THE Birds OF BRITISH COLUMBIA

VOLUME II   NONPASSERINES

DIURNAL BIRDS OF PREY
THROUGH WOODPECKERS

THE Birds
OF BRITISH COLUMBIA

VOLUME II **NONPASSERINES**

DIURNAL BIRDS OF PREY
THROUGH WOODPECKERS

by
R. Wayne Campbell, Neil K. Dawe,
Ian McTaggart-Cowan, John M. Cooper,
Gary W. Kaiser, Michael C.E. McNall

**ROYAL
BRITISH
COLUMBIA
MUSEUM**

 Environment
Canada

Canadian Wildlife
Service

Published by the Royal British Columbia Museum in association with Environment Canada, Canadian Wildlife Service.

This book was prepared and printed with the generous assistance of the Friends of the Royal British Columbia Museum, Employment and Immigration Canada, and the British Columbia Ministry of Environment, Wildlife Branch.

Canadian Cataloguing in Publication Data

Main entry under title:
The birds of British Columbia

    Contents: v. 1. Nonpasserines, introduction, loons through waterfowl – v. 2. Nonpasserines, diurnal birds of prey through woodpeckers.

    ISBN 0-7718-8872-4 (set). – ISBN 0-7718-8973-9 (v. 1). – ISBN 0-7718-8974-7 (v. 2)

    1. Birds - British Columbia. I. Campbell, R. Wayne (Robert Wayne), 1942-   . II. Royal British Columbia Museum. III. Canadian Wildlife Service.

QL685.5.B7B57 1989   598.29711   C89-092228-4

Book design by Chris Tyrrell.
Cover photograph by Ervio Sian.
Bird illustrations by Michael Hames.
Page composition and typesetting in Palatino on MacIntosh II and Linotype 300 systems by Alston Graphics in Victoria, B.C.
Printed by Mitchell Press, Vancouver, B.C.
Bound by Northwest Bookbinding Company, Surrey, B.C.
Dr. G.E. John Smith of the Canadian Wildlife Service developed a system of computer programs to produce the species distribution maps.
The Royal British Columbia Museum
675 Belleville Street
Victoria, British Columbia
V8V 1X4

TABLE OF CONTENTS

INTRODUCTION

This is the second of three volumes on the avifauna of British Columbia; it completes a discussion of the nonpasserine birds begun in Volume 1. The passerine birds are discussed in Volume 3.

The first volume contains the Introduction to the entire set. The Introduction is divided into five sections. The first is a general introduction describing the geology of British Columbia, the bird resource and the history of the project that resulted in publication of this book.

The second section is devoted to the ornithological history of British Columbia, focusing on individuals, institutions, government agencies, and non-profit societies dedicated to the study and preservation of birds and their habitats.

The third section is an extensive treatment of the environment as it relates to birds. It follows a regional ecosystem classification scheme, dividing the province into ten Ecoprovinces and each Ecoprovince into Ecoregions. In this way the province's varied habitats are related to the species that use them.

The fourth and fifth sections lay the foundation for the taxonomy and the treatment of data in the species accounts.

Volume 1 contains species accounts for loons through waterfowl. Volume 2 continues the species accounts for nonpasserine birds: diurnal birds of prey through woodpeckers. Originally, the nonpasserine component of *The Birds of British Columbia* was prepared as one volume with two parts, both relying on a common bibliography. During the editorial phase, however, each book evolved as a self-contained volume, primarily for the convenience of the reader. Due to time constraints in the publication process we chose to include the entire list of references with each volume knowing that repetition occurs.

Citations of unpublished material contain a reference to *A Bibliography of British Columbia Ornithology, Volumes 1 and 2* (Campbell et al. 1979b, 1988). Copies of the papers in these reports are on file at the Royal British Columbia Museum.

SPECIES ACCOUNTS

Checklist of British Columbia Birds

Nonpasserines: Diurnal Birds of Prey through Woodpeckers

This phylogenetic list includes 180 species of birds, diurnal birds of prey through woodpeckers, that have been documented in British Columbia through 31 December 1987*.

Order FALCONIFORMES: Diurnal Birds of Prey
Family CATHARTIDAE: American Vultures

Turkey Vulture

Family ACCIPITRIDAE: Ospreys, Eagles, Hawks, and Allies

Osprey
Bald Eagle
Northern Harrier
Sharp-shinned Hawk
Cooper's Hawk
Northern Goshawk
Broad-winged Hawk
Swainson's Hawk
Red-tailed Hawk
Ferruginous Hawk
Rough-legged Hawk
Golden Eagle

Family FALCONIDAE: Falcons

Eurasian Kestrel
American Kestrel
Merlin
Peregrine Falcon
Gyrfalcon
Prairie Falcon

Order GALLIFORMES: Pheasants, Grouse, Ptarmigan, and Allies
Family PHASIANIDAE: Partridges, Grouse, Turkeys, and Quail

Gray Partridge
Chukar
Ring-necked Pheasant
Spruce Grouse
Blue Grouse
Willow Ptarmigan
Rock Ptarmigan
White-tailed Ptarmigan
Ruffed Grouse
Sage Grouse
Sharp-tailed Grouse
Wild Turkey
Northern Bobwhite
California Quail
Mountain Quail

Order GRUIFORMES: Cranes, Rails, and Allies
Family RALLIDAE: Rails, Gallinules, and Coots

Virginia Rail
Sora
Common Moorhen
American Coot

Family GRUIDAE: Cranes

Sandhill Crane
Whooping Crane

Order CHARADRIIFORMES: Shorebirds, Gulls, Auks, and Allies
Family CHARADRIIDAE: Plovers

Black-bellied Plover
Lesser Golden-Plover
Snowy Plover
Semipalmated Plover
Killdeer

Family HAEMATOPODIDAE: Oystercatchers

Black Oystercatcher

Family RECURVIROSTRIDAE: Stilts and Avocets

Black-necked Stilt
American Avocet

Family SCOLOPACIDAE: Sandpipers, Phalaropes, and Allies

Greater Yellowlegs
Lesser Yellowlegs
Spotted Redshank
Solitary Sandpiper
Willet
Wandering Tattler
Spotted Sandpiper
Terek Sandpiper
Upland Sandpiper
Whimbrel
Bristle-thighed Curlew
Far Eastern Curlew
Long-billed Curlew
Hudsonian Godwit
Bar-tailed Godwit
Marbled Godwit
Ruddy Turnstone
Black Turnstone
Surfbird
Red Knot
Sanderling
Semipalmated Sandpiper
Western Sandpiper
Rufous-necked Stint
Little Stint
Temminck's Stint
Least Sandpiper
White-rumped Sandpiper
Baird's Sandpiper
Pectoral Sandpiper
Sharp-tailed Sandpiper
Rock Sandpiper
Dunlin
Curlew Sandpiper
Stilt Sandpiper
Spoonbill Sandpiper

---

* From January 1988 through to the publication of this volume, three new nonpasserine species have been added to the provincial list (see Addenda).

Buff-breasted Sandpiper
Ruff
Short-billed Dowitcher
Long-billed Dowitcher
Common Snipe
Wilson's Phalarope
Red-necked Phalarope
Red Phalarope

Family LARIDAE: Jaegers, Skuas, Gulls, and Terns

Pomarine Jaeger
Parasitic Jaeger
Long-tailed Jaeger
South Polar Skua
Franklin's Gull
Little Gull
Common Black-headed Gull
Bonaparte's Gull
Heermann's Gull
Mew Gull
Ring-billed Gull
California Gull
Herring Gull
Thayer's Gull
Iceland Gull
Slaty-backed Gull
Western Gull
Glaucous-winged Gull
Glaucous Gull
Black-legged Kittiwake
Ross' Gull
Sabine's Gull
Ivory Gull
Caspian Tern
Elegant Tern
Common Tern
Arctic Tern
Forster's Tern
Aleutian Tern
Black Tern

Family ALCIDAE: Auks, Murres and Puffins

Common Murre
Thick-billed Murre
Pigeon Guillemot
Marbled Murrelet
Kittlitz's Murrelet
Xantus' Murrelet
Ancient Murrelet
Cassin's Auklet
Crested Auklet
Rhinoceros Auklet
Tufted Puffin
Horned Puffin

Order COLUMBIFORMES: Pigeons and Doves
Family COLUMBIDAE: Pigeons and Doves

Rock Dove
Band-tailed Pigeon
White-winged Dove
Mourning Dove
Passenger Pigeon

Order CUCULIFORMES: Cuckoos and Allies
Family CUCULIDAE: Cuckoos

Black-billed Cuckoo
Yellow-billed Cuckoo

Order STRIGIFORMES: Owls
Family TYTONIDAE: Barn Owls

Barn Owl

Family STRIGIDAE: Typical Owls

Flammulated Owl
Western Screech-Owl
Great Horned Owl
Snowy Owl
Northern Hawk Owl
Northern Pygmy-Owl
Burrowing Owl
Spotted Owl
Barred Owl
Great Gray Owl
Long-eared Owl
Short-eared Owl
Boreal Owl
Northern Saw-whet Owl

Order CAPRIMULGIFORMES: Goatsuckers and Allies
Family CAPRIMULGIDAE: Goatsuckers

Common Nighthawk
Common Poorwill

Order APODIFORMES: Swifts and Hummingbirds
Family APODIDAE: Swifts

Black Swift
Vaux's Swift
White-throated Swift

Family TROCHILIDAE: Hummingbirds

Ruby-throated Hummingbird
Black-chinned Hummingbird
Anna's Hummingbird
Costa's Hummingbird
Calliope Hummingbird
Rufous Hummingbird

Order CORACIIFORMES: Kingfishers and Allies
Family ALCEDINIDAE: Kingfishers

Belted Kingfisher

Order PICIFORMES: Woodpeckers and Allies
Family PICIDAE: Woodpeckers

Lewis' Woodpecker
Red-headed Woodpecker
Yellow-bellied Sapsucker
Red-naped Sapsucker
Red-breasted Sapsucker
Williamson's Sapsucker
Downy Woodpecker
Hairy Woodpecker
White-headed Woodpecker
Three-toed Woodpecker
Black-backed Woodpecker
Northern Flicker
Pileated Woodpecker

Regular Species

Turkey Vulture
Cathartes aura (Linnaeus)

TUVU

RANGE: Breeds from southern British Columbia, the southern prairie provinces, southern Ontario and northern New England south through Mexico, the West Indies, and Central and South America. Winters from central California, southern Arizona and New Mexico, Texas, and New Jersey south through the breeding range.

STATUS: *Rare* to *fairly common* migrant and local summer visitant across southern parts of the province, including Vancouver Island. *Very common* autumn migrant on extreme southern Vancouver Island. In winter, *very rare* on the coast, *casual* in the interior. Breeds.

NONBREEDING: The Turkey Vulture is locally distributed across extreme southern British Columbia. It is most often seen in the air, soaring over bluffs, cliffs, and open country including pastures and fields, rangelands, river mouths, marine shores, bays, inlets, roads, and golf courses. Rarely is it seen on the ground except when feeding on a carcass. In autumn, large flocks may be found roosting in trees. Nearly one-quarter of all records are from September, and 81% are from coastal areas.

The centre of abundance on the coast is the area surrounding the Strait of Georgia, including the Gulf Islands. In the interior, most records are from the Okanagan valley. This species has been found from sea level to 1,500 m elevation.

On the coast, it is difficult to differentiate between migrants and the few wintering birds. However, migrants may be seen as early as late February and early March, with most arriving in the first half of April. Autumn migration peaks in early September; by late October most vultures have departed. In the interior, earliest and latest dates for first arrivals are 28 March (Cannings, R.A. et al. 1987) and 15 May; most birds arrive in April. The autumn movement begins in early September and most have departed by mid-October.

Impressive autumn staging areas are located on the extreme southern tip of Vancouver Island and on offshore islands (e.g. Discovery and Chatham islands), where birds roost in tall conifers. It is not uncommon to see a flock of 200 or more vultures soaring there in September.

BREEDING: The Turkey Vulture breeds in 2 well-defined areas

of the province: the south inner coast and the Okanagan valley. On the coast, its range extends from Quadra Island south along the shores and islands in the Strait of Georgia to Sooke on extreme southern Vancouver Island. Small numbers probably also breed throughout the Fraser Lowlands to Hope. In the southern interior, they are known to breed only from Osoyoos north to Shuswap Lake.

Breeding habitat is usually in remote areas, and includes precipitous rocky outcrops and cliffs with protected crevices and caves. The Turkey Vulture also breeds in mixed forests and in areas with large boulder screes. Nests have been found from near sea level to at least 970 m elevation.

Nests: Eight nests have been found in British Columbia: 5 were located in caves, crevices or holes in rocky cliffs, 1 in a sandstone cliff, 1 was located among large boulders at the base of a cliff, and another was found in a mixed forest of Garry oak, arbutus, Douglas-fir, and bigleaf maple. Two nests contained some assemblage of materials: one included green Douglas-fir limbs, the other a few large sticks and other natural debris. Nests found in cliff faces were from 4.6 to 34 m above the base of the cliff; the remaining nests were on the ground.

Eggs: Dates for 6 clutches ranged from 1 May to 1 June, with 4 recorded between 6 and 20 May. Calculated dates indicate that eggs could be found as early as 12 April and as late as 24 June. Clutches contained 1 or 2 eggs (1E-1, 2E-5). Incubation period is variably reported as 28 to 41 days (Kempton 1927; Tyler 1937; Jackson 1983).

Young: Dates for 6 broods ranged from 21 May to 23 August. Calculated dates indicate that young could be found from 15 May to 31 August. Brood sizes ranged from 1 to 2 young (1Y-1, 2Y-5). Nestling period is about 56 to 88 days (Pearson 1919; Kempton 1927; Ritter 1983).

REMARKS: There is some concern about decreasing populations in western North America (see Tate and Tate 1982; Unitt 1984; Wilbur 1978, 1983). In British Columbia, there is no evidence of a decline, but data are limited; areas of known aggregations should be monitored annually.

See Call (1978), Wilbur and Jackson (1983), and P.A. Stewart (1985) for selected papers on the status, biology, and management of the Turkey Vulture in North America.

NOTEWORTHY RECORDS

Spring: Coastal - Sooke Harbour 19 Mar 1945-40; Millstream 24 May 1973-8; Mount Finlayson 26 May 1974-10 (Swift 1975); Cobble Hill 23 Mar 1978-11; Saturna Island 14 Apr 1982-12; Cox Bay 20 May 1979-1; Huntingdon 14 Mar 1943-3 (Munro, J.A. and Cowan 1947); Qualicum Beach 10 Mar 1974-1 (Dawe 1976); Port Hardy 11 Apr 1987-1; San Josef River 25 May 1974-1 (Shepard, M.G. 1975a). **Interior** - Osoyoos 28 Mar 1976-1 (Cannings, R.A. et al. 1987); Newgate 12 Apr 1940-1 (Johnstone, W.B. 1949); Creston 20 May 1986-4; Richter Pass 17 Apr 1976-7; Oliver 17 May 1959-8; Kuskanook 23 Apr 1987-2; Wasa 24 Mar 1980-2; Salmon Arm 14 May 1970-7 (Stevens et al. 1970); Burges and James Gadsden Park 22 Apr 1987-1.

Summer: Coastal - Metchosin 30 Aug 1981-16; Fulford Harbour 26 Jul 1981-10; Chilliwack 24 Jul 1979-12; Sproat Lake 11 Aug 1981-3; Texada Island 22 Jun 1981-11; Duncan Bay (Campbell River) 31 Aug 1973-10; Calvert Island 16 Jul 1939-1 (Munro, J.A. and Cowan 1947). **Interior** - Creston 19-24 Jun 1981-6; Pend-d'Oreille River 4 Aug 1982-3; Osoyoos Lake 22 Jun 1971-10; Oliver

1 Jul 1967-6; Kimberley 12 Aug 1976-4; Arawana 2 Jun 1968-6; Otter Lake (Vernon) 22 Jul 1975-19 (Grant, J. 1975), 20 Aug 1979-39 (Cannings, R.A. et al. 1987); n Kamloops 8 Jun 1986-1 (Rogers, T.H. 1986d).

Autumn: Interior - Swan Lake (Vernon) 15 Sep 1935-10 (Munro, J.A. and Cowan 1947); Skookumchuck 25 Nov 1970-1 (Wilson, M.C. et al. 1972); Flathead (Fernie) 10 Nov 1984-1 (Rogers, T.H. 1984a); Anarchist Mountain 6 Sep 1978-17; Creston 5 Sep 1947-3 (Munro, J.A. 1958a); Newgate 13 Sep 1939-1 (Johnstone, W.B. 1949). **Coastal** - Elk Falls 29 Oct 1975-1; Campbell River (Discovery Passage) 10 Sep 1986-24 at estuary; Comox 9 Oct 1969-3; Qualicum Beach 4 Sep 1976-7; Port Alberni 19 Sep 1951-5; Egmont 5 Sep 1977-5; North Vancouver 2 Oct 1976-18; Vancouver 3 Oct 1979-25; Agassiz 8 Sep 1982-11 perched on fence posts; Mary Hill (Saltspring Island) 1 Oct 1978-160; Pedder Bay 10 Sep 1960-200+, 23 Sep 1984-141, 26 Sep 1981-300+; Metchosin 28 Sep 1983-250, 1 Oct 1980-80; Whiffin Spit 3 Oct 1980-200+; Oak Bay 6 Oct 1952-200+; Rocky Point (Victoria) 16 Sep 1987-44, 22 Sep 1987-144, 27 Sep

1987-240, 10 Oct 1987-76 over 2 hour period.

Winter: Interior - Hat Creek, near Ashcroft 20 Jan 1987-1; Vernon 27 Feb 1970-1 (Rogers, T.H. 1970b); Okanagan Landing 25 Jan 1939-1 (Munro, J.A. and Cowan 1947); Okanagan Lake 17 Feb 1954-2; Vaseux Lake 15 Jan 1967-5 on bighorn sheep carcass; Osoyoos 23 Dec 1984-1 (Cannings, R.A. et al. 1987). **Coastal** - Campbell River 18 Feb 1981-2; Oyster River 4 Jan 1936-1 (Munro, J.A. and Cowan 1947); Comox 24 Jan 1931-1 male (RBCM 12353); Burnaby Lake 13 Feb 1977-1; Coquitlam River 10 Jan 1969-2; Malahat 7 Feb 1981-2; Whiffin Spit 25 Jan 1977-10.

Christmas Counts: Interior - Recorded once: Penticton 27 Dec 1982-1. **Coastal** - Recorded from 5 of 28 localities and on 3% of all counts. Maxima: Vancouver 28 Dec 1968-4, all-time Canadian high count (Anderson, R.R. 1976); Ladner 29 Dec 1979-3; Pender Islands 23 Dec 1978-2.

Extralimital Record: Interior - Horsefly 15 Aug 1938-2 (Munro, J.A. 1945a; Munro, J.A. and Cowan 1947).

Turkey Vulture

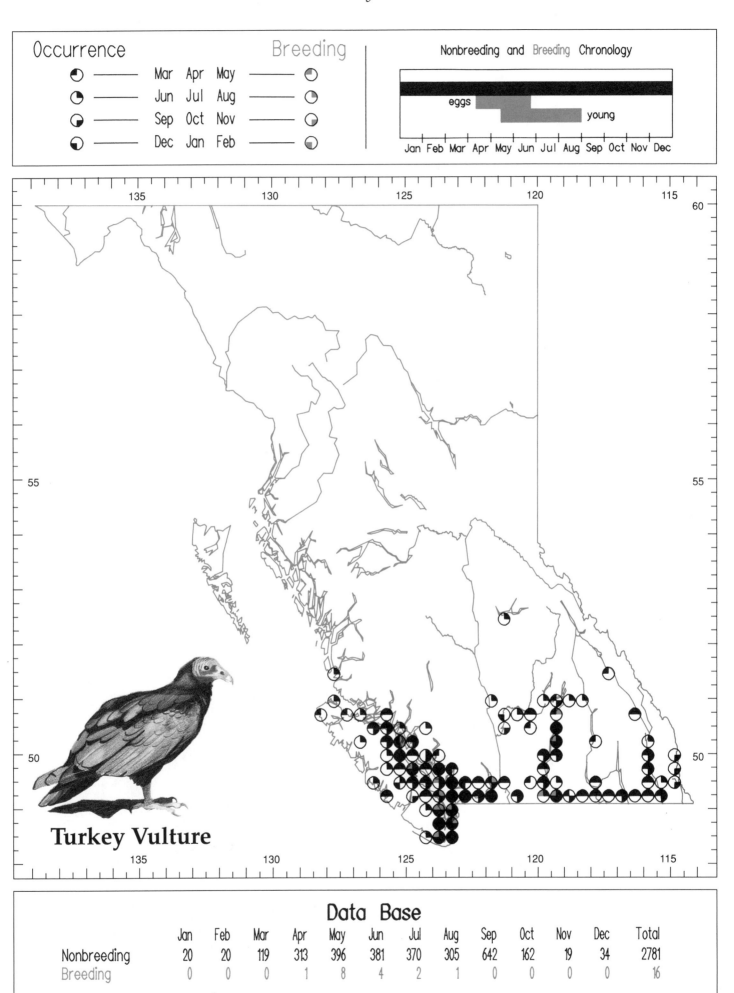

Occurrence — Breeding

Mar	Apr	May
Jun	Jul	Aug
Sep	Oct	Nov
Dec	Jan	Feb

Nonbreeding and Breeding Chronology

eggs

young

Jan Feb Mar Apr May Jun Jul Aug Sep Oct Nov Dec

Turkey Vulture

Data Base

	Jan	Feb	Mar	Apr	May	Jun	Jul	Aug	Sep	Oct	Nov	Dec	Total
Nonbreeding	20	20	119	313	396	381	370	305	642	162	19	34	2781
Breeding	0	0	0	1	8	4	2	1	0	0	0	0	16

Osprey

Pandion haliaetus (Linnaeus)

OSPR

RANGE: Cosmopolitan. Occurs in tropical and temperate parts of all continents. In the Western Hemisphere, breeds from northwestern Alaska and central Canada south to the Bahamas and Mexico. Winters from the southern United States south to Chile and Argentina.

STATUS: *Uncommon* to *fairly common* migrant and summer visitor across the southern third of the province, *rare* north of latitude 56°N. *Very rare* on the Queen Charlotte Islands. In winter, *very rare* on the south coast, *casual* in the interior. Widespread breeder south of latitude 56°N, except the Queen Charlotte Islands.

NONBREEDING: The Osprey is widely distributed throughout the province, occuring chiefly near lakes, rivers, sloughs, and protected coastal waters including lagoons, bays, and inlets. It is reported infrequently on the Queen Charlotte Islands and in far northern mainland areas.

On the coast, the first spring migrants may be seen in late February, but most arrive during the first 2 weeks of April. In autumn, the southward movement begins in September, and by mid-October most have departed. In the southern interior, early spring migrants appear during the second and third weeks of February, but the main influx occurs during the second and third week of April. Migrants arrive in the Chilcotin-Cariboo region during the first week of April. Autumn departure occurs during late August and through September. The main exodus in southern areas occurs during the last 2 weeks of September; most birds have departed by early October. Migrating Ospreys do not regularly aggregate in large flocks in British Columbia as they do in some other areas in North America (see Bull 1974); the largest group reported in the province is 16 birds.

BREEDING: The Osprey breeds throughout the province, except on the Queen Charlotte Islands, generally south of latitude 56°N. Although Cumming (1931) indicates that it "... formerly nested at Tow Hill ... and is now absent from the north end of Graham Island [Queen Charlotte Islands] ... ," there is no conclusive evidence that it ever bred there. The centre of abundance appears to be in the vicinity of Creston and Nelson where approximately 140 pairs nest, making this area one of the most concentrated in the world (Anonymous 1988). The most northern record is from Atlin Lake (3 young in tree nest, 16 July 1980).

The Osprey breeds from near sea level to at least 1,070 m elevation in close proximity to permanent water (see Fig. 13). Occasionally, nests may be located up to 4 km from a source of water. Most nests (87%; n=361) were closely associated with permanent water. Nests close to water were found in the vicinity of lakes (65%), rivers (25%), or marine shores (9%). Three nests were located near drying sloughs. Lake nests were either situated on a man-made structure in the lake (52%), in trees along the shore (39%), or on wooded islands (9%). River nests were situated either along shores (67%) or on man-made structures in the river (23%). Nests on dry land (13%) were located on forested sides of mountains, lightly forested range land, along highways, roads and railway tracks, or on prominent, wooded hills. L.S. Forbes (pers. comm.) found that Ospreys at Creston sometimes nested in Great Blue Heron colonies. He also notes that Ospreys there give nesting Bald Eagles a wide berth and that a relocation of eagle nests caused a redistribution of nesting Ospreys.

Nests: Nests were situated in trees (56%; n=395) and on man-made structures (44%). Most tree nests (64%) were in dead trees (Fig. 1), including black cottonwood and 5 species of conifers. Living trees (36%) included 2 deciduous and 7 coniferous species. Most nests were located at or near the top of the tree. Man-made

Figure 1. *Typical location of an Osprey nest, atop a dead snag along the Thompson River near Ashcroft, August 1983 (Ervio Sian).*

Figure 2. *Osprey nest on top of wooden pilings near Pritchard, 5 June 1968 (Roy W. Phillips). Note Canada Goose eggs in nest which was used by Ospreys the year before.*

Osprey

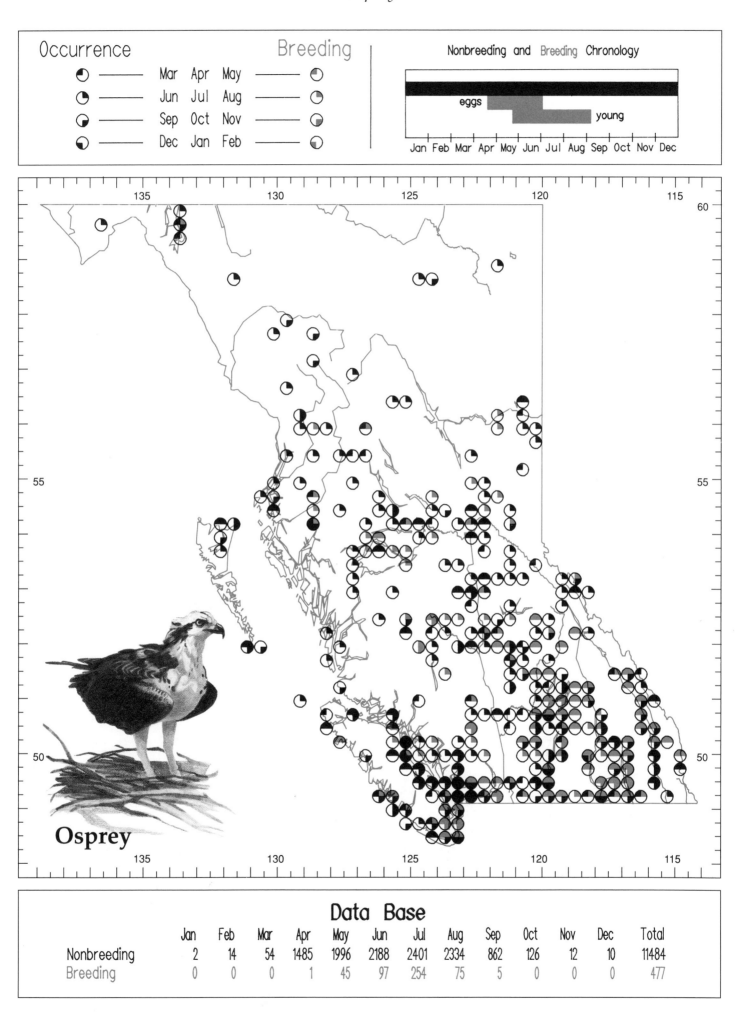

Osprey

Data Base

	Jan	Feb	Mar	Apr	May	Jun	Jul	Aug	Sep	Oct	Nov	Dec	Total
Nonbreeding	2	14	54	1485	1996	2188	2401	2334	862	126	12	10	11484
Breeding	0	0	0	1	45	97	254	75	5	0	0	0	477

structures supporting nests included wooden pilings (53%; Fig. 2), cross members of wooden power poles (32%), navigation lights in lakes (8%), as well as cranes, artificial nest platforms, gas pylons, microwave dishes, a cable across a river, a wharf, and a chimney. Heights of 381 nests above ground or water ranged from 1 to 61 m, with 59% recorded between 9 and 18 m.

Nests ranged from compact to large, bulky structures of sticks, branches, and twigs. They were usually lined with a variety of material, including twigs, grasses, bark (black cottonwood and ponderosa pine), mosses, weeds, fish bones, twine, and down. Measurements for 8 nests ranged from 0.6 to 2.3 m for outside diameter, and 0.3 to 1.7 m in height.

One nest in the east Kootenay was used for 11 consecutive years. Two active Osprey nests built on a wharf were only 6 m from each other. Ospreys have been recorded displacing Canada Geese and Great Horned Owls from their nests, although at Creston, geese often prevent Ospreys from using a nest (L. S. Forbes pers. comm.). Forbes also notes that Ospreys occupying nests from which geese had fledged young rarely reared young successfully.

Eggs: Dates for 46 clutches ranged from 30 April to 23 June, with 51% recorded between 15 and 22 May. Calculated dates indicate that eggs could be found as early as 17 April and as late as the end of June. Sizes for 39 clutches ranged from 2 to 4 eggs (2E-16, 3E-21, 4E-2), with 54% having 3 eggs. Incubation period is about 38 days but may extend to 43 days (Garber and Koplin 1972).

Young: Dates for 419 broods ranged from 21 May to 4 September (2 young fledged), with 52% recorded between 27 June and 20 July. Sizes for 412 broods (Fig. 3) ranged from 1 to 4 young (1Y-117, 2Y-221, 3Y-67, 4Y-7), with 54% having 2 young. Fledging period is 44 to 59 days (Stotts and Henny 1975).

REMARKS: In the Creston area, numbers of breeding Ospreys increased between 1968 and 1981. This increase was attributed, in part, to the installation of a water management system which increased the abundance of prey fish (Fig. 4) available to the birds (Flook and Forbes 1983). In 1981, a mean of 1.5 young was fledged from 27 occupied nests in the Creston area. This mean is above the rate necessary to maintain a stable Osprey population (Henny 1983, 1986; Henny and Wight 1969; Spitzer et al. 1983).

Figure 3. *Pair of adult Ospreys with large young at their nest on the Thompson River, August 1983 (Ervio Sian).*

Figure 4. Osprey with staghorn sculpin (Leptocottus armatus) *at Ashcroft, May 1982 (Ervio Sian).*

NOTEWORTHY RECORDS

Spring: Coastal - Witty's Lagoon 2 May 1982-4; Saanich 18 Feb 1965-1 adult; Denman Island 19 Mar 1978-3; Courtenay 2 May 1928-3; Campbell River 30 Apr 1976-3 (Crowell and Nehls 1970c); Metlakatla 10 May 1904-1 (Keen 1910). **Interior** - Okanagan Landing 27 Mar 1924-1; Merritt 15 Apr 1968-4; Nakusp 15 May 1976-4; Savona 1 Mar 1964-1; Mahood Falls 24 Mar 1977-1; 150 Mile House 7 Apr 1946-1 male (RBCM 15561); Williams Lake 17 Apr 1980-3; Charlie Lake 7 May 1983-1; Atlin 19 May 1981-1 (Campbell 1981).

Summer: Coastal - North Saanich 11 Jun 1982-4; Boundary Bay 20 Aug 1921-5; Royston 19 Aug 1981-5; Triangle Island (Scott Islands) 19 Jun 1974-1 adult; Kimsquit River 8 Jul 1986-1; Lakelse Lake 8 Jul 1976-4. **Interior** - Vaseux Lake 3 Jul 1968-3; Skookumchuck 29 Jun 1976-3; Chilcotin Lake 7 Jun 1977-4; Chetwynd 23 Aug 1975-1 adult; Meziadin Lake 14 Jun 1978-2; Atlin 6 Jun 1978-3; Rainy Hollow 19 Jul 1975-1 adult.

Autumn: Interior - Atlin Lake 6 Sep 1980-3 immatures; Cold Fish Lake 25 Sep 1976-1; Keno Lake 8 Sep 1977-6; Sorrento 12 Nov 1970-1; Swan Lake (Vernon) 10 Sep 1972-15 migrating (Rogers, T.H. 1973a); Okanagan valley 20 Nov 1940-1 female (MVZ 81860); Dutch Creek 3 Sep 1942-16 (Johnstone, W.B. 1949); Upper Arrow Lake 17 Nov 1923-1 (Kelso 1924). **Coastal** - Port Simpson 26 Sep 1969-1 (Crowell and Nehls 1970a); Cape St. James 26 Sep 1978-1; 12 km s Cape St. James-1 within 4 m of fishing boat; Campbell Lake (Discovery Passage) 23 Nov 1923-1 (RBCM 11810); Courtenay 5 Nov 1930-1; Pitt Meadows 8 Sep 1973-3 (Wilson, D. 1977); Stanley Park (Vancouver) 18 Nov 1972-1.

Winter: Interior - 45 km e Kamloops on South Thompson River 29 Dec 1978-1; Chase to Kamloops 8 Feb 1964-3; Trout Creek point (Summerland) 3 Dec 1973-1; Lower Arrow Lake 17 Feb 1923-1 (Kelso 1924); Skaha Lake 6 Jan 1985-1 (Cannings, R.A. et al. 1987); Trail 22 Feb 1972-1. **Coastal** - Willow Point 24 Dec 1973-1; Pitt Meadows 21 Feb 1971-1 (Campbell et al. 1972b); Iona Island 4 Feb 1976-1; Crescent Beach 29 Jan 1950-1, 12 Feb 1956-1; Victoria 17 Feb 1985-1.

Christmas Counts: Interior - Not recorded. **Coastal** - Recorded from 5 of 28 localities and on 2% of all counts. Maxima: Deep Bay 30 Dec 1978-3, all-time Canadian high count (Anderson, R.R. 1980); Terrace 28 Dec 1975-1; Comox 17 Dec 1978-1, 21 Dec 1980-1; Chilliwack 19 Dec 1981-1; White Rock 2 Jan 1983-1.

Bald Eagle

BAEA

Haliaeetus leucocephalus (Linnaeus)

RANGE: Breeds from northwestern Alaska and central Canada south to the southern United States and Baja California, but very locally distributed in interior North America. Winters from Alaska and southern Canada south along the coast and major river systems to at least the southern limits of the breeding range. Formerly bred throughout most of North America north of Mexico.

STATUS: *Uncommon* to *fairly common* resident along the coast of Vancouver Island, the Queen Charlotte Islands, and the adjacent mainland; seasonally and locally *very common* to *abundant*. *Rare* to *uncommon* summer visitant in the northern interior, and *uncommon* resident in the southern interior; local in winter in the vicinity of ice-free rivers and lakes. Widespread breeder.

NONBREEDING: The Bald Eagle is widely distributed throughout the province. It is primarily associated with aquatic habitats including seashores, lakes, rivers, sloughs, and marshes, although it has been found in almost all habitats from sea level to 2,380 m elevation. Habitat preference varies considerably with season.

In spring, migrants follow sea coasts, rivers, and valleys northward. Concentrations are evenly distributed along the coast depending on available food resources. In the interior it is not unusual to find large groups of eagles sitting on frozen lakes awaiting the thaw or gathering near livestock calving grounds (Fig. 6). Some frequent garbage dumps. The spring movement begins in mid-to-late February but occurs mainly in March. Adults have been seen back at nests in Victoria by 7 February, in Lumby by 22 February, in Williams Lake by 29 February, in Prince George by 14 March, in Fort St. John by 24 February, and in Atlin by 1 April.

In summer, aggregations occur only along the coast where "herring balls" and surface-feeding fishes attract both breeding and nonbreeding eagles (Figs. 5 and 7).

The autumn movement is somewhat protracted, and appears to be correlated with the commencement of salmon spawning both on the coast and in the interior. Movements in September and early October are poorly known (Fig. 8). On the coast, salmon spawning begins in late August and September, but eagles move into estuaries and rivers slightly later as spent salmon carcasses become available. Peaks vary, depending on location (Figs. 10 and 11) and spawning species, and may occur from mid-December (Qualicum River) to late January (Squamish River) and early February (Baynes Sound). In the interior, winter numbers and locations depend on open water and populations of waterbirds, especially American Coots. Bald Eagles are also attracted to large mammal carcasses (e.g. elk, deer, moose) killed along highways and railway tracks (Hatler 1983). Garbage dumps are used infrequently in winter.

Figure 5. *Bald Eagles fishing, Imperial Eagle Channel, Barkley Sound, 22 June 1970 (R. Wayne Campbell).*

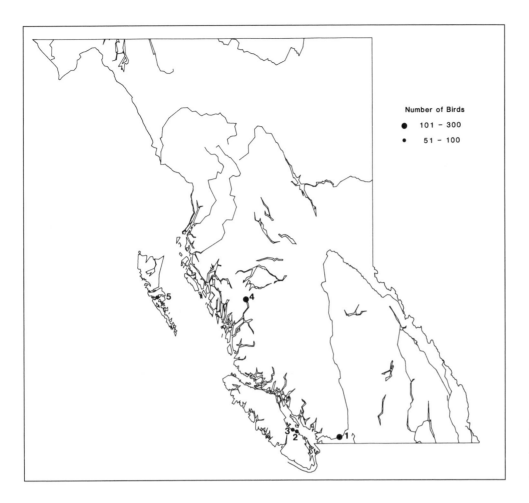

Figure 8. *Major autumn concentrations of Bald Eagles in British Columbia. Coastal: 1 - Harrison Bay; 2 - Little Qualicum River; 3 - Qualicum River; 4 - Kimsquit River; 5 - Pallant Creek estuary.*

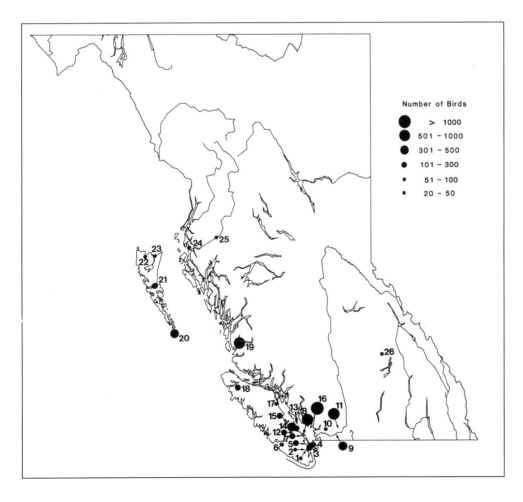

Figure 9. *Major winter concentrations of Bald Eagles in British Columbia. Coastal: 1 - Cowichan Bay; 2 - Somenos Flats; 3 - Fulford Harbour; 4 - Active Pass; 5 - Chemainus River; 6 - Sarita River; 7 - Nanaimo River estuary; 8 - Gabriola Island; 9 - Nicomen Island; 10 - Pitt Meadows; 11 - Lower Harrison River; 12 - Little Qualicum River hatchery; 13 - Little Qualicum River estuary; 14 - Qualicum River; 15 - Puntledge and Tsolum rivers; 16 - Squamish (includes Mamquam River, Lower Squamish River, and Chekamus River); 17 - Campbell River (Discovery Passage) ; 18 - Neroutsus Inlet; 19 - Rivers Inlet; 20 - Cape St. James; 21 - Skidegate Inlet; 22 - Naden Harbour; 23 - Masset; 24 - Prince Rupert; 25 - Terrace. Interior: 26 - Adams River.*

The centre of winter abundance is along the coast (Fig. 9). For example, 4,552 eagles were counted from various coastal sites (Table 1) during the mid-winter Bald Eagle survey in 1987 (Farr and Dunbar 1987). Of the birds classified, 35% were immatures, identical to results obtained on the 1986 count and similar to those reported by Millsap (1986) for 1981 and 1982 counts in the conterminous United States.

BREEDING: The Bald Eagle breeds throughout the province but is only a local breeder in the Boreal Forest regions north of 56°N latitude. The centre of abundance is along the coast, where dense populations are found in the Queen Charlotte Islands and Gulf Islands. An estimate of 9,078±2,024 adult eagles was reported by Hodges et al. (1983) following an aerial survey of coastal British Columbia from 24 April to 3 May 1980.

Bald Eagles breed primarily in coniferous forests—but also in deciduous and mixed woodlands—near seashores, lakes, large rivers, and marshes, and on islands. Large trees are important habitat components. Most nest sites have an unobstructed view of the surrounding area, and a food source is usually nearby. Along the coast, most nests are within 100 m of the shore. This is also generally true for the interior, but some nests are found 1 km from water. Nests have been found from near sea level to 1,370 m elevation.

Nests: On the coast, most nests (65%; n=543) were near the seashore (Fig. 12), on islands, in estuaries, and at the mouths of rivers and creeks. Other nest sites on the coast included lakeshores, marshes, sloughs, lagoons, and rivers. In the interior, nests were found along lakeshores (58%; n=87), on islands in rivers and lakes (22%), and on river banks (16%) also being important. Other nests were located at the mouths of creeks, along railway tracks, and on hillsides.

On the coast, 95% of 511 nests were located in living or dead coniferous trees, including Sitka spruce (74%; Fig. 12), Douglas-fir (19%), western redcedar, western hemlock, and lodgepole pine. Deciduous trees (n=26) included black cottonwood (24 nests), red alder, and willow. In the interior, most nests (67%; n=73) were located in deciduous trees, including black cottonwood (49%), trembling aspen (29%), and balsam poplar. Douglas-fir (21 nests), ponderosa pine (5), and spruces were the coniferous trees used. Nests were more often in living than in dead trees. In addition, 4 nests were located on the ground atop rocky pinnacles, and 1 nest was on a cliff ledge.

TABLE 1
Summary of British Columbia mid-winter Bald Eagle survey, 11 January 1987. Adapted from Farr and Dunbar (1987).

	Age Classes			
	Adult	Immature	Unclassified	Total
Fraser Valley	540	437	184	1161
North Vancouver to Bowen Island	14	1	4	19
Squamish	646	260	46	952
Sechelt	35	15	26	76
Powell River	40	60	6	106
Port Neville	2	1	0	3
Bella Coola	284	96	18	398
Southern Gulf Islands	196	45	15	256
Victoria	34	4	0	38
Cowichan	251	146	14	411
Nanaimo	128	75	30	233
Parksville to Qualicum	90	47	0	137
Comox to Courtenay	175	151	9	335
Campbell River	79	38	1	118
Port Hardy	0	0	7	7
Queen Charlotte Islands	208	88	6	302
TOTALS	2722	1464	366	4552

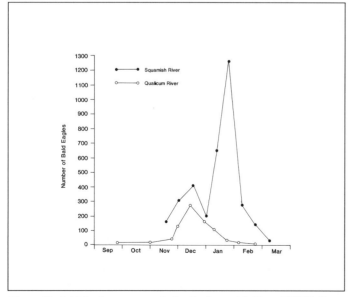

Figure 10. *Bald Eagle census results for the Squamish River, 1980/81 (from Campbell and Van Der Raay 1981) and Qualicum River, 1982/83 (from Cassidy 1983).*

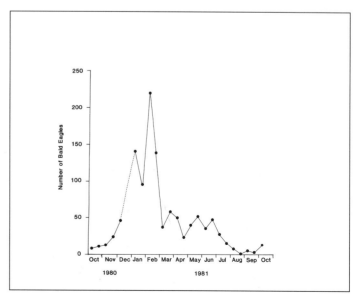

Figure 11. *Biweekly counts (averages) of Bald Eagles, Comox Harbour to Deep Bay, Vancouver Island, 11 October 1980 to 10 October 1981 (courtesy Canadian Wildlife Service). The dashed line indicates a period when counts were not made.*

Nests were usually placed in tree crotches (Fig. 12), on branches next to the trunk, occasionally on branches a short distance from the trunk, or near the crown of the tree. Occasionally old osprey nests were used (Fig. 13). In treeless areas, such as Triangle Island, nests were often built on the top of steep crags or on knife-edge ridges. Although the range of nest heights varied between coastal areas (ground level to 91 m) and inland areas (6 to 38 m), the average range for both areas (50% and 62% of heights respectively) was 12 to 18 m.

Nests were usually massive, cup-shaped platforms with fairly flat tops, and were constructed of dead sticks, branches, and twigs. Some pieces were up to 9 cm in diameter. Nests were lined with grasses, mosses, strips of cedar bark, leaves, and pieces of fresh conifer boughs. Some coastal nests were lined with an assortment of beach debris, including driftwood, bull kelp, eelgrass, cow-parsnip, nylon rope, dry grass, plastic tarpaulin, feathers, sea-lion bones, and assorted seaweeds. Outside diameters of 66 nests ranged from 0.5 to 3.6 m, with 58% recorded between 0.8 and 1.4 m. Outside depths (heights) of 66 nests ranged from 0.3 to 6 m with 53% recorded between 0.4 and 0.9 m. The largest nest was 6 m deep.

Eggs: Dates for 118 clutches ranged from 12 February to 27 June, with 50% recorded between 20 April and 12 May. All eggs collected after late June were addled. Calculated dates indicate that eggs could be found as early as 7 February. Clutch size ranged from 1 to 3 eggs (1E-37, 2E-74, 3E-7), with 63% having 2 eggs. Incubation period is 34 to 35 days (Herrick 1932).

Young: Dates for 425 broods (Fig. 14) ranged from 30 March to 1 September, with 52% recorded between 22 June and 12 July. It is rare to find young (flightless) in the nest in April and after mid-August. Sizes for 425 broods ranged from 1 to 3 young (1Y-253, 2Y-159, 3Y-13), with 60% having 1 young (Fig. 15). Fledging period is 10 or 11 weeks (Harrison , C. 1978).

REMARKS: Gerrard (1983) suggests that Alaska and British Columbia account for 48,000 (69%) of the 70,000 Bald Eagles estimated to occur in North America. Populations in western North America are generally stable.

It has been suggested by many biologists, including Servheen and English (1979), that there are regular migratory movements of Bald Eagles along the Pacific coast and this is supported by our data (Fig. 16). Recently, through radio-tagging, Hodges et al. (1987) have shown that some of the eagles found wintering along the British Columbia coast are from Alaska. Their studies indicate that 73% of first-year and immature eagles disperse through the winter season into British Columbia (and farther south) while 27% remain in southeast Alaska during the summer. They also suggest that immature birds that overwinter in British Columbia may remain there for several years.

The salmon spawning rivers and adjacent forests are undoubtedly important to wintering Bald Eagle populations in British Columbia. The degree of importance has not been determined but can be inferred from studies carried out in Washington State.

Figure 12. *Large Bald Eagle nest in crotch of Sitka spruce on Bonilla Island, 4 June 1970 (R. Wayne Campbell).*

Figure 13. *Osprey nest at Stoney Lake, 30 April 1980 (R. Wayne Campbell). In 1979, this nest was used by Ospreys but the following year it was usurped by a pair of Bald Eagles who successfully raised a single young.*

Stalmaster and Gessaman (1984) note that winter food shortages could naturally limit eagle numbers, and associated food stress could also lower the birds' reproductive performance after they leave the wintering grounds. Since winter densities of raptor populations are thought to be limited by food, protective management policies that reduce energy stress could reduce overwinter mortality. One method of reducing stress would be to ensure that some mature coniferous stands remain near the salmon streams. Anthony, R.G. et al. (1982) note that eagles often select mature and old-growth coniferous forest for roosts. Stalmaster and Gessaman (1984) demonstrate the importance of these forests to the Bald Eagle. In their study on the Nooksack River, they found that the eagles spend 67.5% of their day in roosts, and most of the eagles roosted in coniferous rather than deciduous forests even though the eagles had to expend more energy to travel there. By roosting in conifers, where temperatures and long-wave radiation are higher, wind velocity is low, and rainfall is considerably reduced, the eagles save about 5% of their daily energy budget even after accounting for the energy costs of flying to and from the roost. See Farr (1987) for a description of Bald Eagle roosts in the Fraser Lowlands.

Another stress on wintering eagles is human disturbance—the leading cause of eagle mortality in North America (Newton 1979). Again on the Nooksack River, Stalmaster and Newman (1978) found that the distribution of eagles there reflected the effect of human activity and had a significant influence on their feeding behaviour. Disturbed birds did not return to the same feeding area until several hours after the disturbance occurred, and only when the disturbance had ended. They also found that activities directly on the river, such as boating and fishing, were most disturbing if activities did not regularly occur there. Stalmaster and Newman (1978) suggest that activity restriction zones be created for Bald Eagle wintering grounds, preferably in conjunction with vegetation buffer zones. They note that boundaries of 250 m would be sufficient to protect 90% or more of the population, as most of the eagle avoidance flights were less than that distance.

Steenhof and Brown (1978) list guidelines for preserving and enhancing wintering sites for Bald Eagles.

A very useful bibliography has been published by the National Wildlife Federation (Lincer et al. 1979).

POSTSCRIPT: The mid-winter Bald Eagle survey in 1988 tallied 8,400 birds of which nearly three quarters were in the southern coastal area (Farr and Dunbar 1988). The percentage of immatures was 37, slightly higher than 1986 and 1987 values. A preliminary estimate of the mid-winter population for the province is between 20,000 and 30,000 birds.

Figure 14. *Near fledging Bald Eagles in nest on Joseph Island, 28 June 1976 (R. Wayne Campbell).*

Figure 15. *Nestling Bald Eagle in nest in black cottonwood at Fraser Lake (Fraser Lake), 5 June 1977 (R. Wayne Campbell).*

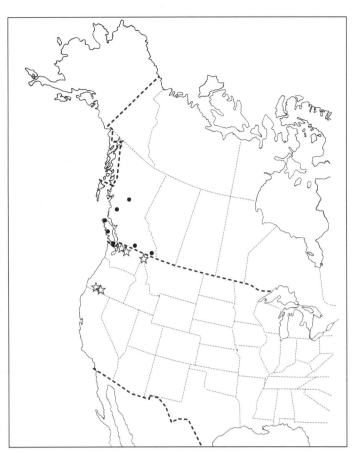

Figure 16. *Banding locations (stars) and recovery sites (circles) of Bald Eagles associated with British Columbia, suggesting the importance of the province to populations in western North America.*

NOTEWORTHY RECORDS

Spring: Coastal - Active Pass 5 Mar 1981-86, 13 May 1983-70; Gabriola Island 7 Mar 1986-35+; Denman Island 15 Mar 1981-36; Pine Island (Queen Charlotte Strait) 30 May 1977-80; Klinaklini River 28 Apr 1986-400; Wanderer Island 23 May 1977-75; Rachel Islands 7 May 1961-84; Skincuttle Inlet 17 Mar 1978-40 to 50; Queen Charlotte City 31 Mar 1982-23 at garbage dump, 22 May 1985-35 on beach; Skeena River (Khyex River to Kasiks River) 27 Mar 1982-242; Nass River 3 Apr 1967-500 (Crowell and Nehls 1967b). **Interior** - Douglas Lake (Quilchena) 6 Mar 1983-16; Otter Lake (Vernon) 30 Mar 1975-30; Glacier National Park 29 Mar 1982-7; Lac la Hache 21 Mar 1977-6; Williams Lake 26 Mar 1983-14 on ice; Peace River (Lynx Creek to Bear Flat) 27 Mar 1983-5 adults, 6 immatures; Chilkat Pass 28 May 1979-6.

Summer: Coastal - Active Pass 4 Jun 1977-74, 3 Jul 1977-41; Imperial Eagle Channel 24 Jun 1970-28; Keats Island 1 Jun 1980-40; Christie Passage 11 Jun 1976-42; Raglan Point 11 Jul 1975-71; Meyers Narrows 17 Jul 1969-60; Klemtu 13 Jul 1969-45; Kimsquit River 1 Jul 1985-4, 2 adults, Aug/Sep 1985-200+ during salmon run, adult:immature ratio 1:1; Tolmie Channel 23 Jul 1969-80; Richardson Passage 10 Jul 1977-60; Prince Rupert 5 Jul 1971-200. **Interior** - 16 km n Flathead (Roosville) 8 Aug 1952-3; Wasa 14 Aug 1977-3; Abuntlet Lake 17 Jul 1979-6; Uncha Lake 10 Jun 1976-6; Nechako River 9 Jul 1974-20; Peace River 18 Aug 1986-11; Basement Creek 9 Jun 1983-12.

Autumn: Interior - Tachie River 12 Oct 1984-650; Peace River 23 Nov 1986-2; Meziadin Lake 15 Sep 1979-10; Kootenay National Park 30 Nov 1983-4. **Coastal** - Pallant Creek 30 Nov 1978-71; Squamish River 24 Nov to 7 Dec 1980-182; Big Qualicum River 29 Nov 1978-51; Hope 26 Nov 1976-60; Harrison River 24 Nov to 7 Dec 1980-302 at mouth.

Winter: Interior - Halfway River 24 Feb 1985-2 adults; Topley 21 Jan 1979-1 feeding on moose carcass; Francois Lake 27 Dec 1987-2; Williams Lake 27 Jan 1979-2 at garbage dump; Brisco 6 Dec 1980-3 feeding on elk carcass; Adams River 21 Dec 1983-23; Summerland 6 Feb 1963-6. **Coastal** - Prince Rupert 9 Jan 1983-40, 25 Feb 1979-54, both at garbage dump; Rivers Inlet late Dec 1975-1,000+; Fulmore Lake 24 Dec 1975-37; Sarita River 10 Dec 1976-100; Chemainus River 18 Jan 1984-74; Fulford Harbour 2 Jan 1982-100+; Active Pass 28 Jan 1984-100+, 27 Feb 1979-117.

Christmas Counts: Interior - Recorded from 14 of 19 localities and on 76% of all counts. Maxima: Shuswap Lake 21 Dec 1982-23; Penticton 27 Dec 1983-15; Vernon 27 Dec 1981-13. **Coastal** - Recorded from 27 of 28 localities and on 94% of all counts. Maxima: Squamish 2 Jan 1984-**1,396**, all-time Canadian high count (Monroe 1984); Deep Bay 27 Dec 1983-424; Comox 21 Dec 1980-180.

Northern Harrier

NOHA

Circus cyaneus (Linnaeus)

RANGE: Circumpolar. Breeds from northern Alaska east across central Canada to Newfoundland and south to Mexico. Winters from southern Canada to northern South America and the West Indies. Widespread in Eurasia.

STATUS: *Uncommon* to *fairly common* spring and autumn migrant on southeastern Vancouver Island, the Fraser Lowlands and generally throughout the rest of the province east of the Coast Ranges. *Rare* migrant on northern Vancouver Island, the Queen Charlotte Islands and the adjacent northern mainland coast. In summer, *rare* on southeastern Vancouver Island, and *uncommon* throughout the Fraser Lowlands and east of the Coast Ranges. In winter *uncommon* on southeastern Vancouver Island, *common* throughout the Fraser Lowlands and *uncommon* in the southern interior except the Kootenays where it is *rare*. Local breeder.

NONBREEDING: The Northern Harrier is widely distributed throughout most of the province. It frequents virtually every type of open country from sea level to at least 2,440 m elevation. Preferred natural habitats include fresh and salt water marshes and sloughs, dry upland fields, grasslands, rangelands, and sagebrush hills and meadows. Human-altered habitats used by the birds include agricultural fields, airports, golf courses, road edges, drive-in theatres, and light station grounds. Alpine meadows are frequented during late summer and autumn.

Spring migration begins in the latter half of March in the south, but occurs mostly during April throughout the province with some movement, especially in northern areas, in early May. The autumn movement begins in late August and continues into November, peaking in southern areas about mid-October.

The marshes and agricultural areas of the Fraser Lowlands support the largest wintering populations of raptors in Canada. The Northern Harrier is the most common migrant raptor frequenting these areas (Douglas, A. 1984) and in 1971 accounted for 36% of all raptors (19 species) counted during organized censuses there (Campbell et al. 1972b). Winter populations in the Fraser River delta and Pitt Meadows areas have remained relatively stable over the period of 1972 to 1987, based on Christmas Bird Count data, although these data suggest that the Northern Harrier is the second most common raptor in winter (see Fig. 18).

BREEDING: The Northern Harrier breeds in open areas on east-central Vancouver Island (King, D.G. 1973), the Fraser River delta, and locally but widespread throughout the interior of the province east of the Coast Ranges. Most nests (64%; n=52) were found in wet or dry cattail and bulrush marshes. Other nests were built in emergent vegetation bordering lakes and beaver ponds, open fields with shrub growth, hardhack and spruce bogs, and open burns. Nests have been found from near sea level to 1,010 m elevation.

Nests: Nests were constructed among bulrush, cattail, reed-grasses, and sedges as well as among shrubs including small and large willows, roses, hardhack, and small pines. All nests consisted of small piles or platforms of vegetation positioned on the ground or over water up to 0.7 m deep. Nests in dry situations were up to 23 cm thick; those over water were up to 36 cm thick. Nests ranged from small pads to large structures of sticks, twigs, and grasses with a shallow depression on the top. Outside diameter of 4 nests ranged from 23 to 56 cm.

Nest materials included sticks, twigs, marsh vegetation, weed stalks, grasses, rootlets, and mosses; most nests were lined with dry grasses and weed stalks. One nest on dry land was built entirely of dry grasses.

Eggs: Dates for 52 clutches ranged from 18 April to 29 June, with 55% recorded between 8 and 20 May. Clutch size ranged from 1 to 6 eggs (1E-1, 2E-2, 3E-7, 4E-12, 5E-22, 6E-7), with 67% having 4 or 5 eggs. Incubation period is 29 to 39 days (Breckenridge 1935; Sealy 1967).

Young: Dates for 21 broods ranged from 21 May to 8 August, with 50% recorded between 7 and 19 June. Calculated dates indicate young could be found as early as 15 May. Brood size ranged from 2 to 6 young (2Y-1, 3Y-4, 4Y-6, 5Y-7, 6Y-2), with 56% having 4 or 5 young. Fledging period is 30 to 35 days (Hammond and Henry 1949; Sealy 1967).

REMARKS: The Northern Harrier was formerly known as the Marsh Hawk. It appeared on the "Blue List" from 1972 to 1986 because numbers were "down or greatly down nearly everywhere" (Tate 1986).

See D. Watson (1977) for a discussion of the life history of the Northern Harrier.

NOTEWORTHY RECORDS

Spring: Coastal - Delta 8 Mar 1975-8 foraging over fields; Sea Island 1 May 1979-10 over marshes; Pitt Meadows 21 Mar 1973-8; Cape St. James 11 May 1982-1; Kimsquit River estuary 18 Apr 1985-1. **Interior** - White Lake (Okanagan Falls) 3 Apr 1979-3, 20 Apr 1978-6; Merritt 15 Apr 1968-6; Columbia Lake 6 May 1939-3 (Johnstone, W.B. 1949); Kamloops 21 Apr 1979-40; Sorrento 8 Apr 1971-4; Burges and James Gadsden Park 17 Apr 1987-1; 100 Mile House 18 Mar 1963-1; Riske Creek 18 Mar 1971-1; Williams Lake 27 Mar 1980-1, 11 Apr 1983-6; Prince George 10 Apr 1976-2; Telkwa 6 Apr 1978-1; Fort St. John 21 Apr 1985-8 migrating, 5 May 1985-5 migrating; Cecil Lake 5 Apr 1981-1; Fort Nelson 20 Apr 1986-1; Atlin 23 Apr 1981-1; Chilkat Pass 14 May 1977-1.

Summer: Coastal - Island View Beach 9 Aug 1984-3; Stubbs Island (Tofino) 31 Aug 1977-1; Sea Island 31 Jul 1979-8, 2 Aug 1963-9 hunting over airport fields; Triangle Island (Scott Islands) 31 Jul 1982-1 (Lemon et al. 1983), 18 Aug 1978-1. **Interior** - Creston 13 Aug 1980-4; Harmer 31 Aug 1983-4

(Fraser 1984); Nicola Lake 10 Aug 1939-8; near Ashcroft 19 Jul 1963-6; Chase 19 Jul 1963-3; Moose Lake (Mount Robson) 30 Jun 1973-1 (Cannings, S.G. 1973); Bowron Lake 6 Jun 1975-3; Nulki Lake 13 Aug 1945-6 (Munro, J.A. and Cowan 1947); Fire Flats 25 Jun 1979-1 pair (Page and Bergerud 1979); O'Donnel River 15 Jul 1981-1.

Autumn: Interior - Haines Road (Kelsall Lake) 21 Oct 1981-1 adult female trapped and released; Pike River 10 Sep 1913-1 male (RBCM 2623); Fort Nelson 4 Oct 1985-1 adult female over airport; n Fort St. John 15 Sep 1984-11; Cecil Lake 11 Sep 1983-5, 6 Nov 1983-1 immature; s Williston Lake 29 Sep 1980-5 over marsh; Alkali Lake (Riske Creek) 25 Sep 1980-5; Revelstoke 21 Sep 1977-3 at airport (Bonar 1978a); Sorrento 25 Sep 1970-3; Kamloops 18 Sep 1983-17; Okanagan Landing 29 Oct 1936-9; Columbia Lake 21 Sep 1938-4 (Johnstone, W.B. 1949). **Coastal** - Masset 20 Sep 1981-1, 12 Nov 1944-1 male (RBCM 10204); Cape St. James 20 Oct 1981-1; Pitt Meadows 1 Nov 1975-11, 6 Nov 1976-15; Sea Island 26 Sep 1966-14

at airport; Delta 14 Sep 1974-7, 11 Nov 1974-17; Long Beach 27 Sep 1984-2 immatures at airport; Victoria 15 Sep 1953-3; Rocky Point (Victoria) 10 Oct 1987-1.

Winter: Interior - Williams Lake 26 Dec 1969-1; Cache Creek 11 Dec 1987-1; Kamloops 15 Dec 1982-3; Swan Lake (Vernon) 17 Dec 1972-4; Wilmer 26 Dec 1982-2; Castlegar 26 Jan 1970-1; Osoyoos 31 Jan 1970-7. **Coastal** - Kitimat 8 Dec 1979-1; Masset 10 Jan 1945-1 female (RBCM 10205); Pitt Meadows 21 Jan 1977-21 (Runyan 1978); Sea Island 29 Jan 1979-13 on airport.

Christmas Counts: Interior - Recorded from 8 of 19 localities and on 32% of all counts. Maxima: Vernon 19 Dec 1982-27; Oliver/Osoyoos 28 Dec 1981-16; Kelowna 20 Dec 1981-8. **Coastal** - Recorded from 13 of 28 localities and on 45% of all counts. Maxima: Ladner 23 Dec 1984-135, all time Canadian high count (Monroe 1985b); Pitt Meadows 27 Dec 1977-55; White Rock 4 Jan 1981-34; Vancouver 18 Dec 1977-34.

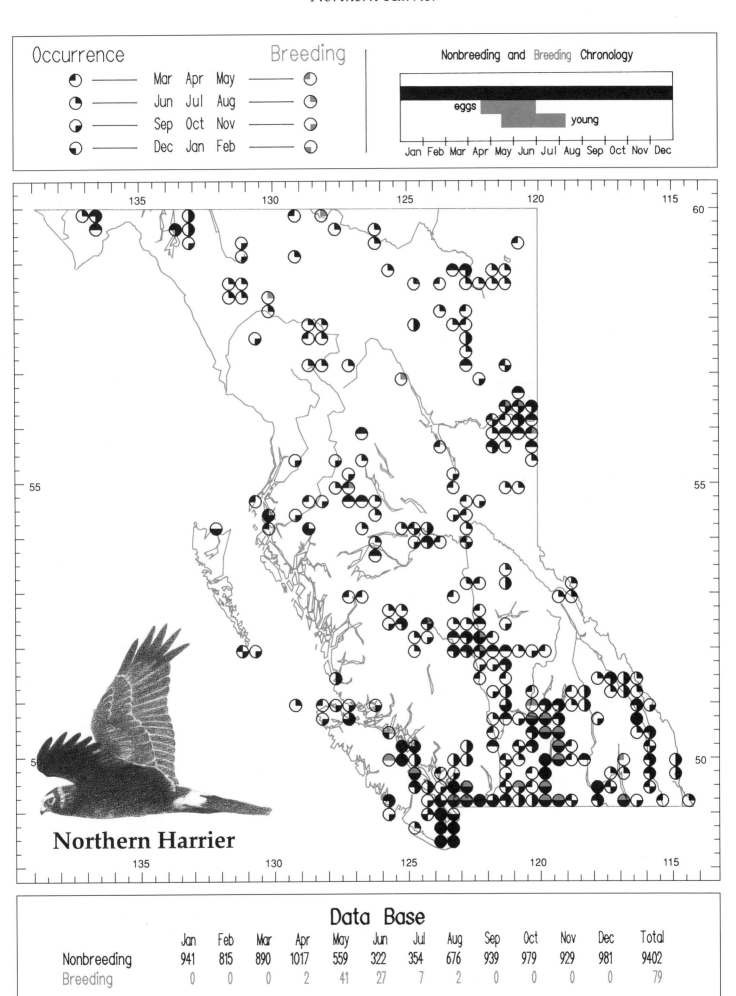

Northern Harrier

Mar Apr May
Jun Jul Aug
Sep Oct Nov
Dec Jan Feb

Breeding

Nonbreeding and Breeding Chronology

eggs   young

Jan Feb Mar Apr May Jun Jul Aug Sep Oct Nov Dec

Data Base

	Jan	Feb	Mar	Apr	May	Jun	Jul	Aug	Sep	Oct	Nov	Dec	Total
Nonbreeding	941	815	890	1017	559	322	354	676	939	979	929	981	9402
Breeding	0	0	0	2	41	27	7	2	0	0	0	0	79

Sharp-shinned Hawk

SSHA

Accipiter striatus Vieillot

RANGE: Breeds from northwestern Alaska and forested parts of Canada south to the southern United States and Mexico. Winters from extreme southern Canada south to Panama.

STATUS: *Common* to *very common* spring and autumn migrant throughout most of the province. *Uncommon* in summer. In winter, *uncommon* in coastal areas and the southern interior; *casual* in the northern interior. Widespread breeder.

NONBREEDING: The Sharp-shinned Hawk is widely distributed in British Columbia from sea level to at least 2,590 m elevation. During migration, it frequents corridors along coasts, lakeshores, rivers, mountain ridges, and meadows where trees and shrubs are prevalent and where updrafts aid movement. In winter, it can be found in almost any type of habitat with trees and shrubs, including bushy edges of pure and mixed coniferous and deciduous woodlands, shrub thickets and fence rows, as well as semi-open areas such as residential communities, cemeteries, golf courses, off-shore islands, and riparian woods. In winter, birds move into lowlands and are rarely found above 600 m elevation.

The Sharp-shinned Hawk is the most numerous diurnal raptor recorded during migration watches. Even so, major migration corridors used throughout the province are not well known. In southern areas, spring migration often begins in late March and lasts until mid-May, peaking during the latter half of April. In northern areas (e.g. Peace Lowlands), the spring movement occurs mainly in May. The autumn movement begins in late August and carries through to late October. The peak occurs in early September in the southern interior, in early October on the south coast.

Main wintering areas on the coast include southeastern Vancouver Island and the lower Fraser River valley, and, in the interior, the Okanagan valley.

BREEDING: The Sharp-shinned Hawk probably breeds throughout most of the province, including the Queen Charlotte Islands and the northern mainland coast. It breeds mostly at higher elevations, frequently above 900 m, east of the Coast Ranges. Of the 14 known, widely-separated breeding sites, 8 were represented only by recently fledged young, an indication of how difficult the nests are to locate. Many summer records, however, were of adults in courtship display, which suggests breeding may occur in the area.

Habitats include fairly dense, mixed coniferous forests such as second growth Engelmann spruce - subalpine fir - western larch and Douglas-fir - western redcedar - western hemlock. Two nests were found in mixed coniferous-trembling aspen woodlands. Most nests were close to water including creeks, bogs, and lakes. Nests have been found from near sea level to 910 m elevation.

Nests: Five nests have been found. All were large, untidy structures in small conifers: 4 in Douglas-fir and 1 in a western redcedar. Tree diameters at breast height ranged from 13 to 23 cm. All nests were placed on branches close to the trunk. They were constructed of western larch, Douglas-fir, or spruce twigs, and lined with finer twigs and pieces of bark. Nest heights ranged from 4 to 12 m.

Eggs: Dates for 3 clutches ranged from 28 June to 7 July. Calculated dates indicate eggs could be found as early as 26 May. Clutch sizes were 4 eggs (2 nests) and 5 eggs (1 nest). Incubation period is 34 to 35 days (Beebe 1974).

Young: Dates for 12 broods ranged from 3 July to 12 August. Calculated dates indicate that young can be found as early as 29 June. Sizes for 8 broods ranged from 1 to 4 young (1Y-1, 2Y-3, 3Y-3, 4Y-1), with 6 broods having 2 or 3 young. Fledging period is 23 to 25 days (Beebe 1974).

REMARKS: Additional information on habitat requirements, breeding ecology and management concerns for accipiters in the Pacific Northwest can be found in Reynolds and Wight (1978), Jones, S. (1981), and Reynolds (1983).

A Sharp-shinned Hawk banded at Goshutes, Nevada on 22 September 1982 was recovered dead on 18 May 1985 in a residential area in Kelowna (Anonymous 1987a).

The Sharp-shinned Hawk appears on the "Blue List" from 1972 to 1986, remaining "very rare as a breeder" (Tate 1986).

POSTSCRIPT: An immature female banded at Albuquerque, New Mexico on 22 September 1987 was recovered on 23 May 1988 at Revelstoke.

NOTEWORTHY RECORDS

Spring: Coastal - Quicks Bottom 9 Mar 1979-3; Mount Tolmie 27 Apr 1983-47 over mountain; Mount Seymour 15 Apr 1971-11 in migration (Campbell et al. 1972b). **Interior** - Osoyoos Lake 28 Apr 1922-a constant succession over north end of lake; White Lake (Okanagan Falls) 19 and 20 Apr 1978-12; Clearwater 27 May 1971-6; Straight Lake 27 Apr 1983-3 (Ducks Unlimited 1983); Williams Lake 30 Mar 1978-1; Boundary Lake (Goodlow) 7 May 1983-1; Bug Lake 28 May 1976-1 (Osmond-Jones et al. 1977); Warm Bay 29 May 1981-1; Liard Hot Springs 11 May 1975-1 (Reid 1975); Haines Road (Kelsall Lake) 15 May 1979-1 (Tull 1979).

Summer: Coastal - Sooke 30 Aug 1974-2; Long Beach 10 Jun 1975-1; Forbidden Plateau 23 Aug to 2 Sep 1943-several each day; Comox 10 Jul 1922-pair; Triangle Island (Scott Islands) 31 Aug 1976-1 immature; Goose Group 4 Jun 1948-pair (Guiguet 1953a); Queen Charlotte City 13 Jul 1946-2 females (UBC 924, 927); Masset and Tow Hill 5

Jul to 9 Aug 1919-6 juveniles (Patch 1922), 21 Jul 1982-1. **Interior** - Rock Creek (Kettle Valley) 7 Jul 1963-2; Okanagan Landing 26 Aug 1909-great numbers flying south; Vinsulla 16 Aug 1975-3; Williams Lake 8 Jun 1977-pair; Sunset Prairie late Aug 1930-3 (Williams 1933a); Chetwynd 5 Aug 1975-2; Parker Lake (Fort Nelson) 24 Jul 1977-1 pair; Strata Mountain 26 Aug 1943-2; Samuel Glacier 28 Jun 1983-1.

Autumn: Interior - Haines Road (Kelsall Lake) 22 Oct 1981-1 female; Mount Hitchcock 6 Oct 1980-1; Stoddard Creek 18 Oct 1986-1; Cecil Lake 1 Oct 1983-1; Dokken Creek 20 Sep 1977-2; Quilchena 20 Sep 1980-4; Summerland 29 Nov 1971-2; Vaseux Lake 11 Oct 1977-3; Blackwall Peak 27 Sep 1975-8. **Coastal** - Mace Creek 15 Sep 1983-2; Gibsons 11 Oct 1981-25 in 2.5 hours; Cypress Park 10 Sep 1979-14, 11 Sep 1979-89, 12 Sep 1979-32, 28 Sep 1979-12, 2 Oct 1979-122, 3 Oct 1979-63, 4 Oct 1979-43, 9 Oct 1979-29, all day counts (Sauppe 1980); Chilliwack 16 Oct 1983-4 drifting

southward; Westham Island 3 Oct 1965-10; Cattle Point 13 Sep 1979-5; Victoria 13 Oct 1973-5.

Winter: Interior - Smithers 4 Dec 1987-1; Williams Lake 26 Dec 1974-2, 2 Jan 1972-1; Horse Lake (100 Mile House) 18 Jan 1976-1; Golden 28 Jan 1900-1. **Coastal** - Masset 16 Dec 1971-2; Bella Coola 13 Dec 1977-1; Cape St. James 17 Dec 1978-1; Malcolm Island 16 Dec 1975-1; Port Neville 17 to 22 Dec 1975-1; Oyster River 2 Dec 1973-1; Fort Langley 8 Dec 1974-4; Swan Lake (Saanich) 13 Dec 1983-3.

Christmas Counts: Interior - Recorded from 8 of 19 localities and on 35% of all counts. Maxima: Penticton 27 Dec 1983-14; Vernon 18 Dec 1983-7; Vaseux Lake 23 Dec 1982-5. **Coastal** - Recorded from 24 of 28 localities and on 69% of all counts. Maxima: Vancouver 19 Dec 1982-24, all-time Canadian high count (Anderson, R.R. 1983); Victoria 17 Dec 1977-16; Ladner 28 Dec 1980-13.

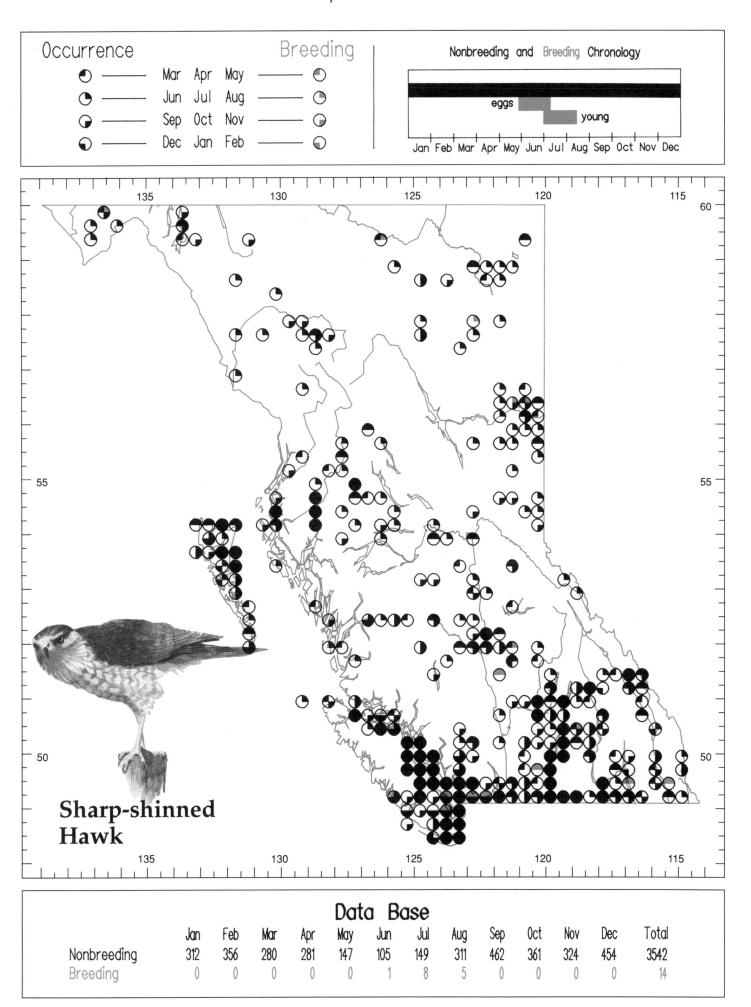

Occurrence · Breeding

Mar Apr May
Jun Jul Aug
Sep Oct Nov
Dec Jan Feb

Nonbreeding and Breeding Chronology

eggs · young

Jan Feb Mar Apr May Jun Jul Aug Sep Oct Nov Dec

Sharp-shinned Hawk

Data Base

	Jan	Feb	Mar	Apr	May	Jun	Jul	Aug	Sep	Oct	Nov	Dec	Total
Nonbreeding	312	356	280	281	147	105	149	311	462	361	324	454	3542
Breeding	0	0	0	0	0	1	8	5	0	0	0	0	14

Cooper's Hawk
Accipiter cooperii (Bonaparte)

COHA

RANGE: Breeds from southern Canada south through the entire United States to northwestern Mexico. Winters from southern British Columbia and the northern United States south to Costa Rica.

STATUS: *Uncommon* resident, at low elevations, in southeastern Vancouver Island, the Gulf Islands, the Fraser Lowlands and the Okanagan valley. Elsewhere, a *rare* to *uncommon* migrant and summer visitant, *casual* in winter south of latitude 52°N; *rare*, becoming *very rare* to the north. Widespread breeder on the south coast and southern interior; rarer elsewhere including the east Kootenay.

NONBREEDING: The Cooper's Hawk is widely distributed across southern British Columbia, south of latitude 52°N, from Vancouver Island to the Alberta border. It also occurs in the central interior to the vicinity of Prince George and Vanderhoof. Elsewhere, its status is unknown.

During migration, the Cooper's Hawk is far less numerous than the Sharp-shinned Hawk, and is usually found below 1,400 m elevation. It uses a wider range of habitat than the other accipiters, including various mixed deciduous/coniferous forests, riparian woodlands, Garry oak - arbutus woodlands, as well as stands of trembling aspen, birches, or alders. In winter, it is frequently found in cities, near Rock Dove and European Starling roosts, and in suburban areas in the vicinity of bird feeders.

Spring migration occurs mainly during the latter half of April. Autumn migration begins in late August, peaks in September, and, in some years, carries on into early November. In winter, centres of abundance on the coast include southern Vancouver Island and the Fraser Lowlands, and, in the interior of the Okanagan valley.

BREEDING: The Cooper's Hawk breeds across southern British Columbia from southeastern Vancouver Island to the east Kootenay and north to Prince George. Nests have been found from near sea level to 1,130 m elevation.

The Cooper's Hawk breeds in small or large, pure or mixed coniferous/deciduous forests and woodlands including dense red alder, trembling aspen, or birches, as well as willow thickets, poplar stands, second-growth western white pine forests, Douglas-fir forests, paper birch - white spruce - lodgepole pine forests, spruce - lodgepole pine associations, Garry oak woodlands, and other semi-open woodlands.

Nests: Most nests (63%; n=62) were situated in coniferous trees (7 species); the remainder were in deciduous trees (10 species). Three species of trees accounted for 52% of the nest sites: Douglas-fir (34%), birches (10%), and black cottonwood (8%). Most nests were positioned in a crotch against the main trunk. Heights of 57 nests ranged from 4.3 to 26 m, with 54% recorded between 9 and 15 m.

Nests were usually rebuilt each year, but some existing nests were added to and used for up to 6 consecutive years. Infrequently (5 nests), crow nests were used as a base. All nests were substantial, sometimes bulky, platforms of sticks and twigs. Nest bowls were shallow and usually lined with bits of coniferous and deciduous bark, as well as green tips of Douglas-fir and western redcedar branches, fine twigs, grasses, and, in one nest, bits of cardboard.

Eggs: Dates for 38 clutches ranged from 27 April to 24 July, with 50% recorded between 10 and 29 May. Those found in late June and July were probably replacement clutches. Sizes for 33 clutches ranged from 2 to 5 eggs (2E-3, 3E-9, 4E-16, 5E-5), with 76% having 3 or 4 eggs. Incubation period is 34 to 36 days (Meng 1951).

Young: Dates for 54 broods ranged from 6 June to 28 August, with 57% recorded between 23 June and 14 July. All August dates represent records of recently fledged young, either of young with traces of natal down, or of young heard and seen begging for food. Sizes for 37 broods ranged from 1 to 5 young (1Y-1, 2Y-9, 3Y-11, 4Y-11, 5Y-5), with 59% having 3 or 4 young. Fledging period is about 30 days for males and about 34 days for females (Meng 1951).

REMARKS: There are no specimen records north of Indianpoint Lake and Bowron Lake, and field identification of North American accipiters can be very difficult (see Mueller et al. 1976, 1979a, 1979b, 1981). Therefore, the distribution of the Cooper's Hawk north of latitude 54°N, including the Queen Charlotte Islands, adjacent northern mainland coast, and Peace Lowlands, requires clarification. There are at least 20 records for these areas, some published (e.g. MacFarlane and Mair 1908; Williams, M.Y. 1933a), all of which we consider hypothetical.

The Cooper's Hawk appears on the "Blue List" from 1972 to 1981 and again in 1986 (Tate 1986). It has suffered declines in all parts of its North American range except in western regions. These declines have been determined from long-term fall migration trends (Hackman and Henny 1971; Robbins 1974), banding studies (Henny and Wight 1972) and shootings (Evans 1982).

A complete treatise on the Cooper's Hawk can be found in Meng (1951). See also Remarks under Sharp-shinned Hawk.

NOTEWORTHY RECORDS

Spring: Coastal - Victoria 6 Apr 1980-3; Mount Tolmie 19 Apr 1973-3 in one hour; Mount Seymour 15 Apr 1971-3 migrants (Campbell et al. 1972b); Campbell River (Langley) 17 Mar 1971-3; Hope 20 May 1977-3; Hansen Lagoon 15 May 1974-1; **Interior** - Newgate 12 Apr 1940-2 (Johnstone, W.B. 1949), 10 May 1930-1 adult male (NMC 24718); Midway 26 Apr 1905-2; White Lake (Okanagan Falls) 10 Apr 1969-5, 20 Apr 1978-26+, 16 riding air currents together in front of a storm as they headed north over mountain tops; Merritt 11 Apr 1976-3; Kamloops 1 Mar 1964-1; Bridge Creek (Revelstoke) 20 Mar 1983-1; Williams Lake 2 May 1954-1 male (NMC 47631).

Summer: Coastal - Victoria 5 Aug 1981-4; Sooke 25 Jul 1979-3; Stubbs Island (Tofino) 8 Jul to 9 Aug 1960-1; Nanaimo 30 Aug 1978-3; Abbotsford 18 Jul 1977-3; Port Neville 30 Aug 1975-2. **Interior** - Manning Park 27 Aug 1974-3; Sparwood 24 Jul 1979-2; Kootenay National Park 26 Aug 1983-3;

Scotch Creek 27 Aug 1966-3; Kleena Kleene 31 Jul 1962-1 (Paul 1964); 10 Mile Lake (Quesnel) 19 Aug 1978-3; Indianpoint Lake 24 Aug 1936-1 (MCZ 281634); Vanderhoof 13 Jun 1952-1 (Munro, J.A. 1955a).

Autumn: Interior - Bowron Lake 3 Sep 1932-1 (MCZ 281632); Williams Lake 15 Sep 1951-1 adult male (NMC 117630); Beaver Lake (Williams Lake) 12 Nov 1980-1; Scotch Creek 10 Sep 1962-5; Greenhills 23 Sep 1983-3 soaring over ridge; Columbia Lake 18 Sep 1938-4 (Johnstone, W.B. 1949). **Coastal** - Triangle Island (Scott Islands) 4 Sep 1976-2; Pachena Point 5 and 10 Nov 1974-2 flying south; Cypress Park 11 Sep 1979-4, 2 Oct 1979-5, 3 Oct 1979-7, 9 Oct 1979-3, all day counts (Sauppe 1980); Maple Ridge 21 Nov 1964-3; Aldergrove 12 Sep 1966-3 chasing crows; Saltspring Island 12 Oct 1977-4; Island View Beach 21 Oct 1984-4.

Winter: Interior - Salmon Arm 3 Jan 1971-1; Summerland 19 Dec 1974-2, 23 Jan 1943-1 female (ROM 86014); Beaver Creek Park 31 Dec 1971-1. **Coastal** - Comox 27 Dec 1946-1 female (RBCM 12420), 6 Feb 1931-1 male (MVZ 81833); Chilliwack 25 Feb 1983-3 together; Huntingdon 29 Jan 1960-1 male (PMNH 71611); Tofino 3 Jan 1976-1 at airport; Victoria 29 Dec 1969-1 male (RBCM 11690); Beacon Hill 29 Jan 1983-2 adults.

Christmas Counts: Interior - Recorded from 9 of 19 localities and on 43% of all counts. Maxima: Vernon 27 Dec 1981-8; Oliver/Osoyoos 26 Dec 1984-6; Vaseux Lake 28 Dec 1978-6; Penticton 27 Dec 1983-5. **Coastal** - Recorded from 18 of 28 localities and on 64% of all counts. Maxima: Victoria 17 Dec 1983-21, all-time Canadian high count (Monroe 1984); Ladner 27 Dec 1981-11; Vancouver 19 Dec 1982-11; White Rock 4 Jan 1981-10.

Cooper's Hawk

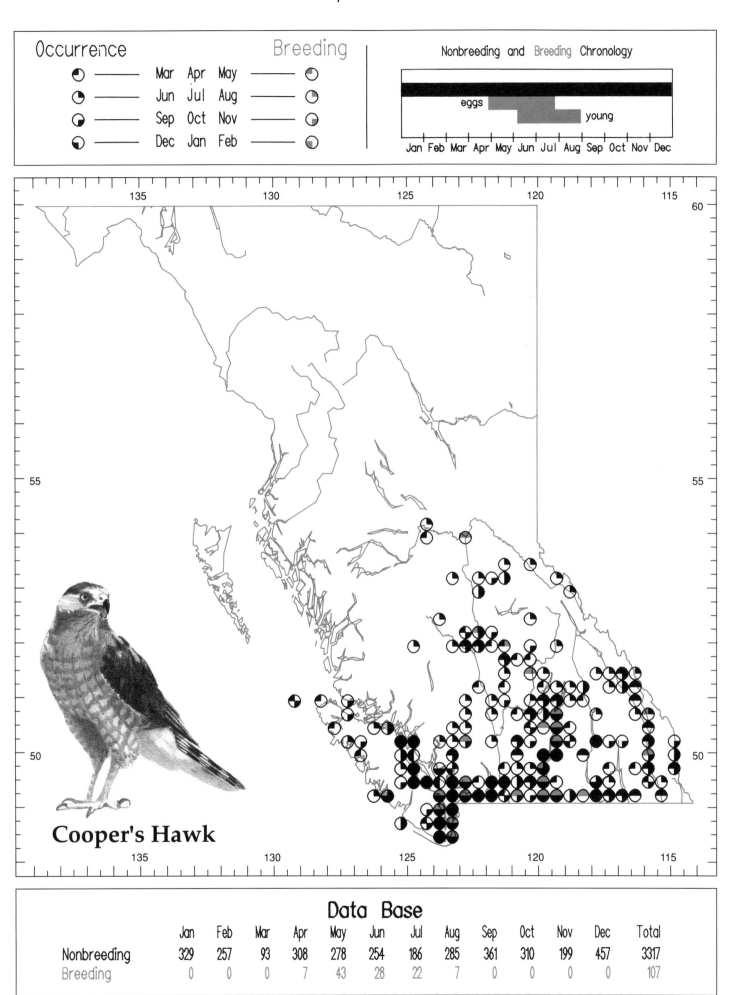

Occurrence Breeding

	Mar Apr May	
Jun Jul Aug	
Sep Oct Nov	
Dec Jan Feb	

Nonbreeding and Breeding Chronology

eggs   young

Jan Feb Mar Apr May Jun Jul Aug Sep Oct Nov Dec

Cooper's Hawk

Data Base

	Jan	Feb	Mar	Apr	May	Jun	Jul	Aug	Sep	Oct	Nov	Dec	Total
Nonbreeding	329	257	93	308	278	254	186	285	361	310	199	457	3317
Breeding	0	0	0	7	43	28	22	7	0	0	0	0	107

Northern Goshawk

Accipiter gentilis (Linnaeus)

RANGE: Breeds in forested parts of Alaska and Canada south through the western mountains to northwestern Mexico, east to South Dakota, the northern Great Lakes states and the Appalachian Mountains. Usually winters in summer range, although there is some southward dispersal to the Gulf states. Also in Eurasia.

STATUS: *Rare* to *uncommon* resident throughout the province including Vancouver Island and the Queen Charlotte Islands. Irregular migrant, *rare* to *uncommon* in spring, *rare* to *fairly common* in autumn. Widespread breeder.

NONBREEDING: The Northern Goshawk is essentially nonmigratory and is widely distributed throughout the province, being least numerous along the coast, and most abundant in the northern interior. Although primarily a bird of mixed, open, and dense forests, it frequents a wide variety of habitats, from sea level to 2,290 m elevation. It has been recorded in almost every forest type in the province, but mostly along forest edges, where accipters are more easily seen than in dense forests. Creeks, rivers, lakeshores, lagoons, sea coasts, islands, and estuaries and their associated habitats are used as hunting areas. The goshawk also frequents man-influenced habitats such as farmlands, parks, cemeteries, airports, orchards, ornamental gardens, and, infrequently, residential areas. Mountain ridges and meadows are used during migration.

Chronology and routes of migration and dispersal are poorly known. When weather and food supplies are favourable, northern populations overwinter (e.g. Atlin, Peace Lowlands), sometimes simply moving to lower elevations. In some years, however, large numbers move southward en masse, as a result of cyclic fluctuations in their prey. In British Columbia, a major invasion of southern areas occurred in 1954 (Keith 1963), and minor peaks in numbers were recorded in 1975, 1978, 1980, and 1983. Mueller and Berger (1967) suggest that many goshawks return to the breeding range after invading the south. This is supported by 4 recoveries of the Northern Goshawk in British Columbia from birds banded at Hawk Ridge Research Station in Duluth, Minnesota (D.L. Evans pers. comm.). All were recovered in the northeastern corner of the province (Dawson Creek, Fort St. John, Fort Nelson) some 2,250 to 2,400 km from their banding location.

Nearly all spring records were of 1 or 2 birds. There was no pronounced northward movement. Any northward movement probably occurs from late February through March along the coast, and in April in the interior. The autumn movement probably begins in September in non-invasion years. The main movement probably peaks about mid-October for immatures and mid-November for adults.

BREEDING: The Northern Goshawk breeds on Vancouver Island and throughout most of British Columbia east of the Coast Ranges. Breeding is suspected but unconfirmed for the Queen Charlotte Islands and adjacent mainland coast.

Dense, mature stands of coniferous forest are the most often reported breeding habitats; mixed woodlands and pure deciduous stands, which vary in size from small groves to large forests, are also used. General habitats described for 19 nests included dense, coniferous forest (6), trembling aspen forest (5), mixed forest (4), open coniferous forest (2), coniferous bog (1) and trembling aspen grove (1). Most nests were near a source of water and were found from sea level to at least 1,400 m elevation.

Nests: Eleven nests were situated in deciduous trees (2 species), and ten were in coniferous trees (4 species). Trembling aspen (9 nests), Douglas-fir (5), black cottonwood (2), and spruces (2) were the most often used trees. Occasionally, dead trees were used. Heights of 17 nests ranged from 6 to 18 m, with 9 nests recorded between 9 and 12 m.

Nests were positioned in main crotches, in forks of branches, against the trunk, or on the broken tops of trees. One nest was built on top of an old red squirrel nest. Nests were fairly large structures of coarse sticks and twigs. Some nests were up to 90 cm in diameter and 36 cm in height. Nest cups, up to 30 cm in diameter and 10 cm deep, were lined with pieces of bark, green, leafy boughs, and poplar twigs. Two nests were unlined.

Eggs: Dates for 5 clutches ranged from 7 April to 15 July. Most egg-laying probably takes place from mid-April to mid-May. Eggs found after mid-June are probably replacement clutches. Clutch size ranged from 2 to 4 eggs (2E-1, 3E-3, 4E-1), with 3 clutches having 3 eggs. Incubation period is 28 to 32 days (Beebe 1974; Reynolds and Wight 1978).

Young: Dates for 25 broods ranged from 24 May to 11 August, with 13 broods recorded between 16 June and 9 July. The earliest date for fledged young was 25 June (Dease Lake). The latest date (calculated) was between 25 and 30 August. Sizes for 22 broods ranged from 1 to 4 young (1Y-3, 2Y-11, 3Y-7, 4Y-1), with 11 broods having 2 young. Nestling period is about 34 to 37 days (Reynolds and Wight 1978).

REMARKS: Two subspecies occur in British Columbia. *A. g. atricapillus* is generally distributed throughout the province, except on Vancouver Island and the Queen Charlotte Islands where *A. g. laingi* is found. The latter race is probably resident (Taverner 1940).

See also Remarks under Sharp-shinned Hawk.

NOTEWORTHY RECORDS

Spring: Coastal - Comox 12 Mar 1958-3; Cranberry 15 Mar 1977-2 adults; Quatse River 14 May 1951-1 immature; Masset Inlet 13 Mar 1981-3. **Interior** - Sparwood 25 May 1983-31; Hazelton 30 May 1921-1 immature (Swarth 1924); Bear Flat 14 Apr 1984-1 adult; Stoddart Creek (North Pine) 16 Apr 1979-1 pair; Fort Nelson 14 May 1982-1 adult male; Atlin 16 May 1981-1 (Campbell 1981).

Summer: Coastal - Campbell Lake (Campbell River) 19 to 25 Jul 1935-3; Tree Point (Alert Bay) 10 Jun 1976-1 adult; Hope Island 28 Jun 1939-1 female (MCZ 281613)); Skidegate 6 Aug 1895-1 male (RBCM 406); Langara Island and northern Graham Island summer 1927-observed daily (Darcus 1930). **Interior** - Glacier Lake (Cathedral Park) 31 Aug 1980-2; Manning Park 20 and 30 Aug 1968-3; 9.6 km e Winfield 16 Jul 1982-2; Alexis Creek 8 Jul 1975-4; Hazelton 16 Jul 1921-1 immature male (Swarth 1924); Fort St. John 2 to 5

Jun 1984-1 adult; Fern Lake (Kwadacha Wilderness Park) 18 Aug 1983-3 (Cooper, J.M. and Cooper 1983); Dease Lake 21 Jul 1962-4, 26 Aug 1962-9; Kotcho Lake 29 Jun 1982-3; Atlin 13 Jul 1985-1 adult.

Autumn: Interior - Haines Road (Kelsall Lake) 22 Oct 1981-2; Atlin 2 Oct 1980-2; Steamboat Mountain (Fort Nelson) 10 Sep 1943-4 immatures (Rand 1944); Fort St. John 27 Nov 1983-1 adult; Lavington 22 Nov 1973-2; Cranbrook 18 Oct 1953-4 immatures. **Coastal** - Masset 19 Nov 1971-1 adult; Khutze Inlet 6 Oct 1935-1 female (MCZ 281605); Kingcome Inlet 21 Sep 1936-2 immatures; Cape Scott 12 Sep and 1 Oct 1935-4; Pulteney Point 5 Sep 1976-1 immature; Oyster River 13 Nov 1922-several; Tofino Inlet 18 Sep 1983-1, 9 to 11 Nov 1952-7, widely scattered.

Winter: Interior - Atlin 5 Dec 1980-1 adult; Fort

St. John 5 Feb 1983-1 adult; Kispiox 23 Jan 1979-1 immature; Prince George 10 Dec 1980-2 adults; 100 Mile House 2 Jan 1984-2; Lavington 10 Dec 1970-2; Osoyoos Lake 28 Dec 1973-2. **Coastal** - Greenville 4 to 14 Jan 1982-1; Masset 20 Dec 1971-1 adult; Port Clements 10 Feb 1983-1 male (RBCM 17885); Port Hardy 11 Jan 1936-1; Chesterman Beach 19 Dec 1981-1 adult; Saanich 4 Dec 1983-1 immature.

Christmas Counts: Interior: Recorded from 11 of 19 localities and on 45% of all counts. Maxima: Penticton 27 Dec 1983-8; Oliver/Osoyoos 29 Dec 1983-5; Vaseux Lake 23 Dec 1983-4; Vernon 26 Dec 1975-4; Smithers 19 Dec 1983-4. **Coastal** - Recorded from 17 of 28 localities and on 21% of all counts. Maxima: Vancouver 21 Dec 1980-3; Pitt Meadows 27 Dec 1983-3; 6 other count areas with 2 birds.

Northern Goshawk

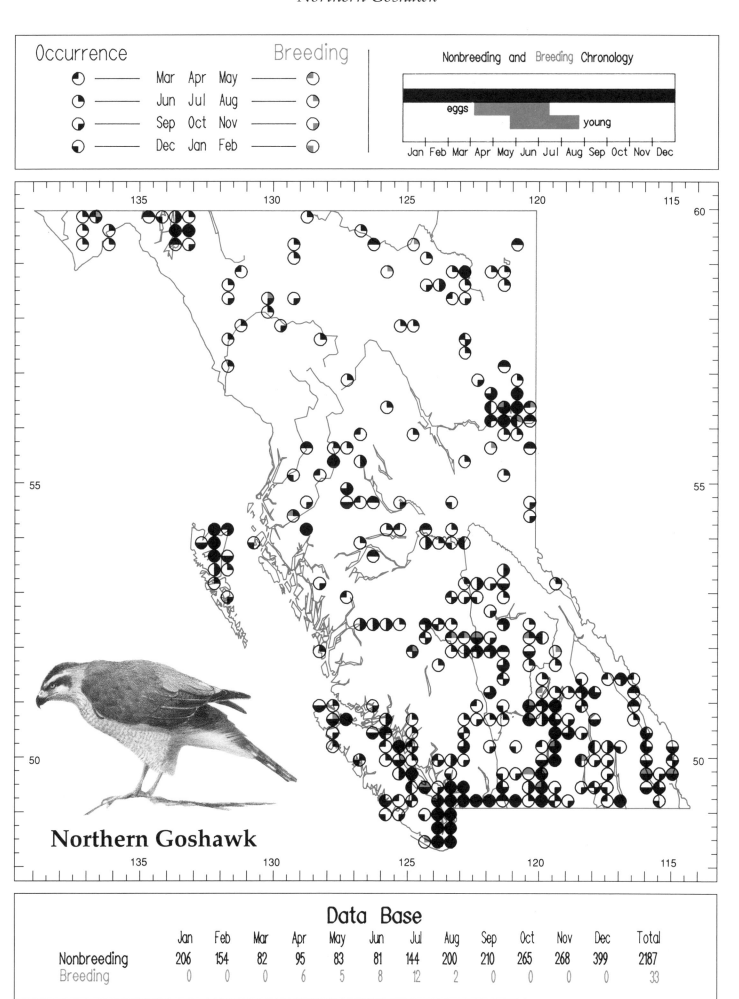

Northern Goshawk

Data Base

	Jan	Feb	Mar	Apr	May	Jun	Jul	Aug	Sep	Oct	Nov	Dec	Total
Nonbreeding	206	154	82	95	83	81	144	200	210	265	268	399	2187
Breeding	0	0	0	6	5	8	12	2	0	0	0	0	33

Broad-winged Hawk

BWHA

Buteo platypterus (Vieillot)

RANGE: Breeds from central Alberta east across southern Canada to Nova Scotia, south to eastern Texas, southern Florida, and the West Indies. Winters in southern Florida and from southern Mexico south to Peru and Brazil.

STATUS: *Rare* summer visitant to the Peace Lowlands, *casual* elsewhere in the interior. Probably breeds.

CHANGE IN STATUS: The Broad-winged Hawk is a recent addition to the avifauna of British Columbia. The first record was a sighting of an adult at Okanagan Landing in 1965, and 9 years later a photograph was obtained of a mounted immature bird collected near Fort St. John, officially adding the species to the provincial list. During the 1980s the Broad-winged Hawk has been seen regularly in the vicinity of Boundary Lake and Fort St. John. It appears to be established there and may be slowly expanding its range throughout the Peace Lowlands.

OCCURRENCE: The Broad-winged Hawk is restricted to the Fort St. John/Boundary Lake area, although small numbers may be present in trembling aspen woodlands in the Fort Nelson Lowlands (Campbell and McNall 1982). Other records are extralimital occurrences.

All but one of the records are of 1 or 2 birds, and nearly half are from May. In spring migration, the small buteo has been recorded in trembling aspen woodlands adjacent to agricultural areas (Fig. 17); in summer, mixed deciduous woodlands (e.g. birch/trembling aspen) seem to be preferred.

Through 1986 there are 21 sightings of the Broad-winged Hawk in British Columbia from 27 April to 27 September. All records, listed in chronological order, are as follows:

(1) Okanagan Lake 22 May 1965-1 flying and circling about 100 m from observer, being harassed by kestrels (Cannings, R.A. et al. 1987).
(2) Mile 54 Alaska Highway (near Fort St. John) 28 August 1974-1 immature (RBCM Photo 448).
(3) Clayhurst 21 June 1978-1.
(4) Mile 54.5 Alaska Highway 27 April 1980-1 adult perched on a power pole.
(5) 20 km southwest of Buick Creek 27 September 1980-1.
(6) Mile 53 Alaska Highway 2 May 1981-2 adults.
(7) Mile 52.5 Alaska Highway 9 May 1981-1.
(8) Beatton Park 10 May 1981-1.
(9) Mount Revelstoke 25 September 1981-1 (Campbell 1983a).
(10) Clayhurst 12 May 1982-1.
(11) Taylor 13 May 1982-2 adults near Johnstone Road.
(12) Charlie Lake 27 May 1982-1 adult.
(13) Kotcho Lake 23 June 1982-1 adult (Campbell and McNall 1982).
(14) Boundary Lake (Goodlow) 14 May 1983-1 adult near an airfield.
(15) 2 km north of Boundary Lake (Goodlow) 12 May 1985-1 adult.
(16) 5 km southwest of Boundary Lake (Goodlow) 12 May 1985-1 adult.
(17) Boundary Lake (Goodlow) 17 May to 20 August 1986 - 5 sightings of a single adult near an airfield. On 20 August, however, 2 adults with 2 young-of-the-year were flushed from an open forest, suggesting the Broad-winged Hawk may breed in the vicinity.

REMARKS: The Broad-winged Hawk is essentially a bird of mixed deciduous forests east of the Rocky Mountains. It was first recorded on the west coast of North America at San Diego, California, on 11 December 1966 (McCaskie 1968). Since that time it has become a regular autumn migrant there. Roberson (1980) suggests that the origin of the birds is the northwest portion of

the breeding range, since dark-phase birds showing up in California are characteristic of that population. Of the 24 birds seen in British Columbia, 4 were dark-phase.

Roberson (1980) lists an additional record of a Broad-winged Hawk at Vancouver on 5 October 1978. Since details are lacking, this observation has not been considered in this account.

Figure 17. *Typical deciduous forest inhabited by Broad-winged Hawks near Fort St. John, May 1987 (R. Wayne Campbell).*

Broad-winged Hawk

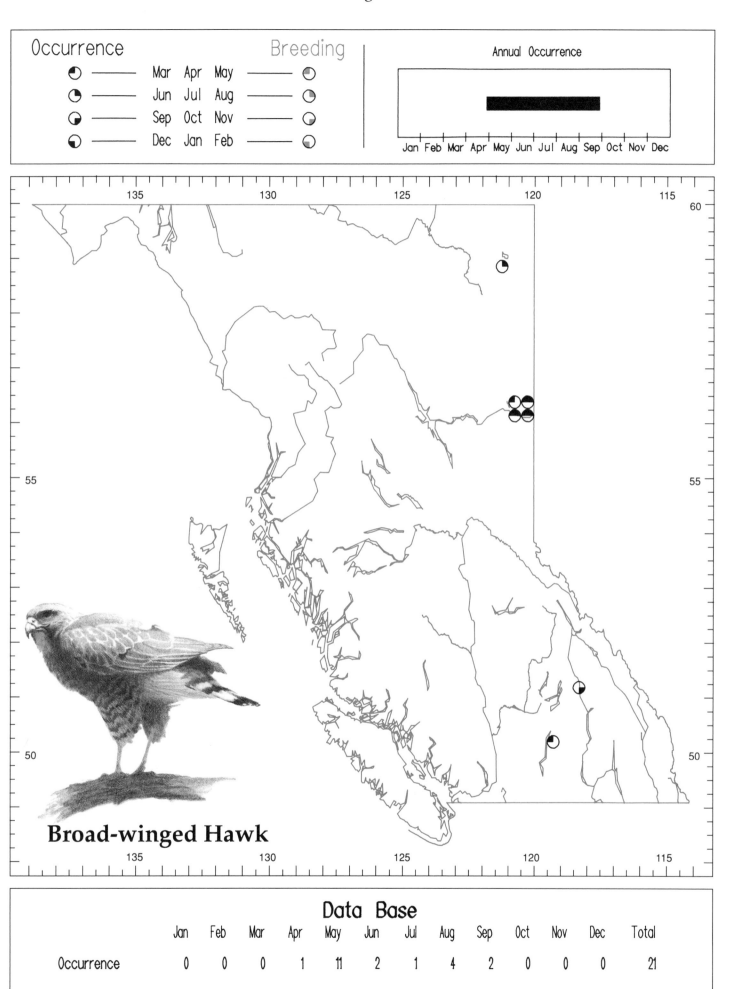

Occurrence

◐	Mar	Apr	May	◔
◔	Jun	Jul	Aug	◑
◑	Sep	Oct	Nov	◔
◕	Dec	Jan	Feb	◑

Breeding

Annual Occurrence

Jan Feb Mar Apr May Jun Jul Aug Sep Oct Nov Dec

Broad-winged Hawk

Data Base

	Jan	Feb	Mar	Apr	May	Jun	Jul	Aug	Sep	Oct	Nov	Dec	Total
Occurrence	0	0	0	1	11	2	1	4	2	0	0	0	21

Swainson's Hawk
Buteo swainsoni Bonaparte

SWHA

RANGE: Breeds locally in central Alaska, northwestern Mackenzie and from central southern British Columbia, central Alberta, central Saskatchewan, southern Manitoba, western and southern Minnesota, and western Illinois south to northern Mexico. Winters primarily in South America.

STATUS: *Uncommon* to *fairly common* migrant and summer visitant in the Thompson-Okanagan Plateau region, becoming *rare* through the Chilcotin-Cariboo to *very rare* farther north. *Very rare* migrant on southeastern Vancouver Island and in the east Kootenay. Local breeder.

NONBREEDING: The Swainson's Hawk occurs mainly in the central interior of the province from the Okanagan valley through the Thompson-Okanagan and Fraser plateaus northwest to the vicinity of Hazelton. It occurs as a migrant in the east Kootenay and on southeastern Vancouver Island.

The Swainson's Hawk inhabits fairly open country, including grasslands and rangelands, alpine meadows (in migration), mountain passes, burns, and clear-cuts. On Vancouver Island, it has been found over agricultural areas and mountain summits. It has been recorded from sea level to 2,290 m elevation.

The main spring movement occurs in late April and early May. Most birds have departed by late August and early September. It has been documented in the province from 7 March to 30 October. Interior records are from 25 March to 7 October; coastal records are from 7 March to 30 October. There is one possible winter record.

BREEDING: The Swainson's Hawk breeds mainly in the southern interior throughout the Thompson-Okanagan Plateau from Princeton, the northern Okanagan valley to the Nicola and Thompson River valleys; also locally in the Bulkley Basin. The centre of abundance is the Nicola and north Okanagan valleys.

Woodlands, including open mixed forests and groves in or adjacent to open areas such as rangeland, pastures, farmland, and marshes were the most often recorded habitats. Rarely, the edges of interior western hemlock - western redcedar forests adjacent to clear-cuts were used for nesting. Nest sites were usually in upland areas of foothills and valleys. One nest, however, was found in a ponderosa pine "in the midst of human activity ... near downtown Vernon" (Cannings, R.A. et al. 1987). Nests have been found from 335 to 457 m elevation.

Nests: Of 14 nests 9 were in conifers: ponderosa pine (7), Douglas-fir (1) and spruce (1). The remaining 5 nests were in black cottonwood (3) and trembling aspen (2). Most nests (11) were situated at or near the tops of trees. Nests were used consecutively for 6 years (Vernon) and for 9 years (near Princeton). All nests were large structures built of sticks. Heights of 12 nests ranged from 4.6 to 23 m, with 6 nests recorded between 13.7 and 18.3 m.

Eggs: Dates for 7 clutches ranged from 10 May to 1 July, with 4 clutches recorded between 10 and 16 May. Calculated dates indicate that eggs could be found by 4 May. Clutch size ranged from 1 to 4 eggs (1E-1, 2E-5, 4E-1). Incubation period is 28 to 35 days (Bent 1938; Fitzner, R.E. 1978).

Young: Dates for 10 broods ranged from 15 June to 13 August, with 5 broods recorded between 4 and 24 July. An early fledging date of 7 July (at Vernon) suggests that nestlings could be found by the first week of June. In normal years, most fledging probably occurs in August. Brood size ranged from 1 to 4 young (1Y-1, 2Y-8, 4Y-1). Fledging period is between 42 and 44 days (Fitzner, R.E. 1978).

REMARKS: In the late 1800s and early 1900s, the Swainson's Hawk was far more abundant and widespread in the province than it is today. R.A. Cannings et al. (1987) attribute the decline to scarcity of prey, namely grasshoppers and crickets, on the breeding grounds and locusts on their wintering grounds in Argentina. Persistent shooting was also a factor.

Population declines were most evident in the Okanagan valley. In late July 1892, Rhoads (1893a) reported a group of 300 to 400 birds feeding on grasshoppers near Vernon. In July 1914, the largest group reported from Okanagan Landing was of 40 individuals (Munro, J.A. 1919). The last large aggregation (75 birds) was reported by A. Brooks near Okanagan Landing in June 1925.

In the east Kootenay, W.B. Johnstone (1949) indicates that the Swainson's Hawk was "reported as being formerly common ... but it is certainly not so in recent years." On the southwest coast, at Chilliwack, Brooks (1917) records "hundreds migrating in the spring of 1889." He mentions that the northward flight "lasted for about five hours."

Since the 1920s, there have been no large aggregations reported in the province, although occasionally, as many as 15 birds can be seen in autumn flocks.

The Swainson's Hawk appears on the "Blue List" from 1972 to 1982; it was delisted to a species of "special concern" in 1986 (Tate 1986).

The specimen record (RBCM 2664) listed by J.A. Munro and Cowan (1947) from Atlin on 19 June 1914 has recently been identified as a dark-phase Red-tailed Hawk.

There is one possible winter record: sometime between November 1913 and February 1914 an immature was collected (UBC 104) at Penticton.

NOTEWORTHY RECORDS

Spring: Coastal - Saanich 28 May 1983-1; Beaver Lake (Saanich) 12 Apr 1974-1 (Crowell and Nehls 1974c); Saltspring Island 7 Mar 1976-1; **Interior** - Oliver to Richter Lake 17 May 1959-4; Penticton 26 Mar 1966-1; Wasa 9 May 1947-2 (Johnstone, W.B. 1949); Minnie Lake 2 May 1979-6; Vernon 28 Apr 1963-4, 1 May 1936-4; Otter Lake (Vernon) 25 Mar 1973-1; Revelstoke National Park 5 May 1890-1 (Cowan and Munro 1944); Horse Lake (100 Mile House) 27 Apr 1977-2; Vanderhoof 8 May 1945-1 (Munro, J.A. and Cowan 1947).

Summer: Coastal - Comox 8 Jun 1953-1 female (RBCM 12444). **Interior** - Manning Park 24 Aug 1977-3 immatures; Osoyoos 10 Jun 1963-2; Anarchist Mountain 19 Aug 1969-13; Rock Creek (Kettle Valley) 25 Aug 1975-5; Newgate 11 Jun 1953-1 (Godfrey 1955); Douglas Plateau 22 Jun 1980-8, 11 Aug 1982-10; Goose Lake (Vernon) 17 Aug 1952-5; Crowfoot Mountain 19 Aug 1970-6 (Stevens et al. 1970); Pyramid Mountain (Wells Gray Park) 23 Aug 1971-1 (Grass 1971); Cottonwood 13 Aug 1929-1 (MCZ 281640); 37 km n Hazelton 24 Aug 1921-1 immature male (MVZ 42049) with toad in stomach (Swarth 1924); Telegraph Creek (Stikine River) 3 Jun 1919-1 (MVZ 39760; Swarth 1924).

Autumn: Interior - Williams Lake 4 Sep 1954-1 female (NMC 47644); Riske Creek 15 Sep 1978-1 immature; Kamloops 1 Sep 1986-7, 2 Sep 1981-7; Okanagan Landing 28 Sep 1920-1 male (ROM 84667); Naramata 3 Oct 1943-1; Wasa 4 Sep 1942-1 male (RBCM 11196); Waldo 7 Oct 1943-1 (Johnstone, W.B. 1949); Bridesville 20 Sep 1973-1. **Coastal** - Victoria Sep 1898-1 (RBCM 1709), 30 Oct 1969-1 (Crowell and Nehls 1970a); Witty's Lagoon 7 Sep 1975-2.

Winter: Interior - See Remarks. **Coastal** - See Christmas Counts.

Christmas Counts: Interior Not recorded. **Coastal** - Recorded from 3 of 28 localities and on 2% of all counts. Maxima: Individual birds were reported from Deep Bay 29 Dec 1979; Pitt Meadows 27 Dec 1977, 30 Dec 1978, 30 Dec 1979; White Rock 30 Dec 1973, 2 Jan 1978, 30 Dec 1978. However, the wide range of plumage variations of the Swainson's Hawk and the close resemblance of it to other buteos makes it one of the more difficult North American birds of prey to identify (Beebe 1974). Because of that, and because we are unaware of any winter records with convincing details, save possibly one (see Remarks), we have not considered the Christmas Count records in the status or seasonal distribution of the species.

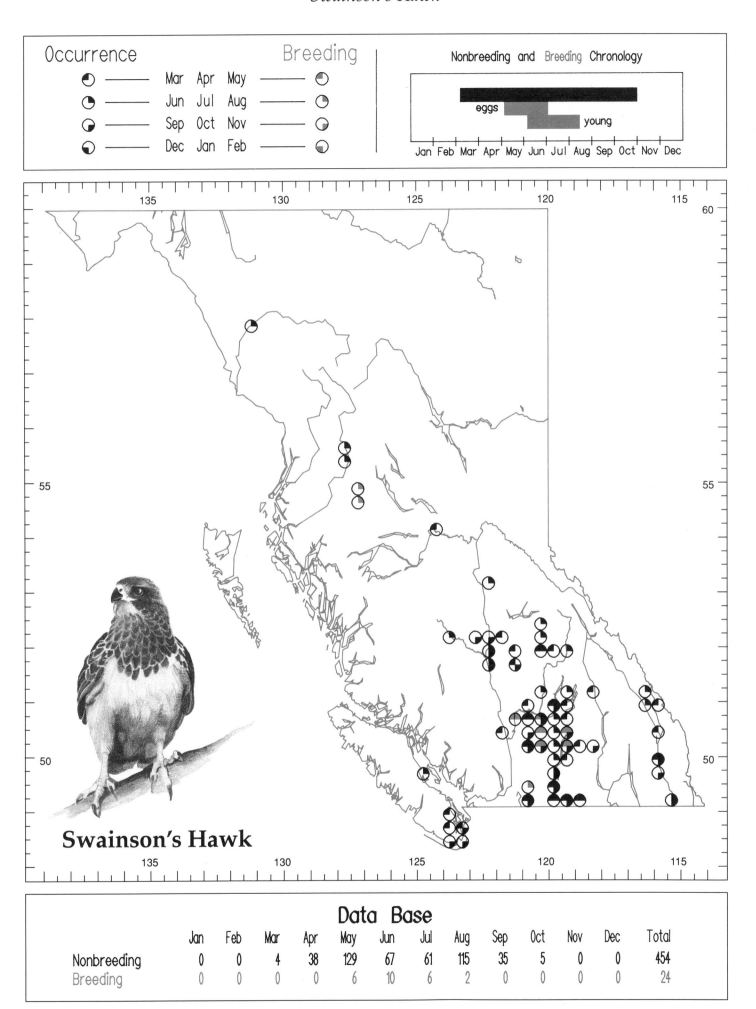

Swainson's Hawk

Data Base

	Jan	Feb	Mar	Apr	May	Jun	Jul	Aug	Sep	Oct	Nov	Dec	Total
Nonbreeding	0	0	4	38	129	67	61	115	35	5	0	0	454
Breeding	0	0	0	0	6	10	6	2	0	0	0	0	24

Red-tailed Hawk

RTHA

Buteo jamaicensis (Gmelin)

RANGE: Breeds from central Alaska, the Yukon, and western Mackenzie, east to southern Quebec and the Maritime Provinces, and south to Florida, the West Indies and Central America. Winters from southern Canada southward.

STATUS: *Uncommon* resident along the coast, including Vancouver Island and the Queen Charlotte Islands, and in the Okanagan, Shuswap and South Thompson regions of the Thompson-Okanagan Plateau. *Uncommon* summer visitant throughout the rest of the province. *Casual* in winter in the interior north of latitude 51°N. *Fairly common* to *common* migrant throughout the province. Widespread breeder.

NONBREEDING: The Red-tailed Hawk is found in almost any open or semi-open habitat from sea level to above the timberline (2,500 m). Open woodlands, grasslands, parklands, rangeland, and agricultural fields with scattered trees are preferred; forest clearings, alpine meadows, airports, estuaries, and marshes are frequented seasonally.

The spectacular migratory flights that occur in eastern North America are not evident in British Columbia. While small numbers are occasionally reported soaring together under certain atmospheric conditions, it appears that most movements are of individuals. Migration routes are poorly known. The spring movement probably follows river valleys and coastlines, and much of the autumn movement is suspected to occur along mountain ridges and meadows.

Spring migration begins in late February and early March in southern areas, but the main movement through the province occurs in April, with some passage in northern areas still evident in early May. The autumn movement begins in the latter half of August, with most birds passing through the province in September. The latest autumn departure date for northern areas is 31 October (Fort St. John).

The major wintering area in the province is the Fraser Lowlands. Populations there are supplemented by birds arriving from the north throughout November and into December (Campbell et al. 1972b). Peaks vary, but most occur in December and February. The Red-tailed Hawk was the most abundant year-round raptor next to the Northern Harrier during counts in the Fraser River delta and Pitt Meadows from January 1975 to May 1980 (Douglas, A. 1984). Christmas Bird Count data indicate a steady increase in numbers of wintering birds from the Fraser River delta and Pitt Meadows between 1972 and 1987, (Fig. 18). In winter, at least, the Red-tailed Hawk is now the most abundant raptor in these areas.

BREEDING: The Red-tailed Hawk breeds throughout the province, including offshore islands, from sea level to at least 2,230 m elevation. Breeding densities are lowest in northern areas (Boreal Forest) as well as on the Queen Charlotte Islands, northern mainland coast, and Vancouver Island, where the diversity of preferred prey (i.e. small mammals) is lowest. The Fraser Lowlands, probably supports the highest breeding densities in the province and compares favourably with other areas in North America. During a study from 1979 to 1985 in Richmond, Runyan (1987) calculated a mean nest density of one nest per 3.6 km². This value is higher than that of one pair per 7.0 km², 7.2 km², and 5.7 km² reported in Wisconsin (Orians and Kuhlman 1956), Alberta (Luttich et al. 1971), and New York (Hagar, D.C. 1957) respectively. The highest density in North America was reported by Fitch et al. (1946) as one pair per 1.3 km² in California.

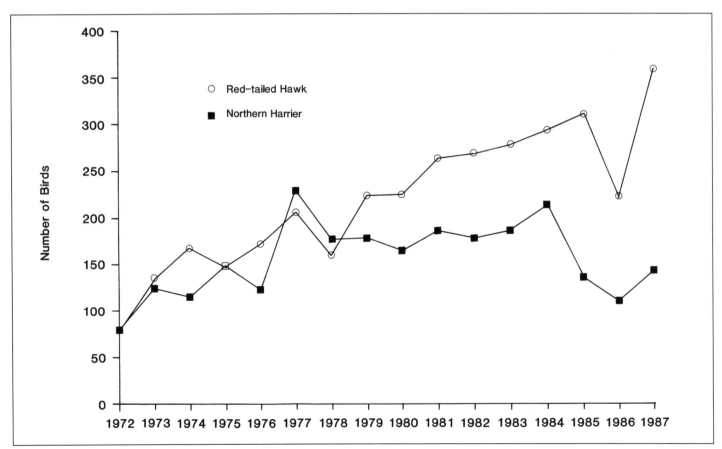

Figure 18. *Fluctuations in numbers of the Red-tailed Hawk and Northern Harrier on Christmas Bird Counts in the Lower Mainland for the period 1972 to 1987. Numbers are aggregate totals for Ladner, Pitt Meadows, Vancouver, and White Rock count areas*

Red-tailed Hawk

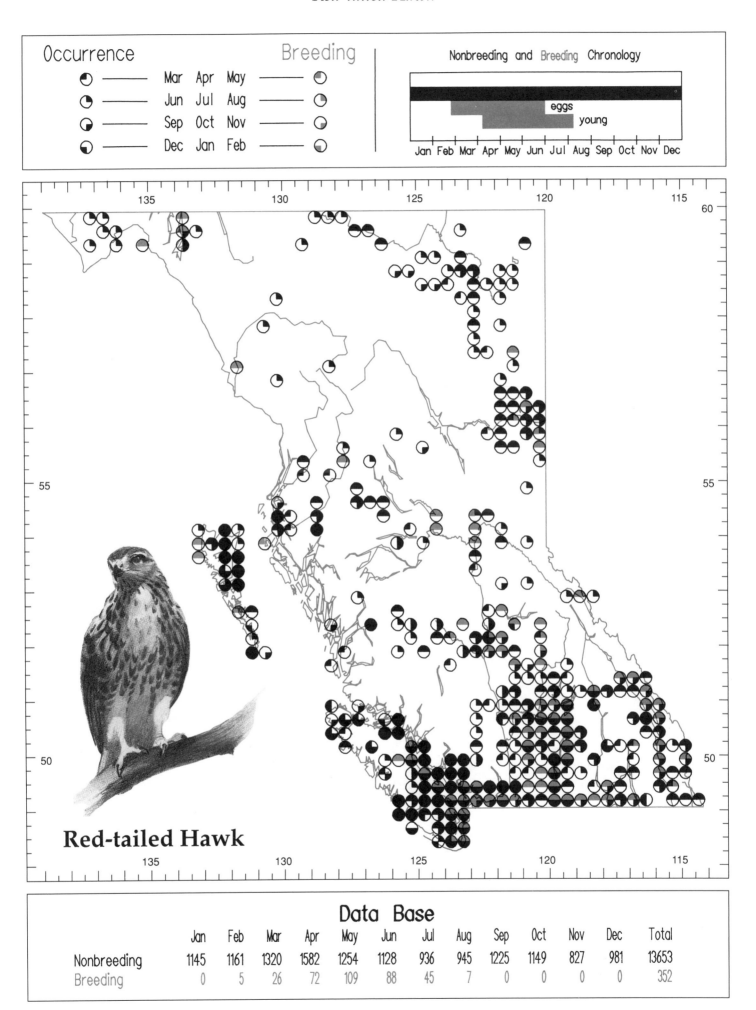

Occurrence / Breeding

	Mar	Apr	May
	Jun	Jul	Aug
	Sep	Oct	Nov
	Dec	Jan	Feb

Nonbreeding and Breeding Chronology

eggs

young

Jan Feb Mar Apr May Jun Jul Aug Sep Oct Nov Dec

Red-tailed Hawk

Data Base

	Jan	Feb	Mar	Apr	May	Jun	Jul	Aug	Sep	Oct	Nov	Dec	Total
Nonbreeding	1145	1161	1320	1582	1254	1128	936	945	1225	1149	827	981	13653
Breeding	0	5	26	72	109	88	45	7	0	0	0	0	352

Breeding habitat varies considerably, but is closely associated with open or semi-open country. Habitat includes the edges of deciduous, coniferous, and mixed woodlands, agricultural areas with woods and fence rows, parkland, river bottomlands, woods bordering lakes, bogs, and marshes, and open woodlands on hills (Fig. 19). Trembling aspen and black cottonwood groves, cliffs, burns, islands in rivers and lakes, large scattered trees bordering highways and roads, and alpine meadows are used less frequently.

Nests: Most nests (92%; n=212) were in trees, and most of the trees were living; the remaining nests were on cliff ledges and in stumps (Fig. 20). Coniferous trees (48%; 8 species) were used slightly more than deciduous trees (44%; 4 species). Black cottonwood (38%), Douglas-fir (19%), and ponderosa pine (19%) were the nest trees most often used.

Nests were well-concealed and situated in or near the tree crown, usually in a crotch or on a branch next to the trunk. Heights of 182 tree nests ranged from 6 to 46 m, with 51% recorded between 12 and 18 m. Cliff nests were up to 76 m above the ground.

There was a great variety of nest structures, from compact to loosely-organized dead and living sticks and twigs. The material ranged in diameter from 0.6 to 9 cm. Outside nest diameters ranged from 36 to 107 cm, outside depths ranged from 23 to 122 cm. Most nests were lined with both fresh and old conifer sprigs, as well as strips of coniferous and deciduous bark, rootlets, leaves, mosses, cones, grasses, feathers, and conifer needles.

Eggs: Dates for 83 clutches ranged from 28 February to 20 June, with 53% recorded between 16 April and 6 May. Calculated dates indicate that eggs could be found as late as 2 July. Sizes for 81 clutches ranged from 1 to 4 eggs (1E-8, 2E-38, 3E-28, 4E-7), with 81% having 2 or 3 eggs. Incubation period is about 34 days (Hegner 1906).

Young: Dates for 237 broods (Fig. 21) ranged from 10 April to 9 August, with 54% recorded between 22 May and 29 June. Most young leave the nest in July. Sizes for 174 broods ranged from 1 to 4 young (1Y-52, 2Y-97, 3Y-21, 4Y-4), with 56% having 2 young. Fledging period is about 45 days (Beebe 1974).

REMARKS: Three of the seven North American Red-tailed Hawk subspecies recognized by the American Ornithologists' Union (1957, 1973) occur in British Columbia. *Buteo jamaicensis alascensis* breeds on the Queen Charlotte Islands (Taverner 1936; Fig. 22) and in coastal areas including Vancouver Island. *B. j. calurus* breeds in the interior and *B. j. harlani* (a valid subspecies, Mindell 1983) breeds in northern British Columbia. The precise ranges of the subspecies are not known.

Figure 19. *Red-tailed Hawk nest at Midway, June 1973 (Martin C. Lee).*

Figure 20. *Red-tailed Hawk nest with young near Princeton, 31 May 1972 (R. Wayne Campbell).*

Figure 21. *Nestling Red-tailed Hawks of the subspecies* B. j. harlani *at Atlin, July 1980 (R. Wayne Campbell).*

Figure 22. *Immature Red-tailed Hawk with Northern Flicker (*Colaptes auratus*) at Sandspit, Queen Charlotte Islands, 12 February 1972 (RBCM Photo 247; Harold Bronsch). This bird belongs to the subspecies* B. j. harlani.

NOTEWORTHY RECORDS

Spring: Coastal - Seymour Hill 30 Mar 1981-5; Saanich 27 Mar 1984-5; Holmes Peak 19 Mar 1983-5; Somenos Lake 16 Mar 1974-4; Boundary Bay 15 Mar 1963-8; Pitt Meadows 6 Mar 1976-14, 8 Mar 1975-19, 13 Mar 1976-33, 10 Apr 1971-10; Vedder River 19 Mar 1961-14. **Interior** - Anarchist Mountain 1 May 1974-7; Richter Pass 21 May 1968-5; Princeton 14 May 1975-4; Fruitvale 11 May 1980-7; Summerland 3 Mar 1964-2; Kamloops 17 Mar 1979-21, 14 Apr 1985-30; 130 Mile House 3 Mar 1982-1; Williams Lake 13 Mar 1979-2; Vanderhoof 2 to 8 May 1945-5 (Munro, J.A. and Cowan 1947); Quick 1 Apr 1978-2; Fort St. John 29 Mar 1981-1, 12 Apr 1986-14, 24 Apr 1983-8; Fort Nelson 12 Apr 1986-1.

Summer: Coastal - Goldstream Park 22 Jun 1984-4. **Interior** - Princeton 24 Aug 1977-6; Okanagan Landing 10 Jun 1925-10 feeding on swarms of large crickets; McQueen Slough 30 Jun 1978-3; Taylor 21 Aug 1975-7.

Autumn: Interior - w Fort Nelson 9 Oct 1985-2; Fort St. John 31 Oct 1982-1; 150 Mile House 7 Sep 1977-6; Douglas Lake (Quilchena) 5 Sep 1972-12; Okanagan Landing 25 Sep 1933-5; Columbia Lake 12 Sep 1981-4; Creston 12 Oct 1975-4. **Coastal** - Cypress Park 11 Sep 1979-17, 4 Oct 1979-14; (Sauppe 1980); Pitt Meadows 10 Nov 1982-19; Sturgeon Slough 30 Nov 1974-17; Sea Island 18 Nov 1979-14; Mount Matheson 14 Oct 1981-10; Nanaimo 26 Sep 1971-4; Rocky Point (Victoria) 10 Oct 1987-20 in several groups of 4 to 6 over 2 hours.

Winter: Interior - Williams Lake 2 Dec 1987-1 adult; Kamloops 29 Dec 1985-2; Otter Lake 9 Feb 1980-3; Nakusp 30 Dec 1984-1, 31 Dec 1978-1; Richter Pass 23 Feb 1974-4 harrasing a Golden Eagle. **Coastal** - Masset 14 Dec 1965-2; Sandspit 12 Feb 1972-1 (RBCM Photo 247-Fig. 22); Bella Coola 12 Jan 1982-2; Pitt Meadows 26 Feb 1977-11; Fort Langley 4 Jan 1976-9; Surrey 22 Dec 1977-8; Sea Island 29 Jan 1979-7; Reifel Island 4 Feb 1981-15; Westham Island 22 Dec 1973-14; Mount Tzuhalem 19 Jan 1974-5.

Christmas Counts: Interior - Recorded from 10 of 19 localities and on 41% of all counts. Maxima: Vernon 19 Dec 1982-35; Penticton 27 Dec 1983- 15; Oliver/Osoyoos 29 Dec 1983-8. **Coastal** - Recorded from 23 of 28 localities and on 79% of all counts. Maxima: Ladner 23 Dec 1984-130; Pitt Meadows 2 Jan 1982-80; Vancouver 18 Dec 1982-63; White Rock 4 Jan 1981-63.

Ferruginous Hawk

FEHA

Buteo regalis (Gray)

RANGE: Breeds from eastern Washington and southern Alberta, Saskatchewan, Manitoba, and North Dakota south to northern Arizona, New Mexico, and Kansas. Winters over much of the breeding range, but mainly from the southwestern United States to central Mexico.

STATUS: *Very rare* summer visitant to the central southern interior. Very local breeder.

CHANGE IN STATUS: The Ferruginous Hawk was first recorded in British Columbia in the spring of 1922, coincidentally in 2 widely separated areas. Records were from the Okanagan valley, at Osoyoos and Vaseux Lake (Brooks 1923b), and from the Peace Lowlands at Fort St. John (Williams, M.Y. 1933b). The latter record we now consider hypothetical (see Remarks). Brooks and Swarth (1925) cite the Osoyoos record, but J.A. Munro and Cowan (1947) consider it hypothetical. J.A. Munro and Cowan (1947) overlook the Fort St. John record. Between 1947 and 1986, 13 sightings were reported including 2 breeding records.

NONBREEDING: The Ferruginous Hawk has been reported mainly in the Okanagan and Nicola regions of the Thompson-Okanagan Plateau north to Shuswap Lake and east to Revelstoke and Wapta Lake.

It inhabits open parkland country with scattered trees and rock bluffs including rangelands, grasslands, and agricultural fields (Fig. 23).

Most records are of single adult birds, from late spring and early summer. Extreme dates are 10 April and 20 September, excluding the one winter record.

All fully documented records, listed in chronological order, are as follows:

(1) Osoyoos 28 April 1922-1 light-coloured adult with "white tail and wing patches; chestnut flank patches very distinct" (Brooks 1923b).
(2) Hody's Bluff (Vaseux Lake) 22 May 1922-1 melanistic bird (Brooks 1923b).
(3) Okanagan Landing 30 August 1944-1 driven away from creek mouth by Peregrine Falcon.
(4) Osoyoos summer 1945-2 adults in open valley just south of Anarchist Mountain.
(5) Aspen Grove mid-June 1968-2 adults seen by a falconer. Another adult seen by the same person late in the month between Merritt and Kamloops. Probably one of the birds seen earlier. See Breeding below.
(6) White Lake (Okanagan Falls) 10 April 1969-1 adult.
(7) Tappen 29 April 1971-1.
(8) Wapta Lake 12 August 1972-1 adult soaring over lake (McLaren and McLaren 1973).
(9) Kelowna 15 May 1977-1 observed for 3 to 4 minutes.
(10) Douglas Lake (Quilchena) 13 June 1978-1 adult.
(11) 16 km south of Logan Lake 20 September 1978-2 adults

with 1 fledgling feeding together in recently cut field. Red-tailed Hawk also feeding on mice scampering about.
(12) Kelowna 10 to 16 January 1979-1 seen by many observers (Cannings, R.A. et al. 1987).
(13) White Lake (Okanagan Falls) 6 June 1980-1 adult.
(14) Anarchist Mountain 8 June 1980-1 adult.
(15) Round Lake (Richter Pass) 10 June 1980-1 adult.
(16) Princeton 13 May 1983-1 adult.
(17) 11 km east of Douglas Lake (Quilchena) 1 May 1984-2 adults.

BREEDING: There is only 1 definite record. A tree nest containing 2 large young was found by falconers north of Aspen Grove in July 1968. One young was taken for falconry purposes and kept for many years. Identification was confirmed by F.L. Beebe (pers. comm.). The nest, large and composed of sticks, was situated about 14 m above the ground in a ponderosa pine.

It is likely, however, that the fledgling, seen in the family group near Logan Lake on 20 September 1978, was raised locally. Isolated pairs may be nesting in scattered locations in the Nicola area, especially where a plentiful prey base of medium-sized mammals exists (e.g. yellow-bellied marmots, northern pocket gophers, and Columbian ground squirrels). The hawks have a more restricted diet than other western hawks, feeding primarily on lagomorphs and large rodents (Smith, D.G. and Murphy 1973; Howard 1975).

Incubation period for the Ferruginous Hawk is about 35 days (Weston 1968); the young fledge at 38 to 50 days (Schmutz 1977)

REMARKS: There are 2 published records, without convincing details, that we consider hypothetical. M.Y. Williams (1933b) mentions, "birds were seen, probably of this species, at Fort St. John, on May 13 and 15, 1922." Callin (1962) reports that a Ferruginous Hawk was observed at Revelstoke in December 1961. There were no other details.

An adult Ferruginous Hawk seen near East Saanich Road on southern Vancouver Island on 29 July 1973 was subsequently found to be a falconer's escaped bird.

The Ferruginous Hawk appears on the "Blue List" from 1972 to 1981 with concern for populations in adjacent Washington and Oregon (Tate 1981). It was delisted to a species of "special concern" in 1982 as it "appears to be holding steady at a reduced level overall or to be locally down" (Tate and Tate 1982) and remained of "special concern" on the 1986 list (Tate 1986).

POSTSCRIPT:
(18) Tranquille 29 July 1989-1 (RBCM Photo 124; Syd Roberts). This record is the first photo-documentation for the province.
(19) Ten Mile Point, Victoria 21 August 1989-1 found dead, shot through wing (RBCM 22247). Bird was seen for a few days previously.

Figure 23. *Typical foraging habitat of the Ferruginous Hawk in the vicinity of Douglas Lake, east of Quilchena (John M. Cooper).*

Ferruginous Hawk

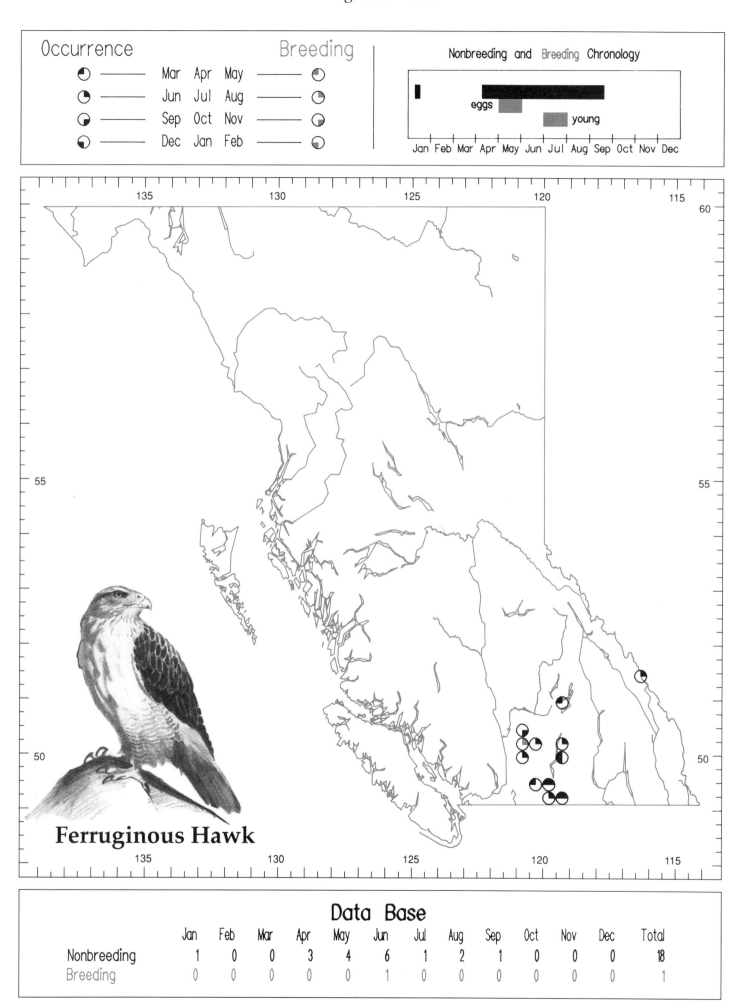

Rough-legged Hawk

RLHA

Buteo lagopus (Pontoppidan)

RANGE: Circumpolar. In North America, breeds from Alaska eastward across low arctic and subarctic Canada to New-foundland. Winters from southern Canada south to California, Arizona, New Mexico, Oklahoma, Tennessee, and Virginia.

STATUS: Generally a regular migrant and winter visitant throughout the province east of the Coast Ranges as well as southeastern Vancouver Island and the Fraser Lowlands. On the south coast, *rare* to *uncommon* in winter on southern Vancouver Island and *uncommon* to *fairly common* through the Fraser Lowlands. *Casual* in summer. In the interior, generally *rare* but locally *uncommon* in winter in the northern Okanagan valley, the Kamloops-Douglas Lake region, and the Creston valley. *Very rare* in summer.

OCCURRENCE: The Rough-legged Hawk occurs as a migrant and winter visitant throughout most of the province east of the Coast Ranges, becoming locally distributed north of 52°N latitude. It also occurs on the south coast primarily along the southeast coast of Vancouver Island and in the Fraser Lowlands.

The Rough-legged Hawk inhabits open, treeless areas including grasslands, rangelands, marshes, alpine meadows, grassy slopes of hills, short-grass fields of airports, and agricultural fields (Fig. 25), but rarely cultivated fields. It has been recorded from sea level to at least 2,130 m elevation, the latter in autumn migration. Eighty-three percent of all records are from coastal areas.

Rough-legged Hawks migrate singly or in small numbers; only rarely are they seen in large flocks. Hardy (1957) reported 2 instances of large flocks: 10 and 22 birds flying "in formation" over Blenkinsop Lake in the autumn of 1952. Spring migration in southern areas occurs mainly in the latter part of March and early April. Late birds can be seen in May. In northern areas, the movement is most noticeable in mid-April. Autumn migrants appear in mid-to-late September some years, but the main autumn movement in southern areas occurs in late October and early November. Banding returns indicate that birds associated with British Columbia breed in Alaska (Fig. 24).

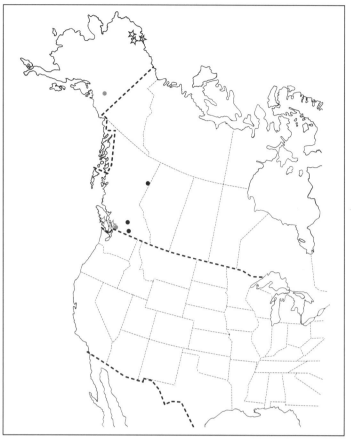

Figure 24. *Banding locations (stars) and recovery sites (circles) of Rough-legged Hawks associated with British Columbia. Red indicates birds banded in British Columbia, black indicates birds banded elsewhere.*

Figure 25. *In the Fraser Lowlands, open agricultural areas bordered by shrubs support the major wintering populations of Rough-legged Hawks in the province (R. Wayne Campbell).*

Rough-legged Hawk

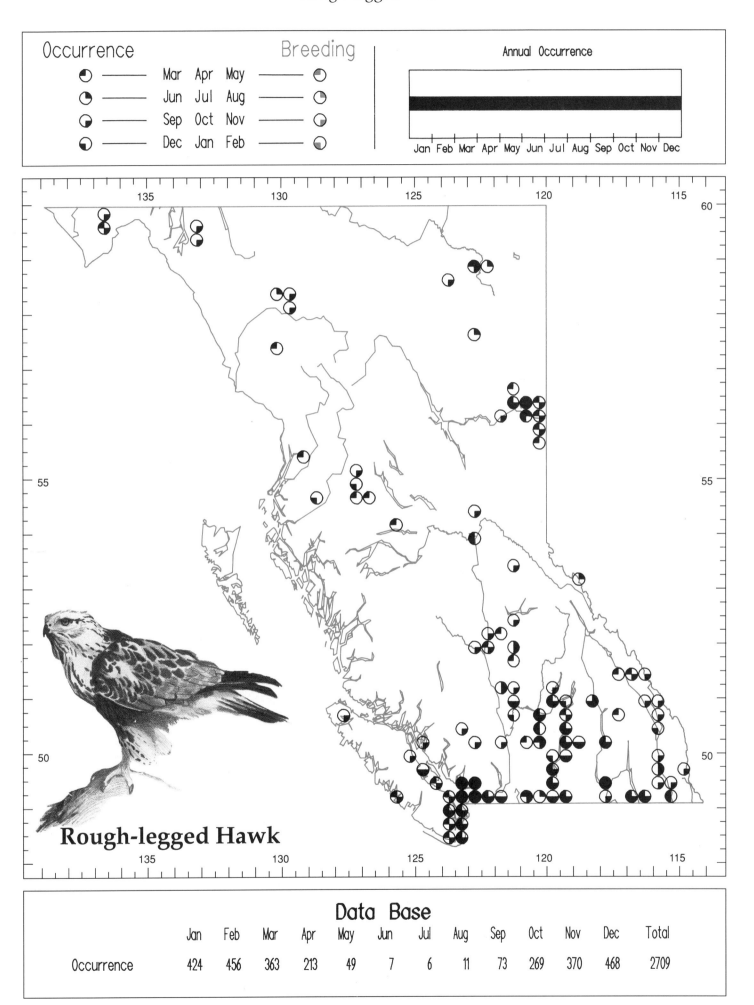

Occurrence

◑ ——	Mar Apr May	—— ◑
◔ ——	Jun Jul Aug	—— ◔
◷ ——	Sep Oct Nov	—— ◷
◕ ——	Dec Jan Feb	—— ◕

Breeding

Annual Occurrence

Jan Feb Mar Apr May Jun Jul Aug Sep Oct Nov Dec

Rough-legged Hawk

Data Base

	Jan	Feb	Mar	Apr	May	Jun	Jul	Aug	Sep	Oct	Nov	Dec	Total
Occurrence	424	456	363	213	49	7	6	11	73	269	370	468	2709

The major wintering area in the province is the Fraser Lowlands especially in the vicinity of Sea Island and Delta (Fig. 26). There, peak numbers occur from December to March. The Rough-legged Hawk was the third most abundant raptor observed in counts in the Fraser River delta and Pitt Meadows from January 1975 to May 1980 (Douglas, A. 1984). In the interior, small numbers winter in the northern Okanagan valley, the Kamloops area, and the Creston valley.

In southern coastal areas, the earliest records for arrivals are 28 August 1966 and 1983 (Sea Island) and 28 August 1975 (Delta); the latest records for departures are 18 May 1976 (Surrey) and 25 May 1974 (Mill Bay). In southern interior areas, the earliest records are 8 September 1982 (Kootenay National Park) and 18 September 1926 (Trout Creek, Summerland - RBCM 11498); the latest records are 18 May 1963 (Manning Park) and 24 May 1986 (Kamloops). These are exclusive of unusual June, July, and early August records.

REMARKS: The plumage of the Rough-legged Hawk varies greatly, with many intergradations between light (Fig. 27) and dark phases (Cade 1955). In British Columbia, the ratio of light-phase birds to dark-phase birds was 2.7:1 (n=236) .

POSTSCRIPT: A single light-phase bird was seen at Delkatla Inlet (Fig. 28) on 26 and 29 November 1988, the first record for the Queen Charlotte Islands (Campbell 1989a).

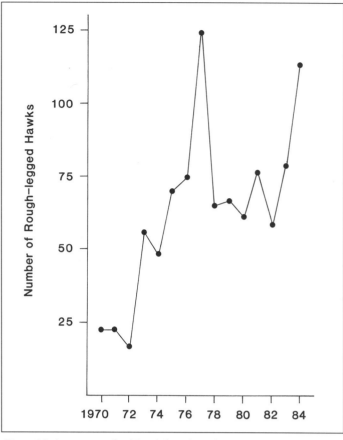

Figure 26. *Aggregate totals of Rough-legged Hawks recorded on Christmas Bird Counts at Vancouver, Ladner, White Rock, and Pitt Meadows, British Columbia, 1970 to 1984.*

Figure 27. *Light-phase Rough-legged Hawk in hedgerow on Iona Island, Richmond, 26 October 1980 (Ervio Sian).*

Figure 28. *Delkatla Inlet at Masset, Queen Charlotte Islands, 28 June 1982. (Dennis A. Demarchi). The open, brackish wetland is an important habitat on the Queen Charlotte Islands for wintering raptors, waterbirds, and wading birds as well as for breeding shorebirds, notably the Least Sandpiper.*

NOTEWORTHY RECORDS

Spring: Coastal - Cedar 2 May 1982-1; Sea Island 3 Mar 1979-11; Delta 8 Mar 1975-9. **Interior** - Anarchist Mountain 3 Apr 1962-8; Creston 19 Mar 1977-1, 3 Apr 1967-5; Chapperon Lake 6 Mar 1983-4; Vernon 6 Apr 1929-7; Kamloops 30 Mar 1985-6, 8 Apr 1984-30, 21 Apr 1979-20, 24 May 1986-2; Riske Creek 2 Apr 1983-1; 141 Mile House 9 Apr 1950-1 male (RBCM 15556); 35 km s Williams Lake 2 Apr 1977-1; Dawson Creek (Peace River) 11 Apr 1985-3; Clayhurst 29 Mar 1981-3; Fort St. John 5 Apr 1986-small flocks appeared, 12 Apr 1986-31; Fort Nelson 19 Apr 1986-1; Chilkat Pass 16 May 1977-1 adult.

Summer: Coastal - Sea Island 28 Aug 1966-3, 28 Aug 1983-1; Surrey 27 Aug 1987-2, 28 Aug 1975-1; Pitt Meadows 1 Jun 1975-1. **Interior** - Manning Park 25 to 30 Jul 1973-2 (Crowell and Nehls 1973d), 10 Aug 1974-1 with freshly killed ptarmigan; Pyramid Mountain (Cathedral Park) 4 Aug 1975-1; St. Mary's Indian Reserve 12 Aug 1976-1; Chapperon Lake 4 Jun 1962-1; Revelstoke 3 Jun 1978-1 at airport (Bonar 1978b); n Clinton 22 Jun 1964-1; Lac la Hache 4 Aug 1940-1 adult (Munro, J.A. and Cowan 1947); Dease Lake 18 Jul 1962-1 (NMC 50413); s Trutch 19 Jul 1987-1 immature; Fort Nelson 15 Jun 1986-1 (RBCM Photo 1121); Kotcho Lake 26 Jun 1982-1 (Campbell and McNall 1982).

Autumn: Interior - Kelsall Lake 4 to 10 Sep 1974-12; O'Donnel valley (Atlin) 3 Oct 1980-2 adults; Muskwa 17 Sep 1943-2 (Rand 1944); Stikine River 5 Sep 1977-1 adult; Cecil Lake 1 Oct 1983-6; nw Fort St. John 27 Oct 1986-1; Jones Creek (Peace River) 11 Sep 1979-1; 114 Mile House 8 Sep 1944-1 (Munro, J.A. and Cowan 1947); Kootenay National Park 8 Sep 1982-1; Adams Lake (Chase) 22 Sep 1980-1; Okanagan Landing 9 Oct 1929-3; Douglas Plateau 22 Oct 1982-15; Black Knight Mountain 13 Oct 1982-1; Waneta 27 Sep 1981-1. **Coastal** - Cortes Island 22 Oct 1975-1; Pitt Meadows 14 Sep 1974-9; Vancouver 6 Sep 1949-1, Sep 1882-1 male (RBCM 421); Sea Island 1 Sep 1976-2, 11 Nov 1973-11, 23 Nov 1982-14; Blenkinsop Lake 19 Sep 1952-10 in migrating flock, 27 Sep 1945-22 in formation, gliding silently (Hardy 1957).

Winter: Interior - Fort St. John 20 Feb 1983-1 (Grunberg 1983a); Smithers 15 Dec 1979-1; 24 km s Prince George 27 Feb 1982-1; Revelstoke 29 Dec 1982-1; 4 km e Cache Creek 20 Jan 1985-1; Kamloops 17 Dec 1983-9, 15 Jan 1984-3; Lake Windermere 26 Dec 1982-1; Vernon 9 Feb 1928-1 (RBCM 9252); O'Keefe 30 Dec 1967-3; Kalamalka Lake 1 Jan 1981-4; Castlegar 27 Dec 1980-1; Creston 21 Jan 1976-27. **Coastal** - Hornby Island 25 Feb 1978-1; Sea and Iona islands 21 Dec 1977-15; Sea Island 26 Jan 1974-12, 22 Feb 1978-14.

Christmas Counts: Interior - Recorded from 7 of 19 localities and on 23% of all counts. Maxima: Vernon 18 Dec 1983-31; Oliver/Osoyoos 28 Dec 1980-6; Kamloops 15 Dec 1984-3. **Coastal** - Recorded from 9 of 28 localities and on 28% of all counts. Maxima: Ladner 23 Dec 1984-72; Vancouver 18 Dec 1977-39; White Rock 2 Jan 1978-32.

Golden Eagle

Aquila chrysaetos (Linnaeus)

GOEA

RANGE: In North America, breeds from northwestern Alaska and Canada south to the southern United States and central Mexico. Winters from northern British Columbia, Alberta, Manitoba and eastern Canada south into Mexico. Also found in Eurasia and North Africa.

STATUS: *Rare* to *uncommon* resident in mountainous and hilly country across southern British Columbia. *Uncommon* migrant and summer visitant in the interior north of latitude 52°N. *Very rare* in winter in the Peace Lowlands; *casual* elsewhere in the north. Breeds.

NONBREEDING: The Golden Eagle is widely distributed in the interior of the province east of the Coast Ranges, throughout the Fraser Lowlands, and along the east coast of Vancouver Island. There are very few records for other coastal areas and none for the Queen Charlotte Islands. Golden Eagles may be seen soaring over almost any habitat from sea level to 3,200 m elevation. They forage in a variety of open habitats, including rangelands, grasslands, marshes, agricultural fields, mountain slopes, highways (for road-kill mammals), and, occasionally, garbage dumps. In winter, Golden Eagles are found at lower elevations.

The Golden Eagle reaches its greatest densities for British Columbia in the highland habitats from Dease Lake northward into the Yukon (F.L. Beebe pers. comm.).

Migration periods are not well known. The spring movement probably occurs from March to mid-April. Autumn migration is more protracted, and probably occurs in September and October.

BREEDING: The Golden Eagle breeds on southeastern Vancouver Island, the Fraser Lowlands, and throughout most of the interior east of the Coast Ranges. Breeding records are lacking from the central part of the province where nesting habitat is marginal and food supplies are limited. It breeds in mountainous areas, along deep river canyons (Fig. 29) and on large coastal islands. Nests have been found from near sea level to 2,380 m elevation, but mostly between 300 and 1,220 m.

Nests: Most nests (51%; n=52) were situated on cliff ledges (Fig. 30). Other nests were found in trees (27%), among overhanging rock faces, on top of rock bluffs and pinnacles, and in caves (Fig. 31). Of the tree nests, 9 were in Douglas-fir, 4 were in ponderosa pine and 1 was in an unidentified snag. Heights of tree nests ranged from 9 to 26 m. Cliff nests ranged in height from 12 to 38 m from the base of the cliff. All nests were built of thick (up to 5 cm diameter) branches and sticks (Fig. 32). Cliff nests were usually less massive than tree nests, although 1 cliff nest was a 7 m pile of sticks, the largest nest reported. Most nests were lined with green Douglas-fir boughs, grasses, bark, and mosses. Nest sizes ranged from 0.8 to 2.7 m in height, and 1.1 to 1.8 m in diameter.

Most nest-building occurred in March, although on 22 December 1979, 2 adults were seen carrying sticks to a nest in the north Okanagan. Some nests were re-occupied; 1 tree nest was used for 5 consecutive years.

Eggs: Dates for 12 clutches ranged from 23 April to 11 June, with 7 clutches recorded between 3 and 9 May. Calculated dates indicate that eggs could be found as early as 13 March. Clutch sizes ranged from 1 to 3 eggs (1E-4, 2E-7, 3E-1). Incubation period is 43 to 45 days (Beebe 1974).

Figure 29. *Mule Creek, Chilkat Pass, 6 June 1988 (William T. Munro). Ledges along deep river canyons provide nest sites for Golden Eagles throughout their range in the province.*

Golden Eagle

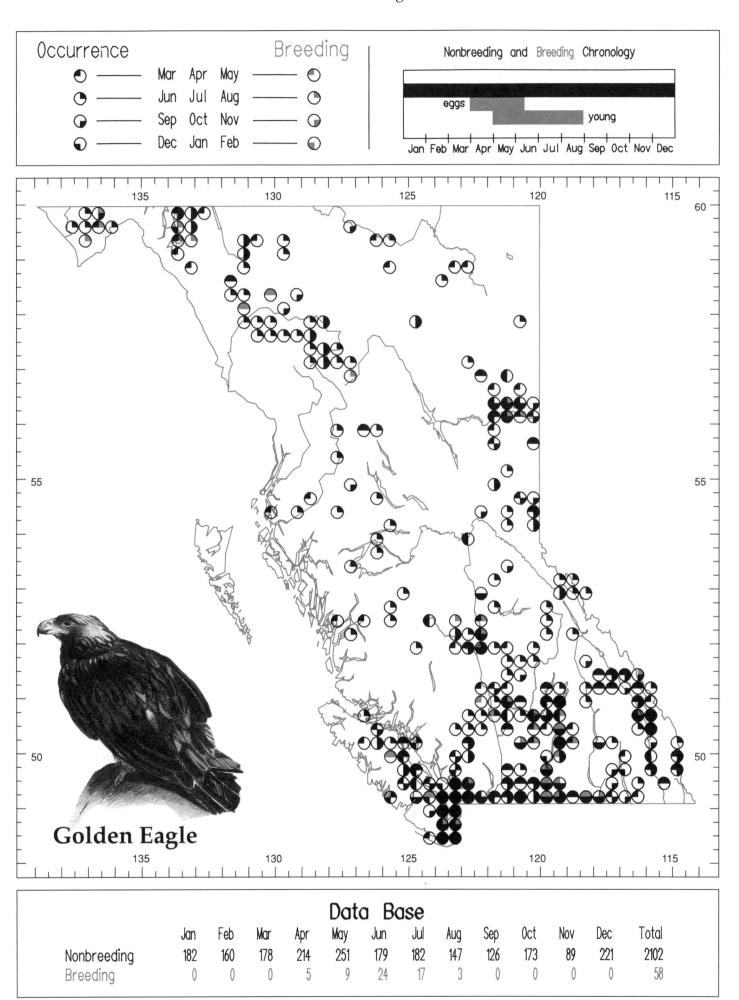

Occurrence — **Breeding**

	Mar	Apr	May
	Jun	Jul	Aug
	Sep	Oct	Nov
	Dec	Jan	Feb

Nonbreeding and Breeding Chronology

eggs — young

Jan Feb Mar Apr May Jun Jul Aug Sep Oct Nov Dec

Golden Eagle

Data Base

	Jan	Feb	Mar	Apr	May	Jun	Jul	Aug	Sep	Oct	Nov	Dec	Total
Nonbreeding	182	160	178	214	251	179	182	147	126	173	89	221	2102
Breeding	0	0	0	5	9	24	17	3	0	0	0	0	58

Young: Dates for 56 broods ranged from 30 April to 28 August, with 50% recorded between 14 June and 18 July. Sizes for 42 broods ranged from 1 to 3 young (1Y-20, 2Y-21, 3Y-1) with 50% having 2 young (Fig. 33). Fledging period is 63 to 70 days (Beebe 1974).

REMARKS: The Golden Eagle has been persecuted for years by ranchers and others because of the partly alleged, partly real damage the birds have caused to domestic livestock (Beebe 1974). From the early 1940s to the 1960s over 20,000 Golden Eagles were killed in the southwestern United States alone (Spofford 1969) as part of eradication programs established by ranchers and government agencies. Since then, public attitudes have changed and laws aimed at preventing the destruction of the species are now in place, although the illegal killing of the birds still continues. Numbers of Golden Eagles in eastern North America, however, appear to be increasing (see review in De Smet 1986) and estimates of the North American population now range from 50,000 to 100,000 birds (see Snow 1973). Populations in the interior of British Columbia appear stable. On the coast, the Golden Eagle has recently become established as a breeding bird along southeastern Vancouver Island. In the early 1940s it was considered casual anywhere near the coast (Munro, J.A. and Cowan 1947). By the late 1940s and early 1950s, sightings of the bird increased, and in 1954, the first breeding record was documented at Upper Campbell Lake (Laing 1956). By 1973, the breeding range had extended southward to Malahat; about the same time, Golden Eagles began to be recorded regularly in Christmas Bird Counts at Victoria. The successful establishment and range expansion of Golden Eagles on Vancouver Island appears to correlate with the introduction of the Eastern Cottontail (*Sylvilagus floridanus*). With large areas of coastal British Columbia now opened through clearcut logging, there may be a further expansion of the Golden Eagle's breeding range along the mainland coast as their favoured prey species move into the clearcuts (see Bruce et al. 1982).

An excellent summary of world literature on the genus *Aquila* has recently been published by the National Wildlife Federation (Le Franc and Clark 1983). Consult W.S. Clark (1983), for details on the identification of North American eagles, especially immatures.

Figure 30. Golden Eagle nests on cliff ledge, 1 km south Kusawa River falls, Chilkat Pass, 2 June 1988 (William T. Munro). In 1988, the site was occcupied by nesting Gyrfalcons.

Figure 31. Golden Eagle nest site at the entrance to an open rock cave, 14 km south of Kusawa River falls, 2 June 1988 (William T. Munro).

Figure 32. Active Golden Eagle nest near Goat Creek, Chilkat Pass, July 1980 (Michael C. E. McNall).

Figure 33. *Golden Eagle nestlings in nest at Tatlatui Park, 1 July 1976 (Ted Osmond-Jones).*

NOTEWORTHY RECORDS

Spring: Coastal - Saanich 12 Mar 1978-3; Malahat 23 Mar 1980-3; Mitlenatch Island 2 May 1971-1 adult (Sirk and Sirk 1971); Ocean Falls 25 Apr 1924-1 female (RBCM 14604). **Interior** - Midway 28 May 1975-3 adults (van Drimmelen and Sullivan 1976); Grand Forks 25 Mar 1978-3; White Lake (Okanagan Falls) 20 Apr 1975-3; Trapp Lake 4 Mar 1984-4; Radium Hot Springs 14 May 1963-2 (Seel 1965); Spences Bridge to Westwold 6 Mar 1983-9; Vernon 6 Apr 1929-6, 8 May 1937-5; Glacier National Park 15 Mar 1979-1; 111 Mile House 6 Apr 1978-3; Williams Lake 30 Mar 1983-1 adult; Halfway River (Fort St. John) 28 Mar 1986-1; Beatton Park 26 Mar 1983-1 adult, 1 immature; Fort Nelson 3 Apr 1986-1.

Summer: Coastal - Victoria 19 Jul 1945-1 male (RBCM 9732); Strathcona Park 24 Aug 1974-2; Mitlenatch Island 2 and 5 Jun 1963-1 (van Tets 1963), 7 Aug 1972-1 (Erasmus and Erasmus 1972).

Interior - Lyle Creek 17 Aug 1985-3; Vernon 17 Jun 1975-3; Kootenay National Park 26 Jul 1981-3; Sherbrooke Lake 2 Aug 1944-3 (Wade 1977); Tonquin Ridge 29 Aug 1974-3 (Cannings, R.A. et al. 1974); Bear Flat 18 Aug 1982-2 adults.

Autumn: Interior - O'Donnel valley (Atlin) 3 Oct 1980 - 9; Gladys Lake 11 Oct 1980 - 5; Cecil Lake (Goodlow) 16 Oct 1983-2 adults, 1 immature; Bear Flat 11 Nov 1985-2; Tocher Ridge 1 Oct 1976-3 (Wade 1977); Invermere 11 Oct 1986-3; Natal Ridge 3 Oct 1983-3; Black Knight Mountain 27 Sep 1982-3; 9.6 km s Oliver 9 Nov 1977-3; Richter Pass 13 Sep 1966-5 (Campbell and Meugens 1971). **Coastal** - Sidney Island 17 Oct 1969-1 female (RBCM 14438); Chatham Islands 22 Oct 1959-3; Matheson Lake 30 Oct 1982-3.

Winter: Interior - Atlin 9 Dec 1980-1 adult; Fort St. John 9 Feb 1983-1 adult; Prince George 31 Dec 1982-1; Williams Lake 1 Jan 1984-1 adult; Kamloops 24 Dec 1980-2; Kootenay National Park 8 Jan 1980-1 adult; Vaseux Lake 14 Dec 1968-2 adults. **Coastal** - Oyster River 23 Jan 1980-1; Comox 23 Jan 1930-1 (RBCM 12453); Grouse Mountain (North Vancouver) 19 Dec 1982-1; Sechelt 5 Feb 1986-1; Brockton Point 26 Dec 1955-1 found exhausted-died 4 Jan 1956; East Sooke 28 Feb 1946-1 male (RBCM 9161).

Christmas Counts: Interior - Recorded from 9 of 19 localities and on 38% of all counts. Maxima: Vaseux Lake 23 Dec 1979-**11**, all-time Canadian high count (Anderson, R.R. 1983); Vernon 19 Dec 1982-6, 18 Dec 1983-6; Oliver/Osoyoos 28 Dec 1979-5. **Coastal** - Recorded from 12 of 28 localities and on 12% of all counts. Maxima: Victoria, 16 Dec 1978-4; White Rock 2 Jan 1977-2, 30 Dec 1978-2; Duncan 15 Dec 1979-2.

American Kestrel

AMKE

Falco sparverius Linnaeus

RANGE: Breeds throughout the Americas from near the tree line in Alaska and Canada south through South America. Winters from southern Canada south through the breeding range. Populations in Canada and the northern United States migrate south as far as Central America and Panama.

STATUS: *Uncommon* to *fairly common* summer visitant throughout the province east of the Coast Ranges, on southern Vancouver Island, and in the Fraser Lowlands. *Fairly common* to *common* migrant, with the exception of the northern mainland coast where it is *very rare*; *casual* on the Queen Charlotte Islands. In winter, *rare* to *uncommon* in the south, *casual* in northern areas. Widespread breeder.

NONBREEDING: The American Kestrel is widely distributed throughout the province. It inhabits open country and clearings, usually in areas with hunting perches nearby. Preferred habitats include open rangeland, grasslands, agricultural areas, sagebrush areas bordered by fence posts, roadsides with utility poles and wires, and meadows and marshes with adjacent trees. During migration, mountain meadows, burns, valleys, and open waterways are used. In winter, kestrels are found at lower elevations where they are often associated with residential areas, airports, farmlands, and parks. They rarely hunt at feeders. They have been found from sea level to 2,560 m elevation.

Kestrels are primarily migratory in the province. Small numbers winter, mostly on southern Vancouver Island, the Fraser Lowlands and the Okanagan valley, a fairly recent trend (see Munro, J.A. and Cowan 1947). During exceptionally mild winters, they may be found farther north (e.g. Peace Lowlands, Chilcotin-Cariboo).

Migration is most noticeable and sometimes spectacular in the interior (see Campbell 1974, 1978a). In southern areas, spring migration may begin from early to mid-March, but the main movement through the province occurs in April, with some migration still evident in early May. Autumn migration in northern areas begins in mid-August. Most kestrels pass through the province in September, but some movement is still evident in southern areas in early October.

BREEDING: The American Kestrel breeds on southeastern Vancouver Island, in the Fraser Lowlands, and throughout the rest of the province east of the Coast Ranges from near sea level to at least 1,770 m elevation. The centre of abundance is the trembling aspen and ponderosa pine parklands in the central and southern interior.

The American Kestrel breeds in semi-open to open country where trees, poles, and cliffs have cavities large enough for nesting. Specific habitats include trembling aspen groves, woodland edges, river bottomlands, wooded lakeshores, farmlands, burns, meadows, orchards, marshes, bogs, and, infrequently, residential areas.

Nests: Nests were situated in woodpecker holes or natural cavities in living and dead trees (73%; n=261), in man-made structures (23%), and in holes in cliffs; sometimes nests of other species of birds were used. Nests were found in coniferous trees (43%; 6 species) more often than in deciduous trees (30%; 6 species). Ponderosa pine (29%) and Douglas-fir (10%) were the most often reported coniferous trees; important deciduous trees were black cottonwood (19%) and trembling aspen (8%). Man-made structures included nest boxes (17%), buildings, power poles, and fence posts. Other birds' nests included those of Belted Kingfisher, Black-billed Magpie (*Pica pica*), and American Crow (*Corvus brachyrhynchos*). Heights of 166 tree nests ranged from 0.9 to 27.4 m, with 94 nests recorded between 4.6 and 9.1 m. Nest sites in cliffs ranged from 6.1 to 8.5 m above the ground or water. Nest cavities were either unlined or contained wood chips, shavings, rotten pieces of wood, sawdust, leaves, grasses, feathers, and straw, the latter material probably brought to the nest site by European Starlings (*Sturnus vulgaris*). Diameters of 15 cavity openings ranged from 6.4 to 36 cm; depths of 12 cavities ranged from 20 to 91 cm, with 8 between 25 and 31 cm. One cliff nest was positioned at the end of a 0.9 m tunnel.

Eggs: Dates for 132 clutches ranged from 17 April to 20 July, with 50% recorded between 21 May and 6 June. Calculated dates indicate that eggs could be found as early as the first week of April in southern areas. Eggs found after early July are probably addled and represent abandoned clutches. Sizes for 104 clutches ranged from 1 to 6 eggs (1E-1, 2E-6, 3E-16, 4E-32, 5E-48, 6E-1), with 77% having 4 or 5 eggs. Incubation period is 29 to 30 days (Sherman 1913).

Young: Dates for 192 broods ranged from 14 May to 26 August, with 51% recorded between 27 June and 15 July. Calculated dates indicate that young could be found in early May in southern areas. Sizes for 148 broods, ranged from 1 to 6 young (1Y-13, 2Y-31, 3Y-43, 4Y-33, 5Y-27, 6Y-1) with 51% having 3 or 4 young. Fledging period is 30 days (Beebe 1974).

REMARKS: The American Kestrel was formerly known as Sparrow Hawk.

NOTEWORTHY RECORDS

Spring: Coastal - Sea Island 1 Apr 1979-7, 6 May 1981-10; Langley 19 Mar 1961-7; Mission 3 Mar 1968-5; Rosedale 30 Mar 1974-14; Terrace 8 Apr 1970-1. **Interior** - Newgate 17 Apr 1939-23; Princeton 22 Apr 1979-10; Cawston 12 Apr 1969-12; White Lake (Okanagan Falls) 20 Apr 1977-14; Merritt 15 Apr 1968-8; Kamloops to Cache Creek 20 Apr 1981-27, 6 May 1977-9; Sorrento 13 Apr 1971-8; Lac la Hache 11 Apr 1979-6, 12 May 1975-14; Soda Creek 14 Apr 1979-6; Quick 27 Mar 1978-1, 27 Mar 1979-1; Decker Lake 30 Mar 1977-1; Vanderhoof 3 May 1961-20+; Pouce Coupe 23 Apr 1979-1; Bear Flat 3 Apr 1986-1 male; Fort St. John 23 Apr 1983-5, 9 May 1968-9; Rose Prairie 10 Apr 1984-1; Fort Nelson 24 Apr 1977-1; Atlin 23 Apr 1981-2; Liard Hot Springs 5 May 1975-1.

Summer: Coastal - Pike Lake 26 Jun 1982-pair; Saanich 22 Aug 1984-2 adults; Chesterman Beach 27 July 1981-1; Iona Island 8 Aug 1971-3; Vancouver 30 Jun 1972-3 adults; Sumner Lake 21 Jul 1981-2; Comox airport 25 Aug 1973-5; Delkatla Creek 5 Jun 1987-1; Terrace 24 Aug 1969-6 migrating. **Interior** - Manning Park 15 Aug 1973-6 in alpine (Belton 1973); Osoyoos 3 Jul 1971-20; Creston 18 Jun 1978-10; Skookumchuk 30 Aug 1976-17; Pennask Lake road 1 July 1978-20; n Okanagan Lake 18 Aug 1975-15 hunting over hay fields; Pemberton 17 Aug 1972-35 (Crowell and Nehls 1973d); Anderson Lake (D'Arcy) 28 Aug 1968-14; nw Pritchard 17 Aug 1975-25+ hunting over hay fields; Marble Canyon (Pavilion) 3 Jul 1961-25; Alkali Lake (Riske Creek) 17 Jul 1978-21; Wells Gray Park 27 Aug 1976-13; Pine Pass 17 Aug 1975-12; Fort St. John 22 Aug 1975-19.

Autumn: Interior - Kelsall Lake 7 Sep 1974-50 to 60; Fort St. John 11 Oct 1986-1; Hanceville 21 Sep 1982-10+; Kamloops to Salmon Lake 3 Sep 1979-110; Chase 8 Sep 1968-10; Stump Lake (Quilchena) 16 Sep 1953-7; Pemberton 24 Sep 1972-14; North Bend 5 Sep 1985-20+; Wasa 7 Oct 1948-4; Edgewood 7 Sep 1919-"a storm of sparrow hawks" (Kelso 1926); White Lake (Okanagan Falls) 7 Sep 1971-10; Manning Park 2 Sep 1973-8, 17 Sep 1981-6. **Coastal** - Masset Inlet 5 Sep 1974-1, 12 Sep 1980-1; Cape St. James 25 Sep to 10 Oct 1981-1; Cypress Park 11 Sep 1979-18; Iona Island 12 Sep 1971-7; Point Grey 3 Oct 1954-25+ on golf course; Prevost Hill 23 Sep 1971-9.

Winter: Interior - Fort St. John 8 Dec 1970-pair (RBCM 12105, 12106); Williams Lake 28 Dec 1975-1 male; Cache Creek (Ashcroft) 31 Dec 1982-1; Kamloops 23 Jan 1979-2 males; Kamloops to Scotch Creek 20 Feb 1964-3; Enderby 26 Jan 1977-1 male feeding on vole; Summerland 26 Dec 1973-3; Nakusp 20 Jan 1976-1; Castlegar 26 Dec 1976-1; Creston 4 Jan 1987-3; Trail 13 Dec 1973-1 male. **Coastal** - Masset 31 Dec 1983-1 male; Abbotsford 9 Feb 1978-3 (2 males, 1 female); Ridgedale 1 Jan 1968-3; Reifel Island 18 Jan 1964-3 (1 male, 2 females); 14 km s Tofino 5 Jan 1975-1 male; Galiano Island 3 Jan 1970-10; North Saanich 30 Jan 1984-3 (1 male, 2 females).

Christmas Counts: Interior - Recorded from 9 of 19 localities and on 41% of all counts. Maxima: Vernon 18 Dec 1983-31; Kelowna 20 Dec 1981-18; Penticton 27 Dec 1983-7; Oliver/Osoyoos 29 Dec 1983-7. **Coastal** - Recorded from 20 of 28 localities and on 46% of all counts. Maxima: Ladner 29 Dec 1979-12; Vancouver 18 Dec 1983-10; White Rock 2 Jan 1977-8; Victoria 21 Dec 1963-8.

American Kestrel

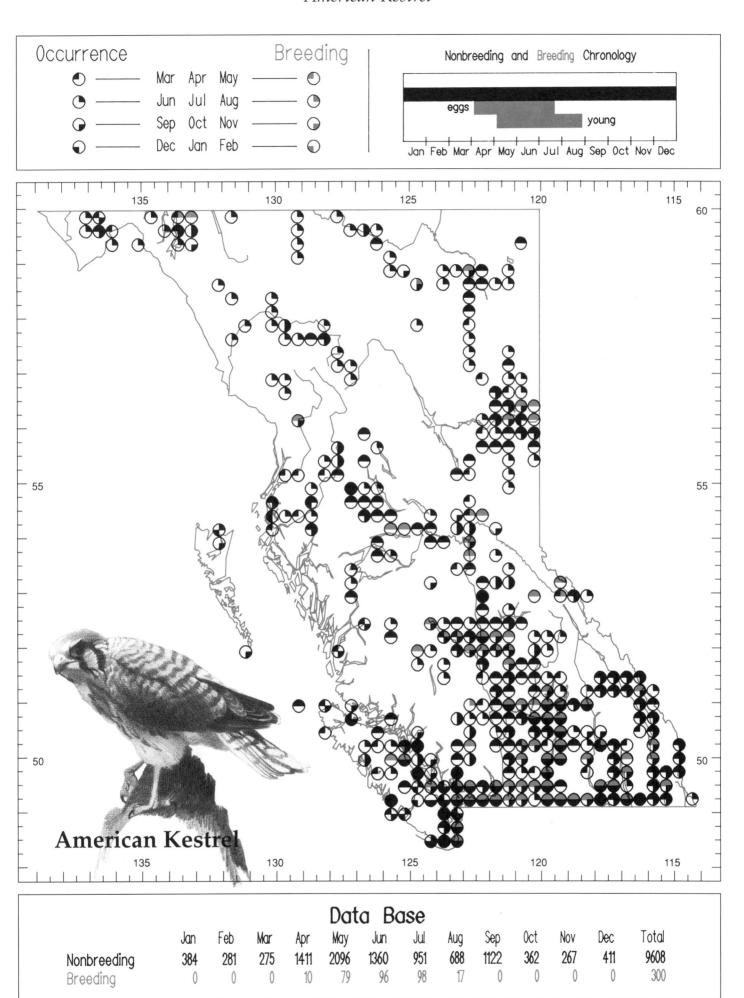

Occurrence / Breeding

Occurrence				Breeding
◑	—	Mar Apr May	—	◕
◔	—	Jun Jul Aug	—	◔
◔	—	Sep Oct Nov	—	◕
◑	—	Dec Jan Feb	—	◔

Nonbreeding and Breeding Chronology

eggs   young

Jan Feb Mar Apr May Jun Jul Aug Sep Oct Nov Dec

American Kestrel

Data Base

	Jan	Feb	Mar	Apr	May	Jun	Jul	Aug	Sep	Oct	Nov	Dec	Total
Nonbreeding	384	281	275	1411	2096	1360	951	688	1122	362	267	411	9608
Breeding	0	0	0	10	79	96	98	17	0	0	0	0	300

Merlin

Falco columbarius Linnaeus

RANGE: Breeds in wooded parts of Alaska and Canada south to central Washington, eastern Oregon, Idaho and eastward along far northern United States to New Brunswick, Nova Scotia and Newfoundland. Winters from south-central Alaska, and southern Canada south to the West Indies, Venezuela and Peru. Also found in Eurasia.

STATUS: *Rare* resident across southern portions of the province below latitude 51°N. *Rare* summer visitant and casual in winter in the north. *Rare* to *uncommon* migrant throughout the province, except the Queen Charlotte Islands where it is *very rare* in autumn. Widespread breeder; breeding not reported from the Queen Charlotte Islands.

NONBREEDING: The Merlin (Fig. 34) is widely distributed throughout the province and can be found in almost any type of country. During migration it prefers open areas along sea coasts, river valleys, lakeshores, and subalpine mountain meadows to at least 2,070 m elevation. Migration in spring is less pronounced than in autumn. It occurs from mid-April through early May in southern areas and about a week later in northern areas. Autumn migration begins in late August, probably peaks in late September and early October, and in some years may continue into early November.

Migration corridors and chronology are poorly known, partly because of the lack of coordinated "hawk watches" and partly because Merlins migrate earlier in the day than other raptors. The movement may start as early as 2 hours before dawn; thus many migrants pass undetected (C.M. Anderson pers. comm.). One known corridor lies along the Alaska Highway between Watson Lake, Yukon and Fort Nelson. Merlins are particularly common there in early September as they prey on, and presumably follow,

migrating Lapland Longspurs (*Calcarius lapponicus*) using this corridor (C.M. White pers. comm.). More than 90% of all records for British Columbia are of single birds; the most reported at once was 6 (see Autumn: Interior in Noteworthy Records).

In winter, Merlins prefer lowlands along sea coasts, valley bottoms, and open waters where small birds abound. Habitats may include estuaries, farmlands, edges of woodlands, marshes, orchards, city parks and cemeteries, school grounds, and residential areas, especially near active bird feeders.

BREEDING: On the coast, the Merlin breeds on Vancouver Island, in Rivers Inlet, and in the Fraser Lowlands. In the interior, it is widely distributed east of the Coast Ranges. It is not known to breed on the Queen Charlotte Islands or the northern mainland coast.

The Merlin is most often reported breeding in coniferous or deciduous woodlands bordering open areas, creeks and rivers, cliffs, hillsides, and lake shores. Nests have been found from near sea level to 790 m elevation. Merlins probably breed near the timberline throughout the province.

Nests: Of 14 nests, 11 were found in conifers, including Douglas-fir (4), spruces (4) and pines (3). The remaining 3 were found in a poplar, a birch, and on a cliff ledge. Thirteen nests were actually old nests of other species of birds including American and Northwestern crows (*Corvus brachyrhynchos* and *C. caurinus*; 6), Black-billed Magpie (*Pica pica*; 4), Steller's Jay (*Cyanocitta stelleri*), Common Raven (*Corvus corax*), and Pileated Woodpecker. Heights of 12 nests ranged from 6.1 to 45.7 m, with 10 heights recorded between 6.1 and 12.2 m. The cliff nest was 41 m above the ground.

Figure 34. Merlin with Dunlin at Iona Island, Richmond, 13 February 1977 (Ervio Sian).

Merlin

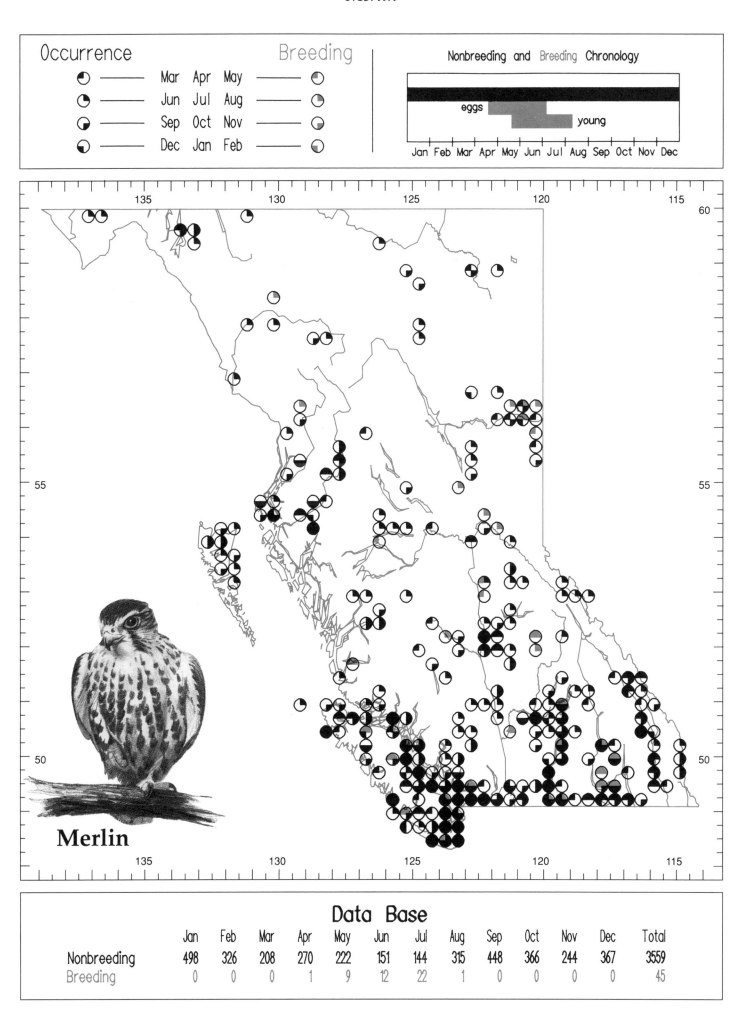

Occurrence

Mar	Apr	May
Jun	Jul	Aug
Sep	Oct	Nov
Dec	Jan	Feb

Breeding

Nonbreeding and Breeding Chronology

eggs

young

Jan Feb Mar Apr May Jun Jul Aug Sep Oct Nov Dec

Data Base

	Jan	Feb	Mar	Apr	May	Jun	Jul	Aug	Sep	Oct	Nov	Dec	Total
Nonbreeding	498	326	208	270	222	151	144	315	448	366	244	367	3559
Breeding	0	0	0	1	9	12	22	1	0	0	0	0	45

Eggs: Dates for 9 clutches ranged from 2 May to 6 July, with 6 clutches recorded between 13 May and 1 June. Calculated dates indicate that eggs could be found as early as 19 April. Sizes for 10 clutches ranged from 1 to 4 eggs (1E-1, 2E-3, 3E-4, 4E-2), with 7 clutches having 2 or 3 eggs. Incubation period is about 29 to 34 days (Beebe 1974; Fox 1971).

Young: Dates for 27 broods ranged from 20 May to 10 August, with 14 broods recorded between 3 and 16 July. It is rare to find young in May and late August. Sizes for 20 broods ranged from 1 to 4 young (1Y-2, 2Y-5, 3Y-11, 4Y-2). Fledging period is about 27 to 30 days (Beebe 1974; Fig. 35).

REMARKS: There is some controversy over the various forms of Merlins found in North America. The American Ornithologists' Union (1957) recognizes 4 subspecies: *F. c. bendirei, F. c. columbarius, F. c. richardsonii* and *F. c. suckleyi.* Temple (1972) suggests that *F. c. bendirei* should be considered a synonym of *F. c. columbarius,* a convention also followed by Stresemann and Amadon (1979).

The limits of range for the species are imperfectly known in British Columbia (Godfrey 1986). The following is a brief summary of details suspected for the 3 subspecies (Temple 1972) known to occur in British Columbia.

F. c. suckleyi [Black Merlin; Fig. 36] - Breeds in the humid Pacific coastal regions and on offshore islands (e.g. Owikeno Lake; upper Campbell Lake). Also, apparently in interior (e.g. Redstone, Chilcotin - Munro, J.A. and Cowan 1947). Winters mainly along the coast south through Washington and Oregon to southern California.

F. c . columbarius (bendirei) [Western Taiga Merlin] - Breeds in the Boreal Forest regions of eastern British Columbia. Winters in the western United States and Canada, along the Gulf and Atlantic coasts, and south to northern South America. Due to human encroachment, now breeds somewhat farther north (Evans 1982).

F. c. richardsonii [Richardson's Merlin] - Breeds in the prairie and grove belt of southern Alberta and southwestern Manitoba, south to northern Montana and northern North Dakota. Winters from Wyoming and Colorado to California and Mexico. Recorded in British Columbia from the Okanagan valley (Munro, J.A. and Cowan 1947), Ta Ta Creek 9 Jan 1945-1 (RBCM 11179), and the Peace Lowlands (Fort St. John, North Pine, Boundary Lake; C. Siddle pers. comm.). There are also 2 specimens of very pale Merlins both from Atlin: 23 April 1931 (RBCM Photo 5894), 12 September 1930 (RBCM 5895). Beebe (1974) suggests that the far northern records of *richardsonii*-like Merlins may represent either a discontinuous extension of the range of true *richardsonii* or the development of a separate population of Merlins with *richardsonii* plumage characteristics.

During the 1970s there was general concern that North American Merlin populations were being affected by organo-chlorine pollutants (see Fox 1971; Trimble 1975; Fyfe et al. 1976; Evans 1982). Recently, however, J.B. Buchanan (1988b) showed, by analysis of Christmas Bird Count data over a 40-year period, no changes in Merlin abundance for any of the North American races. More recent studies indicate that local populations are stable or increasing (see Nagy 1977; Oliphant and Thompson 1978; Oliphant 1985; Oliphant and Haug 1985). As a result, the Merlin appears on the "Blue List" from 1972-1981 and was delisted to a species of "special concern" in 1982 and 1986 (Tate 1986).

The Merlin was formerly known as Pigeon Hawk.

Figure 35. *Merlin young near fledging at Shuswap Lake, July 1977 (Richard J. Cannings).*

Figure 36. *Coastal race of the Merlin (F.c. suckleyi) at Saanich, 15 December 1985 (Tim Zurowski).*

NOTEWORTHY RECORDS

Spring: Coastal - Victoria 18 Apr 1966-3; Mesachie Lake 2 Apr 1974-2; Crescent Beach 14 Apr 1954-3; Sproat Lake 14 May 1974-2; Courtenay 6 May 1969-2; Port Hardy 28 Apr 1951-3. **Interior** - Nelson 10 Apr 1978-2; Invermere 19 Apr 1982-2; Kleena Kleene 27 May 1961-2 (Paul 1964); Hazelton 26 May 1921-2 migrants (Swarth 1924); Fort St. John 23 May 1983-2 adults; North Pine 30 Mar 1986-1; Fort Nelson 20 Apr 1986-1 adult.

Summer: Coastal - Metchosin 15 Aug 1982-3; Tofino 28 Aug 1979-3 flying together; Sutton Pass 16 Jul 1983-2; Hornby Island 10 Jun 1978-2 adults; Cortes Island 20 Jul 1975-2 flying together; Sewall 3 Jun 1980-1 adult. **Interior** - Hedley 8 Aug 1965-3; Nelson 26 Jun 1978-2 males; Okanagan Landing 13 Aug 1910-2; Shuswap Lake 9 Jul 1977-2; Bridge Creek (100 Mile House) 10 Jul 1977-2 adults; Quesnel Lake 21 Jul 1938-2 (Cushing 1941); Fern Lake (Kwadacha Wilderness Park) 22 Aug 1983-2 (Cooper, J.M. and Cooper 1983); Mount Vaughn 5 Jul 1980-2 adults.

Autumn: Interior - Bull Creek (Atlin) 20 Aug 1980-6; Summit Pass 2 Sep 1943-3 (Rand 1944); ne Fort St. John 22 Sep 1986-1; Williams Lake 3 Sep 1981-2; Invermere 10 Sep 1977-2; Swan Lake (Vernon) 10 Sep 1979-3; Okanagan Landing 26 Aug 1909-great numbers of Merlins and Sharp-shinned Hawks flying south (Cannings, R.A. et al. 1987). **Coastal** - Sewall 20 Oct 1981-2 adults; Port Neville 2 Nov 1975-2 adults; Cranberry Lake (Powell River) 20 Oct 1981-4; Roberts Bank 9 Nov 1978-3; Somenos Lake 21 Sep 1974-3; Cowichan Bay 7 Sep 1974-3; Victoria 15 to 31 Sep 1953-6 (Flahaut and Schultz 1954a).

Winter: Interior - Chowade River 26 Feb 1983-1 female (Grunberg 1983a); Williams Lake 3 Jan 1982-1; Yoho National Park 18 Dec 1976-1 male (Wade 1977); Kamloops 18 Jan 1985-1, 14 Feb 1986-1; New Denver 8 Dec 1979-1. **Coastal** - Sewall 25 Feb 1982-2; Port Neville 1 Dec 1975-2 adults; Sayward 8 Dec 1974-2; Cortes Island 4 Jan 1976-2; River Jordan 8 Jan 1984-2.

Christmas Counts: Interior - Recorded from 7 of 19 localities and on 31% of all counts. Maxima: Penticton 27 Dec 1982-8 and 27 Dec 1983-8; Vernon 16 Dec 1984-8; Vaseux Lake 3 Dec 1981-4. **Coastal** - Recorded from 18 of 28 localities and on 55% of all counts. Maxima: Vancouver 16 Dec 1984-13; Ladner 23 Dec 1984-9; Sooke 16 Dec 1984-7.

Peregrine Falcon
Falco peregrinus Tunstall

PEFA

RANGE: Practically cosmopolitan, but absent as a breeder from most of tropical and subtropical America, and New Zealand. In North America, breeds from north of the tree-line in Alaska and Canada south to central Canada, and along the Pacific coast and in the western cordillera south to Mexico. In North America, winters from the northern United States, coastal and south-western British Columbia and southern Ontario southward. Far northern populations are highly migratory, and winter as far south as Argentina and Chile.

STATUS: *Uncommon* migrant, but mostly an *uncommon* resident along the coast where it is more evident in summer in northern areas and in winter in southern areas. Widespread coastal breeder. *Rare* resident in the Okanagan valley. *Very rare* elsewhere in the interior; a local breeder in northern areas.

NONBREEDING: The Peregrine Falcon prefers habitats that support numbers of shorebirds, waterfowl, and other small to medium-size birds. Coastal habitat includes beaches, tidal flats, reefs, islands, marshes, estuaries, and lagoons. In winter, man-altered habitats are also frequented, including farmlands (especially with flooded fields), airports, parks, golf courses, railway yards (with Rock Doves) and bridges (with roosting European Starlings, *Sturnus vulgaris*). In the interior, marshes, lakeshores, river mouths, airports, broad river valleys, and cities (in winter) are preferred. In autumn, migrants have been found in alpine meadows up to 2,410 m elevation.

On the coast, adults disperse from wintering areas in early March, followed by immatures later in the month. The autumn dispersal is more pronounced. Immatures arrive in southern areas (e.g. Fraser River delta) in early August, followed by adults about a month later. Recent banding recoveries (Fig. 37; Anderson, C.M. et al. 1988) indicate first-year birds may migrate southward as far as California. In the interior, spring migration occurs from late March to early April. Fall migration may begin in August, but occurs mostly in September. A very small number of birds winter in the Thompson Basin and Okanagan valley; rarely farther north.

BREEDING: The Peregrine Falcon breeds along the outer and inner coasts but populations are usually localized in the vicinity of colonial nesting seabirds. These areas include the Fraser Lowlands to Hope, the southern Gulf Islands in the Strait of Georgia, northwestern Vancouver Island, islands off the central mainland coast, and the Queen Charlotte Islands. With the exception of eyries in the Fraser Lowlands (Hodson 1980; F.L. Beebe pers. comm.), there are no known coastal mainland breeding sites. All sites are associated with cliff ledges or trees on islands (Fig. 38), with the exception of the Queen Charlotte Islands and northern Vancouver Island, where headlands are also used. At least 50 to 75 pairs breed on the Queen Charlotte Islands, the highest concentration in the province (see Smith, I.D. et al. 1976; van Drimmelen 1986; Munro, W.T. and van Drimmelen 1988). Populations there appeared stable in 1986.

The Peregrine Falcon formerly bred along river canyons and cliffs bordering large lakes of the dry plateaus of the southern interior north to at least the Gang Ranch in the Chilcotin-Cariboo Basin. Breeders may have recently returned to the Okanagan valley. Very little is known about the peregrine population in the far north and Peace River areas. Beebe (1965) mentions active eyries near Fort St. John in 1963 and along the Peace River in 1964; a brood of young was taken from the latter site, but specific details (date and location) are not given.

Nests: On the coast, most nests (93%; n=305) were situated on ledges of vertical rocky cliffs. Other nest sites were found on grassy benches of rocky bluffs (11), and abandoned nests of Pelagic Cormorant (6), Bald Eagle (4); Campbell et al. 1977) and Common Raven (*Corvus corax*; 1). Heights of 67 breeding cliffs

Figure 37. *Banding locations (stars) and recovery sites (circles) of Peregrine Falcons associated with British Columbia. Red indicates birds banded in the province, black indicates birds banded elsewhere.*

ranged from 12 to 366 m, with 50% recorded between 23 and 38 m. Heights of 64 nest sites from the base of the cliff ranged from 4.6 to 335 m, with 50% recorded between 12 and 24 m. Heights of 67 nest sites from the top of the breeding cliff ranged from 0.9 to 61 m, with 60% recorded between 3 and 9 m. Tree nests ranged in height from 12 to 20 m.

Most nest ledges were sheltered by overhanging grass sods, rocks, tree roots, salal, or mosses. A few were partially hidden by trees growing below them, or by tree roots (Fig. 38), and a few were more or less exposed. Nest ledges ranged from 0.3 to 4.6 m deep, and 0.3 to 2.4 m wide. Nesting materials were not used, but some eyries were littered with prey remains, bits of leaves, grasses and mosses, and decayed wood. Interior eyries were situated on ledges in rocky bluffs overlooking large lakes and rivers. Cliff face heights ranged from 6 to 260 m. No other information for interior nests is available.

Eggs: Dates for 155 coastal clutches ranged from 8 April to 30 June, with 56% recorded between 20 April and 7 May. Calculated dates indicate that eggs could be found as early as 28 March. Sizes for 149 clutches ranged from 1 to 5 eggs (1E-3, 2E-31, 3E-46, 4E-65, 5E-4), with 74% having 3 or 4 eggs. In the interior, eggs were probably laid during the first half of May. There is no information on clutch size from interior birds. Incubation period is 32 to 34 days (Beebe 1974).

Young: Dates for 234 coastal broods ranged from 3 May to 20 July, with 51% recorded between 25 May and 6 June. The earliest hatching date was 3 May; the earliest fledging date was 2 June. Most young have left their eyries by the end of June. Sizes for 241 broods ranged from 1 to 5 young (1Y-27, 2Y-77, 3Y-106, 4Y-29, 5Y-2), with 76% having 2 or 3 young (Fig. 39). The only brood

Peregrine Falcon

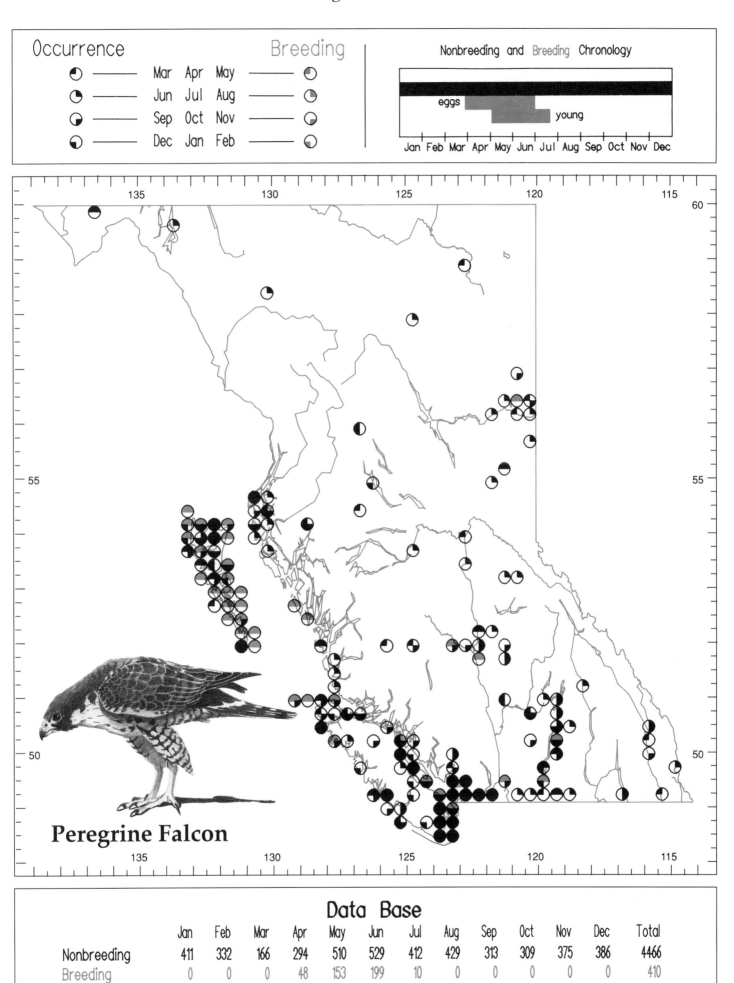

Occurrence / Breeding

Occurrence

◑ ——	Mar Apr May	—— ◔
◔ ——	Jun Jul Aug	—— ◔
◕ ——	Sep Oct Nov	—— ◔
◕ ——	Dec Jan Feb	—— ◑

Breeding

Nonbreeding and Breeding Chronology

eggs   young

Jan Feb Mar Apr May Jun Jul Aug Sep Oct Nov Dec

Data Base

	Jan	Feb	Mar	Apr	May	Jun	Jul	Aug	Sep	Oct	Nov	Dec	Total
Nonbreeding	411	332	166	294	510	529	412	429	313	309	375	386	4466
Breeding	0	0	0	48	153	199	10	0	0	0	0	0	410

Peregrine Falcon

information available from the interior is that, on 20 July 1906, young falcons fledged from a nest near Okanagan Landing which, when back-calculated, indicated they hatched about mid-June. Fledging period in British Columbia is 41 to 43 days (Nelson, R.W. and Myers 1976).

REMARKS: The Peregrine Falcon was formerly an *uncommon* local breeder in the Okanagan valley and the Chilcotin-Cariboo region, where it may still breed. Formerly a *very rare* migrant in the east Kootenay, it also may have bred east of Canal Flats (F.L. Beebe pers. comm.). For more information on Peregrine Falcons in British Columbia, consult the major works by Beebe (1960, 1974), R.W. Nelson (1970, 1977), and R.W. Nelson and Myres (1976). See R.A. Cannings et al. (1987) for a documented description of the decline in breeding peregrines of the Okanagan valley.

Two of the three North American subspecies of Peregrine Falcon (see American Ornithologists' Union 1957; White 1968; White and Boyce 1988) are known to occur in British Columbia, and there is some evidence that the third subspecies passes through the province. A brief summary of their distribution follows:

F. p. anatum [American Peregrine Falcon] - Breeds across interior Alaska south of the Brooks Range eastward across Canada and south to Baja California and Mexico including the south-central United States and the Atlantic coast. It is a resident bird in the southern third of its range, but becomes increasingly migratory northward. It intergrades with *F. p. tundrius*.

F. p. pealei [Peale's Peregrine Falcon] - Essentially resident on the islands and headlands of the Pacific coast from Oregon northwest through the Aleutian Islands to the Commander and Kurile Islands of Asia. It is a marine peregrine and seldom occurs

inland although Jobin (1952a) reports collecting *pealei* at Alkali Lake (Cariboo) on 9 August 1948.

F. p. tundrius [Arctic Peregrine Falcon] - Breeds across the entire Greenland-Canadian-Alaskan Arctic from the tree-line north to about 70°N. It is highly migratory, and winters as far south as southern Brazil and northern Argentina. Two reports suggest that *F. p. tundrius* may occur in the province. A Peregrine Falcon, banded at Inuvik, was found dead at Winfield, and was presumably of the subspecies *F. p. tundrius* or an integrade (R.W. Nelson pers. comm.). Also, C.M. Anderson et al. (1988) report that a bird banded near Colville River, Alaska, was found injured near Olympia, Washington; it likely came through British Columbia to reach Washington.

F. p. anatum and *F. p. tundrius* are the only races officially listed on the Endangered List in the United States (see United States Fish and Wildlife Service 1973; King, W.B. 1981) although the status of *F. p. tundrius* has recently been changed to threatened. Only *F. p. anatum* has "Endangered" status for Canada (Cook, F.R. and Muir 1984) and by the International Union for Conservation of Nature and Natural Resources (1969) for the world. They consider *F. p. pealei* populations to be stable.

The subspecies of birds breeding in the Fraser Lowlands and the Gulf Islands has not been determined.

Since 1890, at least 508 Peregrine Falcons, their eggs or young, have been collected in British Columbia (Fig. 40). Recreational harvest of live nestlings accounted for less than 40% of this total; the remainder were preserved in museum collections as skins or eggs.

For a detailed working bibliography of the Peregrine Falcon refer to R.D. Porter et al. (1987).

Figure 38. Peregrine Falcon nesting habitat on Hippa Island, Queen Charlotte Islands, 12 June 1988 (R. Wayne Campbell). Nest site is on top of rock outcropping among roots of a Sitka spruce.

Figure 39. Adult Peregrine Falcon at eyrie with young, Langara Island, Queen Charlotte Islands, 27 May 1988 (Ervio Sian).

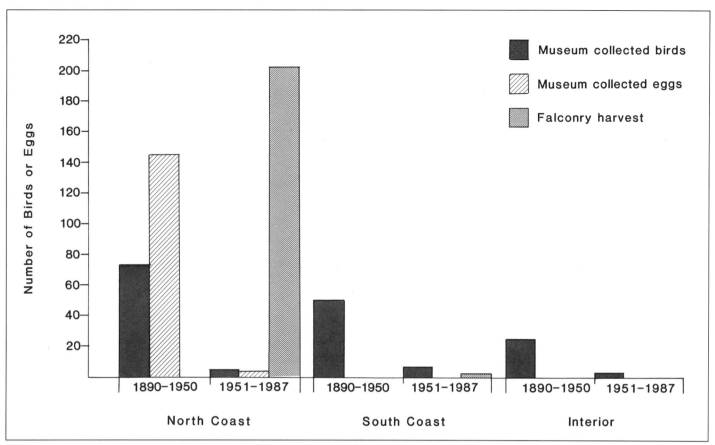

Figure 40. *Scientific and recreational harvest of Peregrine Falcons, their young and eggs in British Columbia between 1890 and 1987.*

NOTEWORTHY RECORDS

Spring: Coastal - Cowichan Bay 21 Mar 1982-2 flying north; Ladysmith 24 May 1980-2; Pitt Meadows 4 Apr 1975-2; Port Hardy 11 Mar 1938-4; Cape Scott 15 to 19 Apr 1980-3. **Interior** - Kilpoola Lake 12 May 1958-1 (Campbell and Meugens 1971); Newgate 9 Apr 1942-1 (Johnstone, W.B. 1949); Mount Knox early Mar 1978-1; Okanagan Landing 21 Mar 1912-1; Kamloops 4 Apr 1982-1; Knot Lakes 28 Apr 1976-1 adult; Kleena Kleene 2 May 1962-1 (Paul 1964); Hanceville 5 May 1981-1 adult; Williams Lake 22 Mar 1977-1 adult; Fort St. John 21 Apr 1985-1 (Grunberg 1985c); Cecil Lake 5 May 1982-1; Fort Nelson 5 May 1986-1 adult; Kelsall Lake 24 May 1979-1.

Summer: Coastal - Metchosin 25 Aug 1975-1; Cleland Island 27 Jun 1976-1; Long Beach 2 Jul 1974-1; Nanaimo River estuary 1 Jul 1967-1; Iona Island 15 Jul 1979-1; Port Mann bridge 7 Jun 1986-1; Ballenas Islands 8 Jun 1981-4 adults; Cape St. James 10 Aug 1981-8 in one flock. **Interior** - Manning Park 28 Aug 1949-1 (Edwards 1949); Sirdar 27 Aug 1947-1 female (Munro, J.A. 1958a);

Rutland 28 Aug 1982-1 immature male; Columbia Lake 4 Jul 1942-1 (Johnstone, W.B. 1949); Mount Revelstoke 3 Jul 1937-1 (Cowan and Munro 1944); 103 Mile Lake 2 Jul 1942-1; Williams Lake 9 July 1948-1 (UBC 2023); Bowron Lake 29 Jul 1961-1 (Ritcey and Verbeek 1961); 11.3 km east Fort St. John 25 Jun 1978-1 adult male; Peace River near Alberta border 5 Jul 1930-2 (Williams, M.Y. 1933a); Spatsizi Plateau 19 Jul 1959-several; Atlin 17 Aug 1977-1 (RBCM 17867).

Autumn: Interior - Riske Creek 25 Sep 1950-1 (RBCM 15568); Kleena Kleene 6 Sep 1962-1 (Paul 1964); Salmon Arm 6 Sep 1970-3 attacking migrating shorebirds (Stevens et al. 1970); Rose Hill 16 Sep 1980-1 immature; Vernon 18 Sep 1979-1, 24 Sep 1945-1 (Munro, J.A. and Cowan 1947); Kelowna 22 Nov 1977-1 adult male; Bummers Flats 24 Oct 1976-1. **Coastal** - Cape St. James 21 Sep 1981-7; Port Hardy 2 Oct 1938-3, 11 Oct 1950-5, 5 Nov 1935-4; Pitt Lake 26 Nov 1974-2; Tofino 10 Nov 1951-3; Roberts Bank 28 Nov 1981-3; Boundary Bay 17 Sep 1922-3; Ucluelet 3 Sep 1983-2, 15 Nov 1950-6; Matheson Lake 4 Oct 1981-4.

Winter: Interior - Tetana Lake Dec 1938-1 feeding on freshly killed adult varying hare (Stanwell-Fletcher and Stanwell-Fletcher 1943); Kamloops 27 Dec 1983-1, 22 Feb 1982-1 adult; Vernon 26 Dec 1968-1, 8 Jan 1969-1 (both Rogers, T.H. 1969); Oyama 28 Jan 1978-1 adult; Okanagan Landing 25 Dec 1924-1 attacking Pine Grosbeak; Trout Creek point (Summerland) 6 Feb 1972-1. **Coastal** - Prince Rupert 2 Feb 1982-1; Masset 4 Jan 1978-2; Kitimat 15 Dec 1979-1 at sewage ponds; Cape St. James 12 Dec 1978-1; Cranberry Lake (Powell River) 21 to 28 Dec 1980-1; Tofino 15 Jan 1981-1; Reifel Island 4 Feb 1981-3; Pachena Bay 23 Jan 1975-1; Cowichan Bay 15 Jan 1974-2 adults; Central Saanich 9 Dec 1980-3; Cadboro Bay 27 Jan 1971-3; Discovery Island 11 Dec 1955-3.

Christmas Counts: Interior - Recorded twice: Kamloops 15 Dec 1984-1 and Vernon 26 Dec 1976-1. **Coastal** - Recorded from 20 of 28 localities and on 44% of all counts. Maxima: Vancouver 26 Dec 1975-7; Ladner 27 Dec 1982-7; Victoria 15 Dec 1984-7, all-time Canadian high counts (Anderson, R.R. 1976, 1983; Monroe 1985b).

Gyrfalcon

GYRF

Falco rusticolus Linnaeus

RANGE: Circumpolar. Breeds in arctic Alaska, northern Canada, Greenland, Iceland, northern Scandinavia, northern Russia, and northern Siberia. In North America, winters from the middle of the breeding range south to the northern United States.

STATUS: *Uncommon* summer visitant and breeder along high mountains in the extreme northwest. *Rare* winter visitant to southeastern Vancouver Island and the Fraser Lowlands. *Very rare* in winter in the central-southern interior. *Casual* in winter in the northern interior.

NONBREEDING: The Gyrfalcon has a scattered but widespread distribution through most of western British Columbia, including Vancouver Island but not the Queen Charlotte Islands. It frequents open and semi-open country, from sea level to alpine meadows, wherever plentiful food supplies exist. In the northern interior, these areas include subalpine and other open lower areas where ptarmigan are common. On the south coast, winter habitat includes areas where waterfowl, gulls, shorebirds, and other waterbirds are concentrated, including tidal flats, marshes, sloughs, wet agricultural fields, offshore islands, lakeshores, airports, golf courses, reservoirs, and occasionally city parks (with Rock Doves). In the southern interior, ice-free lakes, ponds, and river mouths are preferred, but open rangeland, city parks, orchards, chicken yards, and even subdivisions are frequented.

Gyrfalcons wander south mostly during years when ptarmigan populations are low in their breeding range. In some years, this movement may be evident as early as late August or early September, and in other years may occur as late as November. It is rare to find a Gyrfalcon in southern areas before October and after early April.

Earliest and latest dates of occurrence for 5 southern areas of the province are: southern Vancouver Island-11 October and 22 April, Comox-16 August and 27 March, Greater Vancouver-13 September and 20 May, the Okanagan valley-12 September and 23 March, and Kamloops - 3 November and 4 April.

BREEDING: The Gyrfalcon breeds throughout the Northern Mountains and Plateaus region from Spatsizi Plateau Wilderness Park northwest to the St. Elias Mountains. Nest sites are widely scattered on isolated upland cliffs, buttes and rock outcrops, and river bluffs or cliffs surrounded by tundra. All sites have been located between 1,200 and 1,740 m elevation.

Nests: Of 13 nest sites found, 10 were located on ledges; the remaining sites were in unused Golden Eagle nests (see Fig. 30). Nest ledges were up to 24 m long and ranged in height from 6 to 25 m above the ground or water. All were protected by overhangs. Ledge nests were on bare ground with no materials added.

Eggs: We have no records of nests with eggs. Calculated dates indicate that eggs could be found by 3 April. According to Beebe

(1974), most egg-laying probably takes place in late April and early May. Clutch size is usually 2 to 4 eggs. Incubation period is 28 to 35 days (Cade 1960; Beebe 1974).

Young: Dates for 12 broods ranged from 1 June to 19 July. Young could be found as early as 5 May, but only rarely after mid-July. Brood size ranged from 2 to 5 young (2Y-1, 3Y-5, 4Y-5, 5Y-1). Fledging period is 49 to 50 days (Cade 1960; Beebe 1974).

REMARKS: There are 3 recognized colour morphs. Of 114 specimens and observations examined for British Columbia, the colour morph frequencies were: grey - 69%, dark - 27%, and white - 4%, which is consistent with other results for North America (see Snow 1974). Thirty-two of 37 specimens examined from British Columbia were females, That is not unusual, as males do not disperse as far from northern breeding areas as do females (F.L. Beebe pers. comm.). Additionally, females have a lower mortality rate overall, and outnumber males (C.M. White pers. comm.).

A recent band recovery shows that the origin of some yearling birds wintering in southwestern British Columbia is the southern Yukon. A bird found dead near Courtenay on 4 April 1986, had been banded as a nestling near Whitehorse on 21 June 1984.

POSTSCRIPT: From 2 to 6 June 1988 the Boundary Ranges, from Mosquito Flats (Chilkat Pass) to the Yukon/British Columbia border, and east to Rothwell Peak, was surveyed specifically for Gyrfalcons (W.T. Munro pers. comm.). Six sites were located, 4 of which were active and contained young (4Y-3, 3Y-1) at least 20 days old.

On 16 December 1988 a single bird was seen perched on a drift log on Rose Spit (P.J. Hamel pers. comm.). This is the first record for the Queen Charlotte Islands.

NOTEWORTHY RECORDS

Spring: Coastal - Victoria 22 Apr 1975-1; Westham Island 18 Apr 1971-1 immature female (Campbell et al. 1972b); Lulu Island 20 Apr 1975-1, 20 May 1971-1 wounded; Kitimat 14 May 1975-1 adult; Kitsault 13 to 17 May 1980-1. **Interior** - Kalamalka Lake 23 Mar 1979-1; Kamloops 4 Apr 1981-1; Bluff Lake 20 May 1974-1 adult male; Williams Lake 1 Apr 1944-1 (Jobin 1952d); Atlin 18 May 1981-1 (Campbell 1981).

Summer: Coastal - Comox 16 Aug 1902-1 (RBCM 2668); Mitlenatch Island 28 Aug 1976-1. **Interior** - Edozadelly Mountain 2 and 3 Aug 1979-2 (Hazelwood 1979); Taweh Creek to Eve Cone 14 to 18 Aug 1986-2 pairs; Tuya Lake 24 Jun 1974-1;

Chilkat Pass 18 Jun 1980-1, 26 Aug 1983-1.

Autumn: Interior - Kelsall Lake 14 Sep 1980-1 male (RBCM 16611); Chilkat Pass 21 Oct 1981-4; Steamboat Mountain (Atlin Lake) 1 Sep 1981-2; China Head Mountain 15 Oct 1974-1; Enderby 12 Sep 1970-1 (an exceptionally early date); Upper Hat Creek 10 Oct 1964-1 (RBCM 11228); Vernon 29 Oct 1984-1; Okanagan Landing 1 Nov 1929-1. **Coastal** - Comox Sep 1894-1 (RBCM 1716); Qualicum Beach 5 Oct 1982-1; Stanley Park (Vancouver) 13 Sep 1980-1; Westham Island 11 Oct 1971-1 (Campbell et al. 1972b); Saanich 11 Oct 1984-1.

Winter: Interior - Alkali Lake (Cariboo) 18 Jan 1952-1 female (NMC 47659); Kamloops 1 Feb 1982-1, 5 Feb 1984-1; Armstrong 23 Jan 1985-1 female (RBCM 18404). **Coastal:** Westham Island 12 Jan 1980-3; Saanich 6 Dec 1980-1 adult female, 2 immatures harrassing trained Prairie Falcon.

Christmas Counts: Interior - Recorded from 2 of 19 localities and on 5% of all counts. Maxima: Vernon 26 Dec 1977, 27 Dec 1981, 18 Dec 1983, and 16 Dec 1984-all single birds; Quesnel 24 Dec 1981-1. **Coastal** - Recorded from 4 of 28 localities and on 6% of all counts. Maxima: Victoria 19 Dec 1981-2; Ladner 21 Dec 1968, 27 Dec 1981 and 27 Dec 1982 - all 2 birds.

Gyrfalcon

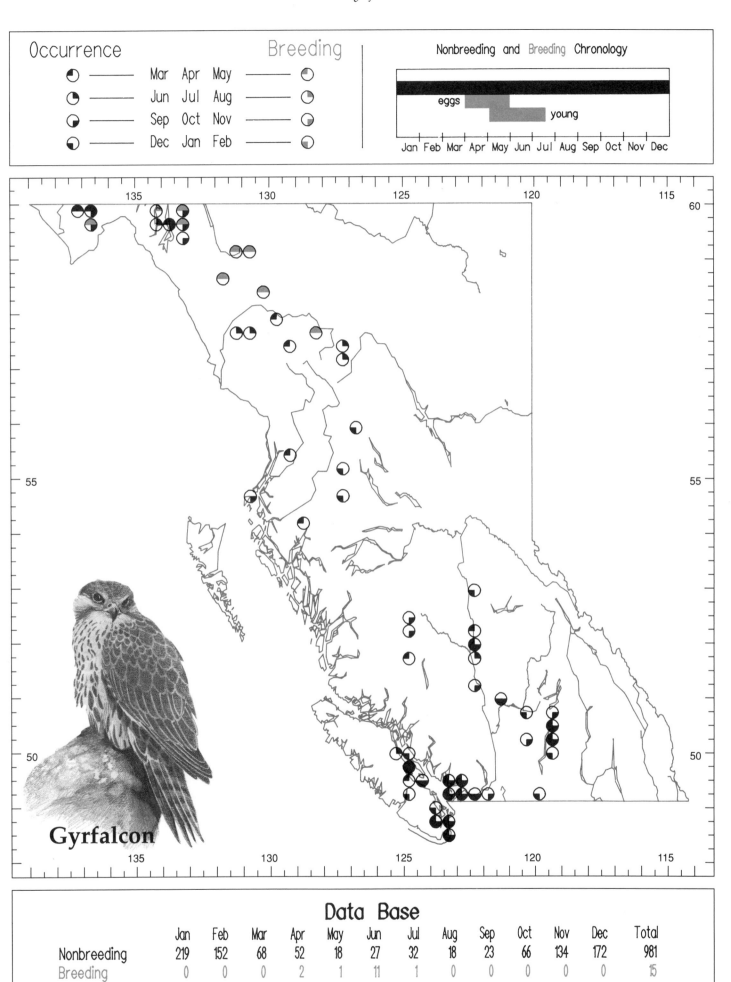

Occurrence   Breeding

◑ ———	Mar	Apr	May	——— ◐
◔ ———	Jun	Jul	Aug	——— ◕
◕ ———	Sep	Oct	Nov	——— ◔
◕ ———	Dec	Jan	Feb	——— ◓

Nonbreeding and Breeding Chronology

eggs   young

Jan Feb Mar Apr May Jun Jul Aug Sep Oct Nov Dec

Data Base

	Jan	Feb	Mar	Apr	May	Jun	Jul	Aug	Sep	Oct	Nov	Dec	Total
Nonbreeding	219	152	68	52	18	27	32	18	23	66	134	172	981
Breeding	0	0	0	2	1	11	1	0	0	0	0	0	15

Prairie Falcon
Falco mexicanus Schlegel

PRFA

RANGE. Breeds in western North America from central-south British Columbia and the southern Canadian prairies south to Baja California, New Mexico, and northern Texas. Winters throughout the breeding range, casually east to the Mississippi River, and south to central Mexico.

STATUS: *Rare* resident in the Okanagan valley. *Rare* late summer visitant to alpine areas of the Cascade Mountains, *very rare* elsewhere in the south-central interior. *Very rare* transient to the southeastern portion of the province. *Casual* in the west Kootenay and on the southwest coast including southern Vancouver Island. *Very rare* local breeder.

NONBREEDING: The Prairie Falcon is widely distributed throughout the central-southern interior including the Okanagan (Fig. 41), Nicola, and South Thompson valleys, north to the Chilcotin-Cariboo Basin region; it is scattered and sparsely distributed elsewhere. The Prairie Falcon inhabits open, treeless country including arid grasslands and sagebrush steppes, alpine meadows and ridges, and, far less frequently, marshes, and farmland. In migration, it has been recorded from sea level to 2,440 m elevation. In winter, it frequents intermontane valleys at the same elevation and latitude as the breeding areas.

Migration periods are poorly known because of the difficulty of distinguishing residents from arriving and departing birds. It is likely that spring migrants arrive in late March and early April. The autumn departure may begin in late August, but most of the movement probably occurs in September and October. This is supported by the small movement discernable in the southern Rocky Mountain Trench (see Autumn: Interior below).

BREEDING: The Prairie Falcon breeds locally in the Thompson-Okanagan Plateau region (Fig. 43) from the Okanagan and Nicola valleys to the vicinity of Dog Creek and Doc English Gulch (Fig. 42) in the Chilcotin-Cariboo Basin.

Prairie Falcons inhabit foothills, valleys, and river canyons with steep rocky cliffs, escarpments, and outcrops or buttes adjacent to the open areas where they hunt. Nest sites are frequently close to water, and have been found from about 450 to 900 m elevation.

Nests: All eyries examined (12) were on cliffs, and were situated on ledges (8), in caves (2), in a crevice and in a pothole. Beebe (1974) indicates that overhangs are important to provide shelter and shade, and all sites reported here had them. One nesting cliff was granite, another sandstone. Dimensions for one nest "hole" were 0.4 m high by 0.9 m wide. Nesting cliffs ranged

Figure 41. *McIntyre Bluff (left) looking towards Vaseux Lake (Stephen R. Cannings). Hunting areas for Prairie Falcons during the nonbreeding and breeding seasons include grasslands, sagebrush environments, and cliffs, especially near lakes and rivers.*

Prairie Falcon

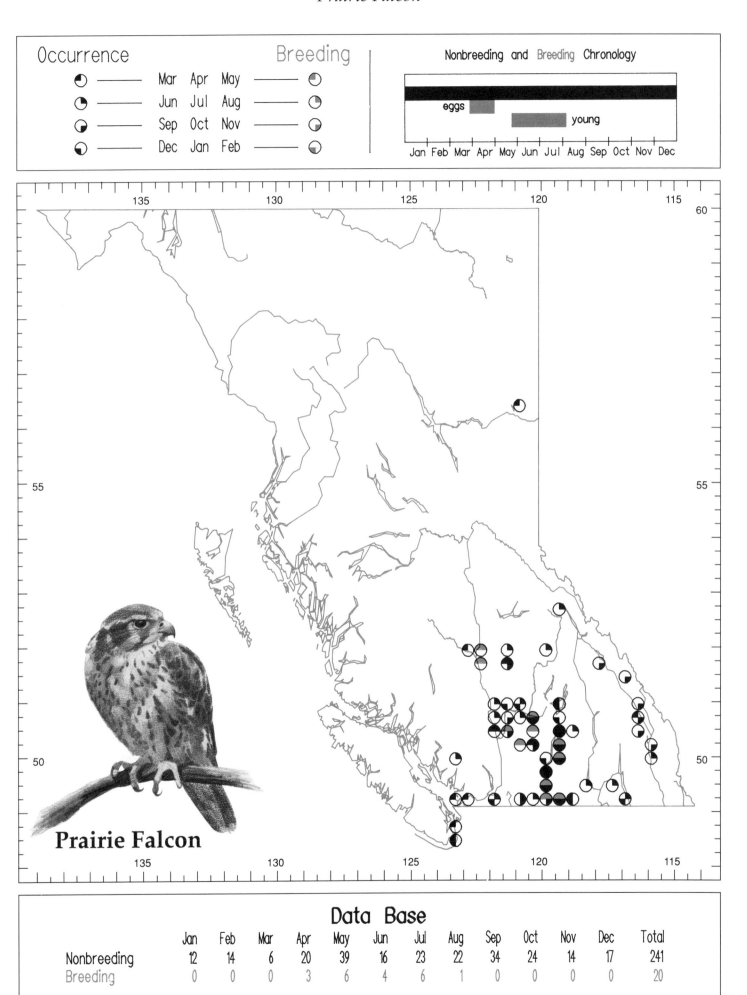

Data Base

	Jan	Feb	Mar	Apr	May	Jun	Jul	Aug	Sep	Oct	Nov	Dec	Total
Nonbreeding	12	14	6	20	39	16	23	22	34	24	14	17	241
Breeding	0	0	0	3	6	4	6	1	0	0	0	0	20

from 15 to 138 m in height, the actual nest site ranged from 9 to 90 m from the base of the cliff. Most nest scrapes were bare, simply the cliff substrate, but one contained a number of Douglas-fir twigs and small pieces of sage.

Eggs: We have no records of dates for nests with eggs. Calculated dates, from the known ages of 4 broods, indicate that eggs could be found as early as 15 March, but probably most eggs are laid in April. Sizes for 3 clutches were 3 or 4 eggs (3E-1, 4E-2). Incubation period is 29 to 33 days (Enderson 1964; Beebe 1974).

Young: Dates for 9 broods ranged from 27 April to 5 August, with 5 broods recorded from 1 to 17 July. Sizes for 8 broods ranged from 1 to 5 young (1Y-1, 2Y-2, 3Y-1, 4Y-3, 5Y-1) with 4 broods having 3 or 4 young (Fig. 44). Calculated dates indicate that young could be found as early as 15 April. Fledging period is about 40 days (Ogden 1973).

REMARKS: Historical populations of the Prairie Falcon are not known. R.A. Cannings et al. (1987) discuss the increase and subsequent decline of the falcon in the Okanagan valley. Information from other parts of its British Columbia range is lacking, but it appears that populations there followed a similar trend to that of the Okanagan birds. Reasons for the decline of the Okanagan birds include direct human interference at nest sites (Fig. 45), perhaps the major cause, and the increasing use of organochlorine pesticides in the valley. In addition, because Prairie Falcons in British Columbia are at the northern limit of their North American range, habitat and food deficiencies may also have contributed to declines.

Whatever the cause of the decline, populations have not fully recovered. Despite recent searches for eyries (see van Drimmelen and Sullivan 1976), few have been found, although foothills away from traditional sites have not been thoroughly investigated. From 1955 through 1985, there is evidence that eyries have been occupied in the vicinity of Kalamalka Lake (1955), Merritt (1970), Spences Bridge (1970, 1982), Kamloops (1975), Kelowna (1975), and Anarchist Mountain (1981). Recent sightings suggest that Prairie Falcons may be re-establishing themselves in arid regions of the province. About one-third of all records are from the period 1975 to 1985, and in the 1980s the species began to appear on Christmas Bird Counts in the Okanagan valley.

Godfrey (1986) reports that the Prairie Falcon has bred at Doc English Gulch and that it has been recorded north to Nulki Lake. We are unaware of any convincing records for these localities.

The American Ornithologists' Union Check-list (1983) erroneously gives the breeding range of the Prairie Falcon as "southeastern British Columbia." Historical and present information indicate that it breeds only in the central-southern interior of the province. There is, however, good Prairie Falcon breeding habitat in the east Kootenay, south of Windermere (F.L. Beebe pers. comm.) and there have been a few recent observations of birds from that area. Observers there should be alert to the possibility of this falcon breeding in the Rocky Mountain Trench.

Figure 42. *The rock-cliffs of Doc English Gulch, Cariboo-Chilcotin Basin region, 20 May 1946 (James A. Munro). Prairie Falcons nest in these cliffs, the most northerly recorded site for British Columbia.*

Figure 43. *Nesting environment for Prairie Falcons at Napier Lake, 27 April 1938 (courtesy Parks Canada, Ottawa).*

Figure 44. *Prairie Falcon young in nest at Napier Lake, 27 April 1938 (courtesy Parks Canada, Ottawa).*

Figure 45. *Disturbance by collectors, photographers, and tourists have resulted in abandonment of some eyries by Prairie Falcons in British Columbia (James A. Munro).*

NOTEWORTHY RECORDS

Spring: Coastal - See Extralimital Records below. **Interior -** Lytton 16 Apr 1971-1; Nicola Lake 28 Mar 1981-1 chasing Horned Larks; Invermere 5 May 1982-1; Sorrento 22 Mar 1972-1; Alkali Lake (Riske Creek) 26 Mar 1951-1 female (NMC 47660; Jobin 1952a); North Pine 25 Apr 1985-1.

Summer: Coastal - See Extralimital Records. **Interior -** Big Buck Mountain 26 Jul 1981-1; Blackwall Peak 27 Aug 1949-1 male (UBC 2123); Cathedral Park 28 Jul 1985-3, 19 Aug 1983-2; Yellow Lake (Richter Pass) 1 Jul 1964-1 (Campbell and Meugens 1971); White Lake (Okanagan Falls) 3 Jun 1922-1 male (NMC 17824); Skookumchuk (east Kootenay) 14 Jun 1976-1; Lillooet 30 Aug 1968-1; Marble Canyon (Pavilion) 3 Jul 1961-2; Dog Creek (Cariboo) 15 Jul 1953-1 male (NMC 47661); 103 Mile Lake 15 Aug 1975-3; Battle Mountain (Wells Gray Park) 16 Aug 1954-1 stooped on wounded ptarmigan (Edwards and Ritcey 1967); Canoe Mountain 25 Aug 1970-1 (Stirling 1971).

Autumn: Interior - 11.5 km nw 100 Mile House 8 Sep 1985-1; Golden 28 Oct 1975-1; Nicholson 17 Nov 1975-1; Brisco 18 Oct 1975-1; Spences Bridge 9 Nov 1971-1 immature male chasing gull over river; Columbia Lake 27 Sep 1978-1; 8 km s Canal Flats 7 Sep 1981-1; Okanagan Centre 16 Sep 1932-1 female with Western Meadowlark in stomach (MVZ 99879); Okanagan Landing 12 Nov 1910-1 male (MVZ 81861); Osoyoos Lake 26 Sep 1922-1 immature female (UMMZ 62290); Poland Lake 1 Sep 1968-1. **Coastal -** No records.

Winter: Interior - Walhachin 25 Feb 1986-1; 18 Dec 1983-1, Kamloops 8 Dec 1984-1, 10 Jan 1931-1 adult male (ROM 83778); Salmon Arm 18 Dec 1970-1 (Schnider et al. 1971); Okanagan Centre 7 Dec 1940-1 female (UBC 584), 12 Jan 1930-1 female with redpoll in crop (MVZ 99877); Creston 7 Dec 1978-1 (Butler, R.W. et al. 1986); Rock Creek (w Greenwood) 7 Jan 1976-1 immature female. **Coastal -** See Extralimital Records.

Christmas Counts: Interior - Recorded from 4 of 19 localities and on 8% of all counts. Maxima: all single birds at Oliver/Osoyoos 28 Dec 1980, 28 Dec 1981, 26 Dec 1984; Vaseux Lake 23 Dec 1984; Penticton 27 Dec 1981; Vernon 23 Dec 1979, 27 Dec 1981, 19 Dec 1982. **Coastal -** Not recorded.

Extralimital Records: All observations of Prairie Falcons outside the central-southern interior should be treated cautiously as some may represent escaped falconer's birds. As Beebe (1974) states, "the Prairie Falcon is the falcon most commonly obtained for recreational use in North America." We closely examined records for the south coast and northern interior and have accepted the following, all of single birds: Saanich Peninsula 5 Apr 1969 (Tatum 1971); Victoria 25 Feb 1975, 1 Apr 1975; Reifel Island 13 May 1979; Chilliwack 27 Jul 1896-1 immature shot (Brooks 1917), 17 Dec 1927-1 male (RBCM 6344); n Fort St. John 25 Apr 1985.

Gray Partridge

GRPA

Perdix perdix (Linnaeus)

RANGE: Widely introduced in North America and established locally from southern Canada south to the northern and middle United States. Native of western Eurasia from the British Isles, southern Scandinavia, and northern Russia south to southern Europe and east to Mongolia.

STATUS: Locally *uncommon* to *fairly common* resident in the Thompson-Okanagan Plateau region. Introduced but subsequently extirpated on Vancouver Island and the south mainland coast. Status elsewhere is uncertain. Breeds.

CHANGE IN STATUS: The Gray Partridge was first introduced to British Columbia in March 1904 when 57 birds were released near Vancouver (Carl and Guiguet 1972). Subsequent releases occurred in 1905 (32 birds), 1907 to 1908 (167 birds), and 1909 (277 birds). Due to the phenomenal success of releases in southern Alberta (Rowan 1925, 1927, 1938) additional stock was liberated around Greater Vancouver and by 1915 the first open hunting season was allowed. In 1908 and 1909 about 500 birds were released on southern Vancouver Island (Victoria, Saanich Peninsula) as well as 72 on nearby James Island, 32 on Sidney Island, and 10 birds on South Pender Island. Introductions on the smaller islands failed after a short time, while those on southern Vancouver Island persisted in 2 small groups near the Uplands Golf Course (Victoria) and the Victoria International Airport (Sidney). By the early 1960s the Victoria population had disappeared due to housing build-up (Carl and Guiguet 1972). At the airport, the population averaged about 13 birds from 1961 to 1971, and reached a high of 31 or more birds in September 1966 (Beckett 1971). The last record there was of a single bird seen on 21 February 1972.

Releases in the Fraser River Lowlands were also unsuccessful (Fig. 48). By the early 1960s small populations still existed at Ladner and on Sea Island. The last birds (3) were reported from the vicinity of the Vancouver International Airport on 7 November 1965.

The Gray Partridge was not initially introduced into the interior; birds spread northward from populations released in north-central and eastern Washington in the early 1900s (Darwin 1916, 1918). Our earliest interior record came in the winter of 1917/1918 when a bird was found dead near Summerland in the Okanagan valley (Munro, J.A. 1925). During the next 6 years small coveys became established and spread 130 km northward to Salmon Arm. Munro predicted that by the mid-1930s the Gray

Partridge would "outnumber all the species of upland game birds combined" in the Okanagan valley. During 1925 and 1926 it was "extremely abundant" there, but following an abrupt decline in 1926 it "maintained a low level of population" (Munro, J.A. and Cowan 1947).

R.A. Cannings et al. (1987) indicate that the Gray Partridge is much more common in the north Okanagan than in the south, because of the more extensive farmlands of alfalfa or grain around Vernon. Westerskov (1966) has shown that the phenomenal success of releases in Alberta lies in choice and quality of food (waste grains and weed seeds) coupled with an abundance of preferred foods that allows the birds to survive the rigorous winters.

Other unsuccessful introductions were made near Alkali Lake and Dog Creek in the Chilcotin-Cariboo Basin in 1940 (Erskine and Stein 1964), the Vanderhoof region (Figs. 46 and 47) in 1931 (which numbered about 200 by 1933; Munro, J.A. 1949a), and the St. Mary prairie (north of Cranbrook) prior to 1937 (Johnstone, W.B. 1949). Immigrants, probably from Idaho, made their way to the Creston area in the late 1940s (Munro, J.A. 1950), but none have been reported since.

NONBREEDING: The Gray Partridge appears to be restricted to the Okanagan valley, although scattered coveys may still persist in the Thompson valley (R.W. Ritcey pers. comm.). Ploughed and irrigated fields and orchards on benchlands and along river bottoms are important habitats. It also frequents sagebrush habitat (Fig. 49) and dry rangeland with open stands of ponderosa pine. It has been found up to 1,280 m elevation.

Very little is known about movements, and most are probably very local. Ample plumage, appreciable layers of subcutaneous and visceral fat (Westerskov 1965), a well-developed flocking behaviour which facilitates finding food, and communal roosting behaviour allow it to survive the cold interior winters (Fig. 50). Family groups remain in coveys throughout the autumn and winter until dispersal in late February and March (Yocom 1943), prior to the reproductive period. The centre of abundance in British Columbia is the northern Okanagan valley, in the vicinity of Vernon.

BREEDING: The Gray Partridge is known to breed only in the Okanagan valley. It breeds in open sagebrush flats and open dry woodlands to at least 460 m elevation.

Nests: Only 6 nests have been described. Three were situated under clumps of sagebrush, one was in tall grass among open

Figure 46. The "Lake District", south of Vanderhoof, where 6 pairs of Gray Partridges were liberated in 1929 (James A. Munro). The population increased to about 40 pairs by 1933; none were seen in the years following.

Figure 47. The Nechako River, at Vanderhoof, where a number of Gray Partridges were released in 1931 (James A. Munro). The population increased to about 200 birds by 1933, then disappeared.

Gray Partridge

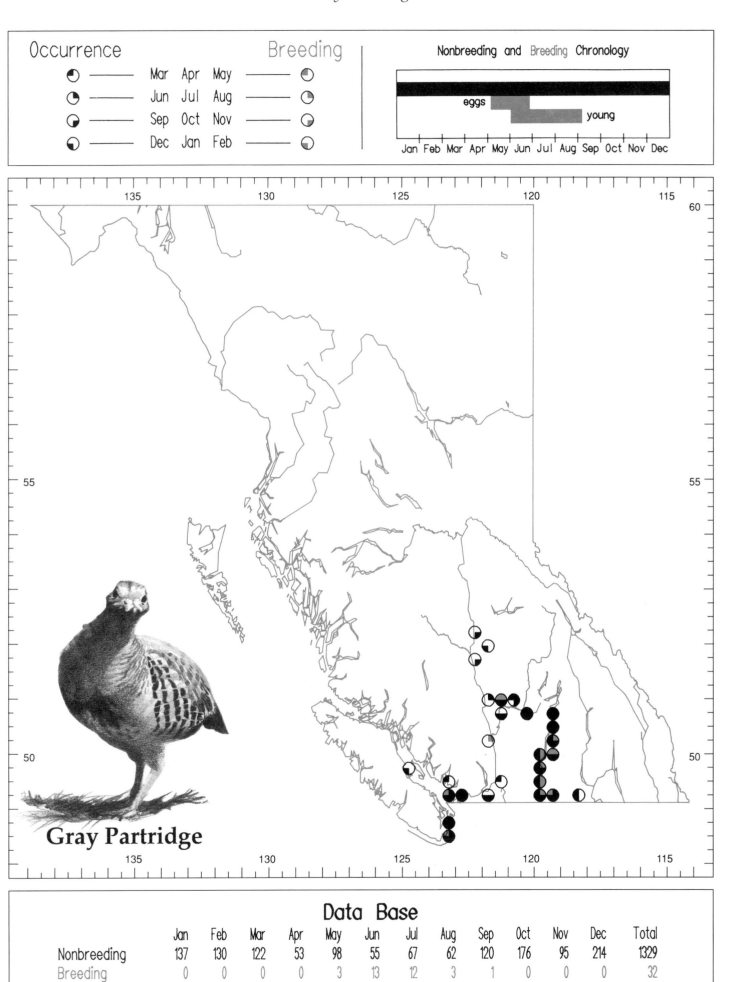

Nonbreeding and Breeding Chronology

eggs

young

Jan Feb Mar Apr May Jun Jul Aug Sep Oct Nov Dec

Gray Partridge

Data Base

	Jan	Feb	Mar	Apr	May	Jun	Jul	Aug	Sep	Oct	Nov	Dec	Total
Nonbreeding	137	130	122	53	98	55	67	62	120	176	95	214	1329
Breeding	0	0	0	0	3	13	12	3	1	0	0	0	32

ponderosa pine woodland, one was under blackberries in an urban area, and one was in grasses bordering a cultivated field. All were shallow scrapes in the ground lined with dry grasses and leaves.

Eggs: Dates for 7 clutches ranged from 5 May to 1 June. Calculated dates indicate that eggs could be found as late as 26 June. Clutch size ranged from 6 to 20 eggs (6E-1, 9E-1, 11E-1, 12E-1, 13E-1, 14E-1, 20E-1). Yocom (1943) gives a clutch range, for Washington, from 10 to 22 eggs, with a mean of 17 eggs. Incubation period is 24 to 25 days (McCabe, R.A. and Hawkins 1946).

Young: Dates for 23 broods ranged from 7 June to 5 September, with 12 broods reported between 22 June and 27 July. In Saskatchewan, downy young were found on the late date of 21 September (Schmidt 1964). Calculated dates indicate young could be found in very early June. Brood sizes ranged from 1 to 19 young (1Y-1, 2Y-1, 5Y-2, 6Y-3, 7Y-2, 8Y-2, 9Y-3, 11Y-1, 12Y-2, 13Y-1, 14Y-2, 18Y-2, 19Y-1) with 12 broods having 5 to 9 young. Fledging period is about 16 days (McCabe, R.A. and Hawkins 1946).

REMARKS: Also known as Hungarian Partridge, and in the Old World as the Partridge.

Figure 48. Adult Gray Partridge at Surrey, 7 May 1982 (Ervio Sian). Small numbers are frequently released by aviculturists throughout the Fraser Lowlands, to date without success.

Figure 49. Dry rangeland and sagebrush habitats are frequented by Gray Partridges in the Okanagan valley, 21 September 1968 (R. Wayne Campbell).

Figure 50. *Chukars foraging near Vaseux Lake, February 1969 (Steve R. Cannings). Gray Partridges also use similar habitats in winter but prefer more open country where nearby rocky outcroppings are not an important habitat component.*

NOTEWORTHY RECORDS

Spring: Coastal - Sidney 3 Mar 1962-6 at airport; Hope 13 Apr 1925-1. **Interior** - Grand Forks 8 May 1983-2; Vaseux Lake 23 May 1983-1; Penticton 16 Mar 1975-2; Savona 20 Mar 1957-covey.

Summer: Coastal - Victoria Jul 1961-10 (Boggs and Boggs 1961c); Ladner 26 Jun 1956-6. **Interior** - Keremeos 4 Aug 1977-15; White Lake (Okanagan Falls) 18 Jul 1979-15; Lavington 3 Aug 1972-14.

Autumn: Interior - Williams Lake 19 Oct 1952-1 female (NMC 47720); Gang Ranch Sep 1952-5 (Erskine and Stein 1964); Cache Creek (Ashcroft) 16 Oct 1954-30 in two flocks; Ashcroft Sep 1983-2; Vernon 10 Sep 1954-41, 20 Oct 1954-45, 28 Nov 1981-20; Okanagan Landing 30 Sep 1927-100+, 15 Oct 1933-30; Summerland 15 Nov 1952-40;

Vaseux Lake 9 Sep 1954-20; Oliver 9 Sep 1954-23; Osoyoos 9 Nov 1946-6. **Coastal** - Chilliwack 16 Nov 1926-1 male (RBCM 12662); Crescent Beach 19 Nov 1945-12; Ladner 21 Nov 1955-12; Sea Island 7 Nov 1965-3 at airport; Sidney Sep 1966-31+ at airport.

Winter: Interior - Lac la Hache winter 1947/1948-10 (Munro, J.A. 1955c); Vernon 26 Dec 1955-127 on Christmas Bird Count (Grant, J. 1956), 11 Jan 1986-8; Okanagan Landing 29 Dec 1924-80, 27 Dec 1926-33 on Christmas Bird Count (Munro, J.A. 1927); Summerland 23 Dec 1928-4 on Christmas Bird Count (Tait 1929), 23 Dec 1934-6 on Christmas Bird Count (Darcus 1935), 13 Dec 1971-14; Penticton 12 Dec 1972-17, 23 Jan 1970-25+; Keremeos 28 Dec 1983-9; Richter Lake 1 Feb

1975-6; Carson 20 Feb 1980-7. **Coastal** - Comox 27 Dec 1959-1 (Pearse 1960); Sidney Jan 1961-12, Jan 1966-13, Jan 1967-16, Feb 1969-14 (all Beckett 1971), 1 Jan 1965-14, 6 Feb 1971-9, 21 Feb 1972-1; Mt. Tolmie Jan 1925-8 (Preece 1925b); Victoria 2 Jan 1955-10 on Christmas Bird Count (Clay 1955), 1 Feb 1959-6; Ladner 2 Jan 1961-6; Chilliwack 6 Feb 1927-1 male (RBCM 6387).

Christmas Counts: Interior - Recorded from 4 of 19 localities and on 7% of all counts. Maxima: Vernon 21 Dec 1980-100; Oliver/Osoyoos 29 Dec 1983-24; Penticton 27 Dec 1983-8. **Coastal** - Recorded from 2 of 28 localities and on 1% of all counts. Maxima: Ladner 2 Jan 1960-14; North Saanich 31 Dec 1960-7.

Chukar

Alectoris chukar (Gray)

RANGE: Introduced in North America and established locally from central southern British Columbia, northern Idaho, central and eastern Montana south to northern Baja California, southern Nevada, northern Arizona, northwestern New Mexico, and south-central Colorado. Native of Eurasia.

STATUS: Introduced. *Fairly common* to *common* local resident in the Thompson-Okanagan Plateau region. Breeds.

CHANGE IN STATUS: Attempts to establish the Chukar in British Columbia were made prior to 1950, but these "private" releases were few in number, undocumented, and are assumed to have been unsuccessful. The first documented release was in 1950 when the British Columbia Fish and Game Branch introduced 17 birds at Kamloops. From 1950 to 1955 a total of 2,606 Chukars were introduced at 8 localities. Regional releases and numbers of birds were as follows: Kamloops - 305, Ashcroft - 501, Spence's Bridge - 72, Vernon - 412, Kelowna - 67, Oliver - 499, Okanagan Falls - 419, and Keremeos - 331 (Martin 1955). Chukars were imported as adult birds from Oregon, and as eggs from Washington. The introductions were successful, and in 1955 the first hunting season was permitted. The Chukar is still a familiar bird in the Thompson-Okanagan Plateau region although its numbers have declined as reflected in the drop in provincial harvests estimated at 22,000 in 1960 down to 560 in 1985 (R.W. Ritcey pers. comm.). Its centre of abundance is restricted to the Thompson-Nicola valleys and the southern Okanagan valley. Butler et al. (1986) report the Chukar as introduced to the Creston area, but no other details are given.

There have been many attempts to introduce the Chukar to southeastern Vancouver Island and the Fraser Lowlands since at least 1932 (Guiguet 1953b). All releases were by local sportsmen, in many instances for dog training, but none was successful.

NONBREEDING: The Chukar has been recorded in the central southern interior from Princeton east to Creston and north through the Okanagan, Nicola, and Thompson River valleys, casually to the southern Chilcotin-Cariboo Basin. It prefers grasslands dominated by sagebrush, cheatgrass, and, occasionally, bluebunch wheatgrass, although the last is an indicator of good range conditions and Chukar prefer overgrazed range (R.W. Ritcey pers. comm.). Usually rocky outcroppings are nearby. It avoids agricultural areas except for some feeding and watering. It also frequents railroad right-of-ways and secondary roads (Demarchi, R.A. 1962). It has been found from 290 to 1,570 m elevation, the highest in the Ashnola range.

The Chukar is primarily sedentary (Christensen 1970). There are, however, local movements, to sources of water in late spring and summer, and to lowlands during the winter. Winter flocks breakup from late February (see Fig. 50) to late March (most birds are paired by mid-March) and begin forming again in mid-June when males and unsuccessful females band together in small groups (Demarchi, R.A. 1962).

BREEDING: The Chukar breeds in the Thompson-Okanagan Plateau from Hedley and the Ashnola River east to Osoyoos Lake and north to Summerland, and from Nicola Lake to Kamloops and Cache Creek. Nests and downy chicks have been recorded between 305 and 670 m elevation. Preferred habitat includes sparsely treed, steeply sloping valleys with open rocky hillsides usually covered with bluebunch wheatgrass, sagebrush, and rabbit-brush.

Nests: Only 4 nests have been reported, all of which contained eggshells indicating chicks had hatched. Three nests were located under bushes on a sagebrush-covered flat. The other nest was found on a shale rock slide. One nest was lined with dry grasses and sagebrush twigs and measured 20 cm in outside diameter and 5 cm in depth.

Eggs: Dates for eggs were calculated by back-dating from the known ages of chicks, using the incubation and egg-laying period determined by R.J. Mackie and Buechner (1963). In British Columbia, eggs could be found from 5 April (Demarchi, R.A. 1962) to late July. Analysis of 3 nests containing eggshells suggests that the clutches contained at least 9, 12, and 14 eggs. Clutch size for 4 active nests reported by R.J. Mackie and Buechner (1963) ranged from 10 to 21 and averaged 15.5 eggs. The incubation period is 24 days.

Young: Dates for 249 broods ranged from 25 May (calculated) to 24 September, with 52% recorded between 27 June and 7 August. Brood size ranged from 2 to 26 young (2Y-3, 3Y-7, 4Y-9, 5Y-15, 6Y-12, 7Y-18, 8Y-36, 9Y-23, 10Y-27, 11Y-21, 12Y-32, 13Y-9, 14Y-11, 15Y-14, 16Y-8, 18Y-2, 20Y-1, 26Y-1), with 56% having 8 to 12 young. In the Thompson River valley, R.A. Demarchi (1962) calculated the average brood size for chicks less than 10 days old to be 11.3 while for chicks from 10 days to 8 weeks old the average brood size was 9.5.

REMARKS: See R.A. Demarchi (1962) and Christensen (1970) for additional life history and management information on the Chukar in British Columbia and North America. *A. chukar* was previously considered a subspecies of *A. graeca* (see Watson, G.E. 1962).

NOTEWORTHY RECORDS

Spring: Coastal - Langley 29 Apr 1982-1; Vancouver 14 Apr 1969-1 male; Pitt Meadows 12 Apr 1974-1. **Interior** - Princeton 30 Apr 1980-1 adult; Anarchist Mountain 1 May 1974-5 at lookout; Vaseux Lake 12 Mar 1977-6 near cliffs; Tranquille 21 Mar 1952-4; Gang Ranch 14 and 16 Apr 1952-2 (Erskine and Stein 1964).

Summer: Coastal - Duncan 16 Jul 1975-1 male; Richmond 18 Jun 1976-2 adults; Vancouver 14 Jul 1966-2. **Interior** - Ashnola River 2 Jul 1963-3; Vaseux Lake 26 Aug 1975-30 on cliffs; Summerland 19 Jul 1965-38 (13 adults, 25 immatures), 26 Jul 1987-20 (2 adults, 18 immatures); Ashcroft 19 Jul 1962-16; Lillooet 29 Aug 1968-19.

Autumn: Interior - 70 Mile House 8 Nov 1979-15; Cache Creek (Ashcroft) 16 Oct 1954-20; Kamloops 21 and 22 Oct 1961-8; Summerland 1 Sep 1970-40+; Vaseux Lake 9 Sep 1954-23; Oliver 17 Sep 1966-30; Richter Pass 10 Nov 1965-15; Ashnola River 1 Sep 1963-5. **Coastal** - Qualicum Beach 18 Sep 1975-1 (Dawe 1976); Vancouver 12 Sep 1977-2.

Winter: Interior - Cache Creek 14 Dec 1977-12, 21 Dec 1981-8; Ashcroft 21 Feb 1964-13; Spences Bridge 12 Jan 1982-14; Lytton to 20 km w Kamloops 8 Jan 1978-48; Pyramid 4 Jan 1977-17; Vaseux Lake 12 Jan 1979-15; Richter Lake 1 Feb 1975-80; Cawston to Keremeos 29 Dec 1982-62; Grand Forks 1 Jan 1980-15 feeding in gravel bank; Creston 5 Feb 1982-1 (Butler, R.W. et al. 1986). **Coastal** - Sooke 3 Dec 1969-2.

Christmas Counts: Interior - Recorded from 4 of 19 localities and on 27% of all counts. Maxima: Oliver/Osoyoos 29 Dec 1983-**193**, all-time Canadian high count (Monroe 1984); Vaseux Lake 28 Dec 1978-118; Kamloops 15 Dec 1984-31. **Coastal** - Recorded once: Deep Bay 30 Dec 1978-1.

Chukar

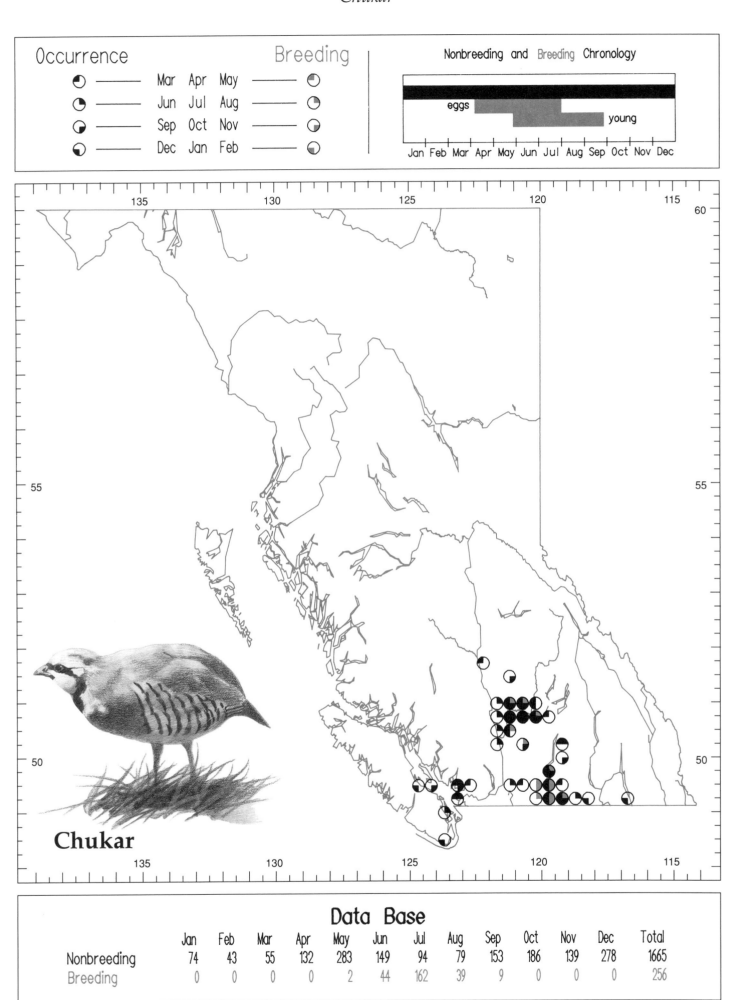

Chukar

Occurrence

	Breeding
Mar Apr May	
Jun Jul Aug	
Sep Oct Nov	
Dec Jan Feb	

Nonbreeding and Breeding Chronology

eggs

young

Jan Feb Mar Apr May Jun Jul Aug Sep Oct Nov Dec

Data Base

	Jan	Feb	Mar	Apr	May	Jun	Jul	Aug	Sep	Oct	Nov	Dec	Total
Nonbreeding	74	43	55	132	283	149	94	79	153	186	139	278	1665
Breeding	0	0	0	0	2	44	162	39	9	0	0	0	256

Ring-necked Pheasant

RNPH

Phasianus colchicus Linnaeus

RANGE: Introduced and established in North America from southern Canada south to Washington, northern California, Utah, and Kansas, east to Virginia and New England. Scattered local populations elsewhere. Native to Asia.

STATUS: Introduced. *Fairly common* to *common* resident on southeastern Vancouver Island, the Fraser Lowlands, the Okanagan valley and the vicinities of Salmon Arm and Creston. Elsewhere, populations are local and the status is unknown. Breeds.

NONBREEDING: The Ring-necked Pheasant (Fig. 51) is distributed along eastern Vancouver Island, from Victoria to Campbell River and east through the Fraser Lowlands to Hope. In the interior, the pheasant occurs primarily in the central southern portion of the province including the Okanagan valley east to Creston and north to Salmon Arm; rarely in the Nicola and south Thompson River valleys and the southern Chilcotin-Cariboo. Small local populations may exist elsewhere in the province as a result of release programs (e.g. Tlell; see Remarks). It has been recorded from sea level to 750 m elevation.

Good pheasant habitat is associated with areas of high soil fertility where agricultural crops and wild vegetation produce the basic requirements of food and cover. It has, however, been found in many habitat types, even dense forests where it occasionally roosts up to 50 m from the forest edge. Other habitats include brackish and fresh water marshes, estuaries, lake shores, open woodlands, beaches, scrubby fields, airports, golf courses, city parks and yards (Fig. 51), and ploughed fields. Climatically, its range varies between the dry interior with its extremes of heat and cold and the more humid, moderate Fraser Lowlands and lowlands of eastern Vancouver Island.

The Ring-necked Pheasant is a sedentary species. Males are polygamous during the breeding season; at other times they are solitary. In winter, females are frequently found in small groups.

BREEDING: The Ring-necked Pheasant breeds from Victoria to Campbell River along the lowlands of eastern Vancouver Island, the southern Gulf Islands, Fraser Lowlands from the Fraser River delta to Chilliwack, throughout the Okanagan valley and the extreme southern portion of the west Kootenay in the vicinity of Creston. It breeds from near sea level to 640 m elevation, but most nests have been found below 300 m.

The Ring-necked Pheasant breeds in most habitats except dense woodlands, but prefers agricultural areas in shrubby, grass and grain fields (Fig. 52). Other habitats include orchards, open deciduous woodlands, marshes, ditches, parks, golf courses and gardens in residential areas (Fig. 53), rangeland, seismic road and powerline cuts, and bogs.

Figure 51. Male Ring-necked Pheasants at feeding station near Courtland Flats, Saanich, 16 March 1986 (Tim Zurowski).

Ring-necked Pheasant

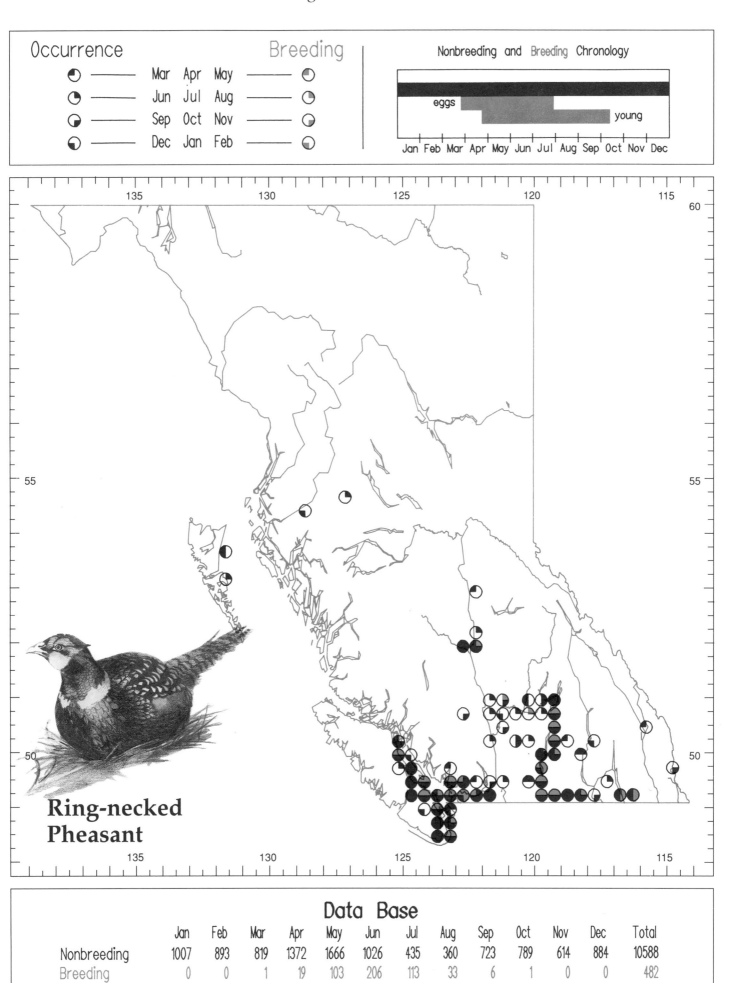

Occurrence

◕	—	Mar	Apr	May	—	◐
◔	—	Jun	Jul	Aug	—	○
◔	—	Sep	Oct	Nov	—	◔
◕	—	Dec	Jan	Feb	—	◕

Breeding

Nonbreeding and Breeding Chronology

eggs

young

Jan Feb Mar Apr May Jun Jul Aug Sep Oct Nov Dec

Ring-necked Pheasant

Data Base

	Jan	Feb	Mar	Apr	May	Jun	Jul	Aug	Sep	Oct	Nov	Dec	Total
Nonbreeding	1007	893	819	1372	1666	1026	435	360	723	789	614	884	10588
Breeding	0	0	1	19	103	206	113	33	6	1	0	0	482

Nests: Nests were located at the bases of clumps of grasses, shrubs, and fence posts, among tall grasses, reeds, cattail, and sagebrush, next to logs, buildings, and construction equipment, and under small trees and brush piles. Nests were frequently close to sources of water. One nest was built inside a metal bucket and another was found in a partially-submerged row boat.

Nests were small depressions in the ground and were formed of grasses, feathers, weed stalks, twigs, and rootlets. They were lined with grasses, leaves, feathers, weeds, and, in-frequently, dried mosses.

Eggs: Dates for 189 clutches ranged from 21 April to 27 July, with 51% recorded between 10 May and 8 June. Calculated dates indicate that eggs could be found as early as 25 March. Sizes for 182 clutches ranged from 2 to 28 eggs (2E-2, 3E-2, 4E-2, 5E-6, 6E-8, 7E-12, 8E-8, 9E-23, 10E-23, 11E-18, 12E-23, 13E-18, 14E-11, 15E-4, 17E-2, 18E-4, 19E-4, 20E-4, 21E-2, 23E-3, 26E-2, 28E-1), with 58% having 9 to 13 eggs. Incubation period is 22 to 25 days (Godfrey 1986).

Young: Dates for 293 broods ranged from 3 May to 11 October with 52% recorded between 4 June and 6 July. Calculated dates indicate that first broods could be found as early as 23 April. Sizes for 291 broods ranged from 1 to 18 young (1Y-17, 2Y-20, 3Y-22, 4Y-29, 5Y-51, 6Y-31, 7Y-33, 8Y-27, 9Y-10, 10Y-18, 11Y-8, 12Y-12, 13Y-6, 14Y-2, 15Y-1, 16Y-1, 17Y-2, 18Y-1) with 59% having 4 to 8 young. Fledging period is 12 to 14 days (Harrison, C. 1978).

REMARKS: From 1882 to 1920, at least 500 Ring-necked Pheasants were released at a number of locations in coastal and interior British Columbia. Some birds were imported from England, but most came from China. From this stock, populations became established and spread throughout suitable habitat, although many additional introductions were made to bolster local populations (see Taylor, E.W. 1959). Some introductions failed. Known pheasant introductions to British Columbia are summarized below. They are discussed by geographic area:

(1) Queen Charlotte Islands: Small numbers were released near Tlell from 1918 to 1920. Spalding (1966) indicates that early introductions were successful and that "a small population was started." By the winter of 1941-42 the Ring-necked Pheasant was "very common" (Cook, F.S. 1947). Thereafter, populations gradually declined. Small introductions were again made in the 1980s, but the population is not large and likely needs regular releases if it is to be maintained.

(2) Vancouver Island: The earliest introduction was at Victoria in 1882. Twenty birds were released, but all died. The following year, 25 pheasants were released at Esquimalt and, apparently, all survived. M. Williams (1964) suggests that pheasant populations on southern Vancouver Island descended from this stock. Populations increased and became well established on the Saanich Peninsula. Spring numbers there were estimated at 900 in 1966 and 2,300 in 1972; autumn numbers were estimated at 5,700 in 1966 and 14,300 in 1972 (Finnegan 1972). Recently, however, T.D. Hooper and Sars (1986) report an all-time low in 1985 based on crowing count indices. For example, an index of 10.8 for Saanich in May 1972 (Finnegan 1972) dropped to 3.3 in May 1985. This decline was attributed mainly to habitat destruction and pesticide use. In spring and autumn 1955, over 700 birds were released at 3 locations north of Victoria (Taylor, E.W. 1959): Duncan (204 birds), Nanaimo (204 birds), and Courtenay (308 birds). Populations there are established but annual winter counts suggest a gradual decline in numbers is occurring.

(3) Gulf Islands: 12 birds were released on Saltspring Island in 1886, 20 on Prevost Island in 1890 and 5 on Jedediah Island in 1895. Today, small numbers exist only on Saltspring Island.

(4) Fraser Lowlands: From 1890 to 1910, at least 400 pheasants were released at various locations from the Fraser River delta to Chilliwack. Introductions were successful and by 1896 the first hunting season was established. In 1955 an additional 6,905 pheasants were released in the same area (see Taylor, E.W. 1959). Populations are now centred in the Fraser River delta and appear relatively stable. See E.W. Taylor (1950) for a detailed study of factors affecting the reproduction and survival of the species in the Fraser Lowlands.

Figure 52. *Incubating female Ring-necked Pheasant, Delta, 12 June 1972 (Ervio Sian). Tall grass fields provide excellent cover for nesting pheasants.*

(5) Okanagan valley: Five birds were brought to Okanagan Falls in 1910, raised in captivity and released in 1911. By late 1912, there were about 200 pheasants in the region (Rye 1952), and by 1942 densities near Vernon reached 3.5 birds per hectare (Cowan 1942b). Numbers declined drastically throughout the valley in 1946 (Rye 1952). Since then, they have fluctuated widely, but with a general downward trend brought about by deteriorating habitat due to urbanization, lack of cereal grain production, and increased use of pesticides (R.W. Ritcey pers. comm.; Spalding and Stoneberg 1981).

(6) Salmon Arm: Birds were introduced and became established long before the 1950s (R.W. Ritcey pers. comm.) although the date of the first release is unknown. Additional birds were released from 1953 to the early 1960s. In April 1961 and 1962, pheasant crowing counts there revealed 362 and 308 birds respectively (Taylor, E.W. 1962). The Salmon Arm and vicinity population is the only real centre of abundance north of the Okanagan (R.W. Ritcey pers. comm.).

(7) Kootenays: Birds were introduced near Ta Ta Creek and Wasa (Johnstone, W.B . 1949). In the Creston area, releases were made in the late 1800s and birds became well established on the flood plain farms and adjacent benchland (Munro, J.A. 1950; Butler, R.W.. et al. 1986). All Kootenay region introductions, with the exception of those in the Creston valley, have failed. The Creston population is small but is of a viable and huntable size (R.A. Demarchi pers. comm.).

(8) Central Interior: Pheasants were introduced near Quesnel and Smithers prior to 1935, when the last birds were seen (Munro, J.A. 1947a). Early introductions in the Alkali Lake and Williams Lake region survived for a number of years although they never became viable. A few pheasants have been released near Alkali Lake over the past few years, with some surviving the winter of 1986/87 to breed the following spring. However, predators appear to have reduced their numbers (A. Roberts pers. comm.).

During the 1950s, pheasant stocking continued in British Columbia but with local, farm-reared birds. In 1955, nearly 9,000 birds were released at 15 coastal locations and 4 interior locations (Taylor, E.W. 1959). New interior locations included Kamloops (265 birds), Merritt (200 birds), Keremeos (240 birds), Grand Forks (262 birds) and Creston (410 birds).

Known in the Old World as the Pheasant.

Figure 53. *Female Ring-necked Pheasant incubating in flower bed in private residence on Reifel Island, 20 April 1973 (Neil K. Dawe).*

NOTEWORTHY RECORDS

Spring: Coastal - Victoria 15 Mar 1969-8 on golf course; Somenos Lake 16 Mar 1974-10; Westham Island 12 Mar 1978-157 on roadside count (Graf 1978); Sea Island 14 Apr 1974-35; Port Alberni 12 May 1974-2; Qualicum Beach 22 Mar 1974-8; Miracle Beach Park 27 Apr 1972-2; Tlell Apr 1987-1. **Interior** - Oliver to Richter Lake 17 May 1959-10; Vaseux Lake 6 May 1976-6 males; Sorrento 16 Mar 1972-4; Riske Creek 12 Mar 1983-1 female left from 80 released in summer of 1981.

Summer: Coastal - Beacon Hill 30 Jun 1975-7; Abbotsford 19 Jul 1963-3; Reifel Island 24 Aug 1968-20; Qualicum Beach 3 Aug 1976-16; Comox 4 Aug 1941-6. **Interior** - Coldstream 11 Jul 1958-14; Lavington 22 Aug 1972-11; Chase to Kamloops 11 Jul 1963-5 along road; Telkwa River valley 10 Jul 1974-1 immature (RBCM 16620).

Autumn: Interior - Alkali Lake (Cariboo) 20 Nov 1949-1 female (NMC 47727); near Cache Creek (Ashcroft) 16 Oct 1954-22; Cherry Creek (Savona) 1 Nov 1954-10; Sorrento 26 Sep 1970-8; Okanagan Landing 17 Oct 1934-150; Lavington 19 Nov 1973-51; Vaseux Lake 22 Oct 1975-4; Creston 28 Oct 1973-12; Grand Forks 21 Nov 1979-5. **Coastal** - Qualicum Beach 7 Oct 1980-13; near Hope 26 Nov 1976-9; Westham Island 2 Oct 1974-70 (Foster 1974); Boundary Bay 12 Nov 1962-44; Duncan 29 Nov 1957-15; Saanich 6 Oct 1980-15.

Winter: Interior - Tranquille 26 Jan 1952-92; Coldstream 13 Jan 1953-60+; Penticton 27 Dec 1976-24; Grand Forks 9 Dec 1979-10. **Coastal** - Lakelse Lake 31 Jan 1976-1 male; Qualicum Beach 22 Dec 1973-11; Sea Island 29 Jan 1979-32; Westham Island 2 Feb 1979-250; Langley 9 Jan 1977-22; Lake Cowichan 24 Dec 1924-8 (Simpson 1925); Saanich 1 Jan 1983-16.

Christmas Counts: Interior - Recorded from 6 of 19 localities and on 41% of all counts. Maxima: Vernon 27 Dec 1981-**371**, all-time Canadian high count (Anderson, R.R. 1982); Penticton 27 Dec 1983-87; Oliver/Osoyoos 29 Dec 1983-71. **Coastal** - Recorded from 16 of 28 localities and on 64% of all counts. Maxima: Ladner 29 Dec 1979-256; Vancouver 26 Dec 1975-208; Pitt Meadows 4 Jan 1976-115.

Spruce Grouse

Dendragapus canadensis (Linnaeus)

RANGE: Resident throughout most boreal forests from tree line in Alaska and Yukon south to the northern United States and east to Labrador and Maine. Introduced in Newfoundland.

STATUS: *Uncommon* but extremely widespread resident thoughout the province east of the Coast Ranges. *Very rare* on the mainland coast; absent from Vancouver Island and the Queen Charlotte Islands. Breeds.

NONBREEDING: The Spruce Grouse is widely distributed throughout interior British Columbia. It occurs in low densities in coniferous forests from approximately 300 to 2,500 m elevation. It is restricted to certain forest types, so local distribution is determined more by elevation than by any other factor. In the southern interior, Spruce Grouse inhabit mountainous regions dominated by lodgepole pine and spruce forests, usually above 800 m elevation. In the north, where spruces and lodgepole pine occur at lower elevations, it ranges from lowland valleys to the timberline. Spruce Grouse are most common in the following habitats, by region: in the Okanagan, subalpine fir - Engelmann spruce forests between 1,300 and 2,000 m (Cannings, R.A. et al. 1987); in the Chilcotin-Cariboo, white spruce swamps (Munro, J.A. 1935b) and Douglas-fir forests (A. Roberts pers. comm.); in Kootenay National Park, spruce and spruce - Douglas-fir forests (van Tighem 1977); in Wells Gray Park, in dense western redcedar -western hemlock stands at lower levels and climax subalpine fir - Engelmann spruce stands nearer the timberline (Webb 1952); Tatlatui Park, lodgepole pine forests, and in Spatsizi Plateau Wilderness Park, white spruce forests (Osmond-Jones et al. 1977).

Spruce Grouse are rather sedentary birds with discrete home territories and overlapping but restricted home ranges. Both sexes remain on home ranges during the non-breeding seasons (Stoneberg 1967). Home ranges are usually only a few hectares in size, thus movements are rather localized for each individual. Adults tend not to move more than a few hundred metres from established territories whereas juveniles disperse from their natal sites up to 6 km from year to year, probably in winter and spring (Stoneberg 1967; McCourt 1969). Most of our records are of 1 or 2 birds or family groups. Family groups (female and young) stay together through to late autumn after the young fledge. Males remain alone and complete a moult after breeding, then may rejoin a family group in late summer or autumn. Spruce Grouse winter in dense cover, singly or in small groups, spending much of their time foraging and roosting in coniferous trees. They are in peak condition in winter when their food is virtually 100% conifer needles (Pendergast 1969). Adults return to traditional territories in April in preparation for breeding, and yearlings search out vacant territories. Unlike Blue Grouse, Spruce Grouse rarely group into large multi-family flocks in autumn and winter, usually staying in single family units. An exceptionally large flock of 30 Spruce Grouse was observed eating gravel from a road along the Green River, west of Anahim Lake, on 11 Dec 1975. These birds were perhaps brought together by gravel availability rather than true flocking behaviour.

BREEDING: The Spruce Grouse is a widespread breeder throughout the interior of the province east of the Coast Ranges at elevations between 400 and 2,100 m. Of 180 breeding records with elevations documented, 80% occurred between 900 and 1,800 m. Males move from thicker winter cover to traditional display sites in more open woods in April. Displaying males are more or less evenly dispersed throughout suitable habitat (Ellison 1971; MacDonald 1968) and remain "on site" until June. Females choose more open habitat for nesting and brood rearing than males do for displaying (Edwards 1949; Ellison 1971; Stoneberg 1967).

Nests: Nests were usually situated in open coniferous forest with a low, sparse understory. Twenty-seven nest sites were shallow depressions in the ground adjacent to or under objects such as the bases of coniferous trees (71%), small shrubs (11%), rail fences (11%), stumps (4%), and birch trees (4%). Thirty-nine nests were lined with loose accumulations of feathers (33%), grasses (26%), evergreen needles (15%), twigs (10%), or bark (3%). One nest measured 12 cm deep and 20 cm in diameter.

Eggs: Dates for 55 clutches ranged from 3 May to 28 July with 51% recorded between 26 May and 19 June. Sizes for 44 clutches ranged from 1 to 10 eggs (1E-2, 2E-1, 3E-3, 4E-3, 5E-9, 6E-15, 7E-3, 8E-1, 9E-4, 10E-3) with 61% having 5 to 7 eggs. Broods of up to 13 young may indicate clutches of 13 eggs, but are more likely the result of mixed broods. Incubation period is about 21 days (Pendergast and Boag 1971).

Young: Dates for 320 broods ranged from 6 June to 24 September with 50% recorded between 9 July and 10 August. Sizes for 300 broods ranged from 1 to 13 young (1Y-35, 2Y-53, 3Y-53, 4Y-58, 5Y-50, 6Y-25, 7Y-9, 8Y-7, 9Y-4, 10Y-3, 11Y-2, 13Y-1) with 71% having 2 to 5 young. Young make short flights in about 10 to 12 days (Harrison 1978).

REMARKS: Three subspecies of the Spruce Grouse are found in British Columbia. The "Franklin's Grouse," *D. c. franklinii* (formerly considered a separate species) inhabits the southern two-thirds of the province, *D. c. osgoodi* inhabits the northern part of the province, and *D. c. canadensis* is the race of central eastern British Columbia (Godfrey 1986).

The Spruce Grouse is a popular game bird in British Columbia. An average of 70,000 were taken each year for the 10 year period 1976 to 1985.

NOTEWORTHY RECORDS

Spring: Coastal - Stuie 29 May 1932-1 female (MCZ 281789). **Interior** - Nelson 30 Mar 1977-1; Radium Hot Springs 28 Apr 1969-1 (Christman 1969); Emerald Lake (Yoho National Park) 13 May 1976-4 (Wade 1977); Knouff Lake road 5 Apr 1983-1; Quesnel 30 May 1932-1 pair (UBC 425, 426); Fort Nelson 15 Apr 1986-1; Atlin 18 May 1981-1 (Campbell 1981); n Kwokullie Lake 26 May 1982-1 (RBCM 17458).

Summer: Coastal - Mount Sproatt 30 Jul 1923-4 (UBC 3769-72); Stuie 26 Jul 1940-1 immature female (UMMZ 122370), 13 Aug 1938-1 adult male (NMC 28787); Porcupine River 23 Jul 1948-

1 male. **Interior** - Flathead River 24 Aug 1958-7; Vermillion River 26 Aug 1970-4; Celista 26 Jul 1960-4; Pisima Mountain 28 Aug 1966-6; Taylor 21 Aug 1975-6; Grant Lake (e Fireside) 28 Aug 1978-5 adults; Moose Lake (Atlin) 13 Jun 1975-1.

Autumn: Interior - Haines Road (Chilkat Pass) 22 Oct 1981-1; Gladys Lake (Atlin) 20 Sep 1976-6; McBride River 8 Sep 1977-6; Stony Lake (e Quintette Mountain) Sep 1977-7, "largest group"; Lake O'Hara 15 Sep 1975-4; Adams Lake (Chase) 18 Sep 1987-8; Johnson Lake (Adams Lake) 20 Sep 1983-5; Cranbrook 2 Nov 1915-1 female; Manning Park 11 Oct 1977-4. **Coastal** - Terrace 12

Oct 1975-1; Stuie 8 Sep 1938-2 females.

Winter: Interior - Milligan Creek 16 Feb 1984-3; Fort St. John 13 Jan 1985-6; Green River (Anahim Lake) 11 Dec 1975-30; Leanchoil 14 Feb 1977-1 (Wade 1977). **Coastal** - Stuie 10 Dec 1971-1.

Christmas Counts: Interior - Recorded from 5 of 19 localities and on 8% of all counts. Maxima: Lake Windermere 4 Jan 1981-2; Smithers 2 Jan 1982-1; Fort St. John 24 Dec 1978-1; Shuswap Lake 19 Dec 1974-1, 3 Jan 1981-1; Yoho National Park 18 Dec 1976-1. **Coastal** - Recorded once: Terrace 30 Dec 1973-1.

Spruce Grouse

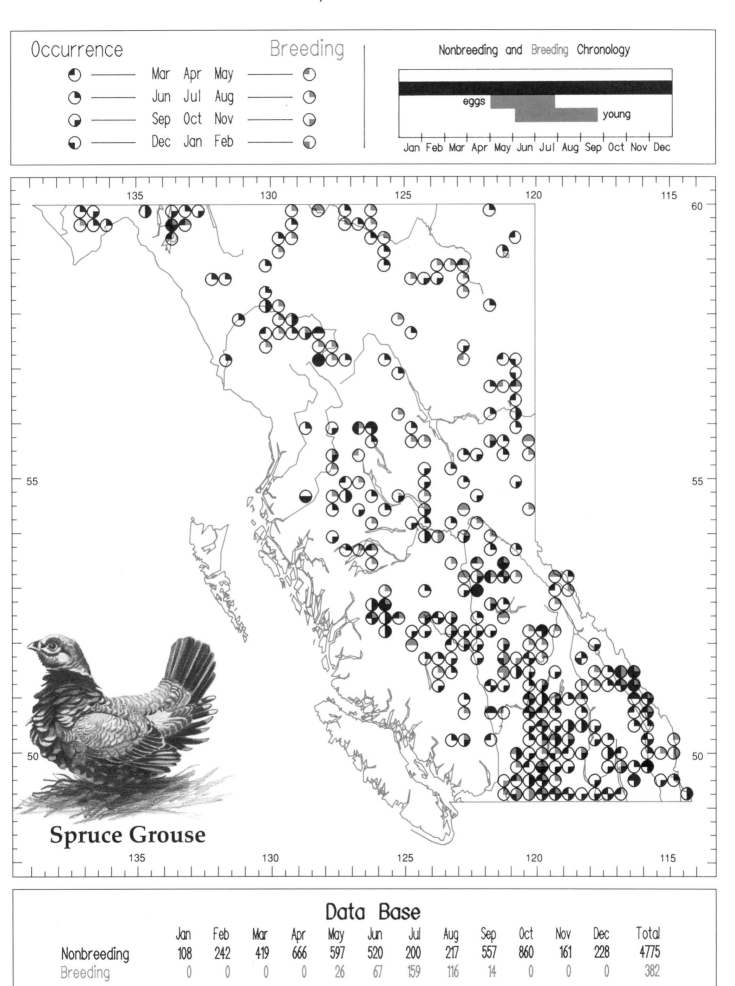

Spruce Grouse

Data Base

	Jan	Feb	Mar	Apr	May	Jun	Jul	Aug	Sep	Oct	Nov	Dec	Total
Nonbreeding	108	242	419	666	597	520	200	217	557	860	161	228	4775
Breeding	0	0	0	0	26	67	159	116	14	0	0	0	382

Blue Grouse
Dendragapus obscurus (Say)

BLGR

RANGE: Resident from southern Alaska and central Yukon east to extreme southwestern Mackenzie, south along the coast to northern California and in the mountains to southern California, Arizona, and New Mexico, east to southwestern Alberta and Colorado.

STATUS: *Uncommon* to *common* resident along the coast including Vancouver Island and the Queen Charlotte Islands. *Rare* to *common* resident in the interior. Widespread breeder.

NONBREEDING: The Blue Grouse is widely distributed throughout British Columbia, including Vancouver Island and the Queen Charlotte Islands. Its distribution is closely associated with mountains throughout its range. North of 52°N and east of the Coast Ranges the species is far less common, and has a scattered distribution. It appears to be absent from large areas, such as the northern Chilcotin-Cariboo and most of the Boreal Forest. The centre of abundance is the east coast of Vancouver Island from Victoria north to Adam River.

The Blue Grouse occupies a wide variety of habitat types throughout the province from near sea level to the alpine regions at 2,050 m elevation. These include mature and second growth coastal forests, small coastal islands, forest openings and edges including logged or burned areas, meadows, and most interior forest types, from the dry forests of the southern interior to the subalpine Engelmann spruce and subalpine fir forests, as well as open plateaus. Winter range is in coniferous forests where birds are principally arboreal, although they may roost in the snow.

Birds may begin leaving their wintering areas as early as February in some years, particularly along the coast. In the southern interior, they begin moving from their wintering grounds by mid-March, somewhat later farther north.

Throughout the summer, most yearling males are not territorial. They wander over extensive areas and probably do not breed (Redfield 1973). Non-territorial adult males (≥2 years) appear to be "not uncommon" within populations of breeding Blue Grouse on the coast (Lewis, R.A. 1984). They wander throughout the summer, their movements encompassing the territories of other males. Although vacant areas, apparently suitable for territories, are present on the summer range, R.A. Lewis and Zwickel (1980) suggest that these males remain non-territorial because the vacant areas are of low quality.

In southern areas, Blue Grouse migrate short distances, if at all, and move uphill to their winter range. In the north and in the interior, migration is downhill from mountain meadows. Along the central and north coast, they tend to migrate to wintering grounds both downward from alpine meadows and upward from open lowland (Fig. 54). Males and unsuccessful females begin moving to their winter grounds from mid-summer through October. During this period, the tendency for the grouse to flock decreases. After November, flocking increases again, peaking in January and early February (Hines 1986). From November through February, Blue Grouse are seldom seen unless specific attempts are made to find them.

BREEDING: The Blue Grouse is a widespread breeder throughout most of British Columbia. The centre of breeding abundance lies south of 52°N latitude; breeding reports are scattered and sparse farther north.

They frequent a wide variety of treed habitats ranging from coastal rain forests near sea level to the open ponderosa pine - sagebrush habitat of the dry interior to the coniferous forests of the subalpine regions, usually in or adjacent to openings such as logging slashes, forest burns, and, occasionally, alpine meadows, farmland, parklands, and bogs. Most summer range is an open landscape with a variety of forbs, shrubs, grasses, and a scattering of coniferous and broadleaf trees (Bendell and Zwickel 1984). There, the females and young spend most of their time on the ground. Males, on the other hand, sometimes select habitat like

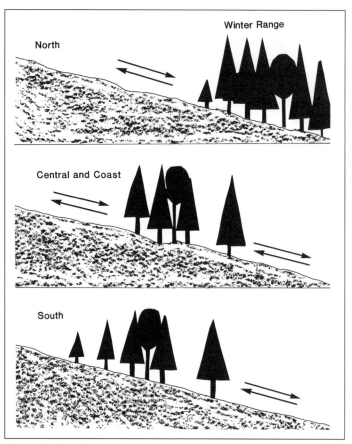

Figure 54. *Direction of migration between winter and summer range for 3 populations of Blue Grouse in British Columbia (from Bendell and Zwickel 1984).*

that of the winter range and spend their time in the conifers adjacent to the openings. On the Queen Charlotte Islands, recent survey work suggests that summer populations occupy mature forests: the birds do not seem to use clearcuts as much as they do farther south (F.C. Zwickel pers. comm.).

Nests: All nests (n=42) were situated in a small depression in the ground (Fig. 55). Most nests (83%) were well hidden under some type of living vegetation (43%), such as small trees, shrubs, and herbs, or under fallen logs (31%). Nests were also found under cut western redcedar boughs; one nest was found in the open in front of a small stump. Nest material seemed to be whatever was near the nest site and included various mixtures of feathers, grasses, twigs, roots, leaves, needles, moss, and herbaceous vegetation, including bracken, fireweed, blackberries, and pearly everlasting.

Eggs: Dates for 85 clutches ranged from 26 April to 4 August with 50% recorded between 21 May and 12 June. Clutch size ranged from 1 to 10 eggs (1E-3, 2E-3, 3E-3, 4E-10, 5E-14, 6E-25, 7E-13, 8E-10, 9E-1, 10E-3) with 61% having 5 to 7 eggs. The average clutch size of 6.3 eggs reported by Zwickel and Bendell (1967) falls within that range. Incubation period is 26 days (Zwickel and Lance 1965; McKinnon and Zwickel 1988). Chicks on uplands hatch about a month later than those on adjacent lowlands (Bendell and Zwickel 1984).

Young: Dates for 355 broods ranged from 16 May to 25 September with 56% recorded between 24 June and 23 July. By late August, most broods start to disband, and by the end of September most juveniles have separated from adult females (Hines 1986). Brood sizes ranged from 1 to 12 young (1Y-46, 2Y-54, 3Y-66, 4Y-53, 5Y-50, 6Y-40, 7Y-31, 8Y-7, 9Y-4, 10Y-2, 12Y-2) with

Blue Grouse

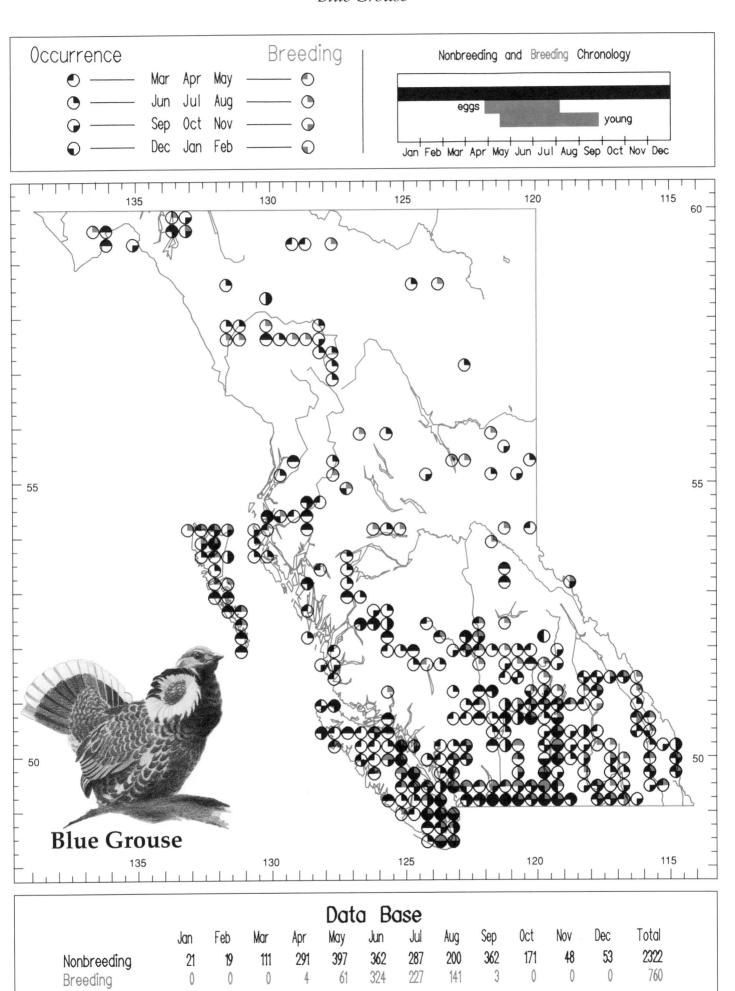

Occurrence

Breeding

	Mar Apr May	
	Jun Jul Aug	
	Sep Oct Nov	
	Dec Jan Feb	

Nonbreeding and Breeding Chronology

eggs

young

Jan Feb Mar Apr May Jun Jul Aug Sep Oct Nov Dec

Blue Grouse

Data Base

	Jan	Feb	Mar	Apr	May	Jun	Jul	Aug	Sep	Oct	Nov	Dec	Total
Nonbreeding	21	19	111	291	397	362	287	200	362	171	48	53	2322
Breeding	0	0	0	4	61	324	227	141	3	0	0	0	760

63% having 2 to 5 young. The 2 broods of 12 were likely a result of brood-mixing. Fledging period is about 14 days for sustained flight (Zwickel 1967).

REMARKS: The Blue Grouse is divided into 8 subspecies in North America, 4 of which occur in British Columbia (Fig. 57). They can be divided into 2 groups: coastal and interior. These groups differ in some plumage, morphological, and behavioural characteristics (Table 2), and are described in detail in Bendell and Zwickel (1984) and in Degner (1988). At one time, the coastal and interior forms were considered separate species: *Dendragapus fuliginosus* and *D. obscurus* respectively, American Ornithologists' Union 1931). The debate on the current status of the 2 groups continues. The American Ornithologists' Union (1983) considers all Blue Grouse as one species but more recently they state that the systematic status is under review (American Ornithologists' Union 1985). Potapov (1985), however, treats the forms as distinct species.

Logging can, in some cases, bring about rapid population increases by creating favourable breeding habitat (Fig. 56; Hatter, J. 1955). On one Vancouver Island study area, maximum spring densities of Blue Grouse reached about 90 adult males/km² (Bendell 1955), one of the highest densities reported for any gallinaceous bird. Usually, however, densities increase to a lesser degree and only for a short while, then stabilize at a moderate level of around 15 to 30 males/km² until the tree canopy begins to close; then they decline to a low density or disappear altogether (Zwickel and Bendell 1985). In some areas of Vancouver Island and the Queen Charlotte Islands, however, open clear cuts did not contain breeding populations of Blue Grouse and were reported never to do so (Bendell and Zwickel 1984). Logging of winter range, however, could reduce or eliminate local numbers, particularly where a large breeding population depends on a small winter range (Bendell and Zwickel 1984).

Although all of British Columbia is within the range of the Blue Grouse, some coastal islands were unoccupied historically. Introductions of Blue Grouse to these islands (F.C. Zwickel pers. comm.) were made as follows:

1) Texada Island: The British Columbia Fish and Game Branch released 135 grouse between 1944 and 1947.. By 1951 they had become established throughout the island. Birds are still present in low densities.
2) Southern Gulf Islands: As part of an experimental introduction, 200 birds were released on Sidney (40), Portland (40), and Moresby (120) islands in 1970 (see Bergerud and Hemus 1975). Apparently, the grouse established only on Moresby Island.
3) Lasqueti Island: Residents introduced 23 birds in 1971. They now occur in low density throughout the island.

Figure 55. Blue Grouse nest and eggs at Sparwood, 17 June 1982 (Mark Nyhof).

Figure 56. Male Blue Grouse, Goldstream Park, Vancouver Island, 4 June 1986 (David F. Fraser). Note the light coloured cervical apteria and wide terminal tail band characteristic of the coastal form.

TABLE 2.
Field marks of the coastal and interior forms of the Blue Grouse in British Columbia (adapted from Bendell and Zwickel 1984; Degner 1988).

Characteristic	Coastal Form	Interior Form
1. Song (hoot)	Loud, most often composed of 5 syllables, mostly from trees in dense site	Soft to inaudible, composed of 6 syllables mostly from the ground in more open sites
2. Terminal tail band	Wide and distinct	Narrow or none at all
3. Number of rectrices (tail feathers)	Usually 18	Usually 20
4. Cervical apteria (bare neck patch)	Yellow	Reddish
5. Flutter flight	Infrequent	Frequent

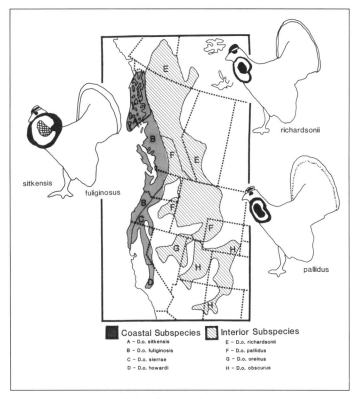

Coastal Subspecies
A – D.o. sitkensis
B – D.o. fuliginosis
C – D.o. sierrae
D – D.o. howardi

Interior Subspecies
E – D.o. richardsonii
F – D.o. pallidus
G – D.o. oreinus
H – D.o. obscurus

Figure 57. Distribution of the subspecies of Blue Grouse in British Columbia (after Bendell and Zwickel 1984). Males of British Columbia subspecies are shown in full display. See Table 2 for a description of field marks.

NOTEWORTHY RECORDS

Spring: Coastal - Sooke Hills 5 Mar 1976-1 hooting, 12 May 1954-15; Adam River 4 to 7 and 10 to 12 May 1982-over 50 seen, hundreds heard; Klemtu 5 Apr 1976-2 hooting; Chief Mathews Bay 9 Apr 1980-2. **Interior** - Summerland 14 Mar 1962-1 hooting; Squilax 7 Apr 1952-9; Riske Creek 14 Mar 1981-2, 20 Apr 1984-1, rare here - move up to fir timber about end of September to winter, 5 May 1978-pair courting; near Williams Lake 27 Apr 1979-2; Torrens River valley 24 May 1977-1 in subalpine; Horseranch Range 12 May 1963-1 (NMC 57668); Three Guardsmen Pass 28 May 1979-3 hooting at timberline.

Summer: Coastal - road to Jordan River 3 Jun 1984-50; Nanaimo River headwaters 14 Jul 1981-1 hooting; Lennard Island 14 Jun 1978-1; on road between Masset and Tlell Jun 1973-50+; Kitsault Lake 17 to 19 Jun 1980-14. **Interior** - Apex Mountain (Penticton) 5 Aug 1962-8 at treeline; Sibola Range 17 Jul 1976-1; North Duti Lake 5 Aug 1976-5; Pink Mountain 11 Aug 1977-5; 16 km s Dease Lake 28 Jun 1962-3 (NMC 49668-70); near Summit Pass Aug 1943-2 (Rand 1944).

Autumn: Interior - Dease Lake 2 Sep 1962-2 (NMC 54195-96); Tumbler Ridge 5 Nov 1976-4; 16 km s Nation River 20 Oct 1972-2; La Forme Creek 10 Sep 1983-12; Scotch Creek 5 Oct 1965-10; n end Okanagan Lake 16 Oct 1962-25; 24 km n Kelowna 29 Sep 1975-6 flushed from steep talus slopes; Oliver 19 Sep 1953-12; Blackwall Peak 27 Sep 1975-13 in subalpine. **Coastal** - Naden River 16 Oct 1975-3.

Winter: Interior - McLure 4 Jan 1952-2; Wells Gray Park winter 1952/ 53-sparsely distributed at lower elevations, a few winter along snow-free s and w slopes of Green Mountain (Ritcey 1953); Beaconsfield Mountain 30 Dec 1978-5 in snow beneath trees at 1,980 m; Manning Park 8 Feb 1980-1 hooting at 1,900 m. **Coastal** - Skip Mountain 28 Feb 1981-1 hooting; Masset Inlet 30 Jan 1982-1; Quadra Island 5 Jan 1976-2; n Ross Lake 20 Feb 1971-1 hooting.

Christmas Counts: Interior - Recorded from 7 of 19 localities and on 22% of all counts. Maxima: Vernon 19 Dec 1982-**13**, all-time Canadian high count (Anderson, R.R. 1983), 18 Dec 1983-4; Smithers 16 Dec 1978-6; Lake Windermere 23 Dec 1979-4. **Coastal** - Recorded from 8 of 28 localities and on 11% of all counts. Maxima: Victoria 27 Dec 1975-3; Squamish 3 Jan 1981-3; all other counts are of 1 or 2 birds.

Willow Ptarmigan

WIPT

Lagopus lagopus (Linnaeus)

RANGE: Holarctic. Breeds in North America from Alaska east across the arctic islands to Baffin Island and south through western British Columbia, Yukon, Mackenzie, northern Manitoba, northern Ontario, Quebec, and Newfoundland. Winters mostly in the breeding range. Also occurs in Eurasia.

STATUS: *Rare* to seasonally *abundant* resident in the western mountainous regions of mainland British Columbia. *Very rare* in eastern portions of the province. Breeds.

NONBREEDING: The Willow Ptarmigan is distributed on the mainland primarily through the western half of the province, although most reports are from the eastern flanks of the Coast Ranges and eastward. It is very rare on the western side of the Coast Ranges. There are few records from the far eastern half of the province.

The Willow Ptarmigan frequents the subalpine and alpine zones of mountains and plateaus, normally just above the treeline, including willow and scrub birch thickets, wet sedge meadows, and stream and lake edges. In winter, birds move to lower elevations, frequenting subalpine forested areas, road and stream edges, and forest openings. They have been recorded from 600 to 1,980 m elevation.

In late spring, winter aggregations break up as birds move from lower elevations and begin pairing. Unpaired males, although usually solitary, may be found in small flocks through the summer. By late August and September, flock formation takes place again, along with increasing movements. Sex-segregation of flocks has been reported (Weeden 1963) although it did not appear in our data. Large autumn flocks of 20 to 200 birds are quite common and, occasionally, birds number in the thousands, particularly in flight to evening roosts.

BREEDING: The Willow Ptarmigan breeds from Garibaldi Park in the southern Pacific and Cascade Ranges north through western British Columbia to the Yukon boundary. It is a very rare breeder in the Northern and Central Rocky Mountains.

Willow Ptarmigan breeding habitat includes the subalpine zone from the timberline, and the alpine zone, from 850 to 1,830 m elevation. Specific habitat includes willow and dwarf birch thickets, sedge-willow marshes, meadows, road edges, gravel bars, forest edge, and open tundra. Weeden (1959a) found that Willow Ptarmigan occupy the warmest and wettest climate of the tundra: the tall shrub zone where shrubs grow from 1 to 2 m in height. After the hatch, family groups concentrate around wet areas, principally marshes and streams.

Nests: All nests (n=84) were situated on the ground. Most nests (74%) were located at the base of a shrub, including willows

(36%), cinquefoils, and dwarf birches. Other nests were located on a hummock surrounded by water, among clumps of sedges and fireweed, at the edge of a stream, on beds of moss or lichen, and on open ground. Weeden (1959a) reports two essential features of nest sites: some kind of permanent overhanging plant material, usually a woody plant, and an open vegetation community extending outward from one side of the nest. Of 53 nests, 43 (81%) consisted of a small scrape lined with grasses and various mixtures of leaves (59%), feathers, or mosses. Other materials included sedges and lichen.

Eggs: Dates for 93 clutches ranged from 26 May to 12 July with 54% recorded between 8 and 28 June. Calculated dates indicate that eggs could be found as early as 21 May. Hannon et al. (1988) found that the mean date of clutch initiation appears to be related to the timing of snow melt. Clutch size ranged from 2 to 12 eggs (2E-1, 4E-6, 5E-5, 6E-12, 7E-18, 8E-24, 9E-23, 10E-2, 11E-1, 12E-1) with 70% having 7 to 9 eggs. Incubation period in British Columbia is 21 to 23 days (n=3). Westerskov (1956) states that this period is 21 to 22 days.

Young: Dates for 114 broods ranged from 12 June to 29 August, with 54% recorded between 2 July and 1 August. Brood sizes ranged from 1 to 12 young (1Y-2, 2Y-11, 3Y-8, 4Y-18, 5Y-21, 6Y-15, 7Y-17, 8Y-14, 9Y-3, 10Y-4, 12Y-1) with 62% having 4 to 7 young. The young fly at 12 to 14 days (R.B. Weeden pers. comm.).

REMARKS: Hannon and Smith (1984) have shown that Willow Ptarmigan yearlings reproduce almost as successfully as adults: yearling territory size, date of clutch initiation, hatching success, and brood size are similar to those of adults. This is unusual among grouse and may be explained by the following factors. Unlike the other tetraonids that leave the hens alone to raise the young, male Willow Ptarmigan are usually very attentive, accompanying broods and defending the young. In addition, Willow Ptarmigan have a high turnover rate in the population with annual mortality ranging from 60% to 72%, much higher than most other species. This mortality opens up large areas, making them available for yearling territories, and reduces competition with adults. Finally, Willow Ptarmigan are dependent on a food source that is readily available and can be obtained without special skills (Hannon and Smith 1984).

See Weeden (1963) for a discussion of ptarmigan management in North America, and Hannon (1982, 1983) for additional information on the biology of the Willow Ptarmigan in British Columbia.

The Willow Ptarmigan has been reported as accidental on Vancouver Island (American Ornithologists' Union 1983); however, we know of no documented records for that location.

NOTEWORTHY RECORDS

Spring: Coastal - Garibaldi Park 29 May 1982-1 male; Porcher Island 29 May 1921-1 pair (MVZ 100118-119); Mount Hays (Prince Rupert) 31 May 1981-1 pair. **Interior** - Kleena Kleene 27 Mar 1968-4+; Berg Lake trail 25 to 26 May 1974-1 female; Pink Mountain 1 Mar 1980-25; Todagin Lake 27 May 1979-2; Wright Creek (Surprise Lake) 20 May 1977-8; White Pass 19 May 1981-3.

Summer: Coastal - Porcher Island summer 1921-adults present (Brooks 1923a); Mount Hayes (Prince Rupert) 21 Jun 1981-1 pair. **Interior** - Mount McLean summer 1920-2 (Glendenning 1921); Sibola Range 17 Jul 1976-1 male; Boulder

Creek (Blunt Mountain) 25 Aug 1957-3 (Gibson, G.G. 1965); Ipec Lake 30 Aug 1979-1 female (Cooper, J.M. and Adams 1979); Spatsizi Plateau 15 Aug 1976-21 old and young birds.

Autumn: Interior - Kelsall Lake 25 Oct 1981-100; Wright Creek (Atlin) 9 Oct 1980-350, large flocks of 20 to 200 birds scattered on hillside, 10 Oct 1980-1,200 flying up draw to roost sites at 1900; Casino Creek valley 10 Oct 1980-2,200 spread in small flocks through entire valley; Glacial Mountain 30 Sep 1961-50 to 100 evening flights; Harold Price Creek 5 Oct 1975-25; Middle River (Takla Lake) 19 Sep 1911-1 (MVZ 100117). **Coastal**

- Alta Lake 6 Nov 1944-14 (Racey 1948).

Winter: Interior - Atlin 4 Jan 1936-2 (MVZ 100100-101); Williams Lake 17 Dec 1949-1 (NMC 47705); Big Creek (Riske Creek) 30 Jan 1959-30; Chimney Lake road 18 Feb 1979-1; Nimpo Lake 6 Feb 1976-6; Kleena Kleene 3 Jan 1953-3 (Paul 1959). **Coastal** - 16 km n Kitimat Jan 1971-4.

Christmas Counts: Interior - Recorded from 1 of 19 localities and on 2% of all counts. Maxima: Smithers 2 Jan 1982-2, 19 Dec 1983-1. **Coastal** - Not recorded.

Willow Ptarmigan

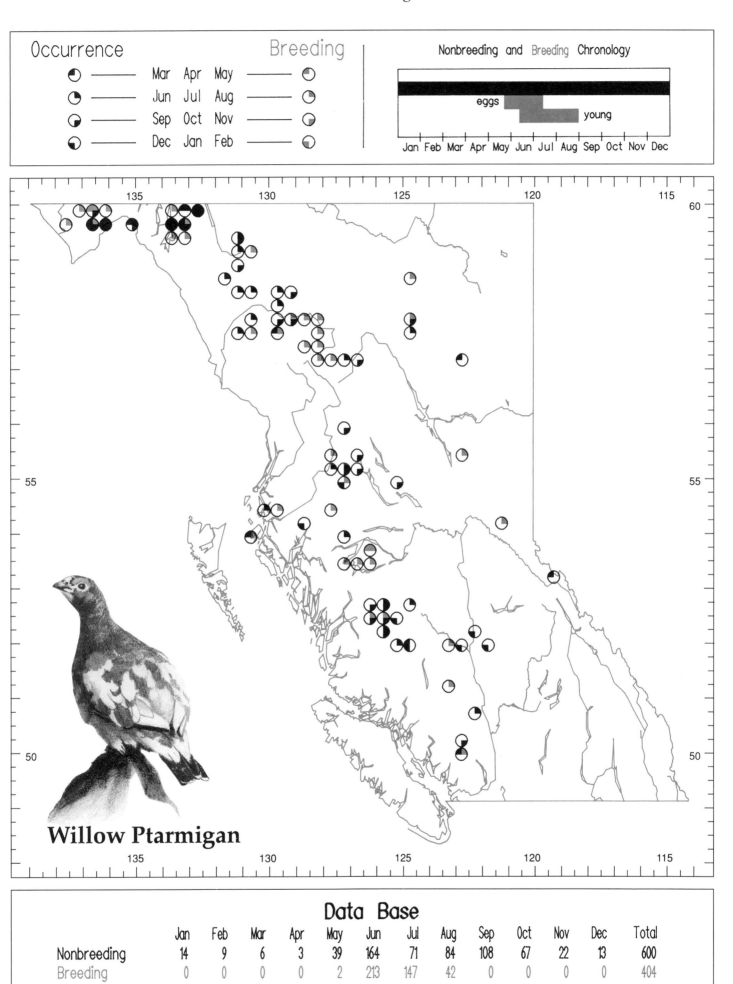

Occurrence Breeding

	Mar Apr May	
	Jun Jul Aug	
	Sep Oct Nov	
	Dec Jan Feb	

Nonbreeding and Breeding Chronology

eggs   young

Jan Feb Mar Apr May Jun Jul Aug Sep Oct Nov Dec

Willow Ptarmigan

Data Base

	Jan	Feb	Mar	Apr	May	Jun	Jul	Aug	Sep	Oct	Nov	Dec	Total
Nonbreeding	14	9	6	3	39	164	71	84	108	67	22	13	600
Breeding	0	0	0	0	2	213	147	42	0	0	0	0	404

Rock Ptarmigan
Lagopus mutus (Montin)

ROPT

RANGE: Holarctic. Breeds in North America from the Arctic islands and coasts south to Alaska, southwestern British Columbia, the Yukon and Northwest Territories, northern Quebec and Newfoundland. Winters primarily within the breeding range. Also occurs in Eurasia.

STATUS: *Uncommon* resident in the Chilkat Pass area and Northern Mountains and Plateaus region. *Rare* to *very rare* resident in western mountains south of 56° N latitude. Locally *rare* in the Northern Rocky Mountains. *Accidental* on the Queen Charlotte Islands. Breeds.

NONBREEDING: The Rock Ptarmigan occurs throughout mountainous regions of northwestern British Columbia, and south through the Coast Ranges where it is more sparsely distributed. It occurs locally in the Northern Rocky Mountains region. Its centre of abundance is the Kelsall Lake-Chilkat Pass region in the extreme northwestern corner of the province.

The Rock Ptarmigan frequents high alpine regions, including plateaus, meadows, and talus slopes throughout its range from 915 to 2,450 m elevation. There are also several records from near sea level. Weeden (1959a) found the Rock Ptarmigan higher on the mountain slopes and farther from the tree limit than the Willow Ptarmigan with little overlap in areas between the species. Birds move to lower elevations, below the treeline, during severe winters.

BREEDING: The Rock Ptarmigan breeds from Garibaldi Park and Panther Peak on the coast sporadically northward through the western mountains to the Yukon boundary. There is one record for the Northern Rocky Mountains region.

The Rock Ptarmigan frequents high elevation plateaus, open alpine meadows, lake edges, and barren rocky areas beyond the zone of tall shrubs throughout its range from 1,066 to 1,980 m elevation. Weeden (1959a) found the Rock Ptarmigan occupying areas with small shrubs less than 1 m tall interspersed among open vegetation, especially berry-bearing members of the Ericaceae. He also found that, following the hatch, Rock Ptarmigan were likely to concentrate in seepage areas at the heads of valleys, moist saddles on ridges, and gravelly stream banks.

Nests: There are no records of nests for the province.

Eggs: Calculated dates (from estimated age of young) indicate eggs could be found in early June. Incubation period is 21 to 22 days (Salomonsen 1950; Watson, A. 1956).

Young: Dates for 24 broods ranged from 29 June to 10 September with 54% between 12 and 29 July. Brood size ranged from 1 to 8 young (1Y-1, 2Y-2, 3Y-3, 4Y-4, 5Y-5, 6Y-6, 7Y-2, 8Y-1)

with 62% having 4 to 6 young (Fig. 58). Young can fly at about 10 days (Weeden 1963).

REMARKS: There are 2 interior records in the literature we consider hypothetical because they lack supporting details. They are Manning Park 25 Jun 1974-1 (O'Brien 1974) and Two Sisters Mountain 11 Aug 1971-1 (Runyan 1971).

See Modafferi (1975), H.A. Roberts (1963), Taverner (1929) and Weeden (1965b) for additional information on the taxonomy, morphology, life history, and food of the Rock Ptarmigan in northwestern North America.

Known as Ptarmigan in the Old World.

The American Ornithologists' Union (1983) reports of Rock Ptarmigan wintering on Vancouver Island, but we know of no documented records from that location.

Figure 58 Female Rock Ptarmigan with brood at Mount Steele, 3 km west of Tetrahydron Peak, 20 July 1988 (RBCM Photo 1231; Richard J. Cannings). This is the southernmost breeding record for the species in British Columbia.

NOTEWORTHY RECORDS

Spring: Coastal - see Extralimital Records. **Interior** - Hudson Bay Mountain 26 May 1980-2 males, 3 females; Pink Mountain 24 May 1981-1 pair (RBCM Photo 761); Spruce Mountain 29 May 1979-1 pair; near Kelsall Lake 31 May 1979-1 male.

Summer: Coastal - Mount Seymour 13 June 1934-1 male collected (Cumming 1935); Garibaldi Park 12 Aug 1968-4; ne Bella Coola 11 Jun 1933-1 pair (MCZ 281875-76), 24 Jun 1934-1 pair (MCZ 281877-78), 24 Jun 1934-1 male (UBC 3943), 25 Jun 1934-3 males (MCZ 281879-81); Swanson Bay 24 Jun 1936-2 males (MCZ 281882-83). **Interior** - Taseko Lake 9 Jul 1953-1; Sibola Range 30 Aug 1969-1 male (MVZ 159873); Burnie Lakes 23 to 30 Aug 1975-1 male (Osmond-Jones et al. 1977); Nine Mile Mountain 5

Aug 1921-1 female (MVZ 42035; Swarth 1924); Mount Trygve 5 Jul 1976-1 male; Pink Mountain 21 Jul 1982-1 (RBCM Photo 824); Cold Fish Lake 5 Jul 1962-1 male (NMC 49720); Haworth Lake 4 Aug 1976-1 male; Beatty Creek 4 Jun 1978-6+; Summit Pass 30 Aug 1943-1 (Rand 1944); Mount McDame 19 Jun 1956-2 males (RBCM 10126, 10157); Kawdy Plateau 4 Aug 1962-3 females (NMC 49721-23); Carmine Mountain 24 Jun 1983-1 male (RBCM 17724); Mile 91, Haines Road (Kelsall Lake) 29 Jun 1980-9 (RBCM 16861-69).

Autumn: Interior - Mile 75, Haines Road (Kelsall Lake) 12 Oct 1982-2; Spruce Mountain 2 Nov 1979-1; Driftwood Range autumn 1938-present (Stanwell-Fletcher and Stanwell-Fletcher 1940); Hudson Bay Mountain 3 Nov 1982-1; Anahim Lake Oct 1967-1

male. **Coastal** - Vancouver late Nov 1975-1.

Winter: Interior - Kelsall Lake 24 Dec 1976-1; Atlin 14 Jan 1977-2; Hudson Bay Mountain 4 Feb 1981-1; Kleena Kleene 20 Jan 1956-12 (Paul 1959). **Coastal** - Vancouver late Nov to 5 Dec 1975-1 on University of British Columbia campus (RBCM Photo 446); White Rock 9 to 18 Jan 1976-1 (RBCM Photo 498 and 720).

Christmas Counts: Interior - Recorded once: Smithers 16 Dec 1978-3. **Coastal** - Not recorded.

Extralimital Records: Coastal - ne end of Queen Charlotte Islands (exact location unknown) 15 Apr 1914-1 (USNM 241646). The specimen, a skeleton, was identified by M. Ralph Browning and David Steadman.

Rock Ptarmigan

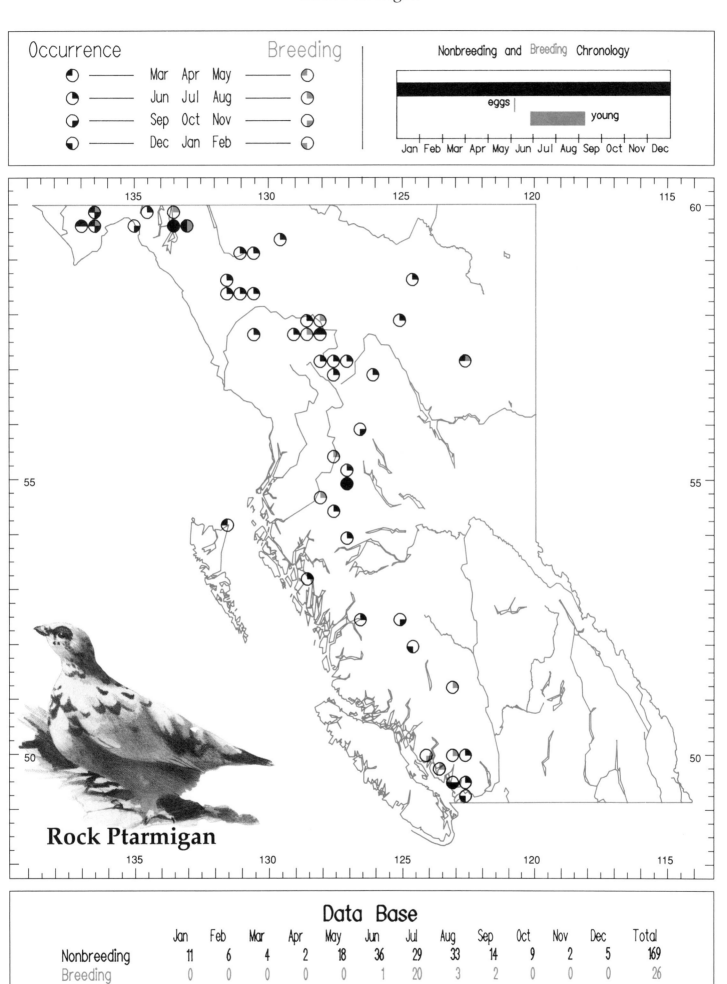

Occurrence / Breeding

Occurrence			Breeding
◐	—	Mar Apr May	◐
◔	—	Jun Jul Aug	◔
◕	—	Sep Oct Nov	◕
◑	—	Dec Jan Feb	◑

Nonbreeding and Breeding Chronology

eggs

young

Jan Feb Mar Apr May Jun Jul Aug Sep Oct Nov Dec

Rock Ptarmigan

Data Base

	Jan	Feb	Mar	Apr	May	Jun	Jul	Aug	Sep	Oct	Nov	Dec	Total
Nonbreeding	11	6	4	2	18	36	29	33	14	9	2	5	169
Breeding	0	0	0	0	0	1	20	3	2	0	0	0	26

White-tailed Ptarmigan
Lagopus leucurus (Richardson)

WTPT

RANGE: Resident in south-central Alaska, Yukon, southwestern Mackenzie, south through British Columbia, including Vancouver Island, and western Alberta to Washington in the Cascade Mountains and to northern New Mexico in the Rocky Mountains. Introduced to California, Oregon, and Utah.

STATUS: *Rare* to locally *common* resident in mountainous regions throughout British Columbia, including southern Vancouver Island, with the exception of the Queen Charlotte Islands and the northeast portion of the province east of the Northern and Central Rocky Mountains. Widespread breeder.

NONBREEDING: The White-tailed Ptarmigan has the widest distribution of all ptarmigan in British Columbia, occuring throughout the mountainous regions of the province, including Vancouver Island, from 900 to 2,800 m elevation. With the exception of the extreme southwest corner of the province, there are few records from the western flanks of the Coast Ranges, probably due to poor observer coverage.

The White-tailed Ptarmigan frequents subalpine and alpine habitats including rocky unvegetated areas, rockslides, alpine meadows, krummholtz, logged and burned subalpine forests, screes, and lake and stream shores.

Weeden (1959a) notes that White-tailed Ptarmigan are typically non-migratory; however, our data suggest they make extensive movements to wintering areas up to 1,200 m lower in elevation and 50 km from the nearest suitable breeding areas. A migration of a wintering population has been noted in Colorado (Hoffman and Braun 1975).

Birds begin moving to breeding areas in late spring when pair formation takes place. In mid-August through September, larger numbers are noted as flocks form once again.

BREEDING: The White-tailed Ptarmigan breeds throughout its range in British Columbia in alpine areas characterized by dynamic physiography and poorly developed vegetation. Specific habitats include rocky alpine tundra and meadows, open scree slopes, rock slides, boulder fields, and glacial cirques. Weeden (1959a) describes their fidelity to a particular habitat type as remarkable, and notes 3 important factors in habitat selection: stable substrate, amount of snow cover, and large size

of rocks (≥ 30 cm in diameter). A stable substrate determines whether or not plants can germinate in the area; the amount of snow cover determines the availability of summer water; and rock size determines the availability of crevices or niches for escape cover. After hatching, White-tailed Ptarmigan habitually feed and loaf near melting snowbanks, surface seepage, or alpine pools (Weeden 1959a).

On Vancouver Island, breeding has been recorded between 1,280 and 1,450 m elevation and in the interior, between 1,830 and 2,650 m elevation.

Nests: All nests (n=11) were in a shallow depression on the ground. Four were among stones on a scree slope and one was under a 1 m subalpine fir tree. Nests contained dried grasses and mixtures of leaves, needles, mosses, sedges, and feathers.

Eggs: Dates for 12 clutches ranged from 11 May to 24 July. Clutch size ranged from 3 to 8 eggs (3E-2, 5E-2, 6E-4, 7E-3, 8E-1) with 7 clutches having 6 or 7 eggs. Incubation period is about 22 to 23 days (Braun 1969).

Young: Dates for 147 broods ranged from 26 June to 9 September with 54% recorded between 20 July and 7 August. Brood size ranged from 1 to 12 young (1Y-8, 2Y-18, 3Y-24, 4Y-29, 5Y-28, 6Y-16, 7Y-16, 8Y-3, 9Y-2, 10Y-2, 12Y-1) with 55% having 3 to 5 young. Broods of 8 or more may be gang broods (R.B. Weeden and C.E. Braun pers. comm.). Fledging period is about 10 days (Choate 1963).

REMARKS: Two subspecies of White-tailed Ptarmigan occur in the province: *L. l. leucurus* occurs throughout the mainland and *L. l. saxatilis* is restricted to Vancouver Island. W.C. Weber (1980) expresses concern for the Vancouver Island subspecies on the basis that the bird was reported so infrequently; he could find only one recent (1976) record. The scarcity of observations is undoubtedly due in part to the birds' restricted habitat, the difficulty of access to observers, and the birds' cryptic colouration. We now have 23 observations, including 8 breeding records, on file for the Vancouver Island subspecies since 1971, and it is being reported in proportions similar to those of the mainland population.

Weeden (1959a) and Braun (1969, 1984) provide additional information on the life history of the White-tailed Ptarmigan in western North America. Habitat requirements are further discussed by Herzog (1977, 1980) and Braun (1980).

NOTEWORTHY RECORDS

Spring: Coastal - Mount Arrowsmith 26 May 1981-2; Mount Wrottesley 24 May 1926-7; Alta Lake 3 Mar 1925-1 male. **Interior -** Crater Mountain 6 Mar 1977-1; Kokanee Glacier Park 23 Apr 1970-1; Emerald Lake (Yoho National Park) 16 to 20 Mar 1977-1 (Wade 1977); Big Creek (Fletcher Lake) 3 Mar 1951-1 female (NMC 47713); Pyramid Mountain (Wells Gray Park) 11 Mar 1953-2; Williams Lake 22 Mar 1987-1 (RBCM Photo 1156); Indianpoint Lake 27 May 1934-1 male (MCZ 281892); Tetana Lake Mar 1941-8 (Stanwell-Fletcher and Stanwell-Fletcher 1943); Pink Mountain 1 Mar 1980-60; Pyramid Mountain (Cassiar) 17 Mar 1954-1 male (RBCM 11133); Atlin 19 Mar 1933-1 female (RBCM 5954); Kelsall Lake 18 May 1957-3 (Gibson, G.G. 1965).

Summer: Coastal - Welch Peak 7 Aug 1936-2 females (RBCM 6887, 6888); Cheam Peak 8 and 9 Aug 1981-25+, includes large chicks; Mount Cokely 25 Aug 1983-1; w Comox 31 Aug 1927-4 (MVZ 100159-62); Stuie 18 Aug 1938-1 male, 1 female (NMC 28792-93). **Interior -** Andy Good Creek 28 Jul 1984-14; Mount Tatlow 20 Aug 1978-

44, 7 coveys over 0.8 km; Mount Huntley Aug 1976-23, mostly adults counted over 1 hour (Goward 1976); Canoe Mountain 21 Aug 1973-18 (Cannings, S.G. 1973); e Bullmoose Mountain 20 Aug 1976-8; Omineca Mountains Aug 1941-3 to 4 pairs (Stanwell-Fletcher and Stanwell Fletcher 1943); Turnagain Lake 13 Jul 1963-2 (RBCM 10798/9); Nazoha Hills 4 Jul 1977-12; Mount McDame 22 Jun 1956-1; Chilkat Pass 5 Jun 1969-4 females.

Autumn: Interior - Kelsall Lake 7 to 14 Sep 1974-12; Summit Lake (Stone Mountain Park) 10 Sep 1971-4 (Griffith 1973); Fern Lake (Kwadacha Wilderness Park) 4 Sep 1979-5 (Cooper, J.M. and Adams 1979); Goat Mountain (Blunt Mountain) 4 Oct 1975-7; Houston Tommy Creek 21 Sep 1974-18; Far Mountain 14 Sep 1982-4; Wolverine Pass (Kootenay National Park) 3 Nov 1962-4 (Seel 1965); Vernon 17 Nov 1905-1 female (FMNH 131080); Quiniscoe Mountain 6 Sep 1979-35. **Coastal -** Stuie 25 Sep 1938-2 females (FMNH 157230-31); 16 km ne Campbell River (Discovery Passage) Nov 1970-1; Mount Arrowsmith 11 Sep

1938-15 (Cowan 1939a); Mount Sproatt 9 Sep 1937-5; Mount Hooper 9 Sep 1979-1; Cowichan Lake 29 Oct 1915-1 (RBCM 2600).

Winter: Interior - Ruby Creek (Surprise Lake) 18 Jun 1981-5; Bear Lake (e Motase Peak) winter 1940/41 - common (Stanwell-Fletcher and Stanwell-Fletcher 1943); Babine Mountains 22 Jan 1979-2; Wells Gray Park early Feb 1953 - common (Ritcey 1953); Amiskwi River 28 Feb 1976-1 (Wade 1977); Lodgepole Lake 15 Jan 1983-1; Silver Star Mountain 17 Dec 1979-2; Halcyon Mountain 27 Feb 1983-1; Apex Mountain (Penticton) 20 Feb 1983-1. **Coastal -** Bella Coola 10 Feb 1981-1 (RBCM 16998); 10 km nw Campbell River (Discovery Passage) 1 to 14 Jan 1975-2, when snow was heavy; Beaufort Range 21 Dec 1977-1; Mount Arrowsmith 8 Jan 1966-2.

Christmas counts: Interior - Recorded from 2 of 19 localities and on 3% of all counts. Maxima: Smithers 19 Dec 1983-19; Yoho National Park 22 Dec 1984-4. **Coastal -** Not recorded.

White-tailed Ptarmigan

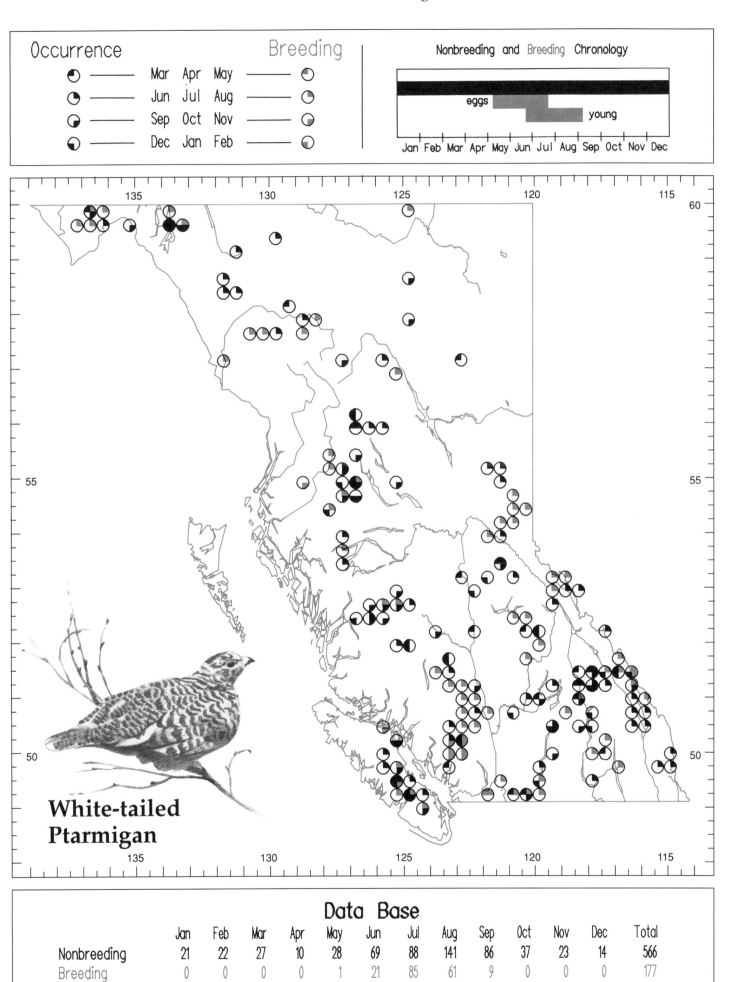

Occurrence   Breeding

◐ ————	Mar Apr May	———— ◖
◔ ————	Jun Jul Aug	———— ◔
◕ ————	Sep Oct Nov	———— ◔
◕ ————	Dec Jan Feb	———— ◒

Nonbreeding and Breeding Chronology

eggs

young

Jan Feb Mar Apr May Jun Jul Aug Sep Oct Nov Dec

White-tailed Ptarmigan

Data Base	Jan	Feb	Mar	Apr	May	Jun	Jul	Aug	Sep	Oct	Nov	Dec	Total
Nonbreeding	21	22	27	10	28	69	88	141	86	37	23	14	566
Breeding	0	0	0	0	1	21	85	61	9	0	0	0	177

Ruffed Grouse

RUGR

Bonasa umbellus (Linnaeus)

RANGE: Resident from central Alaska and forested regions of the Yukon, Mackenzie, Saskatchewan, northern Ontario, southern Quebec, and southern Labrador south to northern California, central Idaho, central Utah, Wyoming, western South Dakota, Minnesota, central Arkansas, northern Georgia and northeastern Virginia. Introduced to Newfoundland and northeastern Nevada.

STATUS: *Fairly common* to *common* resident throughout the province except the Queen Charlotte Islands, islands off the northern mainland coast, and islands in Queen Charlotte Strait. Breeds.

NONBREEDING: The Ruffed Grouse is widely distributed in British Columbia but has not been recorded on the Queen Charlotte Islands or islands off the northern mainland coast from Queen Charlotte Strait north to the Alaska-British Columbia border. Populations appear well established on Vancouver Island and on the mainland, mainly along major water courses. The centre of abundance is in southern areas. The Ruffed Grouse occurs from sea level to 2,225 m elevation, but unlike the Blue Grouse, it prefers lower elevations, especially along river bottoms.

It is a bird of wooded habitats, preferring second-growth deciduous and mixed deciduous-coniferous forests, usually with moderate slopes and nearby water. It prospers best in brushy areas along streams, in alder thickets, shrubby forest edges, brushy areas of logged and burned areas, trembling aspen and vine maple copses, and, occasionally, in dense woodlands. It tends to avoid areas inhabited by man and strictly homogeneous habitats.

Despite its sedentary habits, the Ruffed Grouse does make small seasonal shifts within its home range. In winter, coniferous forests are frequently used for shelter, while in spring, more open, mixed woodlands are occupied. In late summer and early autumn, open brushy areas, often with fruiting trees and shrubs, are favoured. Young birds may wander considerably until they reach sexual maturity. There is some evidence to suggest that small flocks form in the autumn. Altitudinal movements are unknown.

BREEDING: The Ruffed Grouse breeds throughout British Columbia except the Queen Charlotte Islands and islands along the northern mainland coast. Nests have been found from near sea level to 2,130 m, but most were found between 450 and 900 m.

It breeds mainly in woodlands and forests, but nests have been found in farmlands, grasslands, marshes, open burns, and subalpine and alpine areas. In wooded situations, most nests (43%; n=137) were in mixed woodlands, followed by deciduous stands (32%) and coniferous stands (17%). Deciduous stands included alders, willows, trembling aspen, maples, birches, and black cottonwood while coniferous stands were mostly Douglas-fir, lodgepole pine, and spruce.

Nests: All nests (n=137) were on the ground; most were situated near or at the bases of trees (54%), under bushes and shrubs (61%), under or adjacent to fallen logs (16%), or next to or among ferns (5%). The remainder of the nests were in open situations such as fields, burns, and roadways, at the bases of fence posts, among cattails in a damp marsh, on a wooded islet and under fallen branches, One nest was found in a metal pail, and another was under a tractor.

Nests were slight depressions in the ground (or nesting substrate) and were usually lined with leaves (44%; n=101), grasses (27%), feathers and down (18%) as well as materials such as weed stems, bark, mosses, twigs, cones, conifer needles, and catkins. Depths of 6 nests ranged from 2.5 to 9 cm; outside diameters ranged from 18 to 27 cm.

Eggs: Dates for 137 clutches ranged from 10 April to 19 July with 53% recorded between 13 and 27 May. Clutch size ranged from 1 to 15 eggs (1E-1, 3E-3, 4E-3, 5E-8, 6E-8, 7E-12, 8E-16, 9E-20, 10E-32, 11E-21, 12E-9, 13E-2, 14E-1, 15E-1) with 53% having 9 to 11 eggs. Incubation period is 23 to 24 days (Bump et al. 1947).

Young: Dates for 749 broods (Fig. 59) ranged from 4 May to 21 September, with 56% recorded between 15 June and 18 July. Brood size ranged from 1 to 15 young (1Y-86, 2Y-71, 3Y-89, 4Y-116, 5Y-113, 6Y-96, 7Y-54, 8Y-47, 9Y-23, 10Y-29, 11Y-7, 12Y-11, 13Y-3, 14Y-3, 15Y-1), with 55% having 3 to 6 young. Fledging period is 10 to 12 days (Bump et al. 1947)

REMARKS: At least 4 subspecies occur in British Columbia; see Aldrich and Friedmann (1943), Munro, J.A. and Cowan (1947), Dickinson (1953), American Ornithologists' Union (1957), and Godfrey (1986) for discussions on races and their distribution in the province.

The classic work by Bump et al. (1947) provides additional information on the life history of the Ruffed Grouse in North America. For British Columbia consult Davies (1973).

Figure 59. Female Ruffed Grouse with brood of recently hatched chicks near Invermere, June 1979 (Dianne L. Cooper).

NOTEWORTHY RECORDS

Spring: Coastal - Sooke 30 Apr 1953-4; Holmes Peak 19 Mar 1983-9; Campbell Valley Park (Langley) 7 Apr 1968-5; Miracle Beach Park 12 May 1963-7 (Westerborg and Stirling 1963); Klaskish River 15 May 1978-7; Kitsault 13 to 17 May 1980-6+. **Interior** - Balfour to Waneta 16 May 1981-11; Kettle River 17 May 1980-4; Savona 14 Apr 1968-5; McLure 4 Mar 1952-6; Clinton 9 May 1960-10; Alexis Lake 8 May 1977-5.

Summer: Coastal - Holmes Peak 8 Aug 1982-5; Abbotsford 18 July 1977-7; Surrey 4 July 1964-7; Langley 18 July 1977-7; Miracle Beach Park 6 June 1972-8. **Interior** - Mount Revelstoke 15 July 1937-

6; Adams River to Chase 18 Aug 1963-23; Copper Island 21 Aug 1973-10; 150 Mile House 21 June 1970-12; Francois Lake 9 Aug 1944-40 (Munro, J.A. 1947a); Driftwood Range early Aug 1939-14; Cecil Lake 10 Aug 1977-12+; near Fort Nelson 10 Aug 1976-20; Tuya River 27 Aug 1977-6.

Autumn: Interior - Erie Creek (Salmo) 26 Sep 1983-12 along 9.6 km; Rock Creek (Kettle Valley) 16 Sep 1977-11; Scotch Creek to Celista (Shuswap Lake) 19 Oct 1964-22; Horse Lake (100 Mile House) 29 Sep 1957-6; Atnarko River 5 Sept 1948-30 along 11.3 km. **Coastal** - Aldergrove 20 Oct 1966-8; Beaver Point 19 Nov 1955-11; Victoria 25 Sept 1956-9.

Winter: Interior - Prince George 25 Dec 1981-20, some buried in snow; Vernon 9 Dec 1979-2; Testalinden Creek 26 Dec 1985-27; Creston 28 Dec 1981-5. **Coastal** - Aldergrove 23 Jan 1977-5; Duncan 19 Jan 1974-3; Prospect Lake road 30 Dec 1973-6.

Christmas Counts: Interior - Recorded from 13 of 19 localities and on 63% of all counts. Maxima: Smithers 16 Dec 1978-31 and 15 Dec 1979-31; Vernon 19 Dec 1982-15; Shuswap Lake 3 Jan 1981-11. **Coastal** - Recorded from 20 of 28 localities and on 65% of all counts. Maxima: Pitt Meadows 30 Dec 1978-20; Duncan 14 Dec 1974-16; Port Alberni 4 Jan 1976-15.

Ruffed Grouse

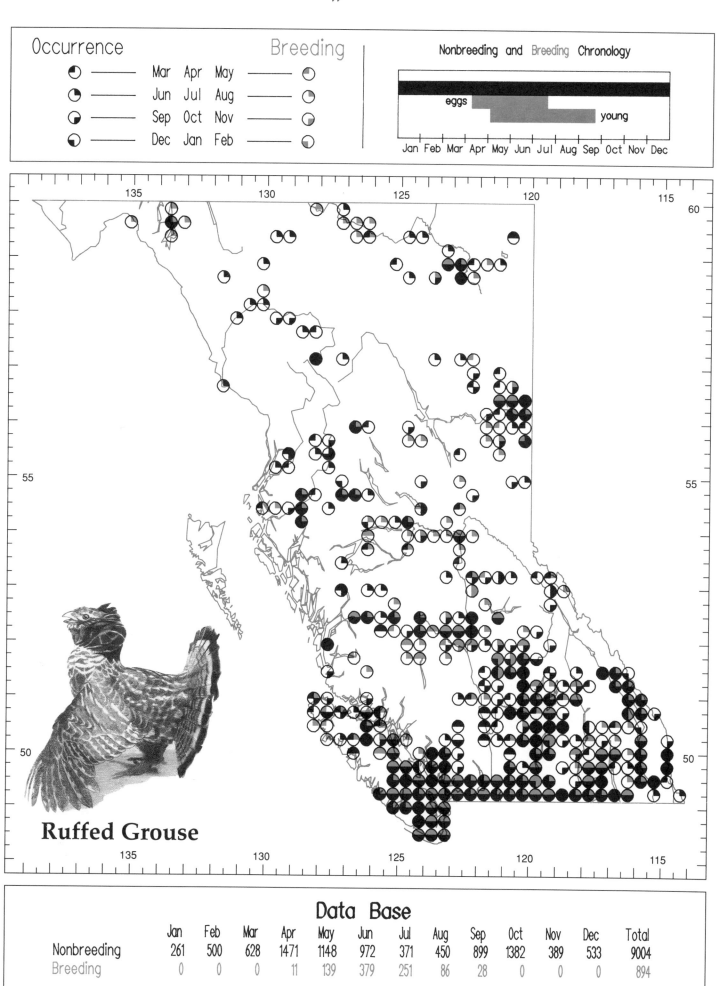

Occurrence   Breeding

	Mar Apr May	
	Jun Jul Aug	
	Sep Oct Nov	
	Dec Jan Feb	

Nonbreeding and Breeding Chronology

eggs

young

Jan Feb Mar Apr May Jun Jul Aug Sep Oct Nov Dec

Ruffed Grouse

Data Base

	Jan	Feb	Mar	Apr	May	Jun	Jul	Aug	Sep	Oct	Nov	Dec	Total
Nonbreeding	261	500	628	1471	1148	972	371	450	899	1382	389	533	9004
Breeding	0	0	0	11	139	379	251	86	28	0	0	0	894

Sharp-tailed Grouse

STGR

Tympanuchus phasianellus (Linnaeus)

RANGE: Resident from north-central Alaska east to central-western Quebec and south through the western North American interior to eastern Oregon, northern Nevada, Utah, northeastern New Mexico, western Nebraska, central South Dakota, northern Minnesota, northern Wisconsin, and northern Michigan. Populations in far northern areas are irregularly migratory.

STATUS: *Uncommon* to *fairly common* resident in the east Kootenay, Thompson-Nicola valleys, Chilcotin-Cariboo region and Peace Lowlands. *Rare* local resident in the Nechako Plateau and Bulkley Basin regions; *uncommon* in the Fort Nelson Lowlands and Liard Basin. Former populations reduced in southern areas, and now more locally distributed. Extirpated in the Okanagan valley.

CHANGE IN STATUS: Even at the time of J.A. Munro and Cowan (1947), the Sharp-tailed Grouse was declining throughout the province. They write:

> At an earlier time the distribution ... was more or less continuous through the Osoyoos and the Dry Forest and Cariboo Parklands, west into the Chilcotin and north to the Vanderhoof region. It is now extirpated over much of its former range. The largest populations now are in the more northerly portion of the range but nowhere is it abundant.

This trend has continued to the present, with central and southern populations gradually becoming more and more restricted due primarily to loss of habitat through urbanization. Losses of open areas through forest succession coupled with loss of riparian habitat and thickets adjacent to open areas also appear to be important factors in the decline of the species. In the 1930s, sharptails occurred up the North Thompson River valley as far as Clearwater, when the large burns there were young. Conversely, in some areas of the Chilcotin-Cariboo today, sharptail populations seem to be increasing because of large clearcuts adjacent to wetlands with willows and scrub birch thickets (R.W. Ritcey pers. comm.). In the Peace Lowlands, sharptails thrive where agricultural practices have opened up forests, and areas under cultivation have good adjacent cover in the form of willow thickets and trembling aspen along their borders. However, where farmers have eliminated the cover to increase yields, sharptail populations have decreased dramatically (Dave Stewart pers. comm.). In addition, R.A. Cannings et al. (1987) suggest that hunting also contributed to the bird's eventual elimination from the Okanagan valley.

According to provincial biologists, populations today are extirpated in the Okanagan valley, low in the northern Fraser Plateau and Boreal Forest regions, low to moderate in the east Kootenay, Nicola, and Thompson River valleys, and the Chilcotin-Cariboo region, and moderate in the Peace Lowlands.

NONBREEDING: The Sharp-tailed Grouse occurs locally in two disjunct populations, one scattered throughout the east Kootenay and the south and central interior north to the vicinity of Babine Lake, and the other in the parklands and Boreal Forest of northeastern British Columbia. It has been recorded from 275 to 2,135 m elevation.

It frequents a variety of habitats but the presence of open lowlands adjacent to brushy or scattered open woodlands is common to all. Such habitats include bunchgrass grasslands,

Figure 60. *Sharp-tailed Grouse habitat – rolling hills, fields, and deciduous thickets – east of Fort St. John in the Peace Lowlands, May 1988 (R. Wayne Campbell).*

Sharp-tailed Grouse

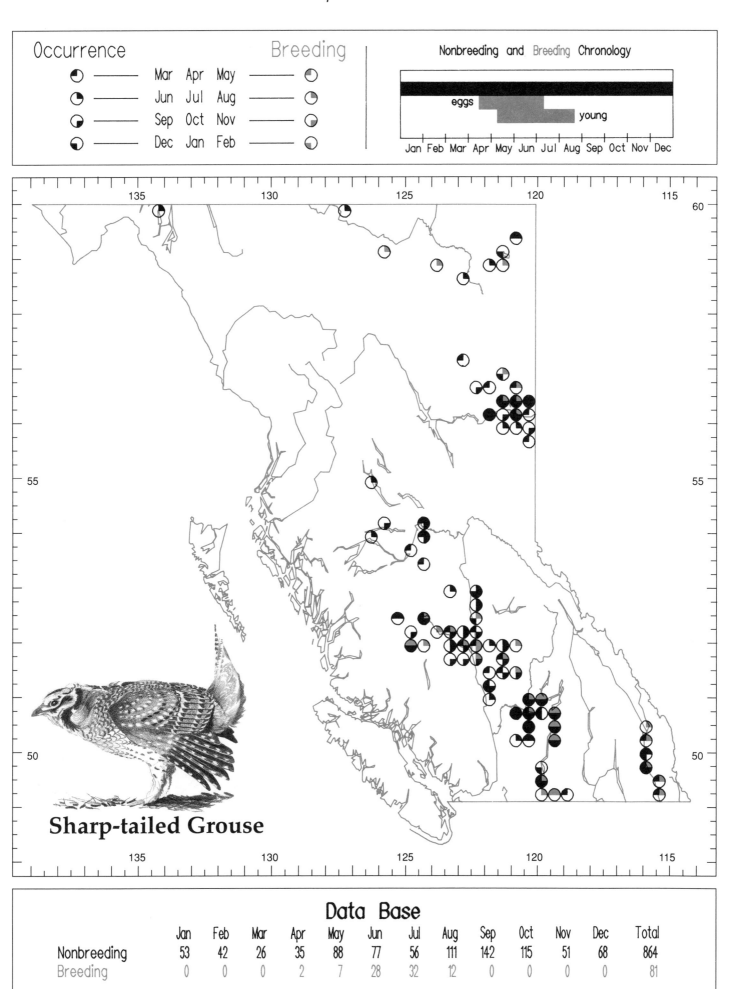

sagebrush flats, and open ponderosa pine, lodgepole pine, and birch woodlands in the southern interior. Young seral deciduous forests are important to the species, especially in northeastern British Columbia. In the Chilcotin-Cariboo and the northern Fraser Plateau regions, habitats include open parklands with adjacent Douglas-fir, trembling aspen, and spruce forests. In the Peace Lowlands, habitats include rolling hills where grain fields and weedy pastures are mixed with brushy trembling aspen and willow thickets (Fig. 60), and in the Boreal Forest, open swamps and muskegs are frequented. Generally, riparian situations as well as swamps, meadows, and burns within coniferous forests are used.

In March and April, small winter flocks begin to break up and males move to leks, followed by the females. There is a subtle, local altitudinal movement from more wooded areas to grassy lowlands. After mating ends in June, males drift away from leks to spend the summer in good foraging areas (Fig. 61).

By September, broods are usually fully grown, and coveys comprising family units of 6 to 8 birds can be found. During the autumn, coveys amalgamate into larger flocks that remain loosely associated throughout the winter. There may be some local movement from lowlands to higher forested wintering areas. In grain-growing areas, the Sharp-tailed Grouse overwinters in lowland fields near food supplies and movements are restricted between foraging and roosting areas. Adequate snow cover is important during severe winters since the Sharp-tailed Grouse may roost in snow burrows rather than in trees (Fig. 62).

BREEDING: The Sharp-tailed Grouse breeds in the east Kootenay, in the central-southern interior from Enderby and Kamloops north throughout the Chilcotin-Cariboo region, and is widespread in the Boreal Forest region from the vicinity of Fort St. John north to at least Muncho Lake and Kotcho Lake. It breeds at elevations from 275 to 1,190 m.

The Sharp-tailed Grouse is the only tetraonid in the province that gathers on traditional "dancing" grounds, or leks; therefore, this habitat requirement is an important factor in the spring distribution of the species. A lek at Charlie Lake containing 19 birds on 13 May 1979 was in an open field surrounded by scrubby areas. Another active lek was found at the Chilco Ranch, near Hanceville, in May 1980; it was on an overgrazed knoll near a pond. Males were displaying there on 16 May 1983 but were absent on 30 May.

Nests: All nests (n=30) were on the ground. Half of the nests were in open grassland; the rest were under sparse canopies of lodgepole pine, ponderosa pine, Douglas-fir, and trembling aspen. Nests were shallow depressions of loosely formed grasses, occasionally lined with a few feathers. Usually they were well concealed in clumps of grass or under branches.

Eggs: Dates for 19 clutches ranged from 22 April to 11 July with 52% recorded between 7 May and 21 June. Calculated dates indicate that eggs could be found as early as 17 April. Clutch size ranged from 5 to 13 eggs (5E-3, 6E-1, 7E-1, 8E-1, 9E-3, 10E-4, 12E-3, 13E-3) with 10 clutches having 9 to 12 eggs. A brood of 14 young (see below) suggests clutches of at least 14 eggs may be found. Incubation period is 23 to 24 days (Ammann 1957).

Young: Dates for 58 broods ranged from 11 May to 22 August with 55% recorded between 28 June and 24 July. Sizes for 56 broods ranged from 1 to 14 young (1Y-6, 2Y-7, 3Y-2, 4Y-5, 5Y-7, 6Y-8, 7Y-9, 8Y-3, 9Y-3, 11Y-1, 12Y-4, 14Y-1) with 52% having 4 to 7 young. Fledging period is about 10 days (Johnsgard 1973).

REMARKS: The classic paper by L.L. Snyder (1935) remains a major reference for the species in Canada.

Formerly placed in the monotypic genus *Pedioecetes*.

Figure 61. *Sharp-tailed Grouse in typical habitat near Alexis Creek, 30 June 1978 (Richard J. Cannings).*

Figure 62. *Adult Sharp-tailed Grouse roosting near Fort St. John, November 1982 (Chris R. Siddle).*

NOTEWORTHY RECORDS

Spring: Coastal - No records. **Interior** - Newgate May 1930-12 (Munro, J.A. and Cowan 1947); Monte Creek 16 Mar 1953-40; Quilchena 4 Apr 1973-24; Merritt 8 Apr 1969-22; Chilcotin River (w Alexis Creek) 22 May 1952-26; Chezacut early Mar 1939-50 in lodgepole pines (Paul 1959), 14 Mar 1942-13; Watson Lake (100 Mile House) 17 May 1954-1 male (UBC 4465); Euchiniko River (w Hay Lake) 6 May 1983-12+; Nechako River 8 May 1983-27 at lek; Mile 59 (Alaska Highway) 13 May 1979-19 at lek; Mile 95 (Alaska Highway) 20 Mar 1983-20; Pink Mountain 1 Mar 1980-20.

Summer: Coastal - No records. **Interior** - St. Mary's Prairie (w Cranbrook) 25 Jun 1974-7, 24 July 1975-3; Stump Lake (Quilchena) Aug 1953-50 to 60; Riske Creek 25 Aug 1978-9; 20 km e Hudson Hope 20 Aug 1980-10; Rose Prairie 18 Aug 1975-11; Kotcho Lake 21 June 1982-2 males calling; Tagish Lake summer 1921-1 (Friedmann 1943).

Autumn: Interior - Cecil Lake 9 Oct 1982-11; Rolla 25 Oct 1978-5; Francois Lake 4 Sep 1948-1 male (UBC 2317); Chilcotin Lake 17 Sep 1979-12, 28 Nov 1939-10; Kleena Kleene 26 Oct 1956-6 (Paul 1959); Separation Lake (Riske Creek) 19 Sep 1978-14; Edith Lake (Kamloops 20 Oct 1953-100 in one flock; Lavington fall 1975-2 or 3; Okanagan Landing 21 to 22 Oct 1924-300 in a mile or two, 29 Sep 1926-150;

Quilchena 8 Oct 1983-60. **Coastal** - No records.

Winter: Interior - Mile 60 (Alaska Highway) 20 Jan 1980-17; Buick Creek 25 Jan 1981-35; Farrell Creek (Peace River) 26 Dec 1985-40; Chilcotin Lake 7 Jan 1947-9; Kleena Kleene 13 Feb 1949-10 (Paul 1959); near Clinton 27 Jan 1975-3; Stump Lake (Quilchena) 19 Feb 1958-15; Pritchard 30 Dec 1952-6; Okanagan Landing 29 Dec 1924-70; Summerland 13 Feb 1970-1. **Coastal** - No records.

Christmas Counts: Interior - Recorded from 1 of 19 localities and on 3% of all counts. Maxima: Fort St. John 3 Jan 1976, 2 Jan 1977, and 26 Dec 1978-all 2 birds. **Coastal** - Not recorded.

Wild Turkey

Meleagris gallopavo Linnaeus

WITU

RANGE: Native to the southwestern and eastern United States and Mexico. Now extirpated or reduced, but reintroduced, in much of its former range. Introduced elsewhere in southern Canada and the United States.

STATUS: Introduced to southern Vancouver Island, the southern Gulf Islands, the Okanagan valley and east Kootenay. Now locally an *uncommon* to *fairly common* resident on Sidney Island, and in the north Okanagan valley and southern west Kootenay, especially near Creston. *Rare* resident, locally, in the east Kootenay. Local breeder.

CHANGE IN STATUS: The Wild Turkey has been introduced to several locations on southern Vancouver Island, the southern Gulf Islands and the Thompson-Okanagan Plateau region since 1910, but most releases have been unsuccessful, except where feeding programs are maintained (e.g. Sidney Island; Fig. 63).

The first introduction was made on James Island in 1910 when 2 pairs were released (Carl and Guiguet 1972). They multiplied but the population had disappeared by 1929. Meanwhile, about 200 birds of Virginia stock were being raised by the British Columbia Game Commission on the Saanich Peninsula. The farm was discontinued in 1954, but birds had been released on Sidney Island, Prevost Island, and, in 1931, on South Pender Island. All these introductions failed. In 1962, 12 more birds were released on Sidney Island and, as of 1985, the population was stable, numbering about 100 individuals.

In the Okanagan valley, the Wild Turkey has been introduced near Vernon and Penticton. Birds were released near Vernon from 1970 to 1973, and by the 1980s, as many as "130 birds were thought to be in the area" (Cannings, R.A. et al. 1987). Four young birds were released near Penticton in August 1975. A lone hen was seen infrequently and was last recorded on 2 January 1978 (see Cannings, R.A. et al. 1987).

It appears that a small resident population has become established in the vicinity of Creston in the west Kootenay. Apparently the birds crossed the border prior to 1967 from releases in northern Washington (Merilees 1971). Two birds were first reported near the Pend-d'Oreille River in March 1967, although Conservation Officers in the west Kootenay had received several alleged reports of turkeys being shot by hunters in the Pend-d'Oreille valley prior to February 1967 and likely in the autumn of 1966. By November 1967, flocks of up to 50 birds were reported. In 1986, the population appeared to be restricted to the vicinity of Creston, where they first nested in 1972 (Butler, R.W. et al. 1986).

The most recent introductions have occurred in the east Kootenay at Skookumchuck, where 20 birds were released in June 1985 (Campbell 1985c; RBCM Photo 1038), and Fort Steele, where 15 birds captured at Rykerts were released in March 1987 (Whittaker 1987).

NONBREEDING: The Wild Turkey is prospering on Sidney Island. Also birds are also still observed in the hills west of Armstrong and in the Falkland area (R. Howie pers. comm.), and small numbers may exist scattered throughout the Okanagan valley. The centre of abundance appears to be in the Creston-Lister area. Turkeys inhabit open wooded valleys, uplands, and

Figure 63. *Male Wild Turkey displaying on Sidney Island, March 1978 (Ervio Sian).*

agricultural fields. It is possible that the distribution of ponderosa pine trees, and hence seeds for food, may limit the numbers and distribution of this exotic bird in the province. However, the Armstrong population survives only around farms with no pine trees in sight.

The Wild Turkey occurs as singles or in flocks, the latter from early autumn to late spring. Winter flocks of over 100 birds have been reported to cause damage at dairy farms in the Lister-Rykerts area, especially since 1984 (B.J. Petrar pers. comm.).

Total records listed in the nonbreeding section of the data base on the accompanying map are misleading because of the sedentary population on Sidney Island. Only select interior records are listed below.

BREEDING: There are 5 breeding records for the province. In April 1979, a nest with 7 eggs was found on Sidney Island. It was described as composed of "leaves and grasses" and positioned "on a slight mound between 2 red alder trees and among a patch of stinging nettles ... not far from water." In the interior, a hen with 2 chicks appeared at a ranch near Naramata (about 500 m elevation) in the summer of 1977. The first breeding record for the province was from Creston: in May 1977, a female was found incubating an unknown number of eggs (RBCM Photo 945). The nest was situated next to a small log in a brushy woodland area. On 3 August 1984, a female with 4 one-month-old chicks was seen on a grassy hillside in dry Douglas-fir forest at Armstrong. Also on that day, a female was seen incubating an unknown number of eggs in a nest partially beneath an unused, vine-covered shed at Armstrong.

Incubation period is 28 days (Bent 1932); fledging period is about 14 days (Harrison, C. 1978).

Data appearing on the accompanying map for breeding chronology are estimated.

REMARKS: The Wild Turkey was formerly known as the Turkey. It is also referred to as the Common or Plain Turkey.

NOTEWORTHY RECORDS

Spring: Interior - Pend-d'Oreille River Mar 1967-2, May 1967-4 adults (Merilees 1971); Roche Lake 9 May 1975-2 on road; near Walker Lake (Kamloops) 12 May 1975-1.

Summer: Interior - Salmon Valley 7 July 1981-1

male, 5 females; Armstrong 3 Jun 1984-10; Paxton Valley 20 Jun 1975-2; Lister 26 Aug 1986-31.

Autumn: Interior - 3 km ne Rykerts 5 Oct 1986-64; Pend-d'Oreille valley Nov 1967-50 (Merilees 1971); Little River (Shuswap Lake) 6 Oct 1975-2 females.

Winter: Interior - Creston area 4 Jan 1987-92, Feb 1978-8 (RBCM Photo 944).

Christmas Counts: Interior - Recorded once: Penticton 27 Dec 1976-1. **Coastal** - Not recorded.

Wild Turkey

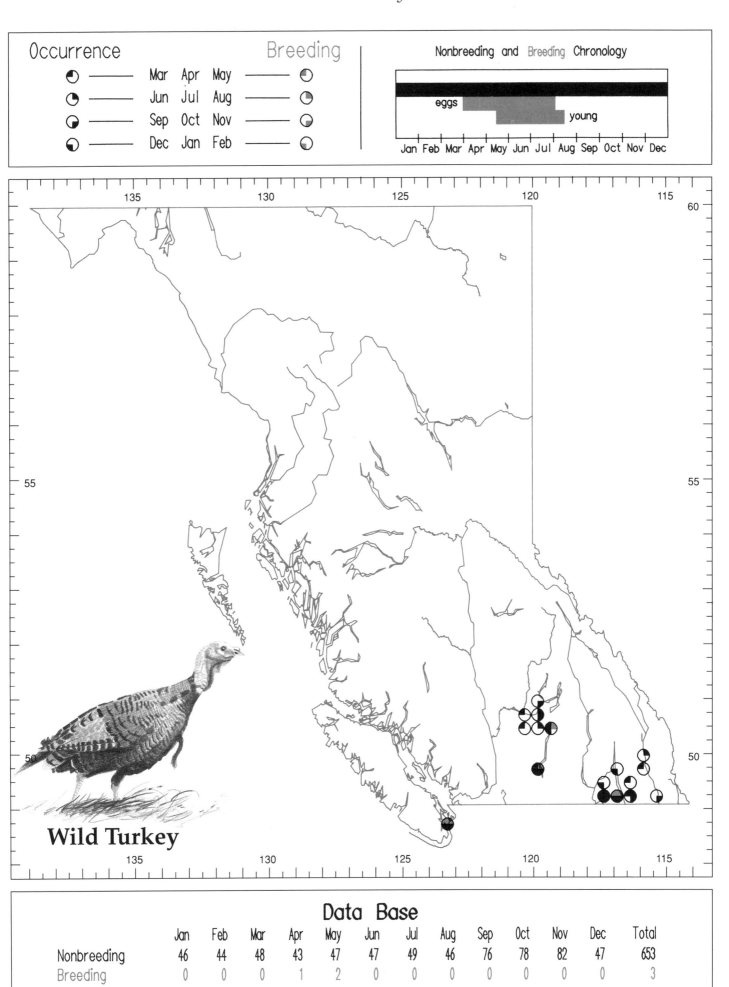

Occurrence

		Mar	Apr	May		
◐	—	Jun	Jul	Aug	—	◐
◔	—	Sep	Oct	Nov	—	◑
◑	—	Dec	Jan	Feb	—	◒

Breeding

Nonbreeding and Breeding Chronology

eggs   young

Jan Feb Mar Apr May Jun Jul Aug Sep Oct Nov Dec

Wild Turkey

Data Base

	Jan	Feb	Mar	Apr	May	Jun	Jul	Aug	Sep	Oct	Nov	Dec	Total
Nonbreeding	46	44	48	43	47	47	49	46	76	78	82	47	653
Breeding	0	0	0	1	2	0	0	0	0	0	0	0	3

California Quail
Callipepla californica (Shaw)

CAQU

RANGE: Resident from southern Brritish Columbia, Washington, Oregon, and western Nevada south to southern Baja California. Established through introductions in southern British Columbia, Washington, western Idaho, and Utah, as well as Chile, Australia, New Zealand, and Germany.

STATUS: Introduced. *Uncommon* to locally *common* resident on southern Vancouver Island and in the southern interior. *Very rare* in the Fraser Lowlands and Creston valleys. Breeds throughout its range.

NONBREEDING: On the south coast, the California Quail is distributed primarily along the east coast of Vancouver Island from Victoria north to Comox (rarely farther north). It may be extirpated in the Fraser Lowlands. In the interior, it is found from the southern Okanagan valley north to Vernon; it is very rare elsewhere in the southern interior and in the Creston valley.

The California Quail frequents a variety of open habitats from near sea level to 1,000 m elevation. It is usually associated with man. On the coast, habitats include shrubland dominated by blackberry thickets or broom, residential gardens, parks, golf courses, farmland, and powerline rights-of-way. Interior habitats include orchards, residential gardens, riparian thickets, and brushy gullies.

By mid-August, adults and young have begun to gather in larger flocks; however, the largest numbers occur in winter as quail congregate in coveys of occasionally over 100 birds. Unusually cold winters can reduce quail numbers considerably; R.A. Cannings et al. (1987) describe the effects of a severe winter (1968-1969) on a quail population of about 300 birds. Even though the birds frequented some of the best quail habitats in the Okanagan valley, the combined effects of low temperatures and heavy snowfall reduced that population to about 30 birds by the end of February.

BREEDING: The California Quail breeds throughout most of its provincial range from near sea level to 900 m elevation. On the coast, it breeds on Vancouver Island from Sooke and Victoria north to Port Alberni and Comox, and locally in the Fraser River delta. In the interior, it breeds locally near Creston, throughout the Okanagan valley north to Salmon Arm, and locally near Clinton. On the coast, its centre of breeding abundance is the Victoria area north to the Saanich Peninsula; in the interior, it is most abundant in the Okanagan valley, especially from Summerland south.

The California Quail frequents a variety of open habitats, including farmland (orchards, pastureland, rangeland, cultivated fields, hayfields), rural and urban residential gardens, city parks, and, to a lesser extent open ponderosa pine forests, deciduous bottomland, sagebrush flats, ravines, riparian woodland and shrubland.

Nests: Of 42 nests, most were hidden under or among vegetation, including shrubs (38%; blackberry, Scotch broom, juniper, rhododendron), grasses and herbaceous plants (21%),

and trees. Ring-necked Pheasant nests were used on 3 occasions. Other sites included under brush piles, logs, and lumber piles. One nest was found under a rock overhang on a mossy cliff, one was under a newspaper (Cannings, R.A. et al. 1987) and another was adjacent to a fencepost in a pasture. All nests were situated in slight depressions on the ground. Materials were principally grasses (57%; n=28), occasionally with mixtures of leaves (29%), twigs, rootlets, or needles. Two nests were made of leaves only.

Eggs: Dates for 76 clutches ranged from 5 March (coastal) and 6 April (interior) to 4 September with 51% recorded between 16 May and 3 July. Clutch size ranged from 1 to 26 eggs (1E-4, 2E-2, 3E-1, 4E-1, 5E-2, 6E-2, 7E-1, 8E-3, 9E-4, 10E-5, 11E-6, 12E-6, 13E-9, 14E-8, 15E-4, 16E-4, 17E-2, 18E-4, 19E-2, 20E-4, 23E-1, 26E-1) with 50% having 10 to 15 eggs. The nest with 23 eggs, as well as the one with 26 eggs, was observed being tended by a single female although the clutches were likely the products of two females. One nest, found at Westholme on 3 June 1955, contained 20 to 30 eggs and was being incubated by 2 females. After the eggs hatched, the hens divided the eggs between them. A male incubated the eggs in one Okanagan nest; this sometimes occurs if the female dies (Harrison, C. 1978). Two nests from British Columbia indicate that the incubation period is 21 to 23 days (see Lewin 1963). Based on the large range of egg dates, it is reasonable to assume that a number of the records are of second clutches or renestings, but none were documented as such. R.A. Cannings et al. (1987) note a second peak in hatching for Okanagan nests, suggesting second nestings or double broods (also see Anthony, R. 1970).

Young: Dates for 537 broods ranged from 18 May to 17 October with 55% between 14 July and 15 August. Calculated dates suggest that young can occasionally be out by early April. Brood size ranged from 1 to 22 young (1Y-16, 2Y-28, 3Y-14, 4Y-21, 5Y-36, 6Y-53, 7Y-27, 8Y-60, 9Y-38, 10Y-65, 11Y-41, 12Y-52, 13Y-18, 14Y-21, 15Y-24, 16Y-12, 17Y-2, 18Y-3, 20Y-4, 21Y-1, 22Y-1) with 52% having 7 to 12 young. Young can flutter short distances at 10 days (Harrison, C. 1978).

REMARKS: California Quail were first introduced to British Columbia near Victoria in the early 1860s (Carl and Guiguet 1972). Introductions were later made to the Fraser River delta (1890), Nicola (1908), the Queen Charlotte Islands (1910), and South Pender Island (about 1910). In the Okanagan valley, quail were first introduced near Penticton in 1912, although a male had been sighted the previous year at Cosens Bay, just south of Vernon (Lewin 1965). That bird may have been from the Nicola introductions or was possibly a colonizer from introductions in northern Washington (see Munro, J.A. and Cowan 1947). California Quail were also introduced near Grand Forks in April 1957 (McKay 1957), several times to the Creston-Lister area (Butler, R.W. et al. 1986), and to the Vanderhoof area (Carl and Guiguet 1972).

NOTEWORTHY RECORDS

Spring: Coastal - Victoria 27 Mar 1982-54, 2 May 1984-85; Witty's Lagoon 6 Mar 1975-40; Jordan River 8 Apr 1973-1 (Crowell and Nehls 1973c); Cowichan River 17 Apr 1974-38 on estuary; Burgoyne Bay 4 Mar 1978-35; Reifel Island 26 Apr 1981-6; 5 km n Little Qualicum River 4 Apr 1977-1 male, 4 females; Comox 19 May 1940-4; Campbell River (Discovery Passage) 21 Apr 1982-1. **Interior** - Creston 12 May 1981-1 pair; Princeton 16 Apr 1977-9; Oliver 18 May 1968-31; 18 km n Spences Bridge 10 Apr 1978-1; White Lake (Sorrento) 20 Apr 1977-15.

Summer: Coastal - Sandcut Creek 11 Jun 1981-2; Sooke 3 Jul 1976-5 adults; Cadboro Bay 12 Jun 1982-9 adults; Island View Beach 3 Jul 1984-3 males; Cowichan River 15 Jul 1974-1 pair; Reifel Island 24 Jun 1981-1 pair; Qualicum Beach 12 Jun 1981-1 female; Comox 10 June 1969-1 pair. **Interior** - Creston 14 Jul 1980-2; Gallagher Lake 18 Jun 1976-4 adults; Summerland 5 Jun 1963-3 pairs; Lytton 12 Jul 1963-10; Vernon 12 Jun 1975-2 pairs.

Autumn: Interior - Okanagan Landing 25 Nov 1959-40; Gallagher Lake 9 Sep 1977-50; Osoyoos 9 Sep 1977-64; Creston Nov 1979-pair at feeder; Princeton 7 Sep 1977-1. **Coastal** - Comox 21 Nov 1924-7; Little Qualicum River estuary 19 Sep 1986-28; Reifel Island 16 Nov 1980-8; Saltspring Island 22 Nov 1977-60; Saanich 10 Oct 1982-30; Cadboro Bay 20 Sep 1973-35; Oak Bay 17 Nov 1981-20.

Winter: Interior - Vernon winter 1968-1; Summerland 12 Dec 1977-80+; Penticton 23 Feb 1976-113; Oliver 10 Feb 1978-23. **Coastal** - Comox 12 Jan 1969-4; Little Qualicum River estuary 12 Dec 1985-20+; St. Mary Lake (Saltspring Island) 9 Dec 1978-51; Cadboro Bay 30 Dec 1973-38.

Christmas Counts: Interior - Recorded from 5 of 19 localities and on 39% of all counts. Maxima: Oliver-Osoyoos 28 Dec 1981-1,339, all-time Canadian high count (Anderson, R.R. 1982); Penticton 26 Dec 1978-1,114; Vaseux Lake 28 Dec 1978-800. **Coastal** - Recorded from 9 of 28 localities and on 31% of all counts. Maxima: Victoria 2 Jan 1966-584; Duncan 20 Dec 1975-119; North Saanich 31 Dec 1960-113.

California Quail

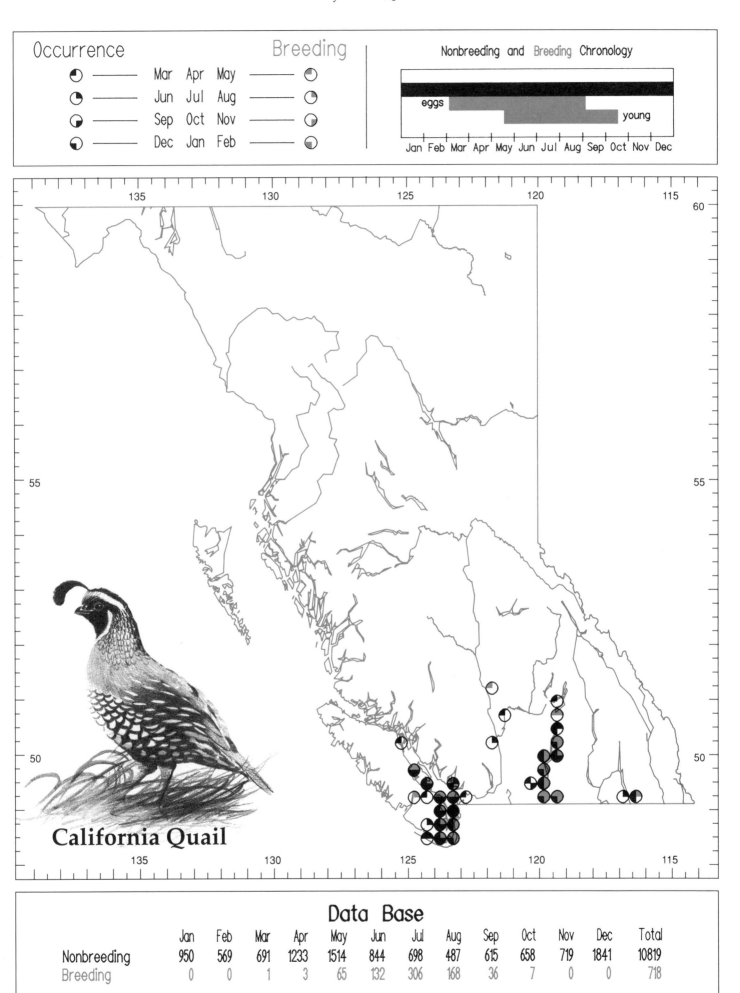

Occurrence

◑	—	Mar Apr May	—	◑
◔	—	Jun Jul Aug	—	◔
◕	—	Sep Oct Nov	—	◕
◓	—	Dec Jan Feb	—	◓

Breeding

Nonbreeding and Breeding Chronology

eggs

young

Jan Feb Mar Apr May Jun Jul Aug Sep Oct Nov Dec

California Quail

Data Base

	Jan	Feb	Mar	Apr	May	Jun	Jul	Aug	Sep	Oct	Nov	Dec	Total
Nonbreeding	950	569	691	1233	1514	844	698	487	615	658	719	1841	10819
Breeding	0	0	1	3	65	132	306	168	36	7	0	0	718

Mountain Quail
Oreortyx pictus (Douglas)

MOQU

RANGE: Resident in extreme southwestern British Columbia, Washington and southwestern Idaho, south to northern Baja California and western Nevada. Introduced to southwestern British Columbia (possibly native) and Washington.

STATUS: Introduced. *Very rare* local resident on extreme southern Vancouver Island. Breeds.

NONBREEDING: The Mountain Quail occurs locally on extreme southern Vancouver Island, from Victoria west to Sooke and north to Tod Inlet and the Malahat. There is one recent record (1986) for Saltspring Island. The Mountain Quail frequents shrubby hills and mountainsides (Fig. 64), coniferous forests, logged hillsides, and areas of dense salal undergrowth from near sea level to 300 m elevation. In the autumn, birds migrate from higher breeding areas to winter at lower elevations.

BREEDING: The Mountain Quail is known to breed only on the extreme southern tip of Vancouver Island.

It frequents the higher elevations of its range during the breeding season. Two broods were reported from logged hillsides.

Nests and Eggs: Only 2 nests have been found: Happy Valley, Metchosin, 10 June 1895-8 eggs, and Victoria 1889-2 eggs.

Calculated dates indicate eggs could be found throughout June. Incubation period is 24 to 25 days (Johnsgard 1973).

Young: Dates for 7 broods ranged from 4 to 24 July. Brood size ranged from 3 to 11 young (3Y-1, 5Y-1, 6Y-2, 8Y-1, 10Y-1, 11Y-1). The most recent breeding record is from the Highland District of Victoria; 13 July 1973-2 adults with 10 chicks.

REMARKS: The Mountain Quail may have been indigenous (see Munro, J.A. and Cowan 1947), but most of its history in the province is obscure. The species was thought to have been first introduced to British Columbia in the early 1860s, and later in the 1870s and 1880s (Wylde 1923; Carl and Guiguet 1972). Apparently, it was introduced to the Fraser Lowlands at about the same time, but the exact date of release is unknown and there are only 3 reports from that area. The Mountain Quail has also been reported north of Victoria to Duncan (Carl and Guiguet 1972; Godfrey 1986), but documented records from that area are lacking.

Observations of Mountain Quail on Vancouver Island have been reported every decade from the 1890s to the present. The largest numbers on file are from the early 1970s (see Tatum 1971); however, Stirling (1986) notes that by the end of that decade "it was generally agreed that the Mountain Quail had vanished." Since 1977 there have been only 4 reports of the species.

Figure 64. *Mountain Quail habitat on the Malahat summit near Victoria, May 1989 (Neil K. Dawe).*

NOTEWORTHY RECORDS

Spring: Coastal - Sooke Mountain Park 18 Apr 1983-1 male; Scafe Hill (Victoria) 26 Apr 1973-2; Victoria 17 May 1971-1 male (RBCM 11780); Munn's Road (Victoria) 27 Mar 1959-4 adult males, Apr 1960-1+ (Stirling 1961); Mount Tuam 19 May 1986-1 (Mattocks 1986a). **Interior** - No records.

Summer: Coastal - Otter Point 6 Jun 1946-1 (Harwell 1946); Mount Finlayson 23 Jun 1974-1 male calling; Malahat 13 Jul 1986-2 males (RBCM 19302-03); Weaver Lake Aug 1966-5 pairs released. **Interior** - No records.

Autumn: Interior - No records. **Coastal** - Weaver Lake 21 Oct 1966-2 males, 1 female; Vedder Mountain 26 Sep 1921-3 (Munro, J.A. and Cowan 1947); Goldstream Park 20 Nov 1921-1 male (ROM 83605); Durrance Lake autumn 1953 - several covies (Guiguet 1953c); Mount Finlayson 23 Nov 1958-6 (Poynter 1960); East Sooke 21 Sep 1960-2 covies: Munn's Road (Gowlland Range) 11 Nov 1977-4; Victoria 20 Nov 1921-2 males (UMMZ 99708-09).

Winter: Interior - No records. **Coastal** - Mill Hill (Langford) 28 Dec 1932-8 (Munro, J.A. and Cowan 1947); Victoria 25 Jan 1889-2 (AMNH 472443-44); Island View Beach 12 Dec 1971-1 male (RBCM 11781); Tod Inlet 20 Jan 1969-8 drowned landing on floating snow in inlet (RBCM 11595-602); Sooke Dec 1897-1 female (RBCM 1663).

Christmas Counts: Interior - Not recorded. **Coastal** - Recorded 3 times, all from Victoria: 21 Dec 1963-9, all-time Canadian high count (Anderson, R.R. 1978), 30 Dec 1973-5, and 18 Dec 1976-2.

Mountain Quail

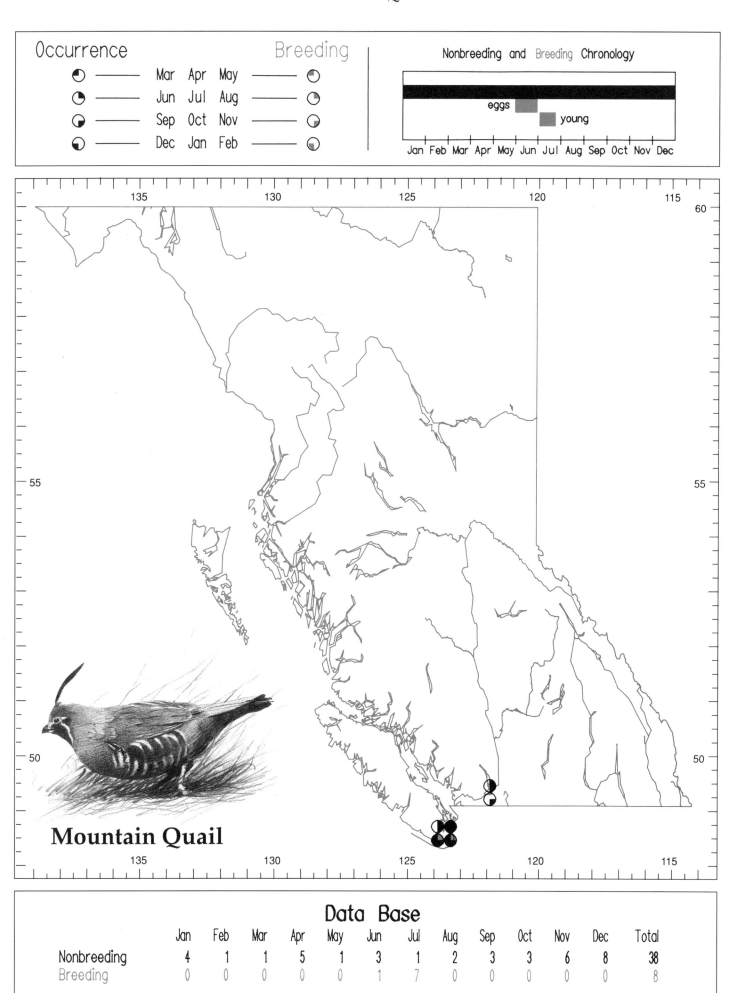

Occurrence / Breeding

Occurrence		Breeding
◕	Mar Apr May	◔
◔	Jun Jul Aug	◔
◑	Sep Oct Nov	◕
◐	Dec Jan Feb	◓

Nonbreeding and Breeding Chronology

eggs   young

Jan Feb Mar Apr May Jun Jul Aug Sep Oct Nov Dec

Mountain Quail

Data Base

	Jan	Feb	Mar	Apr	May	Jun	Jul	Aug	Sep	Oct	Nov	Dec	Total
Nonbreeding	4	1	1	5	1	3	1	2	3	3	6	8	38
Breeding	0	0	0	0	0	1	7	0	0	0	0	0	8

Virginia Rail

VIRA

Rallus limicola Vieillot

RANGE: Breeds across most of southern Canada, south to southern California, Arizona, Oklahoma, northern Virginia along the coast to North Carolina. Winters on both coasts from southern British Columbia and North Carolina south. Also occurs in Mexico and South America.

STATUS: *Rare* to locally *fairly common* resident in southern British Columbia including Vancouver Island, the Fraser Lowlands, and the Okanagan valley. *Very rare* summer visitant to the west Kootenay and the Chilcotin-Cariboo region. *Casual* on the Queen Charlotte Islands, in the east Kootenay, and the northern interior. Breeds.

NONBREEDING: The Virginia Rail occurs locally across the province, south of Quesnel, from Vancouver Island to the east Kootenay. There are only 4 records north of 53°N latitude. It occurs from sea level to 1,060 m elevation. It frequents a wide variety of freshwater and brackish wetland habitats where islands or edges of thick emergent vegetation occur, including lakes, ponds, estuarine and palustrine marshes, bogs, wet meadows, sloughs, and ditches. The Virginia Rail has also been reported from small gardens, including flower boxes, in urban areas.

The timing of spring and autumn migrations is poorly known because the Virginia Rail is so difficult to census in its habitat. Records suggest that the spring movement occurs from late March to early May, while the autumn movement occurs from September through November.

Winter distribution includes coastal areas of Vancouver Island from Victoria north along the east coast to Campbell River and on the west coast to Halfway River, the Fraser Lowlands and the Okanagan valley. It is a casual winter visitant to the Trail area. Its winter centre of abundance is southern Vancouver Island and the Fraser River delta.

BREEDING: The Virginia Rail breeds on southeastern Vancouver Island, from Victoria north to Comox, and throughout the Fraser Lowlands. In the interior, it breeds through the Okanagan valley north to the Shuswap region, in the Creston valley, and locally near 100 Mile House, Williams Lake, and Kleena Kleene. It breeds from near sea level to 915 m elevation.

Breeding habitat includes freshwater marshes, lakes, or sloughs with dense emergent vegetation, principally cattail, bulrush, or sedges, bordering the shore. Occasionally, brackish marshes, wet meadows, ditches, and wet agricultural fields are used.

Nests: All nests (n=34) were situated among dense emergent vegetation, including cattail, bulrush, reed canarygrass, hardhack, sedges, and grasses. Nests were either attached to the stems above the water (54%) or ground (21%), or at the water (13%) or ground (12%). Twenty-two nest heights ranged from ground-level to 45 cm with 65% between ground-level and 15 cm. Most nests were a shallow, woven, basket-like structure of reeds, grasses, or rushes. Some nests were simply loose structures of reeds or rushes with a slight depression in which the eggs were laid. Nests were usually concealed by adjacent emergent stems or leaves bent to cover them.

Eggs: Dates for 55 clutches ranged from 6 April to 20 June with 54% recorded between 20 May and 13 June. Egg-laying at the coast may begin up to one month earlier than in the interior. Clutch size ranged from 2 to 12 eggs (2E-1, 3E-1, 4E-4, 5E-3, 6E-6, 7E-15, 8E-11, 9E-9, 10E-4, 12E-1) with 64% having 7 to 9 eggs. Incubation period is 18 to 20 days (Walkinshaw 1937).

Young: Dates for 61 broods ranged from 3 May to 18 August with 54% recorded between 5 June and 12 July. Brood size ranged from 1 to 9 young (1Y-5, 2Y-10, 3Y-12, 4Y-4, 5Y-2, 6Y-1, 7Y-3, 8Y-2, 9Y-2) with 57% having 1 or 2 young. The low average brood size is misleading: the chicks are precocial, secretive, and difficult to observe in their habitat even when one knows they are there.

REMARKS: R. Johnson and Dinsmore (1986) found that habitat use by breeding Virginia Rails and Soras in northwestern Iowa correlated highly with the availability of emergent vegetation. They also found that practices used to encourage waterfowl use are compatible with the habitat requirements of breeding Virginia Rails and Soras. This secretive marsh bird likely has a wider distribution than our records indicate. Many of our records are the result of direct attempts by observers to find the birds through tape recorded calls or hand claps. See Horak (1964) for a comparative study of the Virginia Rail and Sora.

NOTEWORTHY RECORDS

Spring: Coastal - Quicks Bottom 24 May 1975-2 males, 3 females; Sea Island 11 May 1980-5; Burnaby Lake 23 Apr 1977-3, 28 May 1974-3; Stubbs Island (Tofino) 6 Mar 1985-3; Cranberry Lake (Powell River) 8 May 1981-1; Gunflint Lake 13 Mar 1976-4, 1 Apr 1976-6, 2 May 1977-5; Francis Lake (Port McNeill) 30 Apr 1951-1, 13 May 1951-1. **Interior** - Bridesville 17 May 1970-1; Oliver 10 Apr 1977-1; White Lake (Okanagan Falls) 9 Apr 1976-2; Venner Meadows 18 May 1986-5; Penticton 2 Apr 1966-1; Madeline Lake (Penticton) 18 Apr 1980-2; Hills 12 May 1984-1; Vernon 30 Apr 1985-1; Turtle Valley 12 May 1973-1 (Rogers, T.H. 1973c); 100 Mile House 13 May 1981-1; Pete Kitchen Lake 10 May 1983-1 (Ducks Unlimited Canada 1983); Williams Lake 20 May 1982-1.

Summer: Coastal - Quicks Bottom 13 Jun 1982-7; Burnaby Lake 3 Jun 1969-3; Cleland Island 24 Jul 1967-1, 25 Aug 1967-1 (Campbell and Stirling 1968b); Cranberry Lake (Powell River) 19 and 20 Jun 1981-1; Qualicum Beach 17 Jul 1981-2; Comox 7 Jul 1922-1 female (NMC 17984). **Interior** - Manning

Park 18 and 19 Jul 1985-2 at beaver pond; Yak (Yale) Jul 1883-1 male (RBCM 179); Tamarack Lake 16 Jul 1976-2; Nakusp 18 Jun 1981-1; Wells Gray Park summer 1976-legs found in Merlin nest (RBCM 15304); Quesnel 22 Jun 1980-1 adult; Maclure Lake 15 Jul 1944-1 (Munro, J.A. 1947a).

Autumn: Interior - Williams Lake 19 Sep 1978-1 immature, 19 Sep 1979-1; 100 Mile House 1 Oct 1976-1 (RBCM 15467); Horse Lake (Lone Butte) 22 Sep 1940-1 male (ROM 83210); Elk River and Michel Creek 13 Sep 1983-1 at confluence (Fraser 1984); Duck Lake (Creston) 5 Sep 1952-1 (Munro, J.A. 1958a). **Coastal** - Cape Scott Park 16 Sep 1935-1; Browning Inlet 1 to 21 Nov 1968-2 (Richardson 1971); Cortes Island 28 Oct 1976-2; Long Beach 6 Oct 1973-1; Grouse Mountain 17 Sep 1983-1 at 1,000 m elevation (UBC 14456); Reifel Island 6 Nov 1983-5; Rithets Bog 8 Oct 1972-3 (Tatum 1973).

Winter: Interior - Larkin 30 Dec 1967-1; Vernon 11 Jan 1986-1; Kelowna 17 Jan 1942-1 female

(MVZ 84748); Summerland 22 Dec 1919-1 female (ROM 83211); Penticton 25 Dec 1979-3; Castlegar 17 Dec 1981-1; Hack's Pond (Oliver) 29 Dec 1987-2. **Coastal** - Quatsino Sound 18 Dec 1944-1 (UBC 3850); Cortes Island 13 Dec 1976-14 at three sites; Stubbs Island 29 Dec 1987-3; Tofino 27 Feb 1983-2; Musqueam Indian Reserve 16 Dec 1984-35; Rithets Bog 5 Dec 1971-10+ (Tatum 1972).

Christmas Counts: Interior - Recorded from 3 of 19 localities and on 12% of all counts. Maxima: Vaseux Lake 23 Dec 1982-6; Penticton 27 Dec 1983-4; Vernon 18 Dec 1983-1. **Coastal** - Recorded from 11 of 28 localities and on 21% of all counts. Maxima: Vancouver 16 Dec 1984-39, all-time Canadian high count (Monroe 1985b); Victoria 15 Dec 1984-14; Ladner 23 Dec 1984-7.

Extralimital Records: Interior - Como Lake (Atlin) 8 Jul 1980-1. **Coastal** - Masset 12 Dec 1944-1 male (RBCM 10576); Beal Cove 7 and 9 Jun 1970-1.

Virginia Rail

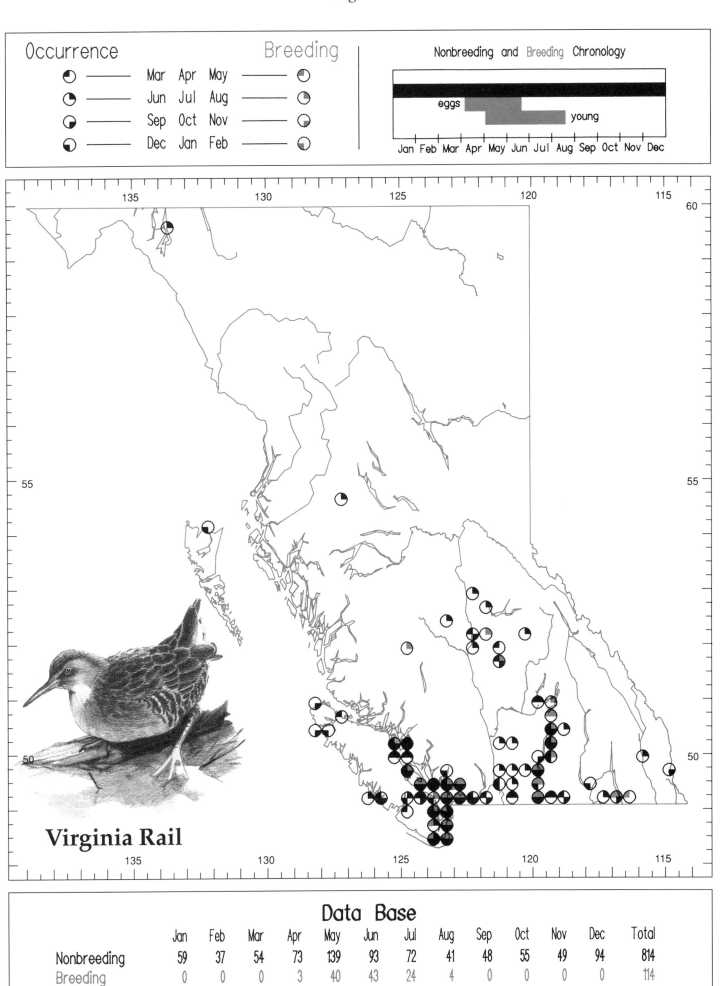

Virginia Rail

Data Base

	Jan	Feb	Mar	Apr	May	Jun	Jul	Aug	Sep	Oct	Nov	Dec	Total
Nonbreeding	59	37	54	73	139	93	72	41	48	55	49	94	814
Breeding	0	0	0	3	40	43	24	4	0	0	0	0	114

Sora

SORA

Porzana carolina (Linnaeus)

RANGE: Breeds throughout most of temperate North America from southeastern Alaska (Trapp et al. 1981), the southern Yukon and Mackenzie east to the Maritime Provinces and south through the northeastern United States to the southwestern United States to Baja California. Winters from the southern United States south to Colombia and Peru including the West Indies; occasionally farther north where marshes remain ice-free.

STATUS: *Rare* to locally *fairly common* summer visitant from southern British Columbia, including southeastern Vancouver Island, the Fraser Lowlands, the southern interior, and the Kootenays, north through the Chilcotin-Cariboo and Nechako Lowland to the Peace and Fort Nelson lowlands. *Very rare* in the Bulkley and Nass basins. *Casual* on the Queen Charlotte Islands, the Teslin Plateau and the Chilkat Pass area. In winter, *very rare* visitant to the Fraser Lowlands; *accidental* in the Okanagan valley and on the Queen Charlotte Islands. Breeds.

NONBREEDING: The Sora occurs infrequently on the northwestern Queen Charlotte Islands and the west coast of Vancouver Island, and regularly along southeastern Vancouver Island, the Fraser Lowlands and generally in suitable habitat throughout the interior to the Peace River and Boreal Forest areas. There are only a few records for the northwestern portion of the province. It has been found from sea level to 1,440 m elevation. The Sora frequents a variety of freshwater and brackish wetlands including lakes, marshes, sloughs, beaver ponds, bogs, estuaries, and sewage ponds. During migration it has been observed in atypical areas including residential lawns and gardens, sandy beaches, open fields, airport runways, city cores, and lighthouse lawns.

Spring migration is usually evident in late April and early May, but may occur as early as mid-March. The autumn movement begins by early September, and most birds have left by mid-October.

Occasionally, small numbers winter in the lower Fraser River valley.

BREEDING: The Sora breeds from extreme southern Vancouver Island, the south mainland coast and Fraser Lowlands, and from the southern interior north through the Chilcotin-Cariboo regions and the Nechako Lowlands to the Peace Lowlands. There is an isolated record from Atlin in northwestern British Columbia.

It breeds from near sea level to 1,220 m elevation, in a variety of freshwater and brackish wetland habitats including marshes, sloughs, lakes, ponds, and wet meadows, that usually contain cattail, bulrushes, and sedges. Willow swamps, marshy river and stream edges, dry grass meadows, drainage and irrigation ditches, and wet fields are used occasionally. In British Columbia, the Sora nests in wetter habitats, and more often in cattail stands, than the Virginia Rail. However, no strong niche-segregating mechanism was found in habitat use by breeding Virginia Rails and Soras in Iowa (Johnson, R. and Dinsmore 1986).

Nests: Most nests (92%; n=48) were in wet situations and were positioned among dense emergent vegetation, including cattail, sedges, and rushes, or in dense grasses. One nest was found in a willow clump. Most nests (86%) were attached to vegetation, above the water. Five nests were on dry ground; 2 were floating. In wet situations, nests ranged in height from 0 to 76 cm above the water's surface with 58% between 5 and 15 cm. Most nests were woven to form a cupped platform and 2 nests were on floating mats of vegetation. Nest materials included reeds, grasses, sedges, bulrushes, and cattails with a lining of dry grasses, weed stalks or sedges. Nests were usually well concealed with vegetation bent over to form a dome.

Eggs: Dates for 81 clutches ranged from 22 May to 30 July with 54% recorded between 1 and 25 June. Calculated dates indicate that eggs could be found on 1 May. Clutch size ranged from 1 to 16 eggs (1E-2, 2E-5, 3E-1, 4E-3, 5E-4, 6E-6, 7E-8, 8E-13, 9E-11, 10E-14, 11E-7, 12E-1, 13E-3, 14E-2, 16E-1) with 65% having 8 to 11 eggs. One nest from British Columbia had an incubation period of about 17 days; Walkinshaw (1935) notes that the period ranges from 15 to 19 days.

Young: Dates for 63 broods ranged from 18 May to 17 September with 56% recorded between 29 June and 25 July. Brood size ranged from 1 to 9 young (1Y-22, 2Y-16, 3Y-10, 4Y-5, 5Y-2, 6Y-5, 7Y-1, 8Y-1, 9Y-1), with 60% having 1 or 2 young. Fledging period is about 36 days (Harrison, C. 1978).

REMARKS: See Virginia Rail for comments concerning the low average brood size and remarks about habitat use by breeding Soras. Walkinshaw (1940) provides noteworthy glimpses into the breeding biology of this secretive species.

NOTEWORTHY RECORDS

Spring: Coastal - Victoria 11 Apr 1976-1, 27 Apr 1984-1 male (RBCM 18106); Quicks Bottom 2 May 1986-4; Westham Island 15 Mar 1973-1; Sea Island 1 May 1982-1; Qualicum Beach 19 Apr 1977-1; Merville 28 Apr 1977-1; Sewall 1 May 1981-1. **Interior** - Creston 8 May 1980-1+; Penticton 18 Apr 1980-1, 10 May 1973-10+; Cranbrook 26 Apr 1916-1; Merritt 15 Apr 1968-1; Douglas Lake (Quilchena) 29 Apr 1980-1 male (RBCM 16445); Trout Lake (Galena Bay) 30 Apr 1977-1; 105 Mile House 28 Apr 1981-1; Riske Creek 4 May 1978-4; Moose Lake (Mount Robson Park) 31 May 1972-1; Smithers 26 Apr 1981-1 male (RBCM 17890); Fort St. John 13 May 1981 -1; North Pine 28 Apr 1980-1; Liard Hot Springs 13 May 1975-1 (Reid 1975); Atlin 7 May 1936-1 (RBCM 5826).

Summer: Coastal - Quicks Bottom early Jun 1971-1 to 2 dozen (Tatum 1972); Chilliwack 24 Aug 1927-1 (RBCM 6254); Hope 19 Jul 1952-1 female (RBCM 10038); Trout Lake (Vancouver) 3 Jun 1984-4; Woodhus Slough (Discovery Passage) 17 Jul 1983-1 immature (Mattocks et al. 1983); Tlell 26 Jul 1974-2, (Shepard, M.G. 1975a), 25 Aug 1974-1. **Interior** - Grave Lake 9 Jun 1984-3+; Wapta Lake 5 Jun 1975-1 (Wade 1977); Stuie 28 Jul 1938-1 immature female (NMC 28748); Moose Lake (Mount Robson Park) 16 Jun 1973-4+; Prince George 18 Jun 1987-2; Topley 6 to 25 Jun 1956-1; Hazelton 8 Aug 1938-1 immature male (UMMZ 97832); Boundary Lake (Goodlow) 23 Jun 1985-6; Fern Lake (Kwadacha Wilderness Park) 22 Aug 1983-1 immature (Cooper, J.M. and Cooper 1983); Kotcho Lake 26 Jun 1982-1 (Campbell and McNall 1982); Helmet (Kwokullie Lake) 9 Jun 1982-4; Twin Lakes (Kelsall Lake) 2 Jun 1981-1.

Autumn: Interior - Fort St. John 18 Sep 1983-1; Gauthier Lake 2 Sep 1981-1; Prince George 3 Sep 1987-1 immature; Springhouse 6 Sep 1981-1 female (RBCM 17260); Yoho National Park 24 Sep 1976-1 (Wade 1977); Bridge Lake 15 Sep 1962-1; Silverton 26 Sep 1976-1; Cranbrook 10 Oct 1913-1; Vaseux Lake 12 Oct 1970-1; Oliver 3 Oct 1981-1. **Coastal** - Masset 3 Nov 1946-1 female (RBCM 10577); Vancouver 13 Oct 1974-1; Ladner 28 Oct 1954-1 female (PMNH 71692); Tofino 6 Sep 1986-1, 20 Oct 1971-1 (RBCM 11966; Hatler et al. 1978); Ascot Pond (Saanich) 4 Sep 1978-2; Victoria 27 Oct 1958-1 (RBCM 10787), 27 Nov 1975-1.

Winter: Interior - See Christmas Counts below. **Coastal** - Masset 28 Dec 1936-1 (RBCM 10578); Richmond 13 Jan 1979-1; Surrey 21 Feb 1977-1; Chilliwack 6 Dec 1927-1 male (RBCM 6255).

Christmas Counts: Interior - Recorded once: Penticton 27 Dec 1980-1. **Coastal** - Recorded from 3 of 28 localities and on 2% of all counts. Maxima: Ladner 14 Dec 1974-2, all-time Canadian high count (tied with Blenheim, Ontario; Anderson, R.R. 1976); Nanaimo 1 Jan 1985-1; Vancouver 17 Dec 1972-1, 29 Dec 1974-1, 18 Dec 1983-1, 16 Dec 1984-1.

Sora

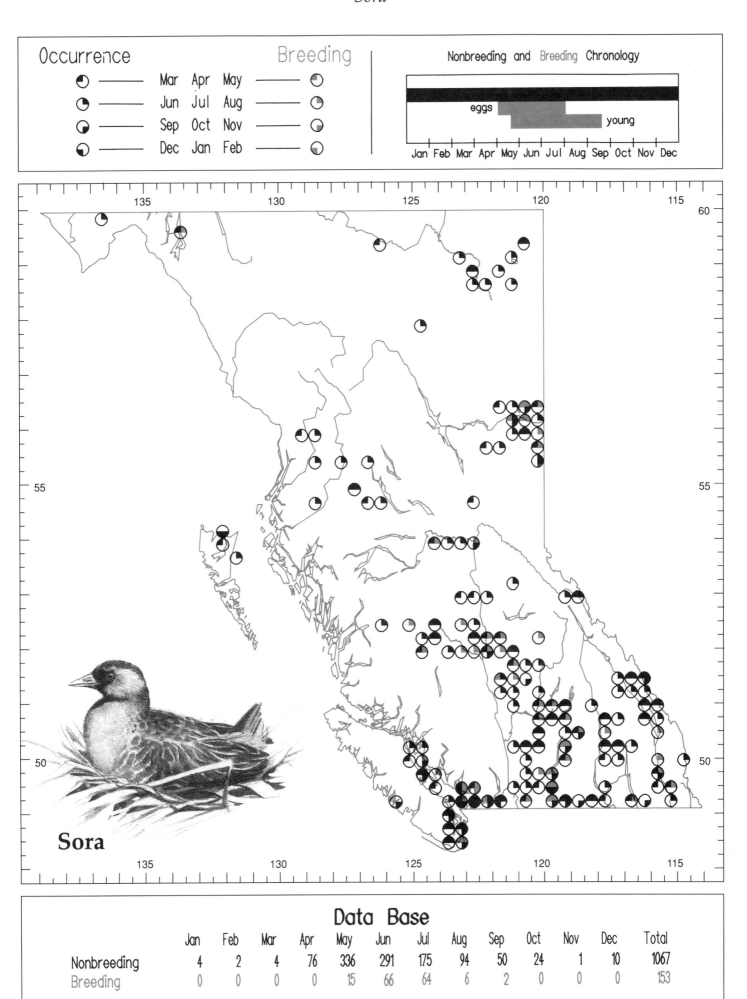

Occurrence

Mar Apr May
Jun Jul Aug
Sep Oct Nov
Dec Jan Feb

Breeding

Nonbreeding and Breeding Chronology

eggs
young

Jan Feb Mar Apr May Jun Jul Aug Sep Oct Nov Dec

Data Base

	Jan	Feb	Mar	Apr	May	Jun	Jul	Aug	Sep	Oct	Nov	Dec	Total
Nonbreeding	4	2	4	76	336	291	175	94	50	24	1	10	1067
Breeding	0	0	0	0	15	66	64	6	2	0	0	0	153

American Coot
Fulica americana Gmelin

AMCO

RANGE: Breeds from the southeastern Yukon and southern Mackenzie east across southern Canada to New Brunswick and south through California, Arizona, New Mexico, Illinois, and southern Florida. Winters from British Columbia and the Pacific coast states, east to Maryland on the Atlantic coast and south to the Gulf coast. Also occurs in Mexico, Central America, the West Indies, northern South America, and the Hawaiian Islands.

STATUS: *Common* to locally *very abundant* spring and autumn migrant and summer visitant from southern British Columbia, including southern Vancouver Island, the Fraser Lowlands, the Okanagan valley, and the west Kootenay north through the Chilcotin-Cariboo to the Peace Lowlands. *Common* to *abundant* winter visitant along the south inner coast; *very rare* elsewhere on the coast. Locally *very common* to *very abundant* winter visitant in the central-southern interior, *very rare* in the Bulkley Basin region, and *rare* in the Liard Basin and Fort Nelson Lowlands. Breeds.

NONBREEDING: The American Coot occurs throughout the southern coast, including Vancouver Island, and sporadically on the northern mainland coast and the eastern Queen Charlotte Lowlands. In the interior, it is widely distributed from southern British Columbia north through the Peace River area east of 128°W longitude. It occurs from sea level to 1,530 m elevation. The American Coot frequents fresh, marine, and brackish waters where aquatic vegetation provides cover and a food source. This includes lakes, ponds, marshes, lagoons, sloughs, estuaries, slow-moving rivers, flooded fields, tidal mudflats, and sewage lagoons

In spring, the main northward movement occurs on the south coast from early April to May. In the interior, it starts in March and peaks in April, with especially large numbers moving through the Creston valley. In summer, most nonbreeders are found within the breeding range. The southern movement begins in late August and continues through to November with the main movement occurring from mid-September to mid-October. Very large numbers move through the Creston and Columbia valleys to winter farther south (Fig. 65). In the Okanagan valley, the autumn movement is protracted, and many birds may overwinter there if lakes remain unfrozen (Cannings, R.A. et al. 1987).

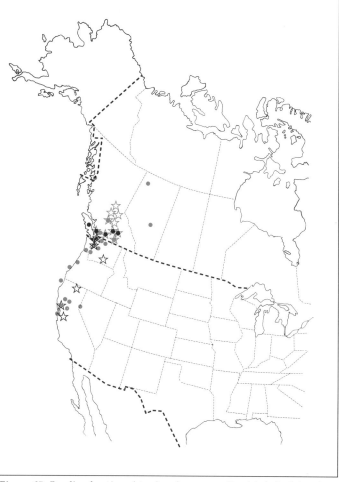

Figure 65. Banding locations (stars) and recovery sites (circles) of American Coots associated with British Columbia. Red indicates birds banded in the province, black indicates birds banded elsewhere.

Figure 66. Wintering American Coots on Beaver Lake, Saanich, 28 January 1984 (Tim Zurowski). Note the 2 male Redheads behind the flock of coots.

American Coot

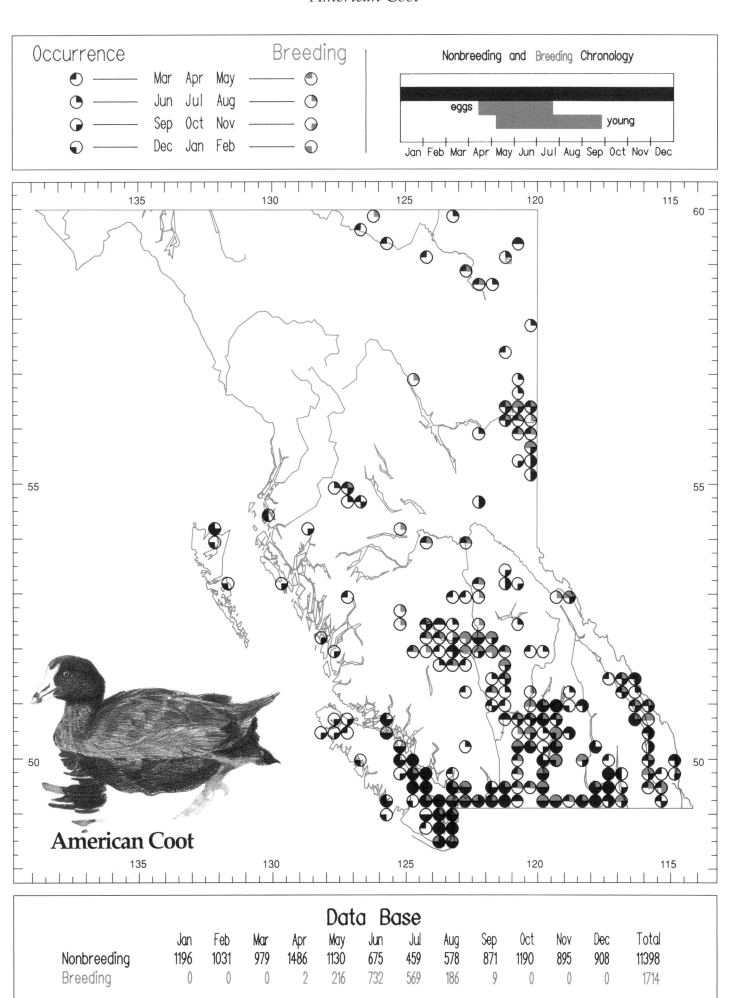

Occurrence

		Breeding
◕ ——— Mar Apr May ——— ◔		
◔ ——— Jun Jul Aug ——— ◔		
◵ ——— Sep Oct Nov ——— ◔		
◕ ——— Dec Jan Feb ——— ◕		

Nonbreeding and Breeding Chronology

eggs   young

Jan Feb Mar Apr May Jun Jul Aug Sep Oct Nov Dec

American Coot

Data Base

	Jan	Feb	Mar	Apr	May	Jun	Jul	Aug	Sep	Oct	Nov	Dec	Total
Nonbreeding	1196	1031	979	1486	1130	675	459	578	871	1190	895	908	11398
Breeding	0	0	0	2	216	732	569	186	9	0	0	0	1714

The American Coot is found along most of the coast in winter (Fig. 66), the centre of abundance on the coast is southeastern Vancouver Island and the Fraser Lowlands. In the interior, the coot is found in winter in the central southern portion from Williams Lake southward, with the centre of abundance in the Okanagan valley south of Kelowna.

BREEDING: The American Coot breeds on southeastern Vancouver Island, from Victoria north to Comox, and throughout the Fraser Lowlands, east across southern portions of the province including the Similkameen, Nicola, Okanagan, Arrow Lakes, Creston, and Columbia valleys, north through the Chilcotin-Cariboo and Fraser Basin regions to the Peace Lowlands, Fort Nelson Lowlands, and Liard Basin.

Nests have been found from near sea level to 1,220 m elevation. The American Coot breeds on freshwater, alkali, and, occasionally, brackish wetlands including lakes, ponds, marshes, and sloughs with extensive stands of dense emergent vegetation usually along the margins. Other breeding sites include sewage lagoons, creek and stream edges, willow swamps, and wide irrigation ditches and canals. The American Coot nests solitarily or in loose congregations of up to 200 pairs (Table 3).

Nests: Most nests (93%; n=258) were situated in dense stands of emergent vegetation including reeds, bulrushes, cattail, sedges, and grasses (Fig. 67). Of the remaining nests, 10 were among waterlilies and 8 were completely exposed on open water. One hundred and thirty-nine nests were located on the water; two were woven baskets attached to sedges just above the water, and two were found on the ground near a lake edge. Of the nests situated over water, 22 ranged from 0 to 30 m from shore with 68% recorded between 2 and 6 m.

Nests were usually bowl or saucer-shaped structures of decaying vegetation (reeds, bulrushes, cattail, or sedges, often lined with dry reeds, grasses, or sedges) floating on the water and anchored to emergent vegetation. Occasionally, a submerged or floating log was used as a substrate. Eight nests were on water where depth ranged from less than 3 cm to 1.2 m. One nest had adjacent reeds pulled over it for concealment. Nests frequently had a "ramp" or "runway" from the water to the top. Heights for

55 nests ranged from 5 to 40 cm with 80% recorded between 5 and 15 cm. One nest diameter was 45 cm at the base and 30 cm at the rim.

Eggs: Dates for 695 clutches ranged from 1 May to 20 July with 52% recorded between 29 May and 15 June. Calculated dates indicate that eggs in the interior could be found as early as 12 April, about 12 days earlier than on the coast. Clutch size ranged from 1 to 23 eggs (1E-19, 2E-43, 3E-41, 4E-43, 5E-48, 6E-60, 7E-89, 8E-100, 9E-114, 10E-74, 11E-34, 12E-16, 13E-6, 14E-4, 15E-1, 16E-2, 23E-1) with 54% having 7 to 10 eggs. Incubation period for 12 clutches in British Columbia was 23 to 24 days.

Young: Dates for 1,044 broods ranged from 5 May to 25 September with 56% recorded between 20 June and 16 July. Brood size ranged from 1 to 12 young (1Y-174, 2Y-263, 3Y-205, 4Y-151, 5Y-95, 6Y-65, 7Y-31, 8Y-34, 9Y-14, 10Y-4, 11Y-5, 12Y-3) with 59% having 2 to 4 young (Fig. 68).

REMARKS: The American Coot is a game bird in British Columbia, although usually less than 1,000 birds are killed each year (Metras 1986).

Four single coots, resembling a Caribbean Coot (*Fulica caribaea*), were discovered on the southwest mainland coast in the mid-1980s (Kautesk 1985b). The records were: Reifel Island 21 October 1984-1 intermediate between typical Caribbean and American coots; Burnaby Lake 27 January to 2 February 1985-1 with bright yellow frontal shield at the centre fading to white towards the edges; 2 February 1985-1 with orange frontal shield (RBCM Photo 1211); and Lost Lagoon 16 February 1985-1 with all-white frontal shield without the reddish plate.

Because some American Coots show considerable variation in the shape, size, and colour of the frontal shield (Guillion 1951; Sykes 1975), and the 2 species hybridize and breed in the same area (Payne and Master 1983), it becomes difficult to reliably identify and separate the 2 species in the field. Although the American Ornithologists' Union (1983) considers the Caribbean Coot a distinct species, it may prove to be a morph of the American Coot.

Fredrickson (1967) provides additional information on the breeding biology of the American Coot in North America.

TABLE 3.

American Coot: location, history, and size of major breeding concentrations in British Columbia.

Location	Site History				
	First Record	Low Survey Results[1] Year	High Survey Results[1] Year	Recent Survey Results[1] Year	Source[2]
Interior - Colonies > 50 nests or pairs					
Westwick Lake	1938		104 Ac 1978	C 1986	1
Cecil Lake	1962	37 Ap 1962	200 P 1980	C 1986	1
Boundary Lake (Goodlow)	1978		50 P 1981	C 1986	1

[1] A - active nests; C - nesting confirmed but no count or estimate made; P - pairs. All data are estimates unless noted as follows: c - complete count.

[2] 1 - British Columbia Nest Records Scheme.

Figure 68. *American Coot chicks at Williams Lake, 17 July 1977 (Ervio Sian).*

Figure 67. *American Coot on nest at west Creston, 14 June 1981 (Mark Nyhof).*

NOTEWORTHY RECORDS

Spring: Coastal - Esquimalt Lagoon 12 Mar 1979-375, 3 Apr 1977-350; Elk Lake (Saanich) 9 Mar 1987-1,000; Westham Island 14 Mar 1974-300, 14 Apr 1973-300, 30 Apr 1974-100; Tofino Inlet 31 Mar 1962-5; Cranberry Lake (Powell River) 23 Apr 1980-15; Port Neville 16 Apr 1977-4; Kimsquit River 22 Apr 1982-1; Masset 21 Mar 1976-11; Prince Rupert 17 Apr 1983-1. **Interior** - Creston 15 Apr 1985-10,110, 18 Apr 1985-19,050, 22 Apr 1985-25,575, 25 Apr 1985-9,250 (Butler, R.W. and Savard 1985); Vaseux Lake 10 Apr 1977-1,050; Okanagan Lake 5 Apr 1979-2,000+; Merritt 15 Apr 1968-100; Vernon 3 Mar 1978-2,400, 20 Apr 1980-1,170; Nicola Lake 6 Mar 1983-1; Stump Lake (Quilchena) 25 Mar 1984-225; Wilmer 28 Apr 1970-1,000+; Burges and James Gadsden Park 9 Apr 1987-51, 16 Apr 1987-252, 21 Apr 1987-679, 27 Apr 1987-300; 100 Mile House 24 Mar 1984-3; Williams Lake 16 Mar 1979-3, 21 Apr 1980-720; Yoho National Park 23 Apr 1977 -2; Toboggan Lake 27 Apr 1979-2; Fort St. John 10 Apr 1986-1; Boudreau Lake 7 May 1981-1,500; Coal River 14 May 1981-1.

Summer: Coastal - Quicks Bottom 14 Jun 1979-8 adults; Burnaby Lake 3 Jun 1946-48 (Munro, D.A. 1947), 20 Aug 1981-50; Iona Island 24 Aug 1969-35; Stanley Park (Vancouver) 23 Jun 1973-30; Cranberry Lake (Powell River) 30 Aug 1981-3; Alta Lake 27 Aug 1968-10. **Interior** - Vaseux Lake 29 Aug 1978-100; Wasa 30 Aug 1977-135+; Munson's Slough (Kelowna) 7 Aug 1950-290, 29 Aug 1950-345 (Munro, D.A. 1952); Rose Hill 16 to 20 Jun 1969-39; 103 Mile Lake 20 Aug 1937-350, 24 Aug 1939-150 (Munro, J.A. 1939g); Williams Lake 26 Jul 1948-53 adults; Clarke Lake 19 Jul 1977-9; Cecil Lake 21 Aug 1980-1,000; Helmet (Kwokullie Lake) 29 May 1982-1.

Autumn: Interior - Boundary Lake (Goodlow) 5 Oct 1986-400; Charlie Lake 22 Oct 1986-294; Fort St. John 27 Oct 1986-38 on sewage lagoons; Blackhawk Lake 15 Sep 1977-100; Kathlyn Lake 22 Nov 1981-1; Round Lake (Smithers) 29 Nov 1987-14; Williams Lake 15 Sep 1980-230, 3 Oct 1979-460, 29 Oct 1979-131, 7 Nov 1978-1; McMurdo to Horse Creek Oct 1963-10,000 aerial survey; Windermere Lake Oct 1963-19,100 aerial survey; Vernon 9 Sep 1977-1,959, 21 Sep 1977-2,030, 6 Oct 1977-3,000; Stump Lake (Quilchena) 28 Nov 1981-500; Sirdar 17 Sep 1947-6,000; Vaseux Lake 29 Sep 1951-1,800; Creston 15 Sep 1967-15,000, 12 Oct 1975-10,000. **Coastal** - Delkatla Inlet 27 Sep 1978-14; Kitimat 5 Oct 1974-2 (Hay 1976); Browning Inlet 30 Oct 1968-1; Cranberry Lake (Powell River) 1 Sep 1980-80+, 30 Sep 1980-375; Pitt Lake 16 Oct 1976-1,300; Westham Island 7 Sep 1968-100; Esquimalt Lagoon 28 Sep 1977-345, 12 Oct 1977-557, 2 Nov 1977-564.

Winter: Interior - Williams Lake 1 Jan 1977-14; Athalmere 22 Jan 1979-15; Penticton area 26 Dec 1964-10,530; Nelson 2 Dec 1978-1,000; Vaseux Lake 21 Dec 1974-1,500. **Coastal** - Prince Rupert 2 Jan 1983-1; Delkatla Inlet 28 Dec 1974-19; Port Neville 23 Dec 1976-6; Campbell River 6 Dec 1975-1 on estuary; Cranberry Lake (Powell River) 1 Dec 1980-130; Fanny Bay (Bowser) 19 Feb 1974-30; Somenos Lake 17 Feb 1985-120; Iona Island 5 Jan 1977-500; Esquimalt Lagoon 26 Dec 1976-275, 8 Jan 1977-300, 26 Feb 1977-300;

Christmas Counts: Interior -Recorded from 8 of 19 localities and on 53% of all counts. Maxima: Penticton 26 Dec 1975-**7,103**, all-time Canadian high count (Anderson, R.R. 1976); Vernon 26 Dec 1977-5,823; Vaseux Lake 28 Dec 1974-3,434. **Coastal** - Recorded from 19 of 28 localities and on 70% of all counts. Maxima: Vancouver 26 Dec 1966-1,886; Victoria 1 Jan 1969-1,672; Duncan 19 Dec 1981-963.

Sandhill Crane

SACR

Grus canadensis (Linnaeus)

RANGE: Breeds from western and central Alaska, across the middle of the Canadian arctic to Hudson Bay and western Ontario south locally to northeastern California, Nevada, Wyoming, Colorado, South Dakota and Michigan; also in Siberia. Winters from the southern United States south to central Mexico. Resident populations from Mississippi to Georgia, southern Florida, and Cuba.

STATUS: On the coast, an *uncommon* to *common* migrant and *uncommon* to *fairly common* summer visitant. *Casual* winter visitant to the south coast. In the interior, an *uncommon* to very *abundant* migrant, *very rare* summer visitant to the north Okanagan valley, *fairly common* in the Chilcotin-Cariboo, and *rare* in the Peace River region. Local breeder.

NONBREEDING: The Sandhill Crane is widely distributed along the coast. In the interior, it occurs mainly in the central-southern portion of the province from the Okanagan valley northwest through the Fraser Plateau region. It is also found widely scattered throughout the Alberta Plateau and Fort Nelson Lowlands. It occurs from sea level to 1,510 m elevation.

Characteristics of nonbreeding habitat include an unobstructed view of surrounding areas and isolation from disturbance (Lovvorn and Kirkpatrick 1981). Roosting and feeding habitats include shallow wetlands such as margins of lakes (Fig. 70), marshes, swamps, bogs, ponds, meadows, estuarine marshes, and intertidal areas as well as dry uplands such as grasslands and agricultural fields. Wide alluvial islands, river banks, frozen waters, beaches, and airports are used less frequently. In the interior, flooded meadows and agricultural fields are almost ideal roost sites; the tendency to roost in shallow water likely provides protection from mammalian predators (T.H. Pogson pers. comm.).

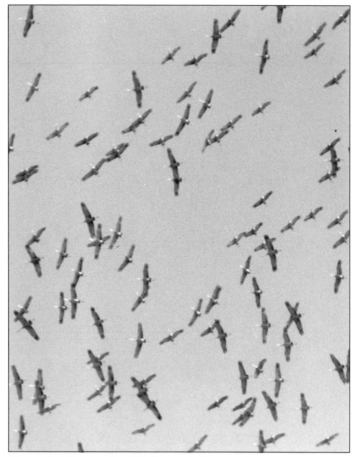

Figure 69. *Migrating Sandhill Cranes circling near Osoyoos, 28 April 1982 (Ervio Sian).*

Figure 70. *Small flock of migrating Sandhill Cranes resting at White Lake, Okanagan Falls, 23 April 1979 (Stephen R. Cannings).*

Sandhill Crane

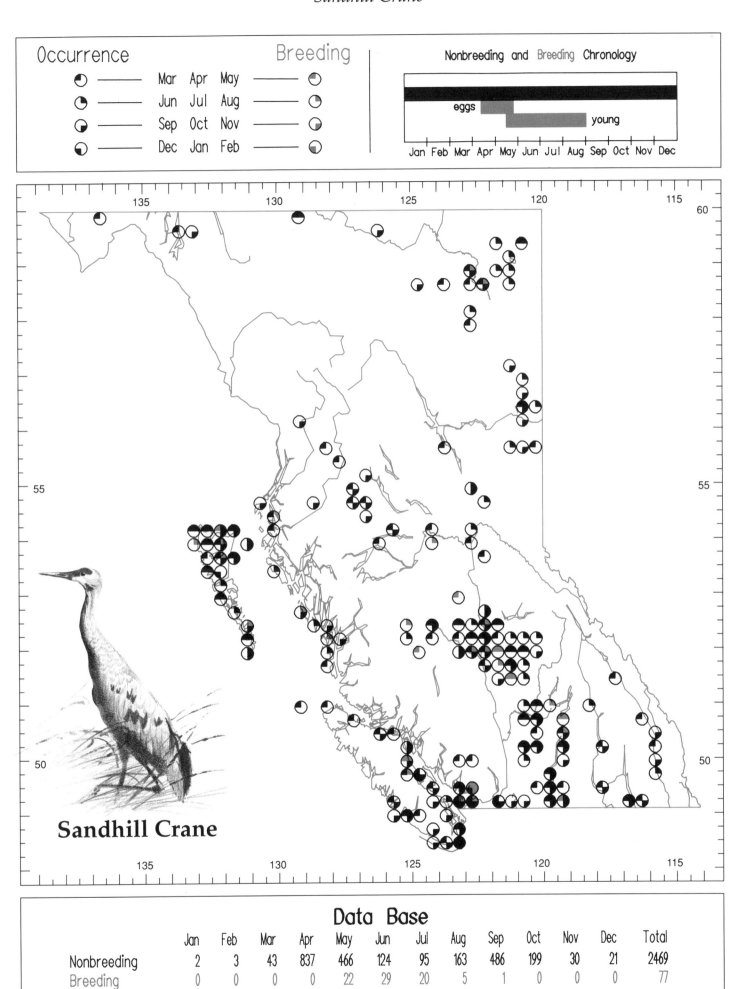

Occurrence

◐	———	Mar Apr May	——— ◐
◔	———	Jun Jul Aug	——— ◔
◕	———	Sep Oct Nov	——— ◔
◑	———	Dec Jan Feb	——— ◑

Breeding

Nonbreeding and Breeding Chronology

eggs

young

Jan Feb Mar Apr May Jun Jul Aug Sep Oct Nov Dec

Sandhill Crane

Data Base

	Jan	Feb	Mar	Apr	May	Jun	Jul	Aug	Sep	Oct	Nov	Dec	Total
Nonbreeding	2	3	43	837	466	124	95	163	486	199	30	21	2469
Breeding	0	0	0	0	22	29	20	5	1	0	0	0	77

The Sandhill Crane migrates mainly by day (Fig. 69); however, there are records of it migrating at night (Melvin and Temple 1982; Kessel 1984). Cranes migrating in favourable weather and within striking distance of a traditional stopover may opt to fly at night rather than land in an unfamiliar area (T.H. Pogson pers. comm.).

There are 3 known migration routes in British Columbia (Fig. 71), each of which is used in spring and autumn: coastal, central interior, and northeastern interior. See Remarks for a discussion of the subspecies using these routes. On the coast, at least 3,500 cranes pass over Cape Flattery, Washington, and enter British Columbia over Juan de Fuca Strait (see Mattocks 1985b). This count is

undoubtedly the best estimate of the number of cranes using the coastal migration route and surely includes all cranes nesting and summering on the coastal islands of British Columbia and southeast Alaska. (T. H. Pogson pers. comm.)

Evidence of a movement farther north along the coast has come from the Barkley Sound region, the east Courtenay area, Johnstone Strait, and the Goose Group. Early spring migrants may appear in February and early March but the main passage occurs in early April. The autumn movement is evident in September, peaks in October, and in some years carries into November. It is not spectacular, but occasionally flocks of 200+ birds are reported. Stopover areas change from year to year.

In the central interior, the route follows the Okanagan valley to Peachland, over Chapperon Lake, the Knutsford/Kamloops area, through the central Chilcotin-Cariboo, over the Fraser Plateau following the Bulkley and Kispiox valleys, probably the Nass River drainage, past the vicinity of Meziadin Lake, and into southeastern Alaska. Between 22,000 and 25,000 birds are thought to use that route (Littlefield and Thompson 1982; C.D. Littlefield pers. comm.). Spring migrants may arrive in the Okanagan valley in early March, but the main movement occurs during the latter half of April, and is usually over by mid-May. The autumn movement is more protracted, and may occur from August through October with the main passage from late September to early October. Flocks at this time may reach 5,000 cranes. Known stopover points include White Lake (Okanagan Falls; Fig. 70), Lac Le Jeune, Bechers Prairie west of Williams Lake, and the Kispiox valley north of Hazelton.

In the northeastern interior, the route generally passes over Fort Nelson and Liard Hot Springs. Kessel (1984) suggests that the birds, numbering between 150,000 and 200,000, enter British Columbia from the Peace River area of northwestern Alberta. We also have reports of large numbers of birds stopping at or passing over Nig Creek and Cecil Lake; we do not know whether these birds are part of the northeastern breeding population or part of the large movement of "Lesser" Sandhill Cranes from the Central Flyway. Spring migration occurs from late April to early May; the return movement occurs mainly during the second and third weeks of September. Birds have been known to stopover at Liard Hot Springs and Nig Creek.

In winter, small numbers have been found infrequently on the Queen Charlotte Islands, east-central and southern Vancouver Island, and the Fraser Lowlands.

BREEDING: On the coast, the Sandhill Crane breeds locally in the Fraser Lowlands (Pitt Meadows, Fort Langley), on islands along the central mainland coast, and on the Queen Charlotte Islands. In the interior, it breeds from the north Okanagan valley (Enderby), north through the Chilcotin-Cariboo region to the vicinity of Vanderhoof. Small numbers breed in the Fort Nelson Lowlands near Fort Nelson.

Breeding habitats include isolated bogs (Fig. 72), marshes, swamps, and meadows from near sea level to 1,220 m. On the Queen Charlotte Islands, one nest was found in the middle of a logging slash near the top of a mountain, and adults with young have been found deep in the mature Sitka spruce-western hemlock forests and on estuarine tidal meadows. This suggests that some family groups may leave their inland nesting sites for better foraging and rearing areas along the coast.

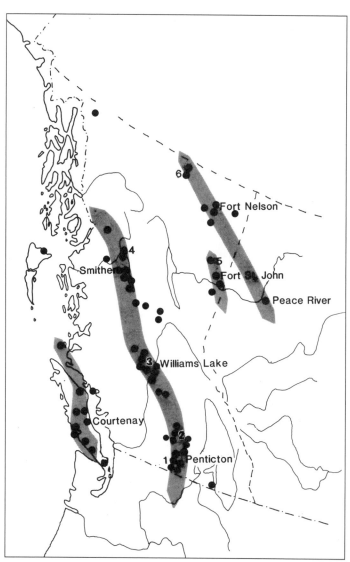

Figure 71. *Suggested migration routes of the Sandhill Crane through British Columbia based on observations of large flocks (>25 birds-coastal; >50 birds-interior). Closed circles indicate observation areas; numbers indicate known stopover points: 1 - White Lake (Okanagan Falls), 2 - Lac Le Jeune; 3 - Becher's Prairie (Alexis Creek), 4 Kispiox valley, 5 - Nig Creek, 6 - Liard Hot Springs. The route through Fort Nelson and Peace River, Alberta is the northeastern route suggested by Kessel (1984). Some of that population may swing south at Fort Nelson to move through the Nig Creek and Fort St. John areas.*

Nests: Nests (n=14) were situated on the ground (8%) or on water, usually among thick shrubs or emergent vegetation such as hardhack, sweet gale, willows, Labrador tea, bulrushes, or sedges (Fig. 74). Two nests ranged from 9 to 25 cm high by 0.9 to 1.5 m in diameter. Nesting material included grasses, bulrushes, sphagnum, hardhack branches, sedges, and leaves, and ranged from a few hardhack branches on dry ground to a large floating platform composed of bulrushes. Water depth beneath 3 floating nests ranged from 15 cm to 1.5 m.

Eggs: Dates for 20 clutches ranged from 2 May to 25 June with 10 recorded between 9 and 24 May. Calculated dates indicate that eggs could be found as early as 12 April. Clutch size ranged from 1 to 3 eggs (1E-2, 2E-16, 3E-1) with 84% having 2 eggs (Fig. 73). Dates from 2 nests in British Columbia suggest an incubation period of 33 to 34 days, more than the 30 to 32 days reported by Walkinshaw (1981), or the 28 days reported by Boise (1977).

Young: Dates for 47 broods ranged from 15 May to 1 September with 57% recorded between 15 June and 15 July. Sizes of 46 broods ranged from 1 to 2 young (1Y-33, 2Y-13) with 72% of the broods having 1 young. Fledging period is about 70 days (Walkinshaw 1949).

Figure 72. *Sandhill Crane flying over nest site in muskeg near Puntchesacut Lake, west of Quesnel, 28 May 1944 (James A. Munro).*

Figure 73. *Nest and eggs of Sandhill Crane near Puntchesacut Lake, 28 May 1944 (James A. Munro).*

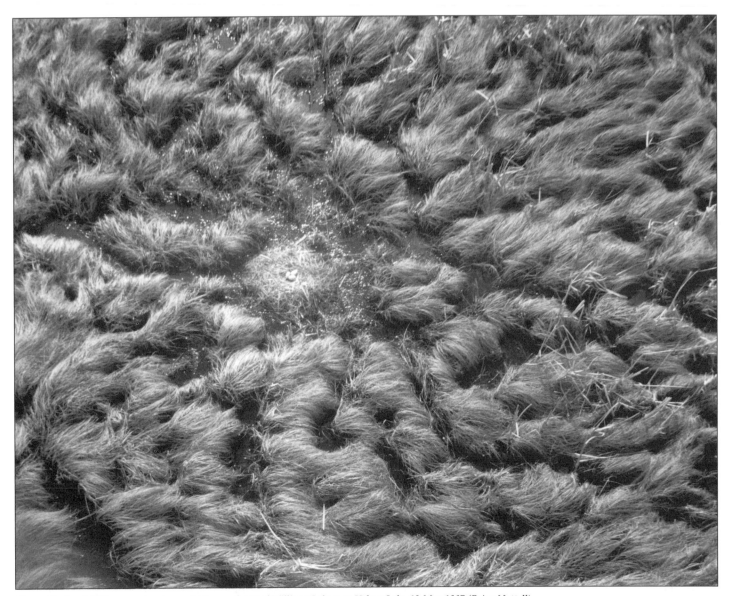

Figure 74. *Sandhill Crane nest and eggs, 50 km southeast of Williams Lake near Helena Lake, 12 May 1987 (Brian Nuttall).*

REMARKS: The Sandhill Crane (Fig. 75) formerly bred in the south Okanagan valley (Osoyoos) and on the south coast (Sumas Prairie, Ladner, Vancouver Island). At the time J.A. Munro and Cowan (1947) was published, the known south coast population was restricted to Lulu Island and Vancouver Island. Pitt Meadows was considered a former nesting area This breeding population now appears restricted to the Pitt Meadows area and one site near Fort Langley. The last Lulu Island breeding record was July 1946, and breeding birds have not been found on Vancouver Island since June 1941. Birds have recently been found nesting in the Shuswap drainage at Mara Meadows near Enderby, and a small breeding population has been found near Fort Nelson.

Based on culmen measurements of Sandhill Crane specimens from British Columbia (see Johnson, D.H. and Stewart 1983), 3 subspecies appear to occur in the province (Fig. 76): *G. c. canadensis, G. c. rowani,* and *G. c. tabida.*

The Lesser Sandhill Crane (*G. c. canadensis*), is described by J.A. Munro and Cowan (1947) as a transient chiefly throughout the interior with the main spring flight arriving about the time the breeding population has begun nesting. This is supported by our data. Two populations of "lessers" are known to occur in the province. The Pacific Flyway Population contains 2 segments. The western segment, between 1,400 (Littlefield and Thompson 1982) and 2,000 (T. Pogson pers. comm.) birds, migrates west of the Cascade-Sierra axis and along coastal British Columbia. The eastern segment corresponds to the large movement of lessers through the central interior of the province. They winter in the Central Valley of California and the vast majority likely nest and summer in the Bristol Bay region of southwest Alaska (T. Pogson pers. comm.), representing a population distinct from the much larger population of the Central Flyway. A portion of the Central Flyway Population (about half of North America's Lesser Sandhill Cranes) migrates through northeastern British Columbia to and from breeding grounds in western Alaska and Siberia.

Little is known of the migration, taxonomy, distribution, or populations of cranes nesting in British Columbia; migration patterns are obscured by movements of the more abundant Lesser Sandhill Crane. J.A. Munro and Cowan (1947) describe the Greater Sandhill Crane, *G. c. tabida,* as the summer visitant and breeding bird in the province. However, Littlefield and Thompson (1979) suggest that cranes nesting "near Prince George and west to the coast" are *G. c. rowani.*

About 5,300 Greater Sandhill Cranes winter in the Central Valley of California. C.D. Littlefield (pers. comm.) estimates that, during the nesting season, 3,400 of these birds are in California and Oregon. He cannot account for the other 1,900 cranes and believes there may be at least 1,900 "greaters" that summer in British Columbia. All 8 track measurements of cranes from the Chilcotin Plateau taken in April 1979 were longer than 115 mm suggesting that these birds belonged to the subspecies *tabida* (see Drewien and Bizeau 1974).

Virtually nothing is known about populations of Canadian Sandhill Cranes, *G. c. rowani,* in the province. Littlefield and Thompson (1979) mention 327 "large cranes" among 1,100 lessers on Sauvie's Island, Oregon, and suggest they might have been *rowani.* Thus, if there are up to 2,000 lessers using the coastal migration route, there could be as many as 1,500 larger birds (*rowani*) summering along the coast of British Columbia, based on the 3,500 cranes counted passing Cape Flattery (see Non-breeding). This is supported by the culmen measurements of birds from the Queen Charlotte Islands; they are more intermediate *(rowani)* than they are greater *(tabida).* In addition, 2 of the 3 specimens from the Fraser Lowlands also appear to be *rowani.* T. Pogson (pers. comm.) notes:

> It seems likely the cranes from coastal British Columbia and southeast Alaska are not the 'lessers' which use the western migration route, but an 'unrecognized population' nesting in coastal marshes and muskegs which probably migrate [with the lessers] and winter together.

We have no further information on subspecies of the birds that breed in the Boreal Forest region of the northeast. It is possible that the birds in the northern portion of their range are "mid-way" between *tabida* and *rowani* (T. Pogson pers. comm.). Whatever the subspecies, all existing evidence (Tacha et al. 1984; Kessel 1984) suggests that the northeastern breeding population migrates through the Great Plains and winters in New Mexico and Texas.

Because of concern for remaining breeding populations on the southwest mainland coast, 17 Sandhill Cranes obtained as eggs from the Rocky Mountain population of *G. c. tabida* at Grays Lake, Idaho, were hatched and subsequently released in 1981 near Pitt Meadows. The success of that project is not known. However, if the birds summering along coastal British Columbia are of the subspecies *rowani,* the wrong subspecies may have been released in the Pitt Meadows area.

See Boise (1977), Melvin and Temple (1982), and Walkinshaw (1949) for additional information on the migration ecology, breeding biology, and general life history of the Sandhill Crane in western North America.

Figure 75. *Adult Sandhill Crane being harrassed by a Red-winged Blackbird* (Agelaius phoeniceus) *near Williams Lake, 12 June 1984 (Ervio Sian). The migration, taxonomy, and distribution of the 3 subspecies that occur in British Columbia are not well known (see Remarks).*

Sandhill Crane

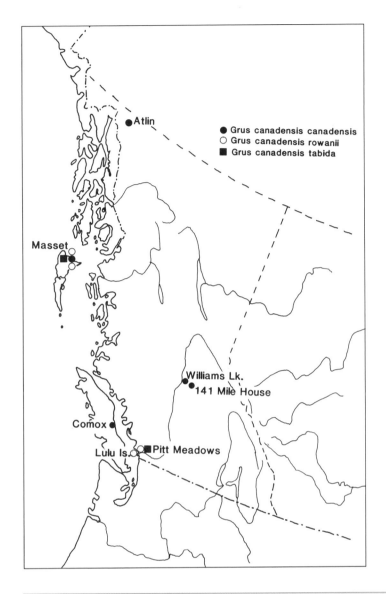

Figure 76. *Distribution of Sandhill Crane subspecies in British Columbia based on exposed culmen measurements of museum specimens.*

NOTEWORTHY RECORDS

Spring: Coastal - Saanich 1 Apr 1975-1; Sidney 9 May 1962-2; Sarita River 10 Apr 1982-150; Delta 1 Mar 1973-4; Pitt Meadows 18 Mar 1982-8; Salmon River (Sayward) 10 Apr 1975-200; Port Neville 8 Apr 1986-80+, 12 Apr 1986-25; Hardy Bay 27 to 30 Apr 1951-1; Triangle Island (Scott Islands) 22 Apr 1987-2; Delkatla Inlet 8 Apr 1980-2, 25 Apr 1972-14. **Interior** - Creston 31 May 1982-100; Oliver 24 Apr 1978-5,000; White Lake (Okanagan Falls) 9 Apr 1976-650, 19 Apr 1978-2,017, 20 Apr 1978-4,531; Summerland 12 Mar 1974-12, 23 Apr 1968-600; Douglas Lake (Quilchena) 28 Mar 1981-1; Nakusp 30 Mar 1979-15, 16 Apr 1983-120; Lac Le Jeune 22 Apr 1986-1,300 to 1,500; Lac la Hache 8 Apr 1981-2; Alexis Creek 24 Apr 1983-200; Smithers 18 Apr 1966-75, 24 Apr 1977-1,250; Hazelton 24 Apr 1980-2,100; Fort St. John 5 May 1985-4; Fort Nelson 25 Apr 1986-several, 27 Apr 1975-100 to 200; nw Fort Nelson 4 May 1975-1,500; Atlin 9 May 1935-1 female (RBCM 5981).

Summer: Coastal - Trial Islands 11 Aug 1953-2; Saanich 31 Aug 1970-8; Barkley Sound 15 Aug 1968-3; Nanaimo 8 Aug 1976-20; Ladner 9 Aug 1967-19; Deas Slough 1 Jul 1981-13, 8 Aug 1978-8 adults, 2 juveniles; Pitt Meadows 23 Jul 1974-15 (Robinson 1974); Campbell River 8 Jul 1976-3; Goose Group 15 Aug 1948-sizeable flock; Porcher Island 8 Aug 1977-2; Rose Spit 17 Aug 1987-13. **Interior** - Osoyoos 31 Aug 1973-2 flocks; Duck Lake (Creston) Jul 1979-1; Summerland 27 Aug 1970-10; Fort Steele 23 Aug 1981-3; Red Lake 1 to 31 Jul 1983-1 pair; Nukko Lake 8 Aug 1982-14; Boundary Lake (Goodlow) 14 Jun 1985-2; Clarke Lake 3 Jul 1986-2; Helmet (Kwokullie Lake) 1 to 5 Jun 1982-2; se Cormier Creek 14 May 1981-2.

Autumn: Interior - Wright Creek (Atlin) 12 Oct 1980-500; Liard Hot Springs 5 Sep 1974-large flock, 17 Sep 1985-2,951 on old airfield; Fort Nelson 6 to 17 Sep 1986-tens of thousands, peak passage with flocks of 200 to 500 passing SE constantly, 16 Oct 1986-5, last record of fall; Nig Creek 15 Sep 1984-500 to 650 (RBCM Photo 938); Cecil Lake 19 Sep 1985-2,000; Meziadin Lake 12 Sep 1979-240; Barren Creek 20 Sep 1980-800; Bechers Prairie (Riske Creek) 21 Sep 1978-1,000; Minton Creek (Hanceville) 13 Sep 1986-165; Kamloops 16 Nov 1982-50; Separation Lake 1 Oct 1951-350; Vernon 13 Oct 1963-1,000; Skookumchuk 20 Sep 1946-6 (Johnstone, W.B. 1949); Nakusp 23 Oct 1976-65; Chapperon Lake 15 Sep 1985-2,000 to 3,000; Summerland 12 Oct 1967-600; Syringa Creek 6 Sep 1979-1; Osoyoos 17 Nov 1979-2. **Coastal** - Masset 3 Oct 1971-1; Sewall 7 Oct 1975-4; Goose Group 15 Aug 1948-sizeable flock; Cape St. James 15 Oct 1978-1; Port Neville 30 Sep 1976-29, 30 Sep 1986-35, 27 Oct 1975-21; Johnstone Strait 19 Sep 1984-130 in 5 flocks; Campbell River 1 Nov 1972-1; Errington 14 Sep 1986-37; Comox 23 Nov 1947-1 female (RBCM 12664); Nanaimo 8 Aug 1976-20; Pitt Meadows 28 Oct 1974-1; Delta 22 Sep 1986-25, 13 Oct 1984-30; Saanich 26 Nov 1984-1.

Winter: Interior - No records. **Coastal** - Skidegate Inlet 3 Feb 1983-2 adults; Pitt Meadows 8 Dec 1985-3, 17 Feb 1980-1; Delta 28 Nov 1980 to 31 Mar 1981-4, 23 Dec 1984-2; Chilliwack 4 Jan 1987-1; Saanich 13 Nov 1974 to 12 Apr 1975-1 (RBCM Photo 377; Hosford 1975).

Christmas Counts: Interior - Not recorded. **Coastal** - Recorded from 4 of 28 localities and on 2% of all counts. Maxima: Ladner 28 Dec 1980-4, all-time Canadian high count (Anderson, R.R. 1981); Comox 21 Dec 1975-1; Chilliwack 15 Dec 1984-1; Victoria 21 Dec 1974-1.

Black-bellied Plover
Pluvialis squatarola (Linnaeus)

BBPL

RANGE: Virtually cosmopolitan. Breeds in northern Canada, Alaska, and northern Siberia. North American birds winter on the Pacific coast from southeastern Alaska to Chile and on the Atlantic coast from New England to Brazil.

STATUS: *Fairly common* to locally *very abundant* migrant on the coast. *Casual* spring migrant and *very rare* to locally *uncommon* autumn migrant in the interior. *Fairly common* to locally *abundant* winter visitant on the coast.

OCCURRENCE: The Black-bellied Plover is widely distributed along the coast of British Columbia and through the valleys of the southern interior; it is sporadic elsewhere. It generally occurs in flocks of 10 to 60 birds, but at favourite staging areas it occurs in aggregations of several thousand (Fig. 77). It may associate with other medium-sized shorebirds such as turnstones and Lesser Golden-Plovers.

On the south coast, large numbers gather during migration at shorebird staging areas, especially Boundary Bay. Fairly large numbers winter on the Fraser River delta and in the Victoria area. Migrants and winter visitants are much less numerous on the outer coast, where plover habitat is limited, although Hatler et al. (1978) describe them as common fall transients at Tofino. Rose Spit is the only locality on the north coast where concentrations have been reported. In the interior, most Black-bellied Plover sightings are of single birds in autumn. Spring migrants are exceptional everywhere in the interior except in the Peace Lowlands where there have been several records in recent years from Charlie Lake and the sewage ponds at Fort St. John.

The Black-bellied Plover frequents several coastal habitats including tidal mudflats, sandy beaches, rocky islets, rocky beaches, short-grass uplands, and man-made habitats such as farmlands and golf courses. The tidal mudflats of Boundary Bay attract the largest numbers. There it forages at low tide on exposed mud and roosts during high tide on nearby fields, beached logs, and spits. In autumn and winter, the Oak Bay golf course consistently attracts the largest concentrations of Black-bellied Plovers on Vancouver Island. Surprisingly few plovers frequent the muddy tidal flats at Witty's Lagoon, whereas several hundred often occur on the gravelly beaches of Esquimalt Lagoon.

In the interior, the Black-bellied Plover frequents lowland short-grass areas such as agricultural fields and airfields, as well as the beaches, gravelly shores and mudflats of sloughs, lakes, and sewage ponds. It may occasionally appear at high-altitude lakes during the autumn migration. The sewage lagoons at Fort St. John and the south end of Swan Lake (Vernon) are the 2 interior localities where the Black-bellied Plover is most frequently reported.

Spring migrants arrive on the south coast in force in mid-April. The main northward movement continues until mid-May and is over by late May. All interior spring records are from May. Stragglers and small flocks of nonbreeders occur on the coast in June and July, but occasionally flocks of up to 1,000, likely early autumn migrants, have been reported in late June. The longer autumn movement begins in July and continues through October, peaking in August and September. Relatively few autumn migrants are reported on the coast north of Comox. Large numbers are found on the Fraser River delta and on southern Vancouver Island. Most autumn migrants move through the interior in September and October, rarely in July, August, or November. Wintering Black-bellied Plovers may occur anywhere on the coast but are most abundant along the southern Strait of Georgia. There are no interior winter records.

REMARKS: The Black-bellied Plover is referred to as the Grey Plover in Johnsgard (1981) and Hayman et al. (1986).

Figure 77. Black-bellied Plovers at Boundary Bay, Delta, 24 April 1971 (R. Wayne Campbell).

NOTEWORTHY RECORDS

Spring: Coastal - Esquimalt Lagoon 20 Apr 1982-350; Chesterman Beach 29 Apr 1969-100+ (Hatler et al. 1978); Boundary Bay 29 Apr 1978-2,010; Mud Bay 24 Apr 1985-5,000, 27 May 1982-250; Comox Harbour to Deep Bay 17 Apr 1981-75 on census; Campbell River (Discovery Passage) 30 Mar 1973-25; Kitimat 21 May 1980-2; Rose Spit 28 Apr 1979-314. **Interior** - Okanagan Landing 24 May 1932-1 (MVZ 100846); Ootsa Lake 17 May 1987-1; Rolla 29 May 1954-1 (NMC 47757); Fort St. John 11 May 1983-1 (first of year), 18 May 1980-1 (first of year), 19 May 1986-1 in winter plumage.

Summer: Coastal - Victoria 19 Jul 1973-35; Boundary Bay 22 Jun 1974-1,000, 11 Aug 1974-5,000 (Crowell and Nehls 1974d), 21 Aug 1978-2,500; Blackie Spit 8 Jul 1979-100; Roberts Bank 10 Jun 1981-90; Goose Group 7 Jun 1948-1 (RBCM 9844); Tlell 18 Jul 1983-1. **Interior** - Wasa 31 Jul 1977-5 (Fitz-Gibbon 1977); Murtle Lake (Blue River) Aug 1959-1; Bowron Lake 18 Aug 1975-1 (Bell 1975); Fort St. John 6 Jun 1983-2 (latest departure), 28 Jul 1983-1 (first arrival), 15 Aug 1986-34, mostly in breeding plumage.

Autumn: Interior - Atlin 1 Oct 1933-1 (RBCM 5796); Fort St. John 22 Sep 1986-21, 10 to 21 Oct 1986-1; Babine Lake 9 Sep 1937-1 (RBCM 7841); Chilco Ranch (Hanceville) 24 Sep 1986-11; Revelstoke airport 21 Sep 1977-20 (Bonar 1978a); Salmon Arm 26 Sep 1970-8+ (Stevens et al. 1970); Kamloops 5 to 18 Sep 1983-2, 28 Sep 1980-15, 30 Sep to 4 Oct 1984-4; Nakusp 10 Sep to 7 Oct 1985-1 to 22 (peaked 22 Sep); Castlegar 2 Nov 1973-1. **Coastal** - Green Island 13 Nov 1977-1 (last of year); Sandspit 17 Sep 1979-14; Union Bay (Comox) 8 Nov 1987-300; Comox Harbour to Deep Bay 19 Sep 1981-706 on census; Boundary Bay 6 Sep 1971-4,000 (Crowell and Nehls 1972a), 22 Oct 1978-595; Chesterman Beach 24 Oct 1983-35; Victoria Int. Airport 5 Nov 1984-300; Oak Bay 30 Nov 1981-300+.

Winter: Interior - No records. **Coastal** - Tlell River 11 Feb 1972-6; Cape St. James 14 Dec 1978-14; Parksville 7 Feb 1981-18; Chesterman Beach 23 Dec 1987-10; Roberts Bank 31 Jan 1982-275; Boundary Bay 1 Dec 1978-1,000+; Patricia Bay 7 Feb 1981-220; Oak Bay 10 Jan 1982-700+.

Christmas Counts: Interior - Not recorded. **Coastal** - Recorded from 13 of 28 localities and on 41% of all counts. Maxima: Ladner 27 Dec 1981-727, all-time Canadian high count (Anderson, R.R. 1982); Victoria 20 Dec 1980-266; Comox 16 Dec 1984-194.

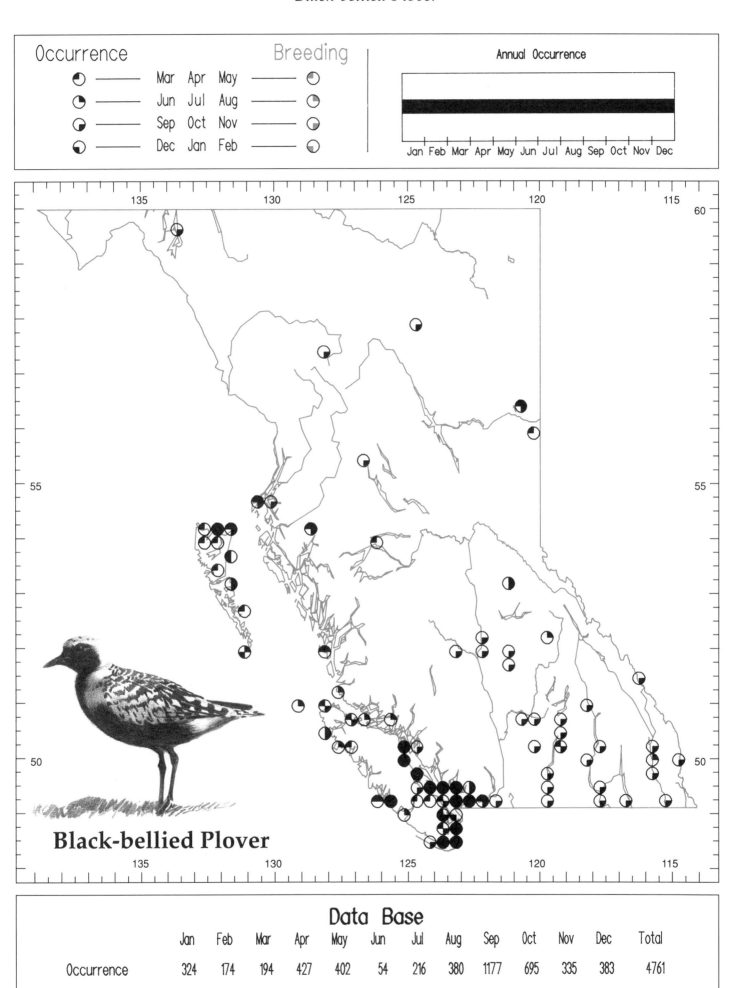

Occurrence   Breeding

◑	——	Mar	Apr	May	——	◔
◔	——	Jun	Jul	Aug	——	◔
◕	——	Sep	Oct	Nov	——	◐
◑	——	Dec	Jan	Feb	——	◔

Annual Occurrence

Jan Feb Mar Apr May Jun Jul Aug Sep Oct Nov Dec

Black-bellied Plover

Data Base

	Jan	Feb	Mar	Apr	May	Jun	Jul	Aug	Sep	Oct	Nov	Dec	Total
Occurrence	324	174	194	427	402	54	216	380	1177	695	335	383	4761

Lesser Golden-Plover

LGPL

Pluvialis dominica (Müller)

RANGE: Nearly circumpolar. Breeds in northern Canada, Alaska, and northern Siberia. Winters in South America and on coasts and islands of the central and western Pacific and Indian oceans.

STATUS: *Very rare* to *rare* spring migrant throughout the province; *rare* to *uncommon* autumn migrant. Locally *rare* summer visitant to alpine plateaus in the northwestern part of the province. *Casual* in winter on the southwest coast. Breeds.

NONBREEDING: The Lesser Golden-Plover has a scattered distribution throughout the province. Most records are of single birds; sightings of 6 or more are exceptional. Larger numbers usually occur only at shorebird staging areas such as Iona Island, Sea Island, Boundary Bay, Salmon Arm, Swan Lake (Vernon), and in the vicinity of Fort St. John in the Peace Lowlands.

The Lesser Golden-Plover frequents habitats similar to those used by the Black-bellied Plover. Inland, it prefers short-grass fields such as playing fields, golf courses, air fields, and flooded pastures as well as slough edges and lake shores. In the Fort St. John area, the plover frequents newly-burned fields far more than other habitat types. On the coast, it uses lagoon shores, sandspits, tidal mudflats, and rocky beaches, although it is most often reported from adjacent uplands. Man-made habitats such as newly ploughed fields, sewage ponds, and lawns are often used as foraging sites.

The weak spring movement occurs mainly in May, with a few early migrants arriving in March or April. Spring migrants are very rare in the interior, except in the Peace Lowlands, although in 1957, Weeden (1960) considered the Lesser Golden-Plover a common spring migrant in the Chilkat Pass area. The much stronger autumn movement begins in late July but does not peak until September when the juveniles pass through. Coastal stragglers occur through mid-November. There are only 7 winter records, 6 of which are from the Fraser River estuary.

BREEDING: There is only one confirmed breeding record for British Columbia: downy young were observed and photographed near Kliweguh Creek, Spatsizi Plateau, on 21 July 1959 (Guiguet 1960a). Guiguet reports that 6 pairs were nesting in an area with very sparse ground cover on top of the plateau above 1,800 m. He notes that a downy young was collected to document breeding, but that specimen has since been lost. At least 2 other small groups of 'breeding' birds were seen in the area, including a downy young on 15 July 1959. Godfrey (1986) cites Guiguet's record and also includes the mountainous regions between Spatsizi Plateau and the Yukon border in the bird's breeding range. See also Remarks. Incubation period is 26 to 27 days (Jehl and Smith 1970) and young are able to fly at about 22 days of age (Johnsgard 1981).

REMARKS: The Lesser Golden-Plover was formerly called the American Golden Plover. Two races, *P. d. fulva* and *P. d. dominica*, occur in British Columbia. Breeding birds and most inland sightings are probably *P. d. dominica* (Munro, J.A. and Cowan 1947; Godfrey 1986; Table 4) although *P. d. fulva* has now been reported from the interior (Cannings, R.A. et al. 1987). On the coast, both forms occur in migration (Munro, J.A. and Cowan 1947). In California, the coastal situation is similar, but winter records there seem to be of *P. d. fulva* (Chaniot 1966), and that might be true for British Columbia also. Recently, some authors have considered these races as full species, *P. fulva* and *P. dominica* (Connors 1983; Hayman et al. 1986). Observers are encouraged to report subspecies when possible; see Hayman et al. (1986) and National Geographic Society (1983) for subspecies determination in the field.

We have 2 records on file that indicate probable breeding by the Lesser Golden-Plover. On 3 July 1976, Osmond-Jones et al. (1977) observed several pairs of golden-plovers in tundra near Black Fox Creek, Spatsizi Plateau, and on 14 June 1986, a pair of golden-plovers was photographed (RBCM Photo 1131) on the Corkscrew plateau at the head of Corkscrew Creek in the Itcha Range. The dates and the activities of the birds suggested breeding. The latter record, if documented, would extend the breeding range of the Lesser Golden-Plover some 600 km south in the province.

TABLE 4.

Examination of specimens (n=25) of the Lesser Golden-Plover for races of *Pluvialis dominica dominica* and *P. d. fulva* in British Columbia.

Region	Month			
	May	September	October	November
Coastal				
P. d. dominica	1m; 1f[1]	3m; 2f	3m; 2f	0
P. d. fulva	0	0	2f	2m; 1f
Interior				
P. d. dominica	0	2m; 4f	2f	0
P. d. fulva	0	0	0	0
Total specimens	2	11	9	3

[1] m-male; f-female; all specimens were juveniles except for 2 adults collected in May.

NOTEWORTHY RECORDS

Spring: Coastal - Oak Bay 4 Mar 1979-1; Iona Island 14 May 1980-5; Vancouver 31 Mar 1974-4; Masset 25 Apr 1942-1 (UMMZ 123234), 6 May 1947-5; Delkatla Creek 7 May 1987-10. **Interior** - Edgewater 11 May 1980-1; Shuswap Falls 29 May 1918-1 (MVZ 100519); Springhouse 30 Apr 1951-1 (NMC 47755); Prince George 26 Apr 1981-1; Fort St. John 11 May 1981-160+ (RBCM Photo 764), 30 May 1983-1 last; Cecil Lake 8 May 1980-1 earliest; Fort Nelson airport 14 May 1982-9 (RBCM Photo 981); Atlin 4 May 1932-2 (RBCM 5793, 5794); Chilkat Pass 19 May 1957-19, two of which were copulating (Weeden 1960).

Summer: Coastal - Oak Bay 10 Jun 1982-1; Long Beach 20 Aug 1978-3; Cleland Island 15 Jul 1978-1; Sea Island 24 Aug 1964-7; Goose Group 6 Jun 1948-5 (Guiguet 1953a); Sandspit 10 Aug 1985-35; Rose Spit 21 Jul 1946-1 (UBC 1908).

Interior - Okanagan Landing 26 Jul 1922-1 (MVZ 100516); Adams River mouth 27 Aug 1973-1 adult (Sirk et al. 1973); Bowron Lake 18 Aug 1975-1 (Bell 1975); Fort St. John 18 Jul 1985-1, 20 Aug 1985-2 (subspecies *dominica*); Mount Edziza 23 Jul 1982-1.

Autumn: Interior - Fort St. John 2 Sep 1985-1, 14, Sep 1986-15 juveniles, 2 Oct 1982-1 last; Prince George 11 Sep 1970-1 (RBCM Photo 71); Williams Lake 4 Oct 1986-4, 12 Oct 1972-1; 103 Mile Lake 11 Oct 1959-1 (Erskine and Stein 1964); Tranquille 7 Sep 1985-10, 30 Sep 1984-10, 2 Nov 1986-1; Salmon Arm 18 Sep 1970-12 (Schnider et al. 1971); Swan Lake (Vernon) 15 Sep 1962-12, 7 Oct 1984-3, 2 *P. d. dominica*, 1 *P. d. fulva* (Cannings, R.A. et al. 1987); Nakusp 15 to 20 Sep 1965-20 (Rogers, T.H. 1966a); Sinclair Pass 26 Sep 1965-1 (Rogers, T.H. 1966a).

Coastal - Masset 17 Oct 1971-19, 9 Nov 1944-1 (RBCM 10613); Green Island 2 Oct 1977-6; Stubbs Island 6 Sep 1987-3; Sea Island 16 Sep 1972-208 (Crowell and Nehls 1973a), 21 Sep 1965-135, 5 Oct 1965-35; Boundary Bay 11 Oct 1971-35 (Campbell et al. 1972b), 20 Oct 1968-68; Oak Bay 18 Nov 1978-1 (last of year).

Winter: Interior - No records. **Coastal** - Lulu Island 4 Jan 1941-2; Reifel Island 25 Jan 1973-1; Iona Island 14 Feb 1968-1.

Christmas Counts: Interior - Not recorded. **Coastal:** Recorded from 2 of 28 localities and on less than 1% of all counts. Maxima: Comox 22 Dec 1974-19, all-time Canadian high count (Anderson, R.R. 1976); Ladner 2 Jan 1966-2.

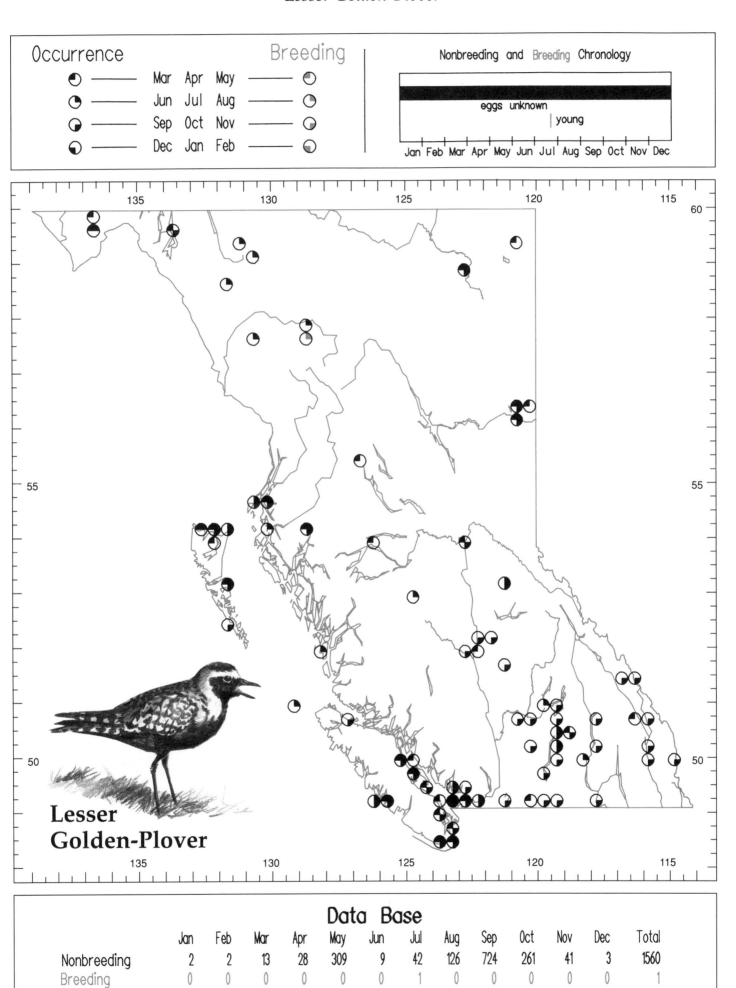

Occurrence / Breeding

Occurrence		Breeding
◐ ——	Mar Apr May	—— ◑
◔ ——	Jun Jul Aug	—— ◔
◕ ——	Sep Oct Nov	—— ◕
◑ ——	Dec Jan Feb	—— ◒

Nonbreeding and Breeding Chronology

eggs unknown
| young

Jan Feb Mar Apr May Jun Jul Aug Sep Oct Nov Dec

Lesser Golden-Plover

Data Base

	Jan	Feb	Mar	Apr	May	Jun	Jul	Aug	Sep	Oct	Nov	Dec	Total
Nonbreeding	2	2	13	28	309	9	42	126	724	261	41	3	1560
Breeding	0	0	0	0	0	0	1	0	0	0	0	0	1

Snowy Plover
Charadrius alexandrinus Linnaeus

SNPL

RANGE: In North America breeds along the Pacific coast from southern Washington south to Baja California and on Gulf coast from Mexico to Florida; also locally in interior Oregon, California, Nevada, Utah, New Mexico, Kansas, Oklahoma, and Texas. Winters in North America in coastal areas from northern Oregon and the Gulf coast south to southern Mexico. Also found worldwide.

STATUS: *Very rare* spring and summer visitant on the south coast; *accidental* on the Queen Charlotte Islands.

OCCURRENCE: The Snowy Plover has been recorded from the Fraser Lowlands, central west coast of Vancouver Island, and the Queen Charlotte Islands. It inhabits hard, sandy or gravel coastal beaches as well as shores of sewage lagoons.

The Snowy Plover was first recorded in British Columbia in 1972 (Poynter 1972). Over the next 14 years, it was found in 5 different years; the observations range from 29 April to 17 July. Three birds is the maximum number recorded from one location.

All records, listed in chronological order, are as follows:

(1) Long Beach (Vancouver Island) 29 April and 6 May 1972-1 bird reported independently by two groups of observers near Comber's Resort. It was seen with migrating Semipalmated Plovers, Western Sandpipers, and Sanderlings (Crowell and Nehls 1972d; Poynter 1972).

(2) Denman Island 28 May 1972-1 (Crowell and Nehls 1972d).
(3) Chesterman Beach (Tofino) 17 July 1973-1 immature (Ward 1973).
(4) Sandspit 12 July 1980-1 on a gravel beach with Semipalmated Plovers (RBCM Photo 724).
(5) Chesterman Beach 2 to 5 June 1981-1 adult with a Semipalmated Plover and two Western Sandpipers. On 4 June good photographs were taken (RBCM Photo 697), one of which includes an adult Semipalmated Plover for comparison.
(6) Iona Island 31 May 1985-1 (RBCM Photo 1055; Mattocks 1985b).
(7) Chesterman Beach 7, 13, and 15 June 1986-1 to 3 birds (Fig. 78). Two birds were photographed together on 7 June (RBCM Photo 1092).

REMARKS: Known in the Old World as Kentish Plover.

Wilson-Jacobs and Meslow (1984) provide a useful summary of current populations and nesting biology of the Snowy Plover in Oregon.

POSTSCRIPT: On 13 May 1989 an adult male was photographed (RBCM Photo 1240; Fig. 79) at the mouth of the Little Qualicum River.

Figure 78. Snowy Plover at Chesterman Beach, Vancouver Island, 7 June 1986 (Adrian Dorst).

Figure 79. Snowy Plover on sand flats at the Little Qualicum River estuary, Vancouver Island, 13 May 1989 (RBCM Photo 1240; Edward L. Nygren).

Snowy Plover

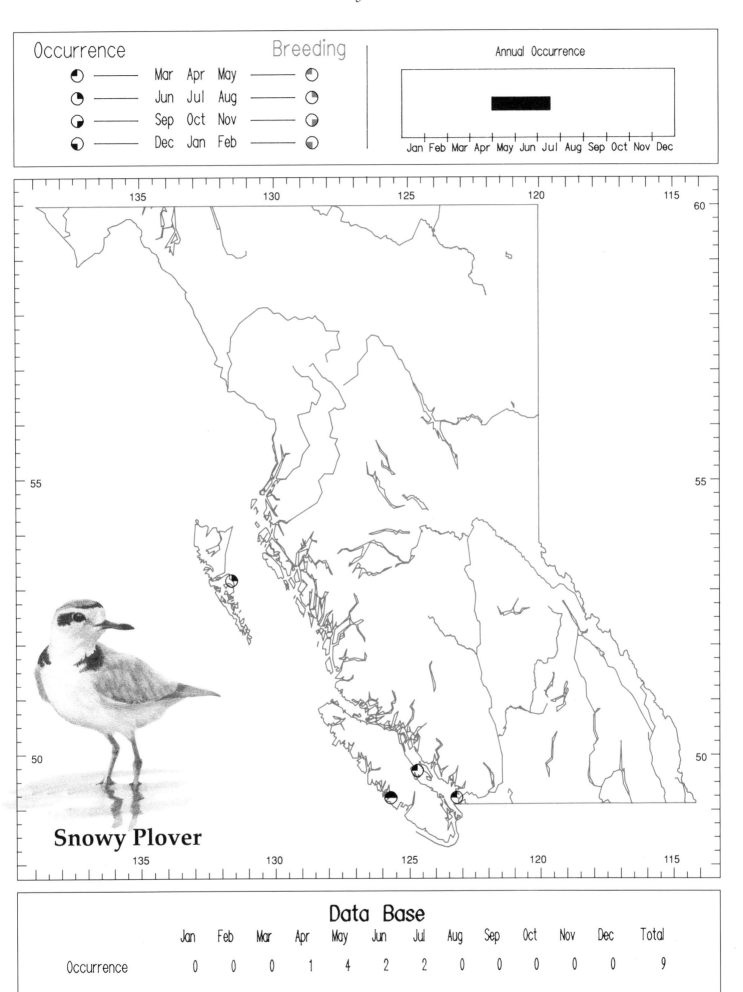

Occurrence

	Breeding
◑ —— Mar Apr May —— ◐	
◔ —— Jun Jul Aug —— ◑	
◕ —— Sep Oct Nov —— ◒	
◖ —— Dec Jan Feb —— ◒	

Annual Occurrence

Jan Feb Mar Apr May Jun Jul Aug Sep Oct Nov Dec

Snowy Plover

Data Base

	Jan	Feb	Mar	Apr	May	Jun	Jul	Aug	Sep	Oct	Nov	Dec	Total
Occurrence	0	0	0	1	4	2	2	0	0	0	0	0	9

Semipalmated Plover
Charadrius semipalmatus Bonaparte

RANGE: Breeds from Alaska eastward across most of northern Canada, except the high Arctic islands, along the Hudson Bay coast, and south through the Maritimes; also very locally on the British Columbia coast south to Vancouver. Winters from central California and South Carolina to southern South America.

STATUS: *Uncommon* to locally *abundant* migrant and summer visitant on the coast. Locally *common* to *very common* migrant in the interior; *fairly common* summer visitant in the Northern Mountains. *Very rare* in winter on the coast. Breeds.

NONBREEDING: The Semipalmated Plover occurs throughout the province. It is far more abundant on the coast than in the interior, where it is scarce in the south. The Semipalmated Plover frequents tidal mudflats, sandy and gravel beaches, small estuaries, and, less commonly, rocky beaches. Major staging areas are the extensive sandy beaches of Long Beach and McIntyre Bay, and the tidal mudflats of the Fraser River delta. In the interior, it frequents exposed shores of sloughs, alkaline ponds, sandy flats along river banks, flooded fields, sewage lagoons, and in alpine areas, melt-water ponds, tundra swamps, and gravel moraines. During the autumn movement it may frequent high mountain lakes.

Spring migration begins on the coast in early April and peaks in late April and early May. Flocks generally number 10 to 50 birds but aggregations of up to 2,000 may occur at major staging areas. By mid-May, migrants have left the south coast except for a few stragglers on the west coast of Vancouver Island. The interior spring movement is quite weak and sporadic, beginning in late April and ending in late May. Highest numbers occur in the Peace Lowlands.

The autumn migration begins in mid-July. On the Queen Charlotte Islands the Semipalmated Plover begins to form small flocks on their breeding beaches in mid-to-late July. The coastal autumn movement continues strongly through August, tapers off in September, and ends in October. The autumn movement in the interior begins in late July and peaks in late August; after mid-September only scattered individuals are present. A few stragglers can be found on the south coast in November, and very few winter in the Strait of Georgia and on Vancouver Island.

BREEDING: The Semipalmated Plover breeds throughout the Northern Mountains and Plateaus and the Chilkat Pass regions, on the Queen Charlotte Lowlands, and at 2 other disjunct localities: in the Chilcotin Plateau, and near Vancouver. It is most abundant on the beaches of the Queen Charlotte Islands where it nests on dunes above the high tide line. Breeding concentrations occur at Sandspit, at the mouth of the Tlell River, and, in particular, near Masset. In June 1985, more than 30 nests were found in a 4 km stretch of beach between Skonun Point and the

Sangan River. Gravel pits also provide breeding habitat for a few pairs on the Queen Charlotte Islands. In the northwest, where the Semi-palmated Plover is more sparsely distributed, it breeds in sub-alpine tundra, near swamps on flat plateaus, and along the margins of lakes. Elsewhere, one pair bred at Le Blanc Lake (Hesse and Hesse 1961) and one pair has bred in various years since 1967 on a rocky breakwater at Iona Island (Campbell and Luscher 1972). Paired birds occupy breeding territories as early as late April on the coast and mid-May in the northwest interior. Nests have been found from near sea level to 1,430 m elevation.

Nests: Nest site selection varies with geographic location. On the Queen Charlotte Islands, most nests were situated within a line of semi-permanent drift logs deposited on sand dunes well above the normal summer high tide line. Nests were in the open between logs or were placed beneath overhanging log ends or planks, completely protected by a 'roof'. Nests farther up the beach, beyond the drift logs, were usually on a slightly elevated patch of sand or on the slope leading to the uppermost edge of the beach. Beach nests were shallow scrapes in the sand, usually lined with bits of seaweed, grasses, white clam shells, or small stones. Of 43 nests, 4 were unlined. Nest materials are gathered from the immediate vicinity of the nests.

In the northwest, nests were situated near water on the bare edges of lakes, on sparsely vegetated slopes, river bars, and man-made habitats such as gravelly road sides and clearings. In these habitats, nests were usually next to an object such as a stone or plant, or in open ground on fresh earth, a clump of lichen, or a low hummock. The site was often visibly different from the surrounding habitat—a dry hump in a wet, muddy area, a gravelly ridge among low vegetation, or a moss clump on a gravel bed. Ten nests measured 4 to 5 cm in depth and 7.5 to 9 cm in diameter. Fourteen nests ranged from 2 to 100 m from water; all but one were less than 35 m from water.

Eggs: Dates for 48 clutches ranged from 9 May to 29 June with 65% recorded between 3 and 12 June. Sizes for 44 clutches ranged from 2 to 4 eggs (2E-1, 3E-5, 4E-38) with 86% having 4 eggs. Incubation period is 23 to 24.5 days (Sutton and Parmelee 1955).

Young: Dates for 27 broods ranged from 7 June to 23 July with 52% recorded between 22 June and 14 July. Calculated dates indicate that young could be found as early as 2 June. Brood size ranged from 1 to 4 young (1Y-8, 2Y-6, 3Y-7, 4Y-6). Nestling period is between 22 and 31 days (Sutton and Parmelee 1955).

REMARKS: Some pairs exhibit nest site fidelity over successive breeding seasons. In 1985, near Masset, a banded male was recaptured on a nest 10 m from its 1984 nest site.

See Burton and McNeil (1976) for a method of aging Semipalmated Plovers.

NOTEWORTHY RECORDS

Spring: Coastal - Iona Island 25 Mar 1951-3; Roberts Bank 30 Apr 1980-106; Long Beach 1 May 1981-300+, 6 May 1981-250+, 8 May 1974-400+; Tofino 29 Apr 1977-280; Tow Hill 22 Apr 1979-9; Tow Hill to Rose Point (survey) 8 May 1983-2,100+. **Interior** - Nakusp 3 May 1982-2; Revelstoke 31 May 1977-4 (Bonar 1978a); Alkali Lake (Riske Creek) 30 Apr 1972-1; Prince George 2 Apr 1979-1; ne Fort St. John 24 May 1986-100; Cecil Lake 7 May 1980-30+; Atlin 16 May 1981-4.

Summer: Coastal - Delta 29 Jul 1984-250+; Boundary Bay 10 Aug 1986-250; Long Beach 1 Aug 1970-200+; Stubbs Island 12 June 1987-4; Vancouver

27 Jul 1985-225; Malcolm Island 28 Aug 1976-80+; Masset Harbour 30 Jul 1977-700. **Interior** - White Lake (Okanagan Falls) 10 Jun 1973-4; Soda Lake 18 Jul 1983-1; Eaglet Lake 4 Aug 1986-1, 24 Aug 1984-1 (RBCM 1205); n Fort St. John 24 Jun 1984-2, 25 Jul 1987-21, 24 Aug 1986-14; Cecil Lake 31 Aug 1980-64; Fort Nelson 31 Aug 1987-4.

Autumn: Interior - Atlin 4 Oct 1980-1; Boundary Lake (Goodlow) 9 Sep 1982-1; ne Fort St. John 5 Sep 1986-5, 21 Sep 1986-4; Rawlings Lake 28 Sep 1973-1; Shuswap Lake 6 Sep 1971-20; Ross Lake 2 Oct 1971-1. **Coastal** - Masset 25 Sep 1982-8; Tofino 4 Sep 1974-80; Iona Island 19 Nov 1978-1; Blackie Spit 14 Nov 1965-4.

Winter: Interior - No records. **Coastal** - Nootka Island 18 Feb 1972-3; Roberts Bank 6 Jan 1979-1; Victoria 6 to 9 Jan 1982-1.

Christmas Counts: Interior - Not recorded. **Coastal**: Recorded from 4 of 28 localities and on 1% of all counts. Maxima: Campbell River 3 Jan 1982-1; Comox 22 Dec 1974-1; Deep Bay 27 Dec 1977-1; Ladner 19 Dec 1976-1. Those are all-time Canadian high counts (Tied with Brier Island, Nova Scotia; Anderson 1976, 1977, 1978, 1982).

Semipalmated Plover

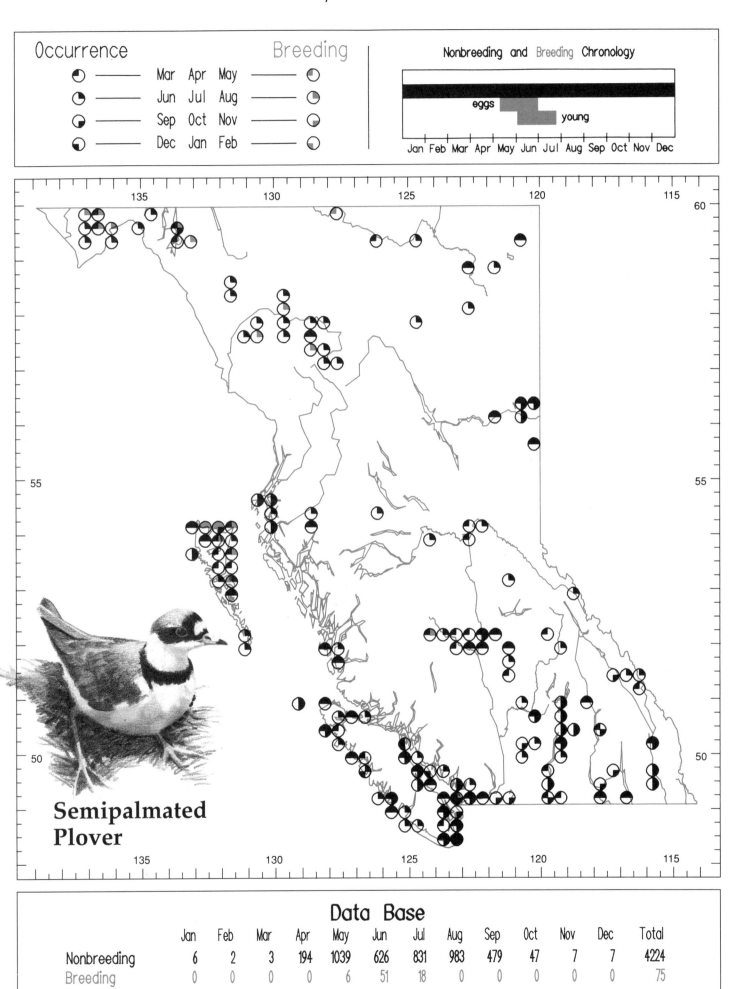

Occurrence — Breeding

Occurrence		Breeding
◑	Mar Apr May	◐
◔	Jun Jul Aug	◔
◕	Sep Oct Nov	◔
◕	Dec Jan Feb	◑

Nonbreeding and Breeding Chronology

eggs — young

Jan Feb Mar Apr May Jun Jul Aug Sep Oct Nov Dec

Semipalmated Plover

Data Base

	Jan	Feb	Mar	Apr	May	Jun	Jul	Aug	Sep	Oct	Nov	Dec	Total
Nonbreeding	6	2	3	194	1039	626	831	983	479	47	7	7	4224
Breeding	0	0	0	0	6	51	18	0	0	0	0	0	75

Killdeer

KILL

Charadrius vociferus Linnaeus

RANGE: Breeds from southern Canada, including the southwestern parts of the Territories, south to Central Mexico; also in Peru. Winters on the Pacific coast north to southeast Alaska and from southern British Columbia and the central United States south to northern South America.

STATUS: *Fairly common* to locally *abundant* migrant and summer visitant. In winter *very common* locally on the coast and *rare* to *uncommon* in the southern interior. Breeds.

NONBREEDING: The Killdeer is widely distributed throughout most of the province becoming scattered and sparsely distributed in the mountainous central northern interior regions including the Skeena and Omineca Mountains, Northern Mountains and Plateaus, and Northern and Central Rocky Mountains. It frequents a wide variety of habitats from seashores to alpine lakes. Coastal habitats include tidal mudflats and sand spits. Log booms and near-shore rocks are used as roost sites. Interior habitats include short-grass uplands, pastures, farmlands, muddy or dried sloughs, river banks, alpine meadows, and lakeshores. Muddy shorelines along lakes, ponds, and rivers are heavily used as well as grassy uplands, especially patches of fresh, green growth within dry areas. During the autumn movement the Killdeer may occur at elevations up to the snowline, wherever meadows or open lakeshores are present. Man-made habitats often hold the highest number of migrants and winter residents. Grass playing fields, newly ploughed fields, stubble fields, flooded pastures, and sewage ponds may hold 100 to 200 Killdeer at times. Estuaries are the primary natural winter habitats on the coast.

The Killdeer, one of the earliest spring migrants in the province, begins arriving in the southern interior in mid-February. These early interior migrants usually encounter snow-covered fields and frozen ponds—harsh conditions for a shorebird. The main movement occurs from mid-March through April and through mid-May in the north.

The presence of winter residents on the coast masks the arrival of spring migrants there. The Killdeer usually arrives as singles, pairs, or in small flocks. Numbers are much lower in the north than in the south.

Small flocks of fledglings and post-breeding adults begin to gather on good foraging grounds as early as June. By August, aggregations of 100+ birds may occur. The autumn movement begins in late July and continues through October in the interior and November on the coast. The Killdeer is only semi-gregarious during the non-breeding season, but autumn flocks are generally larger than spring flocks, especially where shorebirds concentrate, such as Salmon Arm, the Fraser Lowlands, and southern Vancouver Island. A few hardy individuals winter in the southern interior in lowland valleys. Larger numbers winter on the south coast, fewer on the west coast of Vancouver Island and on the north coast.

BREEDING: The Killdeer breeds throughout most of the province including Vancouver Island and the Queen Charlotte Islands, although breeding records in the northwest and central northern interior are scarce or absent. It is most abundant in the south with highest densities in the dry, open valleys and rangelands of the interior, in the Fraser Lowlands, and on southern Vancouver Island.

Figure 80. *Killdeer at nest with eggs in rose garden at the University of British Columbia in Vancouver, 15 April 1970 (R. Wayne Campbell).*

Killdeer

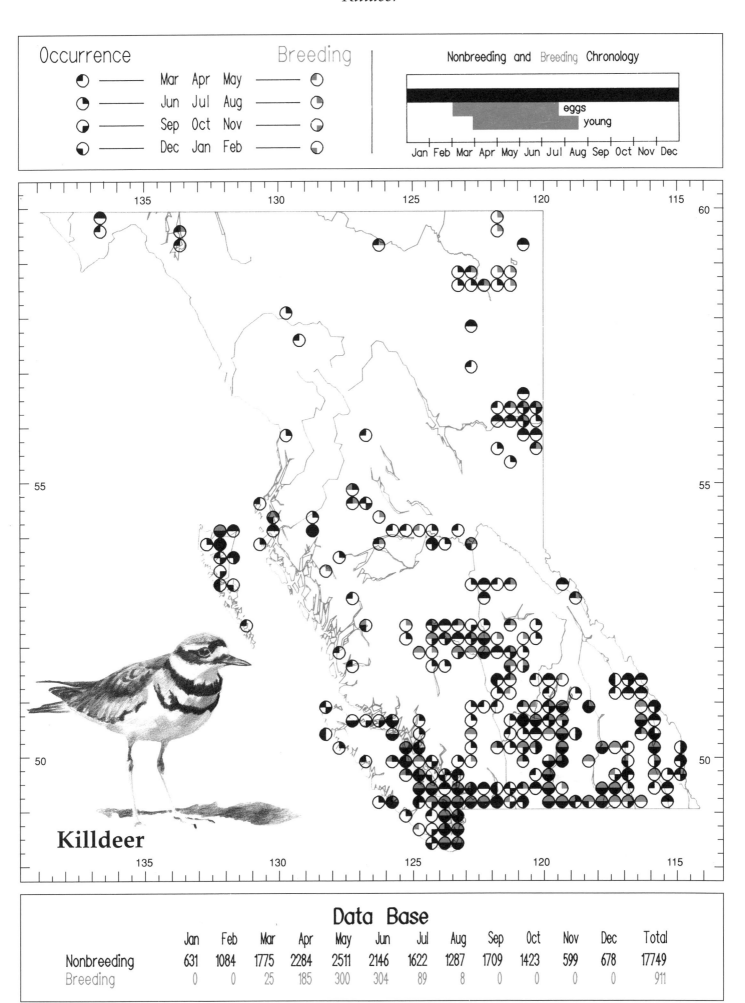

Data Base

	Jan	Feb	Mar	Apr	May	Jun	Jul	Aug	Sep	Oct	Nov	Dec	Total
Nonbreeding	631	1084	1775	2284	2511	2146	1622	1287	1709	1423	599	678	17749
Breeding	0	0	25	185	300	304	89	8	0	0	0	0	911

The Killdeer breeds in a wide range of habitats, a peculiar trait among shorebirds. However, all breeding habitat is characterized by open spaces, and minimal vegetative ground cover, at least at the onset of egg laying. Natural habitats include grassy uplands, lakeshore clearings, open river banks, and marine beaches. Of 447 nests recorded, 53% were found in habitats directly altered or created by human activity (Fig. 80), including agricultural fields, pastures, roadsides, mill yards, lawns, gravel pits, parking lots, and roof tops. Clearing of forested land has increased the amount of breeding habitat available in some areas. For example, in the northeast, gravel-based drilling pads and gravel roads provide nesting habitat in the otherwise unsuitable boreal forest, and in the Okanagan, the Killdeer has moved into subalpine clearcuts (1,500+ m elevation).

Nests: Nests were situated in open areas, not always near water. The Killdeer is attracted to gravelly substrates, particularly on slightly elevated sites. In vegetated sites, nests were placed on bare patches or next to a piece of wood or rock. In rural areas, gravel road sides were often used, while in marine beach habitats, nests were found in gravel above the high tide line, on stone outcrops, among driftwood, and on top of logs.

Nests were shallow scrapes in the ground, usually lined with vegetation or debris gathered from the immediate vicinity of the nest. Nest lining material for 355 nests included wood chips (20%), pebbles (19%), grasses (16%), clam shells (9%), sticks and twigs (9%), bark (5%), and dried cow dung (3%). Twenty-one nests were unlined. Some nests were beautifully constructed saucers of carefully arranged bleached shell fragments, concentric rings of pebbles, or pads of foliose lichens. One nest, on a construction site, was lined with cement chips.

Most nests (99%; n=507) were situated on the ground. Five were on logs, one was on the gravel roof of a department store, and one was 1.3 m above ground in the crotch of a tree. Killdeer are usually solitary nesters, but occasionally, nests only several metres apart are found. Sixteen nests ranged between 6 and 100 m from water, half of which were over 30 m from water. Four nests measured between 8 and 12 cm in diameter and all were about 2.5 cm deep.

A nest on Comox Spit was immersed by the rising tide on 5 consecutive nights for up to 1.5 hours but still produced a brood. Another nest, in the Fraser Lowlands, was incubated while rainwater rose to a depth of 2 cm around the nest. It was also successful.

Eggs: Dates for 511 clutches ranged from 1 March to 21 July with 52% recorded between 21 April and 4 June. Killdeer are double-brooded. Egg laying begins at least a month earlier on the coast than in the interior. Sizes for 520 clutches ranged from 1 to 7 eggs (1E-14, 2E-32, 3E-67, 4E-399, 5E-6, 7E-2) with 77% having 4 eggs. The 2 clutches of 7 eggs (Fig. 81) were likely produced by 2 females. Incubation period is about 25 days (Bunni 1959).

Young: Dates for 391 broods ranged from 15 April to 17 August with 51% recorded between 20 May and 26 June. Calculated dates indicate that nests could contain young as early as 28 March. Sizes for 383 broods ranged from 1 to 5 young (1Y-78, 2Y-83, 3Y-107, 4Y-113, 5Y-2) with 57% having 3 or 4 young (Fig. 82). Young may leave the nest very soon after hatching; a nest with 2 eggs and 2 young at 0830 held 4 young at 1000 and was empty at 1300. Fledging period is about 40 days (Harrison 1978).

REMARKS: Although Godfrey (1986) excludes the Queen Charlotte Islands from the breeding distribution of the Killdeer, it breeds regularly in small numbers near Masset.

Figure 81. *Killdeer attempting to incubate 7 eggs, University of British Columbia campus, Vancouver, June 1971 (R. Wayne Campbell). Note the 2 exposed eggs.*

Figure 82. *Four nestling Killdeer at Osoyoos, 5 June 1984 (Mark Nyhof).*

NOTEWORTHY RECORDS

Spring: Coastal - Long Beach 6 Apr 1982-30+; Serpentine Fen 30 May 1979-35; Pitt Meadows 23 Mar 1976-118; Moresby Camp 2 Apr 1985-15; Masset 7 May 1977-32. **Interior** - Grand Forks 2 Mar 1980-4; Wasa 8 Apr 1982-15; Sorrento 27 Mar 1972-25; Prince George 6 Mar 1983-1; Telkwa 20 Mar 1978-3; Dawson Creek 9 May 1980-50; Fort St. John 1 Apr 1984-1.

Summer: Coastal - Saanich 6 Jun 1982-39 (4 juveniles, 35 adults), 29 Jul 1972-89 (Tatum 1973); Matsqui 25 Jul 1967-110, 1 Aug 1967-132; Little Qualicum River estuary 11 Aug 1976-62 (Dawe 1980); Campbell River estuary 18 Aug 1974-40. **Interior** - Kootenay Flats (Creston) 10 Aug 1947-80+ (Munro 1950); Salmon Arm 26 Aug 1973-300 (Cannings, R.J. 1973); Le Blanc Lake 15 Jul 1978-58; Bald Mountain (Riske Creek) 22 Aug 1978-30;

Dawson Creek 27 Jun 1978-26; ne Fort St. John 6 Aug 1986-41.

Autumn: Interior - Charlie Lake 10 Oct 1982-2 (last); Quick 14 to 29 Nov 1987-1 on ice; Redstone 17 Oct 1940-30; Salmon Arm 11 Sep 1970-150; Radium 26 Oct 1982-9; Swan Lake (Vernon) 22 Nov 1968-50 (Cannings et al. 1987); Lavington 25 Sep 1973-30. **Coastal** - Masset 24 Oct 1982-20; Sewall 21 Nov 1981-5; Little Qualicum River estuary 24 Sep 1975-62 (Dawe 1976); Reifel Island 30 Oct 1972-140; Boundary Bay 17 Sep 1922-250; Garnett Creek 25 Nov 1976-94; Saanich 1 Nov 1982-120, 13 Nov 1982-150.

Winter: Interior - Alkali Lake (Riske Creek) 22 Feb 1970-2; 100 Mile House 10 Feb 1984-1 (first

arrival); Glacier National Park 20 Feb 1982-1; Summerland 24 Feb 1970-8; Castlegar 23 Jan 1977-1. **Coastal** - Prince Rupert 20 Feb 1984-6; Masset 29 Jan 1983-44; Vargas Island 10 Jan 1969-7 (Hatler et al. 1978); Saanich 19 Dec 1981-165; University of Victoria 20 Jan 1979-44; Victoria Harbour 26 Dec 1980-100+ on log boom.

Christmas Counts: Interior - Recorded from 9 of 19 localities and on 32% of all counts. Maxima: Penticton 27 Dec 1976-18; Vernon 18 Dec 1983-12; Shuswap Lake 22 Dec 1979-10. **Coastal** - Recorded from 24 of 28 localities and on 47% of all counts. Maxima: Ladner 22 Dec 1962-**411**, all-time Canadian high count (Anderson 1976); Victoria 30 Dec 1967-375; Vancouver 26 Dec 1961-227; Duncan 18 Dec 1976-227.

Black Oystercatcher

Haematopus bachmani Audubon

RANGE: Resident on the Pacific coast of North America from the western Aleutian Islands eastward and southward to islands off central Baja California.

STATUS: *Fairly common* to *very common* resident along the coast except the Strait of Georgia where it is *uncommon* to *fairly common*. Breeds.

NONBREEDING: The Black Oystercatcher occurs singly or in groups of up to 100 along rocky shorelines in the province at all seasons. It is most frequently seen on rocky islets, reefs, and spits, but also frequents lagoons, gravel and mud flats, rocky beaches, sand bars, and inlets. It visits estuaries, seaside golf courses, and parks infrequently and seems to avoid beaches at times of heavy surf. There are no interior records.

Seasonal movements are not well known. There seems to be a general dispersal from outer exposed coasts to more sheltered areas (e.g. Skidegate Inlet, Chatham Sound, Tofino Inlet, Juan de Fuca Strait) in winter. Flocks have been reported in all months; those in summer are mostly composed of nonbreeding or subadult birds (Fig. 83). Postbreeding birds disperse to favourite areas (e.g. Chatham Sound) and groups build up throughout September and October. Peak numbers are reached in late October and early November. In spring (usually March), large groups are associated with herring spawning areas.

BREEDING: The Black Oystercatcher is a widespread breeder along the inner and outer coastal areas of the province; nesting evidence has been found in 80% of coastal map grids. In the Strait of Georgia, populations are expanding into inlets and sounds (see Campbell 1968e).

All nest sites were located on offshore islands. There are no known mainland sites. Nesting sites varied from large and forested islands, with beaches and rocky headlands (Fig. 84) to

Figure 83. Nonbreeding flock of Black Oystercatchers at Thurston Harbour, Queen Charlotte Islands, 11 July 1977 (R. Wayne Campbell).

Black Oystercatcher

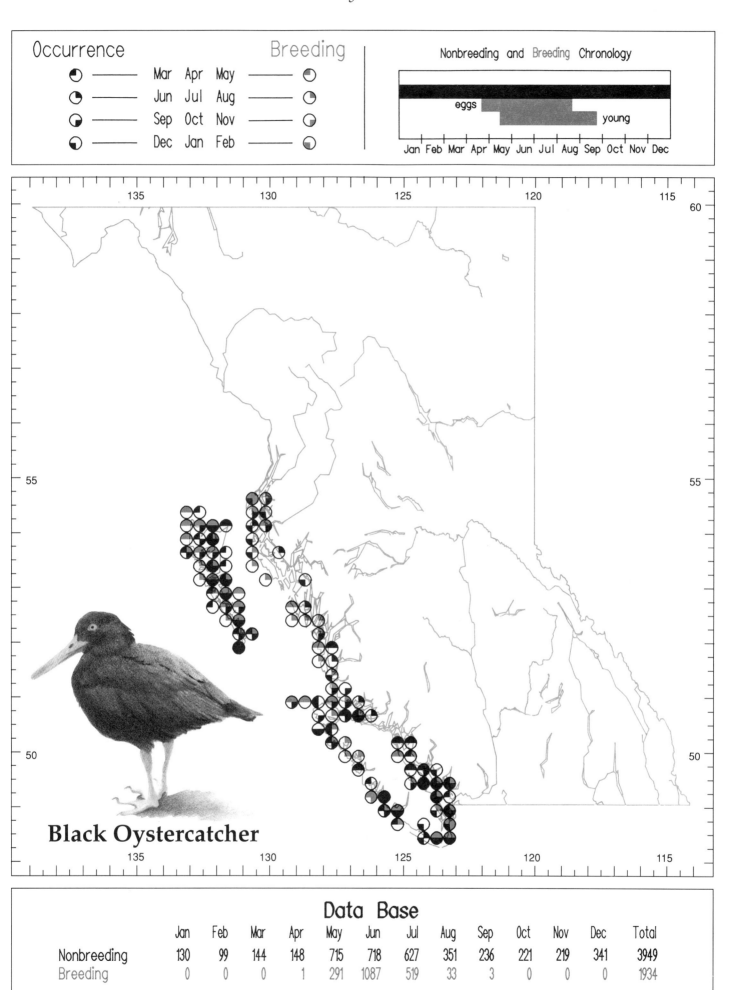

Black Oystercatcher

Data Base

	Jan	Feb	Mar	Apr	May	Jun	Jul	Aug	Sep	Oct	Nov	Dec	Total
Nonbreeding	130	99	144	148	715	718	627	351	236	221	219	341	3949
Breeding	0	0	0	1	291	1087	519	33	3	0	0	0	1934

small, bare islets, with just enough land above high water to provide a suitable nesting substrate (Fig. 85).

The Black Oystercatcher nests singly or in loose colonies on suitable islands (Table 5). For example, Cleland Island, with an area of 7.7 ha, supported 57 breeding pairs in 1971 (Hartwick 1974). In other areas, the number of islets determines the breeding population (e.g. Skidegate Inlet, 15 pairs in 1974 - Campbell 1975b). The centres of abundance are the Queen Charlotte Islands (38%) and the west coast of Vancouver Island (30%). The estimated breeding population is almost 1,000 pairs at 320 sites (Rodway In press).

The Alaskan population is estimated at 1,700 pairs and the Washington population at 200 pairs (United States Department of the Interior 1988; Speich and Wahl 1989).

Nests: Nests, usually well camouflaged, were situated on bare exposed rock, shell, gravel and sand beaches, among driftlogs, on areas of short-grass on rocky headlands, and occasionally on man-made structures (e.g. the concrete base of a navigation light). Most nests were within a few metres of the high tide line; some, however, were up to 8.5 m beyond the waterline. Hatler et al. (1978) and Hartwick (1974) note that a considerable loss in clutches occurs when moderately or unusually high tides or storms wash away eggs laid too close to the mean high-water mark.

Most nests (84%; n=344) were shallow scrapes lined with shells and shell fragments (e.g. mussels, clams, barnacles - Fig. 87), bits of crabs, rock chips and pebbles (Fig. 88), and bits of driftwood. On Glaucous-winged Gull colonies, some nests (9%) looked like small gull nests and were constructed entirely of grasses. Other nests (3%) were lined with beach debris (e.g. dry seaweed, wood chips, string) and the remainder had no nest material at all. Frequently, extra nest scrapes were made (up to 7), but rarely did they contain as much material as those intended for eggs.

Eggs: Dates for 1,371 clutches ranged from 1 May to 19 August, with 53% recorded between 2 and 24 June. Ninety percent of all clutches were found between 18 May and 13 July. Calculated dates indicate that eggs could be found as early as 21 April. Near Tofino, courtship activities were noted on 14 April, and earliest copulation on 24 April (1972) suggesting that, in some years, late April clutches may occur (Hatler et al. 1978). Clutch size ranged from 1 to 5 eggs (1E-288, 2E-660, 3E-419, 4E-3, 5E-1) with 79% having 2 or 3 eggs (Fig. 88). Groves (1984) determined the incubation period in British Columbia to be 26 days.

Young: Dates for 557 broods ranged from 15 May to 22 September, with 54% recorded between 23 June and 20 July. Ninety percent of all broods were found between 10 June and 13

TABLE 5.
Black Oystercatcher: location, history, and size of major breeding concentrations in British Columbia.

Location	First Record	Low Survey Results[1] Year		High Survey Results[1] Year		Recent Survey Results[1] Year		Source[2]
South Coast - Colonies > 10 nests or pairs								
Bordelais Islets	1964	C	1964	12 Nc	1970		1970	4
Clara Islets	1975	2 Nc	1982	11 Nc	1975	4 Nc	1988	1,2
Cleland Island	1967	3 Nc	1967	57 Nc	1971	45 Nc	1986	1,2,3
Gillam Islets	1975	3 Nc	1983	13 Nc	1988		1988	1,2
Grassy Island	1975	5 Nc	1982	16 Nc	1975	16 Nc	1988	1,2
McQuarrie Islets	1975	37 Nc	1988	62 Nc	1975		1988	1
"Mimulus" Islets	1975	12 Nc	1975	15 Nc	1988	15 Nc	1988	1,2
Moos Islet	1975	16 Nc	1982	19 Nc	1975	17 Nc	1988	1,2
Munsie Rocks	1975			18 Nc	1975		1975	1
Starlight Reef	1962	1 Nc	1970	13 Nc	1975	10 Nc	1982	1,2,4
Storm Islets	1975	6 Nc	1975	23 Nc	1976	18 Nc	1987	1,2
Thomas Island	1975	10 Nc	1988	11 Nc	1975		1988	1,2
Thornton Islet	1975	7 Nc	1983	27 Nc	1975	13 Nc	1988	1,2
Triangle Island	1949	3 N	1949	13 Nc	1977	6 N	1985	1,2,5
North Coast - Colonies > 10 nests or pairs								
Anthony Island	1977	11 Nc	1986	19 Nc	1977		1986	1,2
Byers Islands	1976	8 Nc	1976	10 Nc	1988		1988	1,2
"Grassy" Islet	1977	16 Nc	1977	16 Nc	1986		1986	1,2
Harvey Islands	1976	3 Nc	1976	12 Nc	1988		1988	1,2
Langara Island	1910	6 Nc	1981	11 Nc	1969	C	1986	1,2,6
Moore Islands	1970	8 Nc	1976	21 Nc	1988		1988	1,2
"Naden" Rocks	1977	3 Nc	1977	15 Nc	1986		1986	1,2
Sadler Island	1977	2 Nc	1977	10 Nc	1986		1986	1,2
Sandilands Island	1986			10 Nc	1986		1986	2
Tar Islands	1977	2 Nc	1977	10 N	1985		1985	1,2
Tian Islets	1977	18 Nc	1986	31 Nc	1977		1986	1,2

[1]   C - nesting confirmed but no count or estimate made; N - nests. All data are estimates unless noted as follows:
c - complete count.

[2]   1 - British Columbia Nest Records Scheme; 2 - Rodway et al. In prep.; 3 - Hartwick 1974; 4 - Guiguet 1971; 5 - Carl et al. 1951;
6 - Rodway et al. 1983.

Figure 84. *Black Oystercatcher breeding habitat on headlands at Joseph Island, 28 June 1976 (R. Wayne Campbell).*

Figure 85. *Typical low-island Black Oystercatcher breeding habitat on Bunsby Island, 24 June 1975 (R. Wayne Campbell).*

August. The earliest flying young was reported on 27 July. Brood size ranged from 1 to 4 young (1Y-237, 2Y-208, 3Y-108, 4Y-4), with 80% having 1 or 2 young (Fig. 89). Fledging period is about 40 days (Hartwick 1974).

REMARKS: Extensive studies have been completed on the foraging strategy, breeding behaviour, feeding habits, and winter ecology of this species in British Columbia (see Hartwick 1973, 1974; Hartwick and Blaylock 1979; Groves 1982; L'Hyver 1985; Purdy 1985). In spite of its name, the Black Oystercatcher rarely feeds on oysters in the province (however, see Campbell 1966, and Butler and Kirbyson 1979).

Some authors consider *H. bachmani* and *H. palliatus* (American Oystercatcher) to be conspecific (see Jehl 1985). The Black Oystercatcher was previously referred to as the American Black Oystercatcher (American Ornithologists' Union 1983, 1985).

POSTSCRIPT: In 1988 and 1989 a pair of Black Oystercatchers successfully raised a brood from a nest located on the gravel roof of a building on the Nanaimo waterfront (Fig. 86), the first such location for the province.

Figure 86. Black Oystercatchers nesting on the roof of a building on the Canadian Pacific wharf in Nanaimo, 18 June 1989 (William J. Merilees).

Figure 87. Black Oystercatcher nest and egg, Thornton Island, 16 June 1976 (R. Wayne Campbell). Most documented oystercatcher nests in the province were shallow scrapes lined with shell fragments.

Figure 88. Black Oystercatcher eggs laid on a collection of rock chips and pebbles, Gillatt Island, Queen Charlotte Islands, 18 June 1974 (R. Wayne Campbell).

Figure 89. Black Oystercatcher adult and chick at Cleland Island, 2 July 1972 (Ervio Sian).

NOTEWORTHY RECORDS

Spring: Coastal - Victoria 6 May 1963-16; Nanoose Harbour 30 Mar 1977-28 (largest count 1974 to 1979 - Dawe and Lang 1980); Marina Island 30 Mar 1977-15; Pulteney Point 12 Mar 1977-70; Tofino Inlet 24 May 1931-25, 31 May 1931-65 (Racey 1946); Cleland Island 5 May 1982-36; Hesquiat Harbour 7 Mar 1976-49; Triangle Island (Scott Islands) 17 May 1978-32; Cape St. James 3 Apr 1982-30; Copper Bay 21 Mar 1981-36; Queen Charlotte City 20 Mar 1981-42; Masset Inlet 12 Mar 1982-12; Naden Harbour 23 Mar 1976-150, 7 Apr 1975-35+ on new herring spawn. **Interior:** No records.

Summer: Coastal - Victoria 19 Jun 1981-26; Departure Bay 22 Jun 1978-16; Merry Island Jul 1979-50 all month; Mitlenatch Island 28 Jun 1977-13; Storm Islands 13 Jun 1976-99, many breeders; Seabird Rocks 12 Jun 1970-80+; Barkley Sound 19 Aug 1943-25+; Cleland Island 17 Jul 1970-106 nonbreeders; Clark Island 23 Jun 1975-22 nonbreeders; Triangle Island (Scott Islands) 25 Jun 1977-48 nonbreeders, 24 Aug 1978-62; Hasu Cove 22 Jul 1977-64, 42 nonbreeders; Cowley Rock 31 Jul 1977-33; Cape Knox 4 Jun 1947-40. **Interior:** No records.

Autumn: Interior: No records. **Coastal** - Masset Inlet 13 Oct 1976-73; Skidegate Channel 9 Oct 1976-75; Bischof Islands 2 Oct 1976-48; Green Island 18 Sep 1978-13, 26 Sep 1978-35, 6 Oct 1977-20, 10 Oct 1978-45, 24 Oct 1977-88, 31 Oct 1978-108, 11 Nov 1977-110; West Vancouver 23 Sep 1981-16; Departure Bay 2 Oct 1983-40 on islets; Cleland Island 10 Oct 1976-15; Vargas Island 14 Nov 1976-30; Helby Island 1 Oct 1977-71; Sidney 28 Sep 1955-54 (Flahaut and Schultz 1956), 16 Oct 1965-60 (Baldridge and Crowell 1966), 10 Nov 1976-30; Victoria 18 Oct 1970-53 (Tatum 1971), 7 Nov 1962-96, high count (Boggs and Boggs 1963a); Active Pass 5 Nov 1981-15.

Winter: Interior: No Records. **Coastal** - Green Island 14 Dec 1977-2; Digby Island 16 Feb 1978-73 (Savard 1978); Masset 18 Dec 1982-140; Skidegate Narrows 19 Dec 1971-24, 27 Jan 1979-55; Puffin Cove 26 Dec 1970-2 (Campbell 1972b); Edye Passage 16 Feb 1978-50 (Savard 1978); Pulteney Point 18 Dec 1976-74; Vargas Island 4 Dec 1968-35; Lemmens Inlet 27 Jan 1976-90, 7 Feb 1983-52; Victoria 12 Dec 1970-65; Mission Creek (Sechelt) 12 Feb 1982-9.

Christmas Counts: Interior: Not recorded. **Coastal** - Recorded from 13 of 28 localities and on 28% of all counts. Maxima: Masset 18 Dec 1982-140, all-time Canadian high count (Anderson, R.R. 1983); Skidegate Inlet 15 Dec 1984-123; Victoria 22 Dec 1962-96.

Black-necked Stilt

BNST

Himantopus mexicanus (Müller)

RANGE: Breeds locally from southern Washington and Delaware south to Chile and Argentina; also in southern Alberta. Winters from southern Oregon (rarely), the Gulf coast and southern Florida south through Middle America, the West Indies, and South America.

STATUS: *Very rare* spring vagrant in the province.

OCCURRENCE: The Black-necked Stilt has been sighted in southern areas of the province, in 13 widely separated locations, from Victoria to the northern tip of Vancouver Island on the coast and from Vaseux Lake and Creston north to 100 Mile House and near Golden in the interior. It frequents shallow, muddy ponds, lakes, and lagoons, where it forages near the water's edge.

The Black-necked Stilt was first recorded in the province in 1971 (Campbell and Anderson 1972) and subsequently in 5 different years from 13 different locations. All records have been in spring between 17 April and 17 May. At least 59 individual birds were represented in the 21 occurrences, most of which were reported during a noticeable influx in 1987 (Campbell 1987d).

Stilts found in British Columbia are probably individuals that have overshot their normal breeding areas during northward spring migration. Recently a small local breeding population has been found in southern Washington (Rohwer et al. 1979).

All records, listed in chronological order, are as follows:

(1) Sea Island 13 to 14 May 1971-1 adult (RBCM Photo 168 on 14 May; see Crowell and Nehls 1971b; Campbell and Anderson 1972).

(2) Sea Island 4 to 7 May 1974-1 adult (RBCM Photo 357 on 5 May; Shepard, M.G. 1975a; Roberson 1980).

(3) Hansen Lagoon 17 May 1974-1 adult (RBCM Photo 390; Cannings, R.A. 1975a).

(4) Douglas Lake (Quilchena) 9 May 1978-1 adult (Chapman, B.-A. et al. 1985).

(5) Reifel Island 21 April to 4 May 1981 - up to 5 adults (Hunn and Mattocks 1981b). Photographs were obtained on 21 April (RBCM Photo 663; Fig. 90).

(6) Duck Lake (Creston) 10 May 1981-1 adult (RBCM Photo 846; Chapman, B.-A. et al. 1985).

(7) Swan Lake (Vernon; all 1984) 15 May-5, 17 May-6, 25 May-2 (Campbell 1984b; Cannings, R.A. et al. 1987).

(8) Reifel Island 17 to 23 April 1987-maximum 13 on 19 April.

(9) Barnes Lake (Ashcroft) 19 and 20 April 1987-1 (RBCM Photo 1157).

(10) Lulu Island 25 and 26 April 1987-3.

(11) Iona Island 26 April 1987-1 adult.

(12) Clover Point 27 April 1987-3.

(13) Vaseux Lake 27 April 1987-14 in flock.

(14) Okanagan Falls 27 April 1987-9 in flock.

(15) Courtenay 29 April to 4 May 1987-maximum 6 on 3rd (RBCM Photo 1182 on 29th).

(16) 100 Mile House 30 April 1987-4 at marsh.

(17) Palmer Meadows (e Nicola Lake) 1 May 1987-1.

(18) Saanich 5 May 1987-1.

(19) 70 Mile House 7 May 1987-2 adults.

(20) Douglas Lake 9 May 1987-1 on lakeshore.

(21) Burges and James Gadsden Park 12 May 1987-1.

REMARKS: The Black-necked Stilt is often considered conspecific with the Pied or Black-winged Stilt of the Old World. There is considerable debate as to whether or not several species exist within this group (American Ornithologists' Union 1983; Hayman et al. 1986).

POSTSCRIPT:
Another small influx of birds occurred in 1988:

(22) Roberts Lake (Kelowna) 14 and 15 April 1988-2 (Campbell 1988b).

(23) Otter Lake (Vernon) 17 April 1988-2 (Campbell 1988b).

(24) Serpentine Fen (Surrey) 29 April to 2 May 1988-1 (Campbell 1988c).

(25) Duck Lake (Creston) 7 May 1988-2.

(26) Shuswap Lake 7 May 1988-1 (RBCM Photo 1241; Fig. 91).

This influx elevates the status of the Black-necked Stilt in the province to *rare* spring vagrant.

Figure 90. *Black-necked Stilts at Reifel Island, Delta, 21 April 1981 (RBCM Photo 663; Ervio Sian).*

Figure 91. *Black-necked Stilt at Salmon Arm Bay, Shuswap Lake, 7 May 1988 (RBCM Photo 1241; W. Deane Munro).*

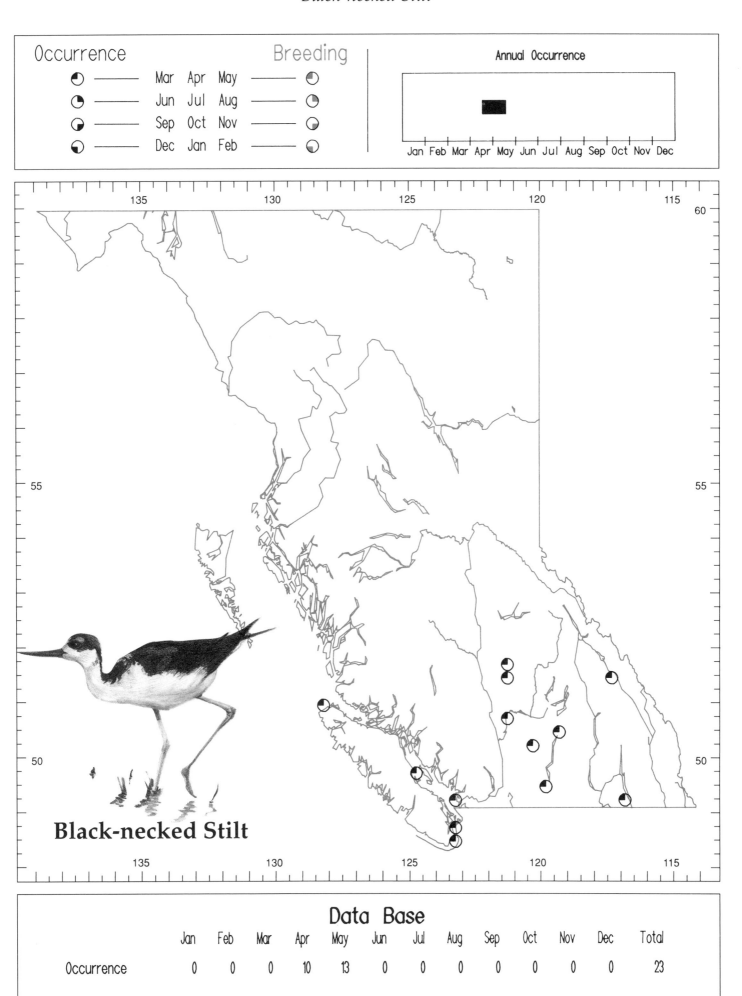

Black-necked Stilt

Occurrence

Mar	Apr	May
Jun	Jul	Aug
Sep	Oct	Nov
Dec	Jan	Feb

Breeding

Annual Occurrence

Jan Feb Mar Apr May Jun Jul Aug Sep Oct Nov Dec

Data Base

	Jan	Feb	Mar	Apr	May	Jun	Jul	Aug	Sep	Oct	Nov	Dec	Total
Occurrence	0	0	0	10	13	0	0	0	0	0	0	0	23

American Avocet

AMAV

Recurvirostra americana Gmelin

RANGE: Breeds from southeastern British Columbia (casually), southern parts of the Prairie provinces, and southwestern Ontario south to the southwestern United States. Winters from the southern United States to Central America.

STATUS: *Rare* spring and summer transient, *casual* autumn transient, *accidental* in winter on the south coast. *Rare* spring and summer visitant in the southern interior. *Casual* in spring and summer in the Peace Lowlands. Four breeding records.

CHANGE IN STATUS: The American Avocet (Fig. 92) was first recorded in British Columbia in 1908 (Brooks 1909a). During the next 52 years it remained a very infrequent visitor to the province, being recorded on only 5 occasions from 3 different locations (see Munro, J.A. and Cowan 1947; Campbell 1972c). During the 1960s a noticeable influx occurred in the province; this trend continued through the 1970s (Cooper, J.M. 1983) and 1980s (Fig. 94). It has been recorded from 31 different locations in the province and recently has become established as a breeding species. The individuals sighted in southern British Columbia likely originate from breeding sites in Montana and Washington, while the Peace River birds are probably vagrants from Alberta.

NONBREEDING: The American Avocet is widely distributed across southern British Columbia from Tofino to the east Kootenay and north through the Thompson-Okanagan and Fraser plateaus to Chilanko Forks. It also has occurred in the Peace Lowlands. Most records are from the Kootenays, Okanagan valley, Fraser River delta (Fig. 92), and Victoria.

On the coast, mud flats, estuaries, and small ponds are preferred. Spits and sparsely vegetated muddy shorelines are frequented. In the interior, habitats include shallow alkaline ponds, lowland marshes, and the shores of larger lakes and sewage lagoons (Fig. 93).

The American Avocet has been recorded in British Columbia from 10 April to 4 December. Most records (58%) are for the spring period. Birds arrive mainly during the first 2 weeks of May, and depart in early September.

Figure 92. American Avocet at Iona Island on the Fraser River delta, 25 July 1979 (RBCM Photo; Ervio Sian).

Figure 93. American Avocets at north sewage lagoon, Fort St, John, 5 May 1988   (Chris R. Siddle).

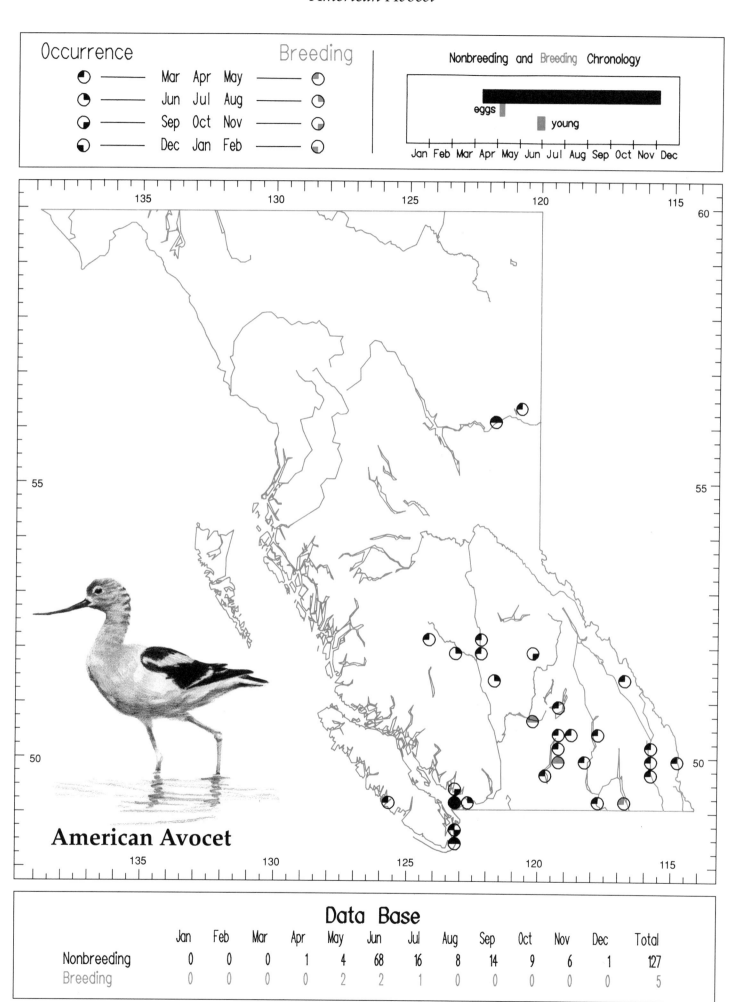

Occurrence

◑	——————	Mar Apr May
◔	——————	Jun Jul Aug
◖	——————	Sep Oct Nov
◕	——————	Dec Jan Feb

Breeding

Mar Apr May	—————— ◑
Jun Jul Aug	—————— ◔
Sep Oct Nov	—————— ◔
Dec Jan Feb	—————— ◔

Nonbreeding and Breeding Chronology

eggs   young

Jan Feb Mar Apr May Jun Jul Aug Sep Oct Nov Dec

American Avocet

Data Base

	Jan	Feb	Mar	Apr	May	Jun	Jul	Aug	Sep	Oct	Nov	Dec	Total
Nonbreeding	0	0	0	1	4	68	16	8	14	9	6	1	127
Breeding	0	0	0	0	2	2	1	0	0	0	0	0	5

BREEDING: There are only 4 breeding records, one from the west Kootenay region, the others from the Thompson-Okanagan Plateau. Details are as follows:

(1) Duck Lake (Creston) – a nest containing 3 eggs was discovered and photographed on 10 May 1968 (Campbell 1972c; RBCM Photo 180). The nest site was completely exposed, situated on a sparsely vegetated mud flat. The height of surrounding vegetation reached 3 to 4 cm. The nest consisted of a scraggly pile of dried plant stems and was approximately 100 m from the lake's edge. The nest site habitat appeared to have been created by a temporary drawdown of the lake's water level. Both adults were present near the nest. The outcome of the nest is unknown.

(2) Beresford Lake 4 May 1987 – a nest containing 4 eggs (Fig. 95) was located 3 m from the alkali lakeshore on a bare substrate. The nest was a small depression lined with grasses and rootlets.

(3) and (4) Alki Lake (Kelowna) spring/summer 1987 - two pairs of adults were located on 16 May. No nest search was conducted but on 25 June, 2 separate broods of 3 young, each with accompanying adults, were noticed. The families were still present on 4 July. The elevation was 354 m.

F. Gibson (1971) gives an average incubation of 24.2 days (range 22 to 29 days) and a fledging period of 27 days in Oregon.

REMARKS: See F. Gibson (1971) and Hamilton (1975) for additional information on the breeding biology and behaviour of the American Avocet.

POSTSCRIPT: In 1988 the American Avocet was reported from 9 widely separated localities in the province. Two pairs bred on the coast at Serpentine Fen (Surrey) for the first time (Wilson, D.J. 1989; Fig. 96).

All records, in chronological order, are as follows: Okanagan Lake 18 April-13, 10 to 12 May-5; Burges and James Gadsden Park 21 April-1; Sea Island 24 April-1; Serpentine Fen (Surrey) 24 April to 28 June, maximum 6 on 1 June, 2 nests with 4 eggs each on 9 June (RBCM Photo 1226); Fort St. John 5 to 12 May, maximum 19 on 11 May; Cecil Lake (Goodlow) 7 May-2; Duck Lake (Creston) 7 and 8 May, maximum 18 on 8 May; Robert Lake (Kelowna) 22 May-1; Alki Lake (Kelowna) 22 May-6; and Iona Island 25 and 26 June-2.

In 1989 Tex Lyon (pers. comm.) reported 2 American Avocets in winter plumage on Stories Beach in Port Hardy on 22 September. Also, for the second year in a row, a pair successfully raised a brood at Serpentine Fen (Surrey) on the southwest mainland coast (Wilson, D.J. 1989).

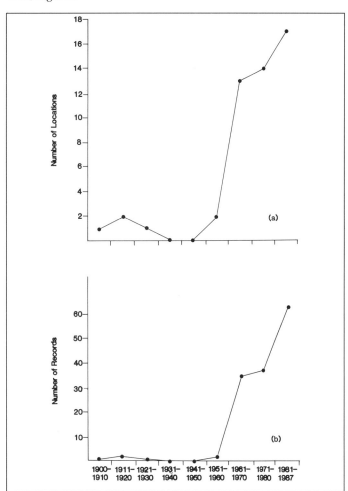

Figure 94. Changes in the number of (a) observation locations and (b) records by decade for the American Avocet in British Columbia, 1900 through 1987.

Figure 95. American Avocet nest at Beresford Lake south of Kamloops, May 1987 (David F. Fraser).

Figure 96. *Douglas J. Wilson inspecting American Avocet nest and eggs at Serpentine Fen, Surrey, 9 June 1988 (Kathleen Fry).*

NOTEWORTHY RECORDS

Spring: Coastal - Saanich 14 May 1974-1 (Shepard 1975b); Reifel Island 4 to 7 May 1985-1 (Campbell 1985c); Sea Island 25 May 1986-1 (Mattocks 1986a); Iona Island 11 May 1968-3 (Campbell 1972c), 15 May 1955-1 adult (Campbell 1972c), 21 May 1968-3 (RBCM Photo 50); Tofino 7 May 1987-4. **Interior** - Duck Lake (Creston) 20 Apr 1986-1; Trail 29 Apr 1976-7 (RBCM Photo 514); Wasa Lake 10 May 1977-12; Nakusp 28 May 1978-1; Okanagan Landing 28 Apr 1908-15 (RBCM 4734); Mabel Lake mid-May 1985-9 (Campbell 1985c); Celista 10 Apr 1962-1 (Schnider et al. 1971), 20 and 21 May 1961-1; Kamloops 22 Apr 1987-11; Beresford 29 Apr to 2 May 1987-2; Riske Creek 15 May 1976-1; Williams Lake 29 May 1986-1; Chilanko Forks 24 May 1980-1; Fort St. John 24 May 1984-2 (Grunberg 1984c), 28 May 1983-4 (Campbell 1983c).

Summer: Coastal - Boundary Bay 31 Aug 1985-3; Reifel Island 5 Aug 1981-1; Iona Island 13 and 22 Jun 1969-2 (Campbell 1972c), 25 Jul 1979-1 (RBCM Photo 714). **Interior** - Kelowna 10 Jul 1987-10; Meadow Lake 4 Jun 1987-2 adults; w Williams Lake Jun 1972-1 pair exhibiting courtship behaviour (Cooper, J.M. 1983); Farrel Creek (Hudson Hope) 13 Jul 1977-1.

Autumn: Interior - Hemp Creek early Sep 1964-1 (RBCM 11233). **Coastal** - Jericho Park (Vancouver) 6 to 12 Sep 1986-1 (Mattocks and Harrington-Tweit 1987; RBCM Photo 1192); Iona Island 5 Sep to 4 Dec 1986-1 (Mattocks and Harrington-Tweit 1987); Fraser River delta 20 Sep 1915-1 (Munro, J.A. 1918); Saanich 1 Oct 1978-1 (RBCM Photo 567).

Winter: Interior: No records. **Coastal** - one record, see Autumn: Coastal.

Christmas Counts: Not recorded.

Greater Yellowlegs

GRYE

Tringa melanoleuca (Gmelin)

RANGE: Breeds in southern Alaska and in Canada in an east-west band from south-central British Columbia to Labrador. Winters mainly from the southern United States to South America; also on the Pacific coast north to the southern Strait of Georgia.

STATUS: *Rare* to locally *very common* migrant throughout most of the province. *Rare* summer visitant to the central-interior. *Rare* winter visitant in the Fraser Lowlands; *fairly common* along the southeast coast of Vancouver Island. Breeds.

NONBREEDING: The Greater Yellowlegs is widely distributed throughout British Columbia from sea level to 1,585 m elevation. In migration it occurs in small numbers throughout the province although it is more abundant in the southern areas.

The Greater Yellowlegs usually occurs in singles or small, loose flocks. It often mixes with Lesser Yellowlegs (see Fig. 97) and other medium-sized waders. Occasionally, large flocks are observed where the birds are concentrated by unusually favourable feeding conditions. Large concentrations can often be found on southern Vancouver Island, the Fraser River delta, (Boundary Bay, and Iona, Sea, and Reifel islands), and to a lesser extent at Salmon Arm and Creston in the central-southern interior. Blackie Spit, on Boundary Bay, consistently attracts the largest numbers in the province.

Coastal habitats include tidal mud flats in protected bays and estuaries, edges of tidal channels, sandy beaches, and spits, but especially areas with shallow waters over a mud bottom. Roost sites include offshore rocks, reefs, and rocky beaches. Inland habitats include shallow slough and pond edges, exposed mud flats, sedge swamps, flooded fields, edges of slow moving creeks, meltwater ponds, and muddy spots in bogs, muskeg, or uplands.

Spring migration begins in late February or March on the south coast and April in the southern interior, peaking in late April or early May, and continuing through to late May. A few stragglers and nonbreeders are found along the coast in June. The autumn movement may begin in late June with adult birds, but it usually begins in early July (also see Buchanan 1988a). The movement peaks in mid-August through September when numbers are swelled by later-migrating juveniles. The northern autumn movement is weak compared to the southern movement. Autumn migration ends by late August in the northern interior, by October on the north coast, and by early November in the southern interior. Some birds remain throughout the autumn and early winter on the south coast and Fraser Lowlands, but the large numbers disappear in November. By December the species is scarce near Vancouver but is still fairly common on southeastern Vancouver Island between Victoria and Comox. Godfrey (1986) considers the species

irregular in winter, but our data indicate regular wintering on southern Vancouver Island.

BREEDING: The Greater Yellowlegs breeds on the plateaus of central British Columbia including the Chilcotin-Cariboo and Nechako Lowland regions. Godfrey (1986) includes all of northeastern British Columbia in this yellowlegs' breeding range but we have no documented breeding records north of 55° latitude in the province.

The Greater Yellowlegs breeds in swampy forested lands between 900 and 1,220 m elevation. Preferred habitats include open or sparsely treed, mixed forests with low and sparse undergrowth near sloughs, wet meadows, or bogs. Burned ridges and clearings within forests are also used.

Nests: The Greater Yellowlegs is a solitary nester; adults not tending nests are constantly alert for danger, often perching on tree tops for a good view of the surrounding area. Nests are extremely difficult to find. Five nests found were scrapes or depressions in the ground sparsely lined with bits of vegetation. Two nests were situated in open lodgepole pine stands near meadows, one nest was in a wet meadow, one in a dry, burned willow area, and one was near a pond. Most nests are probably screened to some extent by vegetation or other debris (Johnsgard 1981).

Eggs: Dates for 10 clutches ranged from 17 May to 20 June with 6 recorded between 21 May and 10 June. Sizes for 9 clutches ranged from 3 to 4 eggs (3E-3, 4E-6). Incubation period is about 23 days (Bent 1927).

Young: Dates for 13 broods ranged from 18 June to 23 July with 7 recorded between 27 June and 4 July. Sizes for 12 broods ranged from 1 to 4 young (1Y-3, 2Y-3, 3Y-3, 4Y-3).

REMARKS: A coastal breeding record was reported by Brooks (1923a) who stated that C. de B. Green found Greater Yellowlegs already hatched in late May 1921 when he arrived on Porcher Island near Prince Rupert. Green considered the species a 'fairly common' breeder there. However, evidence to confirm breeding is lacking, and we have excluded this record from the account. We also have a recent report of 3 pairs of yellowlegs on territory and "obviously breeding" on Banks Island (T.E. Reimchen pers. comm.). The birds were seen in May/June 1987, but unfortunately the species of yellowlegs was not determined. This lends support to the C. de B. Green record and will alert observers visiting islands off the north mainland coast to the possibility that yellowlegs nest there.

Observers in northeastern British Columbia should also be alert to the possibility of nesting birds there. For example, a very agitated Greater Yellowlegs was encountered at Kledo Creek in both July 1985 and July 1986; on the first encounter the bird actually attacked one of the observers (C. Siddle pers. comm.).

NOTEWORTHY RECORDS

Spring: Coastal - Sidney 1 Mar 1976-13; head of Ucluelet Inlet 30 Apr 1974-43; Tofino Inlet 24 May 1984-21; Westham Island 26 Mar 1979-17; Iona Island 1 Apr 1984-75, 12 and 15 Apr 1983-100; Masset 20 Apr 1979-24. **Interior** - Columbia Lake 21 Apr 1979-10; Okanagan Landing 23 Mar 1919-1 (Munro, J.A. and Cowan 1947); Salmon Arm 19 Apr 1971-50+; Kleena Kleene 18 Apr 1950-12 (Paul 1959); Riske Creek 24 Apr 1982-20; Prince George 9 Apr 1985-2; Fort St. John 10 Apr 1984-1; Charlie Lake 22 May 1983-2; Parker Lake (Fort Nelson) 4 to 8 May 1975-2 to 5; Chilkat Pass 8 May 1957-10 (Weeden 1960).

Summer: Coastal - Witty's Lagoon 2 Jul 1983-15; Blackie Spit 22 Jun 1974-22 (Crowell and Nehls 1974d), 23 Jul 1974-40, 28 Aug 1984-53; Reifel

Island 23 Aug 1972-52; Willow Point 15 Aug 1974-30+; Masset 2 Aug 1982-11. **Interior** - White Lake (Okanagan Falls) 25 Jun 1972-7; 16 km w Kamloops 7 Aug 1977-30; Chilco Ranch (Hanceville) 29 Jul 1980-16; Stum Lake 27 Jul 1973-25 (Ryder 1973); Clarke Lake 3 Jul 1986-2 agitated; s Kledo Creek 2 Jul 1986-1 agitated; Parker Lake (Fort Nelson) 13 Jun 1976-6; Level Mountain Range 6 Jun 1978-12+.

Autumn: Interior - Fort St. John 28 Aug 1985-1, last of fall; Springhouse 29 Oct 1952-1 (NMC 47777); Scotch Creek 1 Nov 1962-6; Okanagan 10 Nov 1938-1 (MVZ 100681); Osoyoos 10 Sep 1972-8; Creston 22 Sep 1948-25 (Munro, J.A. 1950). **Coastal** - Masset 11 Oct 1971-6; Cape St. James 22 Oct 1978-1; Courtenay 1 Sep 1986-16; Iona Island

4 Sep 1974-62; Reifel Island 29 Nov 1980-17; Blackie Spit 14 Sep 1980-88, 20 Sep 1977-150, 22 Sep 1982-80; Witty's Lagoon 7 Oct 1983-35.

Winter: Interior - No records. **Coastal** - Little Qualicum River estuary 21 Feb 1978-1 (Dawe 1980); Harrison River 28 Jan 1978-1; Reifel Island 28 Feb 1981-8; Tsehum Harbour 15 Dec 1978-24; Saanich 21 Dec 1974-40; Oak Bay 3 Jan 1983-14.

Christmas Counts: Interior - Not recorded. **Coastal** - Recorded from 9 of 28 localities and on 26% of all counts. Maxima: Victoria 17 Dec 1977-70, all-time Canadian high count (Anderson, R.R. 1978); Deep Bay 19 Dec 1976-29; Vancouver 26 Dec 1963-28.

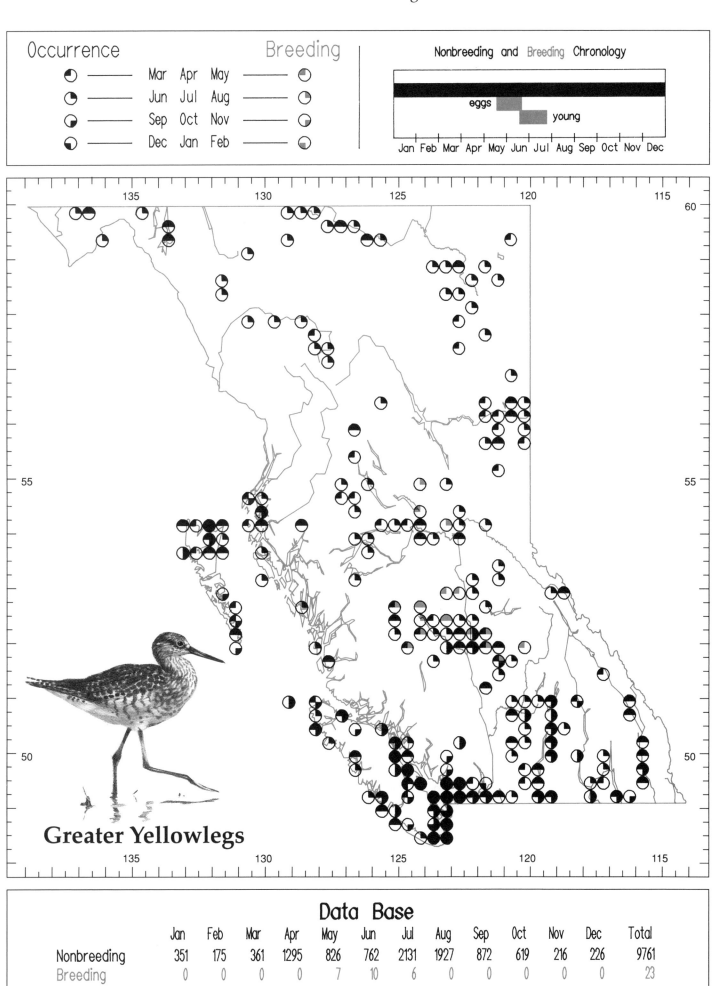

Occurrence

Occurrence		Breeding
◐ ———	Mar Apr May	——— ◓
◔ ———	Jun Jul Aug	——— ◔
◕ ———	Sep Oct Nov	——— ◐
◖ ———	Dec Jan Feb	——— ◒

Nonbreeding and Breeding Chronology

eggs young

Jan Feb Mar Apr May Jun Jul Aug Sep Oct Nov Dec

Greater Yellowlegs

Data Base

	Jan	Feb	Mar	Apr	May	Jun	Jul	Aug	Sep	Oct	Nov	Dec	Total
Nonbreeding	351	175	361	1295	826	762	2131	1927	872	619	216	226	9761
Breeding	0	0	0	0	7	10	6	0	0	0	0	0	23

Lesser Yellowlegs
Tringa flavipes (Gmelin)

LEYE

RANGE: Breeds from central Alaska, the Yukon, and northern British Columbia eastward to James Bay. Winters from the southern United States to southern South America.

STATUS: In spring, an *abundant* migrant in the Peace Lowlands, a *fairly common* to *common* migrant through the rest of the interior, and a *rare* to *uncommon*, locally *very common*, migrant on the coast. In autumn, an *uncommon* to locally *abundant* migrant over most of the province. *Very rare* winter visitant on the south coast. Breeds.

NONBREEDING: The Lesser Yellowlegs is one of the most abundant medium-sized shorebirds in British Columbia. It is widely distributed throughout the province although it is consistently abundant only east of the Rocky Mountains, particularly in the Peace and Fort Nelson lowlands. Elsewhere in the province, it is generally more numerous during the autumn movement than during the spring movement. In southern areas the species is usually less common in spring but more numerous in autumn than the Greater Yellowlegs. It has been reported from sea level to 1,450 m elevation.

The Lesser Yellowlegs occurs in the same habitats as the Greater Yellowlegs (Fig. 97). On the coast it frequents sheltered bays and estuaries with tidal mud flats, preferring slightly more sheltered spots than the Greater Yellowlegs. In tidal marshes it is found in shallower waters along edges of muddy areas but it also occurs on exposed muddy and sandy beaches. The Lesser

Yellowlegs also roosts on rocky beaches, near-shore rocks, and logs. In the interior it frequents muddy areas including wet fields, sloughs, marshes, mudflats, sewage lagoons, ploughed fields, slow-moving creeks, and lake shores. Migrant flocks have been reported roosting on wharves at Parker Lake (Fort Nelson). It is often seen swimming like phalaropes in water too deep for wading. In August, small numbers frequent alpine lakes.

Spring migration begins in March on the south coast and in mid-April in the southern interior, with a province-wide peak from late April through early May. In early summer, small numbers of non-breeders or late migrants occur south of their breeding range. Autumn migration begins in late June and builds through July as adults move south. A second, stronger passage begins in late July in the north, and mid-to-late August in the south as juveniles pass through. Numbers taper off steadily from September to October, except on the Fraser River estuary where high numbers may remain until late September. By November, the species is absent from the interior and scarce on the south coast. In winter, a few birds occur irregularly on southern Vancouver Island or near Vancouver, but it is not a regular winter visitant as is the Greater Yellowlegs.

The Lesser Yellowlegs travels in singles or small flocks, but aggregations of up to 1,000 birds may occur in good foraging localities, particularly at Cecil Lake (Goodlow), the Fort St. John sewage lagoons, Salmon Arm, Iona Island, and Reifel Island.

Figure 97. *Greater Yellowlegs (left) with Lesser Yellowlegs at Reifel Island, Delta, 23 August 1982 (Ervio Sian).*

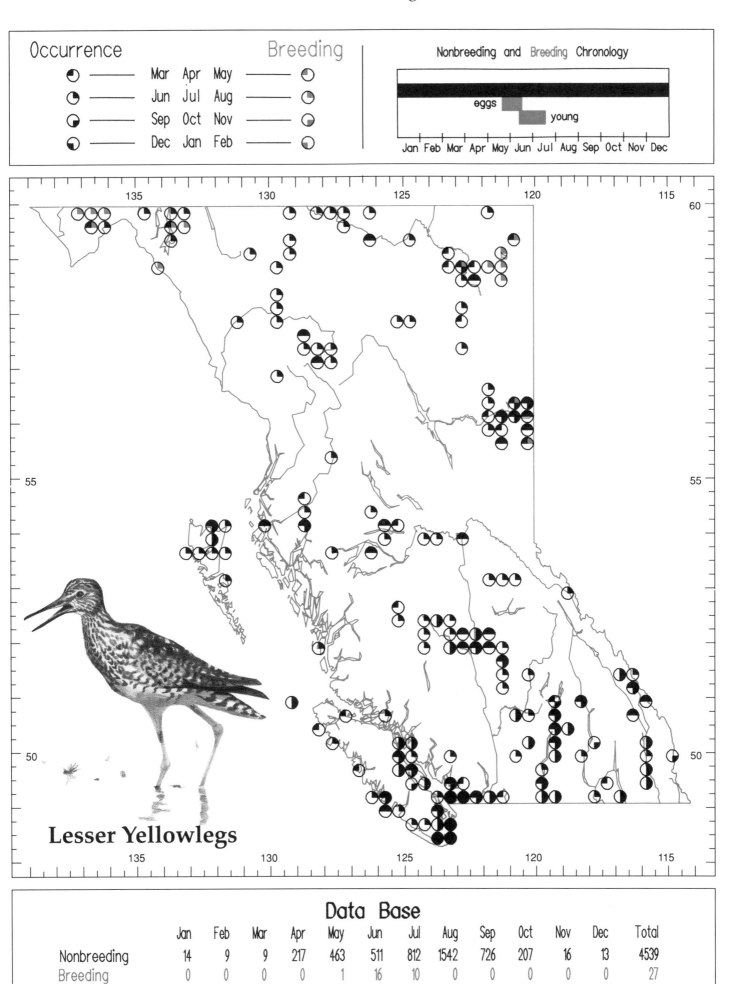

Lesser Yellowlegs

Occurrence · · · · · **Breeding**

Mar Apr May
Jun Jul Aug
Sep Oct Nov
Dec Jan Feb

Nonbreeding and Breeding Chronology

eggs   young

Jan Feb Mar Apr May Jun Jul Aug Sep Oct Nov Dec

Data Base

	Jan	Feb	Mar	Apr	May	Jun	Jul	Aug	Sep	Oct	Nov	Dec	Total
Nonbreeding	14	9	9	217	463	511	812	1542	726	207	16	13	4539
Breeding	0	0	0	0	1	16	10	0	0	0	0	0	27

BREEDING: The Lesser Yellowlegs (Fig. 98) breeds across the extreme northern portions of the province including the Peace and Fort Nelson lowlands, Stikine and Teslin plateaus, and Chilkat Pass area (Fig. 99) at elevations ranging between 750 and 1,200 m. It is most numerous in the Peace Lowlands and the Boreal Forest region east of the Rocky Mountains, becoming less abundant west of the Rocky Mountains. Campbell and McNall (1982) estimated 1 to 2 birds per km of road east of Fort Nelson in June 1982.

The Lesser Yellowlegs frequents semi-open coniferous woodland with sparse, low undergrowth, near swampy or wet areas (Fig. 100) such as boggy openings in spruce swamps, sub-alpine marshes, and lakeside forest clearings. Road allowances and seismic lines have created additional nesting habitat. Wet, swampy marshes are used as brood-rearing sites.

Nests: Nests (n=5) were shallow scrapes in the ground lined with small amounts of debris such as grasses, dry leaves, sedges, or twigs. Two nests were situated in wet sub-alpine marshes, one in a forest clearing, one on a road right-of-way, and one on a seismic line through a black spruce bog. The nest found on the seismic line was on a dry rise, under a 2-m high scrub birch, among stunted black spruce, heather mounds, and wet sphagnum; puddles were within a few metres. One nest was situated on a small hummock.

Eggs: Dates for 5 clutches ranged from 4 to 16 June. Calculated dates indicate that eggs could be found as early as 20 May. Clutch size ranged from 3 to 4 eggs (3E-1, 4E-4). Incubation period is 22 to 23 days (Jehl and Smith 1970).

Young: Dates for 21 broods ranged from 13 June to 17 July (Fig. 101) with 12 broods found between 24 June and 3 July. Sizes for 19 broods ranged from 1 to 3 young (1Y-7, 2Y-5, 3Y-7). Fledging period is probably 23 to 25 days (Johnsgard 1981).

REMARKS: Hayman et al. (1986) discuss the problem of identifying yellowlegs in the field.

Figure 98. Full clutch of Lesser Yellowlegs eggs at Helmet, near Kwokullie Lake, 4 June 1982 (RBCM E2023; John M. Cooper).

Figure 99. Lesser Yellowlegs on breeding territory at Mosquito Flats, Chilkat Pass, 7 July 1980 (Ervio Sian).

Figure 100. Davie Hall Lake north of Atlin, 2 July 1980 (R. Wayne Campbell). For nesting, Lesser Yellowlegs use muskegs adjacent to lakes where wet areas are used for feeding and raising the young.

Figure 101. *Lesser Yellowlegs chick at Como Lake, Atlin, July 1980 (R. Wayne Campbell).*

NOTEWORTHY RECORDS

Spring: Coastal - Iona Island 6 Apr 1976-200+, 24 Apr 1981-25; Reifel Island 18 Mar 1977-6; Campbell River (Discovery Passage) 18 Apr 1974-11; Delkatla Inlet 30 Mar 1983-1. **Interior -** Nicola Lake 16 Apr 1979-75; Revelstoke 12 Apr 1978-1, 4 May 1977-20 (Bonar 1978a); Riske Creek 6 May 1977-62; Fort St. John 26 Apr 1983-151; Cecil Lake 6 May 1981-1,000+ (Siddle 1982), 8 May 1980-400+; North Pine 12 May 1979-150; Parker Lake (Fort Nelson) 14 May 1978-50; Atlin 28 Apr 1981-2; Mosquito Flats (Chilkat Pass) 14 May 1977-60.

Summer: Coastal - Delkatla Inlet 24 Jul 1987-50 (Cooper, J.M. 1987); Cowichan Bay 13 Aug 1977-51, 18 Aug 1987-151; Iona Island 28 Jun 1982-13, 8 Aug 1977-245, 18 Aug 1976-383, 20 Aug 1977-543; Qualicum Beach 9 Aug 1976-77 (Dawe 1980); Delkatla Inlet 26 Jul 1987-50, 2 Aug 1982-15. **Interior -** Creston 25 Aug 1947-85 (Munro, J.A.

1958a); Okanagan Landing 29 Aug 1935-150+ (Munro, J.A. and Cowan 1947); Salmon Arm (Shuswap Lake) 25 Aug 1977-200+; 70 Mile House 13 Jun 1978-4; Williams Lake 15 Aug 1976-70; Bowron Lake 18 Aug 1975-50 (Bell 1975); Fort St. John 27 Jun 1987-400, 29 Jun 1986-150, 5 Jul 1986-300, 17 Jul 1986-114, 25 Jul 1987-275; Boundary Lake (Goodlow) 13 Aug 1986-100 juveniles, 20 Aug 1986-200 juveniles; Charlie Lake 14 Aug 1976-75+; Kotcho Lake 26 Jun 1982-17 singles.

Autumn: Interior - Charlie Lake 6 Sep 1982-10, 21 Oct 1979-1; Boundary Lake (Goodlow) 21 Oct 1986-1; Fort St. John 5 Sep 1986-63 juveniles, 15 Oct 1986-2; Chilco Ranch (Hanceville) 20 Sep 1982-15; Swan Lake (Vernon) 11 Sep 1970-50+, 26 Oct 1951-1 (ROM 84998); Okanagan Landing 2 Sep 1933-100+ (Munro, J.A. and Cowan 1947).

Coastal - Delkatla Inlet 24 Oct 1971-1; Campbell River (Discovery Passage) 11 Sep 1974-20+; Iona Island 28 Sep 1972-200, 10 Nov 1971-10; Reifel Island 10 Sep 1972-97 (Crowell and Nehls 1973a), 4 Oct 1977-84; Esquimalt Lagoon 24 Nov 1980-2.

Winter: Interior - No records. **Coastal -** Burnaby Lake 5 Jan 1975-1; Sea Island 5 Jan 1975-2; Saanich 21 Jan 1979-2; Tsehum Harbour 19 Feb 1977-1; Witty's Lagoon 25 Dec 1981-1.

Christmas Counts: Interior - Not recorded. **Coastal -** Recorded from 3 of 28 localities and on 2% of all counts. Maxima: Vancouver 21 Dec 1969-7, all-time Canadian high count (Anderson, R.R. 1976); Victoria 17 Dec 1977-2; Comox 18 Dec 1983-2.

Solitary Sandpiper
Tringa solitaria Wilson

SOSA

RANGE: Breeds from Alaska, the Yukon, and British Columbia eastward across southern Canada to Labrador. Winters from the southern United States to southern South America.

STATUS: *Uncommon* to *fairly common* migrant and summer visitant in the interior. *Rare* migrant on the south coast; *very rare* on the north coast. Widespread breeder.

NONBREEDING: The Solitary Sandpiper is widely distributed throughout the province east of the Coast Ranges during spring and autumn migrations. At these times, it is scarce on the coast, including Vancouver Island and the Queen Charlotte Islands. It is a quiet, rather inconspicuous species that migrates singly (Fig. 102), and consequently passes through relatively unnoticed. Only in late summer, when the bulk of the southward movement occurs, is it recorded in any numbers. Even then, large flocks are unusual, and most reports are of 1 to 4 birds loosely scattered in good foraging habitats. At times, loose aggregations can number up to 30 birds (Campbell 1987e). The Solitary Sandpiper has been recorded from sea level to 1,600 m elevation.

It usually frequents secluded woodland ponds and pools although it may occur in almost any wet, muddy area, especially if the area is wooded, including habitats not usually frequented by shorebirds. On the coast, it occurs on tidal mud flats and small estuaries. In the interior, it frequents marshes (Fig. 103), wet fields, river edges, creek mouths, lake shores, sewage lagoons, and bogs. In late summer, migrants can occur in alpine meadows and associated ponds. In marshes it prefers the muddy areas between drying rushes and the water's edge. In woodland pools it forages along the water's edge on grassy banks or from exposed stones and branches. It is most common in the Boreal Forest regions of the province.

The spring movement begins in late April and is over by mid-to-late May. The Solitary Sandpiper was very common in May 1982 in the spruce forests northeast of Fort Nelson (Campbell and McNall 1982), but was much less noticeable in June, probably because of the onset of nesting activities. The autumn movement begins in mid-July and peaks in August. The species does not linger in southern British Columbia, unlike many other shorebirds. Most have passed through by late September.

The Solitary Sandpiper has been recorded in British Columbia from 20 April to 20 October.

Figure 102. *Solitary Sandpiper at Cathedral Lake, 19 August 1985 (Chris R. Siddle).*

Figure 103. *Solitary Sandpiper foraging in marsh near Fort St. John, 11 May 1985 (Chris R. Siddle).*

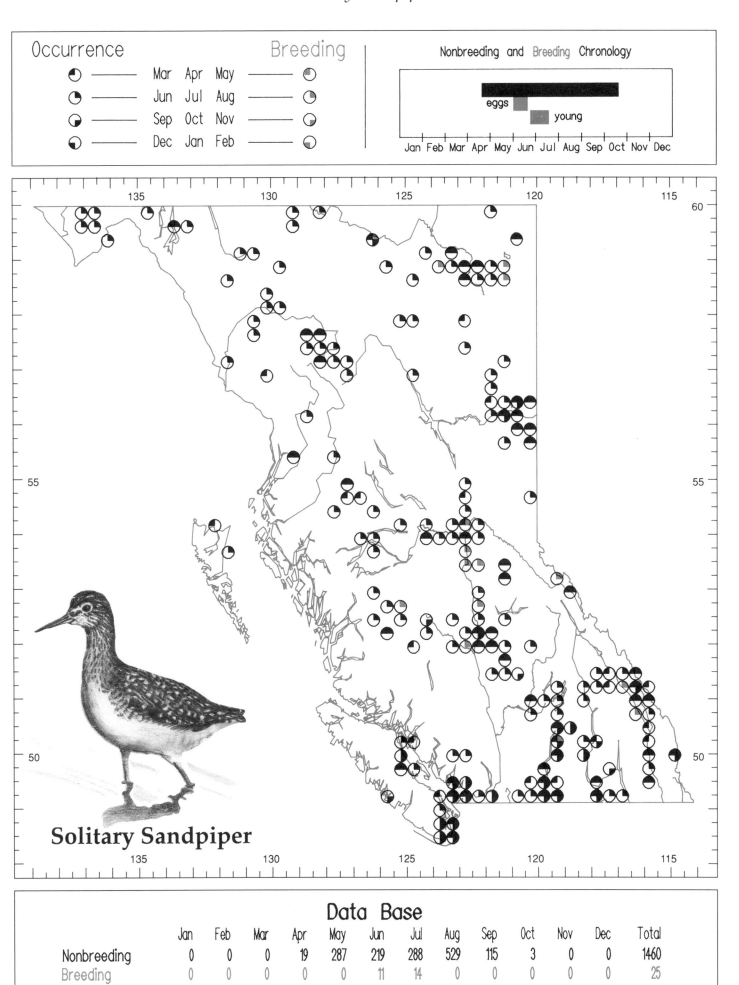

Solitary Sandpiper

Occurrence

		Breeding
◑ ———	Mar Apr May	——— ◑
◐ ———	Jun Jul Aug	——— ◐
◓ ———	Sep Oct Nov	——— ◓
◒ ———	Dec Jan Feb	——— ◒

Nonbreeding and Breeding Chronology

eggs

young

Jan Feb Mar Apr May Jun Jul Aug Sep Oct Nov Dec

Solitary Sandpiper

Data Base

	Jan	Feb	Mar	Apr	May	Jun	Jul	Aug	Sep	Oct	Nov	Dec	Total
Nonbreeding	0	0	0	19	287	219	288	529	115	3	0	0	1460
Breeding	0	0	0	0	0	11	14	0	0	0	0	0	25

BREEDING: The Solitary Sandpiper breeds from the northern Okanagan valley and Northern Columbia Mountains through the Fraser Plateau and Fraser Basin to the Fort Nelson Lowlands and Liard Basin. Breeding has been reported from elevations between 550 and 1,700 m. Preferred habitat is at the higher elevations where spruce and lodgepole pine forests occur in association with open, wet bogs (Fig. 104). Preferred habitats contain water, scattered coniferous trees, and old nests of suitably sized passerine birds. Boggy areas within logged over or burned lands have also been recorded as breeding habitat. Level areas such as valleys, plateaus, and lowlands are used rather than sloping mountain sides.

Of the 6 reported nests, 4 were found at Liard River Hotsprings Park, where the habitat is open sulphurous swamp surrounded by thickets of stunted spruce within a mature spruce forest. A nest at Bald Mountain (Riske Creek) was situated in a logged-over lodgepole pine woodland with only scrub pines left standing. Another nest, at Moffat Lake, was in a patch of young lodgepole pines within a burned area. Young are raised in sedge fens, muskegs, or bogs.

Nests: Solitary Sandpipers have evolved a nesting strategy that is unique among North American shorebirds: they use the nests of other birds as nest sites. Nests of passerines such as robins, waxwings, and blackbirds are used, probably because they are the appropriate size and occur in similar habitats. Nests from the previous year are used; no lining is added by the

sandpiper. The nests are usually situated in conifers (Fig. 105). Of 6 nests reported, 3 were in American Robin *(Turdus migratorius)* nests and 1 was in a Cedar Waxwing *(Bombycilla cedrorum)* nest. Five nest heights ranged between 2 and 4.5 m above the ground.

Eggs: Dates for 6 clutches ranged from 2 to 10 June. Calculated dates indicate that eggs could be found as late as 20 June. Clutch size ranged from 3 to 4 eggs (3E-2, 4E-4). Incubation period is undetermined.

Young: Dates for 16 broods ranged from 25 June to 18 July with 8 broods recorded between 30 June and 16 July. Brood size ranged from 1 to 3 young (1Y-5, 2Y-7, 3Y-4), although broods of 4 young undoubtedly exist. Fledging period is unknown.

REMARKS: Observations of adults, acting in a manner usually associated with nesting, have been made at Manning Park, Kootenay National Park, Charlie Lake (Cowan 1939), Boundary Lake, Kitchener Lake, and Atlin. The Solitary Sandpiper probably breeds throughout its British Columbia range east of the Coast Mountains and observers should be alert for the species in suitable habitat. See Oring (1973) for clues to early reproductive behaviour.

J.A. Munro and Cowan (1947) consider the Solitary Sandpiper a summer visitant only in the northern part of the province and the Peace River Lowlands. They report no nesting records for the species.

Figure 104. *Wetlands near Fort Nelson, July 1982 (Michael C.E. McNall). Quiet, woodland bogs and muskegs with breeding passerines is the preferred nesting habitat for Solitary Sandpipers.*

Figure 105. *Solitary Sandpiper nest at Bald Mountain, Riske Creek, 4 June 1980 (John M. Cooper).*

NOTEWORTHY RECORDS

Spring: Coastal - Blenkinsop Lake 22 Apr 1984-1; Reifel Island 20 Apr 1981-1; Maple Ridge 25 May 1979-1; Nanaimo 9 May 1968-1 (Crowell and Nehls 1968c); Masset 17 May 1920-1 (MVZ 100696). **Interior** - Princeton 23 Apr 1977-1; s 150 Mile House 30 Apr 1981-1; Telkwa 4 May 1978-1; Charlie Lake 26 Apr 1980-1; w Boundary Lake (Goodlow) 11 May 1986-6; Atlin 18 May 1977-10.

Summer: Coastal - Iona Island 10 Jun 1967-1, 28 Aug 1979-3; Salmon Point (Discovery Passage) 22 Jul 1974-3; Tlell 11 Aug 1974-1. **Interior** - Trail 26 Aug 1982-5; Kalamalka Lake 9 to 21 Aug 1975-9; Wilmer 23 Jul 1977-6; Horse Lake (100 Mile House) 1 Aug 1933-12 (Munro, J.A. and Cowan 1947); Felker Lake 10 Jul 1970-6; Beaver Lake (Stum Lake) 26 Jul 1973-16 (Ryder 1973); Fort St. John (counts at northern sewage lagoons in 1987; Campbell 1987e) 14 Jun-0, 18th-1, 24th-8, 17th-30, 29th-25, 30th-4, 9 Jul-5, 12th-7, 13th-2, 15th-2, 17th-3, 18th-1, 20th-3, 22nd-5, 23rd-4, 25th-4, 26th-2, 27th-30 and 30th-4; w Boundary Lake (Goodlow) 23 Jun 1985-1 in flight display; Fern Lake (Kwadacha Wilderness Park) 18 Aug 1979-3 (Cooper, J.M. and Adams 1979); Chilkat Pass 2 Aug 1957-1 (Weeden 1960).

Autumn: Interior - Charlie Lake 5 Sep 1982-1; Fort St. John 20 Sep 1986-1; Bridge Lake 15 Sep 1962-2; Minton Creek (Chilcotin) 13 Sep 1986-2; Okanagan Landing 5 Oct 1929-1; Nakusp 8 Sep 1975-1; Fruitvale 14 Sep 1968-2. **Coastal** - Sea Island 20 Oct 1966-1 (RBCM 11636); Saanich 28 Sep 1978-1; Witty's Lagoon 6 Sep 1971-1 (Tatum 1972).

Winter: No records.

Willet

WILL

Catoptrophorus semipalmatus (Gmelin)

RANGE: Breeds in the prairie regions of Canada, the north-western United States, and on the Atlantic coast from Nova Scotia to northern Mexico. Winters along the coast from the southern United States to northern South America.

STATUS: *Very rare* spring and summer vagrant to south coastal British Columbia including Vancouver Island; *casual* spring vagrant in the southern interior; *accidental* in the Peace Lowlands. *Very rare* autumn vagrant on the south coast; *casual* in the southern interior. *Casual* in winter locally along the Strait of Georgia.

CHANGE IN STATUS: J.A. Munro and Cowan (1947) include the Willet in their hypothetical list on the basis of one bird reported to have been collected near Victoria on 18 August 1898 (Fannin 1898). The species was not reported in the province again until April 1945 when Clay (1946) sighted 50 Willets at Oak Bay. This extraordinary record was apparently discounted at the time by most local bird watchers. The observer, however, noted the unmistakable wing patterns as flocks of 8, 25, and 17 flew past.

OCCURRENCE: The Willet is an irregular vagrant to southern British Columbia; we have one documented record from the Peace Lowlands. Its nearest breeding grounds are in southern Alberta and eastern Oregon. Willets that breed in the west move to the Pacific coast to winter from Oregon to Peru. Birds sighted in British Columbia are individuals that have wandered north of their normal range. Most sightings in British Columbia are of single birds principally from Blackie Spit and Iona Island in the Fraser River estuary and Oak Bay in Victoria.

On the coast, the Willet frequents tidal mud flats, sand beaches, lagoons, and near-shore rocks. In the interior, it uses muddy areas such as marshes, sloughs, wet fields, grassy playing fields, and sewage lagoons. It often associates with other waders such as yellowlegs, whimbrels, plovers, and "peeps."

Figure 106. Willet at Charlie Lake near Fort St. John, 19 May 1984 (Chris R. Siddle).

Figure 107. Willet at Osoyoos, 4 May 1985 (RBCM Photo 1026; Richard J. Cannings).

NOTEWORTHY RECORDS

Spring: Coastal - Oak Bay 17 Mar 1964-1 (Davidson 1966), 29 Apr 1945-50 (Clay 1946); Witty's Lagoon 19 May 1980-1; Iona Island 4 Apr 1983-1; Willow Point 22 May 1973-1. **Interior** - Creston Apr 1979-1; Osoyoos Lake 4 May 1985-1 (RBCM Photo 1026, Fig. 107; Campbell 1985c); Separation Lake 24 May 1985-1; Charlie Lake 19 May 1984-1 (RBCM Photo 919, Fig. 106).

Summer: Coastal - Chain Islets Aug 1957-4

(Davidson 1966); Blackie Spit 22 Jun to 23 Jul 1974-1 (Shepard, M.G. 1975c), 3 Aug 1974-3; Iona Island 14, 24, 26 Jun 1981-1, 27 Aug 1963-2. **Interior** - No records.

Autumn: Interior - Separation Lake 8 Sep 1985-1; Kelowna 13 to 15 Sep 1973-1. **Coastal** - Iona Island 7 Sep 1969-1 (Crowell and Nehls 1970a), 27 Oct 1963-1; Blackie Spit 23 Sep to 20 Oct 1973-1 (Crowell and Nehls 1974a), 6 Nov 1972-1; Oak

Bay 3 Oct and 1 Nov 1959-1 (Stirling 1960a), 2 to 3 Oct 1986-1.

Winter: Interior - No records. **Coastal** - Comox 26 Jan 1950-1 (RBCM 12765); Iona Island 22 and 30 Jan 1972-1 (Crowell and Nehls 1972b).

Christmas Counts: Recorded once: White Rock 30 Dec 1973-2, all-time Canadian high count (Anderson, R.R. 1976).

Willet

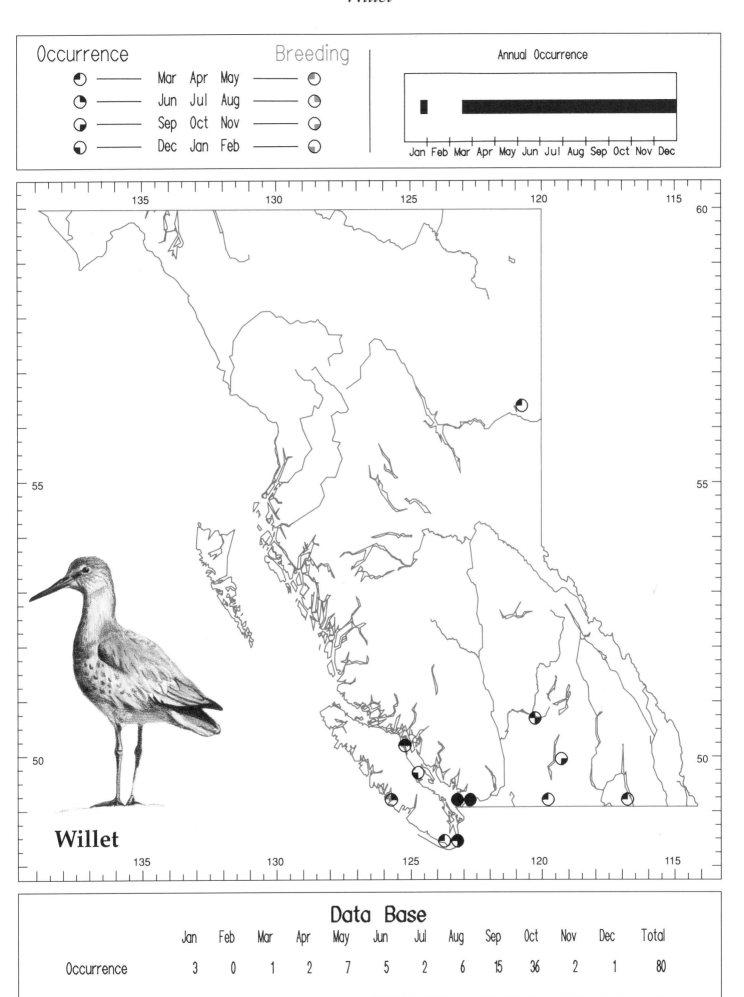

Occurrence

Mar Apr May
Jun Jul Aug
Sep Oct Nov
Dec Jan Feb

Breeding

Annual Occurrence

Jan Feb Mar Apr May Jun Jul Aug Sep Oct Nov Dec

Data Base

	Jan	Feb	Mar	Apr	May	Jun	Jul	Aug	Sep	Oct	Nov	Dec	Total
Occurrence	3	0	1	2	7	5	2	6	15	36	2	1	80

Wandering Tattler

Heteroscelus incanus (Gmelin)

WATA

RANGE: Breeds in mountainous areas of central Alaska, the Yukon, and northwestern British Columbia; also in Siberia. Winters along the coast from southern California to Ecuador and on South Pacific islands south to New Zealand.

STATUS: *Fairly common* to occasionally *common* migrant on the outer coast. *Very rare* migrant along the inner coast and east of the Coast Ranges. *Uncommon* summer visitant in the Northern Mountains and Plateaus region and Chilkat Pass area. *Casual* in winter on the south coast. Local breeder.

NONBREEDING: The Wandering Tattler (Fig. 108) is widely distributed along coastal British Columbia. It migrates singly or in small flocks along reefs, rocks, and peninsulas of the west coast of Vancouver Island, Queen Charlotte Sound, and the Queen Charlotte Islands. Reef-filled Barkley Sound attracts many birds during migration. The Wandering Tattler is quite rare in protected waters, tending to avoid the coastal fiords and even the Strait of Georgia to some extent. In the interior, migrants are exceptionally rare. It has been recorded from sea level to 1,300 m elevation.

The Wandering Tattler mainly inhabits the surf-washed reefs and rocks of the outer coast (Fig. 109). It uses recently exposed rocks covered with barnacles, mussels, and kelp as foraging sites, particularly those amid crashing breakers. It also occurs on nearshore rocks, beaches, and mudflats. In the interior, it has been reported from lakeshore beaches and pond edges.

Figure 108 Wandering Tattler in nonbreeding plumage on the Bunsby Islands, Vancouver Island, 11 August 1984 (Tim Zurowski).

Figure 109. Foraging habitat for migrating Wandering Tattlers on Harvey Islands off the central mainland coast, 24 June 1978 (R. Wayne Campbell).

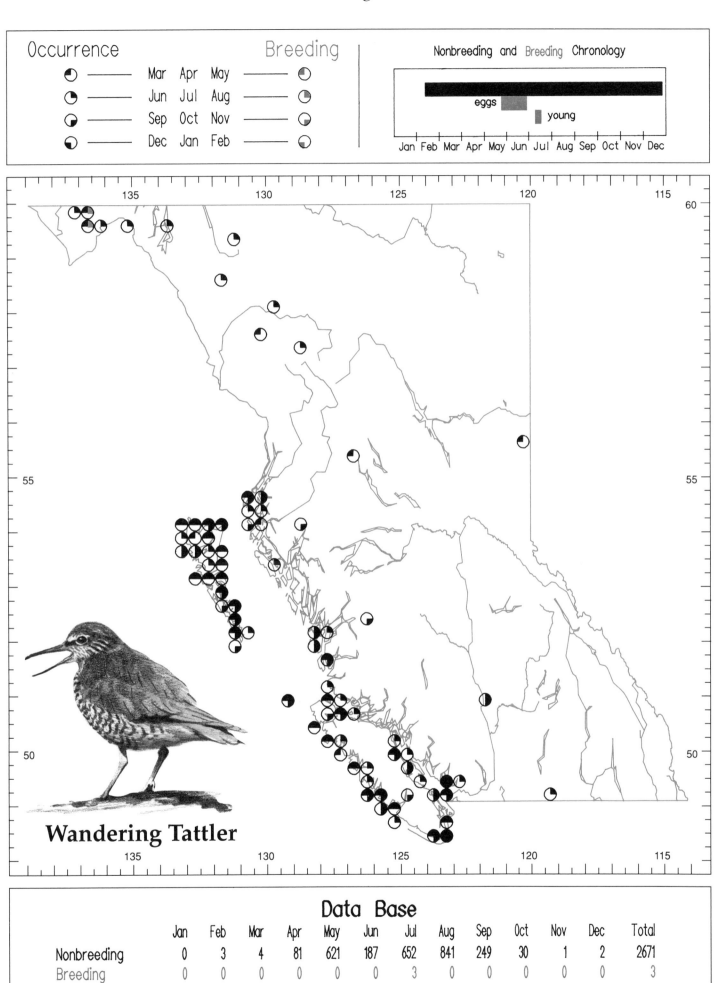

Wandering Tattler

Occurrence

	Mar	Apr	May
	Jun	Jul	Aug
	Sep	Oct	Nov
	Dec	Jan	Feb

Breeding

Nonbreeding and Breeding Chronology

eggs

young

Jan Feb Mar Apr May Jun Jul Aug Sep Oct Nov Dec

Data Base

	Jan	Feb	Mar	Apr	May	Jun	Jul	Aug	Sep	Oct	Nov	Dec	Total
Nonbreeding	0	3	4	81	621	187	652	841	249	30	1	2	2671
Breeding	0	0	0	0	0	0	3	0	0	0	0	0	3

Spring migration begins in mid-April, peaks in early May, and is over by late May, although early spring arrivals have been reported near Victoria in February. A few non-breeders remain on the coast in June. The longer autumn movement begins in mid-July. Numbers peak from late July to late August and taper off through September. Our latest autumn date is 29 October..

BREEDING: The Wandering Tattler (Fig. 110) reaches the southern edge of its breeding range in extreme northwestern British Columbia. The only confirmed breeding localities are in the St. Elias Mountains west of the Chilkat Pass. June records of adults at Gnat Lakes south of Dease Lake, suggest the possibility of breeding in the Northern Mountains and Plateaus region.

Nests of the Wandering Tattler have not been found in the province and only 3 broods have been reported. The remote and rugged terrain the species inhabits reduces the probability of discovering nests or young (Fig. 111). The first breeding record documented in British Columbia was obtained on 11 July 1944 when 2 downy young were collected (ROM 71310, 71311) in a tarn at 1,200 m near the Tatshenshini River at Mile 85, Haines Road (Kelsall Lake). On 18 July 1979, a single downy young was found at the 1,075 m level of west Nadahini Creek near Mile 70, Haines Road. A year later, 2 downy young were found on 14 July near a glacier at the head of Nadahini Creek at 1,180 m elevation. The same pair may have been involved in the last 2 records, because the Wandering Tattler exhibits remarkable nest site fidelity from year to year (Weeden 1959b, 1965a).

In British Columbia, the egg-laying period is not known. Therefore, on the accompanying map, we have used the dates 25 May to 29 June for nests with eggs found by Weeden (1965a) in east-central Alaska. The incubation period is 23 to 25 days.

REMARKS: The Wandering Tattler is considered to form a superspecies with the Gray-tailed Tattler *Heteroscelus brevipes* (Hayman et al. 1986). *H. brevipes* is a vagrant to North America as far south as California, thus observers should examine tattlers carefully, especially those at unusual localities (Paulson 1986).

Knowledge of the breeding distribution of the Wandering Tattler could be enhanced with further field studies in northwestern British Columbia.

Figure 110. *Wandering Tattler in breeding plumage near Kelsall Lake in Chilkat Pass, 22 May 1977 (Ervio Sian).*

Figure 111. *Wandering Tattler breeding habitat west of Nadahini Creek, Chilkat Pass, 18 July 1979 (Sydney G. Cannings).*

Figure 112. *Wandering Tattler in nonbreeding plumage at Crown Lake, between Pavilion and Turquiose lakes in the south-central interior, 2 September 1976 (Winnifred M. Bennie).*

NOTEWORTHY RECORDS

Spring: Coastal - Chain Islets 2 Mar 1974-1 (Shepard, M.G. 1974); Cleland Island 28 Apr 1977-20, 12 May 1976-50; Nootka Island 24 May 1969-6 (Bell 1973); Lyell Island 13 May 1982-3; Green Island 27 May 1978-1. **Interior** - Babine River 22 May 1978-1; Tupper Creek (Tupper) 30 May 1938-1 (RBCM 7909); Chilkat Pass 22 May 1977-14.

Summer: Coastal - Clover Point 8 Jun 1973-2 (non-breeders); Florencia Islet 29 Aug 1977-21; Baeria Rocks 25 Jul 1970-16; Cleland Island 24 Jul 1967-40 (Campbell and Stirling 1968b), 12 Aug 1973-35; Mitlenatch Island 6 Aug 1965-12; Green Island 6 Aug 1978-5. **Interior** - Osoyoos Lake 8 Jun 1985-1; Crown Lake 31 Aug 1976-1 (RBCM Photo 461); Upper Gnat Lake 1 Jun 1978-2.

Autumn: Interior - Crown Lake 1 to 2 Sep 1976-1 (RBCM Photo 461; Fig. 112). **Coastal** - Yakan Point 5 Sep 1919-7; De la Beche Inlet 30 Sep 1976-29; Cape St. James 23 Oct 1978-1; Stuie 2 Sep 1986-1; Tofino Inlet 26 Sep 1970-8 (Campbell and Shepard 1971); Green Point (Long Beach) 22 Oct 1972-1; Florencia Islet 26 Sep 1981-3; Gonzales Bay 29 Oct 1983-1.

Winter: Interior - No records. **Coastal** - Chain Islets 13 Feb 1974-1 (Shepard, M.G. 1974); Oak Bay 25 Feb 1943-1.

Christmas Counts: Interior - Not recorded. **Coastal** - Recorded once: Vancouver 26 Dec 1963-1, all-time Canadian high count (Anderson, R.R. 1976).

Spotted Sandpiper
Actitis macularia (Linnaeus)

RANGE: Breeds from northern Alaska eastward and southward through most of Canada and the United States. Winters on the Pacific coast from southwestern British Columbia to northern Chile, and on the Atlantic coast from South Carolina to southern Brazil.

STATUS: *Uncommon* to locally *fairly common* migrant and summer visitant throughout the province. In winter, *rare* on the southwest coast, *casual* in the southern interior. Widespread breeder.

NONBREEDING: The Spotted Sandpiper is widely distributed throughout the province from late spring through early autumn from sea level to 2,150 m elevation. It inhabits the shorelines of virtually all waterways at all elevations, almost wherever there is ice-free water. It forages by working the margins at the water's edge, rarely wading, but picking among the dry rocks, floating logs, and washed up flotsam. On the coast, it frequents areas where small streams drain across tidal mud (Guiguet 1955a) or boulder-strewn beaches. It generally avoids expansive mudflats and bare sandy beaches. Other coastal habitats include rain pools on small rocky islets, sewage lagoons, and beached seaweed flotsam on sandy beaches. Other interior habitats include gravel pits, roadsides, sewage ponds, and flood plains.

The Spotted Sandpiper does not generally migrate in large numbers, although, occasionally flocks of 10 to 22 birds have been reported. Spring migrants begin to arrive in late April. The spring movement peaks in mid-May in the south and late May in the north. In the Fort Nelson Lowlands, Spotted Sandpipers were scarce from 15 to 20 May in 1982 but became numerous after 21 May (Campbell and McNall 1982). Migration is much more noticeable in the interior than on the coast.

After the breeding season, adults and fledglings gather into small flocks, beginning about mid-July. Adult females migrate first, arriving in the Okanagan valley, for example, in mid-July, followed by adult males and juveniles from mid-August through October (Cannings, R.A. et al. 1987). In winter, a few birds linger on southern Vancouver Island beaches and in the Fraser Lowlands. There are only 2 interior winter records.

BREEDING: The Spotted Sandpiper breeds in all regions of the province but is much more abundant east of the Coast Ranges. It is not a colonial nester although it may be almost a semi-colonial breeder on small islands in coastal inlets. It usually breeds in pairs scattered along the perimeters of most lakes and rivers and on some coastal grassy beaches. It has very broad environmental tolerances and will breed almost wherever there is fresh water. Typical breeding habitat is the edge of an open or semi-open area adjacent to water, with a low ground cover such as shrub-dotted or lightly treed meadows or grazed grasslands, often on a point or peninsula. In heavily forested areas, man-made clearings and weedy roadsides near water are used. It may breed from ocean beaches near sea level up to sub-alpine meadows at elevations of over 1,800 m. Young are raised in wet meadows or bogs, or on shorelines.

Nests: Most nests (93%; n=325) were found near the edges of open areas. The remainder were found under an open forest canopy. The most frequently recorded nesting habitats were clearings at the edges of ponds or lakes (38%), open river banks (22%), and roadsides (8%). Other habitats included marine beaches (7%) and islets (7%) on the coast, open rangeland (5%) in the southern interior, and well-drilling pads (4%) and seismic lines (2 nests) in the boreal forest. Vegetated gravel bars on beaches, rivers, and lakeshores are often used.

Nests were slight hollows or cups scraped in the ground and loosely lined with grasses, leaves, stems, twigs, wood chips, or needles. Only 7 of 270 nests were reported to be unlined. Most nests were partially concealed by overhanging or adjacent vegetation, or objects such as stones and logs. The bases of saplings, tufts of grass, or short clumps of vegetation were preferred sites. Distance to water for 72 nests ranged from 0.25 to 100 m but 72% of the nests were less than 15 m from water. They were often found on the top of a small knoll or on a rise in the ground. When nesting on small islands, the top of the island was preferred. One nest was situated on top of a beaver lodge.

Eggs: Dates for 380 clutches ranged from 17 April to 26 July with 57% recorded between 9 and 29 June. Sizes for 424 clutches ranged from 1 to 5 eggs (1E-10, 2E-10, 3E-28, 4E-372, 5E-4) with 88% having 4 eggs. Incubation period is 20 to 24 days (Hays 1972).

Young: Dates for 255 broods ranged from 5 June to 29 August with 52% recorded between 28 June and 17 July. Calculated dates indicate that young could be found as early as 10 May. Sizes for 252 broods ranged from 1 to 6 young (1Y-61, 2Y-74, 3Y-54, 4Y-62, 6Y-1) with 75% having 2 to 4 young. There is an extraordinary record from Shuswap Lake of 6 newly hatched chicks found in 1 nest. Fledging period is 16 to 18 days (Oring and Maxon 1978).

REMARKS: An incidence of Brown-headed Cowbird (*Molothrus ater*) parasitism was reported from Charlie Lake on 6 June 1984 when 1 cowbird egg was found with a clutch of 3 Spotted Sandpiper eggs (RBCM Photo 920).

NOTEWORTHY RECORDS

Spring: Coastal - Clover Point 20 May 1974-20; Little Qualicum River 26 Apr 1978-1 (Dawe 1980); Cranberry Lake (Powell River) 26 Apr 1980-1; Perry Lake 22 May 1973-26 (Bell 1973). **Interior** - Edgewood 7 Mar 1924-1; Haynes Point (Osoyoos Lake) 23 May 1974-17 (Cannings, S.G. 1974); Emerald Lake (Yoho National Park) 22 May 1976-22 (Wade 1977); Swan Lake (Tupper) 30 May 1938-100 (Munro, J.A. and Cowan 1947); Charlie Lake 9 May 1986-4; Parker Lake (Fort Nelson) 13 May 1975-1.

Summer: Coastal - Mount Douglas Beach (Saanich) 25 Jul 1974-12, 3 Aug 1975-15; Duncan 29 Jul 1974-9 on log; Triangle Island (Scott Islands) 21 Aug 1974-11. **Interior** - Summit Creek (Creston) 13 Aug 1947-35 (Munro, J.A. 1958a); Salmon Arm 24 Aug 1973-60 (Sirk et al. 1973), 25 Aug 1977-20; Charlie Lake 18 Jul 1983-19 (15 adults, 4 immatures).

Autumn: Interior - Kahan Creek 20 Sep 1976-2 (Hazelwood 1976c); Charlie Lake 17 Sep 1983-2; Kelowna 11 Oct 1971-1; Nancy Greene Lake 14 Oct 1978-1. **Coastal** - Malcolm Island 9 Nov 1976-1; Long Beach 8 Sep 1983-19; Duncan 25 Nov 1976-4; Billings Spit 21 Nov 1983-1.

Winter: Interior - Kelowna 19 Dec 1970-1 (Cannings, R.A. et al. 1987); Summerland 20 to 27 Dec 1969-1. **Coastal** - Little Qualicum River 31 Jan 1977-1 (Dawe 1980); Point Grey Beach 9 Jan to 6 Feb 1977-4; Duncan 15 Jan 1977-2; Muir Creek 8 Feb 1970-2 (Tatum 1971).

Christmas Counts: Interior - Not recorded. **Coastal** - Recorded from 13 of 28 localities and on 16% of all counts. Maxima: Comox 18 Dec 1983-6, all-time Canadian high count (Monroe 1984); Vancouver 30 Dec 1967-4; Deep Bay 29 Dec 1981-3; Port Alberni 4 Jan 1976-3; Victoria 27 Dec 1970, 17 Dec 1977, and 17 Dec 1983-3.

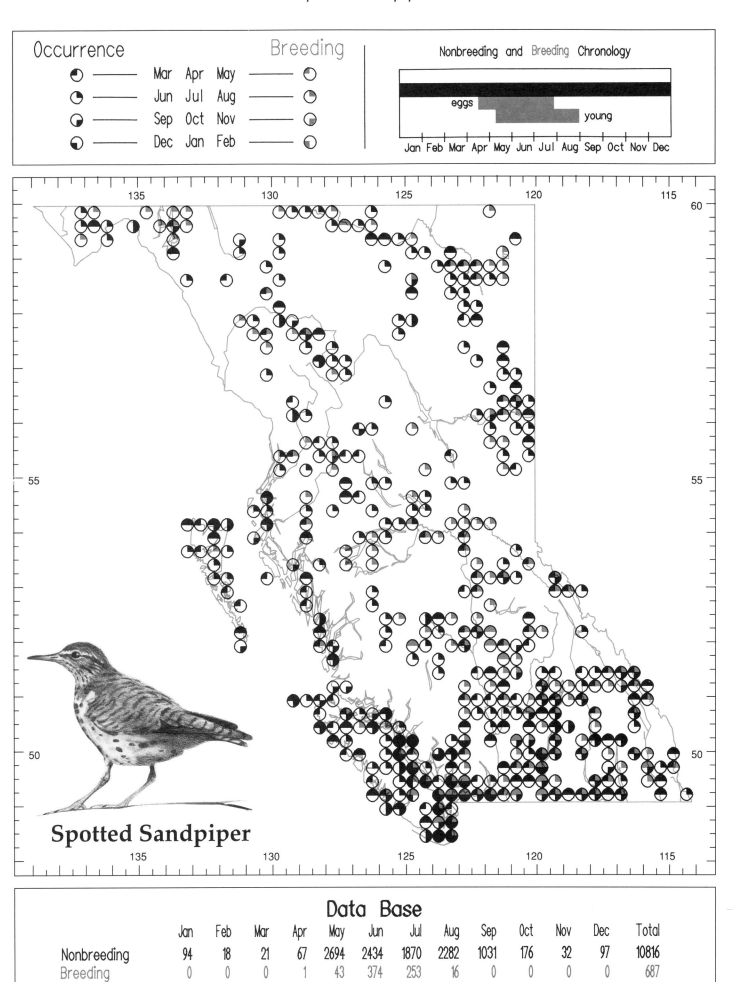

Spotted Sandpiper

Spotted Sandpiper

Occurrence   Breeding

	Mar	Apr	May	
	Jun	Jul	Aug	
	Sep	Oct	Nov	
	Dec	Jan	Feb	

Nonbreeding and Breeding Chronology

eggs   young

Jan Feb Mar Apr May Jun Jul Aug Sep Oct Nov Dec

Data Base

	Jan	Feb	Mar	Apr	May	Jun	Jul	Aug	Sep	Oct	Nov	Dec	Total
Nonbreeding	94	18	21	67	2694	2434	1870	2282	1031	176	32	97	10816
Breeding	0	0	0	1	43	374	253	16	0	0	0	0	687

Upland Sandpiper
Bartramia longicauda (Bechstein)

UPSA

RANGE: Breeds in eastern Alaska and the northern Yukon; through the central Canadian prairies to the American midwest; also in southern Ontario, southern Quebec, and the mountains (locally) south to central Virginia. Winters in the pampas region of central South America.

STATUS: *Very rare* spring transient and *rare* autumn trtansient over most of the province. *Accidental* in spring on the coast. *Rare* summer visitant to the Peace Lowlands.

OCCURRENCE: The Upland Sandpiper is one of the most difficult birds to find in British Columbia. Individuals have been reported irregularly from every geographic region of the province except the north mainland coast. Observations of more than one bird are very rare. The species is a regular visitant only in the Peace Lowlands. It has been found from sea level to 1,830 m elevation.

The Upland Sandpiper frequents open, grassy uplands during all seasons (Fig. 113). In the Peace Lowlands, it frequents overgrown fallow fields (Siddle 1982). In the Boreal Forest, it frequents burned 'jackpine' country (Rand 1944) and open bogs and flats. It also occurs on recent grass burns, wet pastures, golf courses, lawns, meadows, dirt roads, and mudflats.

Our data are too limited to determine periods of migration or routes, but most autumn migrants have been reported between mid-August and late September. Early spring and late autumn dates for the Peace River are 8 May and 9 September and for the province: 24 April and 1 October 1930-2 (Munro, J.A. and Cowan 1947); White Lake (Okanagan Falls) 20 May 1979-2; Lightning Lake 31 May 1981-1 (RBCM Photo 728); Yoho National Park 24 Apr 1975-1 (Wade 1977); Fort St. John 8 May 1985-3, 16 May 1986-2 (last spring record).

REMARKS: The breeding status of the Upland Sandpiper in British Columbia is uncertain. Cowan (1939) and Godfrey (1986) report the Upland Sandpiper as a breeding bird in the Peace Lowlands. Godfrey (1986) also reports it breeding in the Chilcotin-Cariboo region based on a British Columbia Nest Records Scheme record of a brood of 2 young on 20 June 1968 at Pinto Lake, 145 km west of Williams Lake. The brood was foraging on arable land at an elevation of 1,000 m. However, this record provides no description of the young nor any mention of adult birds. Another record reports 4 eggs found near Rossland in 1970, thought to be of the species. Apparently, the Upland Sandpiper was a former breeding bird near Newgate (Brooks 1920) and on the grassy uplands of Anarchist Mountain (Cannings, R.A. et al. 1987). In all those instances, however, evidence of breeding with convincing details is lacking. Most of that evidence is based on observations of adult pairs during the breeding season. We do have recent reports from the Peace Lowlands of pairs of Upland Sandpipers calling and acting in an agitated manner; which suggests they were nesting in the area; but again, nests with eggs or downy young were not found.

It is not surprising that breeding for the Upland Sandpiper has not been documented in British Columbia. It is not a common bird anywhere in the province. When incubating, the birds are very secretive and are difficult to flush, leaving the nest only when an observer is a metre or less from the nest (D.B. Marshall pers. comm.). After the young hatch, the adults are very sensitive to disturbance. They are constantly alert and become more vocal, at times feigning injury, when broods are young and under threat. When the young can fly, the adults become less defensive and more reluctant to flush.

While we suspect that the Upland Sandpiper does breed in the province, based on the circumstantial evidence we have on file, its breeding status remains uncertain.

Tatum (1970) lists 2 possible winter records for southern Vancouver Island: Victoria, 20 December 1969-1 and Panama Flats, 4 January 1970-1. There is some confusion about the identity of these birds and therefore the records are considered hypothetical.

The Upland Sandpiper is reported on the "Blue List" for the period 1975 to 1986 (Tate 1981, 1986; Tate and Tate 1982). It is said to be slowly declining, stable at low levels, or absent over much of its former eastern range (Tate and Tate 1982).

The Upland Sandpiper was previously known as Upland Plover (American Ornithologists' Union 1957, 1983).

Figure 113. Upland Sandpiper near Flatrock Creek, near Clayhurst, 27 June 1987 (Richard J. Cannings).

NOTEWORTHY RECORDS

Spring: Coastal - Victoria 5 May 1979-1. **Interior -** Newgate 28 May 1930-2 (Munro, J.A. and Cowan 1947); White Lake (Okanagan Falls) 20 May 1979-2; Lightning Lake 31 May 1981-1 (RBCM Photo 728); Yoho National Park 24 Apr 1975-1 (Wade 1977); Fort St. John 8 May 1985-3, 16 May 1986-2 (last spring record).

Summer: Coastal - Sea Island 30 Aug 1979-4; Iona Island 16 Jul 1983-1; Cleland Island 3 Jun 1976-1; Mitlenatch Island 1 Jul 1987-1; Masset 6 Jun 1987-1 (Cooper, J.M. 1987). **Interior -** Oyama 30 Aug 1985-1; Glacier National Park 25 Aug 1970-1 (Rogers, T.H. 1971a); Kispiox River valley 17 Aug 1921-4 (MVZ 41996-41999); Fort St. John 20 Aug 1985-4; 3 km e Cecil Lake 26 Jun 1985-1 whistling, 27 Jun 1987-4 adults including 1 displaying bird, 5 Jul 1986-3 (or 4?) very agitated birds, 29 Jul 1987-1 giving migration call; Racing River Wayside Park 8 Jul 1980-10 in fields; Fort Nelson 22 Jul 1985-2, 17 Aug 1986-13 feeding in meadows near airport; Mansfield Creek 14 Jun 1979-1 making "curlee" call.

Autumn: Interior - Fort Nelson 8 Sep 1986-4; Bug Lake 2 Sep 1976-1; 22 km n Eddontenajon Lake 5 Sep 1977-1; Fort St. John 9 Sep 1984-1; Hemp Creek 1 Sep 1939-1 (RBCM 10877); Deadman Lake (Oliver) 13 Sep 1980-1. **Coastal -** Port Hardy 24 Sep 1936-1; Comox 1 Oct 1961-1 (Boggs and Boggs 1962a); Cowichan Bay 14 Sep 1980-2; Esquimalt 27 Sep 1983-1.

Winter: No records.

Upland Sandpiper

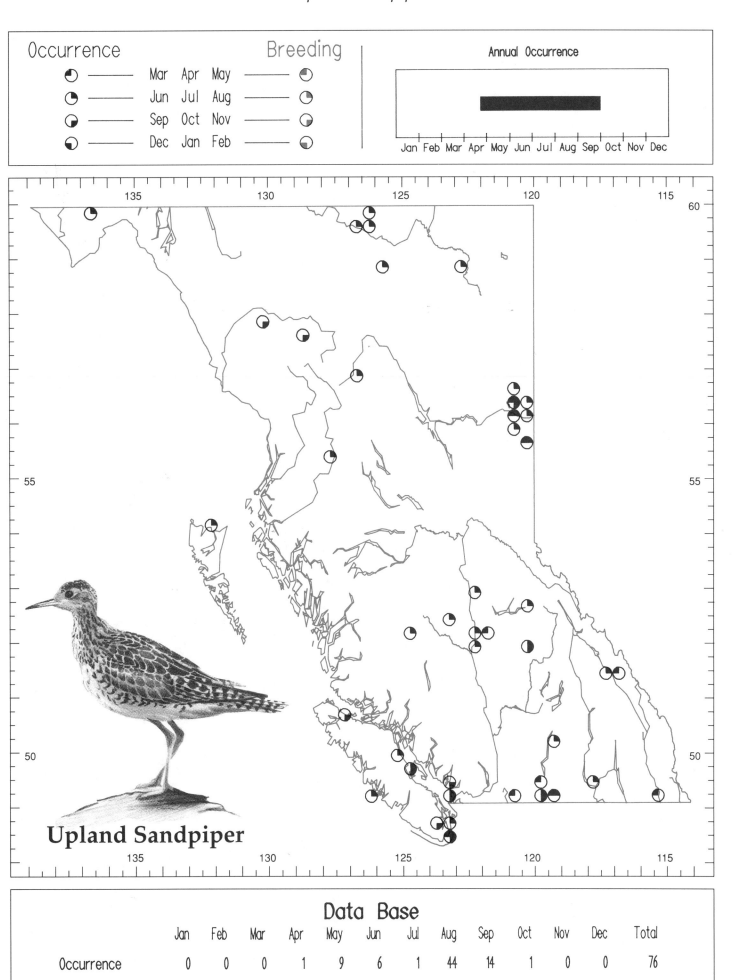

	Jan	Feb	Mar	Apr	May	Jun	Jul	Aug	Sep	Oct	Nov	Dec	Total
Occurrence	0	0	0	1	9	6	1	44	14	1	0	0	76

Whimbrel
Numenius phaeopus (Linnaeus)

WHIM

RANGE: Circumpolar. In North America breeds disjunctly in northern Alaska, the western Yukon, northwestern Keewatin, and on the western shores of Hudson Bay. Winters from Oregon and North Carolina south to southern South America; also in the South Pacific and Africa.

STATUS: *Common* and locally *abundant* transient on the coast. *Very rare* spring transient in the interior. *Very rare* in winter on the southwest coast.

OCCURRENCE: The Whimbrel is widely distributed along the coast, particularly during the major spring and autumn movements. Only 12 interior records are known to us, all from between 1 May and 27 June. On the coast, the Whimbrel frequents offshore islets and rocks, mudflats, wind-swept sandy beaches, and spits. It forages along the water's edge, higher up the beach, or on sand dunes behind beached drift logs. It is found occasionally in ploughed fields and short-grass areas such as golf courses usually near coastal waters. In the interior, it frequents lake shores, sewage lagoons, and sub-alpine swamps.

Taverner (1942) notes that the major Pacific migration route of the Whimbrel is oceanic. Apparently, birds breeding in Alaska fly directly to northern California over the open ocean, although a portion of the flight appears to stop on the west coast of Vancouver Island. Evidently, only the eastern fringe of the migratory movement touches down on the coast of British Columbia. The Whimbrel usually occurs sporadically in small flocks of 5 to 25 birds (Fig. 114); however, in recent years, flocks of up to several hundred Whimbrels have been recorded regularly in May and July near Tofino. Cleland Island is used mainly as a roosting area with flocks resting along rocks at the water's edge in quiet bays. Large numbers appear to forage on the mudflats of Tofino Inlet and Grice Bay and on the sandy beaches of Chesterman Beach. Records by several observers suggest that they forage by day and then fly to Cleland Island and other offshore rocks to spend the night. The Whimbrel has been recorded in the evening leaving the Tofino area and heading out towards the open ocean. Separate observations have noted as many as 750 Whimbrels flying near dusk at Cleland Island.

The spring movement begins in late April or early May and peaks by mid-May. Small numbers of nonbreeders and stragglers occur along the coast throughout June. The first autumn migrants arrive on the south coast in late June. The autumn movement peaks in mid-to-late July. Overall numbers dwindle through August and September although small numbers are reported frequently in September. A few stragglers remain on the coast into November. Winter records are surprisingly numerous considering the species' normal winter range. A few occur in some years near Victoria and the Fraser River delta from December to February. The flocks of 8 and 20 observed at Crescent Beach in February 1957 are exceptional. Equally unusual is the record of 2 birds wintering in Oak Bay.

REMARKS: Only 1 of 4 subspecies, *N. p. hudsonicus*, is known to occur in British Columbia. However, there is a record of a white-rumped curlew, probably of the race *N. p. variegatus* (though *N. arquata* could not be ruled out) photographed near Fort St. John on 11 June 1983 (RBCM Photo 1086). Because of the difficulty in separating small Asiatic curlews, the rare Bristle-thighed Curlew, and the Whimbrel in the field, observers are encouraged to make careful field-notes when any of these species are encountered. Skeel (1983) provides details of Whimbrel breeding biology in Canada.

Figure 114. Whimbrels in flight at Tofino Inlet, late May 1986 (Adrian Dorst).

NOTEWORTHY RECORDS

Spring: Coastal - Blackie Spit 17 Mar 1974-12, 13 May 1979-80; Tofino Inlet 1 May 1974-350, 2 May 1974-300 (Crowell and Nehls 1974c); Tofino 29 Apr 1978-700, 13 May 1976-475 (5 flocks), 10 May 1986-120, 18 May 1987-220; Chesterman Beach 9 May 1982-112; Sewall 15 May 1984-60+; Porcher Island 22 to 24 May 1987-160 in flocks of up to 20 birds, flying and feeding on sandy beach; Rushton Island 19 to 22 May 1987-235 in flocks of 3 to 20 birds, apparent migration. **Interior** - e Osoyoos 17 May 1987-1, 23 May 1983-1 (Cannings, R.A. et al. 1987); McQueen Lake 1 May 1975-1; Separation Lake (Riske Creek) 16 May 1978-4; Fort St. John 28 May 1983-5; Charlie Lake 25 May 1980-1; Parker Lake (Fort Nelson) 13 to 15 May 1974-1 (RBCM Photo 361).

Summer: Coastal - Cowichan Bay 3 Aug 1986-2; Cleland Island 10 Jun 1982-22, 1 Jul 1982-50, 4 Jul 1982-150+ flying south, 23 Jul 1982-750 flying at dusk, 18 Jul 1975-200 roosting; Chesterman Beach 14 Jul 1983-245; Brooks Peninsula 21 Aug 1981-12 (Campbell and Summers In press); Sandspit 9 Jun 1986-7. **Interior** - Duck Lake (Creston) 4 Jun 1980-1; Charlie Lake 17 Jun 1981; North Pine 21 Jun 1984-1; Cold Fish Lake 15 and 27 Jun 1976-1 (Osmond-Jones et al. 1977); Atlin 3 Jun 1933-1 (Munro, J.A. and Cowan 1947); Mosquito Flats (Chilkat Pass) 17 Jun 1980-1.

Autumn: Interior - No records. **Coastal** - Green Island 24 Sep 1978-1; Little Qualicum River estuary 4 Sep 1975-8 (Dawe 1976); Chesterman Beach 1 Oct 1975-20; Blackie Spit 18 Nov 1982 -1; Oak Bay 15 Nov 1952-14; Sooke 22 Sep 1981-6.

Winter: Interior - No records. **Coastal** - Tofino Inlet 26 Dec 1982-1, 14 Jan 1983-1; Crescent Beach 1 Feb 1957-8, 25 Feb 1957-20; Victoria 13 Dec 1982-5; Oak Bay 15 Dec 1951 to 21 Jan 1952-2; Race Rocks 17 Jan 1977-5.

Christmas Counts: Interior - Not recorded. **Coastal** - Recorded from 1 of 28 localities and on 3% of all counts. Maxima: Victoria 23 Dec 1961-6, all-time Canadian high count (Anderson, R.R. 1976), 2 Jan 1964-3, 27 Dec 1964-3.

Whimbrel

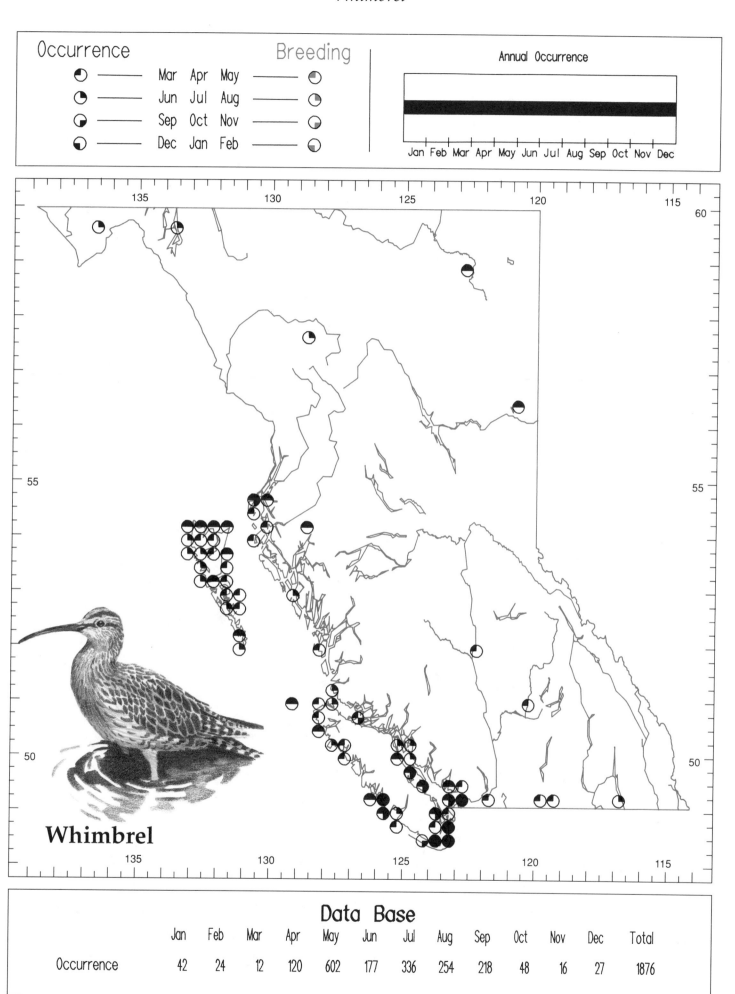

Occurrence

◑	———	Mar	Apr	May	——— ◔
◔	———	Jun	Jul	Aug	——— ◔
◑	———	Sep	Oct	Nov	——— ◔
◕	———	Dec	Jan	Feb	——— ◔

Breeding

Annual Occurrence
Jan Feb Mar Apr May Jun Jul Aug Sep Oct Nov Dec

Whimbrel

Data Base

	Jan	Feb	Mar	Apr	May	Jun	Jul	Aug	Sep	Oct	Nov	Dec	Total
Occurrence	42	24	12	120	602	177	336	254	218	48	16	27	1876

Long-billed Curlew

Numenius americanus Bechstein

RANGE: Breeds from southern interior British Columbia and the southern Canadian prairies south to Utah and Texas. Winters on coastal lowlands from California and Louisiana south to Guatemala.

STATUS: *Uncommon* to locally *very common* spring migrant and *fairly common* summer visitant in the central-southern interior; *casual* in autumn. On the south coast, a *rare* spring migrant, *casual* in summer and autumn, *accidental* in winter. *Accidental* on the north coast. Local breeder.

NONBREEDING: The Long-billed Curlew is widely distributed through the central-southern interior north to the Nechako Lowlands. On the coast, it occurs rarely on Vancouver Island and in the Fraser Lowlands.

In the interior, the Long-billed Curlew frequents grassy steppes (Fig. 116), not necessarily near water, as well as newly-ploughed fields, green hayfields, meadows, and pastures. On the coast, it occurs in wetter habitats, especially on tidal mud flats and beaches, or in nearby fields. Most records on the coast are from the Fraser River delta.

Spring migrants arrive in the interior earlier than any other shorebird except the Killdeer. Major influxes occur from late March to early April. Flocks of more than 50 birds may concentrate in good feeding areas at that time. Most birds have arrived by late April. Coastal migrants occur later, mainly in May, which suggests the birds are mainly nonbreeders. On the breeding grounds, flocks of 6 to 15 Long-billed Curlews, probably nonbreeders, have been occasionally observed flying about in the evenings in May and June.

Figure 115. Long-billed Curlew habitat at White Lake near Okanagan Falls, 19 July 1981 (Michael C.E. McNall).

Figure 116. Pair of Long-billed Curlews on territory near Skookumchuck in the east Kootenay, 27 May 1981 (Neil K. Dawe).

Long-billed Curlew

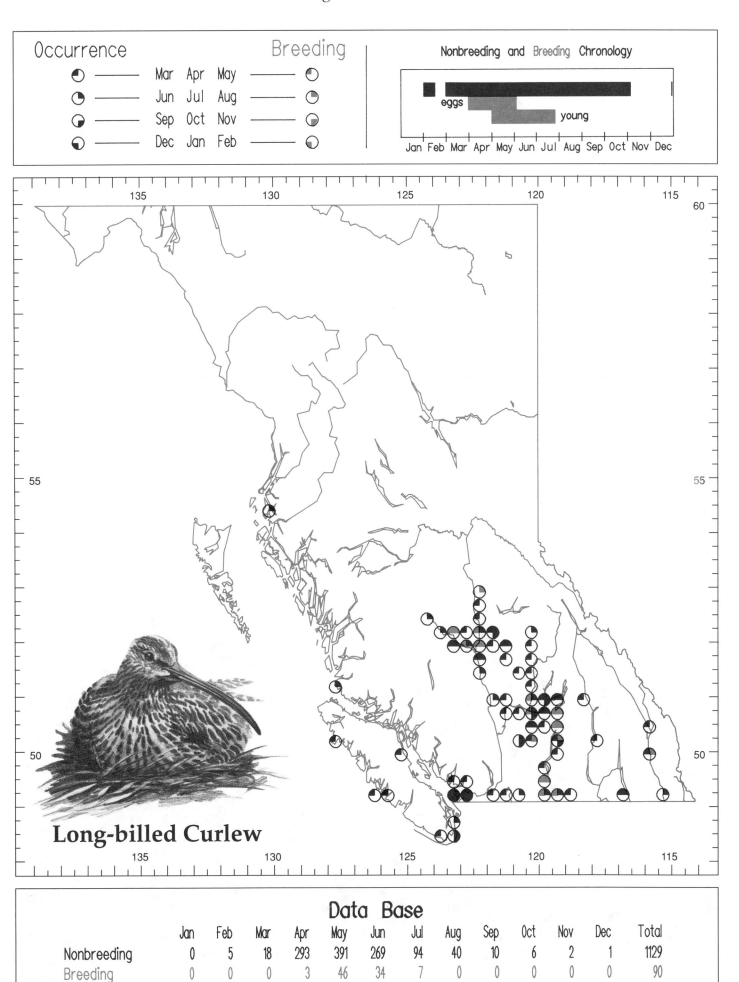

Occurrence

◑	Mar Apr May	◐
◔	Jun Jul Aug	◕
◗	Sep Oct Nov	◔
◕	Dec Jan Feb	◑

Breeding

Nonbreeding and Breeding Chronology

eggs

young

Jan Feb Mar Apr May Jun Jul Aug Sep Oct Nov Dec

Long-billed Curlew

Data Base

	Jan	Feb	Mar	Apr	May	Jun	Jul	Aug	Sep	Oct	Nov	Dec	Total
Nonbreeding	0	5	18	293	391	269	94	40	10	6	2	1	1129
Breeding	0	0	0	3	46	34	7	0	0	0	0	0	90

Small, post-breeding groups of 5 to 10 birds begin to form in July and may disperse from breeding territories at that time. By late July, flocks of up to 20 birds assemble when most young have fledged. The autumn movement occurs from late July through August; sightings after mid-August are few. Most of the movement is south through the central-southern interior. The Long-billed Curlew does not linger in the province in late summer as do many other shorebirds. There are few autumn records; the last birds have usually gone by late October.

There are no real staging areas in British Columbia. Populations are low and migrating birds usually move in small groups. The highest numbers in the province are reported from the Chilcotin-Cariboo region where the largest single flocks have been found on grasslands above Alkali Lake. Concentrations may occur there each spring and summer.

BREEDING: The breeding range of the Long-billed Curlew is restricted to the dry grasslands of the southern interior between 280 and 1,220 m elevation. Highest numbers occur in the Chilcotin-Cariboo region. It also breeds in scattered locations throughout the Thompson-Okanagan Plateau, particularly the Lac du Bois, Douglas Lake, and upper Nicola areas. It is still a fairly common breeder in the north Okanagan valley, but less so in the south Okanagan valley. The most closely watched breeding area in the province is White Lake, near Okanagan Falls, where many of our breeding records originate (Fig. 115). There, up to 8 pairs have bred annually since 1960 (Cannings, R.A. et al. 1987) although only 1 pair has been reported the last 2 years. Ohanjanian (1986b) reports a breeding population of 35 to 40 pairs in the east Kootenay from Grasmere north to Windermere, centred on the Skookumchuk prairie (Fig. 116). However, we have no confirmed breeding records (i.e. nests with eggs or flightless young) for the east Kootenay, other than from the Wasa and Skookumchuck areas. We also lack confirmed breeding records for the Creston area (see Butler, R.W. et al. 1986).

Breeding habitat requirements include large tracts of open grasslands with low vegetative cover (less than 20 cm); the presence of trees or large bushes inhibits breeding. Preferred nesting areas are flat grassy uplands (Fig. 117) or gravelly ridges and hillsides. Wetter areas such as seepages and hay fields are used for brood rearing.

Nests: Nest building begins 1 or 2 weeks after the birds arrive on their breeding territories. Nests were situated on open ridges, hillsides, and flats (15 nests), or fields and pastures (2 nests). Tall, thick patches of grasses and sagebrush are avoided. The scrapes were lined with a bit of fine grass (11 of 17 nests), or twigs (2), thistle stems (1), and cow dung (1). Two nests were unlined. Nests were often placed beside a rock or clump of cow dung. Two nests measured 18 cm in diameter and 6 to 8 cm deep.

Eggs: Dates for 50 clutches ranged from 11 April to 4 June with 56% recorded between 9 and 31 May. Calculated dates indicate that eggs could be found as early as 1 April. Sizes for 30 clutches ranged from 1 to 5 eggs (1E-1, 2E-2, 3E-6, 4E-20, 5E-1) with 66% having 4 eggs. Incubation period is 27 to 28 days (Fitzner, J.N. 1978).

Young: Dates for 33 broods ranged from 2 May (Cannings, R.A. et al. 1987) to 26 July with 55% recorded between 1 and 18 June. Most have fledged by mid-July. Ohanjanian (1986b) reports a flock of 13 juveniles in late July 1986 on breeding grounds in the east Kootenay. Sizes for 19 broods (Fig. 119) ranged from 1 to 4 young (1Y-3, 2Y-8, 3Y-5, 4Y-3) with 13 broods having 2 to 3 young. Harrison (1978) suggests that adults may divide the brood between them, which could account for the high number of observations of broods of 2 young. The fledging period is 41 to 45 days (Fitzner, J.N. 1978).

REMARKS: The Long-billed Curlew is North America's largest shorebird. Its summer range has contracted considerably in the last century due to agricultural and urban expansion into natural grasslands. It appears on the "Blue Lists" of 1981 and 1982 (Tate 1981; Tate and Tate 1982). The fate of the Long-billed Curlew in British Columbia has been of concern since early in this century (Brooks 1918), and the problem of habitat loss and the resulting decline of this symbol of our vanishing natural grasslands continues. Some enhancement and expansion of Long-billed Curlew breeding habitat is planned for the east Kootenay by the British Columbia Wildlife Branch (Ohanjanian 1986b) which may help reverse those losses and declines.

For a discussion of various aspects of the life history of the Long-billed Curlew in the northwestern United States, see J.N. Allen (1980), J.N. Fitzner (1978), Redmond and Jenni (1982, 1986), and Redmond (1986).

Figure 117. *Incubating Long-billed Curlew at Riske Creek, 16 May 1978 (Robert A. Cannings).*

Figure 118. A young John M. Cooper at a Long-billed Curlew nest at Lac du Bois, 5 May 1963 (Louise V. Cooper).

Figure 119. Long-billed Curlew chick at White Lake near Okanagan Falls, 10 June 1979 (Ervio Sian).

NOTEWORTHY RECORDS

Spring: Coastal - Delta 3 Apr 1983-1; Boundary Bay 1 Mar 1980-1, 14 May 1981-6; Iona Island 14 May 1979- 11; Tofino Inlet 3 May 1983-1; Mitlenatch Island 25 Apr 1983-2; Solander Island 5 May 1976-1 (Campbell and Summers In press). **Interior** - Creston 3 Apr 1979-1 adult; Skookumchuck 29 Mar 1978-1; Nakusp 26 Mar 1973-1; Vernon 3 Mar 1969-1, 2 May 1985-13; Kamloops 20 Apr 1984-26; Revelstoke 10 Apr 1983-1; Bonaparte Lake 6 Apr 1987-2; Alkali Lake (Cariboo) 4 Apr 1968-100; Riske Creek 2 May 1986-2, 21 May 1978-16; Marguerite 21 May 1979-1.

Summer: Coastal - Clover Point 11 Aug 1969-1; Sidney Island 16 Aug 1987-1 (RBCM Photo 1161);

Blackie Spit 3 Jul 1983-3; Beach Grove 7 Jun 1981-1; Sea Island 15 Aug 1966-1 (RBCM 11635; Campbell 1972a); Burnett Bay 29 Jul 1987-1. **Interior** - Grandview Lake (Vernon) 4 Jul 1959-40, 14 Jul 1959-50 (Bradley 1959); Stump Lake (Quilchena) 24 Jun 1978-5; Douglas Lake Ranch (Quilchena) 5 Jun 1962-20, flock in meadow; Alkali Lake (Cariboo) 8 Jun 1979-15, 18 Jul 1978-79; s 150 Mile House 8 Jul 1983-6 (Ducks Unlimited Canada 1983); Chilco Ranch (Hanceville) Jul 1983 - flocks of up to 30 birds (Ducks Unlimited Canada 1983); Williams Lake 11 Aug 1978-10.

Autumn: Interior - 11 km n Merritt 9 Oct 1982-1; Separation Lake 4 Sep 1951-32; Okanagan

Landing 11 Oct 1919-2, 29 Oct 1902-1 (FMNH 132791). **Coastal** - Oak Bay 5 Nov 1975-1 (Shepard, M.G. 1976b); Boundary Bay 5 Oct 1983-1, 26 Oct 1958-3 (Erskine 1960), 3 Nov 1979-2; Delta 6 Sep 1983-1; Iona Island 25 Oct 1983-1.

Winter: Interior - Not recorded. Coastal - Boundary Bay 2 to 16 Feb 1980-1.

Christmas Counts: Interior - Not recorded. **Coastal** - Recorded once: Ladner 29 Dec 1979-**1**, all-time Canadian high count (Anderson, R.R. 1980).

Extralimital Record: Coastal - Butze Point 5 Jun 1983-1.

Hudsonian Godwit
Limosa haemastica (Linnaeus)

HUGO

RANGE: Breeds in small disjunct areas of southern Alaska, northwestern British Columbia, the Northwest Territories east of the inner deltas of the Mackenzie and Anderson rivers, northeastern Manitoba, and northern Ontario. Winters in southern South America.

STATUS: *Casual* spring and *very rare* autumn migrant on the south coast. *Casual* migrant in the southern interior and near Atlin. *Uncommon* to *fairly common* spring and autumn migrant in the Peace Lowlands; *very rare* in summer. Local breeder.

NONBREEDING: The Hudsonian Godwit (Fig. 120) has been recorded in 4 widely separated areas in the province: the south coast from Rivers Inlet south to Vancouver Island and the Fraser Lowlands, the central-southern interior, the Peace Lowlands, and the extreme northwest corner from Atlin to the Chilkat Pass area. It occurs regularly only in the Peace Lowlands where it is on the western fringe of the migration corridor. Flocks of up to 26 have been recorded in recent years at the Fort St. John sewage ponds, Cecil Lake, Charlie Lake, and Boundary Lake. Sightings in all other regions of the province have been of 1 to 3 birds only; these birds are well outside the species normal migration routes. On the coast, most records are from Iona Island and Boundary Bay in the Fraser River delta.

In the interior, the Hudsonian Godwit uses thawing areas at outflow streams and muddy shorelines of lakes. Early spring migrants are occasionally seen resting on ice. On the coast, tidal mudflats, sewage lagoons, and sandy beaches are frequented. One bird was observed resting on a log boom.

Spring migrants arrive in the Peace Lowlands in late April or early May with highest numbers recorded between 29 April and 6 May. The spring movement continues there with small numbers (usually singles or groups of less than 5 birds) passing through until the end of May. Few birds remain throughout June. Southward bound autumn migrants arrive in the Peace Lowlands in July, August, and September with peak numbers occurring in mid-July. July flocks consist entirely of adults. A brief autumn passage of juveniles appears to occur in early September (Siddle 1986). The earliest arrival and latest departure dates for the province are 29 April and 8 October.

BREEDING: The only known breeding locality in the province is in the Chilkat Pass area which is a relatively flat, plateau-like area amid the rugged St. Elias Mountains. The area contains shrubby, subalpine vegetation and countless tiny sedge meadows, bogs, pools, ponds, and small lakes. It agrees perfectly with the description of breeding habitat of the Hudsonian Godwit listed by Williamson and Smith (1964) in Alaska.

There is only one documented breeding record. A nest containing 4 eggs was found on 5 June 1963 at Mile 75, Haines Road (RBCM Photo 297). The nest was situated in a "wet grassy area in shrubby marsh close to timberline". The nest itself was described as "a grassy cup in wet area . . . [of] thick moss, grass, and sedge in clusters." The elevation was approximately 915 m.

Three other reports suggest breeding. A pair was observed on territory in the Chilkat Pass from 3 June to 27 July 1957 but neither a nest nor young were found (Weeden 1960). Other pairs were observed exhibiting courtship behaviour in the pass on 8 June 1981 and in June 1983. Although there is only one breeding record, the species is probably a regular breeder in very small numbers. It is also known to breed nearby, on the Chilkat River, in southeastern Alaska (Bailey, A.M. 1948).

The incubation period is 22 to 25 days and the fledging period is about 30 days (Hagar, J.A. 1966).

REMARKS: The Hudsonian Godwit was first documented in the province in 1932 (MVZ 100824, 100624; Brooks, A. 1942). J.A. Hagar (1966) discusses breeding ecology in northern Manitoba and the species' incredible non-stop trans-continental migratory movements.

Figure 120. Hudsonian Godwit at Cordova Spit, southern Vancouver Island, 12 May 1985 (Tim Zurowski).

NOTEWORTHY RECORDS

Spring: Coastal - Cordova Spit 11 and 12 May 1985-1 (RBCM Photo 1100, Fig. 120; see Mattocks 1985b); Reifel Island 15 May 1976-1; Long Beach 30 Apr 1983-1 (Mattocks and Hunn 1983a). **Interior** - 150 Mile House 21 May 1953-1 (NMC 47803); Tupper Creek (Tupper) 8 May 1938-8 (RBCM 7900); n Fort St. John 2 May 1984-26 (Grunberg 1984c), 4 May 1983-18, 5 May 1983-11 (RBCM Photo 855), 25 May 1986-1; Cecil Lake 29 Apr 1980-12; Charlie Lake 3 May 1986-9 asleep on lake ice edge; Boundary Lake (Goodlow) 4 May 1986-20; Tagish Lake 21 May 1983 (Grunberg 1983b); Chilkat Pass 15 May 1977-1.

Summer: Coastal - Reifel Island 14 to 16 Aug 1984-1 (Hunn and Mattocks 1984), 28 to 31 Aug 1975-1 (RBCM Photo 499); Iona Island 8 Jun 1985-1, 17 and 18 Jun 1978-1, 10 Aug 1970-1 (RBCM Photo 37); Crescent Beach 22 to 29 Jun 1974-1 (Crowell and Nehls 1974d); Kwakshna Channel 7 Aug 1937-3 (Laing 1937). **Interior** - Emerald Lake 15 Aug 1974-1 (Wade 1977); Boundary Lake (Goodlow) 30 Jun 1980-1; n Fort St. John 11 Jun 1986-2 adults, 24 Jun 1986-2, 14 Jul 1982-18 (RBCM Photo 823), 15 Jul 1986-9, 20 Jul 1982-12, 8 Aug 1982-12.

Autumn: Interior - n Fort St. John 2 Sep 1984-6 juveniles, 11 Sep 1986-1 juvenile; Vernon 3 to 7 Sep 1987-1 (RBCM Photo 1173). **Coastal** - Iona Island 7 Sep to 1 Oct 1979-1 (RBCM Photo 718), 8 Oct 1979-1; Boundary Bay 1 to 30 Sep 1984-2, 1 and 5 Oct 1986-1 (Mattocks and Harrington-Tweit 1987); Grice Bay 29 Sep 1986-1 (Mattocks and Harrington-Tweit 1987); Cadboro Bay 4 to 9 Sep 1973-1 (RBCM Photo 310).

Winter: No records.

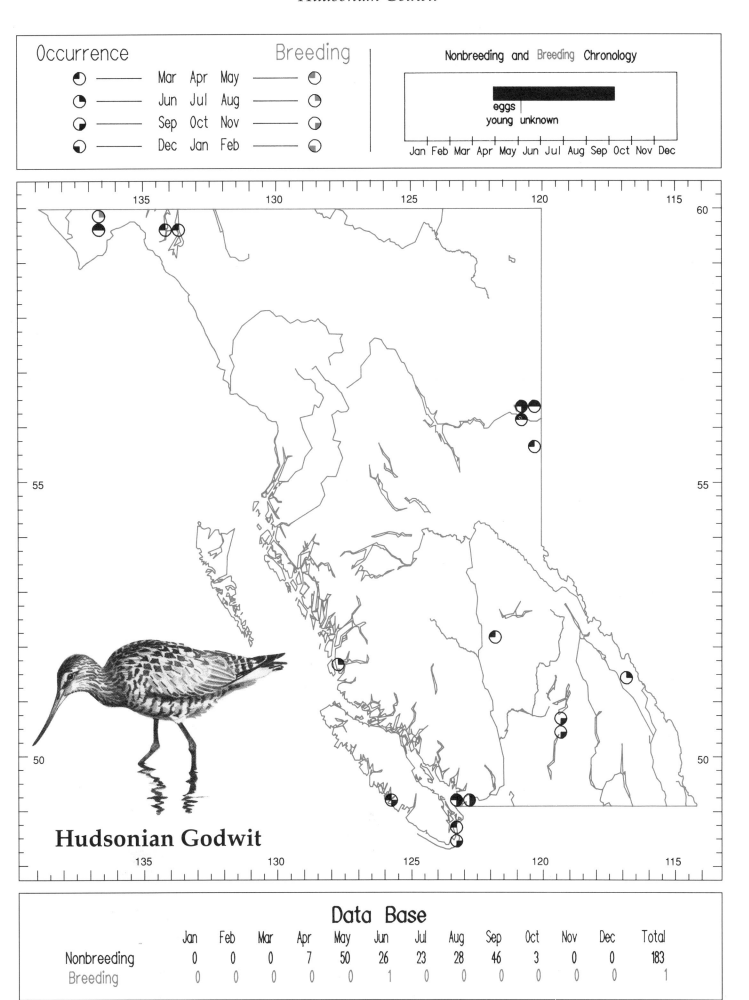

Hudsonian Godwit

Data Base

	Jan	Feb	Mar	Apr	May	Jun	Jul	Aug	Sep	Oct	Nov	Dec	Total
Nonbreeding	0	0	0	7	50	26	23	28	46	3	0	0	183
Breeding	0	0	0	0	0	1	0	0	0	0	0	0	1

Bar-tailed Godwit

BTGO

Limosa lapponica (Linnaeus)

RANGE: Breeds throughout northern Eurasia and locally in western and northern Alaska. Winters in southern Eurasia, west Africa, Australia, and New Zealand. Casual along the Pacific and Atlantic coasts of North America in migration.

STATUS: *Very rare* late summer to late autumn vagrant on the southwest coast.

OCCURRENCE: The Bar-tailed Godwit has been found on the southwest coast of British Columbia on extreme southern Vancouver Island (3 records) and in the Fraser River delta (5 records).

It was first observed in the province (and Canada) in 1931 (see below). Since then the Bar-tailed Godwit has been recorded on seven occasions, between 8 August and 31 October. Most visits were short – the longest was 22 days.

In western North America, south of Alaska, the Bar-tailed Godwit has been recorded in all months except January, April, and December. Most records are for the autumn period (Roberson 1980) and most are coastal.

All British Columbia records, listed in chronological order, are as follows:

(1) Mud Bay (Colebrook) 30 October 1931-1 "bird of the year" (Munro, J.A. 1935a). The bird was mounted and displayed in the office of the British Columbia Game Commission in Vancouver for a period of time (Brooks 1942), then preserved as a museum skin (ROM 81957). The date on the specimen label reads 31 October, a day later than published accounts.

(2) Sidney late August 1972-1. This bird was originally identified as a Marbled Godwit and later photographs revealed its correct identification as a Bar-tailed Godwit (Sparling and Sparling 1974). Tatum (1973) gives a date of 9 September for photo documentation (RBCM Photo 260) at nearby Saanichton Bay.

(3) Reifel Island 16 to 30 September 1972-1 associating with dowitchers and Greater Yellowlegs (Campbell et al. 1974). It was photographed (RBCM Photo 275, not 260 as published) on 30 September (Dawe 1973).

(4) Coburg Peninsula, southern Vancouver Island, 23 September to 14 October 1984-2 (Hunn and Mattocks 1985). The birds were photographed (RBCM Photo 965; Fig. 121) on 30 September.

(5) Mud Bay (Colebrook) 22 to 24 September 1984-1 near foot of 112th Street (Hunn and Mattocks 1985). It was photographed (RBCM Photo 1056) on 23 September.

(6) Boundary Bay 8 August 1986-1 (Mattocks and Harrington-Tweit 1987).

(7) Clover Point 16 August 1987-1.

(8) Boundary Bay 21 and 23 August 1987-1.

REMARKS: Roberson (1980) lists another record for British Columbia, without documentation: Masset 29 and 30 August 1973-1.

All records for the west coast of North America are of the Siberian-Alaska race *L. l. baueri*. See Roberson (1980), Cronau et al. (1986), and Hayman et al. (1986) for plumage characteristics.

Figure 121. Bar-tailed Godwit at Esquimalt Lagoon, southern Vancouver Island, 23 September 1984 (Tim Zurowski). Note the barred tail (left) and the vermiculations in the extended wing (right).

Bar-tailed Godwit

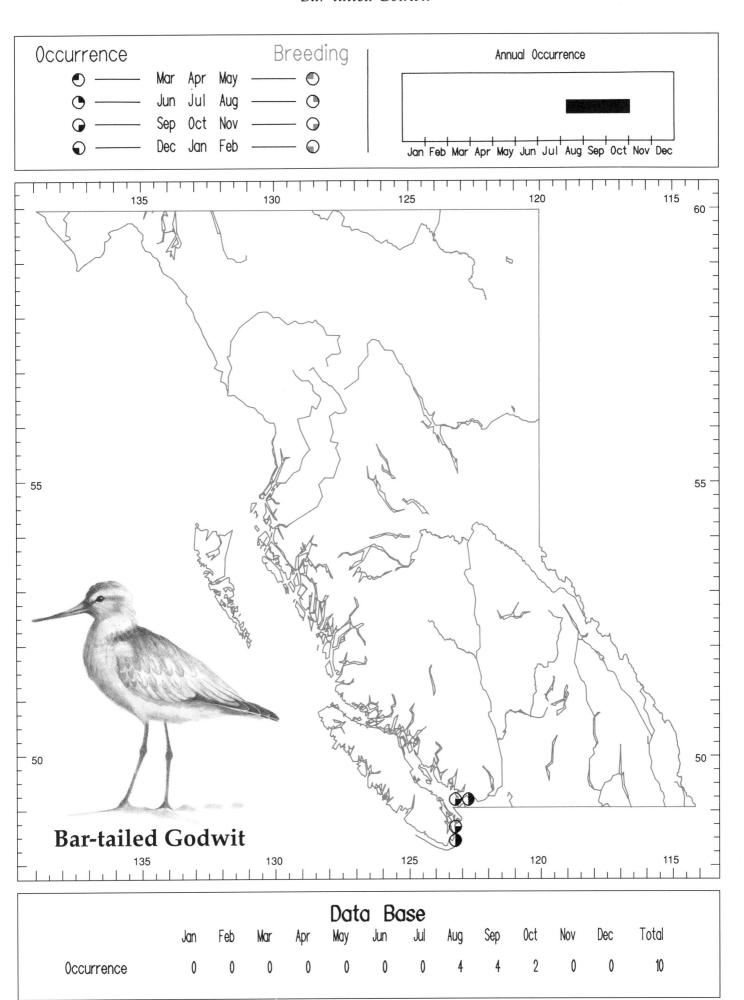

Bar-tailed Godwit

Occurrence

	Breeding
◑ ——— Mar Apr May ——— ◑	
◔ ——— Jun Jul Aug ——— ◑	
◔ ——— Sep Oct Nov ——— ◑	
◕ ——— Dec Jan Feb ——— ◑	

Annual Occurrence

Jan Feb Mar Apr May Jun Jul Aug Sep Oct Nov Dec

Data Base

	Jan	Feb	Mar	Apr	May	Jun	Jul	Aug	Sep	Oct	Nov	Dec	Total
Occurrence	0	0	0	0	0	0	0	4	4	2	0	0	10

Marbled Godwit

Limosa fedoa (Linnaeus)

RANGE: Breeds from the central Canadian prairies to South Dakota and Minnesota; also along James Bay. Winters on the Pacific coast from Oregon to Panama and on the Atlantic coast from Florida to Belize.

STATUS: *Rare* transient on the coast; *casual* in winter. *Casual* transient in the interior.

OCCURRENCE: The Marbled Godwit occurs along inner and outer coastal areas including Vancouver Island and the Queen Charlotte Islands. In the interior it has been recorded 6 times from widely separated locations. Most records (99%) are from the coast, where it is becoming a more regular transient especially during spring migration. This may be due, in part, to recently discovered breeding sites in southwestern Alaska (Kessel and Gibson 1978). Most migrants, however, would bypass British Columbia, since the main movements are primarily through the western interior portions of the continent.

Most records in British Columbia are of single birds (Fig. 122) with small groups of 2 to 4 appearing on occasion; the largest flock reported was 23 birds. Marbled Godwits occur on the coast far more frequently than other species of godwits.

On the British Columbia coast the Marbled Godwit frequents sandy beaches, tidal mud flats, lagoons, and near-shore rocks. It forages among tidal debris above the water line or in the shallow surf. Short-grass areas such as golf courses and airports are frequented when adjacent to marine waters. In the interior it has been found only on lakeshores.

Spring migrants appear in late April or May but disappear in June. Autumn migrants may occur from July through October on the coast. There is only one documented record later than October: 2 godwits wintered in the vicinity of Cadboro Bay, north of Victoria, from 28 Oct 1978 to 20 Apr 1979.

REMARKS: We have one undocumented record of a single bird, possibly wounded, found on farmlands near Victoria on 16 Dec 1954. The number of records shown on the map data base for the period November to February are inflated as those records are of the same 2 birds.

See D.D. Gibson and Kessel (1989) for a recent discussion on the geographic variation and taxonomy of the Marbled Godwit in North America.

Figure 122. Marbled Godwit at Esquimalt Lagoon, southern Vancouver Island, May 1985 (Tim Zurowski).

NOTEWORTHY RECORDS

Spring: Coastal - Blackie Spit 1 May to 25 May 1983-1 (RBCM Photo 1106); Tofino Inlet 29 Apr 1984-2, 26 Apr 1987-3, 2 May 1974-4, 21 and 22 May 1983-1; Port Hardy 28 May 1951-1; Cape Henry 14 May 1986-1 (Campbell 1986e); Delkatla Inlet 27 Apr 1987-23 in a flock; Haida (Masset) 5 May 1983-8; Rose Spit 23 Apr 1979-9; Green Island 3 May 1978-1 (RBCM Photo 581). **Interior** - Felker Lake 20 May 1968-1 (Roberts, A. 1973); Cecil Lake 7 May 1980-1 (Siddle 1982).

Summer: Coastal - Chatham Islands 7 Jul 1984-1; Cleland Island 5 Aug 1978-1; Crescent Beach 28 Jun 1974-1 (Crowell and Nehls 1974d); Iona Island 20 Aug 1983-1; Comox 2 Jul 1971-4; Green Island 14 Aug 1977-1. **Interior** - Okanagan Landing 7 Aug 1910-1 (Brooks 1912, 1920); n Columbia Lake 31 Aug 1941-1 (RBCM 10878).

Autumn: Interior - No records. **Coastal** - Port Simpson 21 Sep 1969-1; Campbell River (Discovery Passage) 11 and 12 Sep 1975-1; Courtenay 29 Sep 1987-1 (RBCM Photo 1169); Boundary Bay 6 Oct 1983-1 (RBCM Photo 1105); Tofino Inlet 3 to 4 Sep 1983-1; Victoria 6 Sep to 8 Oct 1987-1; Oak Bay 1 to 3 Oct 1981-4.

Winter: Interior - No records. **Coastal** - Cadboro Bay (see Occurrence).

Christmas Counts: Not recorded.

Marbled Godwit

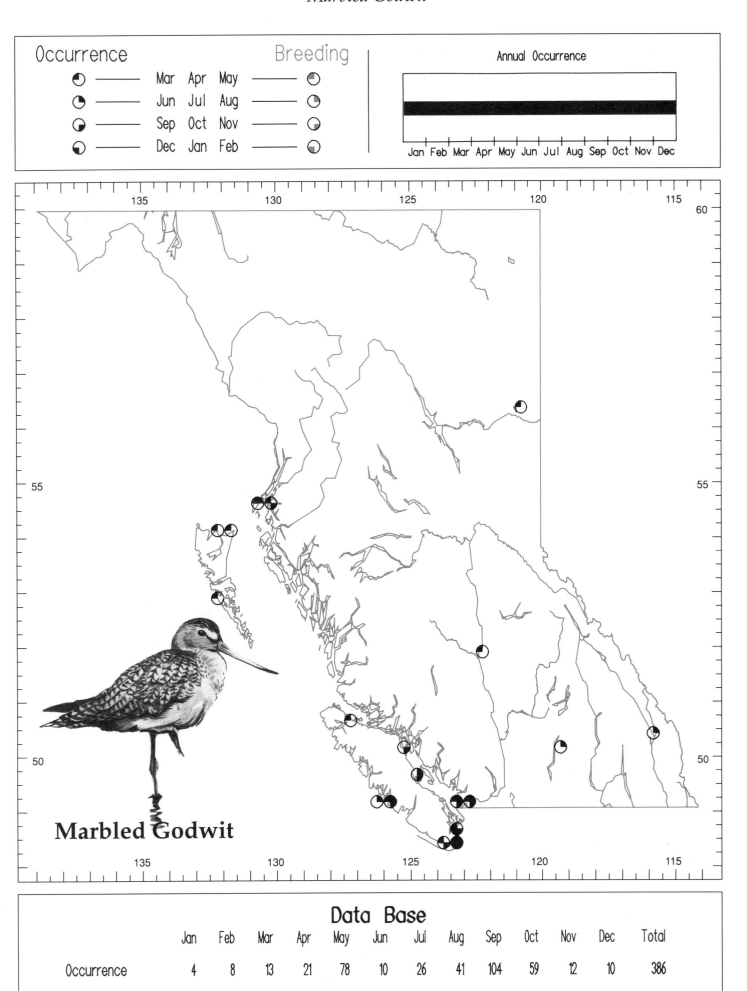

Occurrence

◐	—	Mar	Apr	May	— ◐
◑	—	Jun	Jul	Aug	— ◑
◪	—	Sep	Oct	Nov	— ◔
◕	—	Dec	Jan	Feb	— ◖

Breeding

Annual Occurrence

Jan Feb Mar Apr May Jun Jul Aug Sep Oct Nov Dec

Marbled Godwit

Data Base

	Jan	Feb	Mar	Apr	May	Jun	Jul	Aug	Sep	Oct	Nov	Dec	Total
Occurrence	4	8	13	21	78	10	26	41	104	59	12	10	386

Ruddy Turnstone

Arenaria interpres (Linnaeus)

RUTU

RANGE: Circumpolar. Breeds mainly on the continental coastal fringes around the Arctic Ocean and on most high Arctic islands. Winters in much of the southern hemisphere. In the New World, winters mainly from the southern United States south to Tierra del Fuego.

STATUS: *Uncommon* to *common* spring and autumn transient on the coast; *uncommon* in winter. *Very rare* transient in the interior.

OCCURRENCE: The Ruddy Turnstone occurs regularly throughout coastal British Columbia, but is most abundant on the outer coast. Although the species is a common migrant through much of southern Canada (Godfrey 1986), it occurs only as transient singles or pairs in the interior of British Columbia.

On the coast, the Ruddy Turnstone frequents rocky shores (Fig. 123), especially off-shore islets and reefs or exposed peninsulas where it forages over barnacle and mussel encrusted rocks at the water's edge. It occasionally frequents pebble beaches, sand beaches, and mudflats. On sand beaches it picks through piles of beached kelp and other seaweeds as well as other marine debris, or digs holes with its beak as it forages. In the interior it usually avoids mountainous terrain, but frequents the shores, mudflats, and beaches of freshwater lakes and sloughs and sewage lagoons.

In British Columbia, the Ruddy Turnstone is much less numerous than the Black Turnstone. Flocks of 5 to 15 birds are normal; more than 25 is unusual. It is often seen accompanying large flocks of Black Turnstones or in mixed flocks of turnstones, Surfbirds, and Wandering Tattlers.

The spring migration usually begins in early May (rarely late April), somewhat later than most other shorebirds (Hatler et al. 1978), although the beginning of the movement may be somewhat confused by the presence of overwintering birds. The spring movement appears to peak in mid-May and is less noticeable than the autumn movement. The Ruddy Turnstone arrives at its Arctic breeding grounds each year on a remarkably consistent date (Parmelee and MacDonald 1960) so the fact that the spring migration ends abruptly at the end of May is not surprising. Victoria, Long Beach, and the Queen Charlotte Islands are the best locations to see spring migrants.

Compared to other shorebirds, very few stragglers remain on the coast in June. This may be due to immatures skipping their first northward migration. The autumn movement generally begins slowly in early July but numbers rapidly increase during the last week of July. Peak numbers last through August into early September. Autumn arrivals in July are likely all females since they abandon their broods before the young are fledged (Nettleship 1973). Males follow later in July followed by juveniles throughout August. The rocky islands off Oak Bay, on southern Vancouver Island, consistently attract the largest numbers of late summer migrants. The Ruddy Turnstone is uncommon after mid-

September but a few remain throughout the autumn and into winter in most coastal areas.

In winter, records are usually of single birds. However, flocks of 40 to 50 have been recorded in December near Masset. Although the wintering range is listed as California south to South America, it is evident that small numbers winter north at least to British Columbia. Most of our winter records are from Victoria, Vancouver, and the Queen Charlotte Islands.

REMARKS: M.C. Thompson (1974) and Branson et al. (1978) summarize migratory movements. Two races are reported to occur on our coast; *A. i. interpres* and *A. i. morinella*. However, M.C. Thompson (pers. comm.) suggests that these races are doubtful and may be based on age related plumage variation, not on geography. Some authors suggest that *A. interpres* and *A. melanocephala* constitute a superspecies (American Ornithologists' Union 1983).

Figure 123. *Ruddy Turnstones on the Chatham Islands, off southern Vancouver Island, 12 May 1984 (Tim Zurowski).*

NOTEWORTHY RECORDS

Spring: Coastal - Clover Point 11 May 1975-24; Gabriola Island 24 Apr 1967-2; Boundary Bay 13 May 1983-1; Lennard Island 25 Apr 1977-75; Cleland Island 26 May 1982-3, latest date; Tofino 10 May 1986-10 on mudflats; Goose Group 12 May 1948-8 (Guiguet 1953a); Sandspit 16 May 1985-25; Green Island (Chatham Sound) 21 May 1978-1. **Interior** - Fraser Lake (Fort Fraser) 23 May 1978-1 (Campbell and Garrioch 1978a); Charlie Lake 24 May 1980-2.

Summer: Coastal - Chatham Islands 23 Jul 1984-25, 24 Jul 1983-125, 31 Jul 1982-30; Clover Point 22 Jul 1975-4, 28 Jul 1958-5; Boundary Bay 23 Jul

1983-3; Cleland Island 6 Jun 1970-1, 7 Jul 1982-8 (early date); St. John Harbour 5 Aug 1948-1; Sandspit 15 Jul 1981-25; Big Bay (Prince Rupert) 24 Jul 1987-44; Stephens Island 29 Jun 1976-22. **Interior** - Nakusp early Aug 1978-1; Swan Lake (Vernon) 23 and 24 Aug 1984-1; Blind Bay 24 Aug 1972-1; Salmon Arm 30 Aug 1975-1; Beatton Provincial Park 22 and 23 Aug 1986-1 in winter plumage.

Autumn: Interior - Boundary Lake (Goodlow) 9 Sep 1986-1; Prince George 11 Sep 1970-1; Kamloops 2 to 6 Sep 1986-1; Swan Lake (Vernon) 14 and 15 Sep 1983-1 (RBCM Photo 862); Nakusp

early Aug 1978-1 (RBCM Photo 690). **Coastal** - Green Island 3 Nov 1978-1; Qualicum Beach 12 Sep 1973-10; Long Beach 3 Sep 1983-9; Sidney Island 19 Nov 1980-1 (RBCM 16996).

Winter: Interior - No records. **Coastal** - Masset 15 Dec 1973-45; Vancouver 20 Dec 1975-1; Steveston 19 Feb 1979-1; Clover Point 29 Jan 1955-1 (Clay 1955a).

Christmas Counts: Interior - Not recorded. **Coastal** - Recorded from 6 of 28 localities and on 4% of all counts. Maxima: Skidegate Inlet 18 Dec 1983-4.

Ruddy Turnstone

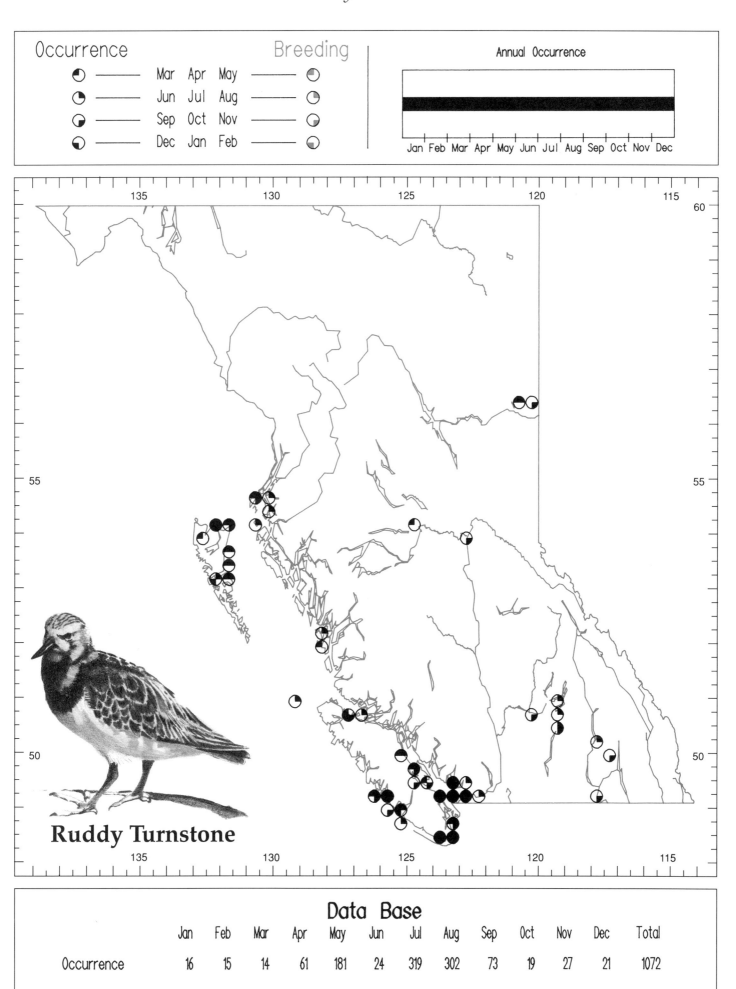

Occurrence

Mar	Apr	May
Jun	Jul	Aug
Sep	Oct	Nov
Dec	Jan	Feb

Breeding

Annual Occurrence

Jan Feb Mar Apr May Jun Jul Aug Sep Oct Nov Dec

Ruddy Turnstone

Data Base

	Jan	Feb	Mar	Apr	May	Jun	Jul	Aug	Sep	Oct	Nov	Dec	Total
Occurrence	16	15	14	61	181	24	319	302	73	19	27	21	1072

Black Turnstone

BLTU

Arenaria melanocephala (Vigors)

RANGE: Breeds on the coastal plain of western and southern Alaska. Winters only on the Pacific coast, from southeast Alaska to central Mexico.

STATUS: *Fairly common* to locally *abundant* migrant and winter visitant on the coast. *Fairly common* in summer. *Casual* in the interior.

OCCURRENCE: The Black Turnstone is widely distributed along the inner and outer coast. Its distribution is largely restricted to rocky coastal shorelines, but it frequents many fiords and protected inlets. It is a vagrant in the interior. The Black Turnstone usually occurs in flocks of 10 to 50 birds, but flocks of up to 4,000 have been recorded during peak migratory movements.

The Black Turnstone (Fig. 124) is the most abundant shorebird of rocky shorelines. Favourite habitats include reefs, rocky beaches, jetties, and gravel bars at the mouths of rivers or along lagoons. It may also forage on adjacent mudflats, wet sandy beaches, floating kelp beds, and piles of washed-up seaweed. Black Turnstones have been recorded roosting on dry rocks, jetties, and floating log booms at which time they may gather into extremely dense flocks.

Overwintering birds occur in substantial numbers along the outer coast, which makes the beginning of the northward spring movement difficult to discern. Hatler et al. (1978) found no obvious spring movement through Pacific Rim National Park. A peak migration seems to occur along the coast in late April and early May. J.A. Munro (1936a) documents increasing numbers from 29 April to 4 May at Tlell followed by a rapid decrease through to 10 May. Dawe (1976, 1980) notes that a large influx occurs at the Little Qualicum River estuary from late April to early May and then ends abruptly. The spring movement ends by mid-May. Late migrants and some nonbreeding yearlings occur from late May through June. The postbreeding southward movement begins in late June and accelerates through the summer. Numbers remain moderate until September when the late-departing juveniles arrive. The Baynes Sound area supports the largest wintering numbers in the province. There, numbers increase through November, peak in late December and early January, and taper off thereafter (Fig. 125). Winter flocks rarely exceed 200 birds and frequently contain Surfbirds, Rock Sandpipers, as well as Sanderlings.

REMARKS: The Black Turnstone is faithful to specific wintering localities year after year (Gill et al. 1983). Thus, flocks observed in winter on the British Columbia coast are probably found there throughout that season.

W.G. Smith (1952) discusses the winter foods and feeding behaviour of the Black Turnstone at Iona Island near Vancouver.

Figure 124. Black Turnstones on the Chatham Islands, off southern Vancouver Island, 5 February 1984 (Tim Zurowski).

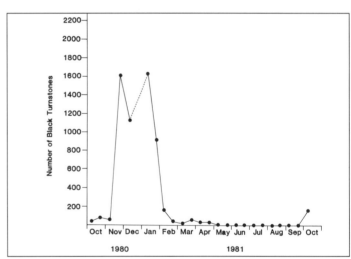

Figure 125. Biweekly counts (averages) of Black Turnstones, Comox Harbour to Deep Bay, Vancouver Island, 11 October 1980 to 10 October 1981 (courtesy Canadian Wildlife Service). Large numbers reported over the period December through January were primarily of birds counted at one roost on log booms north of Union Point. The dashed line indicates a period when counts were not made.

NOTEWORTHY RECORDS

Spring: Coastal - Clover Point 2 May 1971-200; Vancouver 2 May 1974-180; Turtle Island 25 Apr 1972-500; Tofino 2 May 1970-100; Little Qualicum River estuary 22 Apr 1975-9, 29 Apr 1975-113, 7 May 1975-120, latest date; 25 Apr 1976-30, 3 May 1976-155; 4 Apr 1977-7, 25 Apr 1977-134, 3 May 1977-250 (Dawe 1976, 1980); Burke Channel 19 Mar 1983-200; Ridley Island 20 Apr 1979-150; Tlell 4 May 1935-1,000; Rose Spit 28 Apr 1979-105. **Interior** - See Extralimital Records.

Summer: Coastal - Clover Point 26 Jun 1979-14; Sea Island 27 Aug 1934-90; Hudson Rocks 15 Jul 1981-150; Cleland Island 12 Aug 1973-200; Stumaun Bay 24 Aug 1969-321; Rose Spit 17 Jun 1977-10; Green Island (Chatham Sound) 13 Jul

1978-100+; e Port Simpson 28 Jul 1980-4,000, aerial observation (Savard 1981). **Interior:** See Extralimital Records.

Autumn: Interior - No records. **Coastal** - Masset 23 Oct 1971-500+, 16 Nov 1971-300; Port Simpson 28 Sep 1969-351; Port Hardy 15 Sep 1939-1,000; Henry Bay 28 Oct 1978-260; Union Bay (Comox) 29 Nov 1980-3,000 on log boom; Long Beach 1 Oct 1975-62; Ambelside 11 Nov 1974-80; Esquimalt Lagoon 20 Oct 1976-135; Willows Beach 29 Nov 1944-200.

Winter: Interior - No records. **Coastal** - Sewall 20 Dec 1980-100+; Green Island (Chatham Sound) 3 Dec 1978-150; Union Bay (Comox) 13 Dec 1980-

2,000, 10 Jan 1981-2,000, 17 Jan 1981-2,000, and 24 Jan 1981-1,500 all on log boom; Davis Bay (Sechelt) 21 Feb 1981-115; Pachena Bay 11 Jan 1976-150; Ambelside 26 Dec 1966-40; Crofton 4 Dec 1977-150; Clover Point 8 Dec 1973-38.

Christmas Counts: Interior - Not recorded. **Coastal** - Recorded from 19 of 28 localities and on 65% of all counts. Maxima - Comox 19 Dec 1982-**3,560,** all-time North American high count (Monroe 1983); Skidegate Inlet 18 Dec 1983-825; Deep Bay 30 Dec 1980-605.

Extralimital Records: Atlin 14 and 15 May 1930-2 (RBCM 6188, 6189); Nulki Lake 29 Aug 1945-1 female (ROM 85473).

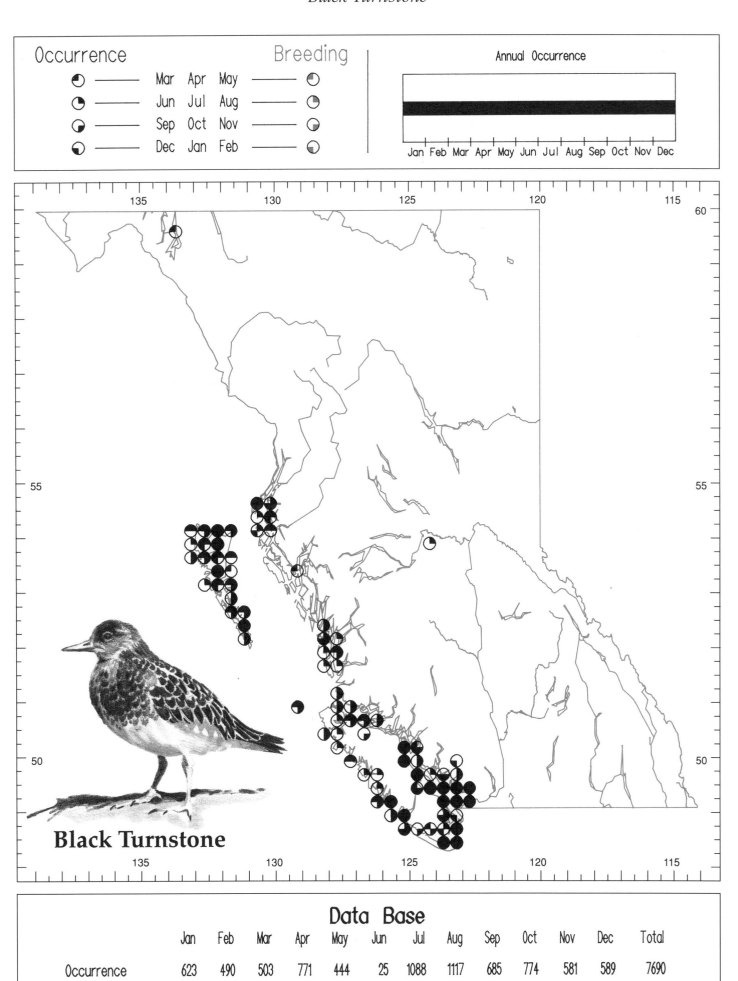

Black Turnstone

Occurrence / Breeding

Occurrence		Breeding
Mar Apr May		
Jun Jul Aug		
Sep Oct Nov		
Dec Jan Feb		

Annual Occurrence

Jan Feb Mar Apr May Jun Jul Aug Sep Oct Nov Dec

Data Base

	Jan	Feb	Mar	Apr	May	Jun	Jul	Aug	Sep	Oct	Nov	Dec	Total
Occurrence	623	490	503	771	444	25	1088	1117	685	774	581	589	7690

Surfbird

Aphriza virgata (Gmelin)

RANGE: Breeds in central Alaska and Yukon. Nonbreeding individuals summer as far south as Panama. Winters along the Pacific Coast from southern Alaska to southern South America.

STATUS: *Very common* spring and autumn migrant on the outer coast, *common* on the inner coast. *Rare* in early summer. In winter locally *uncommon* on the outer coast and *fairly common* on the inner coast.

OCCURRENCE: The Surfbird is widely distributed along coastal British Columbia; there are no interior records. It is mostly restricted to rocky shorelines including islands (Fig. 126), reefs, beaches, headlands, jetties, and breakwaters. Occasionally, it occurs on hard-packed sandy beaches, tidal mudflats, log booms, and short-grass areas of golf courses and peninsulas immediately adjacent to rocky shores. Only rarely does it frequent the heads of inlets.

The Surfbird may be found in singles or flocks of several hundred. It occurs in pure flocks as well as in mixed flocks with Black Turnstones and Rock Sandpipers. As its name implies, it is not disturbed by breaking waves that shower it with water. Rather, the Surfbird seems to challenge the surf as it forages along newly exposed surfaces.

In southern areas, the northward movement is difficult to discern because of the presence of overwintering birds. The spring buildup begins in February and continues through March and into April. Records on file of flocks of 50 or more birds illustrate this trend (January-no flocks, February-4 flocks, March-8, April-7, and May-2). In Victoria, the peak movement occurs from mid-April to early May while in the Barkley Sound area it is from late April through May (Hatler et al. 1978). On northern Graham Island flocks were noted from April to the first week of May; most of the movement was over by mid-May (Darcus 1930). The spring movement appears to be over by mid-May and sightings after 10 May are rare. During spring, Surfbirds are seldom found in flocks of more than a few hundred birds, although, under certain conditions, flocks of thousands occur.

A few nonbreeding stragglers, or late-breeding migrants, are present on the coast in early-to-mid June. At that time they usually occur in small flocks. The southward movement begins in late June and early July and continues in force throughout July and August. Numbers of flocks of 50 or more birds again illustrate this trend (June-no flocks, July-17 flocks, August-37, September-9, and October-2). Large flocks are unusual after mid-September, which likely marks the end of the main autumn movement, although another smaller and shorter movement is evident in November and early December.

In winter, birds are locally but widely scattered until February and March when spring flocking occurs. The sheltered waters of southern Vancouver Island and the Strait of Georgia are preferred wintering areas.

REMARKS: Godfrey (1966) suggests that Surfbirds may be nesting in the western mountains of the province above the timberline. To date there are no known summer occurrences despite field work in the St. Elias Mountains, Atlin Lake, Kawdy Plateau, Level Mountain, Mount Edziza, and Spatsizi areas. Recently, however, the Surfbird has been found nesting in Kluane Game Sanctuary, Yukon, not very far from the British Columbia border (Godfrey 1986). Observers in the northwestern mountains of the province should be alert to the possibility that the Surfbird may breed there.

On their wintering grounds Surfbirds frequently appear "phlegmatic and sleepy" (Johnsgard 1981). Adrian Dorst (pers. comm.) found that statement to be remarkably true. On 27 November 1982, he discovered a flock of 450 Surfbirds foraging among rocks at Chesterman Beach; he was soon able to "lie right amongst them" as the birds foraged.

Figure 126. *Surfbirds near Baeria Rocks, Barkley Sound, September 1988 (Gary W. Kaiser).*

NOTEWORTHY RECORDS

Spring: Coastal - McNeill Bay 25 Apr 1970-80 (Tatum 1971); Turtle Island 25 Apr 1972-4,500 to 5,000 (Hatler et al. 1978); 2 km w Port Alberni 15 Apr 1986-850; Ucluelet 28 Apr 1974-300; Lighthouse Park (West Vancouver) 28 Mar 1982-300; Mission Point 4 Apr 1987-1,000; Tent Island 1 May 1978-50; Masset 30 Apr 1920-150+ (Brooks 1921). **Interior** - No records.

Summer: Coastal - Victoria 28 Jun 1981-9; Tzartus Island 14 Aug 1968-2,000+ in day count; Fleming Island 10 Aug 1967-1,000 in a single flock; Monks Islet 8 Jul 1966-100; Baeria Rocks 3

Jul 1979-64; Conroy Island 27 Jun 1976-9; Sea Lion Rocks 3 Jun 1982-3; Plover Reefs 18 Jun 1975-2; Trail Islands 8 Aug 1979-550; Skidegate Inlet 9 Jun 1980-1. **Interior** - No records.

Autumn: Interior - No records. **Coastal** - Baynes Sound 18 Oct 1980-36; Chesterman Beach 12 Nov 1982-450, 20 Nov 1982-150, 27 Nov 1980-450; Green Point (Long Beach) 7 Sep 1973-50, 14 Sep 1979-48; Clover Point 4 Sep 1975-75, 25 Sep 1983-50, 25 Oct 1980-49.

Winter: Interior - No records. **Coastal** - Kitkatla

Inlet 16 Jan 1978-10; Mitlenatch Island 19 Dec 1965-2 (Campbell 1965); Lighthouse Park (West Vancouver) 2 Dec 1972-50; Clover Point 25 Jan 1976-48; McMicking Point 15 Dec 1975-22, 26 Jan 1980-28; Cattle Point 7 Dec 1982-34; Mary Tod Island 2 Dec 1951-75 to 100.

Christmas Counts: Interior - Not recorded. **Coastal** - Recorded from 9 of 28 localities and on 19% of all counts. Maxima: Nanaimo 31 Dec 1977-**343**, all-time North American high count (Monroe 1978); Sunshine Coast 17 Dec 1983-172; Victoria 27 Dec 1964-70.

Surfbird

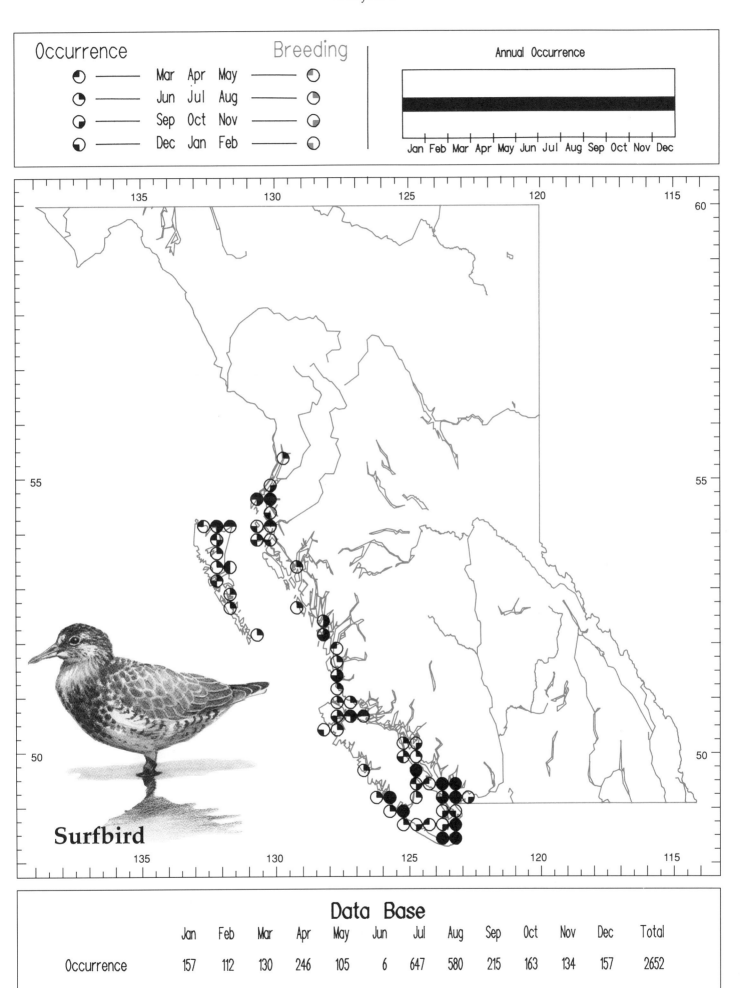

Occurrence

◐	——	Mar Apr May	—— ◑
◔	——	Jun Jul Aug	—— ◔
◓	——	Sep Oct Nov	—— ◒
◕	——	Dec Jan Feb	—— ◑

Breeding

Annual Occurrence

Jan Feb Mar Apr May Jun Jul Aug Sep Oct Nov Dec

Data Base

	Jan	Feb	Mar	Apr	May	Jun	Jul	Aug	Sep	Oct	Nov	Dec	Total
Occurrence	157	112	130	246	105	6	647	580	215	163	134	157	2652

Red Knot

Calidris canutus (Linnaeus)

REKN

RANGE: Cosmopolitan. Breeds in the high Arctic of the New and Old Worlds. Winters in widely scattered areas from California south to southern South America; also in western Europe.

STATUS: *Uncommon* transient on the coast, locally *fairly common* to *very common* in some years; *casual* winter visitant. Not recorded east of the Coast Mountains.

OCCURRENCE: The Red Knot has been recorded at scattered localities along the coast, in low numbers mainly during spring and autumn migrations. It is a long distance migrant that gathers in large numbers at very few, widely spaced localities (Hayman et al. 1986). Since it does not have a major staging area in the province, it probably uses another route to and from its breeding grounds. Most records are from areas where shorebirds concentrate, such as the Fraser River delta, near Victoria, along Long Beach, and at Rose Spit.

This chunky sandpiper (Fig. 127) is usually recorded as a single bird within flocks of other shorebirds such as Black Turnstones, Surfbirds, or Black-bellied Plovers, although flocks of up to 90 Red Knots have been reported. The Red Knot frequents a variety of coastal habitats, more so than most Calidridine sandpipers, including mudflats, hard-packed sandy beaches, offshore rocks, sand dunes, and freshwater sloughs.

The sporadic spring movement occurs from mid-April to early June, peaking from late April to early May. A very small number of nonbreeders linger on the coast in June. The autumn movement begins in late June and may peak anywhere from mid-July through late September. A few stragglers remain in November, and occasionally 1 or 2 birds are seen in winter.

REMARKS: Two to four races are recognized. *C .c. canutus* breeds in Eurasia and in the northern part of the species' range in North America. *C. c. rufa* breeds in the southern part of its Canadian range. All British Columbia specimens examined by Godfrey (1986) were of *C. c. canutus*. Harrington (1983) reviews world migration patterns.

Figure 127. Red Knot at Esquimalt Lagoon, southern Vancouver Island, September 1988 (Tim Zurowski).

NOTEWORTHY RECORDS

Spring: Coastal - Witty's Lagoon 7 May 1974-5; Clover Point 17 Apr 1978-1; Tsawwassen 20 May 1973-14; Iona Island 4 Mar 1950-1 adult male (UBC 2392); Long Beach 2 May 1974-25; Tofino 9 May 1986-17; Hisnit Islands (Tree Island) 15 May 1987-2 (RBCM Photo 1164); Goose Group 20 May 1948-1 adult male (UBC 1940); Rose Spit 23 Apr 1979-11, 28 Apr 1979-80, 29 Apr 1979-90; Port Simpson 13 May 1886-1 male (RBCM 1613); Green Island 27 May 1978-3. **Interior** - No records.

Summer: Coastal - Witty's Lagoon 7 Jul 1973-2; Cattle Point 9 Aug 1963-5; Starlight Reef 24 Jul 1970-1; Boundary Bay 6 Jun 1982-2, 19 and 20 Jun 1982-3, 24 Jun 1982-6, 26 Aug 1981-5; Iona Island 15 to 27 Jun 1981-1, 30 Aug 1980-3; Long Beach 12 Jul 1972-36. **Interior** - No records.

Autumn: Interior - No records. **Coastal** - Tlell 2 Nov 1942-1 (Cook, F.S. 1947); Port Hardy 27 Nov 1940-1; Comox 9 Sep 1950-2 males (RBCM 12778-79); Mud Bay 17 Sep 1984-4; Blackie Spit 30 Oct 1978-5; Saanich 18 Sep 1955-18; Discovery Island 26 Sep 1955-14.

Winter: Interior - No records. **Coastal** - Crescent Beach 8 Feb 1975-1 (RBCM Photo 379), 14 Dec 1975-1 (Shepard, M.G. 1976b); Boundary Bay 5 Dec 1987-2; Oak Bay 12 Feb 1975-1, 19 Dec 1978-1, both on golf course; Chatham Island 6 Jan 1959-1.

Christmas Counts: Not recorded.

Red Knot

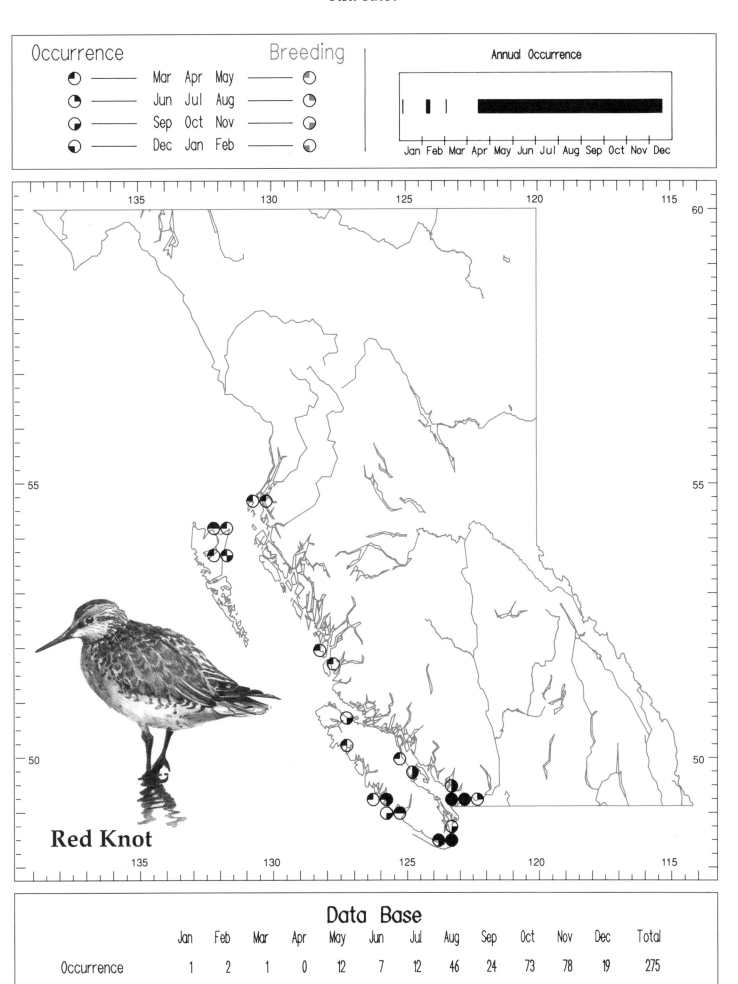

Sanderling
Calidris alba (Pallas)

SAND

RANGE: Cosmopolitan. Breeds in the Arctic of the New and Old Worlds, including land closest to the North Pole. Winters coastally from southern British Columbia and Nova Scotia to Tierra del Fuego; also on the coastlines of Africa, southern Asia, Australia, and western and southern Europe.

STATUS: *Abundant* migrant along the coast; *common* to locally *abundant* winter visitant. In the interior, usually a *very rare* spring and *rare* autumn transient; but, at times, may be locally *very common* in spring and *common* in autumn; *accidental* in winter.

OCCURRENCE: The Sanderling is widely distributed along the coast and widely scattered throughout the interior of the province. It is a long distance migrant with major offshore and coastal movements and, like the Red Knot, has favourite staging areas. It characteristically occurs in tightly-packed flocks of 10 to 30 birds, but may also occur in flocks of several hundred. Pure flocks are seen frequently but the Sanderling associates with almost any other small shorebird. The largest numbers for the province are found on the sandy beaches of northern Graham Island. Surveys from Masset to Rose Spit on 2 May 1982 and 22 September 1982 estimated 1,300 and 2,000 birds respectively. It occurs from sea level to 1,200 m elevation.

The Sanderling frequents hard-packed, sandy beaches on the coast (Fig. 128), normally shunning soft tidal mudflats, cobble beaches, and rocky shorelines. It runs along the tide line, darting in and out as waves wash back and forth, constantly trying to forage on the most recently exposed surfaces. It roosts on logs, rocks, or on drier parts of the beach often in a dense flock above the high tide line. In the interior, it frequents lakeshores, sloughs, and mudflats in lowland valleys and high alpine lakes.

The coastal spring movement begins by late March; numbers increase slowly throughout April and peak in late April to early May. Numbers dwindle rapidly after mid-May. The interior movement is weak. There are many June records of nonbreeders and late migrants from the coast.

The stronger southward movement begins slowly between late June and early July as adults leave the breeding grounds; a peak occurs in August or early September as the juveniles move south. Similar peaks were noted for the west coast of Vancouver Island (Hatler et al. 1978) and the Okanagan valley (Cannings, R.A. et al. 1987). Numbers taper off through the rest of autumn. On the coast, the Sanderling remains as one of the most abundant wintering waders; it occurs over the length of the coast in protected localities with extensive sandy beaches.

REMARKS: Like most Calidridines, Sanderlings prefer to forage during the ebb tide. They may be active nocturnally; one observer watched a flock of 80 forage on Long Beach near midnight under a bright moon.

Figure 128. Sanderlings foraging near Vancouver, 27 May 1986 (Al Grass).

NOTEWORTHY RECORDS

Spring: Coastal - Sidney Spit 4 Apr 1983-250+; Jericho Beach 16 Apr 1978-200; Long Beach 22 May 1983-60; Denman Island 28 Apr 1979-200+; Gray Bay 21 Mar 1981-80; Masset to North Beach 21 Apr 1979-507 (census); McIntyre Bay 6 Apr 1980-350. **Interior** - Duck Lake (Creston)21 May 1956-150 (Munro, J.A. 1958a); Kamloops 15 Apr 1968-4; Fort St. John 30 May 1986-2; Charlie Lake 24 May 1980-1 (early date); Atlin 18 and 19 May 1981-1 (Campbell 1981).

Summer: Coastal - Long Beach 4 Jun 1983-14; Wickaninnish Bay 28 Aug 1977-350; Woodhus Creek 30 Jun 1975-5, 5 Jul 1975-50+, 15 Aug 1974-400; Rose Spit 29 Jul 1977-598 (census), 12 Aug 1977-800. **Interior** - Okanagan Landing 2 Aug 1908-75; Douglas Plateau 11 Aug 1982-3; Soda Lake 7 Jul 1980-2; Fort St. John 17 Jul 1986-7; Atlin 1 Jul 1980-5.

Autumn: Interior - Fern Lake (Kwadacha Wilderness Park) 7 Sep 1979-5 (Cooper, J.M. and Adams 1979); Fort St. John 16 Sep 1986-16, 22 Sep 1986-4 (latest date); Salmon Arm 25 Sep 1970-20; Williams Lake Sep 1966-1 (Roberts, A. 1973); Felker Lake Sep 1971-1 (Roberts, A. 1973); Kamloops 20 Sep 1980-35, 14 Sep 1986-10; Scotch Creek 1 Nov 1962-4; Osoyoos 13 Sep 1981-1, 27 Sep 1924-1. **Coastal** - 16 km e Masset 22 Oct 1971-300; Masset 2 Oct 1971-500; Baynes Sound 3 Oct 1981-200; Buttle Lake 6 Sep 1986-1; Denman Island 28 Oct 1978-200; Long Beach 5 Sep 1982-600, 26 Sep 1985-500; Chesterman Beach 15 Nov 1982-450; Sidney Spit 1 Nov 1982-225.

Winter: Interior - Okanagan Landing 29 Dec 1932-1 (RBCM 9692). **Coastal** - Tow Hill 8 Dec 1971-150; Campbell River (Discovery Passage) 24 Dec 1975-30; Baynes Sound 10 Jan 1981-105 on census; Stanley Park (Vancouver) 6 Jan 1980-150; Iona Island 21 Dec 1941-300; Cordova Bay 11 Jan 1981- 70.

Christmas Counts: Interior - Not recorded. **Coastal** - Recorded from 14 of 28 localities and on 41% of all counts. Maxima: Masset 17 Dec 1983-587, all-time Canadian high count (Monroe 1984); Vancouver 26 Dec 1965-514; Ladner 29 Dec 1979-436.

Sanderling

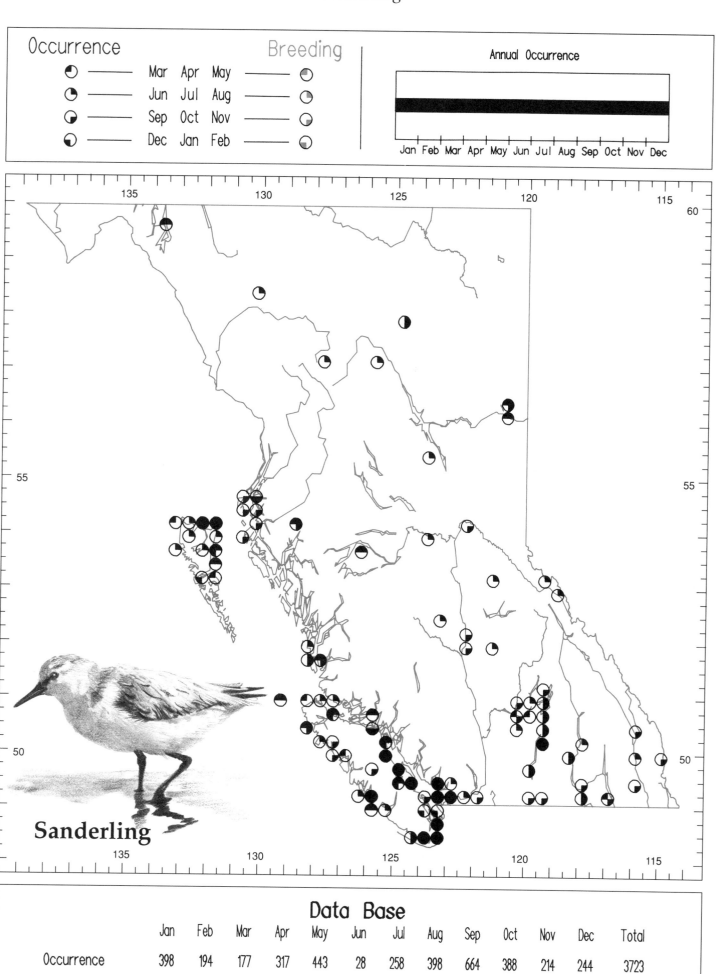

Occurrence

	Mar Apr May
	Jun Jul Aug
	Sep Oct Nov
	Dec Jan Feb

Breeding

Annual Occurrence

Jan Feb Mar Apr May Jun Jul Aug Sep Oct Nov Dec

Data Base

	Jan	Feb	Mar	Apr	May	Jun	Jul	Aug	Sep	Oct	Nov	Dec	Total
Occurrence	398	194	177	317	443	28	258	398	664	388	214	244	3723

Semipalmated Sandpiper
Calidris pusilla (Linnaeus)

SESA

RANGE: Breeds from the Arctic coast of western Alaska across the low and central Arctic of Canada, south along the coast of Hudson Bay and northern Quebec and Labrador. Winters on both coasts from southern Florida and Middle America to northern Chile and northern Argentina.

STATUS: Locally *very common* to *abundant* transient in northeastern British Columbia east of the Northern and Central Rocky Mountains. Generally *uncommon* spring transient and *fairly common* autumn transient throughout the rest of the province except in the southern Strait of Georgia where it may be *very common* in spring and locally *very common* in autumn in some years.

OCCURRENCE: This nondescript small shorebird occurs throughout the province during short migratory periods between its breeding and wintering grounds. It has elliptical migratory routes with most spring migrants moving through the interior of North America and most autumn migrants moving south down both coasts, but principally the Atlantic coast (Harrington and Morrison 1979). On the British Columbia coast, it passes through in low numbers. In the past, the Semipalmated Sandpiper generally went unnoticed among the overwhelming numbers of Western Sandpipers, but today it is seen regularly as birders carefully scan the Western Sandpiper flocks. Groups of 100 or more Semipalmated Sandpipers have been recorded only at the mouth of the Fraser River, in Boundary Bay, and in tidal lagoons near Victoria. It is the third most common 'peep' caught in summer banding operations on the Fraser River delta. Recent banding data indicate that it may be about half as numerous as Least Sandpipers on the Fraser River delta. In the interior, it is a relatively scarce transient except in the northeast. The mudflats at the south end of Charlie Lake and the sewage ponds at Fort St. John regularly attract the largest numbers of transients in the province (Campbell 1987e).

On the coast, the Semipalmated Sandpiper prefers to forage on tidal mudflats in estuaries. It may show less preference for the tide edge than does the Western Sandpiper. In the interior, sewage lagoons and the muddy edges of sloughs and lakes are frequented most often, and it forages in the drainage channels and between clumps of marsh vegetation as does the Least Sandpiper.

Throughout the province the first spring transients arrive in late April, much later than many other shorebirds. Migration continues throughout May and into early June, peaking in the northeast in mid-to-late May. On the coast, up to 40 per day were reported in early May at Browning Inlet (Richardson 1971). The spring movement is weaker than the autumn movement except in the northeast, although migration strength varies from year to year. R.A. Cannings et al. (1987) list the Semipalmated Sandpiper as accidental in spring in the Okanagan, but it does occur more frequently in other parts of the southern interior (e.g. the Chilcotin-Cariboo).

Adult Semipalmated Sandpipers leave their breeding grounds and arrive in the province from late June through July with a peak in numbers from mid-July to early August. Juveniles arrive in mid-July and become more common as the movement progresses. The autumn passage ends in mid-September both in the northeast and in the Okanagan valley (Cannings, R.A. et al. 1987). A few stragglers occur on the coast until mid-October in some years. The species is then absent from the province until April. Extreme dates are 22 April and 14 October.

REMARKS: A bird banded on the Fraser River delta on 16 August 1987 was recovered in Guyana, 23,000 km to the southeast, on 20 October 1987. Substantiated winter records are lacking, but there are 2 undocumented and therefore hypothetical records from Crescent Beach: 4 January 1941-6 and 16 December 1941-10. Observers should be alert to the possibility that Semipalmated Sandpipers may be among the small numbers of Western Sandpipers that occasionally winter on the south coast, although it would be a very unusual occurrence.

Identification in the field is extremely difficult, even at close range (see Figs. 133 and 134) and especially in winter. Browne (1958), Stevenson (1975), Veit and Jonsson (1984), and Hayman et al. (1986) explore problems with field identification. Harrington and Morrison (1979) review migration through North America, and A.R. Phillips (1975) summarizes information on identification, migration, and summer and winter ranges. There is uncertainty regarding the species' status on the coast and in the interior due to confusion with the more abundant Western Sandpiper. Interestingly, Brooks (1927) found the Semipalmated Sandpiper common in the interior "outnumbering the Western Sandpiper 100 to 1." Roberson (1980) concludes that about one-half of the sight records and photographs he examined of this species from Vancouver Island were adult Western Sandpipers in winter plumage, although it would be interesting to know how he separated them using only field notes and photographs when "separation from Western . . . demands a good view and careful observation" (Hayman et al. 1986). Birds not seen well should be left unidentified.

The Semipalmated Sandpiper has also been placed in the genus *Ereunetes* (American Ornithologists' Union 1983).

NOTEWORTHY RECORDS

Spring: Coastal - Blenkinsop Lake 23 Apr 1984-1; Echachis Island 26 Apr 1971-5; Long Beach 22 Apr 1971-5 (Hatler et al. 1978); Browning Inlet early May 1969-40 (Richardson 1971); Kitimat 23 May 1975-1. **Interior** - Skagit Valley 24 Apr 1971-2; Chilco Ranch (Hanceville) 16 May 1983-1 (Ducks Unlimited Canada 1983); Drummond Lake 12 May 1975-3; Telkwa 25 May 1978-1 with 9 Spotted Sandpipers; Fort St. John 24 May 1986-500, 30 May 1986-60; Charlie Lake 30 Apr 1980-5, 24 May 1983-400; Helmet (Kwokullie Lake) 18 May 1982-60 (RBCM 17430-17439); Richter Pass 13 May 1979-4 (Cannings, R.A. et al. 1987).

Summer: Coastal - Saanichton 3 Jul 1965-10; Iona Island 17 Jul 1984-110; Masset 16 Jun 1984-2. **Interior** - Duck Lake (Sirdar) 11 Aug 1948-100 on flooded stubble, 12 Aug 1947-3, 28 Aug 1947-230 (Munro, J.A. 1950); Vernon 22 Aug 1932-35; s 150 Mile House 30 Jul 1983-4 juveniles (Ducks Unlimited Canada 1983); Williams Lake 8 Jul 1973-1; Drummond Lake 11 Jul 1978-3; Vanderhoof 5 Aug 1945-5 (Munro, J.A. 1946); Chief Lake 7 Jul 1944-8 (ROM 83048); Fort St. John 29 Jun 1986-12, 9 Jul 1987-250 (Campbell 1987e), 12 Jul 1986-140, 18 Jul 1987-106, 15 Aug 1986-124; Kotcho Lake 26 Jun 1982-7 (RBCM 17654-17656);

Atlin 27 and 28 Jul 1979-1 with 12 Least Sandpipers; Chilkat Pass 15 and 16 May 1977-16.

Autumn: Interior - Duck Lake (Sirdar) 8 Sep 1947-20 (Munro, J.A. 1950); Kamloops 9 Sep 1984-1; Mud Creek (Shuswap Lake) 22 Sep 1962-7; Riske Creek 29 Sep 1952-1 (RBCM 15640); Fort St. John 1 Sep 1986-32, 14 Sep 1982-1, last seen. **Coastal** - Esquimalt Lagoon 14 Oct 1975-1; Long Beach 5 Oct 1982-1; Grant Bay early Sep 1969-up to 50 (Richardson 1971).

Winter: No records.

Semipalmated Sandpiper

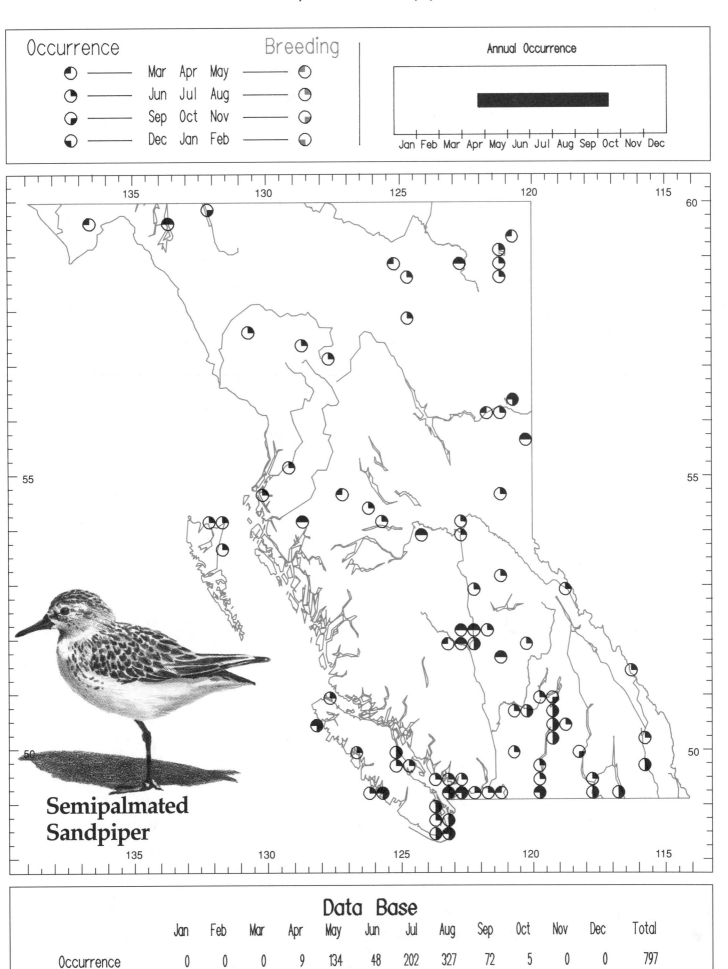

Occurrence   **Breeding**

		Mar Apr May	
		Jun Jul Aug	
		Sep Oct Nov	
		Dec Jan Feb	

Annual Occurrence

Jan Feb Mar Apr May Jun Jul Aug Sep Oct Nov Dec

Semipalmated Sandpiper

Data Base

	Jan	Feb	Mar	Apr	May	Jun	Jul	Aug	Sep	Oct	Nov	Dec	Total
Occurrence	0	0	0	9	134	48	202	327	72	5	0	0	797

Western Sandpiper
Calidris mauri (Cabanis)

RANGE: Breeds on the coastal fringe of western and northern Alaska and on the north-eastern tip of Siberia. Winters mainly from California to Peru on the Pacific coast and from North Carolina to Venezuela on the Atlantic coast.

STATUS: *Very abundant* transient on the coast. *Very rare* spring and *uncommon* autumn transient over most of the interior except in the central-southern portion where it may be locally *abundant* in autumn. *Very rare* in winter, on the south coast except the Fraser River delta where it is *rare*.

OCCURRENCE: The Western Sandpiper is the most abundant shorebird in the province (Fig. 129). Nearly the entire world population migrates along the British Columbia coast during the spring and autumn movements. During these periods most of the population congregates on the rich tidal mudflats of the Fraser River estuary (Fig. 130), the last known major stop before south-central Alaska (Senner et al. 1981). The delta of the Fraser River is the largest on the British Columbia coast and consistently attracts millions of migrating shorebirds and waterfowl (Butler, R.W. and Campbell 1987). Single flocks of 100,000 Western Sandpipers have been reported to concentrate for a day at Roberts Bank and Iona Island during the peak of migration. Their average length of stay is about 3 days (Butler, R.W. et al. 1987, p. 108). Mudflats at Boundary Bay and off Sea Island, Lulu Island, and Westham Island are also heavily utilized. On the west coast of Vancouver Island, the extensive sand beaches of Long Beach, Chesterman Beach (Fig. 132), and the mudflats of Tofino Inlet are important stopping points. Elsewhere along the coast, any estuary or mud or sand beach may harbour some birds, but not approaching the numbers found on the south coast. In the interior, they occur in small numbers over most of the province. There they frequent muddy areas around lake and marsh edges. The mudflats at Salmon Arm are an important stopping place in the southern interior. Very rarely do Western Sandpipers occur in the mountains. On the coast, westerns are typically seen foraging on mudflats or huddled together just above the tide line. At night they roost in very dense groups above the tideline or in adjacent agricultural fields.

Figure 129. Roosting Western Sandpipers at Iona Island, Richmond, 19 August 1982 (Ervio Sian). During strong winds and at evening roosts, thousands of these tiny sandpipers can be found huddled together for protection.

Figure 130. Western Sandpipers foraging on mudflats off Sea Island, Richmond, 26 April 1970 (R. Wayne Campbell). During spring migration, the Fraser River delta is the last known major stop before the sandpipers reach their breeding grounds in Alaska.

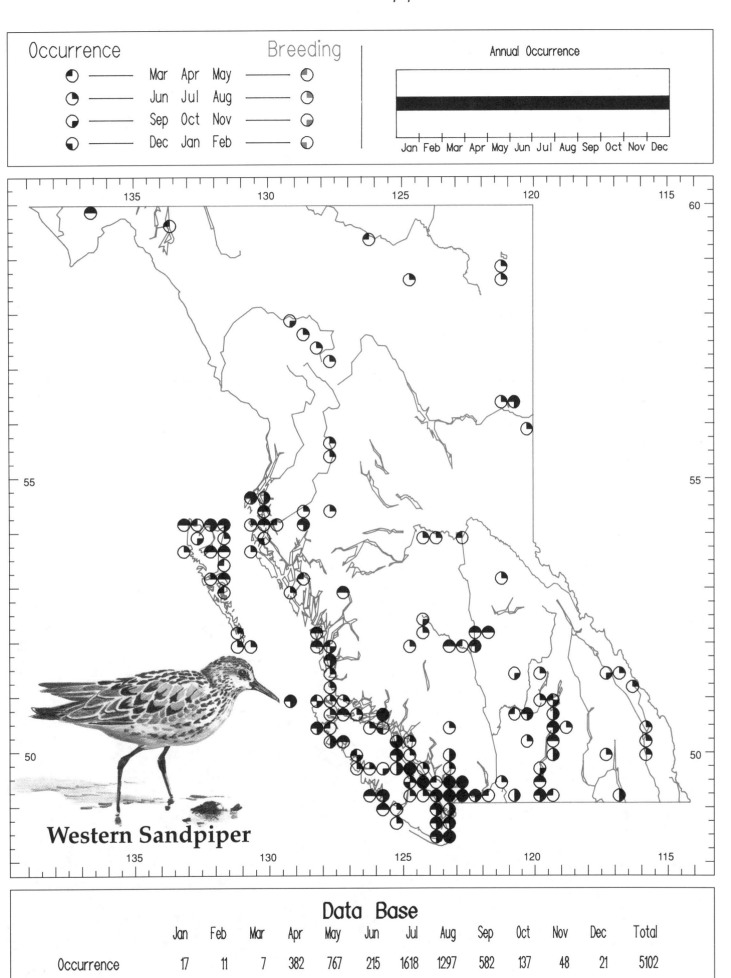

Western Sandpiper

Occurrence

Mar Apr May
Jun Jul Aug
Sep Oct Nov
Dec Jan Feb

Breeding

Annual Occurrence

Jan Feb Mar Apr May Jun Jul Aug Sep Oct Nov Dec

Data Base

	Jan	Feb	Mar	Apr	May	Jun	Jul	Aug	Sep	Oct	Nov	Dec	Total
Occurrence	17	11	7	382	767	215	1618	1297	582	137	48	21	5102

The spring movement begins in early April on the south coast, mid-April on the north coast, and late April in the interior. On the coast, migration peaks from mid-April to early May and ends rapidly after mid-May. Early flocks consist mainly of males, while females predominate in late spring. A few late migrants occur on the coast and in the Peace River area in early June.

The coastal autumn movement begins about 22 June, a week earlier than that of most other shorebirds. There tends to be more adult females than adult males in the early flocks. Adults reach maximum numbers on the south coast in mid-July. Juveniles do not usually arrive until the last week of July; their numbers peak in mid-August. The coastal movement usually lasts until October; a few may remain into November. In the interior, the autumn movement begins in early July, and is much more visible than the spring passage. A few birds winter regularly on the south coast.

REMARKS: The Western Sandpiper is considered by some to be a superspecies with the Semipalmated Sandpiper (Johnsgard 1981). Late migrant juveniles can be extremely difficult to separate from Semipalmated Sandpipers, even in the hand (see Figs. 133 and 134). Stevenson (1975), Veit and Jonsson (1984) and Hayman et al. (1986) provide a guide to field and in-hand identification for these waders. See R.W. Butler et al. (1987) for additional information on sex ratios and weights of Western Sandpipers from the south coast of the province.

Senner et al. (1981) discuss aspects of the spring migration of the Western Sandpiper including a bird banded on the Fraser River delta and recovered 10 days later at Hartney Bay, Alaska. Senner and Martinez (1982) summarize migration data through the interior of North America, including birds banded in autumn on the Fraser River delta and recovered only a few days later in Kansas (see also Fig. 131). We also have a report of a Western Sandpiper colour-marked on the Yukon delta of western Alaska between 19 and 27 July 1979 and observed on the Englishman River estuary that August (M. Wolfe and R. Gill Jr. pers. comm.).

The Western Sandpiper is often placed in the genus *Ereunetes* (American Ornithologists' Union 1983).

Figure 131. Banding locations (stars) and recovery sites (circles) of Western Sandpipers associated with British Columbia. Red indicates birds banded in the province, black indicates birds banded elsewhere.

Figure 132. The extensive sand beaches of Chesterman Beach on the west coast of Vancouver Island are important stopping points for migrating Western Sandpipers in British Columbia (R. Wayne Campbell).

Figure 134. *Adult Western Sandpiper asleep on Sea Island, south of Vancouver, 30 April 1971 (R. Wayne Campbell). Note the band on the bird's right leg.*

Figure 133. *Semipalmated Sandpiper at Cordova Spit, 27 July 1985 (Tim Zurowski).*

NOTEWORTHY RECORDS

Spring: Coastal - Sidney Island 30 Apr 1986-150; Esquimalt Lagoon 18 Mar 1961-2, early arrival date (Stirling 1962); Boundary Bay 31 Mar 1977-6; Roberts Bank 19 Apr 1981-30,000, 25 Apr 1979-100,000, 25 Apr 1982-60,000; Iona Island 30 May 1984-40; Tofino Inlet 1 May 1984-12,000, 5 May 1987-15,000; Hansen Lagoon 17 May 1974-1,650; Ridley Island 19 Apr 1979-9. **Interior** - White Lake (Okanagan Falls) 30 Apr 1974-2; Kamloops 22 Apr 1984-1; Rock Lake (Riske Creek) 24 May 1978-1; Becher's Prairie (Riske Creek) 19 May 1975-10; Williams Lake 10 May 1975-4; Fort St. John 22 May 1986-1; Liard Hot Springs 22 May 1975-1.

Summer: Coastal - Boundary Bay 19 Jul 1978-13,658, 17 Aug 1978-19,000 (survey); Iona Island 21 Jun 1981-150, 1 Jul 1979-100,000, 15 Jul 1978-25,000; Chesterman Beach 23 Jun 1981-45, 25 Aug 1981-15,000; Masset 19 Jun 1919-first arrival, 2 Aug 1920-350 first juveniles (Munro, J.A. and Cowan 1947). **Interior** - Duck Lake (Creston) 10 Jul 1984-2; Deadmans Lake mid-Aug 1981-145; Quilchena 9 Jul 1973-5; Vernon 27 Aug 1961-12; Kamloops 3 Aug 1981-75; Williams Lake 19 Aug 1985-12; Dawson Creek 30 Jun 1978-16.

Autumn: Interior - Fort St. John 16 Sep 1986-1; Felker Lake 9 Sep 1971-10; Bridge Lake 15 Sep 1962-4; Salmon Arm 6 Sep 1970-500; Kamloops 18 Sep 1983-30; Scotch Creek 5 Nov 1962-5; Deadmans Lake (Oliver) 3 to 7 Sep 1980-up to 25. **Coastal** - Naden Harbour 8 Nov 1974-400; Hornby Island 14 Nov 1978-3; Chesterman Beach 4 Sep 1977-35,000, 6 Sep 1979-20,000; Iona Island 6 Sep 1982-20,000, 7 Sep 1982-15,000; Iona and Sea islands 29 Nov 1976-7,000; Boundary Bay 9 Sep 1978-7,700 (survey).

Winter: Interior - No records. **Coastal** - Port Neville 2 Feb 1976-1; Comox 10 Jan 1974-15; Qualicum Beach 11 Feb 1980-11; Sea Island 11 Jan 1975-11, 16 Jan 1975-23; Reifel Island 15 Dec 1968-12; Clover Point 28 Dec 1983-1; Chain Islets 21 Feb 1974-1 (Shepard, M.G. 1974).

Christmas Counts: Interior - Not recorded. **Coastal** - Recorded from 9 of 28 localities and on 10% of all counts. Maxima: White Rock 30 Dec 1978-**33**, all-time Canadian high count (Anderson, R.R. 1984); Vancouver 18 Dec 1983-26; Comox 18 Dec 1983-13.

Least Sandpiper

Calidris minutilla (Vieillot)

RANGE: Breeds in subarctic and northern boreal regions from western Alaska to Labrador and as far south as Sable Island and Cape Cod on the Atlantic coast and the northern Queen Charlotte Islands on the Pacific coast. Winters from the southern United States to central South America.

STATUS: *Fairly common* to locally *very abundant* migrant on the coast and in the southern interior. *Uncommon* to *common* migrant in the northern interior. Locally *fairly common* to *very common* summer visitant. *Very rare* in winter on the coast. Breeds.

NONBREEDING: The Least Sandpiper (Fig. 135) is widely distributed along the coast and through the valleys and plateaus of the interior. Although abundant, it is not nearly as numerous as the Western Sandpiper; maximum counts approach 5,000 birds compared to 100,000 for the Western Sandpiper. Least and Western sandpipers often flock together. Specific localities that consistently attract large numbers of Least Sandpipers are Iona and Sea islands, Boundary Bay, Witty's Lagoon, Long Beach (Fig. 136), and, in lesser numbers, virtually every estuary on the east coast of Vancouver Island. On the central and north coasts, Least Sandpipers usually occur in flocks of less than several hundred birds, even in prime habitats at Hansen Lagoon, Tlell, and Masset. In the interior, Least Sandpipers usually occur much less abundantly. The interior spring movement, most noticeable in the Peace River area, is very weak compared to the coastal movement. In autumn, the birds may be quite abundant in the southern interior. The mudflats of Shuswap Lake at Salmon Arm appear to be the only major interior staging area and attract considerable numbers some years.

Figure 135. Least Sandpiper at Iona Island, Richmond, 8 September 1984 (Ervio Sian). The light, yellowish legs are a reliable field mark that can separate Least Sandpipers from Western and Semipalmated sandpipers.

Figure 136. Long Beach on the west coast of Vancouver Island, 12 August 1968 (R. Wayne Campbell). Seaweed-littered beaches with associated invertebrate prey provide important foraging areas for Least Sandpipers and other shorebirds during migration.

Least Sandpiper

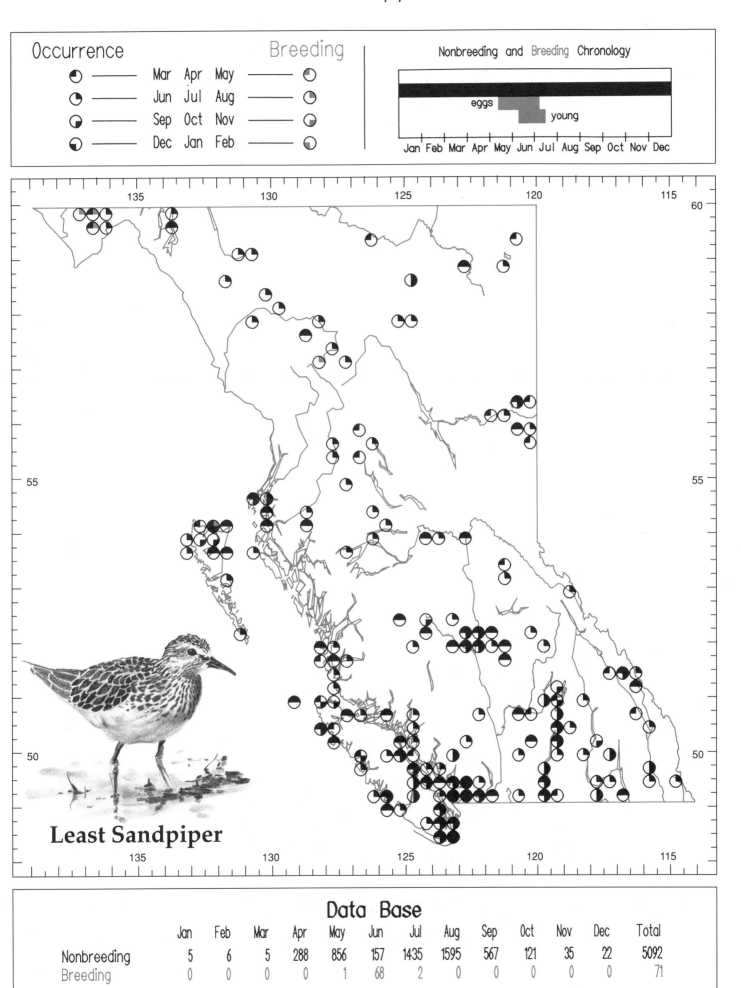

On the coast, the Least Sandpiper is usually found on tidal mudflats and estuaries where it tends to frequent the dendritic drainage channels and the open areas between clumps of emergent estuarine vegetation. It forages by probing in the mud often near or at the base of saltmarsh vegetation, scratching through detritus on the high tide line, or picking under stones. On rocky coastlines, small groups may gather around tide pools. Inland, the soft, muddy edges of lakes, sloughs, ditches, sewage ponds, river banks, and bogs are frequented.

Spring migration begins as early as mid-March on the coast and peaks from late April to mid-May in most of the province, ending by late May (early June in the Peace River area). On the coast, numbers drop off rapidly after mid-May; few stragglers are present in June. The southward movement begins in late June, with an initial peak in early to mid-July, as adult females leave the breeding grounds soon after their clutches hatch. Adult males and then juveniles arrive in force from late July to early September.

The autumn movement ends by mid-September except on the coast where small numbers remain into November in local areas. Several winter records from the south coast and Masset indicate some overwintering.

BREEDING: In North America, the Least Sandpiper breeds farther south than any other Calidridine. It breeds on the Spatsizi Plateau, but the size of that population is unknown. It is also an uncommon but widespread breeder in the Chilkat Pass area and likely breeds in suitable habitat from there through the Northern Mountains and Plateaus. In these areas, it breeds in subalpine bogs and swamps, around the edges of pools and lakes, usually in areas of mixed openings and willow thickets. It breeds from near sea level on the coast to 1200 m elevation in the interior.

It was first discovered breeding on the Queen Charlotte Islands in 1983 when a single nest was found near Masset. Extensive surveys resulted in the discovery of 35 nests in each of 1984 and 1985, and about 70 nests in 1986; most nests were located in a modified brackish estuary in Delkatla Inlet (Fig. 137). A few pairs breed 3 km east of Masset in man-made drainage channels constructed around a military base and in boggy areas along the edge of a sandy beach. The population at Delkatla Inlet is the densest known aggregation of breeding pairs anywhere in the sandpiper's range.

Nests: Nests are shallow depressions in the ground, almost always sparsely lined with a few dried plant stems or tiny leaves. In the Chilkat Pass region, 10 of 16 nests contained only dried willow leaves. Nests are built in open areas well away from taller woody vegetation, usually in moss and sedge covered swampy ground. In extremely swampy areas with many pools, Least Sandpipers select a slightly higher and drier rise or hummock for their nest. Those mounds may be small, dense clumps of sedges or merely a hump of sphagnum. In slightly drier sites, they build nests in sedge growth but always near water. At Masset, nests are built in open grassy and mossy areas; most are situated well away from extensive growths of *Juncus*. One nest was situated on a golf course fairway.

Eggs: Dates for 52 clutches ranged from 1 June to 9 July with 53% recorded between 7 and 18 June. Calculated dates indicate that eggs could be found as early as 12 May. Clutch size ranged from 1 to 5 eggs (1E-2, 2E-2, 3E-6, 4E-41, 5E-1) with 79% having 4 eggs (Fig. 138). Incubation period for 50 clutches in British Columbia was about 22 days.

Young: Dates for 20 broods ranged from 10 June to 3 July with 14 broods recorded between 16 and 29 June. Clutches hatching in early to mid-July would produce fledged young near the end of July and in early August. Sizes for 19 broods ranged from 1 to 4 young (1Y-4, 2Y-1, 3Y-5, 4Y-9) with 14 broods having 3 to 4 young. The fledging period in British Columbia is about 18 days.

Newly hatched young (Fig. 139) usually spend a day near the nest, then wander widely. One nest contained 4 pipped eggs on 16 June, 4 young on 17 June, and 4 young at 0815 on 18 June. At 1350 on 18 June the 4 young were huddled out of the nest and on 19 June one young was spotted 95 m from the nest. Young are reared in well vegetated, swampy grounds.

REMARKS: Veit and Jonsson (1984) and Hayman et al. (1986) discuss field identification of the Least Sandpiper and other smaller sandpipers of the genus *Calidris*.

Figure 137. Delkatla Inlet looking towards Masset, Queen Charlotte Islands, May 1987 (R. Wayne Campbell). This brackish area supports the densest known aggregation of breeding Least Sandpipers anywhere in the bird's range. A proposal to return Delkatla Inlet to its former, natural tidal environment, while beneficial for many reasons, will destroy much of the Least Sandpiper nesting and brood-rearing habitat there.

Figure 138. Adult Least Sandpiper settling on nest near Goat Creek in Chilkat Pass, 15 June 1980 (Ervio Sian).

Figure 139. Adult Least Sandpiper with chicks at Delkatla Inlet, 9 July 1987 (John M. Cooper).

NOTEWORTHY RECORDS

Spring: Coastal - Metchosin 2 to 4 May 1974-1,500; Steveston 2 May 1923-4,000; Iona Island 16 Mar 1975-30, 26 May 1981-100; Long Beach 30 Apr 1983-2,500; Hansen Lagoon 16 May 1974-300; Tlell 30 Apr 1935-400. **Interior** - White Lake (Okanagan Falls) 30 Apr 1974-15; Douglas Lake (Quilchena) 25 Apr 1982-9; Kamloops 3 May 1986-100; Sorrento 5 May 1970-5; 108 Mile House 28 Apr 1980-7; Alkali Lake (Riske Creek) 30 Apr 1972-20; Williams Lake 11 May 1974-40; Fort St. John 26 Apr 1983-first of year, 4 May 1984-21; 24 May 1984-50; Atlin 9 May 1930-2 (RBCM 5822, 5823).

Summer: Coastal - Victoria 30 Jun 1979-52; Saanichton 7 Jul 1974-300; Iona Island 21 Jun 1981-1, 7 Jul 1977-3,000, 9 Aug 1981-1,000; Courtenay River estuary 5 Jul 1941-1,000; Salmon Point (Discovery Passage) 30 Jul 1974-500; Mouat Islands 23 Jun 1981-1; Masset 30 Jul 1977-200. **Interior** - Quilchena 9 Jul 1973-60; Douglas Plateau 11 Aug 1982-50; Salmon Arm 25 Aug 1977-1,000; Le Blanc Lake 30 Jun 1978-7, 15 Jul 1978-50; Westwick Lakes 7 Jul 1978-7; Williams Lake 4 Jul 1973-13, 21 Aug 1985-8; McQueens Slough 30 Jun 1978-12; Fort St. John 9 Jul 1987-45, 12 Jul 1984-48, 10 Aug 1986-30, 17 Aug 1984-36; Chilkat Pass 12 Aug 1957 (Weeden 1960).

Autumn: Interior - Fort. St. John 16 Sep 1986-5, last of year, 2 Sep 1984-2, last of year; Williams Lake 1 Oct 1978-1; Salmon Arm 6 Sep 1970-5,000 (Stevens et al. 1970); Swan Lake (Vernon) 10 Sep 1979-50; Okanagan Landing 19 Oct 1943-1; Deadmans Lake (Oliver) 3 to 21 Sep 1980-up to 130. **Coastal** - Naden Harbour 19 Nov 1974-200; Green Island 23 Oct 1977-1; Tofino 11 Nov 1952-"small numbers"; Chesterman Beach 1 Sep 1981-250; Crescent Beach 31 Oct 1976-65, 14 Nov 1965-22; Martindale Road (Saanich) 20 Nov 1984-1.

Winter: Interior - No records. **Coastal** - Masset 21 Jan 1987-7, 17 Dec 1982-3, 31 Dec 1983-3; Reifel Island 31 Dec 1980-9, 10 Feb 1973-1; Iona Island 7 Jan 1973-2, 26 Dec 1971-13; Crescent Beach 27 Dec 1980-2.

Christmas Counts: Interior - Not recorded. **Coastal** - Recorded from 5 of 28 localities and on 3% of all counts. Maxima: Vancouver 26 Dec 1971-**13**, all-time Canadian high count (Anderson, R.R. 1976); Ladner 30 Dec 1961-8; White Rock 3 Jan 1982-6.

White-rumped Sandpiper
Calidris fuscicollis (Vieillot)

WRSA

RANGE: Breeds across coastal Arctic Canada west to northeastern Alaska. Winters in southern South America.

STATUS: *Rare* transient to the Peace Lowlands. *Casual* elsewhere in the province.

OCCURRENCE: The White-rumped Sandpiper is seldom seen in the province. It normally migrates along the Atlantic coast and through interior eastern North America in autumn, and between the Rocky Mountains and Hudson Bay, concentrated in the eastern prairies, in spring. A few vagrants occur west of the Rocky Mountains.

The White-rumped Sandpiper is listed as a scarce migrant in Alberta (Salt and Wilk 1966), a rare spring migrant in eastern Washington (Larrison and Sonnenberg 1968), and a casual migrant in south coastal Alaska (Kessel and Gibson 1978).

It occurs regularly in spring near Fort St. John where small numbers are seen each year at Charlie Lake or at the Fort St. John sewage lagoons. It has been recorded there only between 18 May and 16 June; the 2 largest flocks on record had 12 birds each. Elsewhere in the province it is extremely rare.

It frequents soft, muddy habitats such as estuaries, tidal mudflats, lake edges, and sewage lagoons (Fig. 140). A group of 5 at Charlie Lake foraged on a gravel road that was dotted with mud puddles. Although the species forms large flocks on its wintering grounds, it tends to migrate in small flocks (Hayman et al. 1986).

The White-rumped Sandpiper has been recorded in the province between 16 May and 16 June and on 30 July, 8 August, and 18 October.

REMARKS: There are several unconfirmed spring and summer records for extreme southern Vancouver Island (Poynter 1958) and an autumn record for the Fraser River delta. See Parmelee et al. (1968) for information on breeding biology for this poorly known species. Burton and McNeil (1976) discuss criteria for aging this species.

Figure 140. *Iona Island, Richmond, showing sewage lagoons and jetty, 29 May 1970 (R. Wayne Campbell). Sewage lagoons throughout British Columbia are attractive habitat to many species of shorebirds from abundant species such as the Western Sandpiper to rare species such as the White-rumped Sandpiper. Such lagoons have also provided the only occurrence records for many accidental species such as the Spoonbill Sandpiper.*

NOTEWORTHY RECORDS

Spring: Coastal - No records. **Interior** - Charlie Lake 18 May 1984-1, 26 May 1980-5; Fort St. John 28 May 1983-6 (Campbell 1983c), 28 May 1985-12, 30 May 1986-8, 31 May 1985-12; Tupper Creek 29 May 1938-1 male (RBCM 7901); Atlin 16 May 1931-1 adult male (MVZ 101004).

Summer: Coastal - Iona Island 15 to 16 Jun 1981-1 (Weber, W.C. 1982), 30 Jul 1974-1 (Crowell and Nehls 1974d). **Interior** - Quilchena 1 Jun 1973-1; Stump Lake (Quilchena) 8 Aug 1976-3; Charlie Lake 6 Jun 1976-3; Fort St. John 3 Jun 1983-5, 6 Jun 1983-3, 16 Jun 1986-4.

Autumn: Interior - Grand Forks 18 Oct 1884-1 male (see Cannings, R.A. et al. 1987). **Coastal** - No records.

Winter: No records.

White-rumped Sandpiper

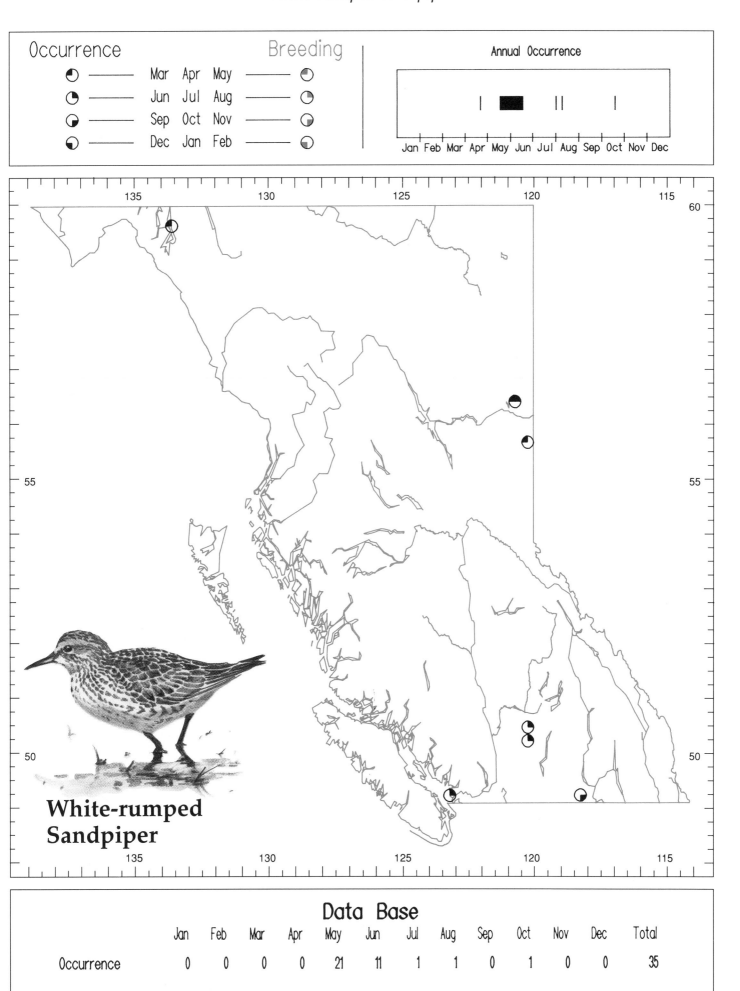

White-rumped Sandpiper

Data Base

	Jan	Feb	Mar	Apr	May	Jun	Jul	Aug	Sep	Oct	Nov	Dec	Total
Occurrence	0	0	0	0	21	11	1	1	0	1	0	0	35

Baird's Sandpiper

Calidris bairdii (Coues)

BASA

RANGE: Breeds from northeastern Siberia across northern Alaska and high Arctic Canada to northwestern Greenland. Winters exclusively in South America from Peru to Tierra del Fuego.

STATUS: *Rare* to locally *fairly common* spring transient. *Very common* to locally *abundant* autumn transient in the southern interior and on the south coast; *fairly common* in the north.

OCCURRENCE: The Baird's Sandpiper is sparsely distributed throughout most of the province during migration periods. In the interior, it frequents the beaches, mudflats, and shallow water of lakes and ponds, alpine areas, and flooded stubble fields. It prefers the drier fringes associated with muddy areas along freshwater ponds and flooded fields where it picks rather than probes for food (Drury 1961). On the coast, it frequents tidal mudflats, lagoons (Fig. 141), and estuaries. On the west coast of Vancouver Island it frequents sandy beaches (Hatler et al. 1978).

The Baird's Sandpiper is an abundant migrant through British Columbia in some years. R.A. Cannings et al. (1987) consider it an uncommon autumn migrant in the Okanagan valley. They also speculate that the Baird's Sandpiper may pass through the Okanagan relatively unnoticed, perhaps largely above treeline. It gathers in large numbers, at times, just to the north at Salmon Arm (Sirk et al. 1973) and to the east at Creston (Munro, J.A. 1958a). Although Jehl (1979) dispels the myth that the species "often travels the full length of the treeless back bone of both continents" during the southward migration, there is evidence that the Baird's Sandpiper does occur in alpine habitats more regularly than any other Calidridine. Such records include a flock of 17 feeding in a glacial stream at 1,950 m on Mount Tatlow, 2 birds picking insects at the edge of a cirque at 1,900 m in the headwaters of the Murray River, and 1 foraging on a snowbank at 2,400 m in Cathedral Park; all 3 records are from mid-summer. The Baird's Sandpiper is surprisingly scarce in the Peace Lowlands. It is a common migrant in Alberta, Saskatchewan, and Manitoba (Godfrey 1986), and most shorebirds that are abundant on the prairies spill over into the Peace River region in fair numbers.

Spring migration begins in mid-to-late April and is over by late May (early June in the northeast). Non-breeders have not been recorded in the province. The southward migration of adults begins in late June or early July, a bit later in the south interior. The autumn movement peaks with the arrival of juveniles in late July in the interior, and August to mid-September on the coast. Some late migrants linger until mid-November but most are gone by mid-October. The Baird's Sandpiper has been recorded in the province from 15 April to 18 November.

REMARKS: The Baird's Sandpiper undertakes one of the longest and most rapid annual migrations of any bird species. During the southward autumn movement, the bulk of the adult population leaves the breeding grounds in the high Arctic and flies to a broad staging area in the American prairies. It then flies 6,000 km directly to northern South America and carries on as far as Tierra del Fuego, all in as little as 5 to 6 weeks (Jehl 1979). The more leisurely movement of juveniles is concentrated in the interior of western North America as well but occurs on a broader coast to coast front.

The Baird's Sandpiper is difficult to identify in the field. Consult Browne (1958) and Hayman et al. (1986) for aids to identification. Jehl (1979) thoroughly covers autumn migration for the species; he believes there are no valid winter records of this sandpiper north of Central America despite numerous reports in official Christmas Bird Counts.

Figure 141. *Baird's Sandpiper at Esquimalt Lagoon, southern Vancouver Island, 28 September 1985 (Tim Zurowski).*

NOTEWORTHY RECORDS

Spring: Coastal - Clover Point 22 Apr 1975-1; Victoria 27 Apr 1978-12; Iona Island 15 Apr 1974-6; Denman Island 18 Apr 1940-3 on spit; Goose Group 11 May 1948-1 adult female (UBC 1969), 23 May 1948-1 female (RBCM 9823); Kitimat 24 May 1975-2; Masset 7 May 1920-1 (Brooks 1921). **Interior** - Vaseux Lake 23 Apr 1962-1; Nakusp 1 May 1976-1; Kamloops 14 Apr 1985-1, 1 May 1982-30+; Kootenay Crossing 17 May 1945-1 adult female (UBC 801); 149 Mile House 28 Apr 1952-1 adult male (NMC 47782); Tupper Creek 8 May 1938-1 female (RBCM 2902); Fort St. John 5 May 1986-2, 30 May 1986-20; Charlie Lake 26 Apr 1980-3, 17 May 1984-25; Fort Nelson 17 May 1986-1; Atlin 6 May 1933-1 (RBCM 5805); Chilkat Pass 15 May 1977-3.

Summer: Coastal - Oak Bay 4 Jul 1982-1; Iona Island 25 Jun 1981-1, 6 Aug 1977-268, 13 Aug 1982-50; Long Beach 28 Aug 1977-13; Kitimat 12 Jul 1975-8 (Hay 1976); Sandspit 21 to 23 Aug 1946 - 2 each day; Masset 28 Jul 1930-1 (Cumming 1931). **Interior** - Duck Lake (Creston) 11 Aug 1948-300 (Munro, J.A. 1950); Douglas Plateau 10 Jul 1983-25; Kamloops 7 Aug 1977-60, 18 Aug 1985-50; Salmon Arm 22 Aug 1973-600, 26 Aug 1973-300 (Sirk et al. 1973); Fort St. John 1 Jun 1986-10, 24 Jun 1987-35, 9 Jul 1987-3, 17 Jul 1987-84, 25 Jul 1987-27, first juveniles, 10 Aug 1986-24 juveniles; Fort Nelson 29 Aug 1987-8 foraging on airport lawn; Chilkat Pass 24 Jun 1973-1 (ROM 119407).

Autumn: Interior - Atlin 9 Sep 1931-1 male (RBCM 5845); Fort St. John 11 Sep 1986-24, 21 Oct 1986-1 juvenile; Rock Lake (Riske Creek) 13 Sep 1978-3; Buffalo Lake 7 Sep 1933-1 (RBCM 11389); Sorrento 1 Sep 1970-100+; Kamloops 12 Sep 1982-75; Columbia Lake 30 Sep 1948-1 (Johnstone, W.B. 1949); Richter Pass 5 Sep 1964-9. **Coastal** - Masset 9 Sep 1938-1 male (RBCM 10651); Triangle Island (Scott Islands) 8 Sep 1975-1 (Vermeer et al. 1976); Comox 19 Sep 1949-100, 27 Oct 1928-1 (MVZ 82016), 8 Nov 1926-1; Reifel Island 18 Nov 1978-1; Chesterman Beach 3 Sep 1974-15; Long Beach 6 Oct 1982-1; Island View Beach 27 Sep 1935-1 male (RBCM 5121); Clover Point 26 Sep 1977-1.

Winter: No records.

Baird's Sandpiper

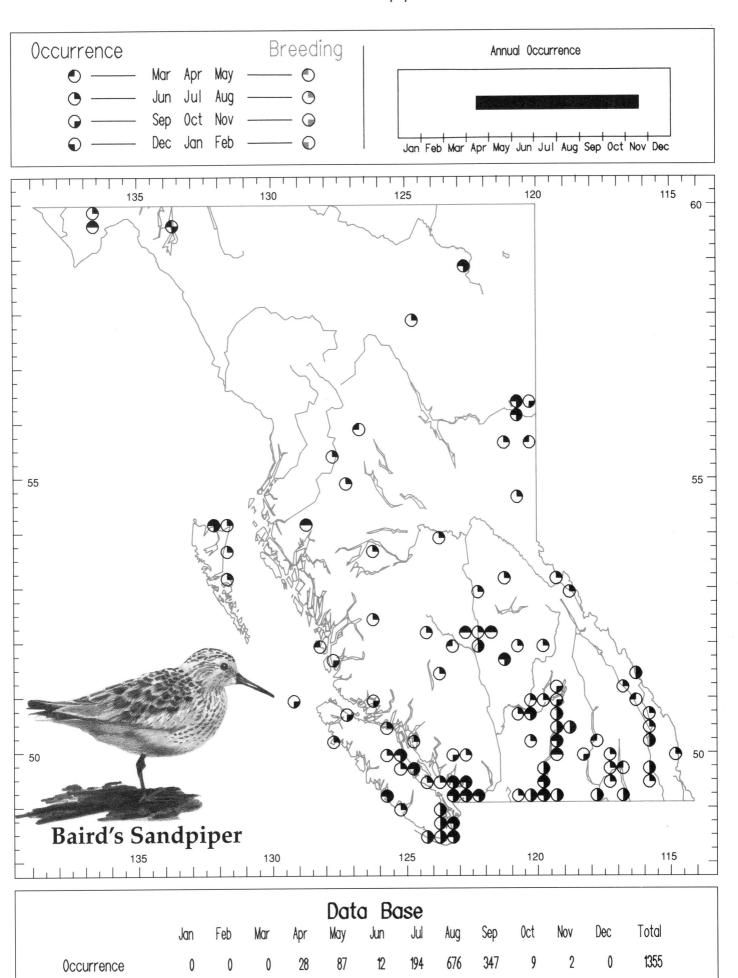

Occurrence

◑	—	Mar Apr May	—	◐	
◔	—	Jun Jul Aug	—	◔	
◕	—	Sep Oct Nov	—	◗	
◕	—	Dec Jan Feb	—	◔	

Breeding

Annual Occurrence

Jan Feb Mar Apr May Jun Jul Aug Sep Oct Nov Dec

Baird's Sandpiper

Data Base

	Jan	Feb	Mar	Apr	May	Jun	Jul	Aug	Sep	Oct	Nov	Dec	Total
Occurrence	0	0	0	28	87	12	194	676	347	9	2	0	1355

Pectoral Sandpiper

Calidris melanotos (Vieillot)

PESA

RANGE: Breeds in northern Siberia and in North America from coastal Alaska east to Hudson Bay including some mid-Arctic islands. Winters mainly in southern South America; a few also winter in Australia and New Zealand.

STATUS: On the coast *rare* to locally *very common* spring transient, *uncommon* to locally *abundant* autumn transient; *casual* in winter on the south coast. In the interior, *casual* to locally *common* spring transient and an *uncommon* to locally *very common* autumn transient.

OCCURRENCE: The Pectoral Sandpiper is sparsely distributed throughout most of the non-mountainous regions of British Columbia with the exception of the plateaus in the northwestern portion of the province. It forages in drier areas than the smaller Calidridines, often well away from the water's edge and among vegetation. On the coast, the drier areas of tidal mudflats and estuaries are preferred. On the west coast of Vancouver Island, it also occurs on sandy beaches and roosts on offshore rocks (Hatler et al. 1978). In the interior, it frequents grassy or flooded muddy fields, slough margins, and sewage ponds. In urban areas, grass fields and golf courses are used. In the Peace Lowlands, freshly ploughed fields and the grassy edges of sloughs and sewage ponds are favoured. In spring in the Boreal Forest of the Fort Nelson Lowlands, it uses the thawing pools between gravel roads and black spruce swamps as stopping places.

The spring movement begins between late April and early May in the south and peaks in mid-May in the south and late May in the north. Spring migrants are most abundant in the Peace Lowlands where flocks of up to 500 birds have been recorded. There are 10 times as many spring records of more than 20 birds from the interior than from the coast, although they are only casual in the Okanagan (Cannings et al. 1987) and the south Thompson River valley (R. Howie pers. comm.).

A few stragglers occur province-wide in June. The autumn movement of adults begins in early July and peaks in late July. Males return first, followed by females. Juveniles arrive by late August and numbers swell through September and October. Their peak movement is several weeks later than that of most Calidridines. Although the Pectoral Sandpiper is listed in some regional accounts as an uncommon autumn migrant (e.g. Cannings, R.A. et al. 1987; Hatler et al. 1978), it is locally common to abundant at Charlie Lake, Creston, Masset, and Iona Island. However, numbers vary from year to year. Numbers dwindle rapidly after mid-October with few present in November, even on the coast.

REMARKS: Early spring migrants have been reported in late March (see Boggs and Boggs 1960) but none of the observations have been adequately documented. We are skeptical, too, of all winter records. The Campbell River and Chilliwack birds are substantiated. However, we have no details of birds reported on the Christmas Bird Counts.

Almost as many Pectoral Sandpipers breed in Siberia as in North America, but the Siberian birds join the American birds in their migration to South American wintering grounds. The majority of the autumn movement is over the west Atlantic, according to Hayman et al. (1986), with some movement through western North America and the Pacific coast. However, the American Ornithologists' Union (1957) reports the autumn migration as mainly through the interior of North America. The spring movement is more westerly, but also through the interior; Pectoral Sandpipers are scarcer on the coast in spring than in autumn. Conversely, they are more abundant in the Peace Lowlands in spring than in autumn.

Kieser and Smith (1982) cover field identification of the Pectoral Sandpiper. Both Cumming (1924) and J.A. Munro (1950) report vegetation (including seeds of pondweeds, sedges, spike-rushes, and bulrushes) in the stomach contents of specimens. This is noteworthy, since Johnsgard (1981) lists only animal matter as food for this sandpiper.

POSTSCRIPT: On 19 December 1988, a bird was photographed (RBCM Photo 1230, Fig. 142) at Burton, the first documented winter record for the interior of the province.

Figure 142. Pectoral Sandpiper at Burton on Lower Arrow Lake, 19 December 1988 (Gary S. Davidson).

NOTEWORTHY RECORDS

Spring: Coastal - Victoria 25 Apr 1958-2 (Schultz 1958); Quicks Bottom 29 Apr 1981-1; Sea Island 27 Apr 1971-1 (Campbell et al. 1972b); Iona Island 15 May 1980-15, 29 May 1980-5; Kitimat 6 May 1980-20, 18 May 1980-100+; Delkatla Inlet 24 May 1987-21 (Cooper, J.M. 1987); Tow Hill 9 May 1979-50. **Interior** - Chilco Ranch (Hanceville) 1 May 1983-first (Ducks Unlimited Canada 1983); Kleena Kleene 21 May 1964-18; Nulki Lake 5 May 1945-30; Fort St. John 24 May 1986-500; Charlie Lake 3 May 1986-6, 24 May 1985-131, 25 May 1980-300+; North Pine 12 May 1979-200+; Chilkat Pass 14 to 16 May 1977-30 per day.

Summer: Coastal - Chain Islets 4 Jul 1970-1; Cattle Point 15 Jul 1964-30; Blackie Spit 7 Jul 1981-7; Cleland Island 18 Jun 1975-1; Iona Island 23 Jul 1973-54, 26 Aug 1973-75; Sandspit 22 Aug 1946-1. **Interior** - Creston 29 Aug 1947-70; Kamloops 25 Jul 1981-2, 18 Aug 1985-25; Salmon Arm 28 Aug 1970-50; Smithers 20 Jul 1977-1; Fort St. John 4 Jun 1986-10, 9 Jul 1987-1, 18 Jul 1987-116, 22 Jul 1987-15, 25 Jul 1987-108; Fort Nelson 16 Aug 1985-1; Atlin 4 Jul 1980-1.

Autumn: Interior - Fort St. John 1 Sep 1984-40 (highest), 27 Oct 1986-13, 31 Oct 1982-1; Bowron Lake 3 Sep 1975-45; Felker Lake 9 Sep 1971-30; Vermilion Crossing 25 Sep 1973-25; Scotch Creek 1 Nov 1962-1; Kamloops 12 Sep 1986-40, 14 Sep 1980-100, 30 Sep 1984-50, 4 Oct 1984-63, 19 Oct 1980-4; Okanagan Landing 6 Nov 1937-10; Wasa 19 Sep 1976-1; Creston 10 Sep 1949-200. **Coastal** - Haida (Masset) 7 Nov 1982-1; Masset 9 Sep 1982-80; Port Hardy 28 Oct 1950-19; Iona Island 24 Sep 1972-300, 27 Sep 1984-285, 2 Oct 1984-400, 7 Oct 1984-270, 17 Nov 1984-1; Sea Island 15 Sep 1971-200; Oak Bay 15 Nov 1982-1.

Winter: Interior - No records. **Coastal** - Campbell River (Discovery Passage) 2 Dec 1975-1; Chilliwack 3 Jan 1927-1 (Munro, J.A. and Cowan 1947).

Christmas Counts: Interior - Not recorded. **Coastal** - Recorded on 2 counts: Nanaimo 31 Dec 1978-3, all-time Canadian high count (Anderson, R.R. 1979); Vancouver 26 Dec 1962-1. Caution should be used with these records as we could find no supporting documentation.

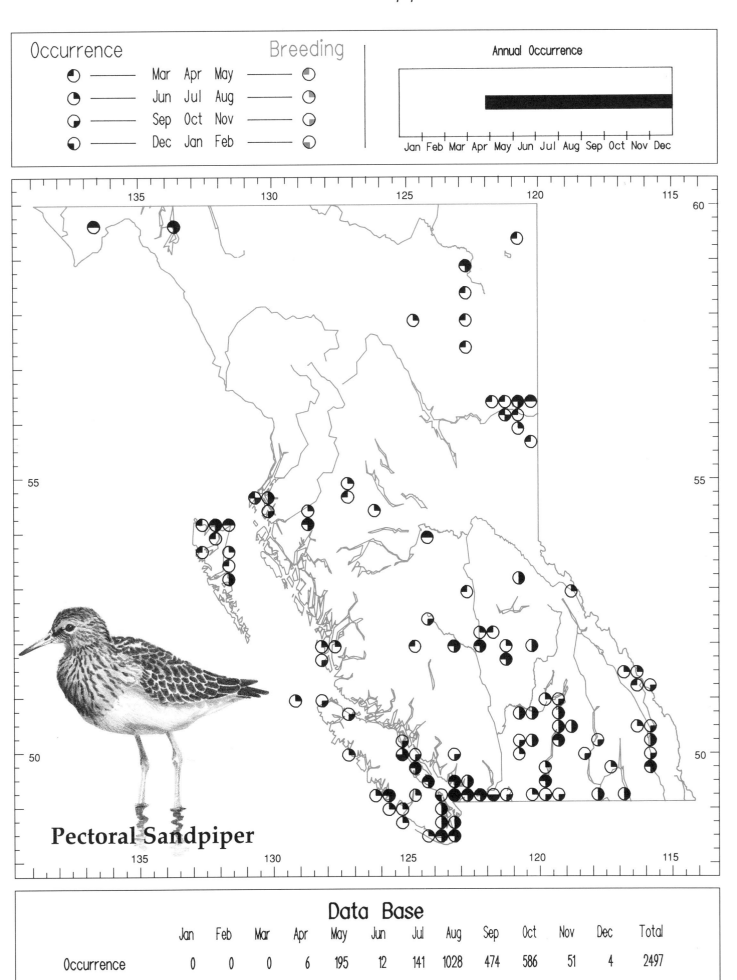

Pectoral Sandpiper

Occurrence / Breeding

	Occurrence	Breeding
Mar Apr May		
Jun Jul Aug		
Sep Oct Nov		
Dec Jan Feb		

Annual Occurrence

Jan Feb Mar Apr May Jun Jul Aug Sep Oct Nov Dec

Data Base

	Jan	Feb	Mar	Apr	May	Jun	Jul	Aug	Sep	Oct	Nov	Dec	Total
Occurrence	0	0	0	6	195	12	141	1028	474	586	51	4	2497

Sharp-tailed Sandpiper

Calidris acuminata (Horsfield)

SHSA

RANGE: Breeds on the tundra of northern Siberia. Winters mainly in Australia and New Zealand.

STATUS: *Uncommon* to locally *fairly common* autumn transient on the coast. *Casual* autumn vagrant in the interior. *Casual* in winter on the coast.

OCCURRENCE: The Sharp-tailed Sandpiper has a scattered distribution along coastal British Columbia; it is rarely found in the interior.

Each year some individuals join the autumn movement of Pectoral Sandpipers and migrate south down the west coast; they are usually found as single birds within flocks of Pectoral Sandpipers. Occasionally small groups of 2 to 20 birds may be found at staging areas such as Iona Island (Fig. 143). It is quite scarce on our coast and is always an exciting find. In some years, however, it may occur locally in larger numbers; it was reported to be "plentiful" at Masset in the autumn of 1941 (Munro, J.A. and Cowan 1947), and occurred in unusually large numbers at Iona Island in August 1977.

The Sharp-tailed Sandpiper arrives relatively late on our coast, usually in late August, and numbers peak in September and October. We have no spring records on file. The earliest arrival date is 22 July. Most of the transients that were aged were immatures which probably accounts for the late arrival dates. By the end of November most have moved on. We have 2 records

that suggest a few may occasionally winter here. All 7 interior records are from early autumn.

The Sharp-tailed Sandpiper frequents habitats similar to those of the Pectoral Sandpiper including short grassy uplands, lawns, tidal mudflats (Fig. 144), estuaries, sewage lagoons, and river banks. On Mitlenatch Island, one rested in an oyster bed. In the interior, it has been reported from sewage ponds and muddy lakeshores. Most records are from Iona Island. The east coast of Vancouver Island and the sandy beaches of the Queen Charlotte Islands are other important localities.

The Sharp-tailed Sandpiper has been recorded between 22 July and 17 November, except for a single confirmed winter record (see also Shepard, M.G. 1977b).

REMARKS: The main migration route for the Sharp-tailed Sandpiper is from breeding grounds in Siberia down the Pacific coast of Asia to Australia and New Zealand where it is an extremely common winter resident. In North America, it occurs as a regular autumn transient in small numbers along the Pacific coast from Alaska to California, including British Columbia, and as vagrants through interior North America.

Field identification is fully discussed by Britton (1980) and Greel (1974). The breeding range of this species is completely enclosed within the breeding range of the Pectoral Sandpiper, its closest relative.

Figure 143. Sharp-tailed Sandpiper at Iona Island, Richmond, 8 October 1978 (Ervio Sian).

Figure 144. Sharp-tailed Sandpiper at Esquimalt Lagoon, southern Vancouver Island, 18 September 1985 (Tim Zurowski).

NOTEWORTHY RECORDS

Spring: No records.

Summer: Coastal - Iona Island 22 Jul 1967-1, 4 Aug 1977-8, 17 Aug 1977- 13, 22 Aug 1977-20; Green Point (Long Beach) 27 Aug 1966-1 (Buffam 1966); Mitlenatch Island 23 Aug 1976-1 (Butler, R.W. and Butler 1976); Masset 9 Aug 1944-1 (RBCM 10660). **Interior** - No records.

Autumn: Interior - Boundary Lake (Goodlow) 9 Sep 1986-2 juvenile; Fort St. John 12 Sep 1987-2 juveniles (RBCM Photo 1165), 8 Oct 1986-1 juvenile; Tranquille 20 Sep 1980-1 juvenile; Swan Lake (Vernon) 12 Sep 1982-1 juvenile. **Coastal** - Green Island 1 Nov 1978-1; Masset 17 Nov 1983-2; Rivers Inlet fall 1913-1 female (UBC 4123); Courtenay 12 Oct 1945-5; Iona Island 18 Sep 1983-5, 3 Oct 1976-6, 10 Oct 1971-6, 10 Nov 1971-4;

Reifel Island 4 Oct 1986-14; Florencia Bay 7 Sep 1986-1 (RBCM Photo 1129); Duncan 2 Sep 1978-1; Saanich 1 Nov 1978; Victoria 6 Nov 1982-1.

Winter: Interior - No records. **Coastal** - Masset 27 Dec 1897-2 (RBCM 207).

Christmas Counts: Not recorded.

Sharp-tailed Sandpiper

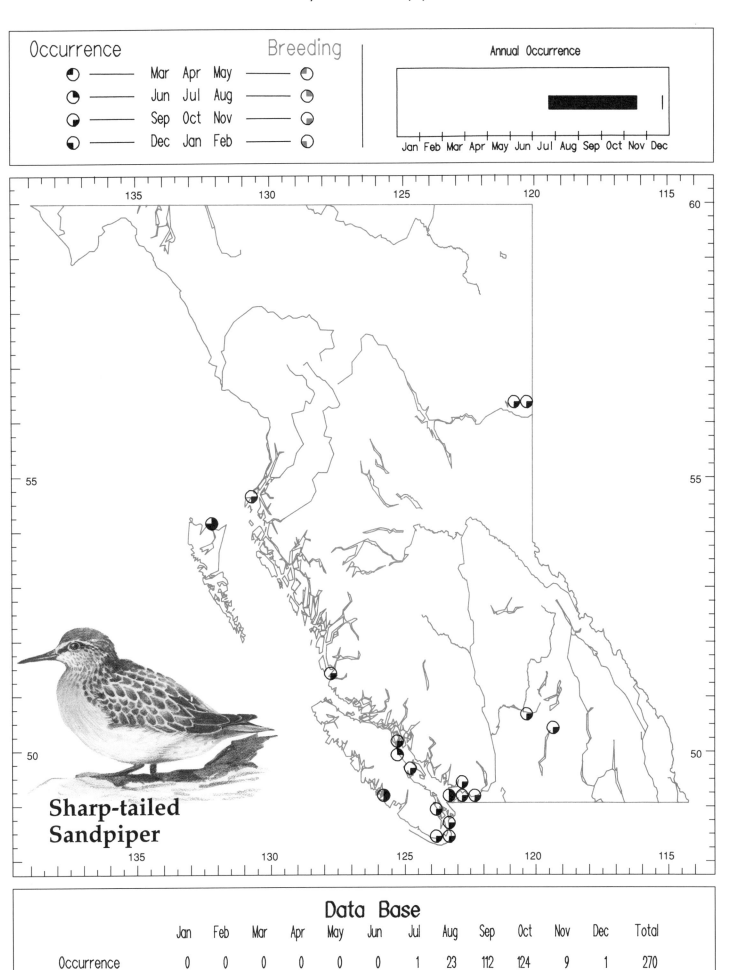

Sharp-tailed Sandpiper

Occurrence

Breeding

Annual Occurrence

	Jan	Feb	Mar	Apr	May	Jun	Jul	Aug	Sep	Oct	Nov	Dec

Data Base

	Jan	Feb	Mar	Apr	May	Jun	Jul	Aug	Sep	Oct	Nov	Dec	Total
Occurrence	0	0	0	0	0	0	1	23	112	124	9	1	270

Rock Sandpiper
Calidris ptilocnemis (Coues)

ROSA

RANGE: Breeds on coastal fringes of eastern Siberia, on many islands in the Bering Sea, and in western and southern Alaska. Resident in more southerly parts of its breeding range. Winters also in the coastal north Pacific Ocean south to northern California and Japan.

STATUS: *Fairly common* to locally *very common* migrant and winter visitant on rocky shores of the north coast. *Uncommon* to locally *common* migrant and winter visitant on the south coast. *Accidental* in the interior.

OCCURRENCE: The Rock Sandpiper is distributed along the rocky coasts of British Columbia. The only interior record is from Atlin. It forages and roosts on offshore rocky islets, rocky headlands, peninsulas, beaches and, occasionally, on mudflats. It is one of the more uncommon regular Calidridines and occurs in small flocks of 6 to 50; it often associates with turnstones, Surfbirds, and tattlers.

The Rock Sandpiper has a very short migration route relative to other Calidridines. It is a late autumn migrant and, conversely, an early spring migrant. Spring migration begins in late March and peaks from mid-April to early May. J.A. Munro (1936a) documents a strong movement at Tlell between 29 April and 11 May peaking at 1 to 3 May. By mid-May, most Rock Sandpipers have left the province. The autumn movement begins in late July

on the north coast and continues sporadically through August. By late August, they begin to appear on northern Vancouver Island but do not reach Victoria in any numbers until October. The autumn movement on the southern island peaks in October and November.

It is locally common in winter in some outer coastal localities such as Victoria (Tatum 1972), Prince Rupert (Fig. 145), and Naden Harbour. It is rare in more protected coastal areas such as Vancouver (Campbell et al. 1972b) and even in some outer coast areas such as Long Beach (Hatler et al. 1978).

REMARKS: The Rock Sandpiper is considered by many to be conspecific with the Purple Sandpiper (American Ornithologists' Union 1983; Hayman et al. 1986). Four races of the Rock Sandpiper have been described: *C. p. tschuktschorum*, which breeds in eastern Siberia and western Alaska, is probably the migratory subspecies and the one responsible for North American records south of Alaska.

J.A. Munro (1936a) examined stomach contents at Tlell and found barnacles and gastropods predominant. W.G. Smith (1952) examined foraging behaviour and diet in winter on the Iona Island jetty and found similar results. Both authors discuss how Rock Sandpiper behaviour changes when interacting with Black Turnstones.

Figure 145. *Three species of shorebirds at Fort Rupert near Port Hardy, Vancouver Island, 15 November 1986 (Richard J. Cannings). Rock Sandpipers often associate with Dunlin and Surfbirds during migration.*

NOTEWORTHY RECORDS

Spring: Coastal - Clover Point 3 Apr 1966-75, 12 Apr 1973-48, 30 Apr 1973-48, 9 May 1968-6 last; Gonzales Point 6 May 1973-76; Snake Island 6 May 1967-15; Malcolm Island 21 May 1976-1; Tlell 1 to 3 May 1935-200 (Munro, J.A. 1936a); Ridley Island 25 Mar 1979-25, 27 Mar 1979-50, 20 Apr 1979-25; Masset to Rose Spit 13 May 1983-24. **Interior:** No records.

Summer: Coastal - Trevor Channel 9 Aug 1968; Sea Island 14 Aug 1966-1; Comox 24 Aug 1934-1 (ROM 85345); Mitlenatch Island 4 Aug 1973-2; Troup Passage 21 Jul 1968-3; e Port Simpson 15 Aug 1934-2 (MVZ 101049, 101050). **Interior:**

No records.

Autumn: Interior - See Extralimital Records below. **Coastal** - Green Island 12 Sep 1978-1 first, 3 Nov 1978-130; Masset 16 Nov 1971-6; Port Hardy 10 Sep 1938-10 first, 18 Sep 1940-60 first; Iona Island 16 Nov 1947-6, first seen; Chatham Islands 28 Nov 1976-40; Clover Point 7 Oct 1978-2 first, 15 Oct 1971-35; Race Rocks 7 Nov 1979-20.

Winter: Interior - No records. **Coastal** - Green Island 28 Dec 1977-80; Naden Harbour 9 Dec 1975-200+, 21 Jan 1975-50+; Green Point 3 Jan 1976-20; West Vancouver 7 Jan 1971-20 (Campbell et al.

1972b); Iona Island 7 Jan 1948-5 on jetty; Chain Islets 27 Dec 1980-90; Cattle Point 9 Jan 1981-32; Clover Point 9 Jan 1979-35, 27 Jan 1953-70

Christmas Counts: Interior - Not recorded. **Coastal** - Recorded from 9 of 28 localities and on 16% of all counts. Maxima: Skidegate Inlet 18 Dec 1983-**161**, all-time Canadian high count (Monroe 1984); Victoria 20 Dec 1969-57; Sunshine Coast 23 Dec 1979-52.

Extralimital Record: Atlin 29 Oct 1932-1 (RBCM 5798).

Rock Sandpiper

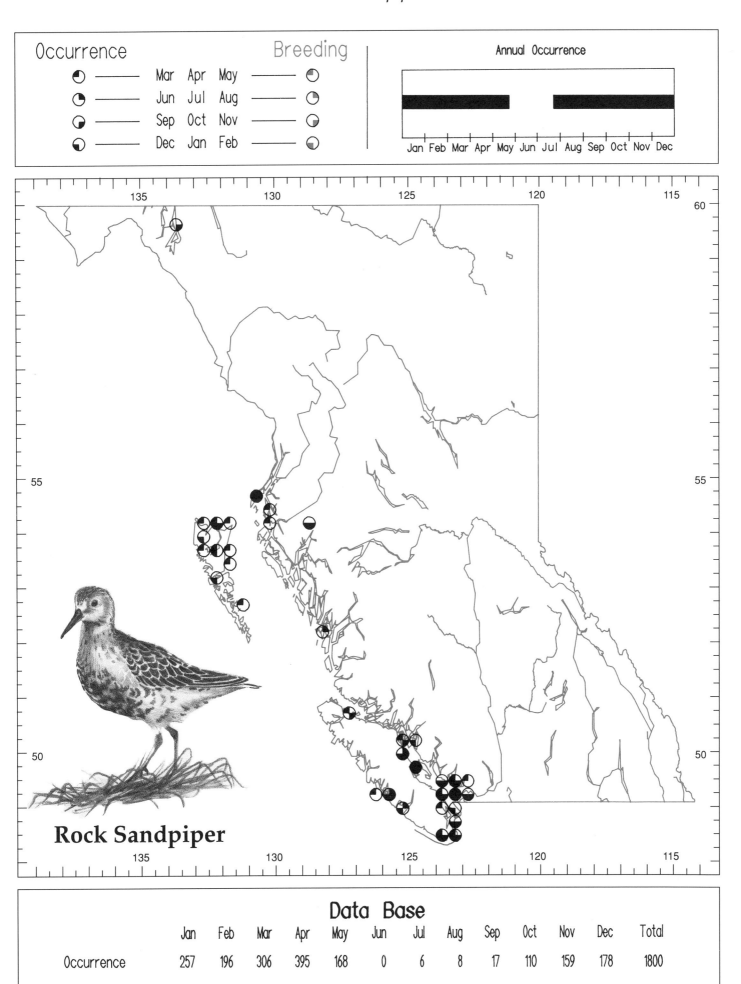

Occurrence

◕ ———	Mar Apr May	——— ◔
◔ ———	Jun Jul Aug	——— ◔
◑ ———	Sep Oct Nov	——— ◔
◕ ———	Dec Jan Feb	——— ◑

Breeding

Annual Occurrence

Jan Feb Mar Apr May Jun Jul Aug Sep Oct Nov Dec

Rock Sandpiper

Data Base

	Jan	Feb	Mar	Apr	May	Jun	Jul	Aug	Sep	Oct	Nov	Dec	Total
Occurrence	257	196	306	395	168	0	6	8	17	110	159	178	1800

197

Dunlin
Calidris alpina (Linnaeus)

DUNL

RANGE: In North America breeds from western Alaska across the low Arctic parts of the Northwest Territories and south along the western shore of Hudson Bay. Winters world wide in north temperate regions, mainly coastal. In North America winters on the Pacific coast from British Columbia to Baja California and on the Atlantic coast from the mid-Atlantic states to northern Mexico. Also breeds in Greenland and northern Eurasia.

STATUS On the coast, a *common* to *very abundant* migrant and winter visitant. In the interior, a *very rare* migrant, *casual* in summer; *casual* in winter in the south interior.

OCCURRENCE: The Dunlin is widely distributed along inner and outer coastal areas and is very abundant from September to May when it may occur in flocks of tens of thousands. In the interior, it occurs infrequently, more often in autumn than in spring, in groups of up to 10 birds.

On the coast, the Dunlin frequents tidal mudflats and prefers to forage along the receding or advancing tide line. At high tide, it roosts on spits, dykes, beached logs, log booms, and breakwaters. It also occurs in small numbers on sandy beaches, rocky points, and, rarely, on offshore rocks (see Fig. 145). The mudflats of the Fraser River delta, Boundary Bay, and on southern Vancouver Island attract the largest concentrations. Smaller numbers occur in the other major estuaries along the coast. Coastal fiords and inlets are generally bypassed. In the interior, it frequents the muddy shorelines of sloughs, lakes, rivers, flooded fields, and sewage lagoons.

The Dunlin has one of the latest southward migrations of any Nearctic shorebird. A few arrive on our coast in July and August, but most of the population that passes through this province (see MacLean and Holmes 1971; Greenwood 1984) gathers in southwestern Alaska from August through September in preparation for migration (Holmes 1966). In late September and early October, this population leaves Alaska and flies rapidly to wintering grounds along the Pacific coast. A large number stops on the British Columbia coast in October when peak numbers are recorded. Numbers drop rapidly after early December as many birds move farther south. A slow northern movement begins in January and continues through early spring. Numbers drop off rapidly after mid-April. Fairly large flocks may occur on the coast throughout May but the latest date for a flock of 1,000+ birds is 9 May. The Dunlin is scarce in spring away from the major estuaries.

In the interior, it occurs very infrequently as a migrant. In some years, a few birds winter in the Okanagan valley and Thompson Basin; there is one record for Prince George. On the coast, the centre of abundance is the Fraser River delta. The largest number reported there was 109,000 birds in November 1979 (Fry 1980) whereas the winter average was calculated to be 40,000 birds (McEwan, E.H. and Whitehead 1984).

REMARKS: The Dunlin is one of the most abundant shorebirds in the northern hemisphere (Soikkeli 1967). It is also one of the most unusual Calidridines in that it is a very late autumn migrant, has a short migration route, winters farther north than most other Calidridines, and juveniles and adults migrate together. Greenwood (1984) discusses worldwide migration of Dunlin. His findings indicate that populations breeding in different areas of eastern Eurasia occupy greatly overlapping regions in winter throughout much of their range. However, this does not appear to apply to most of the North American breeding populations. In North America, Dunlins are separable into 3 distinct groups, each of which has its own wintering area. The Dunlins of northern Alaska winter along the Pacific coast of Asia (Norton 1971), those from western Alaska winter along the Pacific coast of North America, and those that breed in north-central Canada winter along the Atlantic coast (MacLean and Holmes 1971).

Up to 9 subspecies are recognized, but only 7 are accepted by Greenwood (1986), and only *C. a. pacifica* is known to occur in British Columbia (Godfrey 1986).

E.H. McEwan and Fry (1984) found that polychaetes and amphipods were the principal prey taxa of Dunlin wintering at Boundary Bay. Additional information on the winter ecology of Dunlin on the Fraser River delta is supplied by E.H. McEwan and Gordon (1985) and by E.H. McEwan and Fry (1986a, 1986b).

NOTEWORTHY RECORDS

Spring: Coastal - Swartz Bay 9 May 1964-2,000; Long Beach 24 Mar 1978-700; Boundary Bay 10 Mar 1978-25,000, 18 Mar 1975-4,000; Tsawwassen 3 Mar 1963-8,000; Ladner 8 Mar 1978-17,000; Iona Island 27 Apr 1972-15,000; Stubbs Island 23 May 1982-1; Yakoun River estuary 30 Apr 1983-1,080; Naden Harbour 6 Mar 1977-3,000; Masset to Rose Spit 8 May 1983-500. **Interior** - Osoyoos Lake 16 May 1982-2; Okanagan Landing 5 Apr 1941-3; Kelowna 18 May 1986-1; Kamloops 4 Mar 1983-1, 22 Apr 1984-3; 108 Mile Ranch 29 Apr 1981-1; n Riske Creek 19 May 1975-2; n Fort St. John 23 Apr 1984-2; Charlie Lake 4 May 1981-1; Atlin 7 May 1935-1 (RBCM 5800); Mile 75 Haines Road (nw Kelsall Lake) 26 May 1979-1.

Summer: Coastal - Chesterman Beach 29 Jun 1969-40, 30 Jun 1969-100; Tsawwassen 11 Jul 1965-415; Crescent Beach 28 Aug 1965-300; Canoe Pass 18 Jul 1959-80; Spider Island 10 Jul 1939-500 (Munro, J.A. and Cowan 1947); Delkatla Inlet 6 Jun 1984-3. **Interior** - Le Blanc Lake 15 Jul 1978-3; Tupper 2 Jun 1938-1 (Cowan 1939); Fort St. John 17 Jul 1986-1; Parker Lake (Fort Nelson) 7 Aug 1976-10.

Autumn: Interior - Fort St. John 8 to 16 Oct 1986-1; Prince George 27 Nov 1987-7; n 141 Mile House 13 Oct 1950-1 (RBCM 15635); Salmon Arm 15 Sep 1970-1, 13 Oct 1970-1 (Schnider et al. 1971); Goose Lake (Vernon) 18 Nov 1979-5; Swan Lake (Vernon) 25 Nov 1939-1 (ROM 86723); Knutsford 29 Sep 1968-1 (Jacobson 1974). **Coastal** - Big Bay 5 Nov 1977-3,600 (Martin 1978); Masset 16 Nov 1971-1,200; Denman Island 13 Nov 1935-1,000; Crescent Beach 30 Oct 1976-75,000; Mud Bay (Boundary Bay) 26 Oct 1978-15,000, 1 Nov 1975-50,000; Ladner 6 Nov 1966-10,000; Tofino Inlet 10 Nov 1962-1,800; Sidney Island 26 Sep 1958-400.

Winter: Interior - Prince George 12 Dec 1987-1 (RBCM Photo 1206), 31 Dec 1987-11; Tranquille 28 Dec 1986 to 5 Jan 1987-1; Kamloops 25 Dec 1979-7, 3 Jan 1983-1; Vernon 29 Dec 1962-7; Okanagan Landing 21 Dec 1944-1; Kelowna 19 Dec 1987-1, 20 Dec 1970-2 (Rogers, T.H. 1971b); Summerland 15 Jan 1944-2 (RBCM 11395), 11 and 24 Jan 1966-1. **Coastal** - Kitimat 18 Dec 1983-50; Masset Sound 18 Dec 1982-329, 26 Jan 1983-526; Yakoun River estuary 17 Dec 1984-211; Comox 7 Dec 1924-1,000; Harrison River 30 Jan 1977-13; Iona Island 29 Dec 1976-40,000; Mud Bay (Boundary Bay) 1 Dec 1978-60,000, 27 Feb 1975-8,000; Crescent Beach 14 Jan 1966-10,000, 9 Feb 1966-12,000; Martindale Flats (Saanich) 10 Jan 1980-300.

Christmas Counts: Interior - Not recorded. **Coastal** - Recorded from 18 of 28 localities and on 65% of all counts. Maxima: Ladner 19 Dec 1976-45,575, all-time Canadian high count (Anderson, R.R. 1977); Vancouver 26 Dec 1975-27,525; White Rock 2 Jan 1978-22,391.

Dunlin

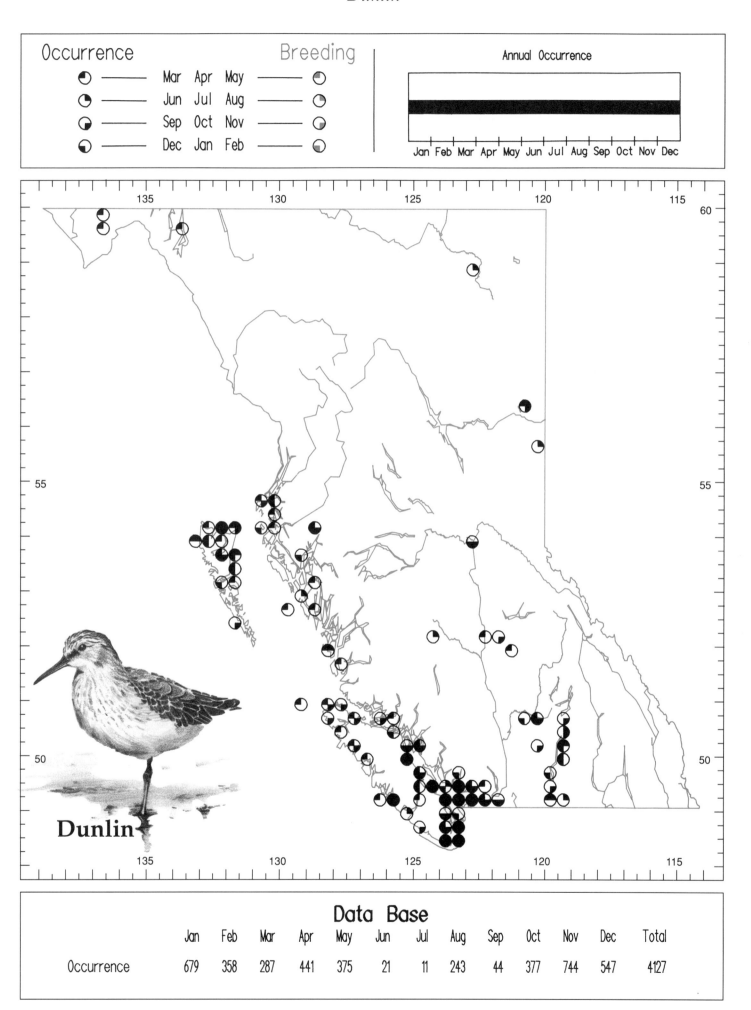

Occurrence   Breeding   Annual Occurrence

Mar Apr May
Jun Jul Aug
Sep Oct Nov
Dec Jan Feb

Jan Feb Mar Apr May Jun Jul Aug Sep Oct Nov Dec

Data Base

	Jan	Feb	Mar	Apr	May	Jun	Jul	Aug	Sep	Oct	Nov	Dec	Total
Occurrence	679	358	287	441	375	21	11	243	44	377	744	547	4127

Curlew Sandpiper

CUSA

Calidris ferruginea (Pontoppidan)

RANGE: Breeds in northern Asia and rarely in northern Alaska. Winters primarily in southern Asia as well as Australia, New Zealand, and Africa.

STATUS: *Very rare* vagrant along the coast.

OCCURRENCE: The Curlew Sandpiper has been recorded on the northern Queen Charlotte Islands, southeastern Vancouver Island, and the Fraser River delta. These occurrences are all from the autumn migration between 11 July and 17 September.
All records, listed in chronological order, are as follows:

(1) 19 km e Masset 31 July 1936-1 male in breeding plumage was collected (MVZ 101094) from among a large group of Sanderlings and Western Sandpipers on the beach (Brooks 1937).

(2) Iona Island 30 and 31 July 1977-1 feeding with dowitchers and Western Sandpipers (Macdonald 1978a). It was photographed on 31 July (RBCM Photos 473 and 491; Fig. 146).

(3) Kye Bay 11 July 1981-1 in breeding plumage.

(4) Witty's Lagoon 14 to 24 July 1981-1 in breeding plumage. It was photographed on 17 July (RBCM Photo 643). When last seen, the bird's rust-red underparts had lost brilliance and showed white and buffy patches. It is possible that this bird and the Kye Bay bird were the same individual.

(5) Iona Island 31 August and 1 September 1981-1 juvenile (Weber, W.C. 1982).

(6) Iona Island 17 September 1983-1 (Hunn and Mattocks 1984).

(7) Iona Island 4 September 1984-1 clearly marked juvenile (Hunn and Mattocks 1985).

REMARKS: The Curlew Sandpiper has been recorded, usually in the autumn, in every state and province along the west coast of North America (Sordahl 1978; Roberson 1980). Holmes and Pitelka (1964) describe the breeding behaviour and taxonomic relationships of this normally Siberian-nesting species that began breeding in northern Alaska in 1962. See Hayman et al. (1986) for details on plumages.

Figure 146. *Curlew Sandpiper at Iona Island, Richmond, 31 July 1977 (RBCM Photo 491; Ervio Sian).*

Curlew Sandpiper

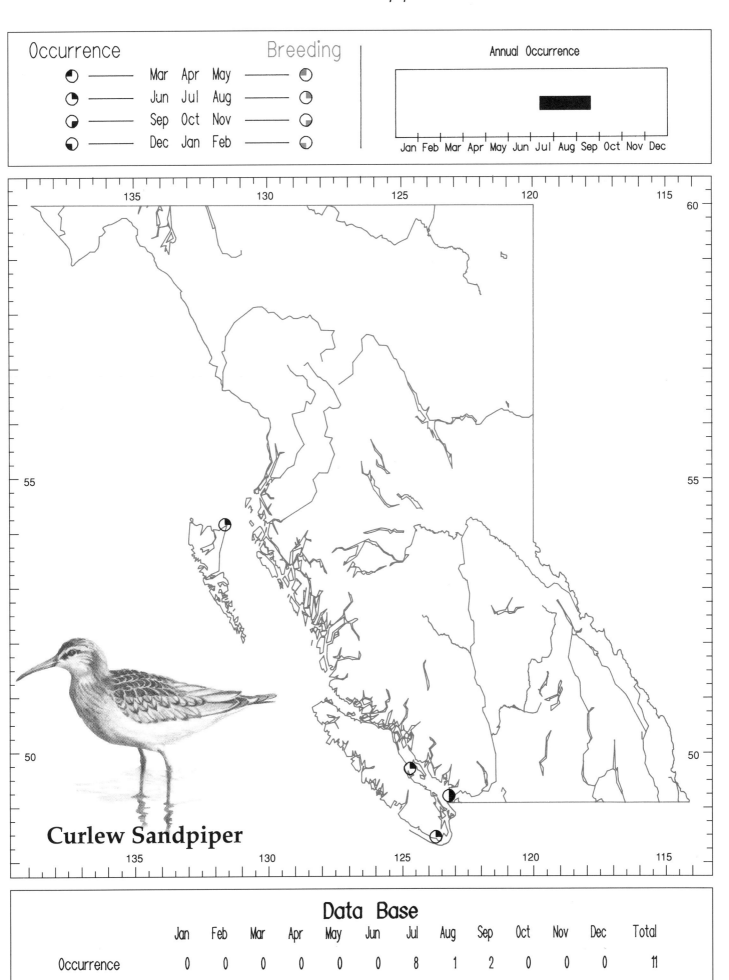

Occurrence

Mar	Apr	May
Jun	Jul	Aug
Sep	Oct	Nov
Dec	Jan	Feb

Breeding

Annual Occurrence

Jan Feb Mar Apr May Jun Jul Aug Sep Oct Nov Dec

Curlew Sandpiper

Data Base

	Jan	Feb	Mar	Apr	May	Jun	Jul	Aug	Sep	Oct	Nov	Dec	Total
Occurrence	0	0	0	0	0	0	8	1	2	0	0	0	11

Stilt Sandpiper

STSA

Calidris himantopus (Bonaparte)

RANGE: Breeds in the low arctic of northern Alaska, across the Yukon and western Northwest Territories, and south along the west shore of Hudson Bay. Winters mainly in central South America but also, in small numbers, north through central America to Florida, Texas, and California.

STATUS: *Uncommon* spring and *common* autumn transient in the Peace Lowlands. *Casual* in spring and *very rare* in autumn elsewhere.

OCCURRENCE: The Stilt Sandpiper has a scattered and sparse distribution in southern British Columbia; it is localized in the Peace Lowlands. It is not a common visitor to the province. Its major migration corridor is through the Canadian Prairies and American Midwest with some movement along the western Atlantic coast. In British Columbia, it is found most regularly in the Peace Lowlands, particularly near Fort St. John, where it is common from mid-summer to early autumn; it is scarcer in the spring. Maximum numbers there in autumn were 90 per day compared to 20 per day in spring. Elsewhere in the province, it is an unusual sight, and summer and autumn records vastly outnumber spring records. In the Okanagan, it is now only a casual autumn migrant; apparently, it was more common earlier in the century (Cannings, R.A. et al. 1987). On the coast, it has been recorded only on southern Vancouver Island and near Vancouver. However, it is listed as a regular but rare migrant from Washington to California (Roberson 1980) and only a casual migrant in southeastern Alaska (Kessel and Gibson 1978). It is considered a regular transient near Vancouver (Campbell et al. 1974) but in extremely low numbers. These coastal birds are probably part of the weak autumn movement headed for the Great Basin area.

The Stilt Sandpiper frequents shallows at the edges of lakes, sloughs, ponds (Fig. 147), and sewage lagoons. Most of the records from Fort St. John and Vancouver are from sewage lagoons. It is an inland wader and rarely occurs on exposed coastal shores although it frequents protected tidal mudflats and estuaries on the coast.

Spring migration of the Stilt Sandpiper is late compared to other shorebirds. All spring birds are recorded late in May, except for a few transients in breeding plumage reported in June. The stronger autumn movement begins in mid-July with the arrival of adult birds, but does not peak province-wide until mid-August through early September. All birds reported in late flocks are juveniles. After September, Stilt Sandpipers are rarely found in the province.

REMARKS: Foraging behaviour changes with the seasons and habitat availability. In summer Stilt Sandpipers probe in the soft mud like other Calidridines. In spring, they usually wade in belly-deep water and pick insects and other aquatic organisms from the surface. A bird at Burnaby Lake was observed foraging on flying insects that had fallen onto the lake's surface (Grass 1968).

Jehl (1973b) discusses the systematics of the Stilt Sandpiper and concludes that there are no strong reasons for maintaining *Micropalama* distinct from *Calidris*, although it is still included in the monotypic genus *Micropalama* by some authors (see Hayman et al. 1986).

POSTSCRIPT: The first records for the Queen Charlotte Islands were reported in 1988. A bird in breeding plumage was present at Delkatla Inlet from 1 to 3 July (D.L. Cooper pers. comm.) and up to 2 juveniles were in the same area from 24 to 26 September (M. Hearne pers. comm.).

Figure 147. Stilt Sandpiper at McIntyre reservoir, Saanich, Vancouver Island, 13 August 1985 (Tim Zurowski).

NOTEWORTHY RECORDS

Spring: Coastal - Saanich 27 to 29 May 1978-1; Burnaby Lake 20 May 1968-1 (Grass 1968). **Interior** - Fort St. John 23 May 1983-1, 24 May 1986-5; Charlie Lake 24 to 25 May 1980-20, 26 May 1980-3.

Summer: Coastal - Witty's Lagoon 21 to 29 Aug 1982-1; Saanich 25 Aug 1973-4 (Crowell and Nehls 1974a); Cowichan Bay 9 Aug 1979-1; Long Beach 8 Jun 1982-1 (RBCM Photo 801); Mud Bay (Boundary Bay) 3 Aug 1985-1 juvenile (first of season); Iona Island 20 to 21 Jun 1980-1, 5 Jul 1980-1, 23 Aug 1973-5 (Crowell and Nehls 1974a), 10 Aug 1973-8, 21 Aug 1985-36 juveniles, 30 Aug 1982-8; Stanley Park (Vancouver) 29 Aug 1966-1 (Orcutt 1967); Wilson Creek (Sunshine Coast) 9 Jul 1987-1; Courtenay 12 to 19 Aug 1987-1 (RBCM Photo 1167). **Interior** - Creston 27 and 30 Jul 1980-1; Okanagan Landing 9 Jun 1927-1 (MVZ 82033), 22 Aug 1932-15 (Cannings, R.A. et al. 1987), 23 Aug 1927-10 (MVZ 101103), ; Vernon 28 Aug 1987-1; Kamloops 20 Aug 1978-20; Golden 29 Aug 1949-1 female (ROM 82733); Yoho National Park 15 and 18 Aug 1976-1 (Wade 1977); Sink Lake 5 Aug 1977-1 (Wade 1977); Fort St. John 1 Jun 1986-2, 7 Jul 1986-1, 14 Jul 1982-90 (survey, one flock of 42), 17 Jul 1986-17, 21 Aug 1985-25, 25 Aug 1986-45, 26 Aug 1982-17, 30 Aug 1986-11; Boundary Lake (Goodlow) 26 Aug 1986-13; Kotcho Lake 26 Jun 1982-1 (RBCM Photo 804).

Autumn: Interior - Fort St. John 5 Sep 1986-92 juveniles, 9 Sep 1986-29, 22 Sep 1986-3; n 150 Mile House 5 Sep 1951-1 male (NMC 47802); 100 Mile House 13 Oct 1982-3; Kamloops 10 Sep 1984-2; Salmon Arm 28 Oct 1970-6 (Schnider et al. 1971); Okanagan Landing 25 Sep 1920-1 (MVZ 82032); Deadman Lake 13 Sep 1980-1. **Coastal** - Comox 11 Sep 1949-1 (Flahaut 1950a); Iona Island 6 to 7 Sep 1981-4, 22 to 25 Oct 1978-1, 17 Oct 1982-1; Reifel Island 29 Sep 1984-7 juveniles, 13 Oct 1984-3 (last of year); s Serpentine River 8 Oct 1980-1; Cordova Spit 27 Sep 1982-1.

Winter: No records.

Stilt Sandpiper

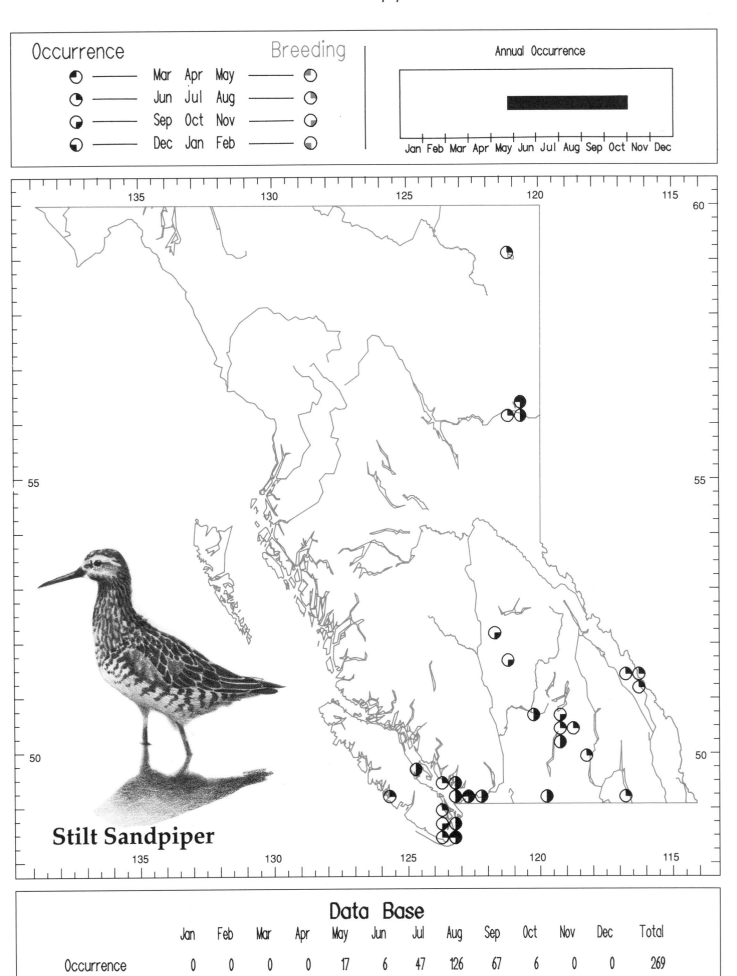

Stilt Sandpiper

Data Base

	Jan	Feb	Mar	Apr	May	Jun	Jul	Aug	Sep	Oct	Nov	Dec	Total
Occurrence	0	0	0	0	17	6	47	126	67	6	0	0	269

Buff-breasted Sandpiper

BBSA

Tryngites subruficollis (Vieillot)

RANGE: Breeds in the Arctic from northern Alaska east to Keewatin. Winters mainly in the interior of Paraguay and northern Argentina.

STATUS: *Casual* transient in spring in the Peace Lowlands. *Rare* autumn transient on the coast; *very rare* in the interior.

OCCURRENCE: The Buff-breasted Sandpiper has a sparse and scattered distribution throughout the province, although the majority of records are from the coast. It has been reported from near sea level to 600 m elevation. It frequents dry, short-grass areas such as golf courses, airports, and residential lawns. Other habitats include sewage lagoons, sandy beaches, damp margins of freshwater lakes and ponds, and damp pastures.

The Buff-breasted Sandpiper is extremely rare in spring or early summer in British Columbia. We have 2 records from the Peace Lowlands in late May and 2 records from the Queen Charlotte Islands in early June. Roberson (1980) reports no records in spring from Washington, Oregon, or California and suggests they are rare but regular migrants in Alaska's western coasts and islands.

Autumn migrants occur more regularly but still in very small numbers. The total number of birds reported during the 1979 autumn movement between British Columbia and California was 58; this was considered an exceptionally large number (Roberson 1980). The largest flock reported in this province contained 8 birds, although 9 were collected over 3 days in August 1946 at Sandspit. The earliest and latest dates reported for the Buff-breasted Sandpiper in the province are 24 May and 8 October.

REMARKS: A record of 200 Buff-breasted Sandpipers reported from Tofino on 2 May 1974 (Crowell and Nehls 1974c) is excluded from this account due to the lack of supporting documentation.

The Buff-breasted Sandpiper is one of the most poorly known Nearctic waders. The major North American migration route is through the Canadian Prairies and American Great Plains (Palmer, R.S. 1967). The spring movement is concentrated almost entirely through this interior corridor; coastal records are exceptional. The southward movement is more widespread although still concentrated in the interior corridor. Apparently, almost all adults move eastward towards Hudson Bay and then southward through the Great Plains. Campbell and Gregory (1976) found that all autumn specimens examined from British Columbia were juvenile birds. J. Strauch (pers. comm.) found similar results for all museum specimens collected on either side of the Buff-breasted Sandpiper's interior migration corridor.

Figure 148. Buff-breasted Sandpiper at Fort St. John, 14 September 1986 (Chris R. Siddle).

Figure 149. Buff-breasted Sandpiper on University of Victoria playing fields, Victoria, 10 September 1987 (Tim Zurowski).

NOTEWORTHY RECORDS

Spring: Coastal - No records (see Remarks). **Interior** - Fort St. John 27 May 1987-2, 30 May 1983-2; Charlie Lake 24 May 1980-5.

Summer: Coastal - Victoria 29 Aug 1947-5; Oak Bay 23 Jul 1950-2; Panama Flats 22 Jul 1974-1; Sea Island 22 Aug 1966-1 (RBCM 11637); Iona Island 7 Jul 1979-1, 11 Jul 1976-2; Sumas 25 Aug 1899-2 (RBCM 1638, 1639); Comox 24 Jul 1948-1, 28 Aug 1922-1 (NMC 18242); Sandspit 9 Jun 1986-1, 21 to 23 Aug 1946-9 (UBC 1035-1043); Masset 5 Jun 1984-1 (RBCM Photo 926); Green Island 13 Aug 1977-1. **Interior** - Okanagan 22 Aug 1932-1 (MVZ 101118), 25 Aug 1978-1; Nulki Lake 19 Aug 1946-1 (ROM 82743); Fort St. John 27 Aug 1985-1.

Autumn: Interior - Atlin 5 Oct 1980-1; Fort St. John 14 Sep 1986-1 (McEwan, C. and Johnston 1987; RBCM Photo 1125; Fig. 148); Riske Creek 12 Sep 1986-1; Tranquille 14 Sep 1986-1; Kamloops 14 to 17 Sep 1980-1 (RBCM Photo 700), 14 Sep 1986-1; Vernon 4 Sep 1970-1, 5 and 6 Sep 1987-1; Vernon Commonage 12 Sep 1985-1. **Coastal** - Grant Bay early Sep 1968-1 (Richardson 1971); Chilliwack 4 Sep 1887-1 (MVZ 101117); Clayoquot 4 Sep 1907-1 (NMC 3526); Iona Island 8 Oct 1974-1; Westham Island 15 Sep 1985-8 immatures; Boundary Bay 18 Sep 1982-1; 9 Sep 1979-4; Victoria 1 Sep 1947-6, 10 Sep 1987-1 (Fig. 149); Witty's Lagoon 28 Sep 1968-1 (Campbell and Gregory 1976); Sooke 7 Oct 1979-1.

Winter: No records.

Buff-breasted Sandpiper

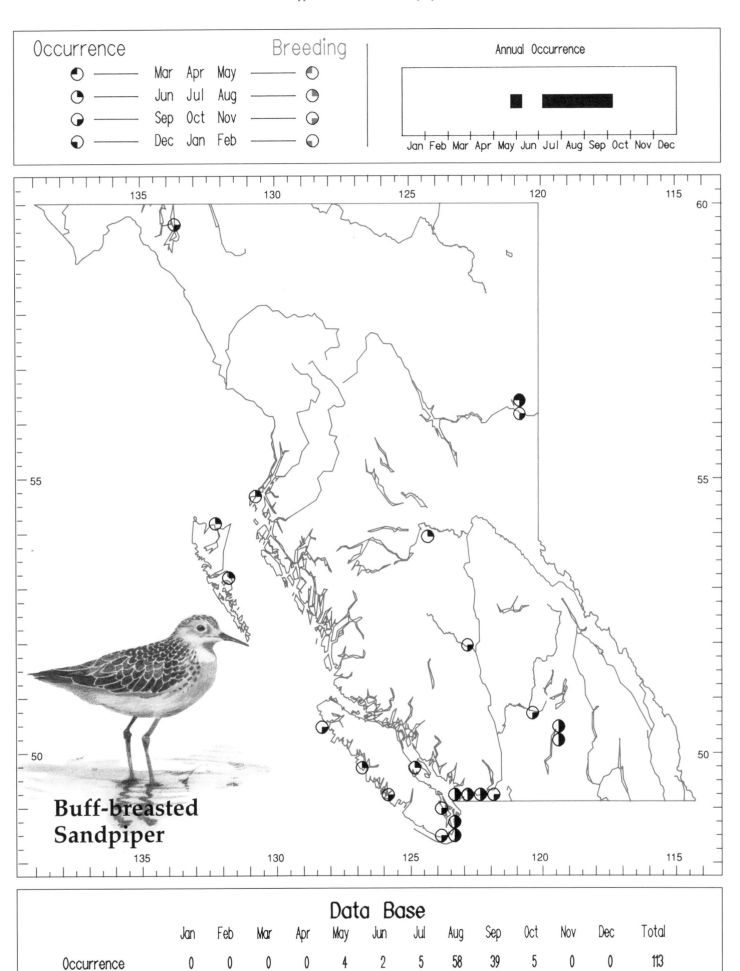

Occurrence

◑	———	Mar	Apr	May	———	◑
◔	———	Jun	Jul	Aug	———	◔
◓	———	Sep	Oct	Nov	———	◓
◕	———	Dec	Jan	Feb	———	◕

Breeding

Annual Occurrence

Jan Feb Mar Apr May Jun Jul Aug Sep Oct Nov Dec

Buff-breasted Sandpiper

Data Base

	Jan	Feb	Mar	Apr	May	Jun	Jul	Aug	Sep	Oct	Nov	Dec	Total
Occurrence	0	0	0	0	4	2	5	58	39	5	0	0	113

Ruff
Philomachus pugnax (Linnaeus)

RANGE: Breeds in northern Eurasia from Norway to Siberia; also in Alaska. Winters mainly in Africa, also in scattered localities in Europe, southern Asia, and Australia; a few in California.

STATUS: *Casual* in spring and *very rare* autumn vagrant on the south coast. *Casual* in the interior.

OCCURRENCE: The Ruff was first recorded in the province at Reifel Island on 7 August 1971 (Campbell et al. 1972b). Since then it has been reported at least once in 10 of the last 14 years. All records from the coast are from the extreme south with most from Iona and Reifel islands. Both interior records are from the Peace Lowlands.

We have only 2 spring records on file: 1 from Iona Island and 1 from the sewage lagoon at Fort St. John. Most summer records are from August. The earliest and latest autumn dates for the province are 26 June and 14 October. Roberson (1980) reports 9 records for British Columbia and 52 records for California, including many winter records. The California peak occurs in September-October (probably juveniles) contrasting with the July-August peak in British Columbia (probably adults).

In British Columbia, the Ruff frequents muddy areas around shorelines, pools, estuaries, sewage ponds, and flooded fields. It usually occurs individually and often spends considerable time at one locality foraging with other shorebirds such as Pectoral Sandpipers. In 1983, a Ruff spent most of September in the vicinity of a flooded field at Duncan; another spent much of September around Clover Point, Victoria. At Oak Bay, one was observed feeding on earthworms under a golf course sprinkler.

REMARKS: The Ruff is a regular spring and autumn visitor to North America, occurring widely but in very small numbers. Vagrant Ruffs occur world wide in the non-breeding seasons. Its North American status has changed in recent years. Godfrey (1966) lists the Ruff as accidental in Canada, but 20 years later he notes its increase to regular status and lists records for all 10 provinces. There is now at least one breeding record from Alaska (Kessel and Gibson 1978), and the suggestion that it breeds in northern Canada (Hayman et al. 1986). The Ruff is apparently the most common Palearctic shorebird in eastern North America (Peakall 1965).

POSTSCRIPT: On 5 September 1989 a Ruff was photographed at Delkatla Inlet for the first Queen Charlotte Islands record (Margo Hearne pers. comm.).

Figure 150. Ruff with Long-billed Dowitcher at Iona Island, Richmond, 7 August 1983 (RBCM Photo 1109; Paul Yorke)

Figure 151. Juvenile Ruff at the Serpentine River, Surrey, 16 September 1982 (RBCM Photo 1245; Ervio Sian)

NOTEWORTHY RECORDS

Spring: Coastal - Iona Island 27 to 29 May 1976-1. **Interior** - Fort St. John 25 to 26 May 1986-1 (RBCM Photo 1126; Campbell 1986c).

Summer: Coastal - Clover Point 24 Jul 1975-1; Saanich 31 Jul to 2 Aug 1975-1; Reifel Island 26 to 27 Jun 1974-1 (Shepard, M.G. 1975c; RBCM Photo 351), 29 Jun 1975-1, 19 and 23 Jul 1986-2

(Mattocks 1986b), 7 and 11 Aug 1971-1 (Campbell et al. 1972b; RBCM Photo 220); Iona Island 7 Jul 1982-1, 30 Jul to 4 Aug 1978-1 to 2, 4 Aug 1980-1, 7 Aug 1983-1 (RBCM Photo 1109; Fig. 150), 23 Aug 1982-1. **Interior** - No records.

Autumn: Interior - Fort St. John 2 Oct 1986-1 juvenile male. **Coastal** - Iona Island 3 to 4 Sep

1981-1, 21 and 23 Sep 1980-1, 25 Sep 1981-1, 12 to 14 Oct 1980-1; Cowichan Bay 9 Sep to 1 Oct 1983-1 (RBCM Photo 875); s Serpentine River 15 to 18 Sep 1982-1 (RBCM Photo 1245; Fig. 151); Clover Point 9 to 10 Sep 1979-1, 24 to 25 Sep 1979-1.

Winter: No records.

Ruff

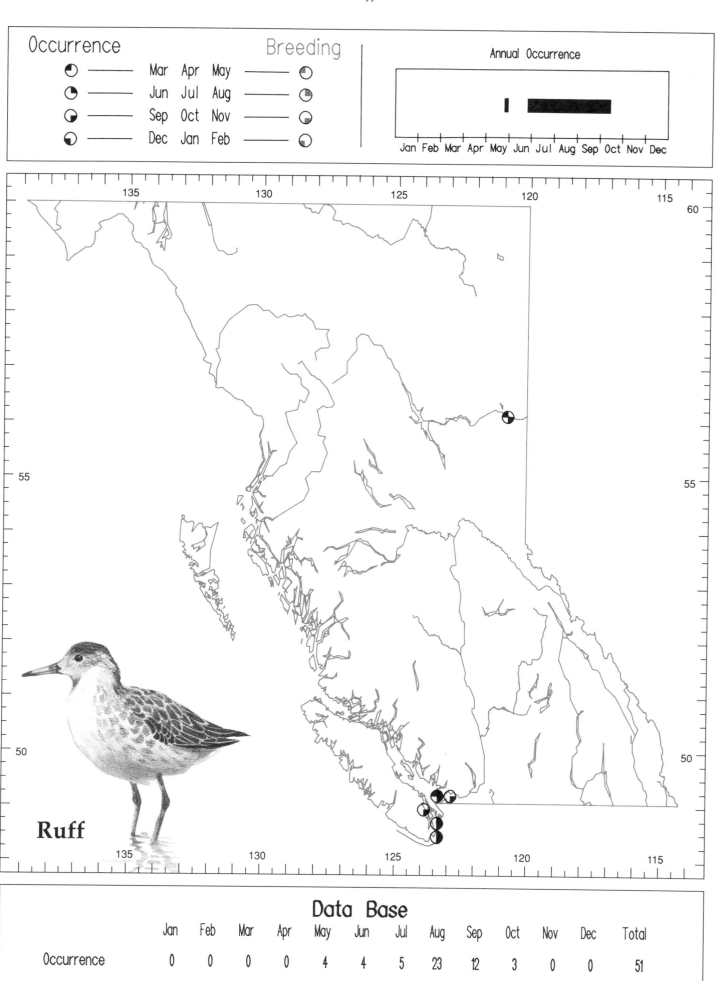

Short-billed Dowitcher
Limnodromus griseus (Gmelin)

RANGE: Breeds in southern Alaska, southern Yukon, northwestern British Columbia and from northern Alberta across the boreal forest to Labrador. Winters from the southern United States to Peru and Brazil.

STATUS: *Common* to *very abundant* spring migrant and summer visitant on the coast, *common* autumn migrant. *Rare* migrant and summer visitant in the interior. Occasionally an *uncommon* autumn migrant in the Peace Lowlands. Breeds.

NONBREEDING: Information is scarce on the relative abundance and status of the 2 dowitcher species anywhere in their ranges due to the difficulty in separating them in the field. Some authors lump their records into a general "dowitcher" category because of the confusion (e.g. Campbell et al. 1972 and Hatler et al. 1978) but most attempt general conclusions based on a few confirmed records. Thus Hatler et al. (1978) suggest there are more Short-billed than Long-billed Dowitchers in Pacific Rim National Park and Campbell et al. (1972b) suggest Short-billed Dowitchers are rare while Long-billed Dowitchers are common in the Fraser Lowlands. Both note that habitat preference explains these trends. The Short-billed Dowitcher appears to be much less common in the interior than the Long-billed Dowitcher; almost all records there are of 1 or 2 birds. In contrast to Long-billed Dowitchers, Short-billed Dowitchers are quite rare in the Peace Lowlands, even though they breed in northern Alberta.

Both dowitcher species probe in soft mud with rapid bill movements. The Short-billed Dowitcher frequents tidal mud flats, farm ponds, muddy fields, golf course greens, and offshore rocks. It forms larger flocks than the Long-billed Dowitcher. The mudflats of Tofino Inlet attract the largest numbers of dowitchers in this province; flocks of 1,000 to 2,000 Short-billed Dowitchers have been confirmed there, but flocks of up to 15,000 dowitchers have been recorded, in all likelihood mostly of this species.

Spring migration occurs mainly from mid-April to mid-May with a few early arrivals beginning in March on the coast. Spring flocks are larger than autumn flocks. The Short-billed Dowitcher is a relatively early autumn migrant, arriving in July and early August, although some of the interior records are from September and October. Like Long-billed Dowitchers, adult females leave for the south first, followed by adult males, then juveniles from late

July on. Short-billed Dowitchers, however, do not linger on the coast and most are gone by October; there are no convincing winter records despite published accounts (see Crowell and Nehls 1970b). Extreme dates in the interior are 6 April and 16 October; the latest interior specimen was taken on 6 October.

BREEDING: The Short-billed Dowitcher breeds only in the vicinity of the Chilkat Pass and St. Elias Mountains in extreme northwestern British Columbia and at Masset on the Queen Charlotte Islands. Godfrey (1986) speculates that breeding probably occurs in the Peace River region but we have no data to confirm this.

Breeding habitat in the St. Elias Mountains is wet, boggy muskeg in sub-alpine meadows, plateaus, and valleys with mixtures of sedges and sphagnum swamps, pools, and willow clumps. Pairs are widely scattered. At Masset 2 or 3 pairs have bred annually, since 1984 when they were first discovered in a brackish estuarine marsh dominated by sphagnum, sedges, and rushes.

Nests: Nests observed were cup-like hollows on the ground usually well concealed in a tuft of grass (3 nests) or on a dry hummock (2 nests). The nests in the tufts of grass were concealed from view by grass stems that had been pulled over them.

Eggs: Five full clutches have been found with dates ranging from 7 to 29 June. Clutch size ranged from 3 to 4 eggs (3E-1, 4E-4). Incubation period is 21 days (Jehl and Smith 1970).

Young: Only 1 brood has been discovered, 2 chicks, 1 to 2 days old, on 27 June in a damp meadow near Mile 71, Haines Road.

REMARKS: Three subspecies exist. *L. g. caurinus* accounts for virtually all coastal records and the breeding birds in British Columbia. Most records considered for this account included notes on the distinctive "tu-tu-tu" call.

On 3 July 1986, on the Squamish River estuary, a single bird was observed calling constantly from the top of a snag and another was flushed nearby from a grassy area, circumstances that suggest breeding.

Observers are encouraged to take great care when identifying dowitchers and to consult the latest references available (see Long-billed Dowitcher).

NOTEWORTHY RECORDS

Spring: Coastal - Sooke 11 Apr 1975-2; Witty's Lagoon 25 Apr 1982-48, 12 May 1974-54; Esquimalt Lagoon 28 Mar 1978-1; Cowichan Bay 12 May 1984-7; Tofino Inlet 28 Apr 1984-3,600; Blackie Spit 26 Apr 1981-35; Boundary Bay 19 Apr 1981-200+; Reifel Island 4 Apr 1984-6; Iona Island 17 Apr 1981-120+, 24 Apr 1982-300, 14 May 1981-30; Long Beach 7 May 1974-180; Tofino Inlet 25 Apr 1979-250, 28 Apr 1984-2,100 and 1,500 (Campbell 1984b); Grice Bay 23 Apr 1974-850; Cleland Island 13 May 1976-15; Willow Point 17 Apr 1974-6; Hansen Lagoon 18 May 1974-15; Calvert Island 1 May 1937-1 (UBC 4413); Tlell 29 Apr 1935-60 (Munro, J.A. 1936a); Ridley Island 8 May 1979-12; Rose Spit 24 Apr 1979-1. **Interior -** Osoyoos Lake 7 to 13 May 1922-10; Manning Park 6 Apr 1983-1; 105 Mile Lake 3 May 1946-1 (Munro, J.A. 1955c); Yoho National Park 18 May 1977-1 (Wade 1977); Fort St. John 9 May 1983-2, 18 May 1982-2, 25 May 1986-1; Atlin 21 May 1981-1 (Campbell 1981); Chilkat Pass 11 May to July 1957-common (Weeden 1960).

Summer: Coastal - Witty's Lagoon 11 Jun 1982-1, 2 Jul 1983-35, 14 Jul 1979-72, 28 Aug 1976-22;

Cadboro Bay 21 Jul 1979-40; Iona Island 15 Jun 1974-1, 25 Jul 1974-30 (Crowell and Nehls 1974d), 28 Aug 1975-20; Chesterman Beach 11 Jul 1983-29; Grice Bay 14 Jul 1974-38; Cleland Island 23 Jul 1976-10; Squamish River estuary 3 Jul 1986-2; Salmon Point (Discovery Passage) 26 Jul 1976-37; Brooks Peninsula 22 Aug 1981-13; Keogh River 8 Aug 1978-4; Port Simpson 19 Aug 1969-7; Green Island 13 Jul 1978-7; Rose Spit 20 Aug 1974-1. **Interior -** Sirdar Lake 3 Aug 1951-1; Richter Pass 5 Aug 1977-present; Chase 19 Jul 1977-1; 108 Mile House 4 Aug 1983-1 (Ducks Unlimited Canada 1983); Chilco Ranch (Hanceville) 9 Aug 1983-several (Ducks Unlimited Canada 1983); Fort St. John 29 Jun 1986-1, 17 Jul 1986-5, 21 Aug 1986-18 juveniles, 27 Aug 1986-10; Rose Prairie 18 Aug 1975-1.

Autumn: Interior - Fort St. John 21 Sep 1986-1 juvenile; 103 Mile Lake 18 Sep 1942-6 (Munro, J.A. 1942b); Kamloops 9 Sep 1984-3; Rawlings Lake 6 Oct 1930-1 (ROM 86673); Swan Lake (Vernon) 30 Sep 1935-2 (ROM 86667, 86674), 16 Oct 1945-3; Kelowna 5 Oct 1957-2 (NMC 47798, 47799); Fort Steele 23 Sep 1937-1 (RBCM 10872).

Coastal - Salmon Point (Discovery Passage) 12 Sep 1976-8; Long Beach 1 Oct 1975-4; Westham Island 5 Oct 1968-55; Blackie Spit 12 Oct 1981-4; Tsehum Harbour 14 Sep 1978-22, 5 Oct 1978-8; Esquimalt Lagoon 29 Nov 1975-3; Witty's Lagoon 3 Sep 1977-50, 10 Sep 1977-47, 21 Oct 1979-30.

Winter: No records.

Christmas Counts: Interior - Not recorded. **Coastal** - Recorded 4 times: Vancouver 3 Jan 1964-4, 21 Dec 1969-68, reported as all-time Canadian high count (Anderson, R.R. 1976); Ladner 2 Jan 1965-12; Duncan 18 Dec 1978-5. The foregoing records should be viewed with caution. We could find no supporting documentation for any of them. In addition, Short-billed Dowitchers have been reported on Christmas Bird Counts in British Columbia only in years when Long-billed Dowitchers were not reported. We have not considered those records in describing the status of the Short-billed Dowitcher in British Columbia.

Short-billed Dowitcher

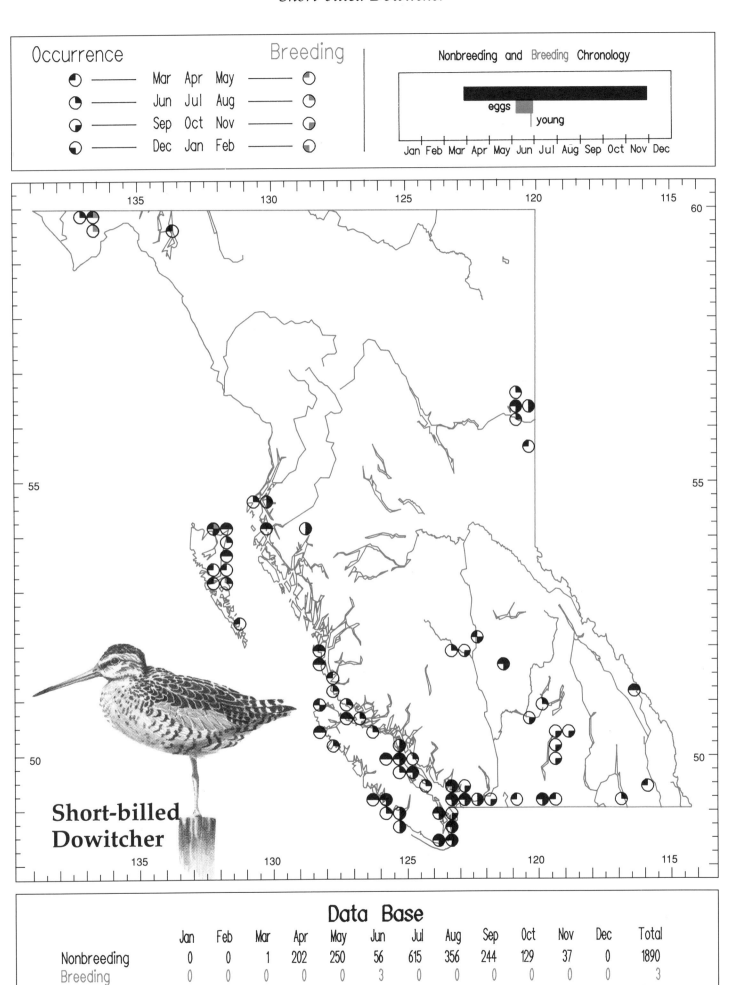

Occurrence · Breeding

	Mar Apr May	
	Jun Jul Aug	
	Sep Oct Nov	
	Dec Jan Feb	

Nonbreeding and Breeding Chronology

eggs · young

Jan Feb Mar Apr May Jun Jul Aug Sep Oct Nov Dec

Short-billed Dowitcher

Data Base

	Jan	Feb	Mar	Apr	May	Jun	Jul	Aug	Sep	Oct	Nov	Dec	Total
Nonbreeding	0	0	1	202	250	56	615	356	244	129	37	0	1890
Breeding	0	0	0	0	0	3	0	0	0	0	0	0	3

Long-billed Dowitcher

Limnodromus scolopaceus (Say)

LBDO

RANGE: Breeds in coastal northeastern Siberia, western and northern Alaska, northern Yukon, and northwestern Mackenzie. Winters mainly from the southern United States to Guatemala.

STATUS: On the coast, a *fairly common* spring transient, *abundant* autumn transient; *uncommon* in winter in the south. In the interior, a *rare* spring transient, *very common* in the Peace Lowlands; *fairly common* autumn transient, *very common* in the Peace Lowlands.

OCCURRENCE: The Long-billed Dowitcher occurs as a transient throughout much of the province but is most abundant on the coast. It is a highly gregarious shorebird that is very difficult to separate from its sibling species, the Short-billed Dowitcher, with which it often mixes. The Long-billed Dowitcher usually occurs in flocks of 10 to 100 birds. It tends to prefer freshwater habitats rather than the brackish and intertidal areas preferred by the Short-billed Dowitcher, although it readily uses salt water habitats when migrating along the coast (Pitelka 1950). On the coast, it forages and rests on tidal mudflats and roosts occasionally on offshore rocks, islands, and log booms. It is also found on nearby inland swamps, flooded fields, reservoir edges, sewage lagoons, and small ponds. In the interior, it frequents the muddy shores of lowland lakes and sloughs, river banks, and sewage ponds; it strays rarely to alpine lakes.

The spring movement in British Columbia occurs from late April to late May. The Long-billed Dowitcher is widespread during migration, rarely concentrating in large numbers in any one locality. Interior migrants are scarce, except in the Peace River parklands where they are usually common in mid-May in the Fort St. John area. The Long-billed Dowitcher is a relatively late autumn migrant; the southward movement begins in July but does not peak until September and October. Adults migrate first, followed by juveniles a month or two later. In 1986, all early July migrants at Fort St. John were adults; the last adult there was recorded on 14 September. Virtually all September and October birds were juveniles (C. Siddle pers. comm.). The Long-billed Dowitcher is much more numerous throughout the interior in autumn than in spring. On the coast, numbers peak in October after building from late August. Most move on in November, and by December only a few remain. Although not mentioned by Godfrey (1986) as doing so, it winters in small numbers in the Fraser Lowlands and on southern Vancouver Island.

REMARKS: Field identification of dowitchers has long been a serious problem for ornithologists and naturalists. The 2 dowitcher species are easily separable only when their distinctive calls are heard. Identification by morphological characteristics alone is difficult for inexperienced observers. In recent years, solutions to this problem have been outlined by Wilds and Newton (1983) and by Hayman et al. (1986). Identification of early specimens also proved troublesome and the early literature on dowitchers is full of misinformation. Separation into 2 species occurred only in 1950 (Pitelka 1950).

A record of 15,000 dowitchers at Tofino on 2 May 1974 was thought to be of mostly Long-billed Dowitchers (Crowell and Nehls 1974c) but this conclusion is suspect, and the record should be viewed with caution.

NOTEWORTHY RECORDS

Spring: Coastal - Albert Head 24 Apr 1936-1 (RBCM 5578); Witty's Lagoon 15 Apr 1976-2; Quicks Bottom 12 May 1978-8; Cowichan Bay 23 Apr 1977-2; Ucluelet 4 May 1977-38; Reifel Island 8 May 1972-170; Iona Island 19 Apr 1979-3, 1 May 1979-150, 19 May 1984-30; Lulu Island 29 Apr 1932-1 (RBCM 14684); Burnaby Lake 7 Mar 1982-48; Clayoquot 24 Apr 1906-3 (RBCM 198, 199, 203); Vertical Point 26 Apr 1983-105; Masset 9 Apr 1980-8, 17 May 1949-3 (RBCM 10708-10710), 20 May 1987-40 (Cooper, J.M. 1987). **Interior** - Duck Lake (Creston) 21 May 1979-2; Richter Pass 13 May 1979-1; Okanagan Landing 19 May 1930-2 (MVZ 100827, 100828); Kamloops 12 May 1982-200, 14 May 1983-100; East Lake 19 May 1970-8; 108 Mile House 29 Apr 1981-6; Prince George 30 Apr 1982-6; Tupper Creek (Tupper) 26 May 1938-1 (RBCM 8244); Fort St. John 13 May 1983-57, 21 May 1983-43; Boundary Lake (Goodlow) 4 May 1986-8, 11 May 1986-36; Cecil Lake 7 May 1980-30, 8 May 1980-70; Atlin 1 May 1930-1 (RBCM 5836).

Summer: Coastal - Witty's Lagoon 5 Jul 1980-18; Victoria 30 Jun 1981-4; Cowichan Bay 16 Jul 1975-31; Bamfield 7 Jul 1973-4; Blackie Spit 18 Jul 1979-64; Reifel Island 15 Jun 1974-6 (Crowell and Nehls 1974d); Iona Island 30 Jul 1978-65, 2 Aug 1976-120, 5 Aug 1975-75, 26 Aug 1973-95, 28 Aug 1973-120; Qualicum Beach 22 Jul 1976-17; Courtenay 23 Jul 1977-25; Comox 10 Jun 1969-1 (Crowell and Nehls 1969c). **Interior** - Duck Lake (Creston) 21 Jul 1951-2 (ROM 84680, 84688); Quilchena 1 Jun 1975-1, 9 Jul 1973-8; Beresford Range (Kamloops) 27 Jul 1950-32; Swan Lake (Vernon) 31 Jul 1951-1 (RBCM 15637); Salmon Arm 26 Aug 1973-20 (Sirk et al. 1973); Revelstoke 21 Jul 1977-4 (Bonar 1978b); Alkali Lake (Cariboo) 19 Jul 1974-7; Beaver Lake (Stum Lake) 26 Jul 1973-20 (Ryder 1973); Prince George 22 Jul 1982-8; Bowron Slough 23 Aug 1975-35 (Bell 1975); Fort St. John 9 Jul 1987-28, 18 Jul 1987-251, 25 Jul 1987-364, 6 Aug 1986-70; Haworth Lake early Aug 1976-30; Atlin 22 Jul 1980-1 (RBCM 17534).

Autumn: Interior - Fort Nelson 4 Sep 1987-2; Fort St. John 5 Sep 1986-118, 14 Sep 1986-47, 22 Sep 1986-55, 15 Oct 1986-11, 21 Oct 1986-9, 27 Oct 1986-7; Williams Lake 12 Oct 1972-2; Fletcher Lake 13 Sep 1986-8; Riske Creek 29 Sep 1952-1 (RBCM 15638); Farwell Canyon 26 Sep 1981-6 (RBCM Photo 646); Emerald Lake (Yoho National Park) 2 Oct 1975-1 (Wade 1977); Revelstoke 15 Sep 1977-13, 17 Oct 1977-4 (Bonar 1978b); Salmon Arm 20 Sep 1970-100, 16 Oct 1970-48, 5 Nov 1970-1 (Schnider et al. 1971); Kamloops 26 Sep 1981-35, 3 Oct 1984-70, 21 Oct 1984-5; Swan Lake (Vernon) 20 Sep 1983-10, 12 Oct 1943-29, 31 Oct 1949-3 (ROM 76867-76869); Nakusp 18 Oct 1975-3; Ta Ta Creek 10 Sep 1939-1 (RBCM 10874); Fort Steele 7 Oct 1918-4 (ROM 24.4.14.202, 204, 205, 207). **Coastal** - Green Island 6 Oct 1978-9; Masset 17 Nov 1983-12; Port Simpson 5 Sep 1886-1 (RBCM 197); Comox 1 Nov 1953-2 (RBCM 12824, 12825); Chesterman Beach 6 Oct 1978-17; Iona Island 23 Sep 1973-395, 30 Sep 1974-216; Reifel Island 21 Sep 1981-300, 28 Sep 1973-700, 13 Oct 1973-1,200, 23 Oct 1973-1189, 16 Oct 1976-600, 12 Nov 1974-400; Westham Island 29 Sep 1976-570, 16 Oct 1976-600, 21 Oct 1972-525 (Crowell and Nehls 1973a); Cowichan Bay 16 Oct 1974-23; Cobble Hill 3 Nov 1974-13; Saanich 1 Oct 1981-63; Witty's Lagoon 15 Sep 1973-35, 4 Nov 1975-11.

Winter: Interior - No records. **Coastal** - Masset 19 Dec 1972-1, 6 Feb 1980-11; Parksville 6 Dec 1981-2; Burnaby Lake 28 Dec 1974-12, 1 Jan 1975-20, 15 Jan 1981-18; Reifel Island 1 Feb 1977-11; Cowichan Bay 9 Dec 1974-2; Swan Lake (Victoria) 2 Dec 1975-8; Oak Bay 7 Feb 1979-2; Victoria 28 Feb 1976-4; Witty's Lagoon 1 Jan 1982-1; Billings Spit 29 Jan 1977-2.

Christmas Counts: Interior - Not recorded. **Coastal** - Recorded from 9 of 28 localities and on 14% of all counts. Maxima: Ladner 21 Dec 1975-683, all-time Canadian high count (Anderson, R.R. - 1976); White Rock 2 Jan 1977-113; Vancouver 20 Dec 1981-82.

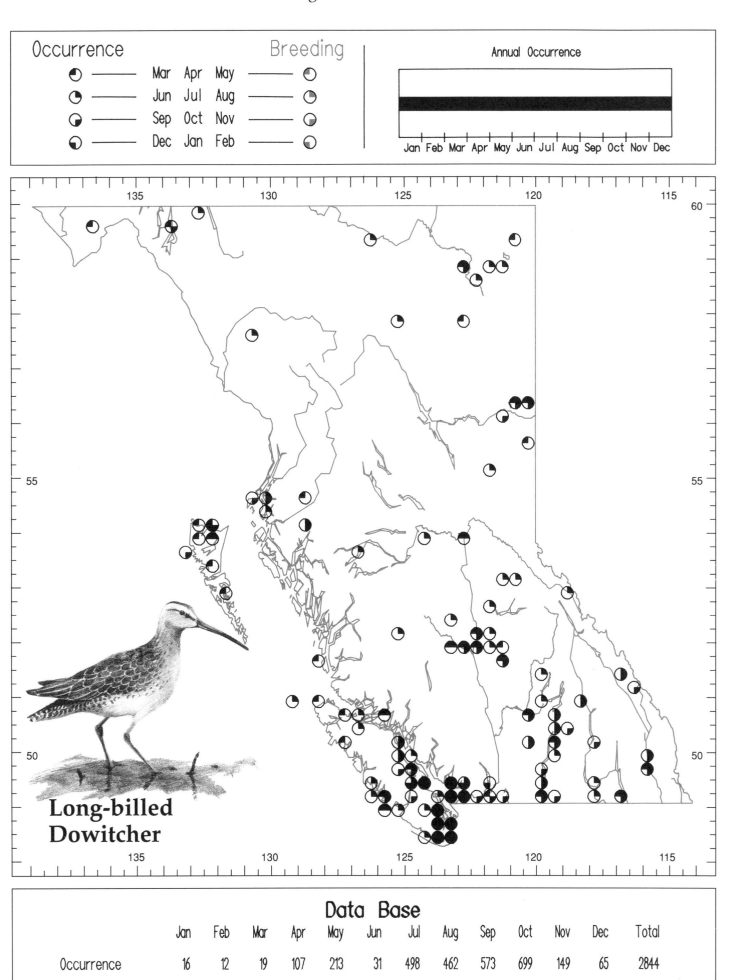

Long-billed Dowitcher

Data Base

	Jan	Feb	Mar	Apr	May	Jun	Jul	Aug	Sep	Oct	Nov	Dec	Total
Occurrence	16	12	19	107	213	31	498	462	573	699	149	65	2844

Common Snipe

Gallinago gallinago (Linnaeus)

COSN

RANGE: Circumpolar. Breeds in temperate northern regions including most of Alaska, all of subarctic Canada, northern United States, and subarctic Eurasia. Winters mainly south of breeding range to northern South America, central Africa, and southern Asia. Some southern populations are resident.

STATUS: *Fairly common* spring migrant on the coast; *uncommon* to *very common* autumn migrant and winter visitant. *Fairly common* spring migrant in the interior; *common* autumn migrant; locally *uncommon* in winter in the southern interior. *Uncommon* to *fairly common* summer visitant throughout most of the province. Breeds.

NONBREEDING: The Common Snipe is widely distributed throughout British Columbia. It frequents bogs, fens, swamps, and muddy or flooded margins along rivers, lakes, and marshes. In urban or rural areas it also frequents flooded or wet spots in stubble fields, pastures, golf courses, ditches, vacant lots, and residential lawns. Winter habitat is quite different from summer habitat. Cattail or bulrush marshes and salt marshes, which are completely unsuitable breeding areas, are very good habitat late in the year, after the vegetation structure has broken down revealing rich muddy soil (Tuck, L.M. 1972). On the coast, snipe favour estuaries and unfrozen uplands such as flooded fields where soils remain soft. In the southern interior, wintering snipe are restricted to unfrozen stream edges or seepages.

The Common Snipe usually occurs singly or in small loosely associated groups in spring but becomes more gregarious in autumn and winter. The largest spring and autumn flocks are 72 and 350 birds, respectively.

The spring movement is difficult to discern but appears to begin in mid-March on the coast, late March in the southern interior, and late April in the northern interior; it peaks in April on the coast and late April to early May in the interior. Snipe flocks disperse before reaching breeding areas and the birds tend to arrive singly (Tuck, L.M. 1972). The autumn movement is more obvious because of more frequent flocking. It begins in late August and peaks anywhere from September to November. In the interior, snipe remain until freeze-up.

In winter, the Common Snipe occurs along the coast north to Kitsault. In the interior, it occurs locally at low elevations from the Okanagan valley and the Kootenays north to Williams Lake.

BREEDING: The Common Snipe is a widespread breeder throughout the valleys and plateaus of British Columbia wherever complexes of peat bogs, fens, and shallow open water occur. Breeding habitat is most often described as marshy meadowland but is usually meadow, fen, or bog rather than marsh. It generally consists of moss hummocks, clumps of sedges or rushes, willow or alder thickets, stunted conifers or low brush, seldom of cattail or bulrush. The Common Snipe breeds from sea level to 1,700 m elevation.

The centre of breeding abundance is the south and central interior, although it is also a widespread breeder in the northern Boreal Forest. It is not known to breed in rugged coastal areas but is present in swampy areas of the Fraser Lowlands and on the east coast of Vancouver Island; there is also a small breeding population on the Queen Charlotte Islands.

Nests: All nests (n=51) were well concealed hollows in the ground. Most nests (51%) were situated in or at the base of tufts of grasses or sedges; 29% were situated on hummocks; and 10% were found in grasses. One was built on a floating log. Five nests in grass tufts were also near the base of small willow shrubs. Nests were usually situated in the drier parts of wet meadows and fens, often at the edge of a clearing, within open brushy areas, or out in the open. Lining material for 47 nests included grasses only (87%), reeds (4%), sedges (2%), and leaves (2%). Two nests were unlined.

Eggs: Dates for 107 clutches ranged from 1 April to 27 July with 53% recorded between 22 May and 20 June. Sizes for 80 clutches ranged from 1 to 5 eggs (1E-4, 2E-3, 3E-9, 4E-63, 5E-1) with 79% having 4 eggs. Incubation period is 17 to 20 days (Tuck, L.M. 1972).

Young: Dates for 44 broods ranged from 23 April to 31 July with 50% recorded between 31 May and 3 July. Calculated dates suggest unfledged young could be found as late as 16 August. Sizes for 37 broods ranged from 1 to 4 young (1Y-14, 2Y-9, 3Y-5, 4Y-9) with 63% having 1 to 2 young. Fledging period is 19 to 20 days (Tuck, L.M. 1972).

REMARKS: See L.M.Tuck (1972) for a complete treatise on snipes. The Common Snipe was formerly known as Wilson's Snipe (American Ornithologists' Union 1957). It is the only wader for which there is a hunting season in British Columbia.

NOTEWORTHY RECORDS

Spring: Coastal - Quicks Bottom 9 Mar 1978-23; Saanich 27 Mar 1982-32; Duncan 15 Mar 1976-44; Iona Island 1 Apr 1979-24; Comox 16 Apr 1954-72; Delkatla Creek 21 Apr 1972-20; Alice Arm 13 to 17 May 1980-1. **Interior** - Oliver 9 Mar 1966-1; White Lake (Okanagan Falls) 30 Apr 1974-3; Kokanee Creek 4 Apr 1977-1; Kamloops 28 Mar 1986-1; Revelstoke 18 Mar 1983-5; Williams Lake 21 Mar 1985-2; Prince George 31 Mar 1984-1; Fort St. John 23 Apr 1986-1; Fort Nelson 14 May 1982-25; Atlin 28 Apr 1981-1.

Summer: Coastal - Matsqui 25 Jul 1967-28; Pitt Meadows 26 Aug 1976-200. **Interior** - Creston 4 Aug 1980-12; Okanagan Landing 26 Aug 1942-13; Felker Lake 19 Aug 1964-30; Boundary Lake (Goodlow) 26 Aug 1986-17.

Autumn: Interior - Fort St. John 28 Sep 1985-2, 20 Oct 1986-1; 25 km w Dawson Creek 18 Sep 1983-8; Chilcotin Lake 2 Nov 1977-2; Revelstoke 1 Nov 1977-1 (Bonar 1978a); Kamloops 27 Sep 1981-10; Nakusp 8 Nov 1975-1; Coldstream 18 Oct 1936-25; Vernon 31 Oct 1944-30. **Coastal** - Green Island 15 Nov 1978-1 last; Prince Rupert 26 Oct 1956-10; Sewall 12 Nov 1981-1; Port Hardy 11 Oct 1950-13; Chilliwack 20 Oct 1978-150; Tofino airport 26 Oct 1982-64; Iona Island 23 Oct 1971-180; Sea Island 29 Sep 1971-100; Reifel Island 17 Sep 1965-350; Martindale Flats (Saanich) 11 Nov 1983-81; Victoria 14 Nov 1970-30.

Winter: Interior - Williams Lake 26 Dec 1974-4; Alkali Lake (Cariboo) 22 Feb 1970-1; Kamloops 24 Dec 1986-2; Leanchoil 14 to 15 Feb 1977-2 (Wade 1977); Columbia Lake 9 Jan 1948-1 (Johnstone, W.B. 1949); Nakusp 1 Jan 1977-1; Coldstream 1 Dec 1954-6; Okanagan Landing 23 Dec 1921-1; Naramata 31 Dec 1964-1; Vaseux Lake 2 Dec 1973-1. **Coastal** - Masset 29 Jan 1983-19; Prince Rupert 4 Dec 1984-1; Kitimat 18 Dec 1983-1; Port Clements 3 Jan 1956-75; Cortes Island 12 Dec 1976-6; Squamish River 26 Feb 1980-15; Burnaby Lake 28 Dec 1974-80; Somenos Lake 24 Jan 1976-40; Otter Point 14 Jan 1978-1.

Christmas Counts: Interior - Recorded from 6 of 19 localities and on 37% of all counts. Maxima: Nakusp 4 Jan 1981-9; Vernon 18 Dec 1983-8; Penticton 27 Dec 1976-5. **Coastal** - Recorded from 23 of 28 localities and on 63% of all counts. Maxima: Vancouver 20 Dec 1981-**151**, all-time Canadian high count (Anderson, R.R. 1982); Ladner 22 Dec 1962-127; Victoria 27 Dec 1964-115.

Common Snipe

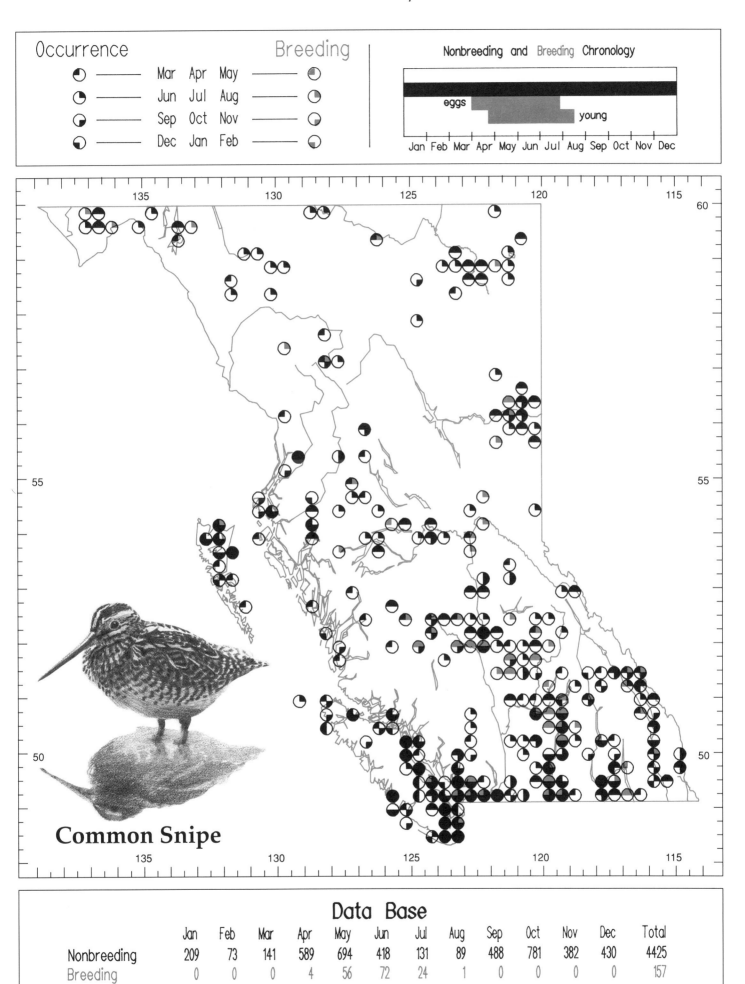

Common Snipe

Occurrence   **Breeding**

	Mar	Apr	May	
Jun	Jul	Aug	
Sep	Oct	Nov	
Dec	Jan	Feb	

Nonbreeding and Breeding Chronology

eggs   young

Jan Feb Mar Apr May Jun Jul Aug Sep Oct Nov Dec

Data Base

	Jan	Feb	Mar	Apr	May	Jun	Jul	Aug	Sep	Oct	Nov	Dec	Total
Nonbreeding	209	73	141	589	694	418	131	89	488	781	382	430	4425
Breeding	0	0	0	4	56	72	24	1	0	0	0	0	157

Wilson's Phalarope

WIPH

Phalaropus tricolor (Vieillot)

RANGE: Breeds in the interior of western North America, mainly in the prairies, but also in the southern Yukon, much of British Columbia, southern Ontario, southern Quebec, and the American midwest. Winters mainly on altiplano lakes in Bolivia, northern Argentina, and Peru; also on pampas to Tierra del Fuego and coastally in central and southern South America.

STATUS: *Fairly common* to *common* migrant and summer visitant within the interior breeding range. On the south coast, a *fairly common* spring migrant and summer visitant; *rare* autumn migrant. Breeds.

CHANGE IN STATUS: The Wilson's Phalarope is currently undergoing an extension of its breeding range in North America (Hayman et al. 1986). In British Columbia it has also been expanding its range since it was first recorded in the province on 15 May 1922 at Osoyoos Lake (Brooks 1923b). J.A. Munro and Cowan (1947) consider the Wilson's Phalarope a regular summer visitant in many parts of the interior, north to Ootsa Lake in the west and Swan Lake (Peace Lowlands) in the east. They report only one coastal record. Since 1947, the Wilson's Phalarope has become a regular summer visitant to the Fraser River delta and the southeast coast of Vancouver Island; breeding has been reported there since 1968 (Campbell 1969b). In the interior, it has become more common and widespread and now occurs north to at least the Fort Nelson region and north of Kotcho Lake; breeding has been reported north to the Fort St. John area.

NONBREEDING: The Wilson's Phalarope occurs in small numbers in the intermontane valleys of southern, central, and northeastern British Columbia where it frequents shallows of sloughs and lakes, flooded meadows, and sewage ponds. On the coast, it occurs regularly on the Fraser River estuary and, occasionally, in wetlands on southern Vancouver Island and along the Strait of Georgia. It prefers fresh or brackish waters, rarely occurring on marine waters. It migrates singly or in small groups; flocks usually number from 2 to 8 birds. Females arrive earlier in spring and leave earlier in summer than males (Hohn 1966; Howe 1975).

Spring migration is mainly through the interior. It begins in early May (early April in some years), and peaks in mid-to-late May. On the coast, the spring movement is stronger than the autumn movement, the opposite to that of most shorebirds.

The autumn movement begins in late July, peaks from mid-August to early September and ends in the third week of September. The movement is primarily through the interior with very few birds reaching the south coast. There are no winter records.

BREEDING: The Wilson's Phalarope breeds in small numbers from the southern Kootenays, through the Thompson-Okanagan and Fraser plateaus west to Kleena Kleene and north to Ness Lake in the Nechako Lowlands; also in the Peace Lowlands from Charlie Lake to Boundary Lake. A few pairs have bred on the coast in recent years at Iona Island and on southern Vancouver Island. The centre of breeding abundance is in the southern Okanagan.

Its breeding habitat is typically shallow, marshy wetlands. It has bred from near sea level to 975 m elevation.

Nests: Nests are hollows in grass or sedge growth usually situated in damp meadows around the perimeter of a marsh or pond. Of 36 nests, 78% were lined with grasses, 9% with sedges, and 6% with wood chips. Three nests were beneath a canopy of vegetation. Nests were usually situated on a dry mound on damp ground in fringes of short-grass (57%), on a hummock (17%), on dykes (18%), in reeds (7%), or at the base of grass or rush clumps (7%). Distance from standing water ranged from 3 to 50 m with 10 of 16 nests less than 15 m from water. The Wilson's Phalarope is loosely colonial in parts of its range but is a sparse nester in this province, although 2 nests 1 m apart were found at Spotted Lake (Cannings, R.A. et al. 1987), and Parham (1937) makes reference to 2 "very small colonies" in the Okanagan.

Eggs: Dates for 48 clutches ranged from 22 May to 3 July with 54% recorded between 2 and 14 June. Calculated dates indicate that eggs could be found as early as 12 May. Sizes for 43 clutches ranged from 1 to 5 eggs (1E-1, 2E-4, 3E-6, 4E-31, 5E-1) with 72% having 4 eggs. Incubation period is 16 to 21 days (Johns 1969).

Young: Dates for 38 broods ranged from 7 June to 4 August with 14 broods recorded between 14 June and 1 July. Sizes for 31 broods ranged from 1 to 5 young (1Y-3, 2Y-9, 3Y-9, 4Y-9, 5Y-1) with 87% having 2 to 4 young.

REMARKS: As in all phalaropes, males perform all incubation and brood rearing duties. They also may attend the nest during egg laying.

Wilson's Phalaropes are more inclined to forage on land than other phalaropes and are often seen walking along the edge of a pond or even on an adjacent field rather than swimming while foraging.

Blomquist (1983) provides a useful bibliography on the 3 species of phalaropes in the world.

J.A. Munro and Cowan (1947) erroneously list 3 records from Atlin: 12 May 1934, 21 July 1924 and 4 September 1924. These should refer to the Red-necked Phalarope (see Swarth 1936).

Often placed in the monotypic genus *Steganopus* (American Ornithologists' Union 1983).

NOTEWORTHY RECORDS

Spring: Coastal - Surrey 4 Apr 1960-1; Serpentine River 17 Apr 1965-6; Reifel Island 28 Apr 1973-1; Iona Island 14 May 1977-15, 14 May 1973-30, 16 May 1973-21, 28 May 1976-15. **Interior** - Osoyoos Lake 16 May 1978-18; Richter Pass 16 May 1964-53 (day count); Fauquier 22 Apr 1980-2; Merritt 16 May 1984-38; Celista 5 Apr 1962-5; Burgess and James Gadsden Park 19 May 1987-11; 150 Mile House 29 Apr 1983-1 (Ducks Unlimited Canada 1983); Fort St. John 20 May 1986-50, 28 May 1983-44; Charlie Lake 4 May 1980-1; Helmet (n Kwokullie Lake) 19 May 1982-1 (RBCM 17743).

Summer: Coastal - Kings Pond (Saanich) 3 Jun 1983-1 (RBCM Photo 897); Cowichan Bay 9 Jun 1980-2; Iona Island 12 Aug 1978-5, 25 Aug 1980-7; Little Qualicum River estuary 21 Jun 1976-1 (Dawe 1980); Mitlenatch Island 23 Aug 1970-1 (Foottit 1970). **Interior** - St. Mary's Indian Reserve 1A 12 Aug 1976-36; Vernon 30 Aug 1950-46; Revelstoke airport 3 Jun 1977-50, 4 Jul 1977-27 (Bonar 1978a); Berg Lake 11 Aug 1973- (Cannings, S.G. 1973); Becher's Prairie (Riske Creek) 20 Jul 1975-25; Beaver Lake (Stum Lake) 26 Jul 1973-25, survey (Ryder 1973); Fort St. John 18 Jun 1987-20, 9 Jul 1987-3, 23 Jul 1987-39, 26 Jul 1987-43, 7 Aug 1986-17, 25 Aug 1986-2; Kotcho Lake 26 Jun 1982-1 (Campbell and McNall 1982).

Autumn: Interior - Kleena Kleene 14 Oct 1961-1 (Paul 1964); Revelstoke airport 21 Sep 1977-8, 17 Oct 1977-4 (Bonar 1978b); Beresford Range 4 Sep 1950-33; Campbell Lake 5 Sep 1950-30; Gallagher Lake 2 Sep 1951-3. **Coastal** - Comox 2 Oct 1928-1 (MVZ 101181); Iona Island 7 Sep 1975-11, 22 Sep 1981-1; Blackie Spit 28 Sep 1972-2; Saanich 5 Sep 1983-1.

Winter: No records.

Wilson's Phalarope

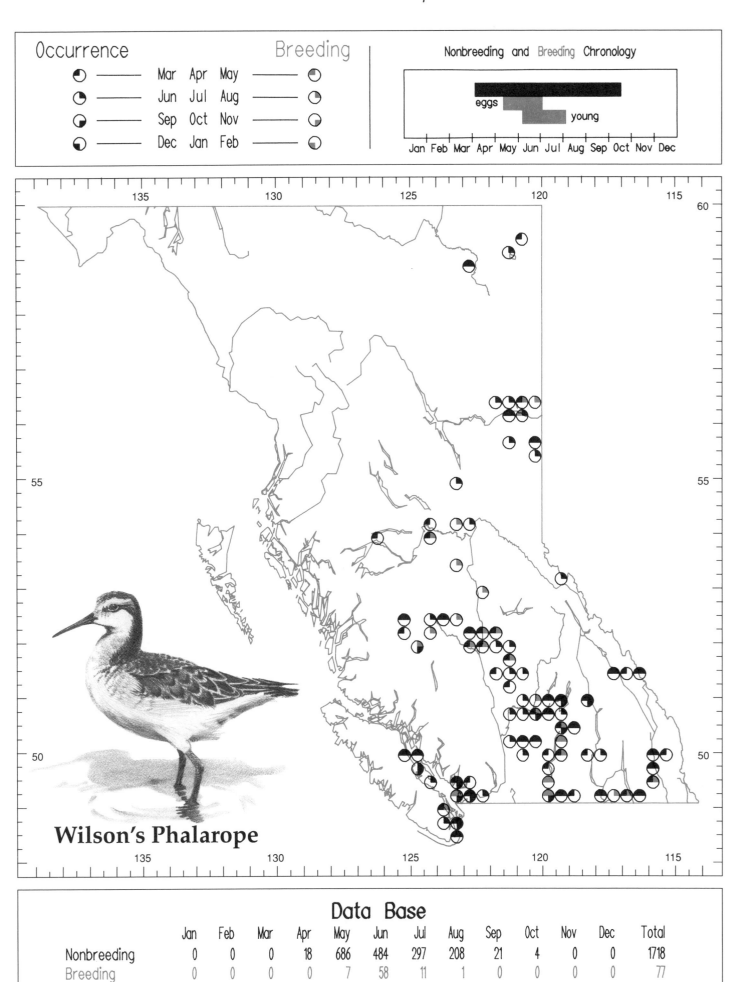

Occurrence ⸻ Mar Apr May ⸻ **Breeding**

◐	Mar Apr May	◐
◔	Jun Jul Aug	◔
◕	Sep Oct Nov	◕
◕	Dec Jan Feb	◕

Nonbreeding and Breeding Chronology

eggs | young

Jan Feb Mar Apr May Jun Jul Aug Sep Oct Nov Dec

Data Base

	Jan	Feb	Mar	Apr	May	Jun	Jul	Aug	Sep	Oct	Nov	Dec	Total
Nonbreeding	0	0	0	18	686	484	297	208	21	4	0	0	1718
Breeding	0	0	0	0	7	58	11	1	0	0	0	0	77

Wilson's Phalarope

Red-necked Phalarope

Phalaropus lobatus (Linnaeus)

RNPL

RANGE: Circumpolar. In North America breeds in the low Arctic across northern Alaska and Canada south to northwestern British Columbia and James Bay. Different breeding populations winter in different areas. Mainly pelagic in winter off Peru, the East Indies, and the Arabian Sea; a few winter in southern California.

STATUS: On the coast a *very abundant* migrant, *rare* in early summer. In the interior an *uncommon* spring migrant and *common* to locally *abundant* autumn migrant; *uncommon* summer visitant in the extreme northwest. Absent in winter. Breeds.

NONBREEDING: The Red-necked Phalarope is the only phalarope that occurs throughout the province from sea level to 1,200 m elevation. Although much of its population migrates far offshore, a major proportion migrates near shore along the coast. Far fewer numbers pass through the interior.

In marine waters, flocks of 5 to 50 are common in the early stages of migration, growing to thousands during peak movements. Flocks congregate along tide lines or the edges of kelp beds where they forage for minute organisms. At sea, flocks skim over the water in long lines or loose groups, settling in the water one moment and rising en masse the next. The Red-necked Phalarope spends virtually all its time on water unless driven ashore by gales. It has been seen foraging along a sandy beach at night after a severe storm. The largest concentrations reported in British Columbia have been from Queen Charlotte Strait, off Cleland Island, and from the Strait of Juan de Fuca. In the interior, the Red-necked Phalarope frequents lakes, marshes, ponds, flooded fields, and sewage lagoons. During the southward migration it occurs on alpine lakes and ponds, often using pools seemingly too small for most shorebirds. Larger lakes such as Charlie Lake are used as regular staging areas during the northward and southward movements.

The spring movement begins in late April or early May and usually peaks in mid-May. It appears to be more pelagic than the autumn movement. Tremendous numbers may gather at offshore staging areas. Just off Cleland Island, Red-necked Phalaropes accumulated to 20,000 birds between 1700 hrs and dusk on 15 May 1969 and were gone the next morning (Hatler et al. 1978). Over the next few days, flocks of up to 5,000 were seen passing all day. Martin and Myres (1969) also reported flocks in excess of 5,000 off Ucluelet in early May. In the interior, the spring movement is a bit later than the coastal movement.

The southward movement begins in early July with the arrival of adult females, followed by adult males late in July and early August. Early flocks usually number from 20 to 200 birds on the coast and from 5 to 20 birds in the interior. In some years, there is a heavy early movement on the coast with flocks

numbering up to 5,000 birds. The autumn movement continues strongly through to early September with arriving juveniles. The strongest interior autumn migrations are through the Peace Lowlands and the Okanagan valley where maximum numbers per day reach 100 to 400 birds. On the coast, several thousands per day may pass any given near-shore locality although they prefer the open ocean to fiords and inlets. Numbers vary considerably from year to year depending on weather and food supply. At Green Island, the absence of "red euphasids" in the autumn of 1978 was cited as a reason for the unusual absence of phalaropes and other regular species (Hart, F.G. 1978a). Most migrants have left by October, with only stragglers remaining until mid-November. Extreme autumn dates are: interior-4 July and 27 October, coast-26 June and 25 November.

BREEDING: The southern edge of the Red-necked Phalarope's breeding range reaches the northwest corner of British Columbia where the species nests in low numbers. There are only 4 confirmed breeding records, all from the Chilkat Pass area of the St. Elias Mountains. However, adults in summer plumage and apparent territorial pairs have been reported in early summer from more southern localities such as Upper Gnat Lake and Stalk Lakes in the Northern Mountains and Plateaus region. On the breeding grounds, the phalaropes occur in small groups early in the season, with several females usually accompanying each male. After incubation begins, females move to the coast.

Breeding habitat is the wet subalpine plateaus around small lakes, bogs, marshes, and pools with damp sedge meadows or mossy-hummocked ground.

Nests: Only one nest has been reported. It was a small cup of sedges on a mossy hummock beside a small pool situated in the subalpine habitat along the Haines Road (Chilkat Pass) at an elevation of 850 m.

Eggs: The lone nest described above contained 3 eggs and 1 young on 2 July 1980. Clutch initiation was about 6 June. Incubation period ranges from 16.8 to 20.7 days averaging about 18 days (Hilden and Vuolanto 1972).

Young: We have 3 breeding records of young out of the nest: on 5 July 1984, 2 adults with 3 fledged young were seen near Holum Creek (Kwatini Creek); a single young bird was seen on 14 July 1980, 80 km north of Haines, Alaska; and a large downy young was reported on 14 July 1944 at Mile 85, Haines Road (Munro, J.A. and Cowan 1947). The fledging period is about 20 days (Hilden and Vuolanto 1972).

REMARKS: Formerly known as Northern Phalarope (American Ornithologists' Union 1957, 1983).

NOTEWORTHY RECORDS

Spring: Coastal - Esquimalt Lagoon 16 May 1970-300; Swiftsure Bank 24 Apr 1972-2, 17 May 1972-1,000; Ucluelet 1 to 4 May 1949-up to 5,000 (Martin and Myres 1969); Cleland Island 15 May 1969-20,000, 18 May 1969-up to 5,000, 19 May 1970-thousands (Hatler et al. 1978); Mitlenatch Island 28 Apr 1980-10, 26 May 1983-42; Milbanke Sound 13 May 1967-118; Langara Island 10 Apr 1927-first of year (Darcus 1930). **Interior** - Osoyoos 27 May 1979-20; Okanagan Landing 25 Apr 1938-4; Kamloops 24 May 1986-12; Jones Lake (Hanceville) 22 May 1980-46; Fort St. John 14 May 1986-1, first of year, 30 May 1986-23; Fort Nelson 17 May 1986-1; Helmet (n Kwokullie Lake) 18 May 1982-20 (RBCM 17740-17742); Atlin 16 May 1981-6.

Summer: Coastal - Cattle Point 31 Aug 1974-4,000; Saanich 26 Jun 1976-1; Johnstone Strait 7 Jul 1976-17; Buckle Group 4 Jul 1982-4,500; Pine Island 14 Jul 1975-3,500; Tree Island 14 Jul 1975-4,500; Queen Charlotte Strait 29 Jul 1970-8,000 day count (Crowell and Nehls 1970d); Milbanke Sound 2 Jul 1969-50; Hecate Strait 11 Jul 1974-200; Stephens Island 30 Jun 1976-52. **Interior** - Wasa 10 Aug 1977-7 (Fitz-Gibbon 1977); Salmon Arm 28 Aug 1970-200+ (Schnider et al. 1971); Felker Lake 29 Aug 1969-20; Jackson Lake (Riske Creek) 26 Aug 1978-63; Towdystan Lake 22 Aug 1978-67; Mirage Lake 11 Aug 1938-88 (Munro, J.A. 1938); Fort St. John 21 Aug 1985-200, 26 Aug 1982-400; Charlie Lake 21 Aug 1986-300+; Kwadacha Wilderness Park 17 Aug 1983-30 (Cooper, J.M. and Cooper 1983).

Autumn: Interior - Fort St. John 6 Sep 1986-62, 19 Sep 1982-1, last; Salmon Arm 2 Sep 1970-200; Kamloops 10 Sep 1978-68, 11 Sep 1983-57, 3 Oct 1982-1; Vernon 27 Oct 1963-1; Duck Lake (Creston) 10 Sep 1947-75 (Munro, J.A. 1958a). **Coastal** - Green Island 18 Sep 1977-50, last of year; Cormorant Island 14 Sep 1967-54; Johnstone Strait 22 Nov 1975-6; Clover Point 2 Sep 1975-2,500, 12 Sep 1972-2,000, 13 Sep 1978-3,000, 7 Nov 1979-35, 25 Nov 1979-2; Gonzales Point 8 Sep 1981-1,255.

Winter: No records.

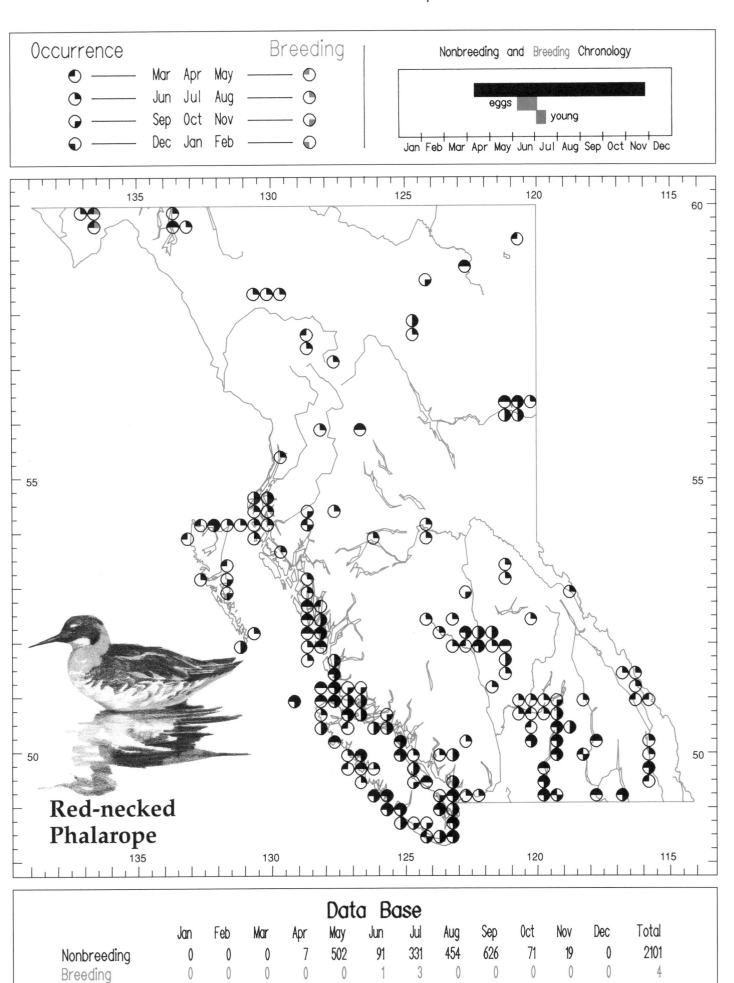

Red-necked Phalarope

Data Base													
	Jan	Feb	Mar	Apr	May	Jun	Jul	Aug	Sep	Oct	Nov	Dec	Total
Nonbreeding	0	0	0	7	502	91	331	454	626	71	19	0	2101
Breeding	0	0	0	0	0	1	3	0	0	0	0	0	4

Red Phalarope
Phalaropus fulicaria (Linnaeus)

REPH

RANGE: Circumpolar breeder. In North America breeds mainly north of the Arctic Circle, south to Hudson Bay and northern Quebec. Also occurs in Eurasia. Winters in pelagic waters, mainly off the coasts of southern South America and Africa.

STATUS: On the coast, a generally *common* transient offshore; in some years *very abundant* near shore; *very rare* in early winter. In the interior, *casual* in autumn.

OCCURRENCE: The Red Phalarope has a scattered distribution along coastal British Columbia; it is rarely found in the interior. It is most frequently observed on the outer coast of Vancouver Island, in Queen Charlotte Strait, and in the Strait of Juan de Fuca. It is rarely encountered in the Strait of Georgia or along the northern coasts and fiords.

The Red Phalarope is almost entirely pelagic during the non-breeding seasons, except when blown inshore by storm fronts. Unique among waders, its migratory routes are entirely oceanic and therefore it is rarely encountered. Only during severe storms, when the species may seek refuge in more protected waters, is it seen near land in significant numbers. It occurs as singles, in pure flocks, or in mixed flocks with Red-necked Phalaropes.

Spring migration occurs from early to mid-May. Martin and Myres (1969) report the Red Phalarope as a regular migrant off Nootka Sound but extremely erratic in appearance from year to year. It has not been reported in spring in the Strait of Georgia. The largest spring concentration recorded is 1,000 birds foraging along a tide line 200 m off Triangle Island (Scott Islands) on 17 May 1974 (Vermeer et al. 1976). Extreme coastal spring dates are 30 April and 28 May.

Few occur in nearshore waters during the summer, traditionally a season of calm weather. However, Martin and Myres (1969) record the Red Phalarope as common, but dispersed, in warm water areas off Cape Flattery, Washington in July and August and suggest that it seems to prefer the warmer waters. Usually, the Red Phalarope is most numerous along the Pacific coast of North America between September and December (Hayman et al. 1986). In British Columbia, most of our records are from October to December, a season with traditionally more violent weather patterns. Extremely large numbers have been reported in autumn, always during severe storms. At Clover Point on 11 Nov 1982, during a gale, several thousand were recorded flying east in a 45 min period. In the autumn of 1934, a heavy movement was recorded on the central coast and northern Strait of Georgia during a period of extreme weather. Various observers noted "countless thousands" near Calvert Island in September and "hundreds" at Black Creek, Courtenay, on 22 and 23 October (Pearse 1935). Some phalaropes at Black Creek even foraged on a wet road. Normally, groups of 5 to 20 occur in autumn, even in severe weather. By mid-December the Red Phalarope has

disappeared completely from British Columbia. Extreme autumn migration dates on the coast are 23 June and 17 December.

There are only 5 documented interior occurrences, all from larger lakes, between 1 August and 29 October.

REMARKS: Also known as the Grey Phalarope (Hayman et al. 1986).

Figure 152. Red Phalarope at Reifel Island, Delta, 23 June 1974 (RBCM Photo 350, Neil K. Dawe).

NOTEWORTHY RECORDS

Spring: Coastal - Ucluelet 12 to 17 May 1949-mixed flocks of 50+ (Martin and Myres 1969); Chesterman Beach 28 May 1980-1 alive on beach; Nootka Sound 14 May 1947-large flocks (Martin and Myres 1969); Triangle Island (Scott Islands) 17 May 1974-1,000 (Vermeer et al. 1976); Cape St. James 16 May 1982-1 (RBCM 17710), 28 May 1982-3; Tlell 30 Apr 1935-1 (ROM 85179). **Interior** - No records.

Summer: Coastal - Clover Point 12 Aug 1974-2; Swiftsure Bank 2 Aug 1971-1 (RBCM 12044); Reifel Island 23 to 25 Jun 1974-1 (RBCM Photo 350; Fig. 152); Long Beach 27 Jul 1983-300; Tofino 31 Jul 1971-2 (Campbell and Shepard 1972);

Mitlenatch Island 7 Jun 1976-1 (Butler, R.W. and Butler 1976); Goose Group 28 Jul 1948-2; Masset 12 Aug 1936-1 (RBCM 9696). **Interior** - Duck Lake (Creston) 1 Aug 1951-1 (ROM 85181).

Autumn: Interior - Swan Lake (Vernon) 28 Sep 1939-1 (ROM 85178), 5 Oct 1955-1 (ROM 85190), 29 Oct 1934-3 (MVZ 82058, 101147, 101148); Okanagan Landing 26 Oct 1963-1 (Cannings, R.A. et al. 1987). **Coastal** - Green Island 13 Nov 1977-1; Sewall 7 Oct 1980-1; Calvert Island Sep 1934-thousands; Port Hardy 16 Oct 1936-common; Black Creek 22 Oct 1934-hundreds (Pearse 1935); Tofino Inlet 13 Sep 1969-20 (Campbell and Shepard 1971); Jordan River 19 Nov 1976-19;

Clover Point 17 Oct 1966-50, 31 Oct 1982-27, 11 Nov 1983-5,000 counted from 0730 to 0815 (Campbell 1983a), 23 Nov 1969-34; Constance Bank to Trial Island 4 Nov 1980-600.

Winter: Interior - No records. **Coastal** - Jordan River 5 Dec 1960-3 (Boggs and Boggs 1961a); Clover Point 3 Dec 1959-large flock (Poynter 1960), 17 Dec 1982-1; Albert Head to Constance Bank 11 Dec 1983-8.

Christmas Counts: Interior - Not recorded. **Coastal** - Recorded once: Victoria 15 Dec 1979-8, all-time Canadian high count (Anderson, R.R. 1980).

Red Phalarope

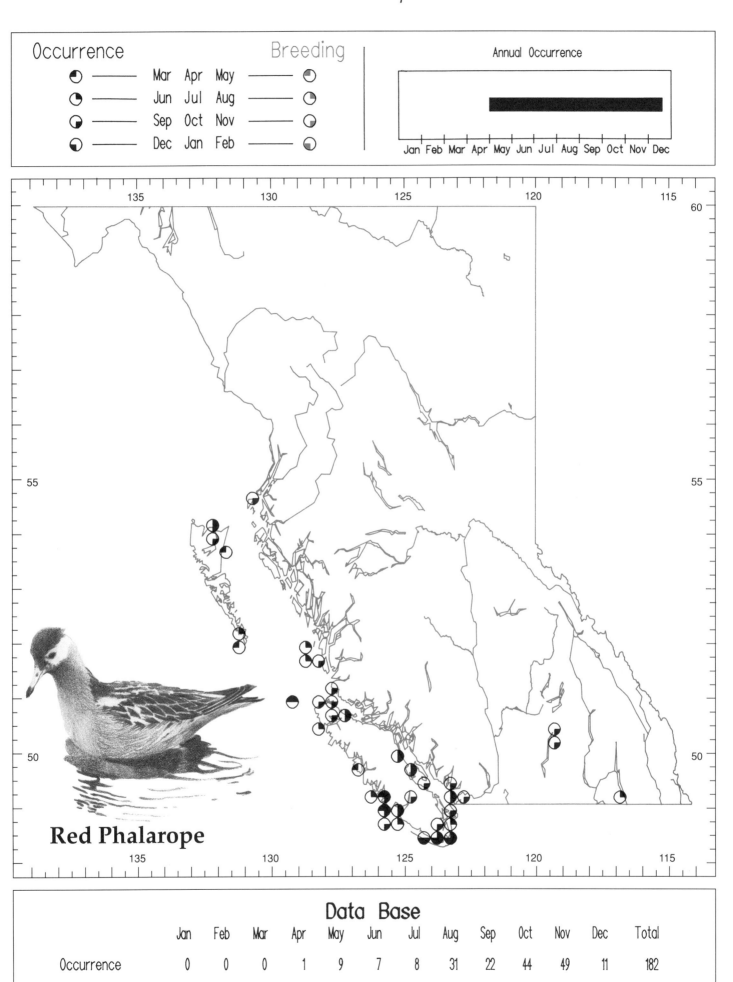

Red Phalarope

Occurrence

	Mar	Apr	May
	Jun	Jul	Aug
	Sep	Oct	Nov
	Dec	Jan	Feb

Breeding

Annual Occurrence

Jan Feb Mar Apr May Jun Jul Aug Sep Oct Nov Dec

Data Base

	Jan	Feb	Mar	Apr	May	Jun	Jul	Aug	Sep	Oct	Nov	Dec	Total
Occurrence	0	0	0	1	9	7	8	31	22	44	49	11	182

Pomarine Jaeger
Stercorarius pomarinus (Temminck)

POJA

RANGE: Breeds from northern Alaska to north-central Arctic Canada and Greenland; also in northern Eurasia. Winters at sea from southern California south to Peru and eastern Australia in the Pacific Ocean and from the southeastern United States to the West Indies and Africa in the Atlantic Ocean. Infrequently occurs inland in migration.

STATUS: *Uncommon* spring transient, *rare* summer visitant and *fairly common* autumn transient offshore. *Very rare* transient in the Strait of Georgia and Juan de Fuca Strait. *Casual* in the interior.

OCCURRENCE: The Pomarine Jaeger occurs mainly as an offshore transient along the outer coast of British Columbia. It is more frequently encountered farther offshore than the Parasitic and Long-tailed jaegers. Wahl (1975) reports a similar situation off Washington: during 34 offshore trips from April to October, 94% of all Pomarine Jaeger observations (n=276) were more than 10 km from shore.

The Pomarine Jaeger occurs infrequently in the protected waters of Queen Charlotte Strait, the Strait of Georgia, and Juan de Fuca Strait. Its status and movements in Hecate Strait are poorly known. Its numbers are probably determined by the distribution of fish. The largest numbers (up to 12 birds at a time) are usually seen in the vicinity of offshore banks (e.g. La Perouse Bank; Fig. 153) and commercial fishing vessels.

Spring migration occurs from late April to early June with the main passage in May. A few nonbreeders remain as summer visitants (mid-June to mid-July), mainly offshore. Autumn migration, when the largest numbers are observed, occurs from mid-July through September. Numbers decline through October and November. Extreme dates for coastal areas are 24 April and 12 November and for the interior, 9 September and 1 December.

REMARKS: Also known as Pomarine Skua or Pomatorhine Skua.

See Furness (1987) for a complete discussion on the taxonomy, biology, and conservation of the Stercorariinae.

Figure 153. *Light-phase Pomarine Jaeger chasing first year California Gull, La Perouse Bank, 27 September, 1986 (Michael Force).*

NOTEWORTHY RECORDS

Spring: Coastal - Clover Point 12 May 1978-2; La Perouse Bank 16 May 1977-1, 16 May 1985-10 (Mattocks 1985b); Tsawwassen 22 May 1971-1 off jetty (Campbell et al. 1972b); Vancouver 8 May 1980-1 dark phase; Elma Bay 31 May 1931-1; 3 km w Sunday Inlet 16 May 1987-2 light phase; Reef Island 31 May 1985-1; 1 km w Skidegate Inlet 12 May 1985-3 light phase; 16 km to 32 km ne Sandspit 24 Apr 1981-4; 29 km e Sandspit 21 May 1982-1; 1 km n Masset 13 May 1978-1. **Interior** - No records.

Summer: Coastal - Victoria 17 Jul 1973-1 (Crowell and Nehls 1973d); Saanich 31 Aug 1974-1; Swiftsure Bank 24 Jul 1977-1; w Ucluelet 24 Jul 1984-6, 30 Aug 1986-10; Barkley Sound 19 Aug 1977-1; Lawn Point (Quatsino Sound) 27 Aug 1967-1; Smith Sound 28 Aug 1948-several; w

Cape Russell 1 Jun 1982-2; Goose Group 13 Jun 1948-1 dark phase (Guiguet 1953a), 27 Jul 1948-7, 14 Aug 1948-8; 32 km w Goose Group 18 Jul 1939-3 females (MCZ 282302 - 282304); Reef Island 9 Jun 1985-1; Marble Island 1 Jun 1986-1 light phase; 5 km w Tasu 19 Jun 1987-1 (Campbell 1987d); McIntyre Bay 15 Aug 1930-1 male (ANS 101136); Tugwell Island (Chatham Sound) 31 Aug 1969-3 (2 light, 1 dark phase). **Interior** - No records.

Autumn: Interior - vicinity Chilcotin Lake Nov 1911-1 (RBCM 112); North Thompson River (Kamloops) 18 Sep 1984-1 immature (Campbell 1984b); Tranquille 21 Sep 1984-1 male found dead on beach of Kamloops Lake (RBCM Photo 939; RBCM 18451). **Coastal** - 1 km w Prince Rupert 25 Sep 1971-2 immatures; Masset 27 Oct 1947-1

(RBCM 10541); Milbanke Sound 1 Oct 1969-1 light phase; Wentworth Island 18 Sep 1967-1 dark phase; Heriot Bay 4 Nov 1975-1 dark phase (Shepard, M.G. 1976b); Oyster Bay 12 Nov 1962-1; Locarno Park (Vancouver) 6 Sep 1985-1 immature; Steveston 8 Oct 1937-1; Cape Beale to La Perouse Bank 10 Sep 1977-9; La Perouse Bank 3 Sep 1983-5, 4 Sep 1983-9, 27 and 28 Sep 1986-12, 1 Oct 1977-3; 13 km s Cape Beale 17 Sep 1977-5; Sidney Island 12 Oct 1967-1; Clover Point 14 Sep 1984-1 immature.

Winter: Interior - Canal Flats 1 Dec 1970-1 immature (PMA 271.59). **Coastal** - No records.

Christmas Counts: Not recorded.

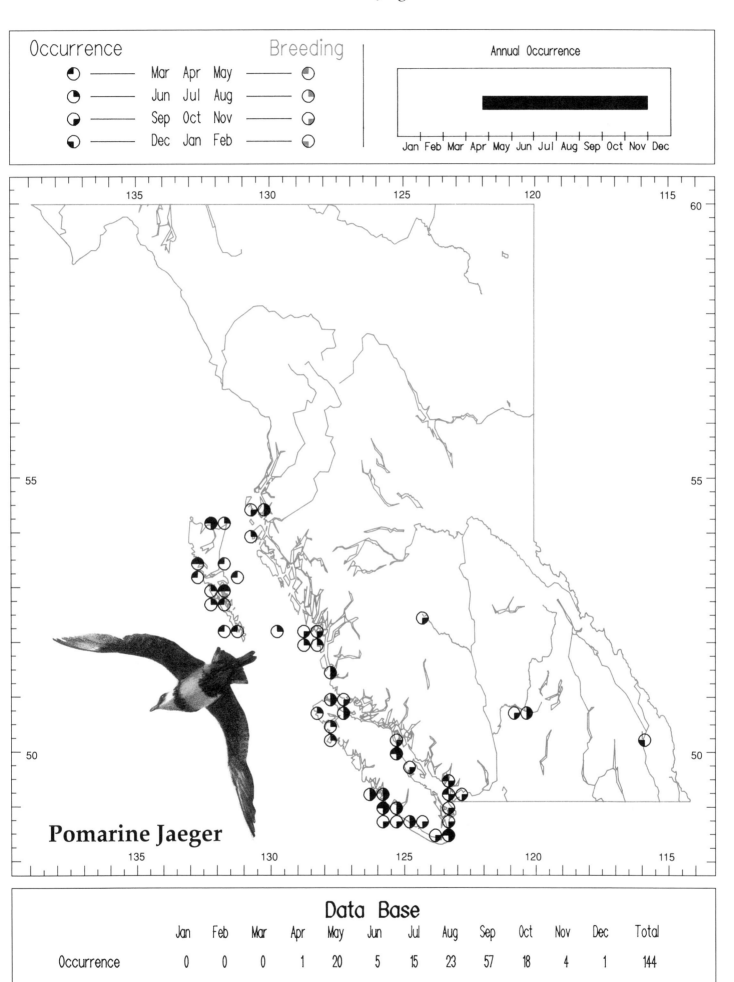

Pomarine Jaeger

Occurrence

◓ ———	Mar Apr May	——— ◔
◔ ———	Jun Jul Aug	——— ◔
◔ ———	Sep Oct Nov	——— ◔
◕ ———	Dec Jan Feb	——— ◔

Breeding

Annual Occurrence

Jan Feb Mar Apr May Jun Jul Aug Sep Oct Nov Dec

Data Base

	Jan	Feb	Mar	Apr	May	Jun	Jul	Aug	Sep	Oct	Nov	Dec	Total
Occurrence	0	0	0	1	20	5	15	23	57	18	4	1	144

Parasitic Jaeger
Stercorarius parasiticus (Linnaeus)

PAJA

RANGE: Breeds from western Arctic Alaska and the Aleutian Islands to north-central Canada and Greenland. Winters at sea in the Pacific Ocean from southern California to southern Chile, Australia and New Zealand and in the Atlantic Ocean from Maine and the British Isles south to Brazil, Argentina, and Africa. At times a regular migrant locally in the interior of North America. Also found in northern Eurasia.

STATUS: *Uncommon* to *fairly common* spring transient, *rare* in summer and *fairly common* to *common* autumn transient along the outer coast. *Rare* spring transient, *uncommon* autumn transient and *casual* in winter in the inner coast. *Casual* in spring and *very rare* in autumn in the interior.

OCCURRENCE: The Parasitic Jaeger, while still oceanic in habits, is seen far more often in nearshore and inner coastal areas than the Pomarine or Long-tailed jaegers. It frequents all coastal areas, especially bays, coves, estuaries, surge narrows, and sewage outlets where it frequently associates with Bonaparte's and Mew gulls, Black-legged Kittiwakes, and Common Terns. Occasionally, coastal lakes and heads of inlets are visited.

In the interior, the Parasitic Jaeger has been recorded in the Peace Lowlands, in the central-southern interior from Wells Gray Park south through the Okanagan valley, and in the vicinity of Creston. It is probably attracted to migrating gulls that frequent larger lakes and rivers.

Nearshore records suggest that spring migration in British Columbia is far less pronounced and of much shorter duration than the autumn movement. Spring migrants move along the coast mainly from late April to mid-May. In early summer, a few nonbreeders are regularly encountered, especially on fish-rich banks off the central coast. Autumn migration begins about mid-July and in some years may carry into early November; the peak movement occurs in September. There are several winter records, all from the Fraser River delta.

The Parasitic Jaeger is usually found solitarily (Fig. 154) or in small groups of 3 or 4 individuals; occasionally, groups of up to 50 individuals have been reported.

Records from British Columbia range from 27 April to 8 December on the coast and from 25 May to 17 October in the interior.

REMARKS: Hilden (1971) suggests that the proportion of colour phases of passage migrants gives some indication of their probable breeding grounds. Southern (1943) has shown that dark birds predominate in southern populations while pale birds inhabit high arctic regions. Of 1,383 birds recorded from May to November in British Columbia, 86% were of the pale colour phase. The monthly breakdown, in percentage of pale to dark colour phases (sample size) is: May 100:0(6), June 71:29(28), July 0:100(8), August 74:26(62), September 88:12(885), October 88:12(382), and November 55:45(22). These results, although incomplete, suggest that pale birds migrate earlier in spring and dark birds earlier in autumn, and that a higher proportion of pale-phase individuals is the norm.

For a discussion of the breeding ecology and behaviour of the species, see O'Donald (1983).

The Parasitic Jaeger is known in the Old World as Arctic Skua.

Figure 154. Juvenile Parasitic Jaeger at Cattle Point, Victoria, September 1983 (Tim Zurowski).

NOTEWORTHY RECORDS

Spring: Coastal - Victoria 9 May 1962-1; Active Pass 1 May 1971-1 (Tatum 1972); 29 km w Barkley Sound 9 May 1972-1; Tofino 15 May 1970-3; Lulu Island 5 May 1924-1 male (RBCM 6812) and 1 female (RBCM 6805); Beresford Island 15 May 1979-4; Lost Islands 3 May 1982-3; 2 km n Gowgaia Bay 15 May 1987-4 (Campbell 1987b); Hecate Strait 4 May 1971-3; 1 km n Masset 27 Apr 1969-1. **Interior** - Creston 25 May 1965-1; Kalamalka Lake 29 May 1927-1.

Summer: Coastal - Victoria 1 Jun 1976-1 and 22 Jul 1966-1 (Crowell and Nehls 1966c); 19 to 32 km w Bamfield 15 Jul 1979-3; Iona Island 2 Jun 1983-1, 15 Jun 1975-2; Cleland Island 19 Jun 1975-1; Tofino 31 Jul 1971-6; Comox 17 Jul 1922-1 female (NMC 18039); Campbell River 29 Aug 1975-25+ chasing Bonaparte's and Mew gulls; Solander Island 24 Jun 1975-1; Hardy Bay 2 Aug 1937-1 male (MVZ 101195); Goose Group 10 Jun 1948-2 (Guiguet 1953a), 28 Jun 1972-1; Anthony Island 30 Jun 1977-2; Reef Island 9 Jun 1985-4; De la

Beche Inlet 16 Jun 1986-1 (Campbell 1986f); Kitimat 2 Jul 1975-1; Naden Harbour 8 Jul 1975-1 harassing Black-legged Kittiwakes; Rose Spit 30 Jul 1974-3. **Interior** - Creston 24 Jun 1981-1 (Butler, R.W. et al. 1986); Okanagan Landing 29 Aug 1942-2 immatures; Salmon Arm 25 Aug 1977-1 harassing Ring-billed Gulls; Stevens Lakes 11 Jul 1962-1 and Aug 1960-1 (Edwards and Ritcey 1967); Charlie Lake 22 Jul 1982-1 harassing Bonaparte's Gull (Campbell 1982c), 24 Aug 1986-1 (Campbell 1986d), 27 Aug 1982-1 (Grunberg 1983c), 27 Aug 1984-1 adult.

Autumn: Interior - Salmon Arm 17 Sep 1970-1, 25 Sep 1970-3 and 26 Sep 1970-1 (Schnider et al. 1971); Scotch Creek 2 Sep 1977-1; Kelowna 17 Oct 1973-1 (Cannings, R.A. 1975b); Penticton 30 Sep 1982-1, 8 Oct 1973-1 (RBCM Photo 318; Cannings, R.A. 1975b); Creston Sep 1984-1 (Butler, R.W. et al. 1986). **Coastal** - Port Simpson 21 Sep 1969-1; Kallum River 16 Sep 1987-1; Kitimat 11 Nov 1974-1 (Hay 1976); Masset 14 Sep 1975-6; Cape St.

James 10 Sep 1982-7; Goose Group 3 Sep 1973-8; Seymour Inlet 18 Sep 1968-9 (Crowell and Nehls 1968a); Comox 18 Sep 1935-12; Qualicum Beach 10 Sep 1975-5 (Dawe 1976); Gibsons 13 Sep 1986-3; English Bay 15 Nov 1975-1; Sea Island 26 Sep 1966-9, 27 Sep 1965-8; Tsawwassen 23 Sep 1978-19 off ferry terminal; Crescent Beach 21 Nov 1968-1; Sumas Sep 1906-1 male (RBCM 122); Active Pass 6 Nov 1976-1; Saanich Inlet 12 Oct 1953-50+ harassing 2,500+ Bonaparte's Gulls, 20 Oct 1953-20; Cape Beale to La Perouse Bank 2 Sep 1984-17; Pedder Bay 10 Oct 1970-25 (Tatum 1971); Trial Islands 1 Oct 1983-11 (6 adults, 5 immatures).

Winter: Interior - No records. **Coastal** - Boundary Bay 2 Dec 1968-1 adult (light morph) chasing Mew Gulls; Crescent Beach 8 Dec 1976-2.

Christmas Counts: Recorded once: White Rock 2 Jan 1978-1, all-time Canadian high count (Anderson, R.R. 1978).

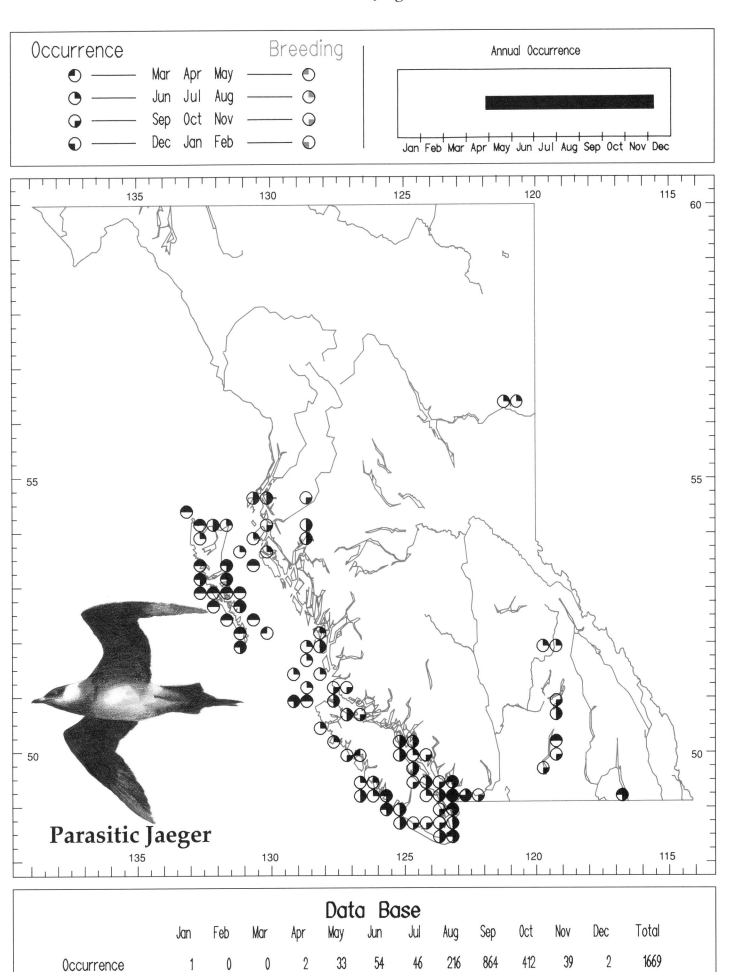

Parasitic Jaeger

Data Base

	Jan	Feb	Mar	Apr	May	Jun	Jul	Aug	Sep	Oct	Nov	Dec	Total
Occurrence	1	0	0	2	33	54	46	216	864	412	39	2	1669

Long-tailed Jaeger

Stercorarius longicaudus Vieillot

LTJA

RANGE: Breeds in Arctic Alaska, Canada, and Greenland. Winters at sea in the Pacific Ocean mainly off South America from Ecuador to Chile and on the Atlantic Ocean from about Pennsylvania south to Argentina. Also found in the Old World.

STATUS: *Very rare* spring transient, *casual* in summer, and *uncommon* to *fairly common* autumn transient along the outer coast. *Very rare* autumn transient on the inner coast. *Very rare* autumn transient in the interior.

OCCURRENCE: The Long-tailed Jaeger is highly pelagic and is not normally seen within sight of land. It has, however, been found in most outer coastal and nearshore areas, as well as throughout the inner coast. It frequents offshore banks, and areas with schools of surfacing small fishes and commercial fishing vessels. Nearshore habitats include areas of upwelling, surge narrows, and bays, especially where mixed-species feeding flocks of gulls, terns, and alcids are found.

In the interior, the Long-tailed Jaeger has been recorded in the northwest, and across southern areas of the province. There it frequents larger lakes and mouths of rivers, especially those with spawning fish where gulls aggregate, and occasionally alpine plateaus and meadows. It has been found up to 2,800 m elevation.

Details for spring migration are poorly known. The main movement probably occurs far offshore and may be relatively compressed with few birds lingering. Some probably begin passing through in early May although extreme dates for nearshore records range from 11 to 28 May. There are no spring records for the interior.

Several early summer records could represent birds that failed to breed and have left breeding grounds as early as mid-June due to rodent scarcity (Anderson, M. 1976).

Autumn migration begins in late July, increases in August, peaks in September, and in some years carries on through October into early November. Records in alpine areas suggest that some Long-tailed Jaegers may migrate at high altitudes through the interior of the province. Unitt (1976) suggests that such a migration route through the North American interior is regularly used by the species.

Extreme dates for the coast are 11 May to 8 November and for the interior, 21 June to November (exact date unknown). Just over 90% of all records are of single birds. The largest concentration was a group of 9 seen in spring off the Queen Charlotte Islands.

REMARKS: Similarities in plumages and colour phases of the 3 species of jaegers make identification challenging. Experience is the best teacher, but Bull (1963), Harrison, P. (1983), and Stallcup (1976) provide useful aids to identification.

See M. Anderson (1976) and Maher (1974) for additional information on the ecology, breeding biology, food, and population dynamics of the Long-tailed Jaeger in North America.

Known as Long-tailed Skua in Old World literature.

NOTEWORTHY RECORDS

Spring: Coastal - west coast Vancouver Island 11 May 1891-1 male (RBCM 1460), 1 female (RBCM 1461); Chesterman Beach 28 May 1931-1; 10 km w Vargas Island 15 May 1971-1; Cape St. James 19 May 1981-2; 3 km w Gowgaia Bay 17 May 1986-9 in loose group with large feeding flock of albatrosses, fulmars, cormorants, eagles, gulls and alcids (Campbell 1986e); 3 km w Milbanke Sound 24 May 1982-2; 5 km w Marble Island 12 May 1985-1. **Interior** - No records.

Summer: Coastal - Mary Tod Island 31 Aug 1980-1; James Island 4 Aug 1955-1; Sumas Lake Canal 23 Aug 1889-1 female (MVZ 101201); Tsawwassen 17 Aug 1974-1 off ferry terminal (Crowell and Nehls 1975a); Seal Islets 3 Aug 1922-1; Buttle Lake 28 Aug 1975-1 male (RBCM 15330); Goletas Channel 6 Aug 1969-1; Cape Scott 29 Jul 1936-2; Goose Group 18 Jul 1939-1 female (RBCM 8787); Naden Harbour 27 Aug 1984-1 adult; McIntyre Bay 21 Aug 1980-1; Somerville Island 15 Jun 1967-1, 21 Jul 1966-1; Portland Inlet 15 Jun 1967-1 (Crowell and Nehls 1967c); Anyox 17 Aug 1966-1. **Interior** - Trail 3 Aug 1984-1; Champion Lakes Park 10 Aug 1984-1; Okanagan Landing 30 Aug 1905-1 female (MVZ 101200); Perkins Peak 29 Aug 1986-1 at 2,800 m (Campbell 1986d); Rainbow Range 21 June 1932-1 (MCZ 282316); n Suscha Lake 15 Aug 1987-1; Kawdy Plateau 4 Aug 1962-1 pair (NMC 49766-67); Atlin Lake 30 Jul 1979-1, summer 1977-1 female (RBCM 17177).

Autumn: Interior - Cold Fish Lake autumn 1958-1; Buffalo Lake 11 Sep 1933-1 (Munro, J.A. 1945a); Lone Butte 4 Sep 1985-2 (Campbell 1985d); Wapta Lake 12 Sep 1976-1 (Wade 1977); Vermillion Pass 18 Sep 1911-1 (Brooks and Swarth 1925); Kootenay Pond 29 Sep 1975-1 (RBCM 17721); Adams River 23 and 25 Oct 1964-1 (Rogers, T.H. 1964a); Salmon Arm 6 Sep 1970-1 immature, 25 Sep 1970-1 (Rogers, T.H. 1971a); Okanagan Landing 2 Sep 1942-1 immature male (MVZ 87841); Trout Creek (Summerland) 18 Sep 1953-1 (Cannings, R.A. et al. 1987). **Coastal** - McIntyre Bay 2 Sep 1980-1 (RBCM Photo 881); Yeo Cove 17 Sep 1968-1; Seaforth Channel 30 Sep 1966-1; Hardy Bay 12 Sep 1934-1; Campbell River (Discovery Passage) 29 Sep 1968-2 (Crowell and Nehls 1968a); Cape Mudge 14 Oct 1966-1; McQuarrie Islets 13 Sep 1970-1; Comox 22 Sep 1928-1 female (MVZ 82069); Southey Island 10 Oct 1967-1; White Rock 11 Sep 1981-1; Sea Island 17 Sep 1966-4 (Campbell 1968d), 8 Nov 1926-1 female (UBC 2901); Ten Mile Point 14 Sep 1952-3 (Flahaut 1953a); Clover Point 20 Oct 1970-1 immature (Tatum 1971); French Beach 6 Sep 1928-1 male (RBCM 4927).

Winter: No records.

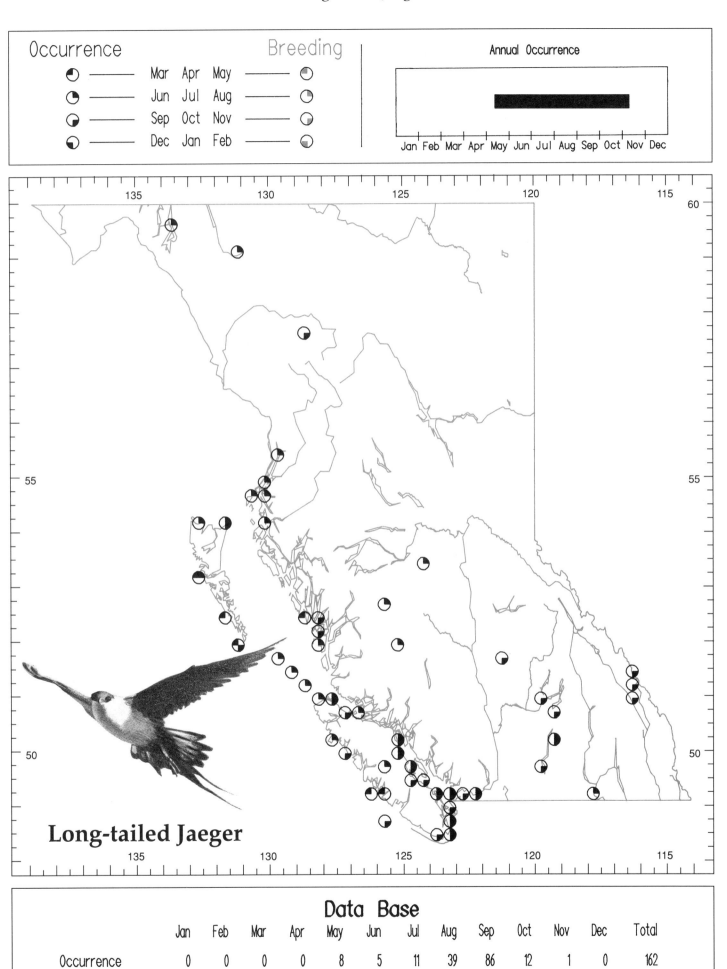

Occurrence

		Mar	Apr	May		
		Jun	Jul	Aug		
		Sep	Oct	Nov		
		Dec	Jan	Feb		

Breeding

Annual Occurrence

Jan Feb Mar Apr May Jun Jul Aug Sep Oct Nov Dec

Long-tailed Jaeger

Data Base

	Jan	Feb	Mar	Apr	May	Jun	Jul	Aug	Sep	Oct	Nov	Dec	Total
Occurrence	0	0	0	0	8	5	11	39	86	12	1	0	162

South Polar Skua
Catharacta maccormicki (Saunders)

SPSK

RANGE: Breeds on the Antarctic continent; migrates to the northern oceans.

STATUS: *Very rare* summer and *rare* autumn transient off the outer coast. *Accidental* in summer and *very rare* in autumn in the Strait of Georgia and Juan de Fuca Strait.

OCCURRENCE: The South Polar Skua is a highly pelagic migrant from the southern hemisphere. Devillers (1977) suggests it regularly migrates into the North Pacific Ocean in a clockwise loop from Japan to North America. The South Polar Skua occurs off Japan between early May and late July with most records in June and July (Kuroda 1962; Kuroda et al. 1958). It occurs in small numbers off the west coast of North America from May to November, with numbers peaking between August and October.

The South Polar Skua has been recorded off British Columbia between 13 June and 22 November with most records (40%) concentrated in September. Off Washington it has been seen between 14 May and 6 October with peak numbers in late August and early October (T. Wahl pers. comm.); off California peak numbers occur between late July and October (Stallcup 1976).

All British Columbia records are of single birds and most are probably immatures; there are no confirmed records of adults. There is one record from terrestrial habitat at Canoe Pass south of Vancouver (Dow, D.D. and Hesse 1969). Skuas have frequently been reported chasing Glaucous-winged Gulls, Herring Gulls, Bonaparte's Gulls, and Common Terns, and have been seen among mixed-species feeding assemblages near fishing vessels, schooling small fishes, and offshore shallows (e.g. La Perouse Bank).

REMARKS: The taxonomy of *Catharacta* is complex and controversial. In the past, some authorities recognized 5 species of skuas, but recently, Devillers (1977) proposed 3 species: Great Skua (*C. skua*), Chilean Skua (*C. chilensis*), and South Polar Skua (*C. maccormicki*). Brooke (1978) has recently added Antarctic Skua (*C. antarctica*) to the list.

Specimens examined recently from the Pacific coast of North America indicate that all are now referable to South Polar Skua (American Ornithologists' Union 1957; Devillers 1977; Godfrey 1986; Jehl 1973a). See Devillers (1977) and P. Harrison (1983) for discussions concerning identification of age-classes of all skuas.

Figure 155. *South Polar Skua, 3 km west of Anthony Island, Queen Charlotte Islands, 15 June 1986 (RBCM Photo 1153; Irene E. Whitney).*

NOTEWORTHY RECORDS

Spring: No records.

Summer: Coastal - Great Chain Island 19 Aug 1960-1; La Perouse Bank 2 Jul 1947-1 (Martin and Myres 1969); nw Cape Cook (Brooks Peninsula) 11 Aug 1970-1 (Crowell and Nehls 1970d); Triangle Island (Scott Islands) 10 Jul 1986-1; 80 km wsw Cape Calvert [not Culvert as listed by Devillers (1977) and Godfrey (1986)] 26 Jun 1938-1 (AUMU 0.37704); 19 km s Goose Group 17 Aug 1948-1 female (UBC 1986); Goose Group 13 Jun 1948-1, 27 Jun 1948-1 female (RBCM 9758), 8 Jul 1939-1 male (RBCM 8801; Cowan 1940); Laredo Sound Jun 1939-1 (Martin 1942); 3 km w Anthony Island 15 Jun 1986-1 (RBCM Photo 1153; Fig. 155). **Interior** - No records.

Autumn: Interior - No records. **Coastal** - w Athlow Bay 22 Sep 1976-1 (McKelvey 1976); Cape St. James 4 Sep 1984-1; Lasqueti Island 16 Sep 1978-1; Norris Rocks 12 Sep 1978-1; Brockton Point 9 Oct 1969-1; Canoe Pass 7 Sep 1968-1 (Dow, D.D. and Hesse 1969); La Perouse Bank 3 Sep 1983-1; Saanich Inlet 25 Sep 1982-1; Mouat Reef 5 and 6 Sep 1987-1; Trial Islands 8 Sep 1959-1 immature (Poynter 1960); Victoria 28 Oct 1972-1 (Tatum 1973); Victoria Harbour 22 Nov 1981-1; Race Rocks 7 Nov 1979-1.

Winter: No records.

South Polar Skua

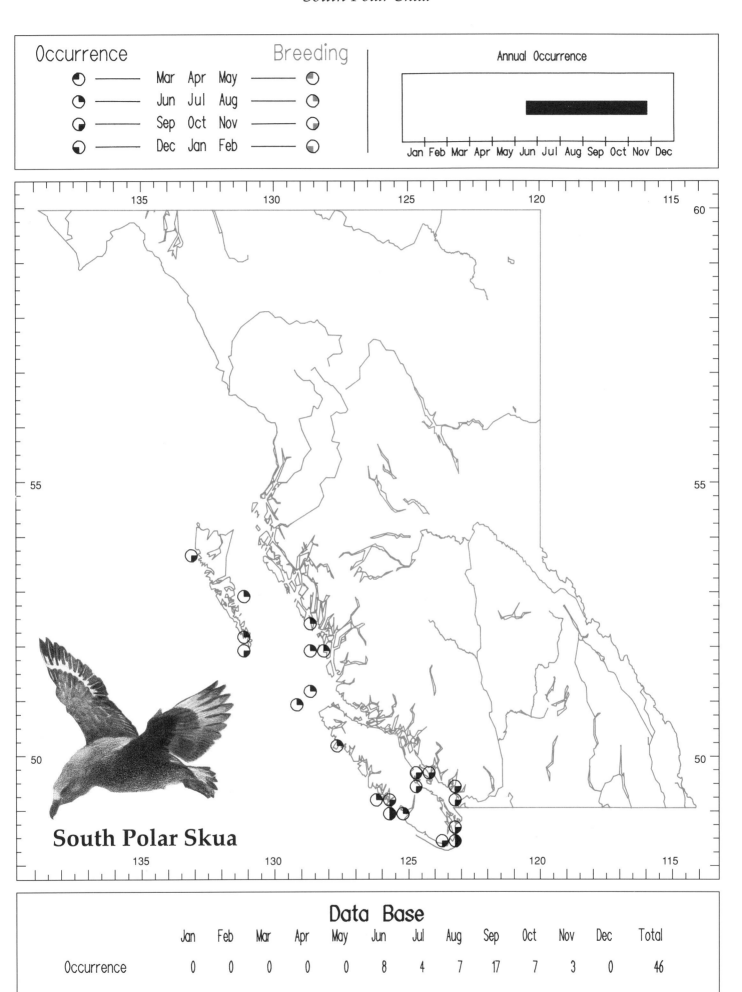

Occurrence

Occurrence		Breeding
◐ ——	Mar Apr May	—— ◑
◔ ——	Jun Jul Aug	—— ◐
◕ ——	Sep Oct Nov	—— ◔
◔ ——	Dec Jan Feb	—— ◕

Annual Occurrence

Jan Feb Mar Apr May Jun Jul Aug Sep Oct Nov Dec

Data Base

	Jan	Feb	Mar	Apr	May	Jun	Jul	Aug	Sep	Oct	Nov	Dec	Total
Occurrence	0	0	0	0	0	8	4	7	17	7	3	0	46

Franklin's Gull

Larus pipixcan Wagler

FRGU

RANGE: Breeds from the Prairie provinces of Canada south to east-central Oregon and Utah and east to Iowa. Nonbreeding birds occur in summer from east-central British Columbia and northeastern Manitoba south to northern New Mexico, Wyoming, Kansas, central Iowa, and the Great Lakes. Winters in the Pacific from Guatemala south to the Gulf of Panama, the Galapagos Islands, Chile, and, occasionally, along the Gulf coast of Texas and Louisiana.

STATUS: *Uncommon* to *fairly common* spring and autumn transient on the southwest coast; *rare* in summer, *very rare* in winter. *Accidental* on the Queen Charlotte Islands. In the interior, locally *very common* to *abundant* summer transient in the northeast, *very rare* spring and summer transient in the southern interior.

CHANGE IN STATUS: J.A. Munro and Cowan (1947) report only 3 records of the Franklin's Gull: the Peace Lowlands, the Okanagan valley, and the Garibaldi Park area. Recently, Hatler et al. (1978) reported the discovery of a previously misidentified specimen (UBC 3004) collected at Tofino on 29 June 1931, the earliest Franklin's Gull record for the province.

The Franklin's Gull remained a casual transient in British Columbia until the late 1950s and early 1960s when it appeared to be increasing its range, becoming more numerous in areas of northern Alberta (Soper 1949; Godfrey 1952; Erskine 1968). This trend was also noted in Oregon (Littlefield and Thompson 1981). By 1970 there were at least 159 records of this gull in British Columbia (see Campbell and Foottit 1972) and it had become much more numerous and regular in occurrence, especially on the south coast. This general trend continues. By the early 1980s the most noticeable change had occurred in the Peace Lowlands, especially along the Peace River. Up to the 1980s, the bird was considered an uncommon transient there with "five to ten birds being recorded each year" (Siddle 1982) but throughout the early 1980s flocks of up to 500 birds were being reported from the vicinity of Fort St. John and Dawson Creek.

OCCURRENCE: The Franklin's Gull occurs in south coastal British Columbia, primarily in the vicinity of the Fraser River delta, the Gulf Islands, and the eastern end of Juan de Fuca Strait.

In the southern interior it is scattered, but in the Peace Lowlands it is concentrated on large lakes. Significant numbers also occur farther north in the vicinity of Kotcho Lake. There is a single record for the Queen Charlotte Islands.

On the coast, the Franklin's Gull is often found with flocks of Bonaparte's and Mew gulls, frequenting harbours, lagoons, estuaries, sewage ponds and outlets, surge narrows, and large lakes. Franklin's Gulls have been observed foraging over salt water, and hawking for insects over sewage lagoons and open fields. They roost regularly on islets, beaches, spits, and log booms, and occasionally on golf courses and fields of city parks. In the interior, the Franklin's Gull frequents lakes, marshes, plowed fields, sewage ponds, and garbage dumps.

In the Peace River area, several hundred adult and immature-plumaged birds are found from May to July, possibly non-breeders that have moved west from Alberta colonies (see Salt and Salt 1976). Birds appear during the latter half of April, and reach peak numbers from late May to mid-June. Large flocks of 200 birds, however, have been found in late August; by September, few remain. Extreme dates of occurrence there are 25 April to 26 October, both from Charlie Lake. Interior records farther south are probably of stragglers attached to migrating flocks of Bonaparte's Gulls. Extreme dates there are 17 May (Lavington) to 19 September (Swan Lake, Vernon).

About 88% of all records are from coastal areas of the extreme southern portion of the province. The Franklin's Gull has been recorded every month, but the main movement occurs in late summer. Small numbers are seen in late July and the main influx occurs in August. By October only scattered individuals are found (Campbell and Foottit 1972). Infrequently, single birds overwinter on the coast. Most observations during migration are of 1 to 3 birds; the largest groups reported have been 40 individuals in spring and 20 in autumn. Extreme dates are 20 January (Victoria) and 27 December (Duncan).

REMARKS: The moult of the Franklin's Gull is unusual in that it is complete both in spring and autumn (Grant, P.J. 1979, 1982). Observers are encouraged to record specific ages of the species so details of migration chronology and routes can be determined.

NOTEWORTHY RECORDS

Spring: Coastal - Clover Point 2 May 1973-1 adult; Chesterman Beach 30 May 1983-1 adult; White Rock (Boundary Bay) 20 May 1970-1 immature (Campbell and Foottit 1972); Iona Island 3 May 1971-40. **Interior** - Creston 16 May 1986-15 (Rogers, T.H. 1986c), 24 May 1986-6 adults; Arrow Lake (Nakusp) 31 May 1984-1 adult; Lavington 17 May 1987-5 adults; Okanagan Lake 18 May 1986-1; Sorrento 20 May 1972-4+; Dawson Creek 8 May 1968-2 adults (Campbell and Foottit 1972); 4 km e Dawson Creek 12 May 1982-40; Fort St. John 25 Apr 1986-5 adults at sewage lagoons; Charlie Lake 14 May 1984-74 adults, 25 May 1985-150 adults, 27 May 1982-300 adults, 28 May 1985-500 adults.

Summer: Coastal - Clover Point 13 Aug to 30 Sep 1961-4 immatures; Witty's Lagoon 30 Jul 1979-1 immature; Duncan 22 Aug 1976-3 immatures; Pachena Bay 4 Aug 1972-1 immature; Stubbs Island (Tofino) 30 Aug 1977-1 immature; Ladner 7 Aug 1973-5, 10 Aug 1973-5, 13 Aug 1973-11 and 26 Aug 1973-11 at sewage pond; Iona Island 6 Aug 1971-15 (Campbell et al. 1972b); Vancouver 4

Jul 1968-3, 30 Jul 1963-3 immatures at Ken Road garbage dump; Comox 23 and 26 Aug 1952-1 (Pearse 1953); Mitlenatch Island 31 Jul 1970-1 immature (RBCM Photo 122). **Interior** - Lightning Lake 6 Jun 1975-1; Osoyoos Lake 11 Jun 1972-12 (8 adults, 4 immatures); Creston 12 Jun 1971-6+ (Stirling 1972a); Sirdar 31 Jul 1951-1 immature female (ROM 82392); Okanagan Lake 3 Aug 1938-1 immature female (MVZ 82089); Wasa Lake 2 and 3 Aug 1971-2 immatures (Dawe 1972); Alta Lake 11 Aug 1941-1 immature female (UBC 488); Salmon Arm 11 Jun 1972-20; Jones Lake (150 Mile House) 10 Jun 1983-1 immature (Ducks Unlimited Canada 1983); Chimney Lake (Cariboo) 1 Aug 1948-1 female (UBC 1794); Williams Lake 18 Aug 1948-2; Swan Lake (Tupper) 9 Jun 1962-60 adults; Charlie Lake 14 Jun 1981-400 adults, 23 Jun 1978-193 (132 adults, 19 immature, 42 unknown), 21 Aug 1986-5 immatures, 27 Aug 1982-200 winter plumage; Kotcho Lake 26 Jun 1982-117 (RBCM 17633-17637) (Campbell and McNall 1982).

Autumn: Interior - Charlie Lake 12 Sep 1982-4, 26

Oct 1982-1; Swan Lake (Vernon) 19 Sep 1983-1; Deadman Lake (Oliver) 15 Sep 1980-1. **Coastal** - Quathiaski Cove 28 Oct 1975-1; Stories Beach 18 Sep 1974-1; Comox 25 Oct 1954-1 in winter plumage (Flahaut and Schultz 1955); Langley 14 Nov 1968-1; Ladner 22 Sep 1973-15, 29 Sep 1972-19; Iona Island 26 Sep 1981-20, 8 Oct 1984-6 immatures; Clover Point 14 Sept 1960-8 immatures, 19 Oct 1975-2 (1 adult, 1 immature), 9 Nov 1967-1.

Winter: Interior - No records. **Coastal** - Port Coquitlam 21 Jan 1964-1; Lost Lagoon 13 Feb 1975-1; Vancouver 22 Dec 1969-1; Duncan 16 to 27 Dec 1970-1; Victoria 20 Jan 1964-1; Clover Point 12 Feb 1983-1.

Christmas Counts: Interior - Not recorded. **Coastal** - Recorded twice: Duncan 27 Dec 1970-1 and Vancouver 21 Dec 1969-1. Both of those are all-time Canadian high counts (Anderson, R.R. 1976).

Extralimital Records: - Hippa Island 7 to 12 Jun 1983-1; Cassiar 16 Jun 1956-1.

Franklin's Gull

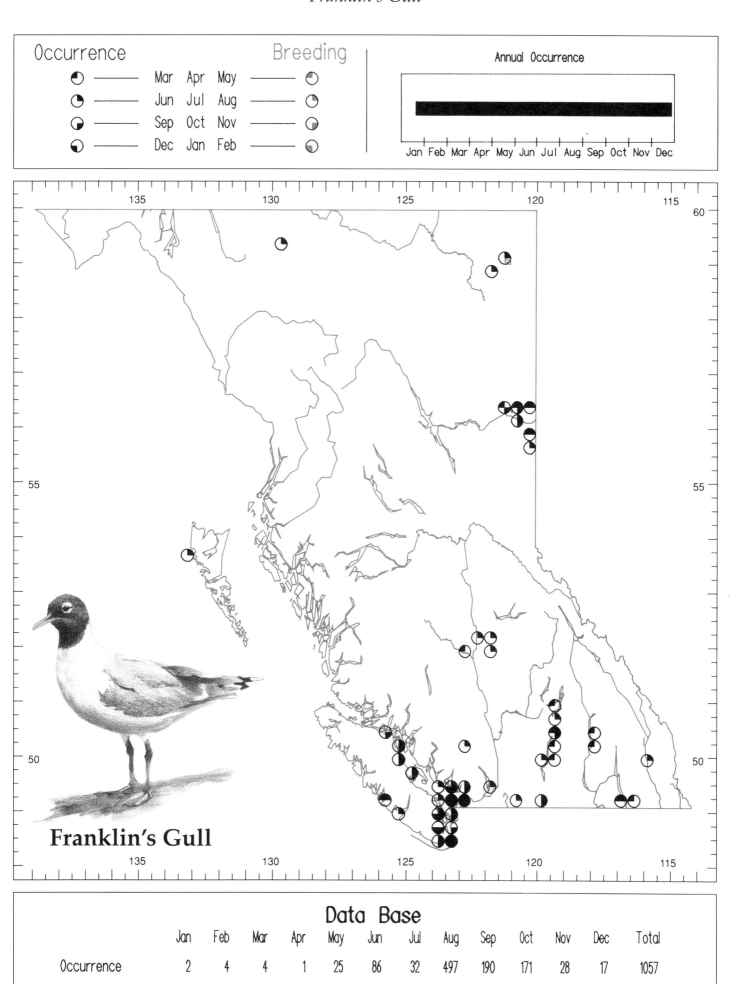

Little Gull

Larus minutus Pallas

LIGU

RANGE: Breeds in Eurasia from southern Scandinavia and northwestern Russia south to northern Europe, south-central Russia, central Siberia, and Lake Baikal. Winters south to the Mediterranean, Black, and Caspian seas. In North America breeds locally in northwestern Manitoba, southern Ontario, and along the Great Lakes in northern Wisconsin and Michigan. Winters on the Great Lakes and along the Atlantic Coast, mainly from Massachusetts to Virginia. Casual throughout rest of the United States and southern Canada.

STATUS: *Very rare* vagrant on the extreme south coast; *accidental* in the interior.

CHANGE IN STATUS: Baillie (1963) documents the invasion of this Eurasian gull into eastern North America. In 1962, it was found nesting in southern Ontario (Scott, G.A. 1963) and today is fairly well established locally in the Great Lakes and northeastern United States.

    The first recorded appearance along the coast of western North America was near Riverside, California in November 1968 (McCaskie 1969). Farther north the Little Gull was first recorded in coastal Washington in September and October 1974 (Crowell and Nehls 1975a). The Little Gull has now been recorded throughout the year from California to British Columbia (Roberson 1980).

    The Little Gull was first discovered in British Columbia at Victoria in October 1972 (Tatum 1973). Over the next 15 years, it was recorded in 11 different years, and in every year between 1982 and 1987. Roberson (1980) suggests that West Coast birds originate from northeastern North America or perhaps northern Europe.

OCCURRENCE: The Little Gull has been recorded along coastal waters of the extreme southern tip of Vancouver Island, the southern Gulf Islands and the Fraser River delta. There is one record from the Peace River area near Fort St. John. The Little Gull is most often found with Bonaparte's Gulls in the vicinity of bays and inlets, off points, and at sewage ponds and outlets.

    Of 38 records, 36 are of single birds. Only twice were 2 birds seen at once. Of the 34 observations that include ages of birds, 19 are of adults. Monthly breakdown of adults (A) and immatures (I) is: February (1A), May (2A, 1I), June (4I), July (3A, 1I), August (3A, 3I), September (5A, 3I), October (2A, 1I) and November (4A). Although the sample size is small, there appears to be no age-segregated movement of birds in British Columbia.

    The Little Gull has been recorded in the province from 5 April to 17 December and on 27 February; most records are from May through November. It is possible that some records represent duplicate sightings of the same bird, as Roberson (1980) suggests. The same individual may wander great distances. All sightings are listed in chronological order as follows:

(1) Ogden Point 24 October 1972-1 and Clover Point 1 November 1972-1 adult (Anonymous 1972; Tatum 1973). Probably the same bird.

(2) Point Grey Beach 17 December 1972-1 on Christmas Bird Count (Campbell 1973a; Crowell and Nehls 1973b).

(3) Sea Island 18 and 19 May 1974-2 (1 adult, 1 immature - see Shepard, M.G. 1975a) and Lulu Island 20 and 21 May 1974-1 adult. The adult is likely the same individual.

(4) Whiffin Spit 31 October 1974-1 winter adult and Clover Point 7 November 1974-1 adult (Crowell and Nehls 1975a). Probably the same bird.

(5) Clover Point 27 February 1976-1 adult.

(6) Iona Island 24 October 1976-1 (Roberson 1980).

(7) Iona Island 17 to 22 June 1978-2 immatures flying and roosting with a flock of Bonaparte's Gulls.

Figure 156. *Adult Little Gull in winter plumage at Holland Point, Victoria, 24 September 1983 (Tim Zurowski).*

(8) Clover Point and Ross Bay 30 August 1979-1 immature; McNeil Bay 17 September 1979-1 immature; Fort Rodd Hill National Historic Park 23 September 1979-1 immature. All locations are along the Victoria waterfront and observations may be of the same bird.

(9) Iona Island 16 and 22 September 1979-1 adult.

(10) Witty's Lagoon 29 August 1982-1 immature.

(11) Active Pass 5 April 1983-1 with 150 Bonaparte's Gulls.

(12) Charlie Lake 9 to 13 June 1983-1, first summer immature with 80 Bonaparte's Gulls. Photographed (RBCM Photo 856) on 9 June.

(13) Iona Island 23 June to 29 July 1983-1 immature, photographed (RBCM Photo 1087) on 29 June.

(14) Clover Point 19 July 1983-1 adult.

(15) Iona Island 21 and 22 September 1983-1 adult in winter plumage.

(16) Holland Point (Victoria) 22 to 27 September 1983-1 adult. Photographed (RBCM Photo 894) on 24 September (Fig. 156); off Albert Head 30 October 1983-1 adult; Clover Point 15 and 16 November 1983-1 adult. All records may be of the same individual.

(17) Iona Island 8 August 1984-1 immature (Hunn and Mattocks 1985).

(18) Victoria 17 September 1984-1, first winter bird (Hunn and Mattocks 1985).

(19) Victoria 25 August to 15 September and 16 and 17 November 1985-1 adult in winter plumage seen at various locations along the waterfront.

(20) Iona Island 9 September 1985-1, photographed (Campbell 1986a; RBCM Photo 1044).

(21) Crescent Beach 3 May 1986-1 adult.

(22) Clover Point 23 July 1986-1 adult (Mattocks 1986a), 13 and 17 August 1986-1 adult, 18 October 1986-1 immature.

(23) Active Pass 8 September 1986-1 adult.

(24) Ten Mile Point 26 July 1987-1 adult.

(25) Clover Point 23 August 1987-1 adult.

(26) Race Rocks 24 October 1987-1.

REMARKS: See Ennis (1969) and P.J. Grant (1982) for field characters of immature Little Gulls.

Little Gull

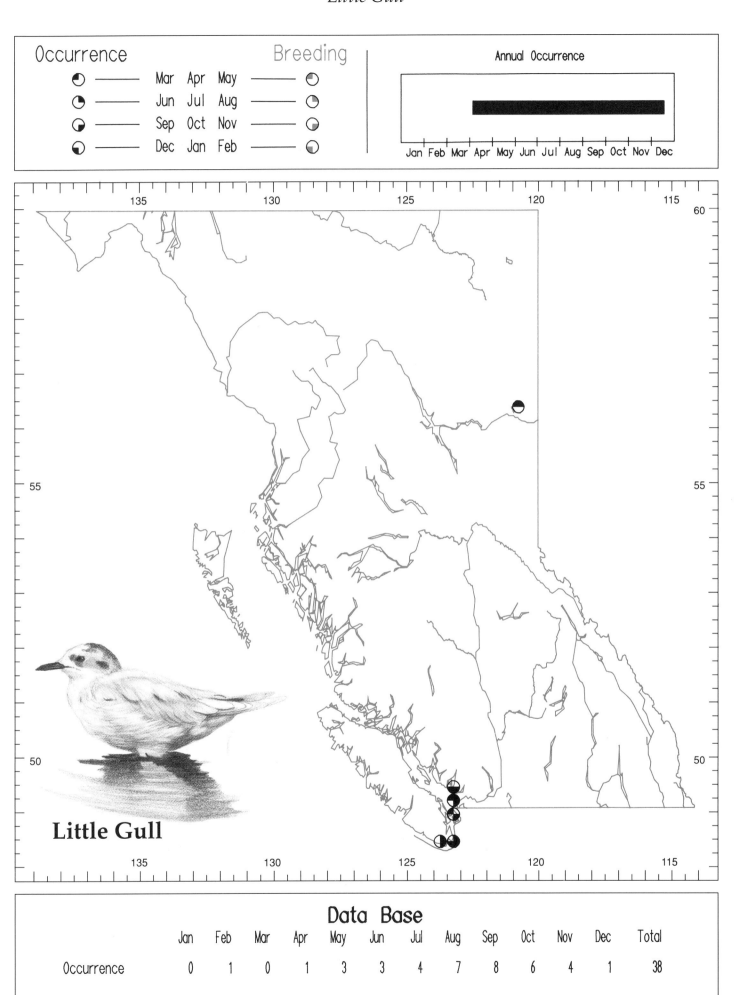

Occurrence

	Mar Apr May	
	Jun Jul Aug	
	Sep Oct Nov	
	Dec Jan Feb	

Breeding

Annual Occurrence

Jan Feb Mar Apr May Jun Jul Aug Sep Oct Nov Dec

Data Base

	Jan	Feb	Mar	Apr	May	Jun	Jul	Aug	Sep	Oct	Nov	Dec	Total
Occurrence	0	1	0	1	3	3	4	7	8	6	4	1	38

Little Gull

Common Black-headed Gull

Larus ridibundus Linnaeus

CBHG

RANGE: Breeds in northern Eurasia and recently northeastern North America. Winters in southern Eurasia, northern Africa and the Philippines; also in North America along the Atlantic coast from Labrador, Newfoundland, New Brunswick, and Nova Scotia south to New York and inland in the Great Lakes region. It is recorded annually along the Pacific coast of North America and is presently considered a rare spring and summer visitor to western Alaska (Roberson 1980).

STATUS: *Very rare* late summer to late autumn vagrant to southern inner coastal areas.

OCCURRENCE: The Common Black-headed Gull has been found, most often in association with Bonaparte's and Mew gulls, on the sea coasts, especially near kelp beds, sewage outlets, lagoons, and golf courses. Nine of the ten acceptable records are from the Greater Victoria area, Vancouver Island. The other is from the southwest mainland coast in Richmond. Except for the 1976 sightings, the birds have all been adults. Extreme dates are 28 July and 13 November.

The records are:

(1) Clover Point (Victoria) 27 October to 1 November and 6 to 13 November 1974-1 in winter plumage (Wood, C. 1976). It was photographed (RBCM Photo 374) on 27 October and 10 November.

(2) Clover Point and McMicking Point (Victoria) 15 August to 8 November 1975-1 in faded summer plumage on arrival. By 25 August it had changed to winter plumage. It was photographed (RBCM Photo 413) on 15 August.

(3) Clover Point 19 October to 8 November 1975-1 adult (second) with brownish hood.

(4) Oak Bay 28 July 1976-1 immature on Victoria Golf Course. Another immature, possibly the same bird but with a slightly different field description, was seen 6 August at McMicking Point.

(5) Clover Point 22 September 1979-1 in winter plumage with Bonaparte's Gulls and a Franklin's Gull on a kelp bed.

(6) McMicking Point 17 October and 19 to 21 October 1980-1 in winter plumage feeding with Mew Gulls and Bonaparte's Gulls.

(7) Victoria 20 August to 27 September 1983-1 in winter plumage seen at various locations along the seafront. It was photographed (RBCM Photo 893) at Esquimalt Lagoon on 20 August (Fig. 157).

(8) Iona Island (Richmond) September 1983-1, photographed (RBCM Photo 1057; Fig. 158).

(9) Esquimalt Lagoon (Colwood) 17 and 19 August and 4, 8, and 30 September 1984-1 in fading summer plumage on arrival and in winter plumage on 4 September.

(10) Oak Bay 1 October 1985-1 in winter plumage with Bonaparte's Gulls in flight off Gonzales Point.

REMARKS: We consider 2 published reports to be hypothetical because field notes are lacking: an immature bird off Harling Point, Oak Bay on 19 June 1976 (Shepard, M.G. 1976c), and one at Tsawwassen on 26 August 1977 (Roberson 1980). The date listed by M.G. Shepard (1976a) of 16 August 1976 for the immature at McMicking Point should probably be 6 August.

The Common Black-headed Gull was previously known as the Black-headed Gull.

POSTSCRIPT: A single bird, in winter plumage, was seen off Spanish Bank on 3 November 1988 and at 5 other sites along the Vancouver waterfront until 17 December 1988 (Cannings, R.J. 1989). The Status of the Common Black-headed Gull should now read: "*Very rare* late summer to early winter vagrant . . . ."

Figure 157. Common Black-headed Gull at Esquimalt Lagoon, southern Vancouver Island, 20 August 1983 (Tim Zurowski).

Figure 158. Common Black-headed Gull at Iona Island, Richmond, September 1983 (RBCM Photo 1057; Ervio Sian).

Common Black-headed Gull

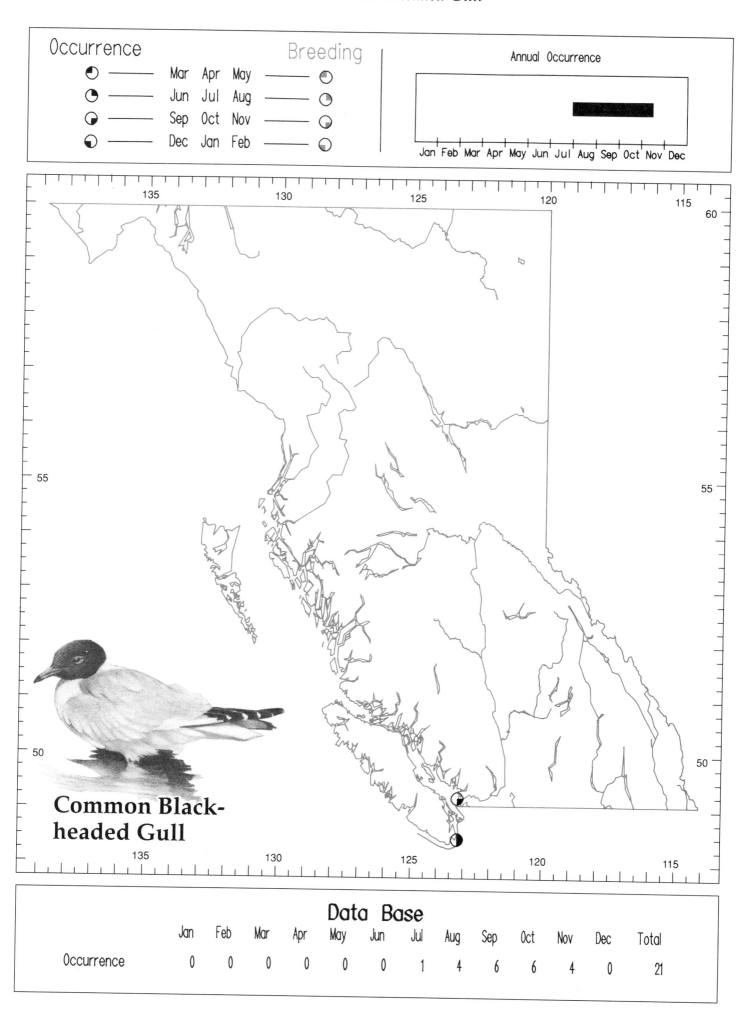

Occurrence

Breeding

Mar Apr May

Jun Jul Aug

Sep Oct Nov

Dec Jan Feb

Annual Occurrence

Jan Feb Mar Apr May Jun Jul Aug Sep Oct Nov Dec

Common Black-headed Gull

Data Base

	Jan	Feb	Mar	Apr	May	Jun	Jul	Aug	Sep	Oct	Nov	Dec	Total
Occurrence	0	0	0	0	0	0	1	4	6	6	4	0	21

Bonaparte's Gull

BOGU

Larus philadelphia (Ord)

RANGE: Breeds from western and central Alaska east to James Bay and south to south-central British Columbia, central Alberta, Saskatchewan, and central Ontario. Nonbreeding birds occur in summer along the Pacific coast south to California, the Atlantic coast south to New England, and on the Great Lakes. Winters on the Pacific coast from southern British Columbia to Mexico and in the east from the Great Lakes south through the Mississippi River to the Gulf of Mexico and from New England to Greater Antilles.

STATUS: On the coast, *very abundant* spring and autumn migrant, *rare* to *uncommon* in summer. In winter, *casual* on the northern mainland coast and *rare* on the west coast of Vancouver Island; *rare* to *very common*, at times *very abundant*, in the southern Strait of Georgia and Juan de Fuca Strait. In the interior, *common* to *abundant* spring and autumn migrant; *accidental* in winter. *Common* summer visitant to the central and northern interior, where it is a widespread breeder.

NONBREEDING: The Bonaparte's Gull occurs throughout the province from sea level to at least 1,700 m elevation. On the coast, it frequents bays, harbours, lagoons, estuaries, areas of tidal convergence and upwelling, passages and narrows, as well as large rivers and sewage lagoons. Wherever food is abundant, concentrations of tens of thousands can occur. Kelp beds, offshore islets, and log booms are favourite roosting sites. In the interior, large lakes and rivers, estuaries, marshes, and ponds are preferred habitats.

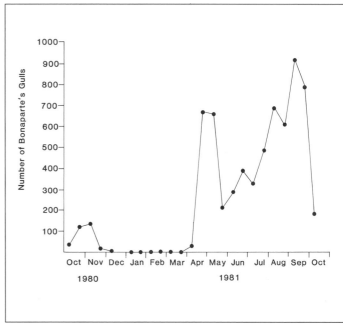

Figure 159. Biweekly counts (averages) of Bonaparte's Gulls, Comox Harbour to Deep Bay, Vancouver Island, 11 October 1980 to 10 October 1981 (courtesy Canadian Wildlife Service). Only one count was made in December.

Figure 160. Migrating Bonaparte's Gulls at Esquimalt Lagoon, southern Vancouver Island, 8 August 1981 (Tim Zurowski).

Bonaparte's Gull

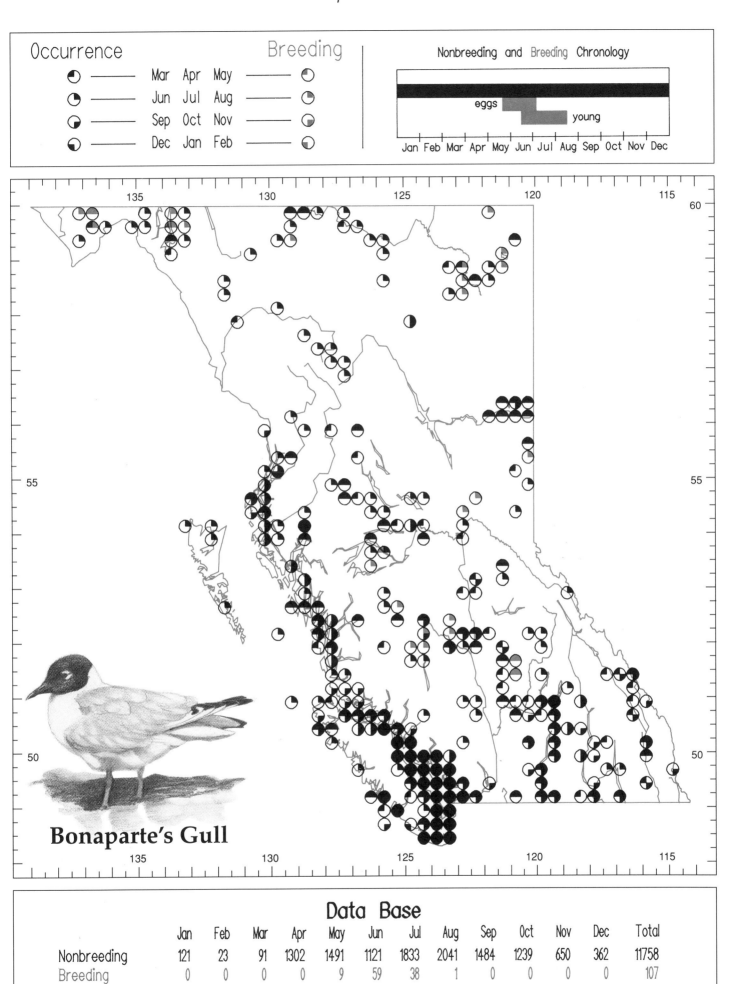

Occurrence

Breeding

	Mar	Apr	May	
Jun	Jul	Aug	
Sep	Oct	Nov	
Dec	Jan	Feb	

Nonbreeding and Breeding Chronology

eggs

young

Jan Feb Mar Apr May Jun Jul Aug Sep Oct Nov Dec

Bonaparte's Gull

Data Base

	Jan	Feb	Mar	Apr	May	Jun	Jul	Aug	Sep	Oct	Nov	Dec	Total
Nonbreeding	121	23	91	1302	1491	1121	1833	2041	1484	1239	650	362	11758
Breeding	0	0	0	0	9	59	38	1	0	0	0	0	107

In spring, the Bonaparte's Gull is most numerous on the coast, especially in the vicinity of Pacific herring spawning areas in the Juan de Fuca Strait and Strait of Georgia, where flocks commonly number in the thousands. The northward movement usually begins in late March and early April. Numbers build throughout the month, peak in late April and early May (Fig. 159), and begin to dwindle by mid-May. In late May, nonbreeders begin to appear in numbers. The latter movement carries on into June. Small but variable numbers remain through the summer. The autumn movement (Fig. 160) begins in late July and continues well into November, when spectacular numbers accumulate on the south coast in areas such as Discovery Passage, Active Pass, Haro Strait, and Juan de Fuca Strait. Again, adults (Fig. 161) precede young and subadults (Fig. 162). In winter, flocks of up to 6,000 gulls occur in inner coastal areas of the Strait of Georgia, especially the southern Gulf Islands, and Juan de Fuca Strait. There is a single winter record from the northern mainland coast near Kitimat.

In the interior, spring migrants appear during the third week of April in southern areas and numbers peak there in very late April and early May. In south-central areas (e.g. Williams Lake), migrants appear consistently during the first week of May. In northern areas (e.g. Fort Nelson) migrants appear late in the first week of May and peak during the second and third weeks of May. Nonbreeding birds are widely scattered in summer, and numbers may reach 300 birds locally. Autumn migration is evident after mid-July and continues into early November, although most birds have departed by mid-October. Adults

precede immatures. There is 1 winter record from Sorrento.

During the warm days of summer and early autumn, flocks of hundreds of Bonaparte's Gulls can be seen capturing large flying insects (e.g. termites, field ants) in the air over forests, beaches, and large lakes.

Extreme dates for the interior are 6 April and 17 November. Regional dates are: Fort St. John, 2 May and 31 October; Williams Lake, 29 April and 15 October; Okanagan, 24 April and 11 November.

BREEDING: The Bonaparte's Gull breeds in the interior from Bridge Lake through the Fraser Plateau and Fraser Basin regions, to the southern Peace Lowlands and across far northern British Columbia. There are no records for the north-central interior, but, the inaccessibility of much of the area prevents a clearer picture of the Bonaparte's Gull's breeding distribution there. For Vancouver Island, there is one unconfirmed breeding record: an adult was seen "probably feeding young" at a nest on Pye Lake, 8 July 1977. Nest contents were not actually observed.

The Bonaparte's Gull breeds in the vicinity of lakes, ponds, muskegs, and alpine marshes in coniferous woodland from 305 to 1,318 m elevation. It prefers small wooded islands for nesting (see Fig. 292 in Volume 1 and Fig. 163). It nests singly or in loose colonies. The number of nesting birds in the province is not known. Estimates for several lakes are listed in Table 6. Bridge Lake, in the Cariboo Plateau, is the most accessible breeding locality and accounts for 27% of all the breeding records.

Figure 161. Adult Bonaparte's Gull at Sidney Spit, southern Vancouver Island, 15 August 1982 (Tim Zurowski).

Figure 162. Immature Bonaparte's Gull at Clover Point, Victoria, 11 September 1982 (Tim Zurowski).

TABLE 6.
Bonaparte's Gull: location, history, and size of major breeding concentrations in British Columbia.

Location	First Record	Low Survey Results[1] Year	High Survey Results[1] Year	Recent Survey Results[1] Year	Source[2]
			Site History		
Interior - Colonies > 10 nests or pairs					
Anahim Lake	1973		12 P 1973	1973	1
Kotcho Lake[3]	1982		11 P 1982	1982	2
Stum Lake	1938	15 P 1971	25 P 1938	15 P 1973	1,3,4

[1]   P - pairs.

[2]   1 - British Columbia Nest Records Scheme; 2 - Campbell and McNall 1982; 3 - Ryder 1972; 4 - Ryder 1973.

[3]   On "Big Island" in lake.

Figure 163. *One Island Lake south of Tupper, July 1978 (R. Wayne Campbell). Conifers on islands are preferred nesting sites for Bonaparte's Gulls in British Columbia.*

Nests: Most nests (62%; n=52) were situated on small, forested islands. Others were found on lake margins, alpine ponds, and marshes in fresh water lakes. One nest was located 60 m from water. Ninety-two percent of nests were in trees, including spruces (81%), Douglas-fir (6%) and western hemlock (3%). Nest heights (n=41) ranged from 1.5 to 17 m, with 58% between 4 and 6 m.

Tree nests were positioned on branches up to 2 m from the trunk. Four ground nests were found on top of mounds of marsh vegetation. Nests were composed of small twigs, mosses, lichens, grasses, sedges, and other marsh vegetation. They were loose to compact structures. Three nests ranged from 23 to 33 cm in outside diameter and 8 to 13 cm in height.

Eggs: Dates for 34 clutches ranged from 20 May to 4 July with 53% recorded between 2 and 19 June. Clutch size ranged from 1 to 3 eggs (1E-1, 2E-12, 3E-21), with 62% having 3 eggs. Incubation period is 23 to 24 days (Godfrey 1986).

Young: Dates for 59 broods ranged from 15 June to 2 August, with 54% recorded between 26 June and 12 July. Calculated dates indicate that nestlings could still be found in mid-August. Fledged young were recorded as early as 26 June at Bridge Lake in the Cariboo. Brood size ranged from 1 to 3 young (1Y-6, 2Y-49, 3Y-4), with 83% having 2 young.

REMARKS: The feeding activity of fish-eating birds and their impact on salmonid fry released from a hatchery on eastern Vancouver Island was studied between 1979 and 1981 (Mace 1983). Significant differences were noted between 2 major predators—the Bonaparte's and Glaucous-winged gulls. The migratory Bonaparte's Gull occurred in tight feeding aggregations with peak numbers corresponding closely to fish density, while the resident Glaucous-winged Gull was distributed

in loose flocks and their numbers did not seem to bear any direct relationship to numbers of fishes (Fig. 164). In addition the Bonaparte's Gull only fed below tidal heights of about 3 m while there was no detectable correlation between feeding activities and tidal height in the Glaucous-winged Gull.

In 1980, 8 species of piscivorous birds captured an estimated 300,900 to 354,200 chinook fry which ranged between 10.4 to 12.2% of the total release (Table 7). The most efficient predator was the Bonaparte's Gull which accounted for 8.3 to 9.9% of the total release.

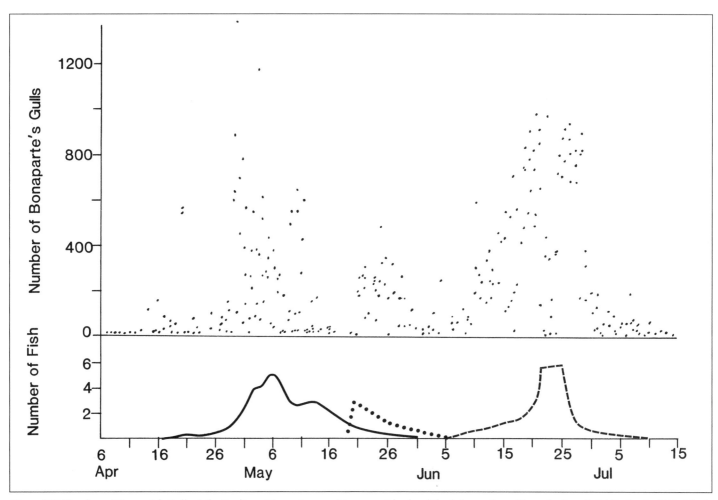

Figure 164. *Numbers of Bonaparte's Gulls at the Qualicum River estuary on Vancouver Island and the daily numbers of juvenile chum (solid line), coho (dotted line), chinook (dashed line), and salmon leaving the hatchery in 1980. Fish numbers have been plotted on different scales: 1 unit on the vertical axis represents 1 million chum fry, 50,000 coho smolts, or 50,000 chinook fingerlings (from Mace 1983).*

TABLE 7.
Estimated number of chinook fry taken by piscivorous birds
in the Qualicum River, Vancouver Island, in 1980
(modified from Mace 1983).

Species	Average	Maximum
Bonaparte's Gull	240,000	289,900
Common Merganser	56,000	56,000
Glaucous-winged Gull	2,600	4,000
Harlequin Duck	1,600	3,000
Pacific Loon	600	1,400
Scoters (3 species)	<50	<50
Total	300,900	354,200
Total as % of release	10.39	12.23

NOTEWORTHY RECORDS

Spring: Coastal - Haro Strait 8 Apr 1978-3,000+, 17 and 18 Apr 1965-3,500+; Active Pass 7 Apr 1984-5,000 most in summer plumage, 26 Apr 1987-7,500, 9 May 1975-4,700; Barkley Sound 3 May 1966-82; Cleland Island 7 May 1982-125; Sea Island 30 Apr 1974-some in summer plumage, 23 May 1975-800 mostly immatures; Comox 20 Apr 1953-1,000 (Flahaut 1953d); Seymour Narrows 13 Apr 1976-1,000; Beaver Cove 3 May 1973-1,000; Namu 9 Apr 1976-200; Lama Passage 7 Apr 1976-800; Kitimat 24 Apr 1975-54. **Interior** - Creston 29 Apr 1956-2; Okanagan Landing 24 Apr 1941-4; Swan Lake (Vernon) 1 May 1979-300; Sorrento 6 Apr 1972-2; Douglas Lake (Quilchena) 5 May 1984-1,000+; Lac la Hache 30 Apr 1943-200, 12 May 1981-400+; Prince George 28 Apr 1982-1; Telkwa 6 Apr 1977-2 adults; Charlie Lake 4 May 1985-17 adults, 14 May 1983-1,000 adults; Parker Lake (Fort Nelson) 1 May 1977-1 adult; Atlin 5 May 1973-1.

Summer: Coastal - Oak Bay 25 Jun 1982-221 mostly immatures, 20 Jul 1958-3,500+; Sarita River 25 Aug 1977-40; Iona Island 28 Jun 1981-1,500, 9 Aug 1981-2,000; Qualicum Beach 2 Jun 1984-20; Comox 10 Jun 1969-325 high count (Crowell and Nehls 1969a); Courtenay 15 Aug 1940-25,000; Oyster Bay mid-Jul 1963-6,000, unprecedented numbers (Boggs and Boggs 1963a); Discovery Passage 10 Jun 1976-1,000+, 25 Aug 1976-10,000+; Kelsey Bay 28 Aug 1965-2,000; Shuttle Island 15 Aug 1979-1 immature; Masset Inlet 10 Jun 1952-10+; nw Graham Island Jun, Jul 1930-present (Cumming 1931); Prince Rupert 9 Aug 1967-2,000; Alice Arm 26 to 28 Aug 1980-100. **Interior** - Penticton 23 Jul 1974-43; 105 Mile House 10 Aug 1968-150; Stum Lake 14 Jun 1973-30, 18 July 1973-800 (Ryder 1973); Charlie Lake 25 Jun 1983-300, 22 Jul 1982-2,400, 21 Aug 1985-1,700; Parker Lake (Fort Nelson) 19 Jul 1985-34; Kotcho Lake 20 Jun 1982-110 (Campbell and McNall 1982); Tagish Lake 15 Jul 1980-47.

Autumn: Interior - Charlie Lake 8 Sep 1984-700, 14 Oct 1979-300+, 30 Oct 1983-1 adult; Drummond Lake 15 Oct 1978-30; Wapta Lake 5 Nov 1976-1 (Wade 1977); Revelstoke 17 Nov 1983-1; Scotch Creek 5 Nov 1962-3; Trout Creek (Summerland) 24 Oct 1950-200+, 11 Nov 1977-1; Sirdar 13 Nov 1947-35 (Munro, J.A. 1958a); Sparwood 7 Nov 1983-2. **Coastal** - Chatham Sound 14 Nov 1975-200+; Masset Inlet 28 Nov 1984-40+; Okeover and Theodosia inlets 12 Nov 1981-3,000; Oyster River 13 Nov 1977-5,000; Qualicum Beach 1 Nov 1977-1,000+; Vancouver 10 Sep 1974-1,300; Blackie Spit 21 Oct 1981-1,500; Tofino 27 Oct 1984-40, 4 Nov 1979-50; Bedwell Sound 18 Oct 1987-650+; Active Pass 2 Sep 1976-6,500, 20 Oct 1976-7,000; Swartz Bay 20 Oct 1976-3,800; Oak Bay 10 Sep 1950-2,000; Trial Island to Race Rocks 28 Oct 1978-10,000, 18 Nov 1979-25,000; Clover Point 9 Nov 1983-20,000.

Winter: Interior - Sorrento 13 Jan 1972-20+. **Coastal** - Greenville 4 to 14 Jan 1982-1; Kitimat 19 Dec 1981-1 adult; Rose Spit 21 Dec 1986-1; Qualicum Beach 13 Dec 1978-340 (Dawe 1980); Tsawwassen 26 Jan 1975-113 off jetty; Active Pass 4 Dec 1976-600; Haro Strait 27 Dec 1978-6,000; Constance Bank 6 Jan 1980-150; Race Rocks 11 Dec 1975-6,000.

Christmas Counts: Interior - Not recorded. **Coastal** - Recorded from 14 of 28 localities and on 33% of all counts. Maxima: Victoria 17 Dec 1977-

Heermann's Gull

HEEG

Larus heermanni Cassin

RANGE: Breeds on islands on the west coast of Mexico. Post-breeding migrant (summer and autumn) along Pacific coast as far north as southern British Columbia. Winters on the Pacific coast from Oregon to Guatemala.

STATUS: *Abundant* to *very abundant* summer and autumn visitant in the vicinity of southwestern and southern Vancouver Island. *Uncommon* to *fairly common* elsewhere in the vicinity of Vancouver Island, including the Fraser River delta. *Very rare* in winter.

OCCURRENCE: The Heermann's Gull occurs in coastal areas surrounding Vancouver Island as well as on the extreme southwest mainland coast north to the Sechelt Peninsula. The area between Clayoquot Sound and Barkley Sound, on the west coast of Vancouver Island, and the extreme southern tip of Vancouver Island are the main centres of abundance. Nearly 72% of all records for the province are from the Greater Victoria area. There are no interior records.

The Heermann's Gull frequents rocky shores (Fig. 165) and bays where offshore islets and kelp beds provide roosting sites. Sand and gravel beaches, sand bars, points and jetties, and log booms are also used for roosting. Salt water lagoons are visited. The Heermann's Gull is also found in offshore waters, usually within 8 km of land. Frequently, small numbers forage in shallower waters farther offshore (e.g. Constance, Swiftsure, and La Perouse banks).

The Heermann's Gull has been recorded in British Columbia from 2 May to 2 January. Early spring migrants first appear in May and June. By the middle of July, flocks of over 100 birds can be found. Peak numbers of up to 600 birds are reached in mid-October, after which numbers decrease rapidly. In some years, a few linger into December and early January.

The ratio of adults to immature plumaged birds (n=8,830) for the period May through November was 91:9. The monthly breakdown in percentage was: May, 100:0 (n=5); June, 97:3 (n=226); July, 94:6, (n=2,764); August, 81:19 (n=1,230); September, 87:13 (n=2,060); October 96:4 (n=2,242); November, 94:6 (n=303). Adults appear to arrive first, mostly from late June through early August, followed by immatures from late August through September. These periods of occurrence need to be better defined (see Tatum 1973).

Although roosting flocks of up to 600 birds have been reported, the Heermann's Gull is not often seen flying in flocks of larger than 40 individuals. In late afternoon and early evening, flights to night roosts are evident from headlands in the Victoria area.

REMARKS: The various plumages of the Heermann's Gull are distinctive at all ages (Harrison, P. 1983) although Hubbs and Bartholomew (1951) report the persistence of a rare colour aberration in the species. Observers are encouraged to record plumages to help determine if waves of different age-classes arrive in British Columbia at different times.

Figure 165. Heermann's Gulls in Barkley Sound, Vancouver Island, 7 September 1980 (Ervio Sian).

NOTEWORTHY RECORDS

Spring: Coastal - Rocky Point (Sooke) 8 Mar 1986-1 in second winter plumage; Clover Point 2 May 1979-1 adult; Oak Bay 30 May 1963-2; West Vancouver 4 May 1975-1 adult. **Interior** - No records.

Summer: Coastal - Trial Island 30 Jul 1976-77; Clover Point 31 Aug 1982-67; Oak Bay 27 Jun 1953-30; Cordova Spit 18 Jul 1975-127; Florencia Islet 11 Jul 1975-10 adults; Sanford Island 25 Aug 1969-150; Gowlland Rocks 13 Jul 1976-20; Wickaninnish Island 1 Aug 1976-150+; Monks Islet 10 Jul 1987-120 adults and immatures; Cleland Island 1 Jun 1976-1, 31 Aug 1969-35; Plover Reefs 24 Jul 1967-100 (Campbell and Stirling 1968b); Hot Springs Cove 22 Jul 1987-20; between Vancouver and Nanaimo 10 Aug 1955-1 (Mills 1960b); Mud Bay (Rosewall Creek) 30 Aug 1962-1; Nootka Island 18 Aug 1972-4 immatures (Bell 1973); Kyuquot Sound 15 Jul 1957-1; Alert Bay 13 to 15 Aug 1917-5 (NMC 10921, 10924-26, 10932; Taverner 1918). **Interior** - No records.

Autumn: Interior - No records. **Coastal** - Cape Calvert 15 Oct 1979-38; Campbell River (Discovery Passage) 30 Sep 1967-1; La Perouse Bank 2 Sep 1984-6 immatures; Stubbs Island (Tofino) 9 Sep 1987-200; Chesterman Beach 26 Sep 1983-150; Wickaninnish Bay 8 to 10 Oct 1983-80, 10 Nov 1983-1 adult; Cape Beale 25 Sep 1976-56; Beach Grove 30 Sep 1973-4; Tsawwassen 11 Nov 1964-12; Mandarte Island 2 Oct 1982-600; Cordova Spit 8 Sep 1984-100; Victoria 16 Sep 1972-180 along waterfront (Tatum 1973); Oak Bay 6 Oct 1982-120, 15 Oct 1982-500; Constance Bank 29 Oct 1980-300; Race Rocks 25 Oct 1980-300, 27 Oct 1984-200, 29 Oct 1983-150, 23 Nov 1974-1.

Winter: Interior - No records. **Coastal** - Howe Sound 18 Dec 1982-1 (Campbell 1983a); Tsawwassen 2 Jan 1969-1 adult (Crowell and Nehls 1969a); Active Pass 3 Dec 1983-2; Oak Bay 12 to 17 Dec 1977-1 adult at marina; Clover Point 4 Dec 1975-1 adult.

Christmas Counts: Interior - Not recorded. **Coastal** - Recorded from 3 of 28 localities and on 1% of all counts. Maxima: Victoria 27 Dec 1964-**1** and 27 Dec 1970-**1**; Duncan 27 Dec 1970-**1**; Sunshine Coast 18 Dec 1982-**1**. The single birds reported in 1964 and 1970, although listed by Anderson, R.R. (1976) as a year later, are, along with 1982 count, all-time Canadian highs. Records from 2 additional counts are considered hypothetical because they lack supporting documentation: New Westminster 26 Dec 1949-10 (unofficial count; Maguire 1950) and Pender Islands 19 Dec 1982-1 (McLardy 1983).

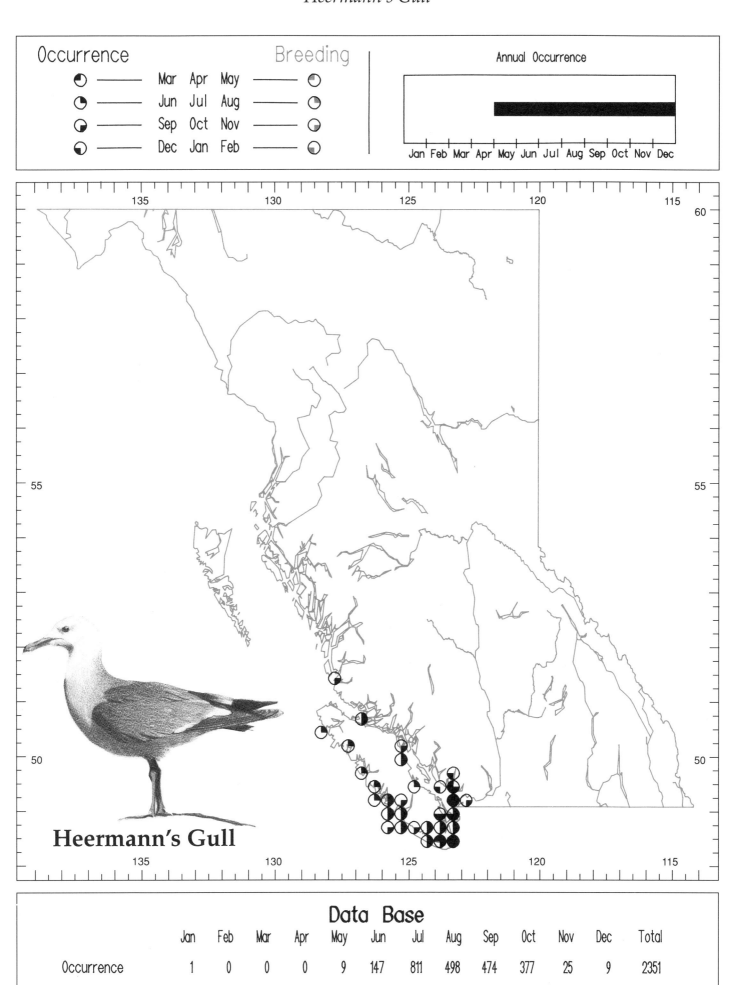

Heermann's Gull

	Jan	Feb	Mar	Apr	May	Jun	Jul	Aug	Sep	Oct	Nov	Dec	Total
Data Base													
Occurrence	1	0	0	0	9	147	811	498	474	377	25	9	2351

Mew Gull

Larus canus Linnaeus

MEGU

RANGE: Breeds from central and southern Alaska and northwestern Canada south to northern and coastal British Columbia and east to northern Saskatchewan. Winters along the coast from southeastern Alaska south to Baja California. Also occurs in Eurasia.

STATUS: *Abundant* to *very abundant* spring and autumn migrant on the coast. In winter, *very abundant* on the southwest mainland coast, *common* to *very common* on the northern mainland coast and the Queen Charlotte Islands. *Uncommon* to *common* summer visitant along the coast. In the southern interior, *rare* spring and autumn transient, *very rare* summer and winter visitant. In the northern interior, *very common* spring and autumn migrant, and *uncommon* summer visitant. Breeds.

NONBREEDING: The Mew Gull is widely distributed along coastal British Columbia. It has a widespread but sparse distribution throughout the interior. Along the coast, it frequents a variety of habitats including bays, estuaries, surge narrows, beaches, mudflats, harbours, and sewage outlets, and follows inlets and rivers up to 150 km inland. The Mew Gull regularly joins other gulls at abundant food sources such as Pacific herring and salmon spawning areas and along lines of tide convergence. During migration and winter, tens of thousands of birds are found in fields throughout the lower Fraser River valley, and are frequently seen in cultivated lands following ploughs. The Mew Gull is seldom found offshore. In the interior, it frequents rivers, sand bars, lakes, garbage dumps, sewage ponds, and marshes. It has been found from sea level to 1,280 m elevation.

On the coast, spring migration occurs from early March through mid-May. Peak numbers in the Fraser River delta were reported in early May. Early autumn migrants appear in August; numbers build up until winter maxima are reached about early December. The Strait of Georgia is the main wintering area; Victoria and the Fraser River delta support the largest concentrations.

In the northern interior, migrants and breeding birds first arrive in late April and early May; most depart in August and by early September few remain. Extreme dates in the northeast are 29 April and 12 October (Fort St. John); in the northwest they are 3 May and 14 September (Atlin). In the southern interior, spring migrants occur mostly in May, autumn migrants in August and early September. Small numbers are found some winters. Extreme dates there are 25 March (Summerland) and 8 January (Vernon).

BREEDING: The Mew Gull breeds throughout Vancouver Island, along the mainland coast west of the Coast Mountains from Harrison Lake to Prince Rupert, and in the interior generally across the province north of 57°N latitude. It nests singly or in small colonies (Table 8). Along the coast, nest sites are associated with freshwater lakes (Fig. 167) where bare or treed rocky islets, large boulders, and, occasionally, fallen trees and stumps provide nesting sites. In the interior, the Mew Gull nests in marshy areas, shallow lakes, on beaches, ponds, and other wetlands where tussocks, hummocks, and islands are evident. Occasionally, sites are shared with other larids including Herring and Bonaparte's gulls (see Fig. 292 in Volume 1). Nesting sites have been found from 15 to 1,158 m elevation.

Figure 166. Adult Mew Gull at nest, Kennedy Lake, Vancouver Island, June 1969 (R. Wayne Campbell).

Mew Gull

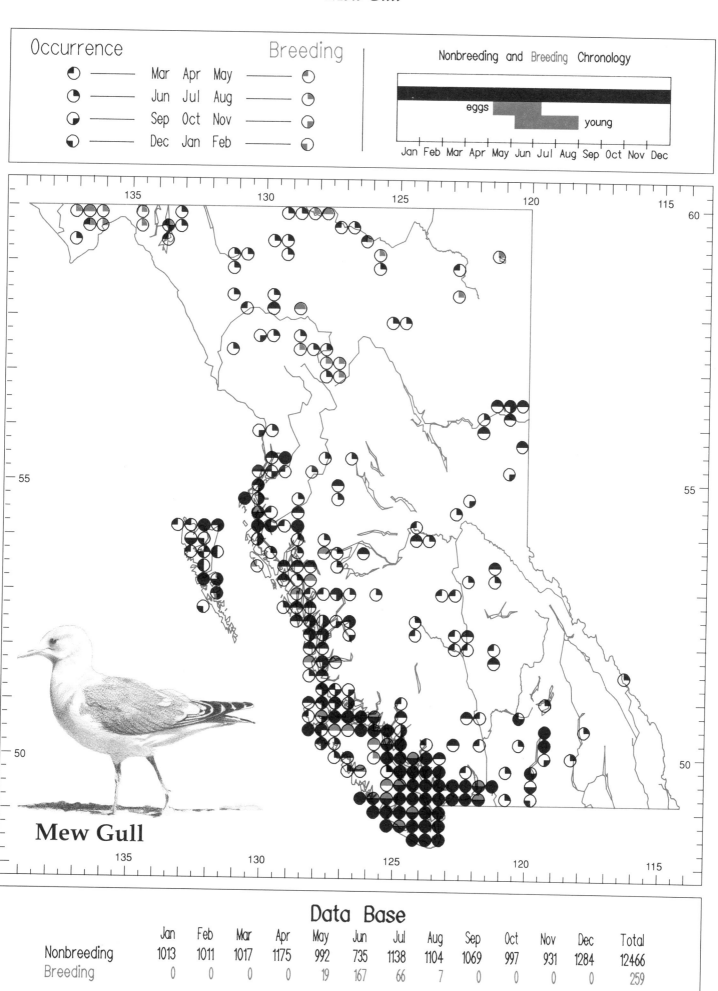

Occurrence

| Mar Apr May |
| Jun Jul Aug |
| Sep Oct Nov |
| Dec Jan Feb |

Breeding

Nonbreeding and Breeding Chronology

eggs

young

Jan Feb Mar Apr May Jun Jul Aug Sep Oct Nov Dec

Mew Gull

Data Base

	Jan	Feb	Mar	Apr	May	Jun	Jul	Aug	Sep	Oct	Nov	Dec	Total
Nonbreeding	1013	1011	1017	1175	992	735	1138	1104	1069	997	931	1284	12466
Breeding	0	0	0	0	19	167	66	7	0	0	0	0	259

Nests: Nests (n=152) were situated on bare rock (50%; Fig. 166), hummocks/tussocks (23%), living trees (13%), bare ground (6%), fallen trees/stumps (4%), and river pilings (4%). Some eggs were simply laid on sphagnum with no materials while others were laid in more typical nests constructed mainly of grasses, twigs, rootlets, and sticks (66% of all nests). Other materials included mosses, sedges, lichens, conifer cones, bark, and leaves. See Fig. 168 for a comparison of typical coastal and northwestern interior nests. Outside diameters of 37 nests ranged from 36 to 56 cm; inside diameters ranged from 22 to 29 cm; inside depths ranged from 9 to 19 cm; heights ranged from 16 to 24 cm.

Eggs: Dates for 161 clutches ranged from 8 May (Cowichan Lake) to 12 July (Chilkat Pass), with 52% recorded between 5 and 20 June. Clutch size ranged from 1 to 5 eggs (1E-10, 2E-39, 3E-108, 4E-2, 5E-2), with 67% having 3 eggs. Incubation period in British Columbia averages 25 days (Vermeer and Devito 1986).

Young: Dates for 89 broods ranged from 10 June to 31 August, with 56% recorded between 21 June and 12 July. Calculated dates indicate that young could be found by the first week of June. Brood size ranged from 1 to 3 young (1Y-19, 2Y-49, 3Y-21), with 55% having 2 young. Fledging period in British Columbia is 30 to 32 days (Vermeer and Devito 1986).

REMARKS: Previously known as Short-billed Gull in North America; also as Common Gull in Old World.

TABLE 8.
Mew Gull: location, history, and size of major colonies in British Columbia.

| Location | Colony History | | | | |
	First Record	Low Survey Results[1] Year	High Survey Results[1] Year	Recent Survey Results[1] Year	Source[2]
Coastal - Colonies > 10 nests or pairs					
Kennedy Lake	1960	14 N 1960	32 Nc 1969	27 Ac 1985	1,2
Interior - Colonies > 5 nests or pairs					
Kotcho Lake	1982		8 Ac 1982	1982	3
Mile 71 Haines Road (Chilkat Pass)	1980		10 Ac 1980	1980	4

[1] A - active nests; N - nests. All data are estimates unless noted as follows: c - complete count.

[2] 1 - Campbell 1970d; 2 - Vermeer and Devito 1986; 3 - Campbell and McNall 1982; 4 - British Columbia Nest Records Scheme.

Figure 167. Site of Mew Gull nesting colony in Kennedy Lake, July 1968 (R. Wayne Campbell).

Figure 168. *Comparison of nest structure and materials for Mew Gull nests on the coast and in the Tatshenshini Basin: nest and eggs at Kennedy Lake (left), 26 June 1968 (R. Wayne Campbell), and nest with egg and young at Shini Lakes (Alsek River), June 1983 (John M. Cooper).*

NOTEWORTHY RECORDS

Spring: Coastal - Clover Point 2 Mar 1976-2,500; Cape Beale 16 Apr 1972-150+; Active Pass 14 Mar 1975-1,600; Delta 28 Mar 1976-2,500, 3 May 1980-5,000; Langley 29 Apr 1977-2,500+; Pitt Lake 1 hr counts of migrants 27 Apr 1976-1,300, 1 May 1976-2,000, 5 May 1976-8,630, 6 May 1976-4,000; Agassiz 8 Apr 1976-3,500; Qualicum 23 Mar 1976-4,000 on herring spawn (Dawe 1980); Comox 31 May 1969-150; Kimsquit River 11 and 12 Apr 1985-500+ feeding on eulachons; Skidegate Inlet 16 Apr 1972-40; Kitimat 4 Mar 1975-415, 24 Apr 1975-1,700; Skeena River 20 Mar 1983-thousands feeding on eulachons between Khyex River and Kasiks River; Prince Rupert 1 Apr 1976-500. **Interior** - Summerland 25 Mar 1977-1 adult (RBCM Photo 496); Okanagan Landing 2 May 1944-3 (MVZ 89864, 101236); Tranquille 10 May 1983-20 adults (Rogers, T.H. 1983c); 105 Mile Lake 11 May 1939-48; Riske Creek 5 May 1978-5 adults; Toboggan Lake 6 May 1980-3; n Fort St. John 29 Apr 1979-8 adults; Charlie Lake 4 May 1983-51; Fort Nelson 3 May 1986-2 adults; Atlin 3 May 1981-1 adult.

Summer: Coastal - Whiffin Spit 5 Aug 1983-250; Gotha Point 6 Jun 1984-40 immatures; Sarita Bay Aug 1976-291; White Rock (Surrey) 25 Aug 1976-1,500; Sea Island 27 Jun 1974-40; Vedder Canal 24 Aug 1982-450; Comox 20 Jun 1978-500; Alert Bay 9 Aug 1973-600; Grenville Channel 27 Jul 1966-300+; Skidegate Inlet 17 Jul 1977-3; Kitimat 2 Jul 1975-167; Prince Rupert 14 Jul 1966-350 in harbour, 8 Aug 1969-1,300 (peak count - Crowell and Nehls 1969c). **Interior** - Okanagan Landing 13 Aug 1944-1 immature; Nakusp 29 Jul 1978-9; Anderson Lake (D'Arcy) 27 Aug 1968-120; Field 14 Jul 1976-2 (Wade 1977); Charlie Lake 23 Jul 1982-35; Bear Flat 26 Jul 1985-30; Tatshenshini River 8 Jun 1983-16 migrating.

Autumn: Interior - Atlin 14 Sep 1972-2; Charlie Lake 12 Oct 1985-1 adult; Kamloops 9 Nov 1980-1 immature. **Coastal** - Prince Rupert 29 Sep 1966-500; Kitimat 1 Oct 1974-320, 13 Nov 1974-163; Bella Coola 7 Nov 1979-50; Quadra Island 17 Nov 1973-500+; Comox 2 Oct 1974-162; Steveston 28 Sep 1963-1,000; Sea Island 31 Oct 1973-1,000; Boundary Bay 12 Nov 1962-2,000+; Tofino 3 Sep 1974-150 in harbour; Clover Point 19 Sep 1974-1,500, 29 Oct 1984-2,000+, 6 Nov 1976-2,000; Finlayson Point to Trial Island 9 Nov 1983-30,000 estimated feeding along 3 km tide line.

Winter: Interior - Kamloops 21 Dec 1974-1 adult; Vernon 8 Jan 1984-2; Okanagan Landing 11 Dec 1913-1 immature. **Coastal** - Green Island 2 Dec 1977-100+; Prince Rupert 6 Jan 1983-350; Masset 26 Dec 1972-110; Kitimat 22 Dec 1974-188; Quatsino Sound 14 to 16 Feb 1973-962; Campbell River (Discovery Passage) 10 Dec 1952-1,000 passed over in less than an hour (Flahaut 1953b); Powell River 12 Jan 1982-800; Nanoose Harbour 10 Feb 1977-255 (largest count from 1974 to 1979 - Dawe and Lang 1980); Clayoquot Sound 11 to 13 Dec 1972-804; Pachena Bay 14 Jan 1976-300; Agassiz 24 Feb 1977-600; Sea Island 12 Jan 1966-7,000 on airport fields; Delta 1 Dec 1973-6,000+; Active Pass 9 Feb 1975-1,800 (Rodway and Campbell 1977); Macaulay Point 3 Dec 1983-3,000.

Christmas Counts: Interior - Recorded from 3 of 19 localities and on 4% of all counts. Maxima: Vernon 18 Dec 1983-2; Penticton 26 Dec 1974-1; Oliver/Osoyoos 28 Dec 1981-1. **Coastal** - Recorded from 25 of 28 localities and on 89% of all counts. Maxima: Victoria 21 Dec 1974-**16,375**, all-time Canadian high count (Anderson, R.R. 1976); Vancouver 26 Dec 1960-9,741; Ladner 23 Dec 1972-7,243.

Ring-billed Gull
Larus delawarensis Ord

RANGE: Breeds in western North America from central and southern interior British Columbia (locally) and southern Canada south to northeastern California, southeastern Wyoming, and northeastern South Dakota; and in eastern North America from southern Ontario, southern Quebec, and northeastern Newfoundland south to central Michigan, northeastern Illinois, northern Minnesota and Wisconsin, and New England. Winters from southern British Columbia south along the Pacific coast to southern Mexico and in the interior from the Great Lakes and Maine south to Mexico and Cuba.

STATUS: On the south coast, *fairly common* to *common* spring migrant, *very common* to *abundant* in summer; *abundant* to *very abundant* autumn migrant and *uncommon* in winter. *Uncommon* on the west coast of Vancouver Island and on the north coast. *Fairly common* to *common* resident in the southern interior, *abundant* autumn migrant. *Rare* summer visitant in the northern interior. Local breeder.

CHANGE IN STATUS: In the mid-1940s the Ring-billed Gull was considered a transient in the interior and uncommon on the south coast (Munro, J.A. and Cowan 1947). There were no breeding records, but a few individuals were reported to summer in the southern interior. In the mid-1950s the status was essentially the same (Guiguet 1957), but a decade later the species was "locally abundant, seasonally" in the Fraser Lowlands (Edwards 1968). Numbers also increased in the central-southern interior about this time. R.A. Cannings et al. (1987) attribute the change to "rapid

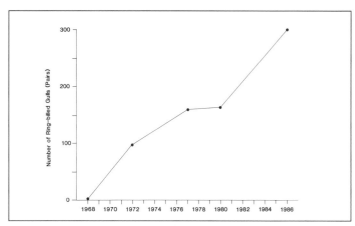

Figure 169. Population increase in Ring-billed Gulls breeding on Grant (Whiskey) Island, Okanagan Lake, 1968 to 1986.

growth of the human population . . . and the concomitant increase in garbage dumps and beach and playground refuse." In addition, the continental population was increasing rapidly, expanding its range and numbers during the 1960s (Godfrey 1986). Breeding was first documented in 1968 on Whiskey Island in Okanagan Lake. In 1985, a second colony was found at Ellis Island on Fraser Lake, 610 km to the northeast. According to local residents, the Ellis Island colony did not exist in 1984. The Ring-

Figure 170. Whiskey Island, 12 June 1978 (R. Wayne Campbell). This island has recently been officially renamed Grant Island in memory of James Grant, an Okanagan naturalist.

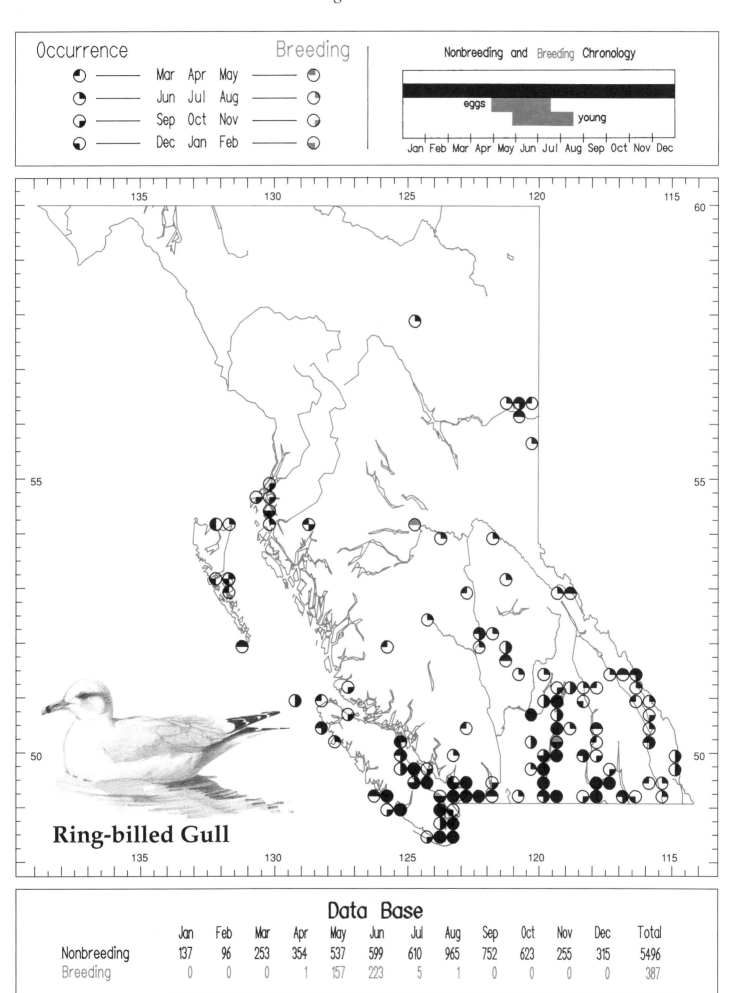

Occurrence

	Mar Apr May	
Jun Jul Aug	
Sep Oct Nov	
Dec Jan Feb	

Breeding

Nonbreeding and Breeding Chronology

eggs

young

Jan Feb Mar Apr May Jun Jul Aug Sep Oct Nov Dec

Ring-billed Gull

Data Base

	Jan	Feb	Mar	Apr	May	Jun	Jul	Aug	Sep	Oct	Nov	Dec	Total
Nonbreeding	137	96	253	354	537	599	610	965	752	623	255	315	5496
Breeding	0	0	0	1	157	223	5	1	0	0	0	0	387

billed Gull is still expanding its range and increasing its numbers throughout the southern half of the province.

NONBREEDING: On the coast, the Ring-billed Gull is widely distributed in the Fraser Lowlands, the Strait of Georgia, and Juan de Fuca Strait. It occurs locally on the central west coast of Vancouver Island and is scattered in small numbers north of Vancouver Island including the Queen Charlotte Islands. Largest numbers occur on the Fraser River delta. In the interior, it is widely distributed, generally south of 52°N latitude, from the Okanagan valley to the east Kootenay. Elsewhere, it is local. It has been recorded from sea level to 1,550 m elevation.

Preferred habitats on the coast include bays, lagoons, estuaries, freshwater and brackish lakes, large rivers, beaches, agricultural fields, garbage dumps, municipal parks, and golf courses. The Ring-billed Gull is rarely found on the open ocean. Similar habitats are used in the interior, although beaches and man-made grassy areas are preferred. It is frequently seen following agricultural machinery. In winter, garbage dumps are especially important.

Since the Ring-billed Gull has only recently expanded its range into British Columbia, seasonal occurrence and numbers, especially as they relate to age classes, are not well known. Generally, it is far less numerous in spring than in autumn migration. The buildup of summering and wintering populations further confuses arrival and departure dates.

On the south coast, spring migrants have been reported from early March through late May with the peak movement occurring in April. Autumn migration can begin in early June and continue into October. There appears to be two peak movements, one in July and another in September, which may represent different age-classes. Small numbers, usually in groups of less than 10 birds, winter on inner coastal sites and occasionally along outer or northern coastal areas.

In the southern interior, spring migrants arrive in late February or early March, but the main movement occurs from late March through April. By early May, the northward movement is "virtually complete" (Cannings, R.A. et al. 1987). The autumn passage begins from mid-July to early August, although there are reports of flocks containing more than 100 birds in late June. This movement continues through September and peaks between late September and mid-October. The main interior wintering area is in the vicinity of Kelowna.

In the Peace River area, spring migrants arrive in late April and early May. Most have departed by early September. The latest departure date from Fort St. John was 13 October.

BREEDING: The Ring-billed Gull breeds at 2 widely separated sites in British Columbia. The largest and oldest colony is on Whiskey Island in Okanagan Lake in the Okanagan valley (Fig. 170); the other is on Ellis Island in Fraser Lake in the Bulkley Basin (Fig. 171).

Whiskey Island is small (40 x 10 m) and only 4 m high with 10 or so ponderosa pines. The site is shared with a few pairs of nesting California and Herring gulls. Since its discovery in 1968 the colony has increased about 16 pairs per year and nearly doubled in size during the periods 1972 to 1977 and 1979 to 1986 (Fig. 169). It has probably reached its maximum size.

Ellis Island is a medium-sized rocky island with aspens and shrubs along its shores. In 1985, nests were restricted to a 5 x 6 m site on a low, rocky outcropping on the southwest tip of the island. Egg-laying was complete and incubation had begun (Campbell 1985e). The site was shared with 14 pairs of Herring Gulls.

In 1986 the total breeding population in the province was estimated at between 300 and 350 pairs (Table 9).

Nests: Nests were built on bare rock or soil, against a rock face, among driftwood, or at the base of a shrub or tree. On Whiskey Island, several clutches were laid in abandoned Canada

Figure 171. *Ellis Island in Fraser Lake (Fraser Lake), a nesting site for Ring-billed and Herring gulls, 5 June 1977 (R. Wayne Campbell).*

Goose nests and several birds did not build any nest at all. Nests were usually small mounds composed of grasses, reeds, bits of driftwood, pine needles, dried bulrush, feathers, plant stalks, and rootlets. They were usually lined with grasses, mosses, weeds, and bark strips. Dimensions were highly variable.

Eggs: Dates for 375 clutches ranged from 23 May to 5 July. Most egg laying occurred in May, but a pipped egg found on 23 May indicates that eggs could be found as early the last week of April (Cannings, R.A. et al. 1987). An incubated clutch found on 5 July, was probably a replacement clutch and indicates that viable eggs could be found in mid-July. Clutch size ranged from 1 to 6 eggs (1E-35, 2E-88, 3E-192, 4E-30, 5E-21, 6E-9) with 51% having 3 eggs. The high proportion of very large clutches (4 to 6 eggs) is considered characteristic of young colonies. Incubation period is 25 days (Vermeer 1970).

Young: Only 11 distinct broods have been recorded; most counts involved grouped and mobile young. Brood dates ranged from 11 June to 5 July but a pipped egg found on 23 May indicates that some hatch by at least 25 May. R.A. Cannings et al. (1987) estimate the earliest date for flying young at 29 June and flightless young have been seen on Whiskey Island in mid-August. Broods ranged from 1 to 3 young (1Y-5,2Y-5,3Y-1). Fledging period averages 37.2 days (Vermeer 1970).

REMARKS: See Blokpoel et al. (1985) for a discussion of plumage characteristics of nesting Ring-billed Gulls of different ages. Lauro and Spencer (1980) provide helpful suggestions for separating plumages of juvenile and first-winter Ring-billed Gulls and Mew Gulls.

TABLE 9.
Ring-billed Gull: location, history, and size of major colonies in British Columbia.

Location	First Record	Low Survey Results[1] Year	High Survey Results[1] Year	Recent Survey Results[1] Year	Source[2]
Interior - All colonies					
Whiskey Island	1968	3 P 1968	163 Nc 1978	300 P 1986	1,2,3
Ellis Island	1985		24 Nc 1985	1985	4

[1] N - nests; P - pairs. All data are estimates unless noted as follows: c - complete count.

[2] 1 - Merilees 1974a; 2 - Campbell 1978b; 3 - Cannings, R.A. et al. 1987; 4 - Campbell 1985e.

NOTEWORTHY RECORDS

Spring: Coastal - Victoria 28 Apr 1950-4; Faber Islets 10 May 1972-4 (RBCM Photo 291); Roberts Bank 25 May 1980-40; Delta 8 Mar 1975-60 mostly adults; Cape Scott 15 Apr 1980-3; Cape St. James 2 Apr 1982-3; Skedans Islands 26 Apr 1983-1 adult; Masset 8 May 1938-1 collected; Kitimat 27 Apr 1975-1 adult. **Interior** - Osoyoos Lake 31 Mar 1978-6 adults, 11 Apr 1978-30; Creston 18 Mar 1972-44, 20 Apr 1986-50+; Kelowna 7 Apr 1978-159 adults, 9 May 1981-200; Vernon 24 Mar 1984-30+; Columbia Lake 5 May 1945-6 (Johnstone, W.B. 1949); Kamloops 2 Mar 1986-3; Williams Lake 30 Apr 1984-2 adults; Moose Lake (Mount Robson Park) 29 May 1972-8; Cecil Lake 24 Apr 1986-1 adult.

Summer: Coastal - Cowichan Bay 11 Jun 1983-9, 23 Jul 1984-48 (45 adults, 3 immature); Seabird Rocks 24 Jul 1972-6+ (Hatler et al. 1978); Boundary Bay 22 Jul 1981-500, 10 Aug 1973-500; Sea Island 7 Jun 1986-500; Comox 21 Jun 1953-40; Cape St. James 14 Jun 1982-6; Sandspit 7 Aug

1957-2 (Mills 1960a); Rose Spit 2 Jul 1983-4; Port Edward 27 Aug 1979-1 adult. **Interior** - Manning Park 2 Jul 1971-4; Osoyoos Lake 29 Jun 1969-75, 15 Aug 1971-100+; Creston 29 Jun 1980-61, 11 Aug 1948-148; Penticton to Summerland 23 Jul 1974-130, 20 Aug 1974-148 (Cannings, S.G. 1974); Trout Creek (Summerland) 25 Jun 1983-100+; Fairmont 24 Aug 1976-50; Salmon Arm 30 Jul 1973-50, 20 Aug 1973-600; 150 Mile House 10 Jun 1983-5; Fort St. John 24 Jun 1985-9 immatures; Fern Lake (Kwadacha Wilderness Park) 16 Aug 1983-1 adult (Cooper, J.M. and Cooper 1983).

Autumn: Interior - Fort St. John 13 Oct 1985-1 immature; Williams Lake 24 Oct 1978-1; Salmon Arm 8 Sep 1985-200+, 14 Oct 1982-500; Swan Lake (Vernon) 29 Nov 1977-17; Winfield 30 Sep 1973-125; Alki Lake 30 Sep 1973-1,201; Nelson 9 Oct 1968-218; Penticton 21 Nov 1979-200; Creston 14 Sep 1985-500; Oliver 6 Sep 1980-150. **Coastal** - Tracy Island 15 Sep 1966-1; Agamemnon Channel 3 Oct 1974-10; Stubbs Island 7 Nov 1987-11 adults

with 200 California Gulls; Burnaby Lake 7 Oct 1971-43; Delta 12 Oct 1974-90; Ladner 21 Sep 1981 -1,500 mostly adults; Westham Island 8 Sep 1974-550; Crescent Beach 5 Nov 1951-25; Tofino 3 Sep 1974-3; Clover Point 19 Sep 1974-200.

Winter: Interior - Kamloops 28 Dec 1986-37, a rare occurrence; Kelowna 19 Dec 1987-355; Nelson 19 Jan 1969-26; Penticton 17 Dec 1974-100, 19 Jan 1976-70+; Vaseux Lake 8 Dec 1973-55, 22 Feb 1974-1; Trail 29 Dec 1979-1. **Coastal** - Masset 12 Dec 1982-1; Skidegate Inlet 19 Dec 1982-1; Chilliwack 28 Dec 1982-1 immature; Westham Island 18 Dec 1970-3; White Rock 28 Jan 1968-4.

Christmas Counts: Interior - Recorded from 7 of 19 localities and on 33% of all counts. Maxima: Kelowna 20 Dec 1981-195; Penticton 27 Dec 1981-106; Vernon 19 Dec 1983-26. **Coastal** - Recorded from 16 of 28 localities and on 35% of all counts. Maxima: White Rock 4 Jan 1981-254; Vancouver 30 Dec 1967-210; Ladner 14 Dec 1974-178.

California Gull

Larus californicus Lawrence

CAGU

RANGE: Breeds from southern Mackenzie through the prairie provinces and locally in central southern British Columbia to Washington, southeastern Oregon, east-central California, northern Utah, central Montana, and central North Dakota. Winters from southern British Columbia south along the Pacific coast to Mexico.

STATUS: On the coast, a *very common* to *abundant* spring migrant on the mainland and Vancouver Island; *casual* on the Queen Charlotte Islands. In summer, *common* on the south coast, *rare* on the north coast, and *very rare* on the Queen Charlotte Islands. *Very abundant* autumn migrant on the south coast; *common* to *very common* on the north coast including the Queen Charlotte Islands. *Uncommon* to *fairly common* in winter on the south coast including Vancouver Island.

In the interior, *fairly common* to *common* spring migrant in southern areas; *rare* north of the Okanagan valley. *Uncommon* in summer away from Okanagan Lake. *Very common* to *abundant* autumn migrant in the southern third of the province; *rare* elsewhere. *Rare* to *uncommon* in winter in the Okanagan valley and locally in the west Kootenay. Local breeder.

Figure 172. Adult California Gull at the Delta garbage dump, April 1974 (Ervio Sian).

Figure 173. Immature California Gulls at Long Beach, west coast of Vancouver Island, 26 August 1968 (R. Wayne Campbell).

California Gull

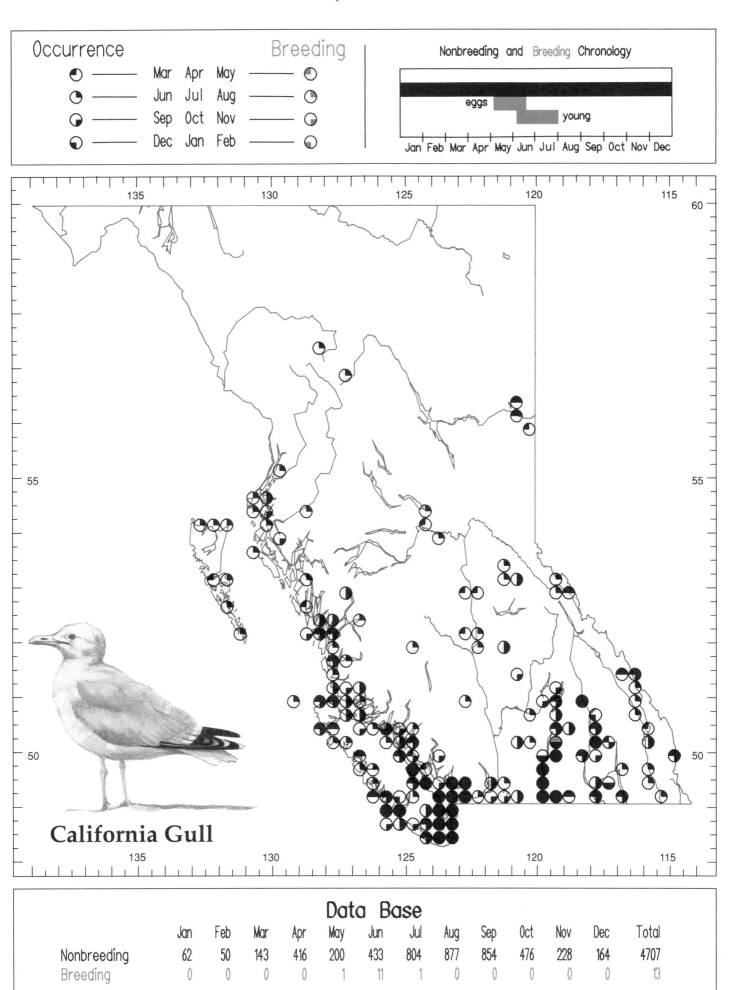

Mar Apr May
Jun Jul Aug
Sep Oct Nov
Dec Jan Feb

Nonbreeding and Breeding Chronology

eggs   young

Jan Feb Mar Apr May Jun Jul Aug Sep Oct Nov Dec

California Gull

Data Base

	Jan	Feb	Mar	Apr	May	Jun	Jul	Aug	Sep	Oct	Nov	Dec	Total
Nonbreeding	62	50	143	416	200	433	804	877	854	476	228	164	4707
Breeding	0	0	0	0	1	11	1	0	0	0	0	0	13

CHANGE IN STATUS: J.A. Munro and Cowan (1947) consider the California Gull a "transient, in small numbers, on the southern coast and in the interior." Its status remained unchanged until the early and mid-1960s when numbers and frequency of occurrence increased on the south coast (Oldaker 1961, 1963b) and in the Okanagan valley (Cannings, R.A. et al. 1987). Historically, expanding colonies on the prairies may have contributed to this change, but the increased availability of garbage from a larger human population may have also played a role. Appropriately, the bird's status was monitored at various garbage dumps in the Vancouver area by R.F. Oldaker who read leg bands through a telescope (Oldaker 1960; Houston 1963). He found that the California Gulls there originated from Saskatchewan, Alberta, North Dakota, Montana, Wyoming, Idaho, California, Oregon, and Washington (Fig. 174). By the mid-1970s Houston (1977) reported that since "virtually all California Gulls of Saskatch-ewan origin apparently pass through British Columbia, it is not surprising that a high percentage of young-of-the-year at Vancouver in the first fall migration were from Saskatchewan." Hatler et al. (1978) reported that the west coast of Vancouver Island was an important late summer/early autumn staging area for the California Gull and groups of up to 5,000 were not uncommon at the mouths of coastal rivers.

On 29 May 1972, Merilees (1974a) found the first nest for the province in a colony of Ring-billed Gulls on Okanagan Lake. Two more nests were found on 12 June 1978 (Campbell 1978b). By 1985 the population was estimated at 10 pairs and in 1986 it had increased to 17 pairs.

NONBREEDING: The California Gull (Fig. 172) occurs primarily as a spring and autumn transient in the central southern interior and the vicinity of Vancouver Island. Occurrence elsewhere probably represents wanderers from the main movement to and from the breedingcolonies in the interior of the continent.

It occurs widely on the coast, frequenting beaches (Fig. 173), bays, estuaries, lagoons, agricultural fields, airports, garbage dumps, sewage outlets, and, less often, brackish sloughs and freshwater lakes. It also frequents the open ocean. In autumn, the California Gull is the most abundant gull off the British Columbia coast, a situation similar to that reported by Wahl (1975) for Washington.

In the interior, the California Gull uses lakes, rivers, river bars, beaches, lake shores, agricultural fields, and garbage dumps.

Recently, spring movements have been obscured by increasing numbers of overwintering birds. Migration on the coast appears to begin in mid-March and continues into early May. The peak movement is in the first half of April. Flocks of over 300 have been found on the west coast of Vancouver Island in June, suggesting that at least some subadults may not migrate to the breeding colonies until they are older. In summer, only small numbers remain in inner coastal areas.

The autumn movement begins in the second week of July (Oldaker 1960) and increases during August. On the west coast of Vancouver Island, large groups are unusual after mid-September in most years (Hatler et al. 1978), but on the Fraser River delta, hundreds are still present in late October. Small numbers winter on both the west and the east coasts of southern Vancouver Island and on the Fraser River delta.

Spring migration in the central southern interior is evident from mid-March through early May. Most of the movement occurs in April, peaking in mid-April. In the Peace River area, migration occurs from late April to mid-May. Small numbers are widely scattered in summer. As on the coast, autumn migration in the interior is more spectacular than the spring movement. It begins in late July, peaks in late August, and may carry on into late November. Small numbers winter locally in the Okanagan valley and west Kootenay.

BREEDING: The California Gull nests only on Grant (Whiskey) Island in Okanagan Lake. See the Ring-billed Gull account for details on the nesting location (Fig. 175). The following

information is based on the contents of 15 nests (1E-4, 2E-2, 3E-5, 1E1Y-3, 3Y-1) recorded between 29 May and 15 June. Calculated dates indicate eggs could be found from 5 May to at least 18 June. Incubation period ranges from 21 to 33 days with an average of about 25 days (Behle and Goates 1957). Calculated dates indicate young could be found least 6 June to at least 30 July. Young fledge during their sixth week (Vermeer 1970).

REMARKS: Eleven species of gulls (California, Herring, Thayer's, Slaty-backed, Iceland, Western, Glaucous-winged, Glaucous, Lesser Black-backed, Yellow-footed, and Great Black-backed) are so closely related that their taxonomy presents a difficult problem in ornithological systematics (American Ornithologists' Union 1983).

The California Gull is currently regarded as a monotypic species (American Ornithologists' Union 1957). Recently, however, Jehl (1987) suggests that it is separable into a small, dark mantled race (*L. c. californicus*) and a larger, paler race (*L. c. albertaensis*). Birds breeding in the province are likely of the former race.

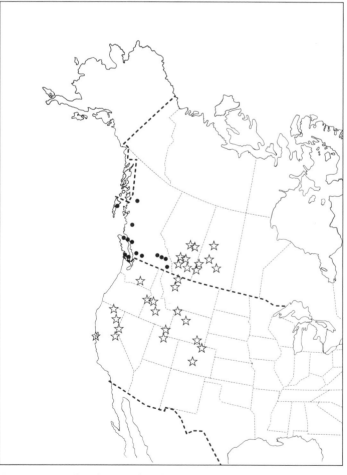

Figure 174. *Banding locations (stars) and recovery sites (circles) of California Gulls associated with British Columbia.*

Figure 175. *Adults and mobile young Ring-billed and California gulls at Whiskey Island, Okanagan Lake, July 1986 (John M. Cooper).*

NOTEWORTHY RECORDS

Spring: Coastal - Saanich 2 Apr 1984-20+ at garbage dump; Cleland Island 15 May 1970-20; Delta 9 May 1981-250; Richmond 24 Mar 1985-100; Qualicum River 16 Apr 1941-100+; Teal Island 8 Apr 1976-200; Gunboat Passage 8 Apr 1976-100; Cumshewa Inlet 15 Mar 1976-1 adult. **Interior** - Trail 22 Mar 1984-1 adult; Vaseux Lake 23 May 1977-10; Penticton 17 Mar 1977-10 adults; Windermere Lake 28 Apr 1979-10; Kamloops 11 Mar 1979-4, 18 Mar 1978-40; Sorrento 30 Mar 1972-50; Yoho National Park 13 Apr 1976-4 (Wade 1977); Moose Lake (Mount Robson Park) 29 May 1972-6; Puntchesakut Lake 27 May 1944-1 female (ROM 83470); Vanderhoof 7 May 1968-12; Charlie Lake 28 Apr 1985-1, 25 May 1981-20.

Summer: Coastal - Clover Point 22 Jul 1983-548; Jordan River 24 Jul 1980-5,000; Cowichan Bay 11 Jun 1983-50; Klanawa River 13 Aug 1970-5,500; Wizard Islet 17 Aug 1970-2,000+; Long Beach 12 Jul 1982-5,300, 22 Jul 1970-5,100; Tsawwassen 15 Jun 1981-27; Richmond 21 Aug 1985-915 passed in 20 min; Johnstone Strait 6 Aug 1969-207; Brooks Peninsula 5 to 15 Aug 1981-1,800; Naiad Islets 5 Jul 1982-350 immatures, 2 Aug 1987-1,500; Bella Bella 14 Aug 1968-40; Shuttle Passage 10 Jul 1977-34; Cumshewa Inlet 12 Jul 1977-60+; Naden Harbour 29 Aug 1984-40; Green Island 21 Aug 1977-15+. **Interior** - Sirdar 30 Jul 1948-28; Manning Park 25 Jul 1973-23 (Crowell and Nehls 1973d); Trout Creek Point (Summerland) 12 Jul 1974-70 (Cannings, S.G. 1974), 30 Aug 1967-27; Revelstoke 17 Aug 1978-27; Field 5 Aug 1975-50 (Wade 1977); Williams Lake 2 Jul 1979-4 adults; Bowron Lake 25 Aug 1975-11; Tatlatui Lake 26 Jul 1974-2 adults; Fort St. John 24 Jun 1985-5; Klahowya Lake 20 Jul 1976-1 (Osmond-Jones et al. 1977).

Autumn: Interior - Lac la Hache 23 Oct 1951-1 adult male (NMC 47821); Wapta Lake 3 Nov 1975-3 (Wade 1977); Revelstoke 6 Sep 1978-204, 19 Sep 1978-387, 16 Oct 1978-82 (Bonar 1978b); Adams River 14 Oct 1982-100's; Merritt 7 Sep 1971-24; Burton 7 Sep 1985-1,000; Penticton 8 Oct 1973-89, 18 Oct 1973-1,440, 30 Oct 1973-1,027, 11 Nov 1973-55; Trail 11 Nov 1984-23. **Coastal** - Yeo Cove 9 Sep 1968-45; Nakwakto Rapids 18 Sep 1967-50; Little River (Comox) 24 Oct 1937-500+; Delta 28 Sep 1980-125 at garbage dump; Boundary Bay 19 Sep 1947-100+; Tofino 10 to 13 Nov 1961-500; Long Beach 25 Sep 1971-1,500, 10 Oct 1975-700+; Ucluelet 2 Oct 1971-2,500; Bamfield to La Perouse Bank 2 Sep 1984-10,000; La Perouse Bank 3 Sep 1983-3,000; Witty's Lagoon 5 Oct 1979-500; Esquimalt Lagoon 9 Sep 1979-200.

Winter: Interior - Galena Bay (Upper Arrow Lake) 1 Jan 1984-15; Nakusp 4 Jan 1981-2; Kelowna 1 Jan 1981-15; Penticton 19 Dec 1976-6; Skaha Lake 22 Feb 1974-15. **Coastal** - Comox 20 Dec 1966-2; Vancouver 21 Dec 1986-250; Spanish Banks 5 Feb 1984-32 adults; Trout Lake (Vancouver) 5 Jan 1985-65, 3 Feb 1985-98; Delta 7 Dec 1974-9 at garbage dump; Oak Bay 6 Jan 1943-30, 18 Jan 1962-16.

Christmas Counts: Interior - Recorded from 6 of 19 localities and on 29% of all counts. Maxima: Penticton 22 Dec 1984-40; Nakusp 30 Dec 1984-11; Vaseux Lake 23 Dec 1981-7. **Coastal** - Recorded from 11 of 28 localities and on 22% of all counts. Maxima: Vancouver 16 Dec 1984-**92**, all-time Canadian high count (Monroe 1985b); Victoria 21 Dec 1974-74; Ladner 27 Dec 1981-16.

Herring Gull
Larus argentatus Pontoppidan

RANGE: Breeds in North America from Alaska, the northern Yukon, and Mackenzie east to Labrador and Newfoundland, south to south-central British Columbia, through central Alberta and Saskatch-ewan, southern Manitoba and southern Ontario to northern Minnesota, Wisconsin, northern New York, and along the Atlantic coast to northern South Carolina. Winters from Alaska, the Great Lakes region and Newfoundland south to Panama and the West Indies. Also in the Old World.

STATUS: Offshore a *common* to *very common* spring and autumn migrant; in winter, *fairly common* to *common*; *rare* in summer. In inner coastal areas, *uncommon* to *fairly common* in winter and in spring and autumn migration; *very rare* in summer. In the interior, *common* to *abundant* spring migrant, *fairly common* to *common* autumn migrant, at times locally *abundant*. *Common* to *abundant* locally in winter in the Okanagan valley and west Kootenay. Widespread but local breeder in the interior.

NONBREEDING: The Herring Gull is widely distributed thoughout the province from sea level to at least 1,675 m. On the coast, it frequents the open ocean as well as beaches, bays, harbours, inlets, estuaries, and garbage dumps. It roosts with other large gulls, especially the Glaucous-winged Gull, in flooded fields, on golf courses, and in city parks as well as on coastal buildings. In the interior, it prefers lakes, rivers, fish-spawning streams (Fig. 176), and garbage dumps (mostly in winter).

The status on the coast is not well understood. Available data suggest that on the south coast the Herring Gull is a passage migrant, mostly along the west coast of Vancouver Island. In winter, small numbers are found throughout the Strait of Georgia and Juan de Fuca Strait with larger flocks recorded on the west coast. Individuals are occasionally seen in the area in summer. The Herring Gull appears to be far more numerous throughout the year on the Queen Charlotte Islands. Spring migration occurs mainly from late March through mid-May; the autumn movement occurs mainly between mid-September and late October. In winter, the Herring Gull is most numerous and widespread offshore (Sanger 1970, 1973a); there is a dispersal away from land in autumn and a return to land in spring.

In the southern interior, spring migration is evident from late March through early May, and in northern areas (e.g. the Peace River region), from the third week of April through May. Autumn migration begins in late August, peaks mainly during September and October, and in some years in southern areas, carries into early November. All winter occurrences, except one (Atlin), are from Shuswap Lake south through the Okanagan valley and from Revelstoke to Trail in the west Kootenay. Winter populations are mostly concentrated around garbage dumps.

Coastal records listed below have been carefully scrutinized, but may not accurately reflect the species' occurrence (see Remarks). Interior records are more representative.

***Figure 176.** Adult Herring Gull in winter plumage feeding on spawning salmon at the Goldstream River, Vancouver Island, 30 November 1985 (Tim Zurowski).*

Herring Gull

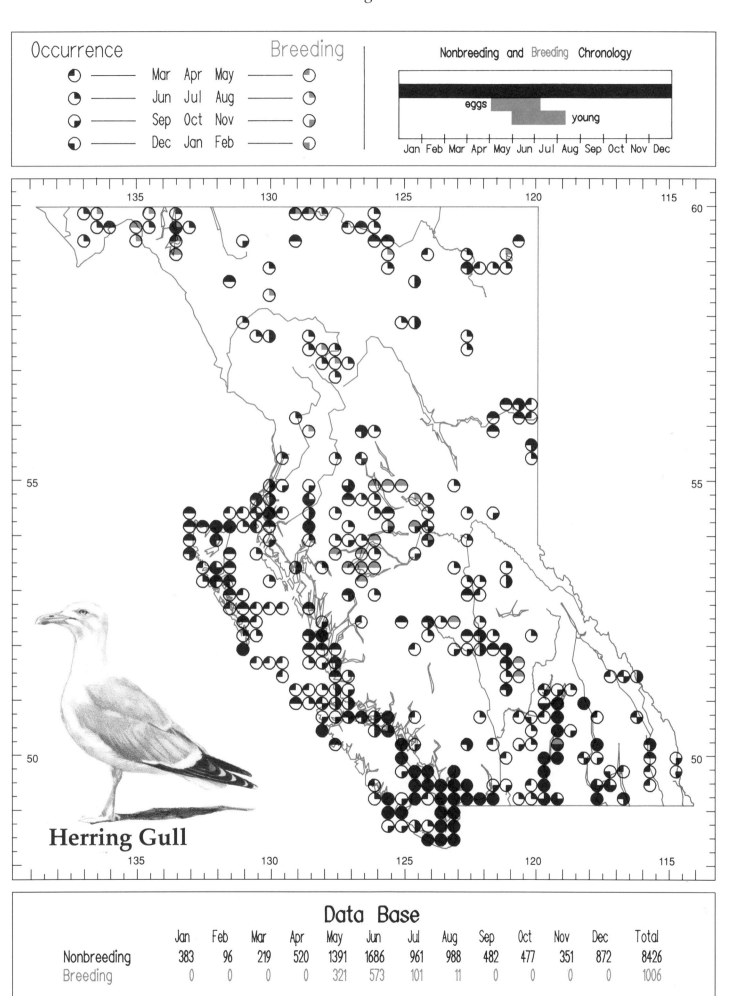

Occurrence

Breeding

◓	Mar	Apr	May
◔	Jun	Jul	Aug
◕	Sep	Oct	Nov
◕	Dec	Jan	Feb

Nonbreeding and Breeding Chronology

eggs

young

Jan Feb Mar Apr May Jun Jul Aug Sep Oct Nov Dec

Herring Gull

Data Base

	Jan	Feb	Mar	Apr	May	Jun	Jul	Aug	Sep	Oct	Nov	Dec	Total
Nonbreeding	383	96	219	520	1391	1686	961	988	482	477	351	872	8426
Breeding	0	0	0	0	321	573	101	11	0	0	0	0	1006

BREEDING: The Herring Gull breeds from Okanagan Lake in the Thompson-Okanagan Plateau northwest through the Fraser Plateau, Babine Upland in the Fraser Basin, Nass Basin, and the Northern Mountains and Plateaus region to Kelsall Lake in the Chilkat Pass area and east through the Liard Basin to Kotcho Lake in the Fort Nelson Lowlands.

It nests singly, or in loose or compact colonies (Fig. 179). All sites are associated with lakes and are situated on rocky islands, low islets (Fig. 177), and large boulders, either bare or with grasses, shrubs, and occasionally large trees. On large, forested islands, rocky headlands are frequently used for nesting (Fig. 178). Some nest in mixed colonies with California Gulls (Okanagan Lake), American White Pelicans (Stum Lake), Ring-billed Gulls (Fraser Lake and Okanagan Lake), Mew and Bonaparte's gulls (Kotcho Lake), and Arctic Terns (Atlin Lake).

There are about 40 known nesting sites in the province. Histories of the 7 largest colonies are given in Table 10. Generally, populations appear to be increasing very slowly. Nesting sites have been found from 518 to 1,341 m elevation.

Nests: Nests were built on rock surfaces, with or without vegetation, usually in open situations (Fig. 180). Infrequently, some were found among tall grasses, under shrubs, or at the base of tall conifers. Nests (n=114) were usually sparse to bulky mounds, with shallow to deep cups, and large bases. They were composed mainly of grasses (41%), sticks and twigs (34%), mosses (10%), and feathers (9%). Other materials included reed stems, lichens, driftwood, bark, pine cones, aquatic weeds, bones, and leaves. Outside diameters for 63 nests ranged from 34 to 86 cm; inside diameters ranged from 23 to 36 cm; outside depths ranged from 4 to 36 cm.

Eggs: Dates for 742 clutches ranged from 14 May to 9 July, with 71% recorded between 25 May and 9 June. Calculated dates indicate that eggs could be found as early as 4 May. Clutch size ranged from 1 to 6 eggs (1E-126, 2E-183, 3E-416, 4E-16, 6E-1) with 56% having 3 eggs. Incubation period is 25 to 28 days (Godfrey 1986).

Young: Dates for 232 broods ranged from 31 May to 12 August with 54% recorded between 17 and 25 June. Brood size ranged from 1 to 4 young (1Y-109, 2Y-86, 3Y-35, 4Y-2), with 84% having 1 or 2 young (Fig. 181). Fledging period is about 45 days (Harris, M.P. 1964).

REMARKS: J.A. Munro and Cowan (1947) treated the Herring and Thayer's gulls as separate species. The former was considered a "summer and winter visitant to the interior" and a "winter visitant to the coast" while the latter was listed as an "abundant winter visitant to the Strait of Georgia" where at times it greatly outnumbered the Herring Gull. In 1956, the Thayer's Gull was considered a subspecies of the Herring Gull (*Larus argentatus thayeri*) (American Ornithologists' Union 1957) but was reinstated as a full species in 1972 (American Ornithologists' Union 1973, 1983). During the period from 1957 to at least 1973 there was little attempt by observers to differentiate between the races and most birds were simply listed as "Herring Gull." By the late 1970s, and throughout the 1980s, observers became more confident in identifying the 2 species, mainly because of the available literature (see Gosselin and David 1975; Monaghan and Duncan 1979; Lehman 1980; Grant, P.J. 1982). Therefore, this necessarily incomplete account is based mainly on information during the past decade. The species requires further study, most of which should be concentrated in coastal areas offshore.

Godfrey (1986) indicates that 2 races of the Herring Gull occur in British Columbia. The subspecies *Larus argentatus smithsonianus* occurs throughout the province, as a breeder and migrant. There is one record of the Siberian race *L. a. vegae*, which is larger and has a darker mantle: Henderson Lake, 27 November 1922 (MVZ 101280).

The Herring Gull interbreeds with the Glaucous-winged Gull in areas of sympatry in southeastern Alaska (Patten and Weisbrod 1974), further complicating identification of coastal gulls.

Figure 177. Low, wooded islet in Babine Lake used by Herring Gulls for nesting, June 1977 (R. Wayne Campbell).

TABLE 10.
Herring Gull: location, history, and size of major colonies in British Columbia.

Location	First Record	Low Survey Results[1] Year	High Survey Results[1] Year	Recent Survey Results[1] Year	Source[2]
			Colony History		
Interior - Colonies > 20 nests or pairs					
Atlin Lake	1914	39 Np 1977	53 Nc 1980	C 1981	1,2
Babine Lake	1944	28 Nc 1980	31 P 1974	1980	1,3
Bridge Lake	1933	15 P 1933	30 N 1980	1980	1,4
Ootsa Lake	1944	8 Nc 1986	21 N 1974	1986	1,3
Stuart Lake	1945	46 Nc 1977	53 Nc 1985	1985	1
Stum Lake[3]	1938	48 Nc 1960	200 N 1938	103 Nc 1986	1
Trembleur Lake	1977	35 Nc 1986	36 Nc 1977	1986	1,5

[1] C - nesting confirmed but no count or estimate made; N - nests; P - pairs. All data are estimates unless noted as follows: c - complete count; p - partial count.

[2] 1 - British Columbia Nest Records Scheme; 2 - Anderson, E.M. 1915; 3 - Munro, J.A. 1947a; 4 - Munro 1935c; 5 - Campbell and Garrioch 1978a.

[3] A complete census on 29 May 1988 revealed 136 active nests, 3 of which were empty; the remainder contained clutches of up to 5 eggs. On 16 June 1988, an additional 11 nests were found on a nearby island.

Figure 178. *The rocky headlands of large, forested islands in Babine Lake are used by pairs of breeding Herring Gulls, June 1977 (R. Wayne Campbell).*

Figure 179. *Herring Gull breeding colony at Trembleur Lake, 7 June 1977 (R. Wayne Campbell).*

Figure 180. *Typical habitat for Herring Gull nesting site in Kotcho Lake, east of Fort Nelson, 26 June 1982 (R. Wayne Campbell).*

Figure 181. *Herring Gull chick and egg on Ellis Island, Fraser Lake (Fraser Lake), 5 June 1977 (R. Wayne Campbell).*

NOTEWORTHY RECORDS

Spring: Coastal - Clover Point 17 Apr 1973-10; Whiffen Spit 20 Mar 1976-3; Stubbs Island (Tofino) 12 Apr 1979-45; Long Beach 18 Mar 1981-12 adults, 21 Apr 1966-14+ (Edwards 1968); Iona Island 27 Apr 1971-2 (Campbell et al. 1972b); Vancouver 26 Mar 1974-3 adults; Sechelt 3 Apr 1977-4; Fitz-Hugh Sound 7 May 1977-19, mostly singles; Skeena River 27 Mar 1977-180 at eulachon run; Skincuttle Inlet 27 Mar 1976-400; Rose Spit 25 Apr 1979-60, 28 Apr 1979-80, 29 Apr 1979-350, 30 Apr 1979-600, 4 May 1979-982 (725 adults, 257 immatures), 5 May 1979-140 (90 adults, 50 immatures). **Interior** - Trail 1 Mar 1984-142, 7 Apr 1983-62; Creston 28 Mar 1962-2,000+ unusually large numbers, 15 Apr 1980-30; Kelowna 22 Mar 1978-45 adults, 7 Apr 1978-103 adults, 9 May 1981-10 immatures; Revelstoke 5 Apr 1978-1; Williams Lake 27 Mar 1983-2 adults, 14 Apr 1979-40 adults, 8 May 1978-300+; Dawson Creek 19 Apr 1986-2 adults; Charlie Lake 30 Apr 1983-1 adult, 4 May 1983-100 adults, 25 May 1980-40 (30 adults, 10 immatures); Parker Lake (Fort Nelson) 1 May 1977-6 adults; Liard River 1 May 1981-3; Atlin Lake 29 Apr 1981-1 adult.

Summer: Coastal - Clover Point 28 Jul 1983-5 immatures, 19 Aug 1978-5 adults; Cleland Island 12 Aug 1973-5; Starlight Reef 30 Aug 1977-7 immatures; Port Alberni 22 Aug 1983-8; Campbell River (Discovery Passage) 20 Aug 1972-5; Rogers Islands (Queen Charlotte Strait) 7 Jul 1982-1; Burnaby Narrows 8 Jul 1977-1 adult; Garcin Rocks 10 Aug 1979-90; Rose Spit 30 Jul 1974-340 (50 adults, 290 immatures), 21 Aug 1974-80; Kitimat 23 Aug 1975-4; Port Simpson 29 Aug 1969-13. **Interior** - Castlegar 1 Aug 1979-50; Kootenay Flats 27 Jun 1956-25 adults (Munro, J.A. 1958a); Wasa Lake 14 Aug 1937-3 adults; Revelstoke 29 Aug 1977-6; Williams Lake 2 Jul 1979-30 adults at dump; Driftwood River 5 Aug 1981-80+; Charlie Lake 23 Jun 1978-34 immatures, 24 Jun 1985-12 immatures; Spatsizi River 16 Jul 1977-3 adults; Fern Lake (Kwadacha Wilderness Park) 19 Aug 1983-26 (25 adults, 1 immature) (Cooper, J.M. and Cooper 1983); Fort Nelson 4 Jun 1979-18 adults at dump; Tatshenshini River 3 Jun 1983-13 adults.

Autumn: Interior - Atlin Lake 15 Oct 1980-1 immature male (RBCM 17133); Kahan Creek Sep 1976-100's migrating through valley; Charlie Lake 29 Sep 1985-1 adult; Tchesinkut Lake 3 Oct 1982-9; Williams Lake 23 Oct 1978-1; 100 Mile House 8 Nov 1984-1 immature; Adams River 1 Oct 1970-36, 25 Oct 1982-500, 16 Nov 1970-150+; Columbia Lake 10 Sep 1939-13, 11 Nov 1983-19; Nelson 13 Nov 1978-100, 20 Nov 1978-200 at dump; Penticton 30 Oct 1973-59 immatures; Trail 1 Oct 1984-2, 3 Nov 1984-53. **Coastal** - Masset 12 Sep 1982-30, 9 Oct 1982-10; Kincolith 21 Sep 1980-30+; Kitimat 28 Sep 1974-5, 5 Oct 1974-35, 12 Oct 1974-75; Campbell River (Discovery Passage) 15 Sep 1974-10; Hornby Island 17 Sep 1978-15; Vancouver 27 Sep 1959-3; La Perouse Bank 3 Sep 1983-100, 18 Sep 1976-44, 23 Sep 1978-10, 14 Oct 1978-30; Race Rocks 27 Sep 1977-12+.

Winter: Interior - Atlin Lake 12 Dec 1980-1 immature after severe wind storm; Columbia River (Revelstoke) all winter 1982/83-23; Salmon Arm 7 Jan 1971-20+; Kelowna 3 Jan 1987-2,068, 19 Dec 1987-645; West Arm (Kootenay Lake) 2 Dec 1978-200, 21 Jan 1979-400, 11 Feb 1979-200; Okanagan Lake (Penticton) 5 Dec 1970-35, 2 Feb 1976-10+; Trail 1 Dec 1983-75, 7 Jan 1984-50, 18 Feb 1984-128, all at garbage dump, numbers increased when lakeside dump at Nelson was closed; Osoyoos Lake 10 Jan 1970-11. **Coastal** - Masset 18 Dec 1982-26; Campbell River (Discovery Passage) 21 Dec 1968-5; Vedder River 5 Jan 1975-3 adults; Iona Island 17 Feb 1973-5; Chesterman Beach 18 Dec 1982-Herring Gulls made up a significant portion of thousands of gulls passing by in south-easterly direction; Long Beach 10 Jan 1983-40+; Pachena Bay 7 Dec 1978-50; Swartz Bay 16 Feb 1974-40; Goldstream River 3 Dec 1983-7; Constance Bank 11 Dec 1983-10.

Christmas Counts: Interior - Recorded from 9 of 19 localities and on 51% of all counts. Maxima: Kelowna 20 Dec 1981-138; Vernon 19 Dec 1982-91; Penticton 22 Dec 1984-75. **Coastal** - Due to inconsistencies in recording Herring/Thayer's Gulls a summary would be meaningless. Three high counts for 1984 (W. C. Weber pers. comm.) were Ladner (215 birds), Pender Islands (128 birds) and Comox (90 birds).

Thayer's Gull
Larus thayeri Brooks

THGU

RANGE: Breeds on the Arctic islands of Canada east to Baffin Island. Winters mainly along the Pacific coast from British Columbia to Mexico. Rare but regular in interior North America.

STATUS: *Abundant* to *very abundant* migrant and visitant from mid-autumn to mid-spring in the vicinity of the Strait of Georgia and Juan de Fuca Strait. *Common* to *abundant* for the same period on the west coast of Vancouver Island, the northern mainland coast and the Queen Charlotte Islands. *Rare* in summer. *Very rare* in the interior.

OCCURRENCE: The Thayer's Gull occurs in coastal areas of the province. Its centre of abundance is the southeastern and southern shores of Vancouver Island, the southern Gulf Islands, and the Fraser River delta. It frequents most coastal habitats including estuaries, bays, lagoons, harbours, spits, as well as garbage dumps, sewage lagoons, and lakes. Thayer's Gulls frequently roost with other wintering gulls (e.g. Glaucous-winged Gull) on offshore rocky islets, log booms, wharves, agricultural fields, beaches, and spits. The largest aggregations are food-related, and occur in bays and harbours (e.g. Nanoose Harbour, Qualicum Bay) during Pacific herring spawning periods in spring and at garbage dumps during winter. In the interior, the Thayer's Gull frequents garbage dumps and lakes.

Early autumn migrants may arrive in late July and August but the main movement begins in September. Numbers generally increase through November and peak in December and January.

Spring departure occurs mostly from late March through April; during this time it is likely that migrants from Washington and southern coastal states pass through southwestern British Columbia. By mid-May only scattered individuals remain on the coast, mostly immatures.

The status of the Thayer's Gull in the interior requires clarification. Recent field work suggests that small numbers regularly occur in winter in the Okanagan valley, especially in the vicinity of garbage dumps. It has been seen there in May and from 8 November to 26 March. There is one recent record from Fort St. John.

The Thayer's Gull has been recorded in the province from 12 July through 22 June. Ninety-seven percent of all records are for the period September through April. Of those, 41% are for the winter months.

REMARKS: The Thayer's Gull was reinstated as a full species, distinct from the Herring Gull (q.v.), in 1973, mainly as a result of research by Macpherson (1961) and N.G. Smith (1966) in the Canadian arctic (American Ornithologists' Union 1973). While Macpherson's (1961) research showed that *thayeri* was not a subspecies of the Herring Gull, he did not give the bird full species status as suggested by the American Ornithologists' Union (1973), but rather considered it a subspecies of the Iceland Gull (*L. glaucoides*). Subsequently, research at Howe Bay, Baffin Island by Knudsen in 1975 and 1976 (see Godfrey 1986, p. 262) revealed widespread interbreeding between *L. thayeri* and *L. g. kumlieni*, which was contrary to N.G. Smith's (1966) results from the same area. Later, Gaston and Decker (1985) also found interbreeding between *L. thayeri* and *L. g. kumlieni*, on Southampton Island. The lack of verification of N.G. Smith's (1966) results and abundant specimen evidence that "colour and pattern differences between *thayeri* and *kumlieni* are completely bridged by individual variation" caused Godfrey (1986) to treat *thayeri* as conspecific with *L. glaucoides*.

The status, distribution, and populations of the Thayer's Gull in British Columbia, including offshore areas, require further study. Observers should consult Gosselin and David (1975) and Lehman (1980) for assistance in field identification of Thayer's Gulls.

NOTEWORTHY RECORDS

Spring: Coastal - Victoria 1 Mar 1976-12, 22 May 1973-2; Cowichan Bay 5 Mar 1974-50; Tofino 18 Mar 1981-102, 26 Apr 1974-2; Richmond 11 Mar 1984-200, 17 Mar 1985-160, 24 Mar 1985-100 (counts at garbage dump); Barnston Island 14 May 1977-55; Departure Bay 5 Mar 1928-80+ (Munro, J.A. and Cowan 1947); Nanoose Harbour 6 Mar 1974-1,130, 14 May 1974-1,200, 20 May 1974-800; Little Qualicum River estuary 15 May 1975-1 (Dawe 1976); Denman Island 15 Mar 1981-60; Comox 27 Apr 1974-50; Campbell River 6 Mar 1974-125; Goose Group 18 May 1948-1; Skincuttle Inlet 18 May 1985-15; Queen Charlotte City 15 Mar 1972-20; Kitimat 24 Apr 1975-288, 23 May 1975-23; Prince Rupert 29 Apr 1975-75; 72km w Terrace 27 Mar 1977-125. **Interior** - Penticton 5 May 1985-1 (RBCM Photo 1024); Kelowna 6 Mar 1985-4+ at dump (RBCM Photo 1021), 26 Mar 1985-1; Carrs 2 Mar 1985-1.

Summer: Coastal - Oak Bay 19 Aug 1981-1 adult; Cowichan Bay 7 Aug 1950-1; Sandhill Creek (Long Beach) 10 Aug 1973-2 immatures; Departure Bay 19 Aug 1974-1; Iona Island 18 Aug 1985-1 adult; Little Qualicum estuary 22 Jul 1975-1 (Dawe 1976); Quadra Island 8 Aug 1982-1 adult; Whistler 12 Jul 1980-1 adult; Tlell 25 Aug 1974-2 adults; Prince Rupert 31 Aug 1969-2. **Interior** - see Extralimital Records.

Autumn: Interior - Sorrento 8 Nov 1971-1 immature. **Coastal** - Prince Rupert 30 Sep 1969-34; Kitimat 12 Oct 1974-238, 7 Nov 1974-98; Masset Sound 19 Nov 1983-4; Queen Charlotte City 26 Oct 1971-3; Princess Royal Island 4 Sep 1946-1 male (UBC 1001); Bella Bella 18 Sep 1968-18 adults; Cracroft Island 3 Oct 1968-50; Rosewall Creek 20 Nov 1975-750; Nanoose Harbour 8 Oct 1976-21 (Dawe and Lang 1980); Iona Island 15 Sep 1985-4 adults, 26 Sep 1985-100, 23 Oct 1973-700, 11 Nov 1984-400, 23 Nov 1980-500; Long Beach 1 Oct 1975-12 adults; La Perouse Bank 18 Sep 1976-10, 14 Oct 1978-20; Cordova Spit 6 Sep 1982-1 adult; Esquimalt Lagoon 30 Sep 1982-200 adult; Clover Point 1 Nov 1980-126 mostly adults.

Winter: Interior - Okanagan Landing 25 Feb 1985-1; Kelowna 19 Dec 1987-11, 3 Jan 1987-8, 4 Jan 1986-1; Penticton 26 Jan 1984-1; Okanagan Falls 27 Dec 1980-1 adult. **Coastal** - Port Edward 22 Feb 1975-75; Masset 10 Dec 1982-8, 29 Jan 1983-55, 1 Feb 1983-15; Minette Bay 2 Dec 1974-9; Campbell River (Discovery Passage) 19 Feb 1974-30; Rosewall Creek 12 Jan 1976-164; Little Qualicum River estuary 14 Feb 1977-960 (Dawe 1980); Nanoose Harbour 28 Jan 1978-720 (Dawe and Lang 1980); Departure Bay 23 Feb 1938-25 (Munro, J.A. and Cowan 1947); Vedder River 17 Jan 1983-1 adult; Fort Langley 26 Jan 1974-80+;

Richmond 14 Dec 1985-600+, 26 Jan 1986-300, 2 Feb 1986-300, all at dump; Sea Island 18 Feb 1974-200; Pachena Bay 7 Dec 1978-100; Cowichan Lake 2 Dec 1970-2 (ROM 108931, 108932); Cowichan Bay 7 Feb 1974-530; Victoria 1 Dec 1984-2,000+, 17 Dec 1983-200 at dump; Beaver Lake (Saanich) 5 Jan 1986-90 on ice; Esquimalt Lagoon 26 Dec 1985-240, 13 Jan 1979-500.

Christmas Counts: Interior - Not recorded. **Coastal** - Figures used for counts are since 1973, when the Thayer's Gull was considered a separate species (see Remarks). Recorded from 21 of 24 localities and on 47% of all counts. Maxima: Pender Islands 20 Dec 1976-**1,433**, all-time North American high count (Monroe 1977); Vancouver 26 Dec 1975-1,220; Victoria 15 Dec 1984-1,000. Mark (1981), in his analysis of data for all Christmas counts in coastal western North America for the period 1973 to 1978, shows that there are inconsistencies in separating Thayer's Gulls and Herring Gulls. Therefore, data for those species should be treated cautiously.

Extralimital Records: Fort St. John 22 June 1987-1 (RBCM Photo 1160); Atlin 10 Aug 1932-1 (RBCM 5919).

Thayer's Gull

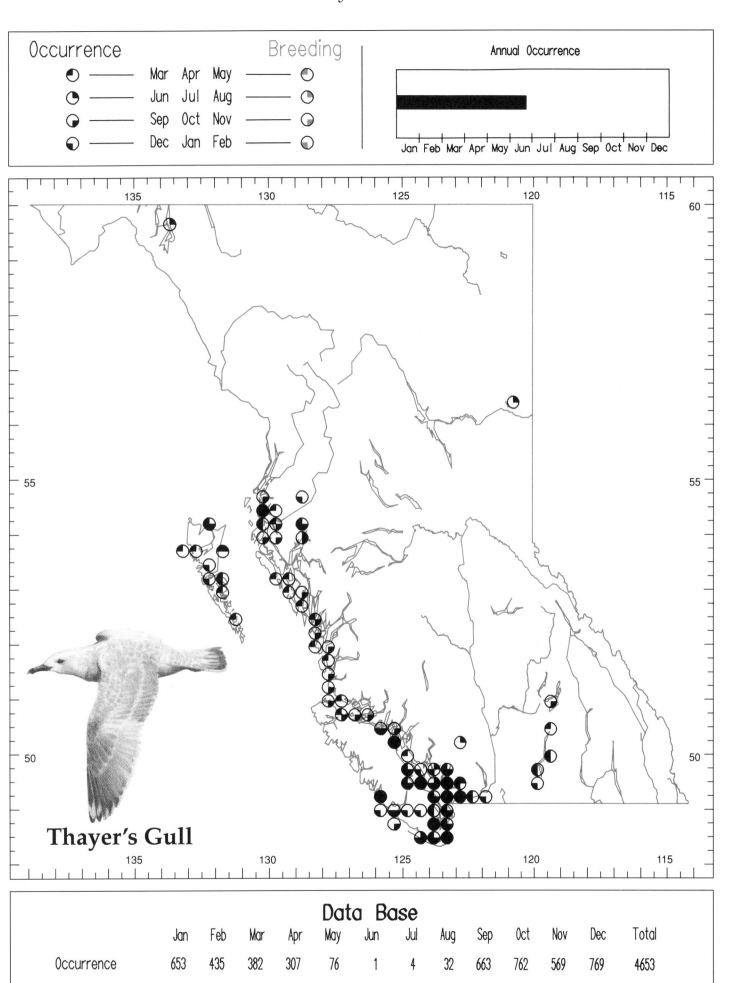

Occurrence

◐	——	Mar	Apr	May	——	◐
◐	——	Jun	Jul	Aug	——	◔
◕	——	Sep	Oct	Nov	——	◔
◕	——	Dec	Jan	Feb	——	◑

Breeding

Annual Occurrence

Jan Feb Mar Apr May Jun Jul Aug Sep Oct Nov Dec

Thayer's Gull

Data Base

	Jan	Feb	Mar	Apr	May	Jun	Jul	Aug	Sep	Oct	Nov	Dec	Total
Occurrence	653	435	382	307	76	1	4	32	663	762	569	769	4653

Western Gull

Larus occidentalis Audubon

WEGU

RANGE: Breeds along the Pacific coast from south coastal Washington south to central Baja California. Winters from southern coastal British Columbia south to southern Baja California.

STATUS: *Uncommon* to *fairly common* resident on the southwest coast of Vancouver Island. *Very rare* to *rare* summer visitant, *rare* to *uncommon* winter visitant, in the vicinity of the Strait of Georgia and Juan de Fuca Strait. *Very rare* elsewhere along coastal British Columbia. Not reported from the interior of the province.

OCCURRENCE: The Western Gull occurs regularly, throughout the year, from Clayoquot Sound to Barkley Sound on the southwest coast of Vancouver Island and in the vicinity of Victoria. Elsewhere, it occurs infrequently and is rarely encountered north of Vancouver Island. All records are from the Queen Charlotte Islands, mostly of adults, are sight records by competent observers. The Western Gull is accidental in Alaska (Kessel and Gibson 1978).

Nearly 82% of all records are of 1 or 2 birds; they are usually found among flocks of Glaucous-winged Gulls. The largest numbers occur in late spring and summer. The Western Gull is ubiquitous in all marine habitats and regularly visits garbage dumps. Occasionally it travels inland short distances to freshwater lakes, rivers, and flooded fields, in company with other gulls. It occurs inland to at least Chilliwack.

The Western Gull is most numerous on the outer coast of Vancouver Island. Over 80% of records there are for the period May through August. Records suggest that an influx of birds occurs in May (most noticeable offshore - Campbell and Shepard 1971) and again from late June into August (Hatler et al. 1978). The late summer influx probably involves post-breeding movements of immatures from colonies in Washington and Oregon. Banding recoveries suggest some of these birds remain in winter (Munro, J.A. and Cowan 1947).

In the protected waters of the Strait of Georgia and Juan de Fuca Strait, the Western Gull is primarily a winter visitant. There, it is most numerous along the east coast of Vancouver Island. Birds arrive in October and November and most have departed by March; a few can be found in summer.

REMARKS: The breeding distribution of the Western Gull in British Columbia is not well understood, mainly because it interbreeds with Glaucous-winged Gulls (Scott, J.M. 1971), producing intermediate morphs in breeding populations, which are difficult to identify without collecting. Hoffman et al. (1978), in their analysis of hybridization between these 2 species in the Pacific Northwest, indicate a 180 km zone of interbreeding along the Washington coast. At Cape Flattery, the Washington colony closest to British Columbia, about 7% of the population was pure Western Gull, about 2% were hybrids, and the remainder were pure Glaucous-winged Gulls. The same authors found Western Gull characteristics in birds breeding on the Chain Islets off Victoria.

These results confirm Pearse's (1946) suggestion that hybridization was evident on Seabird Rocks in Pachena Bay. Later, Campbell and Stirling (1968b) reported an adult Western Gull with an adult Glaucous-winged Gull on territory on Cleland Island, northwest of Tofino. On 26 July 1970, a mixed Glaucous-winged Gull-Western Gull pair was photographed (RBCM Photo 129; see Hatler et al. 1978) on Sea Lion Rocks off Long Beach. During field work on Cleland Island during the summers of 1983 and 1984, M.A. Purdy (pers. comm.) estimated that 5% to 10% of the 2,000+ breeding pairs of gulls involved Western Gulls. If pure breeding pairs of Western Gulls were involved, there has been a significant northward expansion of the species' breeding range along the Pacific Coast of North America since the studies of Hoffman et al. (1978). However, we have no documented information on nests, or chronology of eggs or young, resulting from pure Western Gull breeding pairs in British Columbia, and have decided to exclude it as a breeding species on these grounds.

The American Ornithologists' Union (1983) states that "hybridization between Western and Glaucous-winged Gulls occurs in mixed colonies from southern British Columbia to western Oregon, and these two will probably prove to be conspecific." See also Hoffman et al. (1978) for additional discussion on the taxonomy of the 2 species.

The unusually high number of 40 birds tallied during the unofficial New Westminster Christmas Count in 1949 (Maguire 1950) is considered questionable since no accompanying field notes were published.

NOTEWORTHY RECORDS

Spring: Coastal - Clover Point 6 Mar 1974-3; San Juan River 1 May 1974-4; Barkley Sound mid-Mar 1946-comprised 5% to 10% of gull population (Martin and Myres 1969); Cape Beale 23 Mar 1946-1 female (UBC 876); Long Beach 20 Apr 1966-40 (Edwards 1968); Tofino 19 Apr 1976-2 adults, 4 immatures; w Tofino 2 May 1970-100+ (Campbell and Shepard 1971); 8 km w Tofino 19 May 1974-7 adults, 3 immatures; Tsawwassen 17 May 1970-1 on jetty (RBCM Photo 171); Comox 22 May 1938-1 male (FMNH 158550); Cortes Island 7 Apr 1976-4; Port Hardy 7 Mar 1935-1; Gunboat Passage 8 Apr 1976-1; Tow Hill 16 Apr 1987-2 adults. **Interior** - No records.

Summer: Coastal - Chain Islets 2 Aug 1983-1 adult, 5 immatures; Imperial Eagle Channel 12 Aug 1964-4; Long Beach 28 Aug 1962-20; Cleland Island 24 Jul 1967-3 (Campbell and Stirling 1968b); Iona Island 15 Jul 1980-1; Courtenay 17 Jun 1938-1; Brooks Peninsula 16 Jun 1978-5; Triangle Island (Scott Islands) 9 Jul 1984-1 immature. **Interior** - No records.

Autumn: Interior - No records. **Coastal** - Masset 23 Oct 1971-1; Sangan River 7 Oct 1971-1; Vancouver 9 Sept 1973-13; Delta 29 Oct 1984-1 adult, 4 immatures, 24 Nov 1985-4 adults, 1 immature; Henderson Lake 26 Nov 1922-1 male (MVZ 101260); Chesterman Beach 5 Sept 1974-12, 9 Oct 1983-4 adults, 4 immatures; Long Beach 24 Nov 1965-42 (Edwards 1968); Long Harbour 22 Nov 1977-3; Port Renfrew 21 Sep 1974-4; Becher Bay 21 Nov 1983-9; Clover Point 10 Sep 1982-3, 5 Nov 1974-7.

Winter: Interior - No records. **Coastal** - Rose Spit 17 Dec 1987-5; Seymour Inlet 26 Jan 1936-1 (band recovery; Ferris 1942); Quatsino 20 Jan 1936-1 (band recovery); Comox 20 Jan 1920-1 male (MVZ 101299); Vancouver 2 Jan 1985-45 (hybrids with Glaucous-winged Gulls); Burnaby Lake 15 Jan 1981-1; Vedder River 25 Jan 1981-1; Long Beach 28 Feb 1982-2 adults, 2 immatures; Ucluelet 29 Feb 1974-5; Folger Island 11 Feb 1976-3; Todd Creek (Saanich) 8 Dec 1983-6; Port Renfrew 14 Feb 1939-1 (band recovery); Albert Head 11 Dec 1983-10; Clover Point 24 Jan 1971-4.

Christmas Counts: Interior - Not recorded. **Coastal** - Recorded from 11 of 28 localities and on 16% of all counts. Maxima: Victoria 15 Dec 1984-7, all-time Canadian high count (Monroe 1985b); Ladner 27 Dec 1981-6; Vancouver 26 Dec 1965-5; Pender Islands 27 Dec 1966-5.

Western Gull

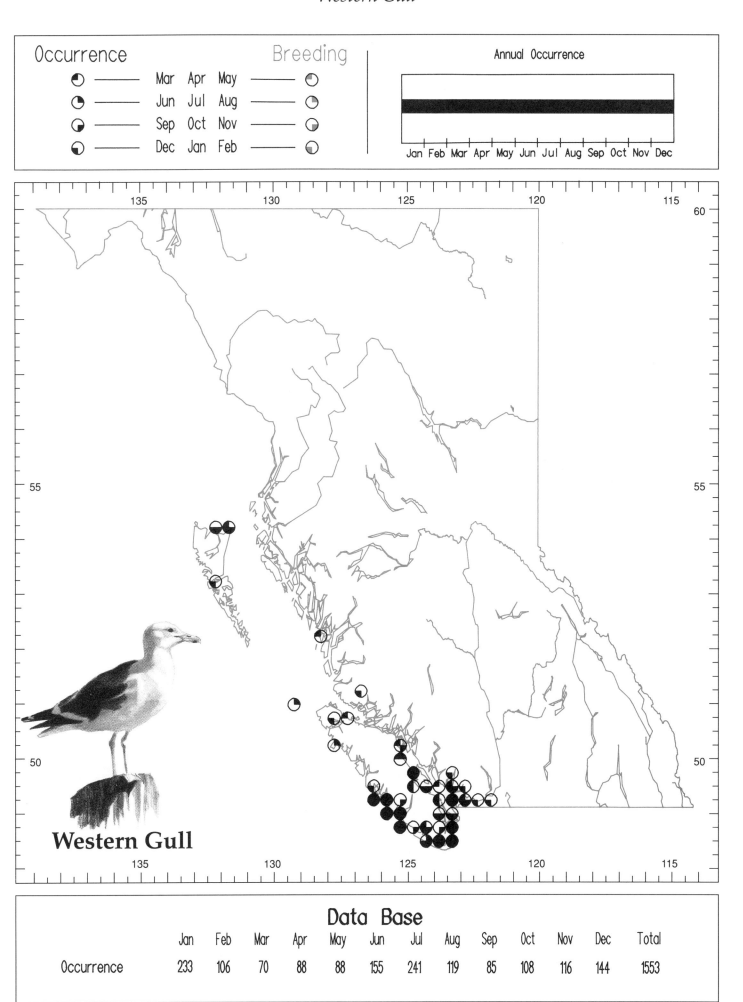

Occurrence

Occurrence		Breeding

Mar Apr May

Jun Jul Aug

Sep Oct Nov

Dec Jan Feb

Annual Occurrence

Jan Feb Mar Apr May Jun Jul Aug Sep Oct Nov Dec

Western Gull

Data Base

	Jan	Feb	Mar	Apr	May	Jun	Jul	Aug	Sep	Oct	Nov	Dec	Total
Occurrence	233	106	70	88	88	155	241	119	85	108	116	144	1553

Glaucous-winged Gull

Larus glaucescens Naumann

RANGE: Breeds from the southern Bering Sea and southern Alaska south along the Pacific coast to northwestern Washington; also on the Commander Islands. Winters throughout the breeding range south along the coast to southern Baja California; also on the Pacific coast of Asia south to Japan.

STATUS: Along the coast, a *very abundant* spring and autumn migrant and *very common* to *very abundant* summer visitant. A *very common* to *abundant* winter visitant on the north coast, including the Queen Charlotte Islands; *very abundant* on the south coast including the Fraser Lowlands. In the central-southern interior, a *very rare* visitant; *casual* in northeastern British Columbia. Widespread breeder along the coast.

NONBREEDING: The Glaucous-winged Gull is widely distributed along the coast. It prefers nearshore areas, but regularly visits fishing vessels well offshore, and may be partially pelagic in some seasons (Sanger 1970, 1973a; Wahl 1975). In the interior, it has been recorded from Anderson Lake, Kamloops, and Squilax south through the Okanagan valley and in widely separated locations in the northeast. It occurs from sea level to 1,200 m elevation.

The Glaucous-winged Gull is found in all coastal habitats at all seasons. It is the "sea gull" of the coast. It occurs in extremely large numbers in bays, harbours, estuaries, and rivers where spawning Pacific herring, salmon, and eulachon are found. It is very gregarious and often congregates with other marine-foraging birds over schools of sandlance and Pacific herring (Porter, J.M.

1980). It roosts at night in large flocks on sheltered bodies of water along the coast, including bays, inlets, rivers, islands, log booms (Fig. 183), and on larger freshwater lakes. Man-influenced habitats used along the coast include garbage dumps (Fig. 182), city parks, athletic fields, school yards, airports, agricultural fields, buildings, and structures along waterfronts. In the interior, the Glaucous-winged Gull has been found at garbage dumps, lakes, river mouths, and city parks.

Even though the species is present along the coast in numbers throughout the year, there is a definite migration. In spring, the movement generally occurs between late March and early May, and in autumn between late September and late October. Most large spring and autumn concentrations are related to herring and salmon spawning sites, respectively.

In summer, flocks are usually small except near colonies and garbage dumps. Tagging and banding studies by Drent and Ward (1970) and R.W. Butler et al. (1980) indicate that a portion of the breeding population, mostly immatures, shifts southward along the coast during winter. Many of these gulls collect in the Vancouver region and Fraser River delta where 70% to 80% forage at refuse sites (Ward, J.G. 1973). For example, results of Christmas counts at 13 locations in the Strait of Georgia and Juan de Fuca Strait in 1980 produced 101,968 Glaucous-winged Gulls, 72% of which were tallied at 5 locations in the Fraser Lowlands. At dusk they move to night roosts in the vicinity of Burrard Inlet, Steveston, Boundary Bay, and Sapperton. These winter roosts are active from October to March. Peak movements (65,100 in 1970) occur in late November (Campbell et al. 1972a).

Figure 182. Gulls, mostly Glaucous-winged, at Delta garbage dump, March 1976 (Ervio Sian).

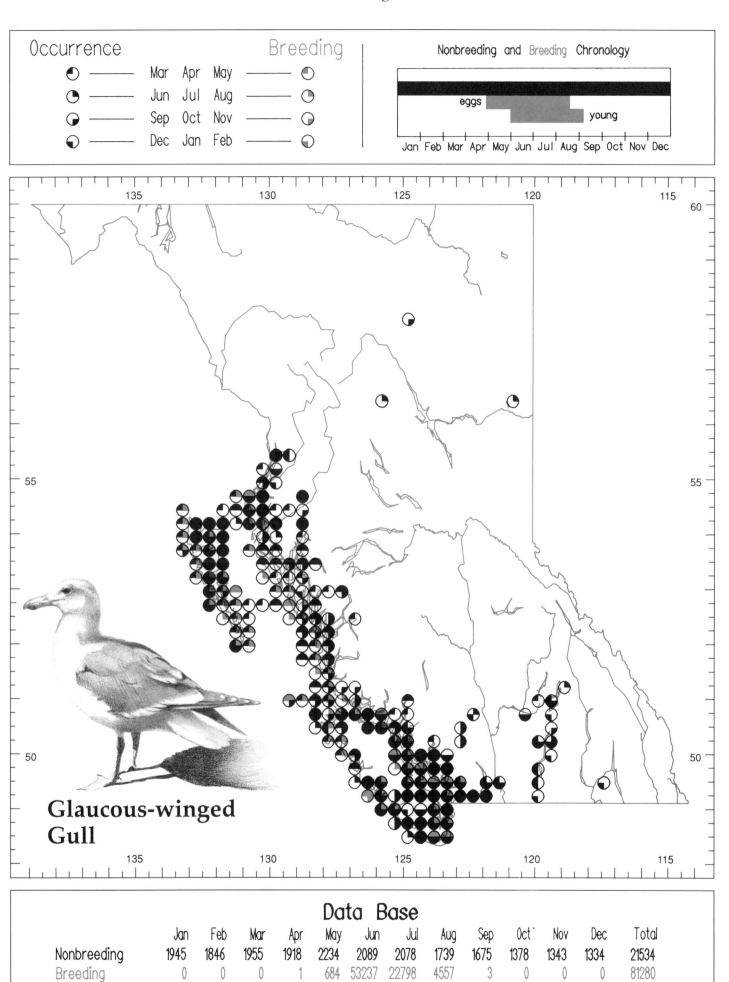

Glaucous-winged Gull

Figure 183. *Fraser River at New Westminster, 20 June 1970 (R. Wayne Campbell). Log booms are used by gulls, mainly Glaucous-winged Gulls, for roosting throughout the year.*

BREEDING: The Glaucous-winged Gull breeds along inner and outer coastal waters from Race Rocks off southern Vancouver Island north to Zayas Island, including the Queen Charlotte Islands. It has also been found breeding on Fulmore Lake, a freshwater lake near Port Neville (Rodway In press). Similar situations have previously been reported (Wahl 1972; Weber, J.W. and Fitzver 1986). It breeds from near sea level to 90 m elevation.

The Glaucous-winged Gull is primarily colonial but frequently nests singly. Preferred sites are on small, offshore islands, less than 25 m high and ranging in size from 2 to 10 ha. All major colonies are on islands less than 25 ha in size and 100 m in height. Colony sites are usually treeless (Fig. 184), often bare (Fig. 185), or with large patches of grasses, herbs, or shrubs. On large forested islands, small numbers of gulls use bare, rocky headlands and cliffs.

During the past 2 decades an increasing and expanding Glaucous-winged Gull population has forced gulls to colonize new habitats, often near urban environments (Campbell 1975c; Hooper, T.D. 1988). The first nests on the roofs of buildings were reported by Oldaker (1963a) and Sanford (1974) at Vancouver. In 1971, the first mainland site was established on a man-made jetty (Campbell 1975c) and this site had expanded along the Vancouver waterfront by 1976 (Poynter 1976). By 1984, small colonies had become established on the support beams of bridges in Vancouver (Hobson, K.A. and Wilson 1985). By 1986, the nesting population in downtown Vancouver was estimated at 500 pairs (Vermeer et al. 1988).

In Victoria, T.D. Hooper (1988) located 99 nests on the roofs of buildings in numbers ranging from 1 to 9 per roof. Other urban sites, often used by isolated pairs, include derricks, light beacons, barges, wooden pilings (Fig. 186), log booms, large trees, building ledges (Fig. 187), a control house of an operating crane, a drydock, a water tower, and a marine buoy.

During the past 50 years, the Glaucous-winged Gull population in British Columbia has increased about 3.5 times (Drent and Guiguet 1961; Campbell 1975c; Verbeek 1986). In the 15 year period from 1960 to 1974, the population nearly doubled in the Strait of Georgia and Juan de Fuca Strait (Campbell 1975c; Verbeek 1986). The total breeding population in British Columbia, as of 1987, is estimated at 25,000 pairs.

The centre of the breeding population is situated in the vicinity of Vancouver Island where 56% of all colonies are located. Populations of Glaucous-winged Gull colonies (in pairs) from 4 geographical areas are: the Strait of Georgia (13,004 at 72 sites in 1986-Vermeer and DeVito 1989), the west coast of Vancouver Island (6,828 at 53 sites in 1986), the Queen Charlotte Islands (2,600 at 85 sites in 1986-Rodway 1988), and Queen Charlotte Strait (844 at 22 sites in 1987-Rodway In press). Histories of the major British Columbia colonies are summarized in Table 11.

In Alaska the breeding population is estimated at 133,000 pairs and in Washington it is about 18,500 pairs (United States Department of the Interior 1988; Speich and Wahl 1989).

Nests: Most nests (99%; n=68,077) were on islands or rock islets. The rest were on the mainland, on waterfront buildings or other man-made structures. Some were in mixed colonies of other ground-nesting species such as Double-crested, Brandt's, and Pelagic cormorants, and Common Murres.

Nests were usually situated on the ground on rock surfaces, with or without vegetation, along the upper reaches of sandy beaches, among driftwood, on cliffs, and on headlands. Nesting substrates for 81 nests on the roofs of buildings in Victoria included gravel, tar paper, asphalt shingles, wood, concrete, and metal (Hooper, T.D. 1988). A few nests were in coniferous trees such as Sitka spruce, Douglas-fir, and western redcedar. Heights of tree nests ranged from 2 m (on a branch) to 18 m in a Bald Eagle nest; on buildings and other structures nest heights ranged from 4 to 61 m.

Nests were usually meagre to substantial saucers or mounds, with shallow to deep cups, often with large bases. Occasionally, eggs were laid on bare rock, in sand or dirt, or on roofs of buildings without nesting materials. Materials are usually available in the immediate vicintiy of the nest, that is, within the territory (Patten 1974). Some adults in British Columbia, however, have been known to fly up to 10 km from colonies in search of nesting material. Nests were composed variously of grasses, mosses, seaweeds and other marine vegetation, plant stalks, rootlets, twigs, driftwood, feathers, bark, leaves, and man-made material such as string, plastic bags, pieces of fishing net, and paper. Lining materials included grasses, feathers, leaves, cones, rootlets, conifer needles, mosses, lichens, and bark.

Figure 184. *Christie Islet, a typical small, treeless nesting site for Glaucous-winged Gulls along the south coast of British Columbia, 18 July 1970 (R. Wayne Campbell). Rudolf Drent is rowing Robin Weber (bow), Rick Jerema (left), and William J. Anderson to the islet for annual gull-banding activities.*

Figure 185. *Glaucous-winged Gull colony on bare rock on Sea Lion Rocks off Long Beach, Vancouver Island, August 1968 (R. Wayne Campbell).*

TABLE 11.					
Glaucous-winged Gull: location, history, and size of major colonies in British Columbia.					

		Colony History			
Location	First Record	Low Survey Results[1] Year	High Survey Results[1] Year	Recent Survey Results[1] Year	Source[2]
South Coast - Colonies > 100 nests or pairs					
Ada Islands	1974	86 Nc 1980	171 Nc 1974	124 Nc 1986	2,4,23
Arbutus Island	1976	39 Nc 1976	150 Nc 1986	1986	2,23
Baeria Rocks	1958	175 Nc 1988	380 Nc 1975	1988	2,5,21
Ballingall Islets	1936	1 N 1954	150 N 1968	145 Nc 1986	2,7,8,23
Beresford Island	1950	S 1961	122 N 1987	1987	2,18,21
Bremner Islet	1982		144 Nc 1982	1982	21
Buckle Group	1975	60 Nc 1975	127 Nc 1982	65 Nc 1987	4,11
Bunsby Island	1955	124 Nc 1988	190 Nc 1975	1988	4,5,21
Chain Islets	1924	80 N 1943	2432 Nc 1986	1986	2,5,23
Christie Islet	1914	30 N 1956	718 Nc 1978	454 Nc 1986	2,5,20,23
Cleland Island	1925	150 N 1930	2236 Nc 1982	1622 Nc 1988	5,21
Five Finger Island	1958	110 Nc 1968	671 Nc 1986	1986	2,6,23
Florencia Island	1968	75 N 1968	479 Nc 1975	346 Nc 1982	2,4,21
Franklin Island	1950	173 Nc 1972	480 Nc 1971	216 Nc 1986	2,23
Gillam Islets	1958	297 Nc 1983	646 Nc 1988	1988	2,5,21
Grassy Island	1958	141 Nc 1975	188 Nc 1988	1988	4,5,21
Great Bear Rock	1962	18 Nc 1970	274 Nc 1975	247 Nc 1982	4,11,14
Grebe Islets	1974	7 Nc 1974	108 Nc 1986	1986	2,4,23
Hudson Rocks	1958	75 N 1959	308 Nc 1981	247 Nc 1986	2,5,23
Imrie Island	1905	0 N 1905	355 Nc 1978	216 Nc 1986	2,5,23
Java Islets	1900	181 N 1980	531 Nc 1969	298 Nc 1986	2,5,7,23
Mandarte Island	1900	350 N 1921	2500 N 1970	2363 Nc 1986	2,5,9,23
McQuarrie Islets	1975	25 N 1982	256 Nc 1975	203 Nc 1988	4,21
McRae Islet	1969	97 Nc 1969	262 Nc 1986	1986	2,4,23
Merry Island	1950	100 N 1950	362 Nc 1978	158 Nc 1981	2,5
"Mimulus" Islets	1975	210 Nc 1975	222 Nc 1988	1988	4,21
Mitlenatch Island	1896	150 N 1927	3500 N 1967	2100 Nc 1986	2,3,23
Moos Islet	1975	221 Nc 1982	321 Nc 1975	148 Nc 1988	4,21
"Naden Base" Islet	1981		143 Nc 1981	1981	2
Nipple Rocks	1975	82 Nc 1982	149 Nc 1988	1988	4,21
Norris Rocks	1968	17 Nc 1968	170 N 1975	287 Nc 1986	2,23
O'Leary Islets	1975	54 Nc 1978	117 Nc 1988	1988	2,4,21
Pam Rock	1956	10 N 1956	109 Nc 1986	1986	2,5,23
Passage Island	1958	16 Nc 1958	798 Nc 1978	384 Nc 1986	2,5,23
Race Rocks	1924	72 N 1953	471 Nc 1981	1981	2
Ragged Islets	1923	0 N 1923	130 Nc 1978	69 Nc 1986	2,7,23
Rogers Islands	1975	75 N 1975	138 Nc 1982	1982	4,21
Rose Islets	1963	1 N 1972	211 Nc 1981	116 Nc 1986	2,7,23
Sartine Island	1950	C 1950	740 B 1975	240 P 1987	18,19,21
Sea-Lion Rocks	1967	131 Nc 1967	175 Nc 1973	133 Nc 1982	12,13,21
Seabird Rocks	1943	181 Nc 1988	400 N 1970	1988	14,15,21
Sisters Islets	1940	25 Nc 1986	151 Nc 1981	1986	2,5,23
Snake Island	1947	330 Nc 1968	719 Nc 1981	673 Nc 1986	1,2,23
Solander Island	1954	C 1954	347 P 1988	1988	2,4,6,21
Starlight Reef	1962	159 Nc 1970	306 Nc 1975	279 Nc 1982	4,14,21
Thornton Islet	1975	295 Nc 1983	1053 Nc 1988	1988	4,21
Triangle Island	1949	100 N 1961	340 N 1977	337 N 1984	2,18,21
Tsawwassen[3]	1974	115 Nc 1974	238 Nc 1986	1986	2,4,23
Victoria[4]	1958	1 Nc 1958	110 Nc 1986	1986	5,10
Vivian Island	1966	59 N 1966	245 N 1975	208 Nc 1986	2,23
Volcanic Islets	1975	0 N 1982	153 Nc 1988	1988	4,21
"Wallis" Rocks	1961	7 Nc 1981	100 N 1963	1981	2
White Islets	1923	279 Nc 1974	490 Nc 1986	1986	2,4,5,23

		TABLE 11. (Continued)				
			Colony History			
Location	First Record	Low Survey Results[1] Year	High Survey Results[1] Year	Recent Survey Results[1] Year		Source[2]

North Coast - Colonies > 100 nests or pairs

Location	First Record	Low Survey Results		Year	High Survey Results		Year	Recent Survey Results		Year	Source[2]
Anthony Island	1971	247	Nc	1977	352	Nc	1986			1986	16,17,22
Byers Islands	1976	61	Nc	1976	112	Nc	1988			1988	2,21
Conroy Island	1976	97	Nc	1976	208	Nc	1988			1988	2,21
Dugout Rocks	1976	133	Nc	1976	141	Nc	1988			1988	2,21
Egg Rock	1976	122	Nc	1976	140	Nc	1988			1988	2
Flatrock Island	1900	12	Nc	1972	145	Nc	1986			1986	5,16,21
Garcin Rock	1971	100	Nc	1971	102	Nc	1986			1986	2,22
Green Island	1920	84	Np	1976	248	Nc	1988			1988	2,5,21
Grey Islet	1976	48	Nc	1976	108	Nc	1988			1988	2,21
Joseph Island	1976	115	Nc	1976	245	Nc	1988			1988	2,21
Joyce Rocks	1977	94	Nc	1977	197	Nc	1986			1986	17,22
Langara Island	1926	50	Nc	1959	200	Nc	1958	73	Nc	1986	2,5,22
Major Brown Rock	1977	136	Nc	1977	299	Nc	1988			1988	2,21
Moore Islands	1936	67	Nc	1976	150	Nc	1988			1988	2,5,21
"Naden" Rocks	1977	42	Nc	1977	110	Nc	1986			1986	17,22
North Pointers	1976	109	Nc	1988	122	Nc	1976			1988	2,21
Sadler Island	1977	67	Nc	1977	114	Nc	1986			1986	17,22
Simpson Rocks	1976	155	Nc	1976	176	Nc	1988			1988	2,21
Tian Islets	1947	212	Nc	1988	289	Nc	1986			1988	5,17,21,22
Wells Rock	1970	90	Nc	1970	139	Nc	1976			1976	2

[1] B - breeding birds; C - nesting confirmed but no count or estimate made; N - nests; P - pairs; S - nesting suspected. All data are estimates unless noted as follows: c - complete count; p - partial count.

[2] 1 - Munro, J.A. and Cowan 1947; 2 - British Columbia Nest Records Scheme; 3 - Cooke 1915; 4 - Campbell 1976a; 5 - Drent and Guiguet 1961; 6 - Pyle and Sarles 1958; 7 - Rodway and Campbell 1977; 8 - Sprot 1936; 9 - Munro, J.A. 1925b; 10 - Hooper, T.D. 1988; 11 - Rodway et al. In prep.; 12 - Campbell and Stirling 1968a; 13 - Hatler et al. 1978; 14 - Guiguet 1971; 15 - Pearse 1946; 16 - Summers 1977; 17 - Campbell and Garrioch 1979; 18 - Carl et al. 1951; 19 - Vermeer et al. 1976; 20 - Sullivan 1985; 21 - Rodway In press; 22 - Rodway 1988; 23 - Vermeer and Devito 1989.

[3] On the breakwater.

[4] Gulls breeding in urban areas.

Figure 186. *Glaucous-winged Gull nest and eggs atop wooden pilings at Burrard Drydocks in Vancouver, 25 May 1975 (R. Wayne Campbell).*

Figure 187. *Young Glaucous-winged Gull away from nest on building window sill at Victoria, August 1987 (Tracey D. Hooper).*

Occasionally, nests were built entirely of seaweeds or eel-grass.

The dimensions for 366 nests ranged as follows:

outside diameter	20 to 86 cm
inside diameter	10 to 36 cm
outside height	4 to 41 cm
bowl depth	<1 to 20 cm

Eggs: Dates for 68,077 clutches ranged from 30 April to 20 August with 78% recorded between 5 and 26 June. Exceptionally bad weather can delay the timing of egg-laying (Verbeek 1986). Clutch size ranged from 1 to 5 eggs (1E-9,681, 2E-20,632, 3E-37,631, 4E-125, 5E-8), with 55% having 3 eggs (Fig. 186). Gulls will lay a second clutch if the first is destroyed, but it will usually contain fewer eggs. The incubation period for Mandarte Island gulls was about 27 days (Vermeer 1963; Verbeek 1986), based on the time from laying of the "c" egg to its hatching.

Glaucous-winged Gull eggs have also been found in active and inactive nests of Double-crested, Brandt's, and Pelagic cormorants, Great Blue Heron, Canada Goose, Bald Eagle, Black Oystercatcher, and Northwestern Crow.

Young: Dates for 13,178 broods ranged from 8 June to 8 September with 68% recorded between 7 and 25 July. Calculated dates indicate that young could be found as early as 3 June. Brood size ranged from 1 to 4 young (1Y-2,133, 2Y-4,587, 3Y-6,432, 4Y-26) with 84% having 2 or 3 young (Fig. 189). Fledging period ranges from 37 to 53 days with an average of 44 days (Vermeer 1963).

REMARKS: More specific information on the breeding biology and ecology of the Glaucous-winged Gull throughout its range in western North America can be found in Henderson (1972), McMannama (1951), Patten (1974), Vermeer (1963), J.G., Ward (1973), and Verbeek (1986).

This species interbreeds with the Western Gull in Washington (Scott, J.M. 1971; Hoffman et al. 1978) and British Columbia (Pearse 1946) and with the Herring Gull in Alaska (Williamson and Peyton 1963; Patten and Weisbrod 1974) and British Columbia (Merilees 1974b). This interbreeding creates a continuous gradation in primary feather pigmentation and abnormal plumages (see also Pearse 1947; Vermeer et al. 1963). Verbeek (1979) discusses timing of primary moult for this species in the province.

Glaucous-winged Gull chicks have been banded in British Columbia at various south coast colonies on and off since 1921 (Pearse 1923). Analysis of banding returns have shown that most Glaucous-winged Gulls disperse southward along the west coast of North America in autumn. Early reports by Pearse (1923) and Woodbury and Knight (1951) indicate that young Glaucous-winged Gulls disperse more widely, up to 2,050 km, than adults. This is supported by Gabrielson and Jewett (1970) and Baltz and Morejohn (1977). Recently, however, Butler et al. (1980) have shown that "although first-year gulls dispersed farther than older age classes, the mean dispersal distance between age classes showed little difference."

The most significant conclusion from banding returns is the seasonal shift in mortality of immatures that has occurred over the years as an apparent consequence of the increased gull population (Fig. 188).

The time of peak mortality has changed in the following manner:

1938 to 1941	January (Woodbury and Knight 1951)
1959 to 1963	November through February (van Tets 1968)
1966 to 1969	mid-winter
1975 to 1979	late summer and autumn

Verbeek (1986) suggests that the "food supply in the early autumn is no longer adequate to meet the demands of the adults and the recently fledged young, the latter losing out in the resulting competition".

First year mortality is about 60% (Butler, R.W. et al. 1980), and gulls rarely live beyond 15 years. The 5 oldest birds recorded from British Columbia were 20 years 62 days (Campbell 1968a), 21 years (Vermeer 1963), 25 years 6 months (Campbell 1975a), 29+ years (Wakefield 1987; K.S. Wakefield pers. comm.), and 32 years (J.B. Waddell pers. comm.; Brown, B. 1985).

POSTSCRIPT: In 1988 the total breeding population was estimated at 28,575 pairs, 49% found in the Strait of Georgia and 25% along the west coast of Vancouver Island. There are 331 nesting sites known in the province.

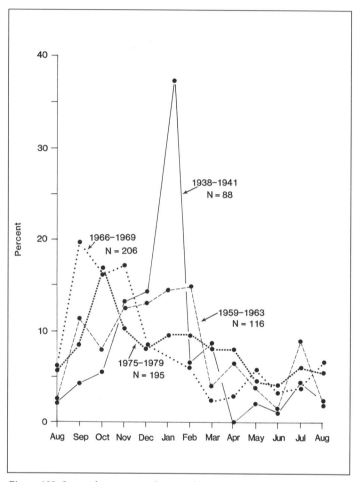

Figure 188. *Seasonal occurrence of 1-year old Glaucous-winged Gulls banded in British Columbia and recovered dead in western North America, expressed in percentage/month of annual mortality. Sample size and the years the birds were banded is shown for each curve (from Verbeek 1986).*

Glaucous-winged Gull

Figure 189. *Downy Glaucous-winged Gull chicks on Mitlenatch Island, 6 August 1966 (R. Wayne Campbell). Note band on right leg of front chick.*

NOTEWORTHY RECORDS

Spring: Coastal - Chain Islets 2 Mar 1974-3,000; Ganges Harbour Mar 1972-3,871 in Captain's Pass area at herring spawn (Rodway and Cambpell 1977); Delta 8 Mar 1975-3,000 at garbage dump; Iona Island 11 May 1974-2,000+; Departure Bay 6 Mar 1929-3,000 at herring spawn (Munro, J.A. and Clemens 1931); Tofino 12 Mar 1980-20,000 on mud flats; Englishman River to French Creek 10 Mar 1976-25,000 at herring spawn; Hesquiat Harbour 7 Mar 1976-2,000; Nanoose Harbour 7 Apr 1957-2,000; Lama Passage 7 Apr 1976-2,000; Burnaby Island 16 Apr 1985-600 on mud flat; Sandspit 11 Mar 1972-400; Kitimat 14 Mar 1975-1,550 on tidal flats off Eurocan dock; Rose Spit 29 Apr 1979-800; Skeena River 27 Mar 1977-2,800 at eulachon run, counted from Skeena to 72 km west of Terrace; Langara Point 23 May 1981-320 immatures roosting; Prince Rupert 1 Apr 1976-3,000; Finlayson Island 24 Mar 1987-11,000 on aerial survey; Alice Arm 10 and 11 Mar 1980-118. **Interior** - Okanagan Lake (Penticton) 5 May 1985-1 (RBCM Photo 1025); Okanagan Lake (Summerland) 4 Mar 1977-1; Squilax 2 Apr 1971-1.

Summer: Coastal - Clover Point 4 Jul 1976-150; Oak Bay to Mandarte Island 19 Jul 1961-900 counted over water during 3-hr boat trip; Imperial Eagle Channel 30 Aug 1977-1,336+ foraging; Fraser River 15 Jun 1973-1,250 roosting; Alta Lake 31 Aug 1932-several (Racey 1948); Comox Harbour 1 Jun 1969-1,000; Campbell River (Discovery Passage) 6 Jul 1968-504 mostly immatures; Checleset Bay 13 Jun 1978-1,500+ roosting on islet in evening; Storm Islands 4 Jul

1982-600, half adults and half immatures, roosting on reef; Sandspit 7 Aug 1957-350 (Mills 1960a); Langara Point 1 Jun 1981-208 roosting in tidal zone; Port Simpson 22 Jul 1969-456 off wharf; Green Island 21 Aug 1977-250+ arrived with California, Mew and Herring gulls. **Interior** - Whiskey Island 29 May 1972-1 adult mated to Herring Gull (Merilees 1974b).

Autumn: Interior - Kamloops 30 Nov 1980-1 adult near garbage dump; Swan Lake (Vernon) 8 Nov 1949-1 male (ROM 76586); Okanagan Landing late Nov 1984-1 (Rogers, T.H. 1984a). **Coastal** - Pearl Harbour 2 Sep 1969-200; Prince Rupert 29 Sep 1966-250; Minette Bay 19 Oct 1974-476; Graham Reach 27 Sep 1985-165; Cape Scott to Quatsino 2 Oct 1935-1,000; Salmon Point (Campbell River) 15 Sep 1974-600; Alta Lake 12 and 13 Sep 1946-present (Racey 1948); Point Holmes (Comox) 15 Nov 1939-2,000; Tofino Inlet 10 to 13 Nov 1961-500; Henderson Lake 16 Nov 1922-400+ (Munro, J.A. 1923); Hope 18 Nov 1968-45; Chain Islets 22 Oct 1975-1,025.

Winter: Interior - Kamloops 26 Dec 1986-3 adults, 1 immature; Anderson Lake 2 Feb 1922-1 immature male (ROM 24.11.3.4); Kelowna 20 Dec 1982-1 adult, 3 immature (RBCM Photo 839), 7 Jan 1983-1 (RBCM Photo 840); Okanagan Lake (Summerland) 27 Dec 1976-1; Penticton 26 Dec 1970-2 immatures (Rogers, T.H. 1971b). **Coastal** - Alice Arm 10 to 12 Dec 1980-92; Prince Rupert 23 Feb 1975-800 adults and 750 immatures along waterfront at noon; Kitimat 15 Dec 1974-416

adults and 416 immatures at dump in early afternoon, 20 Jan 1975-1,200 at Eurocan dock; Alliford Bay 12 Feb 1973-310; Tasu Sound 29 to 31 Jan 1973-148; Campbell River (Discovery Passage) 1 Feb 1975-1,532 at estuary; Nanoose Harbour 28 Feb 1974-5,000; Squamish River 29 Jan 1980-371; Indian Arm 4 Jan 1979-2,500; Sandhill Creek (Long Beach) 18 Feb 1982-8,000 at mouth, 21 Feb 1982-15,000 at mouth; Hope 5 Dec 1976-150; Stanley Park (Vancouver) 25 Jan 1974-1,000; Cultus Lake 10 Jan 1971-4,000; Burns Bog (Delta) 14 Jan 1973-10,000 in vicinity; Sarita River 10 Dec 1976-2,000+; Active Pass 28 Jan 1975-1,100; Cowichan Bay 22 Jan 1974-1,330 on wharf; Saanich 17 Dec 1983-2,500 at Hartland dump; Elk Lake (Saanich) 21 Jan 1984-5,000 resting on ice; Tod Creek 8 Dec 1983-9,000 on flats; Clover Point 5 Jan 1974-700.

Christmas Counts: Interior - Recorded from 3 of 19 localities and on 3% of all counts. Maxima: Shuswap Lake 22 Dec 1979-1; Penticton 27 Dec 1982-1. **Coastal** - Recorded from 28 of 28 localities and on 95% of all counts. Maxima: Ladner 28 Dec 1980-**44,832**, all-time North American high count (Monroe 1981); Vancouver 2 Dec 1959-35,442; Victoria 16 Dec 1978-14,943.

Extralimital Records: Interior - Fern Lake (Kwadacha Wilderness Park) 7 Sep 1979-1 (Cooper, J.M. and Adams 1979); Charlie Lake 9 Jun 1981-1 (Siddle 1982), 15 Jun 1983-1 with Herring, California, and Ring-billed gulls resting in field, 8 Jun 1983-1.

Glaucous Gull
Larus hyperboreus Gunnerus

GLGU

RANGE: Breeds in North America on Arctic coasts and islands of Alaska and Canada. Winters from the Bering Sea south along the Pacific coast to California and on the Atlantic coast from Labrador to Florida. Also occurs across northern Eurasia.

STATUS: On the coast, *rare* to *uncommon* winter visitant. In the interior, *very rare* to *rare* winter visitant.

OCCURRENCE: The Glaucous Gull occurs throughout the year in small, scattered numbers along the coast. It is most numerous in winter. In the interior, it has been recorded from widely separated locations, mostly in winter. Most interior records are from the Okanagan valley.

On the coast, it occurs chiefly in the vicinity of garbage dumps but also frequents fish processing plants, harbours, mud flats, beaches, sewage lagoons, log booms, flooded fields (Fig. 190), and fish spawning areas. Individuals usually associate with flocks of other roosting and feeding gulls such as Glaucous-winged and Herring gulls. In the interior, the Glaucous Gull frequents garbage dumps, as well as lakes, salmon spawning streams, rivers, and sewage lagoons.

Nearly 89% of all records are from coastal areas, and of those, 87% are from early November through mid-April. The main influx of wintering birds occurs in December and by late March only a few remain. Occasionally, individuals remain throughout the summer, mostly in the vicinity of garbage dumps. In winter, most birds are found near the Fraser River delta.

Similar results were found in the interior where 84% of records are for the period November through April. Extreme dates in the north are 2 October and 10 July (Fort St. John); in the south, they are 28 October (Salmon Arm) and 8 June (Thrums).

Nearly 90% of all records, excluding Christmas Counts, were of single birds. The largest group was 9 individuals counted at the Vancouver garbage dump during the winter of 1964-65. Of birds whose ages were recorded, 87% were first- or second-year birds. D.W. Johnston (1955) notes similar proportions in his study of distribution patterns of Glaucous Gulls in North America wintering south of their Arctic breeding grounds.

REMARKS: Extensive hybridization between the Glaucous Gull and the Herring Gull (*L. argentatus*) occurs in Iceland (Barth 1968), although sympatry without interbreeding apparently

exists in Canada (Smith, N.G. 1966). Hybridization also occurs with the Glaucous-winged Gull (*L. glaucescens*) in the eastern Bering Sea region (American Ornithologists' Union 1983).

Pacific coastal birds usually belong to the subspecies *L. h. barrovianus*; as were all specimens examined by Banks (1986).

Dwight (1925), D.W. Johnston (1961), and P.J. Grant (1982) should be consulted for discussions of problems concerning plumage variation and field identification. In particular, D.W. Johnston's study "should caution field observers in the identification of large white gulls in late winter, spring and summer, because a white-appearing gull is not necessarily *hyperboreus* but may be a worn, faded *glaucescens*."

***Figure 190.** Glaucous Gull at Delta, 1 March 1972 (Neil K. Dawe).*

NOTEWORTHY RECORDS

Spring: Coastal - Clover Point 1 Apr 1970-1 immature (RBCM Photo 96), 11 May 1968-2 (1 adult, 1 immature); Tofino 24 Apr 1976-2 immatures, 18 May 1931-1 female (UBC 5646), 25 May 1971-1 immature (RBCM Photo 181); Departure Bay 28 Mar 1928-5 (Munro, J.A. 1935d); Richmond 17 Mar 1985-3 immatures at dump; Nicomen Island 17 May 1972-4; Denman Island 23 May 1976-1; Comox 24 Apr 1969-1 immature; Sliammon 22 Mar 1981-3; Campbell River (Discovery Passage) 28 Apr 1980-2 immatures; Cape St. James 8 May 1982-3 immatures; Bella Bella 19 May 1979-1 immature; Kitimat 30 Apr 1975-1 immature; Langara Island 15 May 1947-1 immature (Johnston, D.W. 1955); Masset 20 Mar 1976-2 immatures; Prince Rupert 8 May 1983-8 along waterfront; 88 km w Terrace 27 Mar 1977-1 adult, 1 immature at eulachon spawn. **Interior -** Okanagan Landing 7 Apr 1938-1 immature female (MVZ 101334), 4 May 1944-1 immature female (MVZ 101333); Sorrento 14 May 1971-2; Prince George 1 May 1982-1 adult.

Summer: Coastal - Clover Point 12 Jun 1973-1 immature; Helby Island 25 Aug 1977-1 immature; Long Beach 4 Jun 1975-1 immature (Hatler et al.

1978); Vancouver 18 Jun 1972-1 immature at dump; Pender Harbour 30 Jul 1983-4; Comox 4 Aug 1937-1; Storm Islands 4 Jul 1982-2 immatures; Skonun Point 11 Jun 1984-1 (RBCM Photo 927); Rose Spit 30 Jul 1974-1. **Interior -** Thrums 8 Jun 1971-1 adult; Charlie Lake 24 Jun 1980-1 immature, 10 Jul 1980-1 immature; Cold Fish Lake 23 Jun 1976-1 (Osmond-Jones et al. 1977); Tatshenshini River 7 Jun 1983-1 immature (Campbell et al. 1983).

Autumn: Interior - Fort St. John 2 Oct 1986-1 immature; Bridge Lake 22 Nov 1981-1 immature; Adams River 31 Oct 1982-2 immatures; Salmon Arm 5 Nov 1970-2; Kamloops 19 Nov 1983-1, first winter bird; Skaha Lake 8 Nov 1966-1 immature. **Coastal** - Minette Bay 22 Oct 1974-1 immature; Comox 15 Sep 1903-1 (Johnston, D.W. 1955); Richmond 1 Sep 1971-1 immature (Campbell et al. 1972b); Ganges Harbour 22 Nov 1977-4; Victoria 3 Sept 1928-2 (Hagenstein 1928).

Winter: Interior - Adams River 9 Dec 1970-6 (Schnider et al. 1971); Sorrento 18 Dec 1970-3; Okanagan Landing 27 Dec 1965-2 (Rogers, T.H. 1966b); Kelowna 2 Jan 1977-1 adult, 2 immatures

at dump; Nelson 21 Jan 1977-1 immature at dump; Osoyoos Lake 11 Jan 1969-1 immature. **Coastal** - Prince Rupert 25 Jan 1979-1 immature; Kitimat 15 Dec 1974-1 immature; Masset 7 Dec 1945-1 (RBCM 11324); Alliford Bay 7 and 8 Jan 1942-1 immature (Cook, F.S. 1947); Tahsis Inlet Jan to May 1949-3 or 4 seen weekly (Mitchell 1959); Comox 18 Dec 1935-1 (RBCM 12869); Delta 1 Dec 1985-3, 31 Jan 1976-1 adult, 3 immatures, 26 Feb 1971-12 (total for 4 dumps in area - Campbell et al. 1972b); Long Beach 12 Feb 1983-1 adult, 2 immatures; Kildonan 11 Jan 1921-1 (RBCM 4972); Goldstream Park 14 Dec 1978-2 immatures, 11 Jan 1986-3 immatures.

Christmas Counts: Interior - Recorded from 3 of 19 localities and on 8% of all counts. Maxima: Penticton 26 Dec 1974-4; Shuswap Lake 21 Dec 1982-2. **Coastal** - Recorded from 14 of 28 localities and on 20% of all counts. Maxima: Ladner, 4 counts with 6 birds, 26 Dec 1970, 26 Dec 1977, 27 Dec 1982 and 23 Dec 1984; Victoria 19 Dec 1981-4; Vancouver 17 Dec 1972-3; Skidegate Inlet 15 Dec 1984-3.

Glaucous Gull

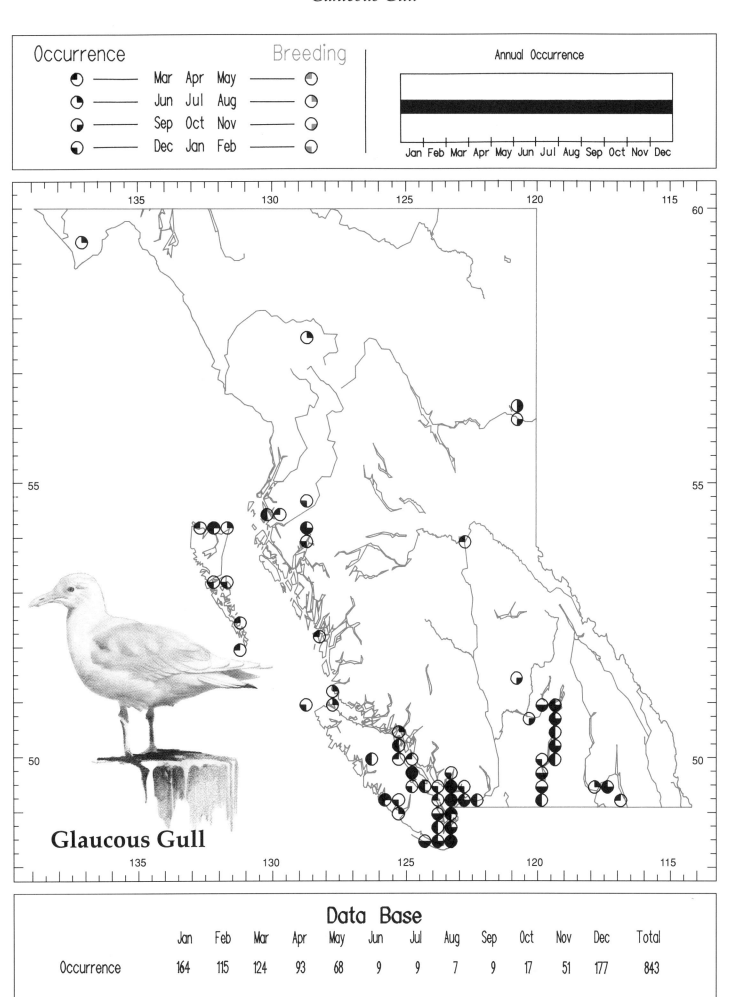

Occurrence

Breeding

	Mar	Apr	May	
	Jun	Jul	Aug	
	Sep	Oct	Nov	
	Dec	Jan	Feb	

Annual Occurrence

Jan Feb Mar Apr May Jun Jul Aug Sep Oct Nov Dec

Glaucous Gull

Data Base

	Jan	Feb	Mar	Apr	May	Jun	Jul	Aug	Sep	Oct	Nov	Dec	Total
Occurrence	164	115	124	93	68	9	9	7	9	17	51	177	843

Black-legged Kittiwake
Rissa tridactyla (Linnaeus)

BLKI

RANGE: Circumpolar. In North America, breeds on some high Arctic islands south to the Aleutian Islands and southern Alaska, Newfoundland, and southeastern Quebec. Nonbreeding birds occur in summer along the Arctic coast of Alaska and Canada, infrequently south along the Pacific coast to California. Winters along the Pacific coast from the southern Bering Sea and southern Alaska south to Baja California and along the Atlantic coast from Newfoundland south to North Carolina.

STATUS: *Abundant* spring and autumn migrant in offshore waters, *uncommon* in nearshore waters; *very rare* elsewhere. In summer, irregularly *abundant* to *very abundant* along outer coastal areas, *rare* in protected waters such as Juan de Fuca Strait and the Strait of Georgia. In winter, *very rare* in inshore waters, *uncommon* along the outer coast and probably *common* offshore. *Accidental* in the interior.

OCCURRENCE: The Black-legged Kittiwake is a pelagic gull that is more frequently encountered in offshore waters than nearshore and inner protected coastal waters. When away from the open ocean it can be found, often in substantial numbers, roosting on rocky islets and headlands (Fig. 191), sandy beaches, and spits. It often associates with other gulls. Frequently, large numbers are blown inshore by strong winds. When this happens, kittiwakes frequent a variety of coastal habitats including bays, harbours, surge narrows, estuaries, sewage lagoons, as well as open waters. Most of these birds are immatures. There is a single record from an interior lake.

It is well known that marine birds forage in mixed flocks (Morse, D.H. 1970). Along the British Columbia coast, the assemblages are mostly seen 1 to 3 km from shore from May to August when nonbreeding birds are present. Sealy (1973a) notes that the it was the most frequently seen species in mixed species flocks near Langara Island from 5 May to 8 August. Numbers ranged from 25 to 500 per flock and Sealy suggests that the Black-legged Kittiwake helped other species (e.g. Glaucous-winged Gull, Rhinoceros Auklet) find places where food was available.

Our knowledge of patterns of occurrence in British Columbia still remains somewhat confused. Numbers vary considerably from year to year. These fluctuations may be weather related, but most may be attributed to the lack of long term coastal studies. Records suggest that a spring movement occurs offshore, mainly from the second week in March through April and perhaps into May. At Victoria, for example, nearly 83% of all records (n=223)

Figure 191. *Nonbreeding Black-legged Kittiwakes roosting on Portland Point, Long Beach, Vancouver Island, 4 August 1969 (R. Wayne Campbell).*

are from the month of May. The largest spring flock (Reef Island) was 3,000 to 10,000 birds.

The Black-legged Kittiwake is most abundant in British Columbia from May through September (89% of records), the period when nonbreeding birds are present. At this time the ratio of immature versus adult-plumaged birds (n=2,615) is about 8:1. It is likely that many immatures do not fly directly to breeding grounds but remain in British Columbia waters from early spring to mid-autumn. Roosting flocks of nonbreeding birds may reach about 1,000 individuals; however, most groups are in the low hundreds.

The autumn movement begins in August, peaks in September, and is usually over by late October. A few birds remain as winter visitants along the outer coast.

REMARKS: There are 2 recognized subspecies, but only *Rissa tridactyla pollicaris* is found in British Columbia (American Ornithologists' Union 1957). Plumage characteristics are discussed in detail by P.J. Grant (1982).

NOTEWORTHY RECORDS

Spring: Coastal - Clover Point 29 May 1976-165; e Oak Bay 28 May to 4 Jun 1971-50; w Ucluelet 20 May 1949-150 to 200 (Martin and Myres 1969); Tofino 30 May 1976-150; Vancouver 3 Apr 1961-3 (Boggs and Boggs 1961b); Comox 28 Apr 1934-2 (CMNH 115457-58); Brooks Peninsula 12 Mar 1976-100; w Triangle Island (Scott Islands) 13 Mar 1976-200; w Goose Group 30 May 1948-20; Reef Island 22 Apr 1985-3,000 to 10,000, 13 to 14 May 1985-thousands with shearwaters; Tlell 9 Mar 1972-350, 11 Apr 1972-200; n Rose Spit 27 May 1983-335+. **Interior** - No records.

Summer: Coastal - Clover Point 2 Jun 1975-2 adults, 6 immatures, 18 July 1975-5 immatures; Oak Bay 4 Jun 1971-50; Imperial Eagle Channel 10 Jul 1973-1,200 feeding at entrance; Delta 29 Jun 1985-1 immature; Florencia Island 11 Jul 1975-300; Cleland Island 12 to 16 Jun 1975-120; McQuarrie Islets 23 Jun 1975-325; Campbell River (Discovery Passage) 27 Jun 1975-160+; Sutil Point 8 Jun 1975-120+; Solander Island 27 Jun 1975-550; Heater

Harbour 5 Jun 1985-40; Hippa Island 25 Aug 1983-110; Naden Harbour 1 Jul 1975-200; Masset Sound 10 Jun 1982-80; Shag Rock 28 Aug 1984-150; Rose Spit 21 Aug 1974-120; Hudson Bay Passage 6 Jul 1970-200 (Crowell and Nehls 1970d). **Interior** - No records.

Autumn: Interior - See Extralimital Records. **Coastal** - Green Island 9 Sep 1977-125, 17 Sep 1978-300, 18 Sep 1977-250, 9 Oct 1977-250+, 2 Nov 1978-4; Masset Sound 10 Oct 1982-10; Freeman Island 15 Sep 1983-30; Port Hardy 8 Sep 1937-10; Campbell River (Discovery Passage) 31 Oct 1982-250 at estuary; Iona Island 12 Sep 1971-3 (Campbell et al. 1972b); 11 Oct 1971-1 (RBCM Photo 183); Blackie Spit 13 Nov 1977-1 immature; Port Alberni 5 Sep 1977-1 immature; w Tofino 13 Sep 1969-800 (Crowell and Nehls 1970a); s Port Renfrew 5 Oct 1974-15; Victoria 2 Sep 1977-1 immature.

Winter: Interior - No records. **Coastal** - Green

Island 16 Dec 1977-10+; Triple Islands 11 Jan 1985-2; Beresford Island 14 Dec 1975-6 adults, 1 immature; Little Qualicum River estuary 12 Jan 1983-1 (RBCM 18265); Pitt Lake 13 Jan 1976-1 adult being eaten by an immature Red-tailed Hawk; White Cliff Point (West Vancouver) 6 Jan 1978-1 immature; La Perouse Bank 13 Feb 1977-33; Oak Bay 28 Feb 1976-2; Jordan River 12 Dec 1975-4 at mouth; Victoria 3 Dec 1968-3, 27 Dec 1907-1 immature male (MVZ 101394);

Christmas Counts: Interior - Not recorded. **Coastal** - Recorded from 2 of 28 localities and on 1% of all counts. Maxima: Victoria 18 Dec 1982-3, 21 Dec 1974-1, 16 Dec 1978-1; Nanaimo 26 Dec 1982-1.

Extralimital Records: Interior - Atlin Lake 7 Oct 1980-1 adult.

Black-legged Kittiwake

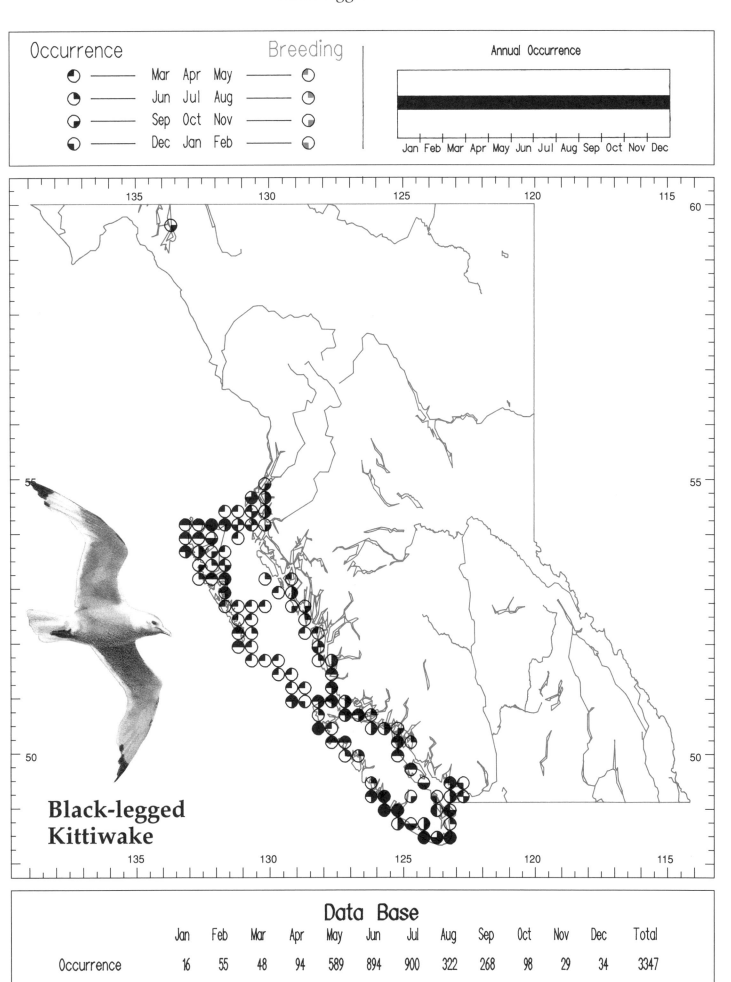

Occurrence   Breeding

◐ ———	Mar Apr May	——— ◑
◔ ———	Jun Jul Aug	——— ◔
◕ ———	Sep Oct Nov	——— ◒
◑ ———	Dec Jan Feb	——— ◓

Annual Occurrence

Jan Feb Mar Apr May Jun Jul Aug Sep Oct Nov Dec

Black-legged Kittiwake

Data Base

	Jan	Feb	Mar	Apr	May	Jun	Jul	Aug	Sep	Oct	Nov	Dec	Total
Occurrence	16	55	48	94	589	894	900	322	268	98	29	34	3347

Sabine's Gull
Xema sabini (Sabine)

SAGU

RANGE: Circumpolar in the high Arctic. In North America breeds on arctic coasts and islands in Alaska (south to Bristol Bay) and arctic Canada. Winters at sea in the eastern Pacific from Panama south to central Chile. Highly pelagic in migration.

STATUS: Offshore, a *very common* to *abundant* spring migrant, *abundant* to *very abundant* autumn migrant, and *very rare* in summer. *Very rare* in inner coastal waters during migrations and in summer, and *casual* in winter. In the interior, *casual* in spring, *very rare* in summer and autumn through eastern parts of the province.

OCCURRENCE: The Sabine's Gull migrates well offshore between its high Arctic breeding grounds and tropical wintering areas. It usually occurs in large flocks. Only a small portion of migrants are seen near land, and flocks there are rarely larger than 100 individuals.

Most records and largest numbers are from the late summer and autumn (Fig. 192). On the coast, stragglers are blown inshore by storms where they are seen in protected waters of the Juan de Fuca Strait and the Strait of Georgia (Campbell 1970a).

In the interior, the Sabine's Gull frequents large lakes, sewage lagoons, and rivers. Most records are of single birds, usually in company with other small gulls, such as Bonaparte's and Ring-billed gulls. One was observed at Okanagan Landing on 9 Sep 1897, hawking for insects with a flock of Common Nighthawks (Brooks 1900).

On the coast, spring migration usually begins in early April and in some years extends into early June. Records are too limited to detail peak movements and trends. A few stragglers remain on the coast all summer. Most summer records are from the central mainland coast between Laredo and Smith sounds. Autumn migration begins in late July, peaks in late August to mid-September, and most of the movement is over by early October. The earliest confirmed record of a bird-of-the-year was from the Goose Group on 20 July 1948 (RBCM 975). In winter, 1 or 2 birds have been reported from widespread areas along the coast, most from protected waters. In the interior, spring migrants have been recorded from late May and June, autumn migrants from August through late October.

The earliest spring dates for coastal areas are 4 February (Masset) and 1 March (Victoria), and the latest autumn date is 26 December (Iona Island). In the interior, the earliest spring dates are 27 May (Charlie Lake, Peace River), and 18 June (between Hudson Hope and Halfway River), and the latest autumn dates are 6 August (Charlie Lake) and 27 October (Adams River, Shuswap Lake).

REMARKS: Two subspecies migrate off the British Columbia coast: *Xema sabini woznesenskii* breeds in western Alaska, while *X. s. sabini* breeds in northern Alaska, Canada, and Siberia. The former subspecies is usually slightly darker. Vaurie (1965) questions the validity of the 2 subspecies.

Figure 192.Sabine's Gulls at La Perouse Bank, west of Vancouver Island, September 1985 (David F. Fraser).

NOTEWORTHY RECORDS

Spring: Coastal - Clover Point 1 Mar 1974-1 (Crowell and Nehls 1974c), 15 Apr 1969-1 (Campbell 1970a); La Perouse Bank 16 May 1985-30; w Ucluelet 3 Apr 1972-small flock, 17 May 1949-50+ (Martin and Myres 1969); w Tofino 2 May 1970-8 (Campbell and Shepard 1971); 8 May 1971-4 (Campbell and Shepard 1972), 19 May 1974-5; Iona Island 31 May 1975-1; Jericho Beach 29 May 1975-1; Esperanza Inlet 28 May 1966-66; Reef Island 2 May 1985-35+; Tlell 9 Mar 1972-1 in winter plumage; Masset Inlet 30 May 1975-50+ feeding along tide rip. **Interior** - Charlie Lake 27 May 1982-6 adults (Grunberg 1982).

Summer: Coastal - w Juan de Fuca Strait 29 Aug 1968-1,000 in 1 flock flying south; Cattle Point 28 Jun 1953-1; Swiftsure Bank 2 Aug 1946-300; Barkley Sound 31 Aug 1977-54; w Tofino 31 Jul 1971-6 (Campbell and Shepard 1972), 31 Aug 1964-40+; Iona Island 13 Jun 1973-16; w Goose Group 9 and 26 Jun 1948-1 (Guiguet 1953a); Hecate Strait 3 Jun 1970-39; Masset 7 Aug 1986-1, 9 Aug 1939-1 (Munro, J.A. and Cowan 1947); Port Simpson 13 Aug 1969-5. **Interior** - Sirdar 28 Aug 1947-1 female (ROM 82116); Sorrento 2 to 4 Jun 1971-1; Tupper Creek (Tupper) 2 Jun 1938-1 male (RBCM 7916); Fort St. John 4 Jun 1986-1 at sewage lagoons; Charlie Lake 3 Jun 1983-5, 6 Aug 1986-1; between Hudson Hope and Halfway River 18 Jun 1977-1 (RBCM Photo 694).

Autumn: Interior - Charlie Lake 1 and 8 Sep 1984-1 adult and 1 immature respectively; Fort St. John 19 Sep 1986-1 immature at sewage lagoons; Bowron Lake 18 and 23 Sep 1975-1 in summer plumage (O'Brien and Bell 1975); Myrtle Lake (Wells Gray Park) 17 Sep 1959-1 female (Edwards and Ritcey 1967); Buffalo Lake 16 Sep 1933-1 male (RBCM 11372); Adams River 27 Oct 1963-1 (Schnider et al. 1971); Okanagan Landing 9 Sep 1897-1 immature female MVZ 82102), 15 Sep 1931-1 male (MVZ 101399); Deadman Lake (Oliver) 3 Oct 1981-1 immature. **Coastal** - w Athlow Bay 22 Sep 1976-1 (McKelvey 1976); Queen Charlotte Strait 12 Sep 1968-6; Vargas Island 23 Oct 1977-1 female (RBCM 16245); Hornby Island 20 Sep 1978-1 immature; Pitt Lake 24 Sep 1978-1; Vancouver 31 Oct 1967-1; 22 km w Tofino 13 Sep 1969-500 (Campbell 1970a), 26 Sep 1970-90 (Campbell and Shepard 1971); La Perouse Bank 2 Sep 1984-500, 4 Sep 1983-150, 5 Sep 1982-900, 21 Sep 1974-46; Victoria 24 Oct 1963-5 (Campbell 1970a), 29 Oct 1963-7, 25 Nov 1966-6 (Campbell 1970a).

Winter: Interior - No records. **Coastal** - Masset 4 Feb 1942-1 female (RBCM 10538); Cumberland 20 Dec 1987-1 immature at garbage dump; Victoria 3 Dec 1968-3 (Crowell and Nehls 1969a), 7 Dec 1964-4, 10 Dec 1967-2 (Campbell 1970a); Point Grey (Vancouver) 7 Dec 1947-1 female (UBC 1669); Iona Island 26 Dec 1947-1 female (UBC 1670).

Christmas Counts: Interior - Not recorded. **Coastal** - Recorded once: Victoria 21 Dec 1963-1, all-time North American high count (tied with 6 United States localities; Monroe 1973, 1979, 1982).

Sabine's Gull

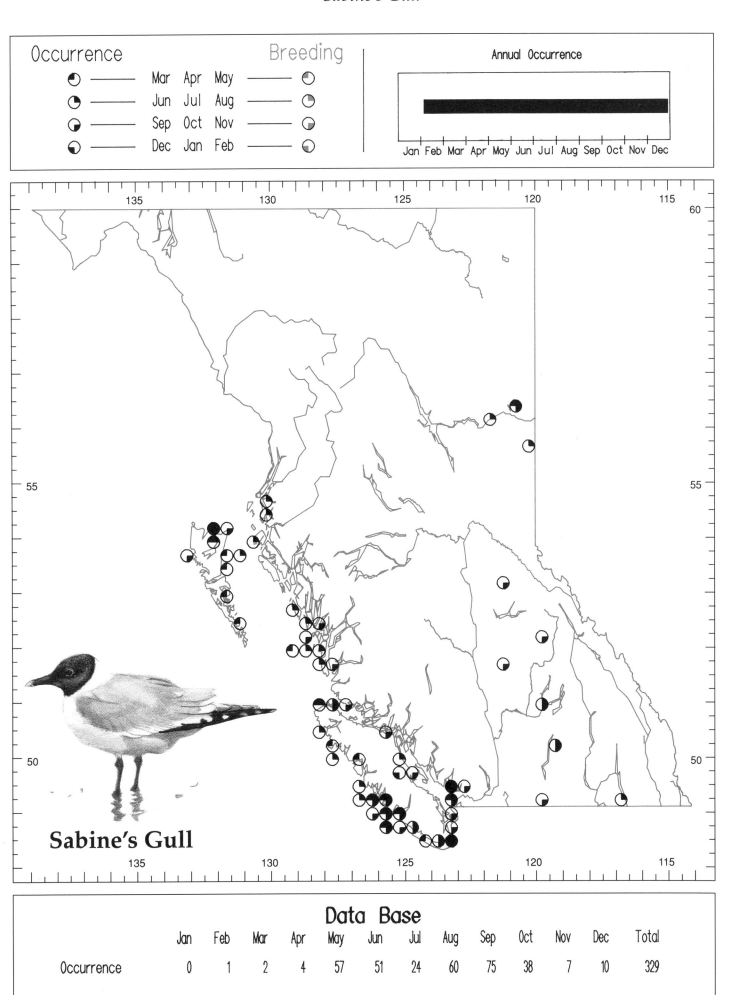

Caspian Tern
Sterna caspia Pallas

CATE

RANGE: Breeds locally in western North America from southwestern British Columbia, Washington and Oregon to Utah and Wyoming, south through interior of California to Baja California, and from south-central Mackenzie, central Saskatchewan and Manitoba, southeast to Great Lakes and northeast to Newfoundland. Also breeds on the Atlantic coast from Virginia to central Florida and along the Gulf coast to Texas and south into Mexico. Winters from central California south to Baja California and adjacent mainland Mexico, and from North Carolina south along the Atlantic and Gulf coasts to eastern Mexico and the West Indies. Also winters throughout the Old World.

STATUS: *Fairly common* to locally *very common* summer visitant on the southwest and southeast coasts of Vancouver Island, the Strait of Georgia, Juan de Fuca Strait, and the Fraser River delta. *Very rare* elsewhere along the coast including the Queen Charlotte Islands. In the interior, *very rare* summer visitant to the Okanagan valley; *casual* elsewhere. Local breeder.

CHANGE IN STATUS: The earliest records of the Caspian Tern (Fig. 193) in British Columbia are sightings of single birds in the Okanagan valley in 1905, 1910, and 1922 (Brooks 1912; Brooks and Swarth 1925). They are considered hypothetical by J.A. Munro and Cowan (1947), but are accepted by R.A. Cannings et al. (1987). The first coastal record is of 2 birds seen at Nanaimo in 1959 (Davidson 1963). During the next decade, the Caspian Tern became a regular summer visitor to southern coastal areas of the province (Campbell 1971c). Its status was upgraded to a rare summer visitant on the southwest coast but it remained a casual summer visitant in the interior. This trend in northern range expansion of the Caspian Tern correlated with the establishment and growth of breeding colonies in California (Gill 1977) and Washington (Alcorn 1958; Penland 1981).

Figure 193. Two Caspian Terns, of a flock of seven, on sandbars in the Okanagan River at the north end of Osoyoos Lake, 26 June 1975 (Ervio Sian).

Figure 194. Florencia Bay, August 1967 (R. Wayne Campbell). Protected bays on the west coast of Vancouver Island are preferred foraging locations.

Caspian Tern

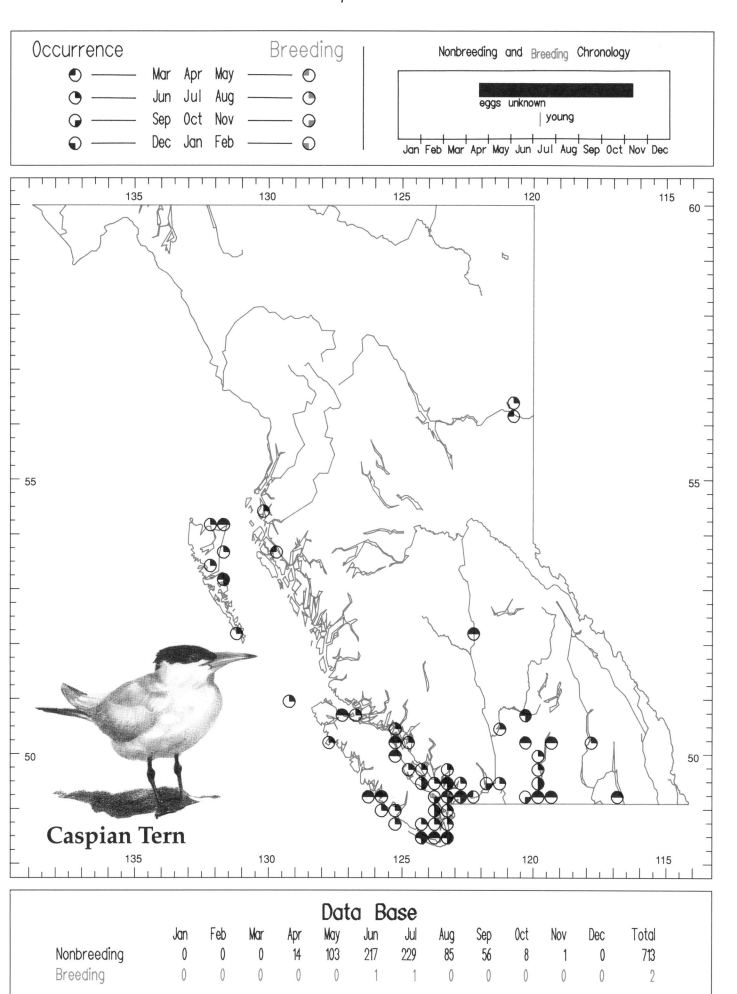

During the 1970s, the number of records and sizes of flocks increased gradually; since 1980, they have increased dramatically, especially in the vicinity of the southern Strait of Georgia. In the Vancouver area, nearly 58% of all records are from 1980 to 1986; during this period, flocks of up to 84 terns were seen. In the same period, the Caspian Tern expanded its range to the north coast and Queen Charlotte Islands.

The El Niño current, bringing warm waters to the eastern Pacific in 1983 and 1984, may have contributed to the northward extension of range, but the extension is most likely due to a general population expansion of breeding colonies along the Pacific coast. In the early 1900s, the Caspian Tern population gradually shifted from interior freshwater nesting sites to coastal areas (Gill and Mewaldt 1983). Populations became well established on human-created habitats and increased dramatically. From the mid-1960s through the 1970s, breeding numbers in the San Francisco, California area increased from about 400 pairs to 1,500 pairs (Gill 1977). Colonies in Gray's Harbor and Willapa Bay, Washington increased from 50 pairs in 1957 to 3,000 pairs in 1981 (Alcorn 1958; Penland 1976).

Gill and Mewaldt (1983) estimate that in 1981 about 6,000 pairs of Caspian Terns nested in 24 colonies at 20 sites along the Pacific coast, a 74% increase over numbers reported at the sites in the early 1960s. They also predict that, given suitable habitat, Caspian Terns could soon be found nesting from coastal British Columbia to southeast Alaska. Breeding was first documented in British Columbia in 1984.

NONBREEDING: The Caspian Tern occurs along the inner and outer coast from southern Vancouver Island north to Prince Rupert and the Queen Charlotte Islands and throughout the Fraser Lowlands to Hope. In the interior, it has been found throughout the Thompson-Okanagan Plateau, and in the west Kootenay, Chilcotin-Cariboo Basin, and Peace Lowlands.

On the coast, it frequents beaches, tidal mudflats, and sheltered bays (Fig. 194) where it forages over shallow water. Favourite roosting and loafing areas include sandbars, mudflats, beaches, and rocks, where it often associates with gulls. Most records near Vancouver are from mudflats at Roberts Bank, Iona Island, and Boundary Bay. In the interior, the Caspian Tern frequents larger lakes where it is usually found loafing on sand spits and shores (Fig. 193).

Extreme dates for the coast are 19 April and 11 November, and for the interior, 7 May and 10 November. Of all records (n=713), 95% are from coastal areas; 32% are from July, while 77% are from May to July.

BREEDING: There are only 2 records, probably involving the same birds, both from Roberts Bank in the summer of 1984. On 21 June an adult with two flightless chicks was seen along a sandy strip of beach near the jetty and on 10 July a single large young was photographed in the same area (Fig. 195).

REMARKS: The Caspian Tern is often placed in the monotypic genus *Hydroprogne*.

Figure 195. *Adult Caspian Tern with recently fledged young at Roberts Bank, 10 July 1984 (Ervio Sian). This is the only breeding record for British Columbia.*

NOTEWORTHY RECORDS

Spring: Coastal - Esquimalt Lagoon 19 Apr 1982-1; Florencia Bay 13 May 1982-3; Blackie Spit 28 Apr 1984-5; Mud Bay (Surrey) 16 May 1984-84 adults; Roberts Bank 9 May 1981-73, 25 May 1980-35; Miracle Beach Park 19 May 1983-4; Klewnuggit Inlet 29 May 1983-2; Alliford Bay 13 May 1983 (Campbell 1983c); Rose Spit 27 May 1983-1 (Campbell 1983c). **Interior** - Oliver 25 May 1982-20; Okanagan River (Osoyoos Lake) 7 May 1922-1 (Brooks and Swarth 1925); Kalamalka Lake 29 and 31 May 1972-2; Chapperon Lake 12 May 1984-1; Kamloops 17 May 1984-2; Williams Lake 9 May 1987-2 adults; Peace River 24 May 1975-3.

Summer: Coastal - Sooke River estuary 2 Jun 1985-14, 16 Jun 1985-50; Port Renfrew 1 Jul 1978-7; Chesterman Beach 14 Jun 1983-7, 30 Jun 1984-12; Stubbs Island (Tofino) 12 Jun 1987-21, 3 Jul 1984-24 (RBCM Photo 942); Blackie Spit 2 Jul 1981-34; Roberts Bank 6 Jun 1985-49, 28 Jul 1981-34; Iona Island 4 Jun 1984-24, 12 Jul 1983-65, 23 Aug 1981-35; Cleland Island 14 Jun 1976-10, 12 Jul 1979-11; Brooks Peninsula 7 Aug 1981-1 (Campbell and Summers In press); Triangle Island (Scott Islands) 12 Jul 1984-4; Sandspit 6 and 8 Jul 1983-4; Rose Spit 28 Aug 1987-3; Prince Rupert 18 Jun 1985-4. **Interior** - Osoyoos Lake 9 Jun 1985-2, Jul 1905-1 (Brooks 1912); Okanagan Landing 8 Jul 1910-1 (Brooks 1912); Nakusp 19 Jun 1982-2 (Campbell 1982c); Chapperon Lake 10 Jul 1982-2; Tranquille 10 Jul 1978-2 adults; Williams Lake 24 Aug 1985-1 adult; Charlie Lake 4 Jul 1984-2.

Autumn: Interior - Kamloops 12 Sep 1986-1; Tranquille 1 Sep 1980-2, 12 and 13 Sep 1987-1 adult and 1 immature; Vaseux Lake 10 Nov 1932-1; Cathedral Lakes 7 Oct 1984-1 found dead (Campbell 1985a). **Coastal** - Sandspit 6 Sep 1985-3; Hope 15 Sep 1978-3; Little Qualicum River estuary 22 Sep 1974-2 (Dawe 1976); Brockton Point 12 Oct 1983-10+; Roberts Bank 12 Sep 1982-7; Mud Bay (Surrey) 7 Oct 1975-1; White Rock (Boundary Bay) 11 Nov 1971-1 (Crowell and Nehls 1972a); Duncan 25 Sep 1970-2 (Tatum 1971); Victoria 22 Sep 1976-1.

Winter No records.

Common Tern

COTE

Sterna hirundo Linnaeus

RANGE: Breeds in North America from Alberta east to Newfoundland and south to northeastern Montana, South Dakota, southern Michigan, northern Ohio, northern and central New York, and on the Atlantic coast to North Carolina; also southeastern Texas and Florida. Winters along the coasts of the southern United States, but mostly in South America. Also found in the Old World.

STATUS: *Common* to *abundant* spring transient, *very common* to *very abundant* late summer and autumn transient in the vicinity of the Strait of Georgia and Juan de Fuca Strait. In the southern interior, *uncommon* to *fairly common* spring transient, *fairly common* to *common* late summer and autumn transient. *Uncommon* transient in the Peace River area. *Casual* elsewhere.

OCCURRENCE: The Common Tern is a transient in the Strait of Georgia, Juan de Fuca Strait, the southern interior, and northeastern British Columbia. On the coast, it frequents open marine waters as well as bays, estuaries, harbours, lagoons, narrows, and beaches. It frequently rests on kelp beds (Fig. 196), floating driftwood, and log booms. Fewer numbers are seen in spring than in autumn. Migrants have been reported in late April but most arrive in early May with numbers peaking in mid-May. Most birds are gone by late May, although a few immatures may remain through June to mid-July. Autumn migrants begin to arrive in late July; large numbers are present from late August to mid-October when numbers decline rapidly into November.

Monthly high counts in the southern Strait of Georgia are as follows: March-10, April-13, May-1,200, June-24, July-100, August-650, September-3,000, October-100, and November-130.

In the interior, the Common Tern is seen less frequently; only 17% of all records are from east of the Coast Ranges. Most interior records are from large lakes in the vicinity of the Okanagan valley. Spring migrants have been recorded as early as late April and early May but most pass through during the latter half of May. A few immatures from widely separated locations are reported in June and July each year. Autumn migration is evident by late August, peaks around mid-September, and most have passed through by the end of the month. Stragglers have been found in southern areas in late October.

Extreme dates for the coast are 28 March and 29 November; for the interior they are 30 April and 28 October.

REMARKS: There are 2 published winter records, both without supporting documentation; they are considered hypothetical:

Surrey 27 Dec 1961-5 (Holdom 1962), Victoria 10 Dec 1967-4 (Crowell and Nehls 1968b). It is difficult to separate juvenile Common and Arctic terns in the field; consult P.J. Grant and Scott (1969) for identification.

The Common Tern appears on the "Blue List" from 1978 to 1981 (Tate 1981) but it was delisted to a species of "special concern" in 1982 (Tate and Tate 1982).

Figure 196. Common Terns at rest on kelp in Oak Bay, Victoria, September 1975 (R. Wayne Campbell).

NOTEWORTHY RECORDS

Spring: Coastal - 1.6 km w Victoria 4 May 1962-200+ (Boggs and Boggs 1962c); Crescent Beach 8 May 1940-22; Iona Island 25 Apr 1982-13, 16 May 1971-1,200 (Campbell et al. 1972b); 8 km w Fraser River delta 27 Apr 1936-3 females (MCZ 282375-282377); Seymour Narrows 18 May 1975-400+. **Interior** - Trail 18 May 1973-1; Okanagan Landing 6 May 1940-2, 21 May 1927-60; Chapperon Lake 9 May 1982-30; Shumway Lake 5 May 1984-24; Columbia Lake 6 May 1939-2 adults (Johnstone, W.B. 1949); Shuswap Lake 13 May 1970-1, 24 May 1980-17; Bridge Lake 19 May 1958-2 (Erskine and Stein 1964); Williams Lake 30 Apr 1980-7, 30 May 1980-5 adults; Fort St. John 24 May 1985-1 adult; Boundary Lake (Goodlow) 29 May 1983-2 adults.

Summer: Coastal - Clover Point 22 Jul 1984-6, 31 Jul 1973-100 (Crowell and Nehls 1973d); Gonzales Point 30 Aug 1983-850; Tsawwassen 13 Jun 1976-4 off jetty; Boundary Bay 30 Jun 1976-4, 16 Jul 1969-100+, 21 Aug 1962-500, 31 Aug 1982-450;

Mitlenatch Island 16 Jul 1969-2; Alta Lake 21 Aug 1937-17 (Racey 1948). **Interior** - Osoyoos Lake 18 Jun 1974-1 (Cannings, S.G. 1974), 8 Aug 1970-11; Lone Duck Lake (Manning Park) late Jul 1973-1 (Belton 1973); Okanagan Lake (Summerland) end Jul 1974-100+ (Cannings, S.G. 1974); Merritt 10 Jul 1982-3; Columbia Lake 28 Aug 1948-30 (Johnstone, W.B. 1949); Golden 12 Jun 1979-3; Emerald Lake (Yoho National Park) 22 Aug 1977-4 (Wade 1977); Chilcotin Lake 6 Jun 1977-10+; Williams Lake 20 Jun 1979-1, 17 Aug 1979-20, 24 Aug 1985-40 (10 immatures); Bowron Lake 16 Aug 1975-9 (O'Brien and Bell 1975); Tupper Creek (Tupper) 26 Jun 1938-1 male (RBCM 7919); Boundary Lake (Goodlow) 10 Jun 1984-6; Charlie 11 Aug 1977-100+; Fern Lake (Kwadacha Wilderness Park) 17 Aug 1983-6 (Cooper, J.M. and Cooper 1983); Kotcho Lake 26 Jun 1982-1 (RBCM 17638), 2 Jul 1982-6 (Campbell and McNall 1982).

Autumn: Interior - Swan Lake (Tupper) 2 Sep

1981-25; Williams Lake 4 Sep 1984-20 (10 immatures); Columbia River (Revelstoke) 6 Sep 1983-23; Campbell Lake (Kamloops) 5 Sep 1950-35; Columbia Lake 28 Oct 1945-5 (Johnstone, W.B. 1949); Nicola Lake 2 Sep 1977-14, 9 Oct 1981-3; Sirdar 2 Sep 1947-30, 10 Sep 1947-75, 11 Sep 1947-30; Osoyoos Lake 15 Sep 1984-50, 24 Oct 1971-15. **Coastal** - Bardswell Group 19 Sep 1935-1 female (MCZ 282374); Powell River 11 Oct 1976-8 on log booms; Little Qualicum River estuary 4 Sep 1976-40, 10 Oct 1976-3 (Dawe 1980); Tofino 12 Sep 1974-2, 29 Nov 1972-1 (Hatler 1973); Stanley Park (Vancouver) 4 Oct 1982-286; Spanish Bank 2 Nov 1975-1; Blackie Spit 9 Sep 1973-485 (Crowell and Nehls 1974a), 20 Sep 1984-500; Victoria 8 Sep 1979-2,550, 27 Sep 1979-3,000, 2 Oct 1983-1,500, 16 Oct 1977-1,000, 9 Nov 1983-250, 28 Nov 1983-5.

Winter: No records.

Common Tern

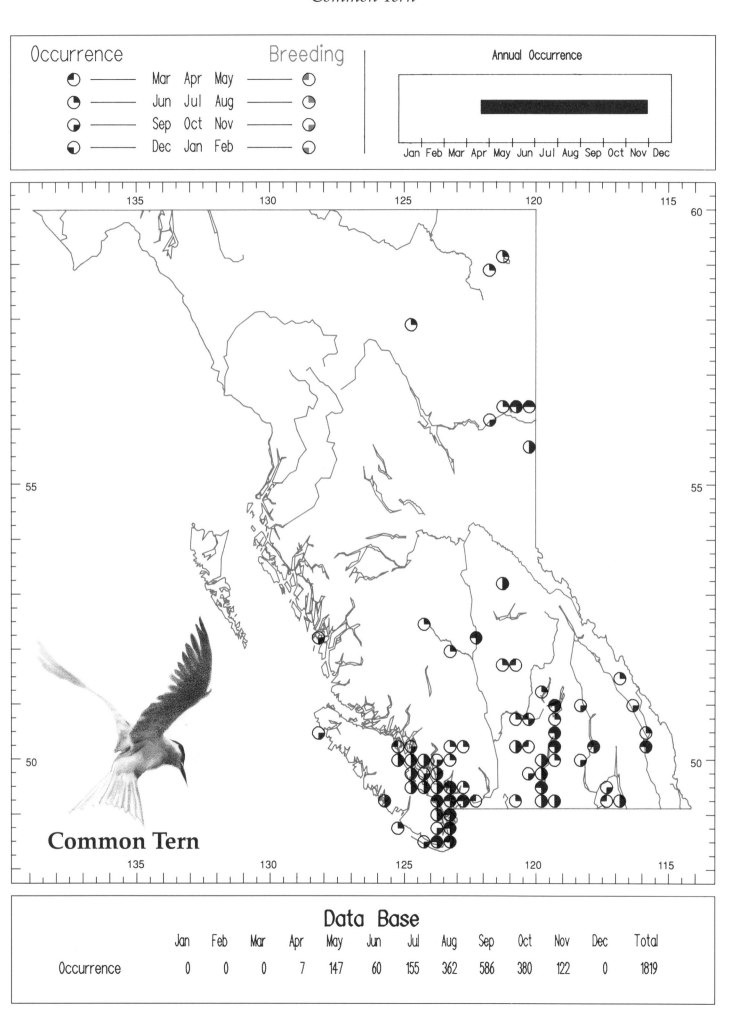

Common Tern

Data Base

	Jan	Feb	Mar	Apr	May	Jun	Jul	Aug	Sep	Oct	Nov	Dec	Total
Occurrence	0	0	0	7	147	60	155	362	586	380	122	0	1819

Arctic Tern

Sterna paradisaea Pontoppidan

RANGE: In North America breeds from the high Arctic coasts south to the Aleutian Islands, Alaska, northwestern British Columbia, and across northern and Atlantic Canada and locally in Washington and Massachusetts; also breeds in northern Eurasia. Winters in the oceans of the Southern Hemisphere.

STATUS: Migrates at sea. *Rare* spring and *uncommon* to *fairly common* autumn migrant on the coast, mostly offshore. *Very rare* spring and *rare* autumn migrant in the interior. Breeds.

NONBREEDING: The Arctic Tern has a scattered but widespread distribution throughout the province. It migrates primarily far offshore, passing to and from its breeding grounds in the Arctic and its wintering grounds in the Antarctic. Small numbers appear in outer and inner coastal areas of British Columbia during its passage in spring and autumn. It is recorded far less frequently during the spring movement.

Spring migration occurs from late April through mid-May. Infrequently, a few stragglers are seen in summer through mid-July. Autumn migration begins in late July and continues into the first two weeks of September. A few stragglers linger into October. The peak movement probably occurs during the first half of August.

In the interior, very early spring migrants have appeared in April but most are seen during the latter half of May. Most autumn records are from late July through mid-August. Lakes and marshes are preferred habitats in British Columbia. Arctic Terns have been found from sea level to 1,554 m elevation.

No large flocks of migrating Arctic Terns have been reported in British Columbia. Most records (71%) are of single birds in autumn; the largest flock was of 10 individuals. Extreme dates for coastal areas are 27 April and 14 October; for the interior they are April (date unknown) and 15 May and 30 September.

Figure 197. Arctic Tern on nest near Tatshenshini River in Chilkat Pass, July 1980 (R. Wayne Campbell).

Figure 198. Kelsall Lake in Chilkat Pass, August 1980 (R. Wayne Campbell). Several pairs of Arctic Terns nest on gravel bars and sand beaches surrounding the lake.

Arctic Tern

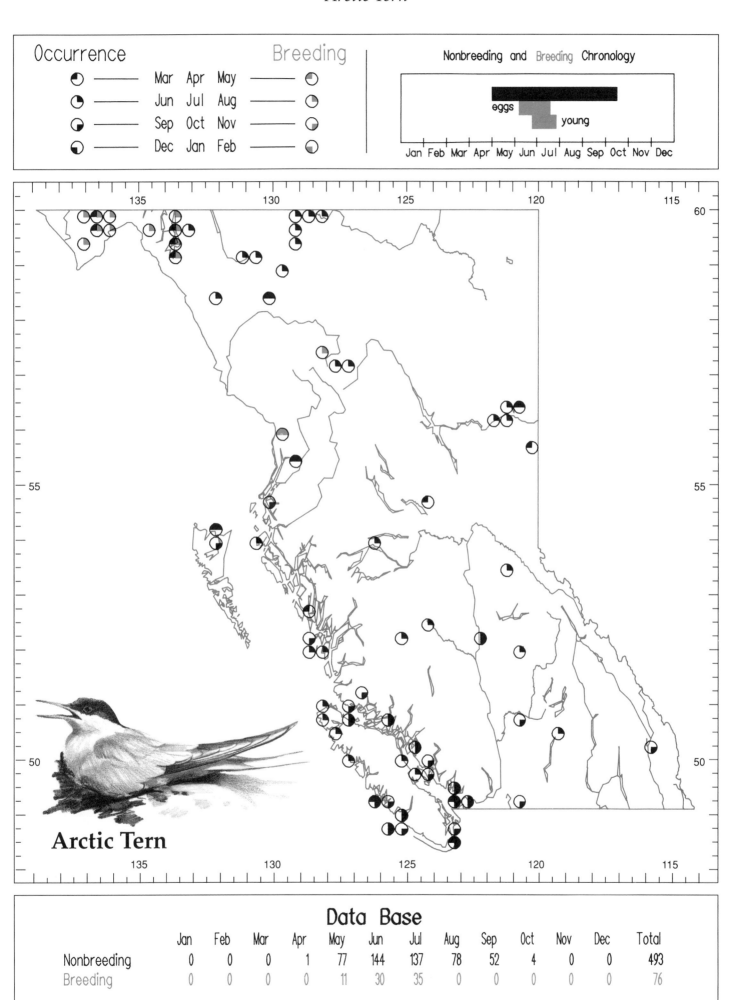

Figure 199. Arctic Tern breeding habitat at the Tatshenshini River, July 1983 (R. Wayne Campbell). Note the agitated bird and the nest with 2 eggs.

TABLE 12.
Arctic Tern: history and size of the colony at Stewart, British Columbia, 1960 to 1972.[1]

Year	Spring arrival	First eggs	Total nests	Estimated pairs	First young	Last seen
1960	14 May	21 May	2[2]	5	—	—
1961	13 May	22 May	4	7	9 June	2 July
1962	8 May	10 June[3]	2	5	—	—
1963	15 May	26 May	2	7	—	7 July
1964	14 May	24 May	1	4	—	—
1965	16 May	23 May	2	8	—	—
1966	15 May	5 June	1	6	—	—
1972	—	2 July[4]	2	5	—	—

[1] Data in letter from P.F. Blokker dated 24 January 1973 to Canadian Wildlife Service.

[2] Most nests contained 2 eggs; several had 3 eggs.

[3] Disturbance due to dyke construction.

[4] Due to flooding conditions.

BREEDING: The Arctic Tern (Fig. 197) breeds in northwestern British Columbia (Fig. 198) from the vicinity of the Tatshenshini River east to Atlin Lake and south to Spatsizi Plateau (57°15'N, 128°10'W) and Stewart. It breeds in isolated pairs or small loose colonies in subalpine wetlands, gravel river bars (Fig. 199), and on islands in large lakes. Most nests have been found between 670 and 1,006 m elevation.

The total breeding population is not known. Only the colony at Stewart has a history of continuous visits. From 1960 to 1966, and in 1972, the colony ranged in size from 4 to 8 pairs (Table 12). Between 1960 and 1966 the colony was located on the tide flats at the head of Portland Canal. A small sawmill was constructed on the site and the terns relocated to a low gravel bar directly in the flightpath of the Stewart airport. The present status of the colony is unknown.

Nests: Most nests were depressions or scrapes in the bare ground with no nest material. Occasionally, nests were lined with a few dead leaves or dry grasses. The most substantial nest was situated on a 50 cm wide rock and consisted of a 2.5 cm pad of twigs and grasses required to accommodate eggs on the hard, uneven surface of the rock. Nests were usually at the water's edge but several were up to 20 m from water.

In subalpine areas (e.g. Chilkat Pass) they were mere depressions on mounds of sphagnum at the edge of a pond or on hummocks in the pond. In forested areas, nests were found on gravel river bars as shallow scrapes in sand. At large lakes, all nests found were on rocky, relatively open islands.

Eggs: Dates for 40 clutches ranged from 20 May to 16 July with 21 clutches recorded between 26 May and 15 June. Clutch size ranged from 1 to 3 eggs (1E-6, 2E-30, 3E-4), with 75% having 2 eggs (Fig. 199). Incubation period is 21 to 22 days (Godfrey 1986).

Young: Dates for 29 broods ranged from 9 June to 24 July with 15 broods recorded between 4 and 16 July (Fig. 200). Fledged young have been recorded as early as 16 July (Atlin Lake), and all records after that date are of recently fledged young. Brood size ranged from 1 to 3 young (1Y-4, 2Y-22, 3Y-2) with 76% having 2 young. Fledging period is 20 to 22 days (Harrison, C. 1978).

REMARKS: A small breeding colony of Arctic Terns has been established in Washington state since 1977 (Manuwal et al. 1979).

Figure 200. *Arctic Tern chick at Atlin Lake, 5 July 1980 (R. Wayne Campbell).*

NOTEWORTHY RECORDS

Spring: Coastal - Victoria 16 May 1974-9 (Crowell and Nehls 1974c); Iona Island 4 May 1974-1 (Shepard, M.G. 1975a); Steveston 4 May 1981-1; 7 km w Tofino 19 May 1974-1; Masset Sound 30 May 1983-1; Kitsault 13 to 17 May 1980-1; Stewart 8 May 1962-1. **Interior** - Pinchi 30 May 1977-2; Tupper Creek (Tupper) 29 May 1938-1 (Cowan 1939); Charlie Lake 25 May 1983-9 adults; Dease Lake 29 Apr 1894-1 male (RBCM 1486); Atlin 11 May 1934-1 (Swarth 1936), 17 May 1981-4 spring arrival (Campbell 1981), 19 May 1977-1 adult spring arrival; Chilkat Pass 15 May 1977-1 adult, 16 May 1977-3 adults.

Summer: Coastal - Cadboro Bay 18 Aug 1974-2;

Barkley Sound 26 Aug 1977-3; Iona Island 8 Aug 1982-4; Burrard Inlet 10 Jun 1985-1 adult; Cleland Island 30 Aug 1977-5; Rugged Point 22 Jun 1975-2; Lawn Point (Quatsino Sound) 27 Aug 1967-4; Cape Russell (San Joseph) 27 Aug 1967-8; Cape Scott 27 Aug 1967-10; Port Hardy 30 Aug 1938-7; Wiah Point 16 Aug 1947-1 male (UBC 1490). **Interior** - Manning Park 17 Aug 1968-1; Okanagan Lake 15 Jul 1961-3 adults; Charlotte Lake (Kleena Kleene) 21 Jul 1974-1 (RBCM Photo 363); Chezacut Lake 30 Jul 1931-1 adult female (UBC 3100); Williams Lake 11 Aug 1936-8 (Munro, J.A. and Cowan 1947); Ootsa Lake 10 Aug 1976-3; Indianpoint Lake 27 Aug 1931-3 (MCZ 282394-96); Charlie Lake 8 Jun 1983-2

adults, 24 Aug 1986-2 adults; Butte Lake 1 Jul 1977-3 adults; Chilkat Pass 17 Jun 1972-30 in small groups.

Autumn: Interior - Williams Lake 3 Sep 1978-1 adult and 2 immatures, 10 Sep 1978-1 adult; Columbia Lake 30 Sep 1944-1 male (RBCM 11154). **Coastal** - Seymour Inlet 18 Sep 1967-7; Port Hardy 10 Sep 1938-6; Bargain Harbour 10 Oct 1978-6; Ferguson Point 1 Sep 1973-5; Blackie Spit 14 Oct 1984-1 immature.

Winter: No records.

Forsters's Tern

Sterna forsteri Nuttall

FOTE

RANGE: Breeds from southeastern British Columbia and across southern Canada to Manitoba, south through eastern Washington and Oregon to southern California, Colorado and Iowa. Also along Atlantic coast from New York to North Carolina, and Gulf coast from Alabama to Mexico. Winters on the Pacific and Atlantic coasts from central California and Virginia south to Mexico.

STATUS: *Uncommon* summer visitant and local breeder in the Creston valley. *Very rare* in the Thompson-Okanagan Plateau; *casual* in the Peace Lowlands. *Very rare* in late summer and early autumn on the extreme southern coast.

CHANGE IN STATUS: J.A. Munro and Cowan (1947) include the Forster's Tern on the extralimital list for British Columbia birds on the basis of a specimen collected at Okanagan Lake in 1928. During the next 46 years there was only 1 additional record, from Nelson, in 1943. Since 1974, however, "white terns," probably Forster's Terns, have been reported near Creston nearly every summer (Goossen et al. 1982). Breeding was suspected in 1976 but was not confirmed until 1980. Goossen et al. (1982) suggest that Forster's Terns were probably prevented from colonizing areas near Creston because of annual flooding. Dyking and water control activities, providing stable and suitable nesting habitat in the Creston valley, probably contributed to the successful establishment of the small breeding colony there. During the late 1970s and early 1980s, single birds have been seen regularly in late summer and early autumn on the extreme south coast.

NONBREEDING: The Forster's Tern (Fig. 201) occurs primarily in the vicinity of the Creston valley but wanderers have been recorded near Merritt, in the north and south Okanagan valley, and at Fort St. John in the Peace Lowlands region. On the coast, it has been found on the Fraser River delta and at Victoria. It frequents lakes and marshes in the interior and shallow, inshore marine and brackish waters on the coast.

Migration periods are not well known. Birds probably return to breeding areas during the second and third weeks of May. Autumn migration may begin in late July but occurs mostly in August. On the coast, autumn migration is evident from late July through mid-October. The largest group (21 birds) was reported near Creston on 25 May 1980.

Extreme dates for the interior are 1 May and 20 September and for the coast they are 12 July and 18 October.

In the Noteworthy Records section, all coastal but only select interior occurrences are listed.

BREEDING: The Forster's Tern breeds only at Duck Lake in the Creston Valley Wildlife Management Area. The colony is situated in a shallow, freshwater marsh with a heavy growth of submerged aquatic plants and dense stands of emergents including cattail and reed canarygrass. The colony, possibly present since 1974, was first confirmed in 1980 (Goossen et al. 1982). The nearest breeding colonies are located at Stobart Lake, Alberta (310 km northeast), Ninepipe National Wildlife Refuge, Montana (270 km southeast), and Brook Lake, Washington (280 km southwest).

In 1980 the size of the colony was estimated at 5 pairs. Subsequently, 9 nests were found in 1981, 4 in 1983, 6 in 1984, and nesting was confirmed for 1987 although nest counts were not made (Anonymous 1987).

Nests: Nests were described in 1980 as composed of "plant stems and a few feathers built on a mat of vegetation," in 1981 as a "base of sedges and grass, lined with finer grasses, 8 to 10 cm deep," in 1983 as composed of "marsh grasses," and in 1984 as "small pads of submerged aquatics pulled together into a shallow nest scrape 4 cm deep." Of 16 nests observed, 15 were constructed on floating pads of vegetation, either small pads of plants gathered by the terns (6 nests), naturally occurring mats of floating vegetation, or on old grebe or muskrat platforms (2 nests). One nest was situated on the side of a muskrat lodge.

Eggs: Dates for 8 clutches ranged from 29 May to 10 July. The clutch found on 29 May contained 3 partially incubated eggs, indicating a slightly earlier egg date (perhaps 21 May). In 1984 egg-laying was just beginning on 10 July (empty-5 nests, 1E-1 nest), suggesting eggs could be found as late as 26 July some years. Sizes for 8 clutches ranged from 1 to 3 eggs (1E-1, 2E-2, 3E-5). Incubation period is 23 to 25 days (Godfrey 1986).

Young: The only brood observed consisted of 2 young on 20 June; they were from a clutch of 3 eggs found on 31 May. The young were found dead on 23 June. On 26 June 1983, 1 nest contained an unspecified number of young. Calculated young dates range from 15 June to 25 August.

REMARKS: The date of the specimen from Okanagan Lake, cited as 3 August 1938 by J.A. Munro and Cowan (1947) and Godfrey (1966), is actually 24 June 1928 (Brooks 1900, 1942; Godfrey 1986).

Figure 201. *Forster's Tern with Common Tern on kelp bed at Ogden Point, Victoria, 12 to 18 October 1986 (Tim Zurowski).*

NOTEWORTHY RECORDS

Spring: Coastal - No records. **Interior** - Duck Lake (Creston) 1 May 1981-2, 3 May 1981-3, 24 May 1986-15+, 25 May 1980-21 (Goossen et al. 1982); Swan Lake (Vernon) 17 May 1987-2 adults; Fort St. John 25 May 1985-1 adult.

Summer: Coastal - Iona Island 12 Jul 1981-1 (Weber, W.C. 1982), 21 Aug 1979-1 (Mattocks and Hunn 1980); Crescent Beach 25 to 31 Aug 1984-1.

Interior - Duck Lake (Creston) 10 Jul 1984-11, 28 Aug 1980-15; Osoyoos Lake 10 Jun 1974-1; Okanagan Lake 24 Jun 1928-3 (1 female - MVZ 101451); Charlie Lake 12 Jun 1983-1 immature, 16 Jun 1983-1 adult.

Autumn: Interior - Nicola Lake 20 Sep 1978-2 adults, 3 immatures; Swan Lake (Vernon) 15 to 17 Sep 1984-1; Nelson autumn 1943-18. **Coastal** - Stanley Park (Vancouver) 7 and 8 Sep 1974-1 immature; Vancouver 1 Sep 1984-1 adult; Tsawwassen 30 Sep 1978-1 off jetty; Boundary Bay 13 Sep 1982-1; Crescent Beach 1 to 11 Sep 1984-1, 11 Sep 1983-1; Ogden Point 12 to 18 Oct 1986-1 (Campbell 1986d; Mattocks and Harrington-Tweit 1987; RBCM Photo 1122; Fig. 126).

Winter: No records.

Forster's Tern

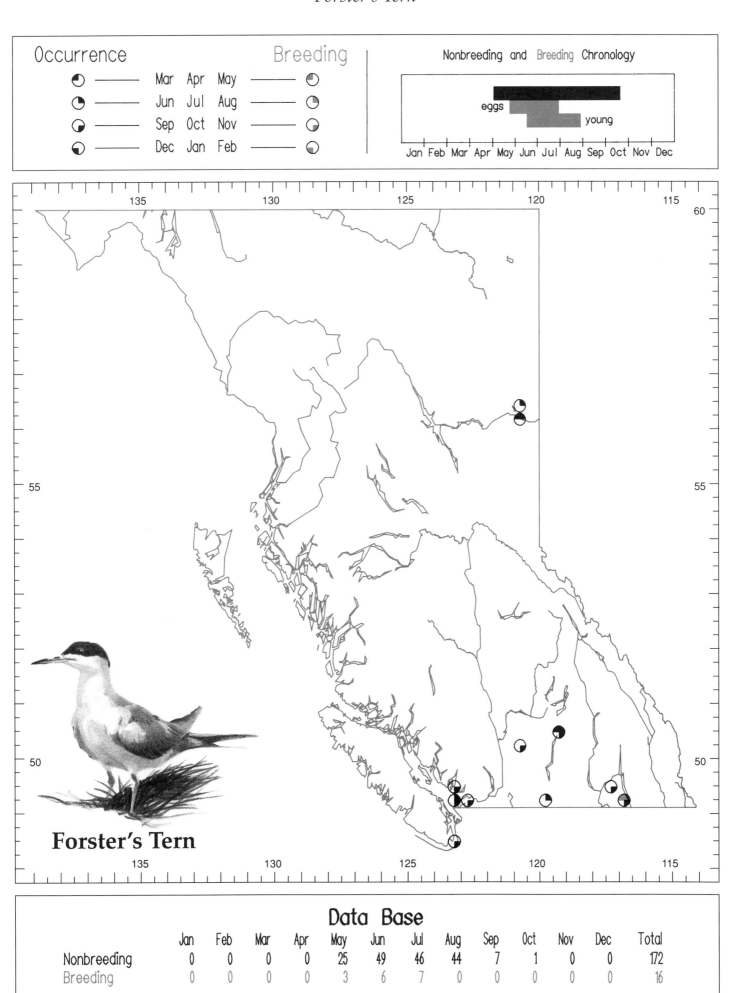

Occurrence / Breeding

	Mar Apr May	
Jun Jul Aug	
Sep Oct Nov	
Dec Jan Feb	

Nonbreeding and Breeding Chronology

eggs / young

Jan Feb Mar Apr May Jun Jul Aug Sep Oct Nov Dec

Forster's Tern

Data Base

	Jan	Feb	Mar	Apr	May	Jun	Jul	Aug	Sep	Oct	Nov	Dec	Total
Nonbreeding	0	0	0	0	25	49	46	44	7	1	0	0	172
Breeding	0	0	0	0	3	6	7	0	0	0	0	0	16

Black Tern

BLTE

Chlidonias niger (Linnaeus)

RANGE: Breeds in much of interior North America from British Columbia east to New Brunswick and south to central California and New York. Winters in northern and western South America. Also occurs in Eurasia and Africa.

STATUS: In the southern half of the interior, locally *fairly common* to *abundant* spring and autumn migrant and summer visitant; *uncommon* in the northeast. On the coast, *rare* summer visitant throughout the Fraser Lowlands; *casual* on southeastern Vancouver Island. Breeds.

NONBREEDING: The Black Tern is widely distributed in the interior south of the Fraser Basin region and east of the Coast Ranges. In the northeast, it occurs in the Peace and Fort Nelson lowlands regions. On the south coast, it occurs from the Fraser River delta to the vicinity of Chilliwack; on Vancouver Island it has been recorded from Nanoose Harbour south to Victoria. It has been found from sea level to at least 1,400 m elevation. The Black Tern frequents interior lakes, marshes, and rivers in major valleys and plateaus enroute to and from breeding areas.

It is a highly migratory species that spends only a short nonbreeding period in British Columbia. Early spring migrants have been found from mid to late April but most arrive in mid to late May. Soon after arrival, numbers quickly build around colony sites. In summer, small numbers of nonbreeders are widely scattered in appropriate habitat. Autumn migration may begin in late July and by mid-August most birds have departed.

Extreme dates for 3 areas of the province are as follows: southern interior - 11 April and 20 September; Peace River region - 19 May and 16 September; south coast - 17 April and 10 October.

BREEDING: The Black Tern is a widespread, but local breeder, east of the Coast Ranges and south of the Fraser Basin region (Summit Lake). Small numbers also breed east of the Rocky Mountains in the Peace and Fort Nelson lowland regions. The

only coastal breeding locality is Pitt Lake (Campbell 1970b). It breeds at elevations between 61 and 1,220 m.

The Black Tern nests on shallow, freshwater lakes, marshes, sloughs, and ponds in open and forested regions (Fig. 202). Still waters with emergent vegetation or waterlilies are required. Colonies vary in size from 3 to 100 pairs, (1 to 5 pairs-3 colonies, 6 to 10 pairs-13, 11 to 20 pairs-24, 21 to 50 pairs-14, 51 to 100 pairs-3), with 66% having 11 to 50 pairs. The largest reported colonies (Table 13) are at Tachick Lake near Vanderhoof and Cecil Lake, east of Fort St. John. Several satellite colonies may occur in one large marsh or lake such as Swan Lake (Vernon) where in 1937 a population of 114 pairs was clustered in 5 colonies of 6 to 46 pairs each. In the Creston valley, breeding numbers ranged from 600 terns in 1981 to 200 in 1984. This is the largest local population known in British Columbia (Chapman-Mosher 1986).

Nests: Most nests (91%; n=218) were situated in openings in or at the edges of emergent vegetation (such as cattail, bulrush, and marsh horsetail) over water ranging in depth from 10 cm to 1.7 m.

Nests were small cups or pads of aquatic vegetation, either floating platforms anchored to emergents or built on mats of floating debris (Fig. 203), muskrat cuttings, old grebe nests, muskrat lodges, and floating boards and logs. At Creston, 49 nests were composed of marsh horsetail and 114 were composed of reed canarygrass. Few other nests were described but other materials included dead leaves, mosses, cattail and bulrush stems, and rootlets. Nests at Cecil Lake were the only ones described as "lined with fine grasses."

Nest diameters ranged from 13 to 23 cm and nest heights ranged from 1.3 to 6.4 cm. Nest building generally begins in late May.

Eggs: Dates for 533 clutches ranged from 24 May to 22 July with 53% recorded between 5 and 18 June. Clutch size ranged from 1 to 6 eggs (1E-54, 2E-133, 3E-336, 4E-7, 5E-1, 6E-2), with 63% having 3 eggs. At Creston, egg failure was frequently caused

Figure 202. *Adult Black Tern foraging at Swan Lake near Dawson Creek, 7 July 1986 (Chris R. Siddle).*

Black Tern

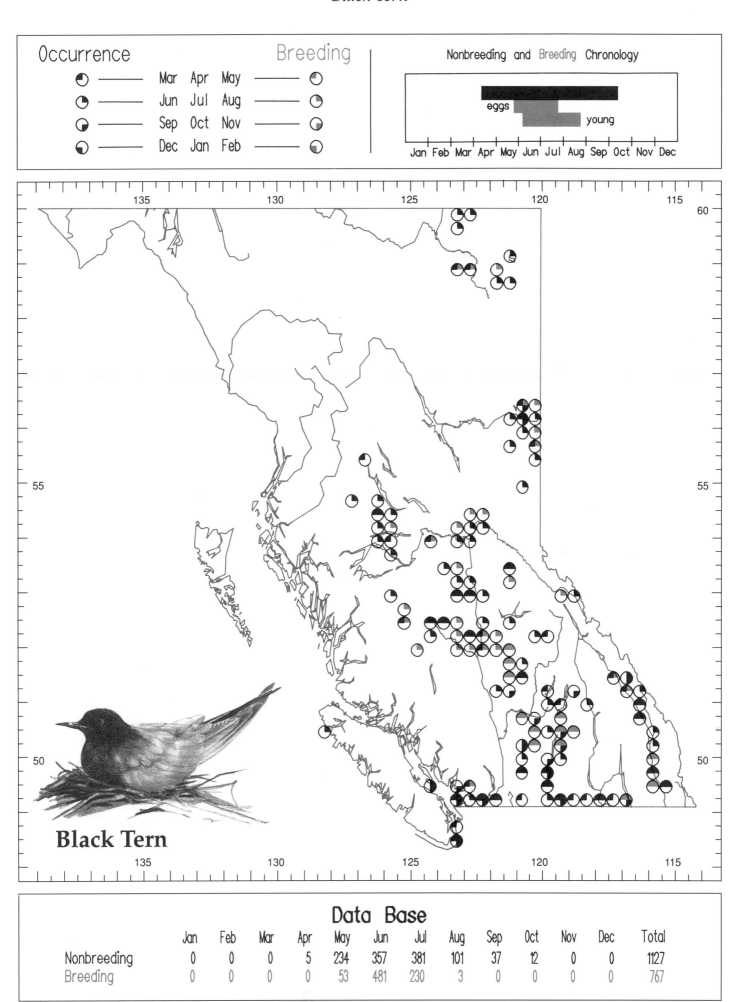

Occurrence / Breeding

Occurrence
- Mar Apr May
- Jun Jul Aug
- Sep Oct Nov
- Dec Jan Feb

Breeding

Nonbreeding and Breeding Chronology

eggs

young

Jan Feb Mar Apr May Jun Jul Aug Sep Oct Nov Dec

Data Base

	Jan	Feb	Mar	Apr	May	Jun	Jul	Aug	Sep	Oct	Nov	Dec	Total
Nonbreeding	0	0	0	5	234	357	381	101	37	12	0	0	1127
Breeding	0	0	0	0	53	481	230	3	0	0	0	0	767

Black Tern

by wave action or rising water levels; Chapman-Mosher (1986) reports that 30 clutches were lost from 1981 to 1984. One nest site there was reclaimed by a muskrat. One female laid 2 successive 3-egg clutches and both were destroyed by "washouts." Incubation period in British Columbia is 21 to 22 days.

Young: Dates for 214 broods ranged from 6 June to 22 August (Fig. 204) with 51% recorded between 23 June and 9 July. Most young fledged in mid to late July. The earliest date was 12 July. There are only 3 records of young in August; the latest brood date of 22 August was of adults feeding a recently fledged young. Brood size ranged from 1 to 3 young (1Y-61, 2Y-87, 3Y-66), with 71% having 2 or 3 young. Brood sizes are difficult to determine because young terns scatter and hide when their colonies are disturbed. Fledging period is 21 to 28 days (Harrison, C. 1978).

REMARKS: Two theses (Bailey, P.F. 1977; Chapman-Mosher 1986) provide additional information on the breeding biology of the Black Tern in British Columbia.

There is concern over the decline of Black Tern populations in North America, especially in the northern Great Plains region (see Tilgham 1980; Tate and Tate 1982). It appears on the "Blue List" from 1978 to 1986; for the 1986 list it was considered "down or greatly down throughout its range" (Tate 1986).

The status of the Black Tern in Canada has recently been reviewed by Gerson (1987). She suggests that the Black Tern be considered threatened in Canada because of the continuing loss of its habitat and its continent-wide decline. Trends in British Columbia are generally unknown. In the Okanagan valley, however, R.A. Cannings et al. (1987) document a decline in breeding numbers from about 200 pairs between 1925 and 1940 to only a few pairs in 1978. These data should be treated cautiously as breeding numbers of Black Terns fluctuate greatly from year to year.

Figure 203. Black Tern nest near Wilmer, June 1979 (Dianne L. Cooper).

TABLE 13.
Black Tern: location, history, and size of major colonies in British Columbia.

Location	Colony History						
	First Record	Low Survey Results[1] Year		High Survey Results[1] Year		Recent Survey Results[1] Year	Source[2]
Interior - Colonies > 30 nests or pairs							
Cecil Lake	1945			90 P	1978	1978	1
Creston							
Corn Creek Marsh	1982			24 Ac	1982	C 1987	1
Leach Lake	1982			84 Ac	1982	C 1987	1
Dawson Creek	1962			30 P	1962	1962	1
Horse Lake	1937			36 P	1937	1937	1
McQueen's Slough	1978			50 P	1978	1978	1,2
Ness Lake	1974			50 P	1974	1974	1
Nukko Creek	1944			20-30 P	1944	1944	2,3
150 Mile House	1979			30 P	1979	1979	1
Tachick Lake	1945			100 P	1945	1945	2,3
Vernon							
Swan Lake	1937			114 P	1937	E 1978	1,4

[1] A - active nests; C - nesting confirmed but no count or estimate made; E - colony extinct; P - pairs. All data are estimates unless noted as follows: c - complete count.

[2] 1 - British Columbia Nest Records Scheme; 2 - Campbell 1979; 3 - Munro, J.A. and Cowan 1947; 4 - Cannings, R.A. et al. 1987.

Figure 204. *Adult Black Tern feeding chick at Stum Lake, in the Chilcotin-Cariboo Basin, 10 July 1973 (Ervio Sian).*

NOTEWORTHY RECORDS

Spring: Coastal - Sumas 29 May 1896-1 female (RBCM 1489); Iona Island 17 Apr 1982-1 adult, 16 May 1971-2. **Interior** - Lightning Lake 15 May 1980-1; Creston 10 May 1980-1; Vaseux Lake 9 May 1922-1 (Thacker 1923); Okanagan Lake (Penticton) 18 May 1974-10 (Cannings, S.G. 1974); Cranbrook 14 May 1915-2 (RBCM 2154-55); Swan Lake (Vernon) 28 May 1940-156 at colony sites; Stump Lake (Quilchena) 11 Apr 1976-1, 20 Apr 1975-3; Shumway Lake 24 May 1986-30; Shuswap Lake 18 Apr 1962-1; 100 Mile House 22 Apr 1977-10; Williams Lake 18 May 1985-35; Riske Creek 13 May 1981-1; Nulki Lake 22 May 1945-2 (Munro, J.A. and Cowan 1947); Babine River 22 May 1978-2; Old Man Lake 24 May 1979-100+; Swan Lake (Tupper) 29 May 1939-150 (Munro, J.A. and Cowan 1947); Fort St. John 19 May 1983-1; Cecil Lake 28 May 1980-50.

Summer: Coastal - Chilliwack 3 Jun 1929-2 (RBCM 6468-69); Iona Island 12 Jul 1971-3. **Interior** - Hahas Lake 14 Aug 1980-16+; Columbia Lake 31 Aug 1977-10; Revelstoke 26 Aug 1977-1 at airport (Bonar 1978b); Salmon Arm 26 Aug 1973-2; Horse Lake (100 Mile House) 19 Aug 1937-200 (Munro, J.A. and Cowan 1947); Kleena Kleene 24 Jun 1948-12 (Paul 1959); Williams Lake 8 Jun 1978-40, 24 Aug 1985-2; Squiness Lake 16 Jul 1975-8; Francois Lake 15 Jun 1951-6; Charlie Lake 21 Aug 1980-1 immature; Boundary Lake (Goodlow) 22 Aug 1984-1 adult, 1 immature; Parker Lake (Fort Nelson) 13 to 18 Jun 1976-25, 3 Aug 1968-several (Rogers, T.H. 1968b); Kotcho Lake 25 Jun 1985-3 adults.

Autumn: Interior - Fort St. John 16 Sep 1986-1; Loon Lake (Clinton) 2 Sep 1975-1; Shuswap Lake 18 Sep 1965-1 (Stevens 1969); Knutsford 2 Sep 1977-4; Nicola Lake 20 Sep 1978-1; Peachland 5 Sep 1960; Okanagan 3 Sep 1921-2 (MVZ 82116, 101407); Osoyoos 3 Sep 1973-1; Sirdar 10 Sep 1947-1 immature (Munro, J.A. 1958a). **Coastal** - Nanoose 3 Oct 1980-1; Iona Island 19 Sep to 10 Oct 1981-1; Sumas Lake 1 Sep 1899-1 immature (Brooks 1917); Esquimalt Lagoon 12 Sep 1974-1.

Winter: No records.

Extralimital Records: Coastal - Grant Bay 22 to 31 Aug 1968-1 (Richardson 1971).

Common Murre

Uria aalge (Pontoppidan)

COMU

RANGE: Breeds in North America from western Alaska and the Aleutian Islands south along the Pacific coast to central California; in eastern North America from Labrador and southeastern Quebec south to Nova Scotia. Winters near the breeding grounds, in the Pacific Ocean south to southern California, in eastern North America south to Maine. Also in northern Eurasia.

STATUS: *Very common* to *abundant* spring migrant along the outer coast; infrequently *common* to *abundant* along the inner coast. In summer, *very abundant* in the vicinity of major colonies, otherwise *fairly common* to *very common* on the outer coast, *rare* to *uncommon* on the inner coast. *Very abundant* migrant in late summer along the outer coast, remaining *very abundant* on the south coast through autumn; *common* along the northern mainland coast and the Queen Charlotte Islands. Locally *very common* to *very abundant* in winter. Local breeder.

NONBREEDING: The Common Murre is widely distributed along all inner and outer coastal areas. Its distribution in the offshore (pelagic) zone is unknown, but it may be the most abundant seabird there throughout much of the year. It is not known to occur inland or on coastal lakes.

The Common Murre prefers protected marine waters off straits (Fig. 205), inlets, bays, and channels, especially in areas of upwelling and mixing. It congregates in certain favoured regions such as Pacific herring spawning areas in the Strait of Georgia in spring, and feeding grounds around the Gulf Islands, near Tofino, and in Queen Charlotte Sound in autumn. Occasionally, single birds or small flocks are found in brackish areas of rivers and marshes. In migration, open, offshore waters are preferred.

Population movements of the Common Murre in British Columbia are not fully understood. There appears to be a distinct northward and southward migration but little is known about the source of the birds (see Remarks). In addition, there is an impressive influx of murres into southern areas from colonies in Washington and Oregon in mid-summer. However, movements between inner and outer coastal areas throughout the year prevent a clear interpretation of dispersal and migration patterns.

Peak numbers of Common Murres are encountered in the Strait of Georgia from late January to early March (see Edwards 1965), but this may be more related to movement towards Pacific herring spawning sites than any real migratory movement. On the west coast of Vancouver Island, there is a noticeable spring movement from late April through the first half of May. From mid-July through September, there is a spectacular influx of moulting adults and young of the year, often in family groups of males and fledglings. Part of this influx moves up the west coast of Vancouver Island as far as Checleset Bay (Campbell and Summers In press) and part moves through Juan de Fuca Strait into the Strait of Georgia. Banding returns indicate that most of these birds originate from colonies in Oregon and will form part

Figure 205. Common Murre in winter plumage off Albert Head, Victoria, 23 January 1983 (Tim Zurowski).

Common Murre

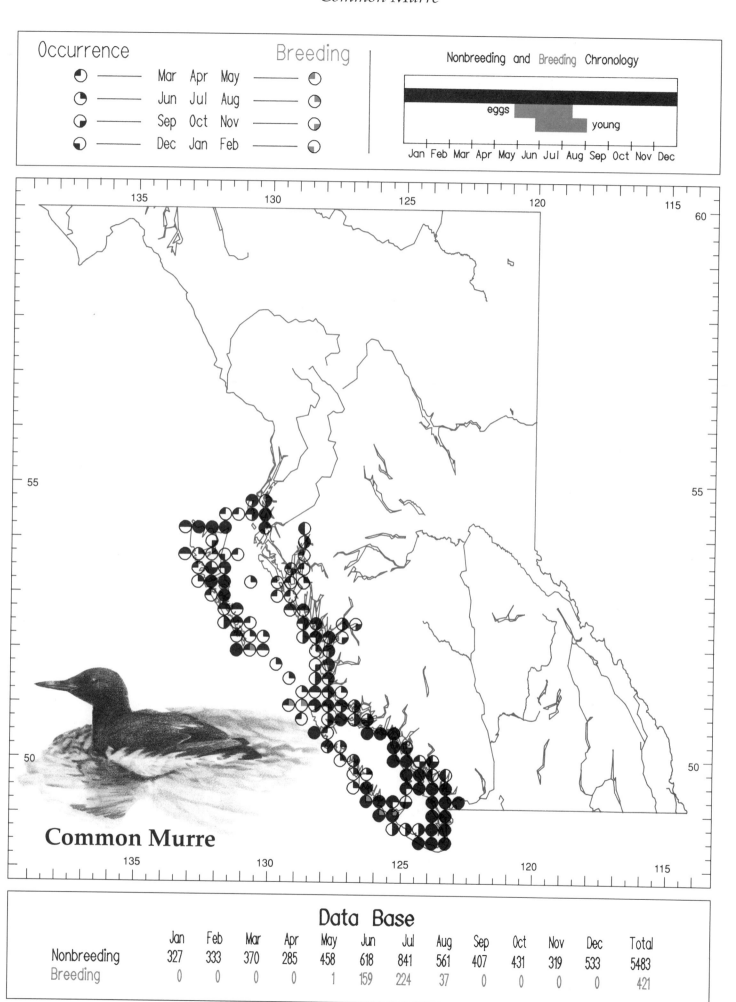

Occurrence / Breeding

Occurrence		Breeding
◕	Mar Apr May	◔
◕	Jun Jul Aug	◔
◔	Sep Oct Nov	◔
◕	Dec Jan Feb	◑

Nonbreeding and Breeding Chronology

eggs — young

Jan Feb Mar Apr May Jun Jul Aug Sep Oct Nov Dec

Data Base

	Jan	Feb	Mar	Apr	May	Jun	Jul	Aug	Sep	Oct	Nov	Dec	Total
Nonbreeding	327	333	370	285	458	618	841	561	407	431	319	533	5483
Breeding	0	0	0	0	1	159	224	37	0	0	0	0	421

of the wintering population in British Columbia (Tuck, L.M. 1960). Other birds that winter along the coast could be arriving from colonies in Alaska; this autumn movement probably occurs in September and October. Major winter concentrations occur off southern Vancouver Island and at the northern end of the Strait of Georgia.

BREEDING: The Common Murre breeds locally on the outer coast from Barkley Sound on southwestern Vancouver Island north to the Kerouard Islands on the southern tip of the Queen Charlotte Islands (Fig. 207). Although it has been found breeding at 6 sites (Table 14), only the colonies in the Scott Islands and Kerouard Islands are permanent and well established.

All nesting sites are on offshore islands. Isolated nesting pairs and small colonies are located on small, low, bare rocky islets and reefs (Campbell et al. 1975). On Triangle Island (Fig. 206), the Common Murre nests on rocky peninsulas, headlands, and islets, and among grass tussocks on the crest of headlands (Guiguet 1950a). Habitat on the Kerouard Islands is bare rock.

The small number of colonies in British Columbia may be due to the scarcity of suitable cliffs. Many offshore islands are low and rounded, lack protection from rain, or may present the wrong aspect to the prevailing wind. About 2,800 pairs of Common Murres breed in the province, most of which are in the Scott Islands off northwestern Vancouver Island.

About 940,000 pairs breed in Alaska and 15,400 pairs breed in Washington (United States Department of the Interior 1988; Speich and Wahl 1989).

Nests: No actual nests are built. Rather, eggs are simply laid on bare rock or soil, usually on cliff ledges, from 4 to 91 m above the high water mark. Some eggs, however, are laid on the slopes and tops of low rocky islands.

Eggs: Dates for 362 clutches ranged from 26 May to 12 August with 72% recorded between 15 June and 10 July. All clutches consisted of a single egg. Incubation period is 28 to 35 days (Tuck, L.M. 1960).

Young: Dates for 53 broods ranged from 20 July to 31 August (end of field season) with 56% recorded between 16 and 24 August. Calculated dates indicate that young could be found as early as 25 June. All broods consisted of a single young (Fig. 208). Young leave for the sea at about 18 to 25 days and are cared for and fed by the male of the pair. The young fledge at least 21 days after that (Tuck, L.M. 1960).

REMARKS: Of the 7 subspecies described in the world, only 1, *U. a. inornata*, is known to occur in British Columbia. L.M. Tuck (1960) provides an overview of the murres of the world.

There appear to be 2 distinct groups breeding along the Pacific coast of North America. A "California" group, which breeds early and migrates north with its young as early as mid-July, and a "Northern" group, which includes those in British Columbia whose young are just beginning to hatch in mid-July.

Every August, dozens of dead Common Murres wash ashore in Boundary Bay with clear lesions where the wing joins the body. They have presumably been removed from nets and discarded by fishermen. On a much larger scale, W.B. King et al. (1979) suggest that mortality of murres (*Uria* spp.) and other seabirds resulting from commercial fishing operations is affecting world populations.

Chilton and Sealy (1987) discuss the role of Common Murres in mixed-species feeding flocks of seabirds. They found that flocks in which Common Murres participated were larger and lasted longer than flocks without the murres and suggested that Common Murres enhance the foraging of other seabirds, particularly the surface-feeding gulls. Of the 8 species observed in mixed-feeding flocks, Common Murres were the most important flock initiators, being first in attendance at nearly 24% of the feeding flocks.

The Common Murre is sometimes referred to as the Thin-billed Murre and in the Old World as the Guillemot.

All species of seabirds off the British Columbia coast are affected by oil pollution but the Common Murre suffers most heavily (Fig. 209). The Nestucca oil spill off Washington State in December 1988, impacted on wintering populations of seabirds both in coastal Washington and southern British Columbia. Of the 12,877 dead birds identified, most were Common Murres: 80% of mortalities in Washington and 42% of mortalities in British Columbia (Rodway et al. In press).

TABLE 14.
Common Murre: location, history, and size of all known colonies in British Columbia.

Location	Colony History				
	First Record	Low Survey Results[1] Year	High Survey Results[1] Year	Recent Survey Results[1] Year	Source[2]
South Coast					
Cleland Island	1969	0 N 1984	8 N 1982	1984	1,2,8
Florencia Island	1969	0 N 1975	1 N 1969	1975	1,9
Sartine Island	1968	236 B 1968	600 B 1975	270 B 1987	3,6,7
Starlight Reef	1975	0 N 1977	2 N 1980	1980	1,10
Triangle Island	1900	3000 B 1949	4910 B 1982	1984	2,4,5
North Coast					
Kerouard Islands	1977	90 B 1977	400 B 1987	1987	1,2,3

[1]   B - breeding birds; N - nests or burrows. All data are estimates.

[2]   1 - British Columbia Nest Records Scheme; 2 - Rodway et al. In prep; 3 - Campbell and Garrioch 1979; 4 - Guiguet 1950a;
5 - Carl et al. 1951; 6 - Hancock 1970; 7 - Vermeer et al. 1976; 8 - Campbell et al. 1975; 9 - Hatler et al. 1978; 10 - Campbell 1976a.

Figure 206. *Common Murre colony at Triangle Island, August 1974 (R. Wayne Campbell).*

Figure 207. *Common Murre colony at Kerouard Islands, Queen Charlotte Islands, August 1985 (Alan G. Whitney).*

Figure 208. *Adult Common Murre with chick on Cleland Island, 20 August 1969 (R. Wayne Campbell).*

Figure 209. Oiled Common Murre washed ashore at Stanley Park, Vancouver, March 1969 (R. Wayne Campbell). Of all seabirds breeding in British Columbia, the Common Murre suffers most heavily from oil pollution.

NOTEWORTHY RECORDS

Spring: Coastal - Otter Point 11 Mar 1986-400; w Tofino 8 May 1971-130 (Campbell and Shepard 1972); Squamish River 11 Mar 1980-68 off estuary; Quadra Island 28 Apr 1980-1,000+ with 400 Marbled Murrelets; Klaskish Inlet 13 Mar 1976-300; Pulteney Point 21 Mar 1977-127; Cape St. James 11 Apr 1982-100; Sandspit 4 May 1986-60; Kitimat 21 Mar 1975-22; Langara Island 26 May 1952-500 to 600 in small flocks; Rose Spit 27 May 1983-100+; Green Island (Chatham Sound) 21 Apr 1978-630+. **Interior** - No records.

Summer: Coastal - Beechey Head 14 Jul 1984-900; Oak Bay 23 Jun 1984-250; Clover Point 29 Jul 1983-900; Barkley Sound 19 Aug 1977-9,000; Portland Point to Sea Lion Rock 25 Jul 1972-10,000 (Hatler et al. 1973); Mitlenatch Island 30 Jun 1963-30 (van Tets 1963); Miracle Beach Park 6 Jul 1966-500 (Crowell and Nehls 1966c); Checleset Bay 13 Jun 1978-335, 22 Jul 1978-1,250, 5 Aug 1981-2,200; Triangle Island (Scott Islands) 10 Jul 1982-4,890, including breeders and nonbreeders on cliffs, 22 Jul 1984-7,500+; Goose Group 10 Jun 1948-25; Rankine Island 10 Aug 1979-50; Hecate Strait 9 Aug 1972-900 in small area; Cape Naden 25 Aug 1984-200; Port Simpson 26 Aug 1969-57. **Interior** - No records.

Autumn: Interior - No records. **Coastal** - Prince Rupert 29 Nov 1974-25; Skidegate Inlet 3 Sep 1974-500+, 4 Oct 1978-100; Finlayson Channel 27 Sep 1985-90; Cape Scott Park 27 Sep 1935-200; Bella Coola 7 Nov 1979-5 off estuary; Namu 18 Oct 1981-60; Schooner Channel 12 Sep 1967-158; Cape Mudge 10 Oct 1968-365; Tofino 12 Sep 1970-2,000; Bamfield to La Perouse Bank 10 Sep 1977-4,633 (Shepard, M.G. 1978); Active Pass 7 Oct 1981-600+; Ross Bay (Victoria) 3 Sep 1958-1,000; Juan de Fuca Strait 1 Oct 1983-3,300; Clover Point 2 Nov 1983-9,000 flew past in 30 minutes.

Winter: Interior - No records. **Coastal** - Prince Rupert 27 Jan 1979-1,200; 6 km n Rose Spit 28 Feb 1983-394; Masset 28 Dec 1986-415; Queen Charlotte City 19 Feb 1972-250; Seymour Narrows to Discovery Passage 31 Dec 1977-5,011, 28 Jan 1979-1,200; Egmont 21 Feb 1974-150; Nanoose Harbour 5 Feb 1974-774; Ambleside 13 Feb 1983-180; Somass River 7 Jan 1983-10, 3 km from mouth (Campbell 1983a); Lennard Island 1 to 5 Dec 1976-1,000+ in raft; Departure Bay 10 Jan 1942-2,000 (Munro, J.A. and Cowan 1947); Iona Island 30 Dec 1967-200+; Active Pass 1 Feb 1981-thousands; Saanich Inlet 26 Feb 1983-760; Haro Strait 5 Feb 1964-2,500+ on feed; Race Rocks 11 Dec 1983-5,000.

Christmas Counts: Interior - Not recorded. **Coastal** - Recorded from 22 of 28 localities and on 72% of all counts. Maxima: Victoria 30 Dec 1973-**7,831**, all-time Canadian high count (Anderson, R.R. 1976); Campbell River 16 Dec 1979-7,518; Sooke 16 Dec 1984-1,935.

Thick-billed Murre

TBMU

Uria lomvia (Linnaeus)

RANGE: Breeds on the Pacific coast of North America in northern Alaska, the Bering Sea, the Aleutian Islands, Kodiak Island, and locally in British Columbia; on the Atlantic coast from Ellesmere Island, Greenland, northern Hudson Bay, Labrador, northern Quebec, and Newfoundland to the Gulf of St. Lawrence. Winters within much of breeding range; on the Pacific coast, mainly in the Bering Sea south to southeastern Alaska, infrequently south to central California; on the Atlantic coast from Greenland south to Maryland. Also occurs in northern Eurasia.

STATUS: *Very rare* migrant and summer visitant along the coast; *accidental* in winter. Local breeder.

CHANGE IN STATUS: The first 2 reports of the Thick-billed Murre in British Columbia were specimens: the first from Seymour Narrows (Bent 1919, p.199); the second found dead at Boundary Bay near Ladner on 8 December 1941 (Racey 1947). Both specimens were subsequently examined and reidentified as Common Murre (Brooks and Swarth 1925; S.G. Sealey pers. comm.).

The first acceptable sight record was from Langara Island in 1970, but the species' presence was not documented until 1980 (RBCM Photo 664). Two adult Thick-billed Murres were also noted among a Common Murre colony on Triangle Island in 1980. In 1981, a small breeding nucleus became established and the following year at least 70 adults were in attendance (Vallee and Cannings 1983).

The Triangle Island breeding colony represents a southeastward extension of the murre's known breeding range of about 800 km into the eastern Pacific (Sowls et al. 1978; Vallee and Cannings 1983).

NONBREEDING: The Thick-billed Murre has been found only on the Queen Charlotte Islands and off the west coast of Vancouver Island. All records are from open marine waters, often the same as those frequented by Common Murres. Records are too few to determine movements or migration patterns. It has been recorded from 8 May to 29 August; there is also one winter record.

BREEDING: In British Columbia, the Thick-billed Murre breeds only on Triangle Island off the northwestern tip of Vancouver Island (Fig. 210). General habitat of the island is described by Carl et al. (1951). The colony is situated on the southwest peninsula, from 76 to 91 m above sea level. It is shared with several thousand Common Murres (q.v.).

In 1981, the colony was estimated at 19 pairs and in 1982 about 70 Thick-billed Murres were counted at the colony site.

The breeding population in Alaska is large, nearly 925,600 pairs (United States Department of the Interior 1988). None breed in Washington.

Nests: No nests were built; eggs were laid on bare ground on exposed narrow ledges of steep, rocky cliffs, or on level, open areas near the cliff top.

Eggs: Only 2 clutches, both with single eggs, have been recorded: 18 and 21 August 1981. Calculated dates indicate that eggs could be found as early as 23 July, which is a late date compared to arctic Thick-billed Murres. Incubation period probably lies between 31 and 34 days (Gaston and Nettleship 1981).

Young: Seven adults, each with a chick, were counted on 27 August 1981. Thick-billed Murres were still present on 29 August but had fledged sometime before 5 September (Vallee and Cannings 1983). Data are insufficient to determine brood dates. Young leave the colony for the sea at between 15 and 30 days from hatching (Gaston and Nettleship 1981).

REMARKS: There are 2 subspecies in North America: *U. l. lomvia* is found in the eastern Arctic and the Atlantic coast; *U. l. arra* in the north Pacific Ocean, including British Columbia. There are 3 additional races in northern Siberia (Portenko 1944).

P. Harrison (1983) emphasizes that "any dark-headed alcid in autumn or early winter should be scrutinized." The Thick-billed Murre begins "a post-nuptial head moult from late July onwards, and by mid-August most populations have the diagnostic white sides to face and dark post-ocular stripes." Also see Forsell and Gould (1980) and Roberson (1980).

See Gaston and Nettleship (1981) for detailed information on the breeding ecology of the species in the Canadian arctic.

The Thick-billed Murre is also known as Brunnich's Murre and in the Old World as Brunnich's Guillemot.

Figure 210. *Thick-billed Murres on Triangle Island, 16 July 1985 (Michael S. Rodway).*

Thick-billed Murre

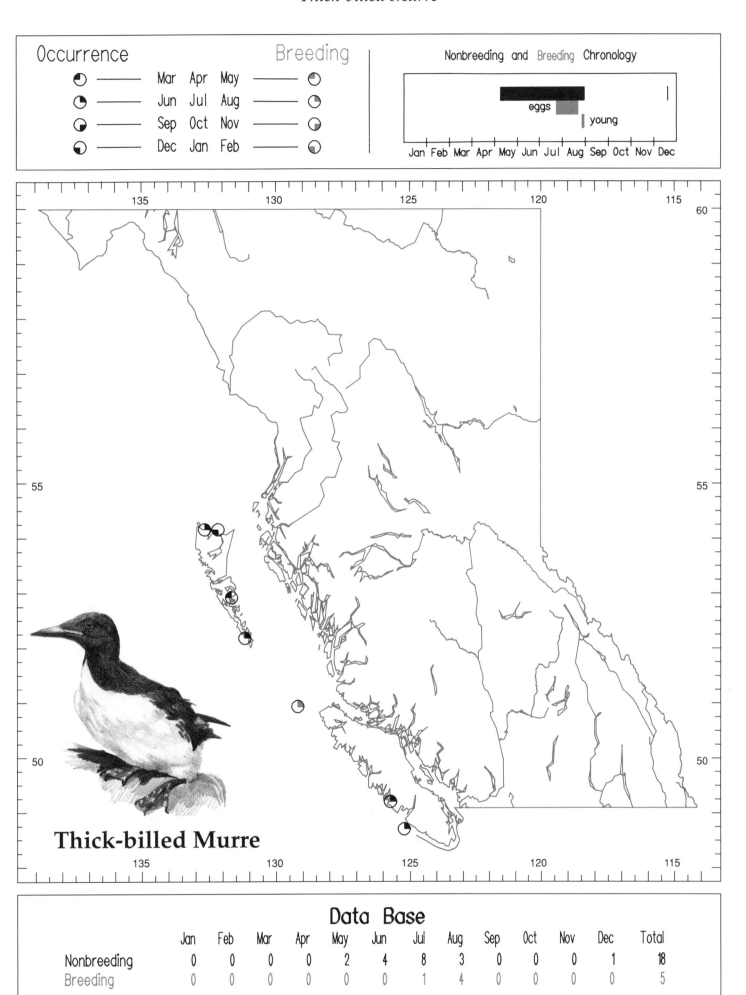

Occurrence / Breeding

Occurrence		Breeding
◐	Mar Apr May	◑
◔	Jun Jul Aug	◔
◕	Sep Oct Nov	◕
◕	Dec Jan Feb	◒

Nonbreeding and Breeding Chronology

eggs young

Jan Feb Mar Apr May Jun Jul Aug Sep Oct Nov Dec

Thick-billed Murre

Data Base

	Jan	Feb	Mar	Apr	May	Jun	Jul	Aug	Sep	Oct	Nov	Dec	Total
Nonbreeding	0	0	0	0	2	4	8	3	0	0	0	1	18
Breeding	0	0	0	0	0	0	1	4	0	0	0	0	5

Pigeon Guillemot

Cepphus columba Pallas

PIGU

RANGE: Breeds from the Kurile Islands and Bering Sea south along the coast to southern California; winters throughout the breeding range. Also found on the northern Pacific coast of Asia.

STATUS: *Common* to *abundant* migrant in spring, locally *very common* to *abundant* summer visitant and *fairly common* to *very common* along the coast during the post-breeding dispersal in autumn. In winter, locally *common* to *abundant* on the inner south coast, *uncommon* on the north coast including the Queen Charlotte Islands. Widespread coastal breeder.

NONBREEDING: The Pigeon Guillemot is widely distributed along all coastal areas throughout the province. It inhabits the nearshore zone, especially along stretches of rocky coastline. It is neither a deep diver nor a species of the open ocean, and is regularly found in bays, inlets, channels, surge narrows, sounds, coves, and harbours. It generally avoids brackish areas and only occasionally frequents heads of deep inlets.

Although present along the coast throughout the year, the Pigeon Guillemot is mostly reported from April through September when it can be locally numerous. Migration periods and seasonal movements between breeding, foraging, and wintering areas are not well known.

Lightkeepers along the north coast have noted a spring movement of guillemots from about mid-March through April. On the south coast, pre-breeding birds may congregate locally in February before dispersing to colonies. Most adults arrive in the vicinity of colonies in April and early May. On the south coast, first landings of adults on the colonies occur during the last 2 weeks of April. In summer, subadult birds form small flocks that occupy marginal habitats close to the breeding neighbourhoods. At Mandarte Island, a significant portion of an intensively watched colony were nonbreeders, including small numbers of yearlings, and larger numbers of 2-year olds, which were mostly evident from mid-June onwards (Drent 1965). Groups of more than 50 are unusual during the summer period in areas away from important breeding sites. See Storer (1952) and Drent (1965) for a discussion of attendance of adults and immatures at the colony.

The autumn movement is not well defined; rather, there appears to be a slow but steady dispersal of birds from colonies in August and early September. Loose aggregations of 100 or so guillemots have been reported at a few sites along the coast, many of which are also favourite wintering areas. There may also be a general southward movement from colonies along the north coast, including the Queen Charlotte Islands, to main wintering areas in Queen Charlotte Strait, the Strait of Georgia, and Juan de

Figure 211. Adult Pigeon Guillemot with sculpin at Cleland Island, August 1974 (R. Wayne Campbell).

Pigeon Guillemot

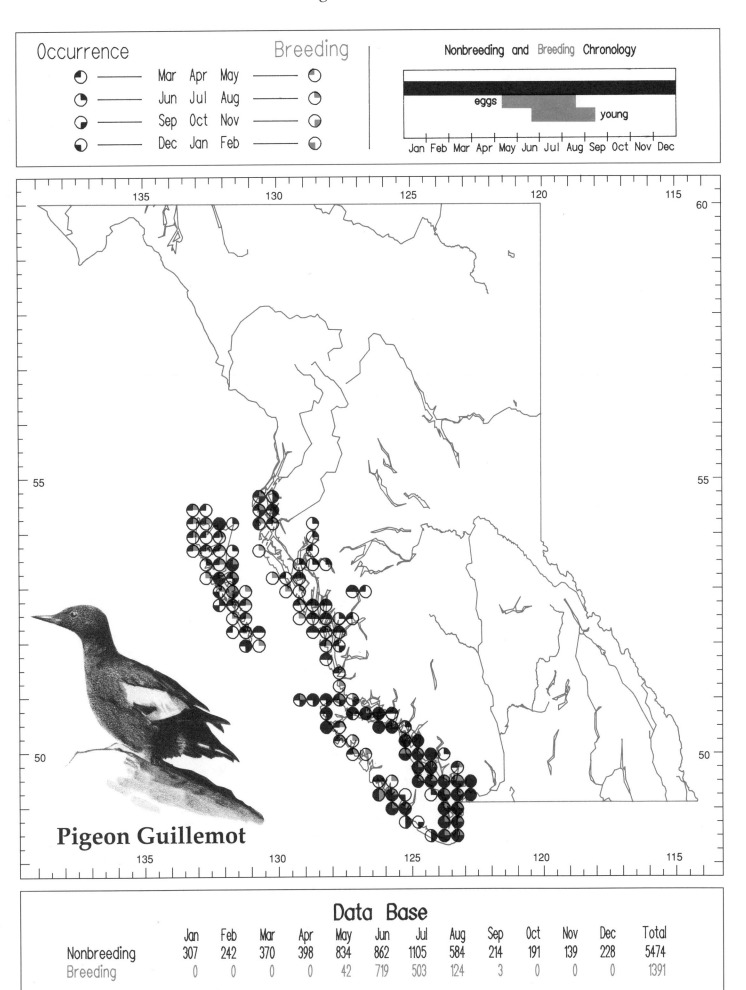

Pigeon Guillemot

Occurrence / Breeding

	Mar	Apr	May
	Jun	Jul	Aug
	Sep	Oct	Nov
	Dec	Jan	Feb

Nonbreeding and Breeding Chronology

eggs   young

Jan Feb Mar Apr May Jun Jul Aug Sep Oct Nov Dec

Data Base

	Jan	Feb	Mar	Apr	May	Jun	Jul	Aug	Sep	Oct	Nov	Dec	Total
Nonbreeding	307	242	370	398	834	862	1105	584	214	191	139	228	5474
Breeding	0	0	0	0	42	719	503	124	3	0	0	0	1391

Fuca Strait. In winter, individuals are widely scattered throughout the inner coastal areas, but at times may form loose groups of up to 200 birds (Munro, J.A. 1921). However, details of its winter distribution are generally unknown.

BREEDING: The Pigeon Guillemot (Fig. 211) breeds throughout coastal British Columbia from Sooke north to Langara Island and Dundas Island. Although breeding has been reported on only 63% of all coastal map grids, the Pigeon Guillemot has been seen on most islands, cliffs, and headlands, and probably breeds wherever suitable nesting substrate exists (Fig. 213). It is not known, however, to breed along inlets and fiords on the northern mainland coast. It is the most conspicuous breeding seabird in the province.

The Pigeon Guillemot is a colonial species only in the vicinity of large rocky islands and headlands that provide suitable nest-sites. Otherwise, it readily breeds as isolated pairs along the shoreline provided sites are devoid of mammalian predators and soft banks (for burrowing) or crevices are available for nesting (Fig. 212). Colony sites can be bare rock, heavily forested, grassy, or shrub-covered, and steep to gently sloping. The species is very plastic in its choice of nest sites, and small colonies have become established on man-made structures (Campbell 1977b). Accurate population estimates for the province are not available because of the difficulty of locating actual nests (see Remarks). Recent surveys tallied 9,382 birds, presumed to breed at 310 sites along the coast. Over one-half of all birds sighted were in the Queen

TABLE 15.
Pigeon Guillemot: location, history, and size of major breeding concentrations in British Columbia.

Location	First Record	Low Survey Results[1] Year		High Survey Results[1] Year		Recent Survey Results[1] Year		Source[2]
South Coast - Colonies > 100 birds around nesting area.								
Beresford Island	1950	C	1950	267 Bc	1987		1987	3,11
Cleland Island	1903	150 Bc	1975	1000 Bc	1961	205 Bc	1988	1,2,3
Mandarte Island	1945	15 B	1945	349 Bc	1981	241 Bc	1987	5,15,22
Mitlenatch Island	1920	43 Bc	1977	500 B	1922	134 Bc	1987	5,14,22
Race Rocks	1953	14 Bc	1977	400 B	1974	78 Bc	1987	5,7,22
Sartine Island	1950	176 Bc	1987	290 Bc	1975		1987	3,11,13
Storm Islands	1975	25 Bc	1976	111 Bc	1987		1987	3,5,7
Swiss Boy Island	1969			200 Bc	1969		1969	4
Triangle Island	1949	86 Bc	1982	241 Bc	1984	144 Bc	1985	3,11,12
North Coast - Colonies > 100 birds around nesting area.								
Anthony Island	1971	35 Bc	1971	395 Bc	1985		1985	3,5,18
Conroy Island	1976	15 Bc	1976	148 Bc	1988		1988	3,5
Jewell Island	1974	284 Bc	1977	311 Bc	1974		1977	5,9
Kunghit Island	1977	47 Bc	1977	155 Bc	1986		1986	5,19
Langara Island	1926	71 Bc	1972	187 Bc	1988		1988	3,5,16
"Lepas" Islet	1927	50 Bc	1972	218 Bc	1977	173 Bc	1986	5,17
Lillihorn Island	1977	82 Bc	1977	200 Bc	1986		1986	5,17
Low Island	1972	45 Bc	1986	115 Bc	1983		1986	5,19
Lucy Islands	1976	4 Bc	1976	197 Bc	1983	54 Bc	1984	3,5
Moore Islands	1936	131 Bc	1976	567 Bc	1970	187 Bc	1988	3,5,21
"Naden" Rocks	1977	77 Bc	1977	142 Bc	1986		1986	5,17
Nedden Island	1977			174 Bc	1977		1977	5
Reef Island	1971	24 Bc	1977	338 Bc	1985		1985	5,8
Sandstone Islands	1977	162 Bc	1977	200 Bc	1986		1986	5,17
Skedans Islands	1971	60 Bc	1977	200 Bc	1972	136 Bc	1983	5,10,19
Solide Islands	1977			110 Bc	1977		1977	5
Steilta Islets	1977	90 Bc	1977	131 Bc	1986		1986	17,20
Titul Island	1971	1 Bc	1982	115 Bc	1977	114 Bc	1983	5,19
Torrens Island	1967	7 Bc	1967	261 Bc	1974	167 Bc	1977	5,9

[1] B - birds; C - nesting confirmed but no count or estimate made. All data are estimates unless noted as follows: c - complete count.

[2] 1 - Western Foundation of Vertebrate Zoology; 2 - Campbell and Stirling 1968b; 3 - Rodway et al. In prep.; 4 - Guiguet 1971; 5 - British Columbia Nest Records Scheme; 6 - Hatler et al. 1978; 7 - Campbell 1976a; 8 - Gaston and Noble 1985; 9 - Campbell 1975b; 10 - Summers 1974; 11 - Carl et al. 1951; 12 - Lemon and Rodway 1983; 13 - Vermeer et al. 1976; 14 - Pearse 1923; 15 - Meugens 1945; 16 - Young 1927; 17 - Rodway 1988; 18 - Rodway et al. 1989; 19 - Rodway et al. 1988; 20 - Hatter, I. and Stordeur 1978; 21 - Drent and Guiguet 1961; 22 - Emms and Morgan 1989.

Figure 212. Vivian Island, west of Powell River, 13 June 1981 (R. Wayne Campbell). A large proportion of the nesting Pigeon Guillemot population in the province uses available crevices in cliffs on islands and headlands along the coast.

Figure 213. Small Pigeon Guillemot colony on Testlatlints Rock, Langara Island, Queen Charlotte Islands, June 1988 (Neil Holmes). Note adults and burrows in salal tangle on top of rock.

Charlotte Islands. Location, history, and size of major breeding concentrations in British Columbia are given in Table 15.

In Alaska, 46,908 birds are thought to be breeding at nearly 600 sites and in Washington, 4,270 birds probably nest at 144 sites (United States Department of the Interior 1988; Speich and Wahl 1989).

Nests: Most nests (96%; n=1,036) were associated with natural sites. Of those, 39% were situated in rock crevices (Fig. 214), 28% under or between large boulders and rocks, 16% under beach logs, driftwood and other marine debris (see Campbell 1975b), 14% in burrows (mostly excavated), and 2% in caves. Forty-one nests were situated in man-made structures such as wharves (Campbell 1977b), piers, light beacons, drain pipes, beached ship hulls, and log pilings. Man-made sites are rarely explored and may be used more frequently than our records indicate. Most nests were well hidden; eggs were occasionally discovered on open ledges and in open areas without cover, among talus, on boulder beaches, and among tall grasses. Nest heights ranged from 0.9 to 55 m.

Nest site tenacity, as with other auks, is pronounced in the Pigeon Guillemot. Returning adults prepare their nest-site about 1.5 to 5.5 weeks before egg-laying:

> The nest sites are cleared out. Old eggs are ejected, plants plucked out, the floor scraped clear, and any loose stone chips, shell fragments, etc. present in the burrow are pulled together into a little heap with a central depression, where the eggs are eventually deposited. (Drent 1965).

Adults have not been observed carrying new material into the nest (Thoreson and Booth 1958). Many nest sites were without materials, eggs being laid directly on bare soil, rock, or wood.

Pigeon Guillemot eggs have been discovered in the burrows of the European Rabbit (Drent et al. 1964), Tufted Puffin, and Rhinoceros Auklet. In Masset and Juskatla inlets on the Queen Charlotte Islands, the Pigeon Guillemot is primarily a burrow nester (Campbell 1977c). Measurements for 12 burrows there were: entrance diameter - 14 to 24 cm; length - 32 to 58 cm.

Eggs: Dates for 1,036 clutches ranged from 10 May to 17 August (partially incubated) with 60% recorded between 5 and 22 June. Clutch size ranged from 1 to 3 eggs (1E-420, 2E-612, 3E-4) with 59% having 2 eggs. Drent (1965) mentions that the Pigeon Guillemot cannot "effectively incubate more than 2 eggs," therefore clutches of 3 eggs are likely the work of 2 females.

The incubation period ranges from 28 to 32 days (Drent et al. 1964). At Mandarte Island, hatching success was 62% (Drent et al. 1964), while in Washington, it was 54% (Thoresen and Booth 1958).

Young: Dates for 348 broods ranged from 20 June to 7 September (Fig. 215) with 61% recorded between 5 and 30 July. Calculated dates indicate young could be found as late as 13 September. Brood size ranged from 1 to 2 young (1Y-193, 2Y-155) with 55% having 1 young (Fig. 216). The nestling/fledging period averages 35 days with a range of 29 to 39 days (Drent et al. 1964). In British Columbia, fledging success at Mandarte Island in a "normal" year was 99% (Drent et al. 1964); in Skagit County, Washington, it was 86% (Thoreson and Booth 1954).

REMARKS: Two subspecies have been reported in British Columbia: *Cepphus columba columba* is the resident and common race (American Ornithologists' Union 1957; Godfrey 1986); in addition, Dickinson (1953) reports the race *C. c. kaiurka*, based on a female collected at Lund (MCZ 282440) on 24 August 1934; this race breeds in the western Aleutian Islands.

Censusing Pigeon Guillemots is very difficult because nest-sites are usually hidden in inaccessible nooks and crannies. No colony in British Columbia has been completely searched for nests. Population estimates for a few of the larger colonies are from early morning counts of adults displaying on the sea near the colony before the egg-laying period. Counts should be made systematically around the colony, on calm days, and the census time should be noted. Nettleship (1976) provides additional comments that would help standardize census techniques.

For other aspects on breeding biology, see Thoresen and Booth (1958), Drent and Guiguet (1961), Drent (1965), and Aitchison (1972).

The Pigeon Guillemot and Black Guillemot (*C. grylle*) constitute a superspecies (American Ornithologists' Union 1983).

Figure 214. *Pigeon Guillemot nest site with eggs in a rock crevice at Skidegate Inlet, Queen Charlotte Islands, 18 June 1974 (R. Wayne Campbell).*

Figure 215. *Recently hatched Pigeon Guillemot chick on Five Finger Island near Nanaimo, 5 July 1974 (R. Wayne Campbell).*

Figure 216. *Pigeon Guillemot chick leaving nest site in the hollow of a beach log on Cleland Island, 2 August 1974 (R. Wayne Campbell).*

NOTEWORTHY RECORDS

Spring: Coastal - Race Rocks 26 Apr 1977-58, 16 May 1977-136; Esquimalt 16 Apr 1968-103; Saanichton Bay 11 Mar 1973-400 off spit; Crescent Beach 6 Apr 1968-12; Cleland Island 22 May 1931-150 (Munro, J.A. and Cowan 1947); Mitlenatch Island 30 May 1981-361 on count around island in morning; Port Neville 26 May 1976-30 adults; Anthony Island 28 May 1985-267, survey; Titul Island 12 May 1983-114 at 1100 hrs; Kimsquit River 8 Apr 1980-1 near estuary; Kagan Bay 11 May 1977-356; Hecate Strait 24 to 32 km e Lawn Point 21 Apr 1987-142; Masset Inlet 14 Apr 1935-300 (Munro, J.A. and Cowan 1947); Entry Point 22 May 1983-70+; Parry Passage 30 Mar 1976-57; Green Island (Chatham Sound) 16 Mar 1978-90+ arrived from south; daily flocks present after this date. **Interior** - No records.

Summer: Coastal - Haystack Islets 30 Jun 1983-200 feeding on "fish boils" with gulls and cormorants at 1930 hrs; Mandarte Island 25 Jun 1974-400 counted on trip around island; Active Pass 23 Jun 1983-25; Swiss Bay Island 21 Aug 1969-200; Cleland Island 12 Aug 1973-310 around islands; Mitlenatch Island 9 Aug 1969-406 counted between 0630 and 0715 hrs (Foottit 1969); Triangle Island (Scott Islands) 16 Jun 1974-200 in tight raft off north side; Goose Group 16 Jul 1948-68; Luxana Bay 2 Jul 1982-200+; Louscombe Point 3 Jul 1977-600+; Sinnett Islets 27 Jun 1976-68 fishing with loons and scoters; Dean Channel 21 Jul 1985-1 adult at head of channel; Torrens Island 8 Jul 1960-300, 13 Jul 1977-511; Tian Islets 24 Jul 1977-148; Lucy Island 10 Jun 1977-104, survey; Port Simpson 19 Jul 1969-80. **Interior** - No records.

Autumn: Interior - No records. **Coastal** - Green Island (Chatham Sound) 28 Sep 1969-4; Skidegate Inlet 15 Oct 1971-20; Port Neville 4 Oct 1977-50; Secret Bay 6 Sep 1965-30; Oyster Bay 4 Sep 1975-20+; Qualicum Beach 9 Sep 1980-60; Crescent Beach 16 Oct 1966-10 well offshore; Cordova Bay 18 Sep 1973-105 off spit; Oak Bay 8 Nov 1980-30.

Winter: Interior - No records. **Coastal** - Masset 17 and 26 Dec 1972-1; Masset Sound 21 Feb 1983-5, boat survey; Tasu Sound 29 to 31 Jan 1973-2 (Robertson 1974); Pulteney Point 21 Jan 1977-188 in individuals and small groups counted between 1640 and 1730 hrs; Port Neville 22 Jan 1977-18; Qualicum Beach 9 Jan 1974-10; Howe Sound 6 Feb 1921-200 around Bowen and Gambier islands (Munro, J.A. 1921); Departure Bay to Horseshoe Bay 8 Jan 1965-39 counted during ferry trip; Burrard Inlet 25 Feb 1893-30; Vancouver 26 Dec 1948-18 (Middleton 1949); Bamfield 9 Dec 1976-30; Active Pass 15 Feb 1973-100; Saanichton Bay 22 Feb 1973-200 off spit; Baynes Channel 27 Jan 1979-30; Oak Bay 26 Jan 1985-58, mostly around Chain Islets.

Christmas Counts: Interior - Not recorded. **Coastal** - Recorded from 18 of 28 localities and on 61% of all counts. Maxima: Victoria 2 Jan 1966-260, all-time Canadian high count (Anderson, R.R. 1976); Vancouver 27 Dec 1959-75; Nanaimo 27 Dec 1976-50.

Marbled Murrelet
Brachyrhamphus marmoratus (Gmelin)

RANGE: Breeds from the central Aleutian Islands and northern Gulf of Alaska south along the coast to central California. Winters throughout the breeding range. Also winters on northern Pacific coast of Asia.

STATUS: *Very common* to *abundant* resident on salt water along the coast; locally *very abundant* at times, especially in spring and winter. *Uncommon* on coastal fresh-water lakes during the breeding season (April to September); *very rare* at other times of year. Breeds.

NONBREEDING: The Marbled Murrelet is the most widely distributed alcid in the province, occurring on marine waters along the coast, usually within 2 km of land, as well as on many coastal lakes up to 75 km inland.

It inhabits protected coastal waters throughout the year, such as bays, inlets, fiords, lagoons, harbours, and coves, as well as exposed coastal waters (Fig. 217). Tidal rips through narrow passages, shelves at the mouths of inlets, and shallow banks are important foraging sites.

Coastal lakes are also used year-round by Marbled Murrelets. Of 83 records, 18% were from the nonbreeding season, October to March. This percentage is close to figures reported by H.R. Carter and Sealy (1986) for the west coast of North America. They also mention that British Columbia has a preponderance of coastal lakes and most of the lakes used by murrelets are within 20 km of the ocean. The farthest inland lakes used were Cultus, Harrison, and Swan lakes (se Meziadin Lake).

Although the Marbled Murrelet frequently occurs in pairs or loosely knit groups of 12 or so birds throughout nearshore coastal areas, it has a clumped at-sea dispersion, which may be a response to localized food concentrations. The largest concentrations have been reported from Skookumchuck Narrows and near Cortes Island in spring and winter, and from Sechelt in winter only. In summer, Sealy and Carter (1984) found large concentrations off Flores Island.

There is probably a general north and south migration by portions of the Marbled Murrelet population. However, because of the difficulty in separating migrant and resident birds, and of determining movements between inner and outer coastal areas, these migration periods are not well known. Seasonally large numbers first appeared off Qualicum Beach in 1976 on 5 April (Dawe 1980) and in Pacific Rim National Park there is a general influx of Marbled Murrelets in May (Hatler et al. 1978). In the vicinity of Langara Island in 1971, Marbled Murrelets were absent during late winter and early spring, but returned in pairs on 25 April (Sealy 1975b). Tatum (1973) noted increased numbers off southern Vancouver Island during the first half of September.

The centre of the wintering population is the Strait of Georgia, Howe Sound, and Juan de Fuca Strait. On the northern mainland coast, numbers are generally small and consist mostly of singles and pairs; flocks of up to 100 birds are frequent but local on the Queen Charlotte Islands (e.g. Skidegate Inlet).

BREEDING: The Marbled Murrelet probably breeds along the entire coast of the province, although a nest containing eggs or downy young has not been discovered. Its range may include larger forested coastal islands and mainland forests, and extend inland in the vicinity of large lakes to at least 75 km from the sea. Strong evidence for breeding throughout this range includes completely formed eggs taken from the oviduct of collected females (Sutton and Semple 1941), egg fragments gathered from beneath felled trees (Guiguet 1956), adults seen carrying fish to coastal and inland locations, the discovery of flightless young in forested habitats (Munro, J.A. and Cowan 1947), and recently fledged young seen in inshore waters.

Breeding evidence accepted for inclusion on the distribution map consists of the following detailed records of eggshell fragments or nest fugitive young found in forested environments along the coast.

(1) Gilloyees Inlet 26 August 1919-2 downy young on the ground near a marsh (Brooks 1926; MVZ 101538; H.R. Carter and Sealy 1987).

(2) Point Grey Beach 23 July 1941-1 fledgling male, completely feathered, but egg-tooth apparent with some down adherent (Munro, J.A. and Cowan 1947; UBC 478). Drent and Guiguet (1961) note that the habitat is within "1/2 mile of second-growth forest on the east, largely [red] alder with a bit of Douglas-fir and [western] hemlock; and within 3/4 mile of extensive second-growth forest to the south, largely fir with some [red] alder and [western] hemlock."

(3) Masset 15 July 1947-1 juvenile female, unable to fly, picked

Figure 217. Marbled Murrelets off Albert Head, Victoria, 25 October 1986 (Tim Zurowski).

Marbled Murrelet

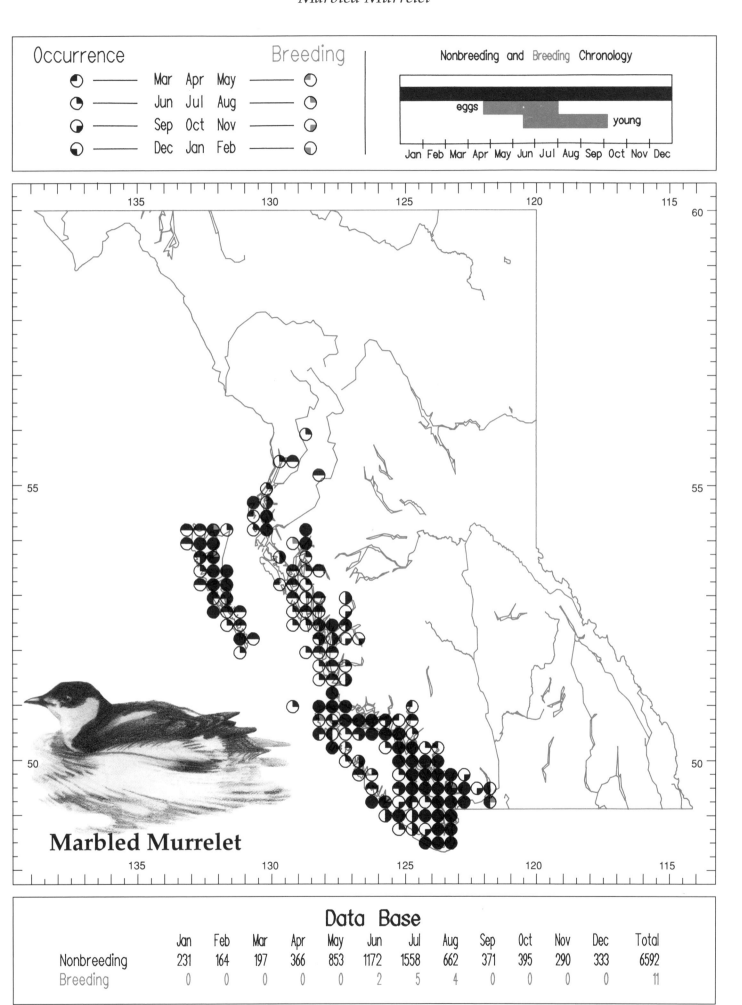

Occurrence

◐	Mar Apr May	◐
◔	Jun Jul Aug	◑
◕	Sep Oct Nov	◕
◕	Dec Jan Feb	◕

Breeding

Nonbreeding and Breeding Chronology

eggs

young

Jan Feb Mar Apr May Jun Jul Aug Sep Oct Nov Dec

Marbled Murrelet

Data Base

	Jan	Feb	Mar	Apr	May	Jun	Jul	Aug	Sep	Oct	Nov	Dec	Total
Nonbreeding	231	164	197	366	853	1172	1558	662	371	395	290	333	6592
Breeding	0	0	0	0	0	2	5	4	0	0	0	0	11

up near the road, about 3.2 km from salt water (Drent and Guiguet 1961; RBCM 10555).

(4) Kumdis Slough 26 July 1947-1 fledgling on the water (Carter, H.R. and Sealy 1987).

(5) Masset 4 June 1953 - an adult and broken egg shells found in the forest, on the ground, after a tree was felled (Guiguet 1956).

(6) Holberg 24 August 1967 - 2 flightless young dropped out of a tree being felled by loggers. The egg teeth were intact and primary feathers were still sheathed. R.D. Harris (1971) mentions that the birds would have been ready to leave the nest within 10 to 14 days. The nest was approximately 18 m from the ground in a western redcedar, about 6 km from salt water.

(7) Kennedy Lake 19 June 1969-1 half grown fledgling (Campbell 1970d).

(8) Stanley Park (Vancouver) 18 July 1970-1 flightless fledgling with an egg tooth picked up alive; it died later (UBC 13470; Campbell et al. 1972a).

(9) Franklin River 13 August 1970-1 downy young on the ground (RBCM 14700; H.R. Carter and Sealy 1987).

(10) Powell Lake 7 August 1979-1 fledgling on the water (Carter, H.R. and Sealy 1987).

(11) Chilliwack 7 July 1987-1 flightless young with an egg tooth found in downtown Chilliwack (RBCM Photo 1242; Fig. 218) The bird weighed 140 g. It was banded and released on 8 July at Stanley Park in Vancouver.

In addition, there are numerous reports (not mapped) of small young along the coast, some with egg teeth, others flightless, and many recently fledged. These young birds arrive on the sea mainly from late June through August with complete juvenal plumage (Sealy 1975b).

The Marbled Murrelet generally nests solitarily (Binford et al. 1975; Simons 1980; Sealy and Carter 1984) but may also breed in small colonies according to Varoujean and Williams (1986). As a result, population sizes are poorly known. Recently, however, Sealy and Carter (1984) have shown that the size of breeding populations may be determined by censusing Marbled Murrelets at sea. The method assumes that birds seen on the water nest in adjacent forested areas. In a study area of 1,236 h of inshore waters surveyed from Cape Beale to Estevan Point along the west coast of Vancouver Island the total breeding population was calculated to be 8,460 individuals. The mean density of 8.1 birds/km² was higher than that calculated for other areas along the Pacific coast of North America (Gould, P.J. et al. 1982; Sealy and Carter 1984).

Speich and Wahl (1989) suggest that as many as 5,000 Marbled Murrelets may nest in Washington.

Nests: No nests with descriptions have been discovered in British Columbia, and less than 10 definite nests are known from throughout its world range. The Marbled Murrelet is known to nest on tree branches (Kuzyakin 1963; Binford et al. 1975), on the open ground (Simons 1980; Hirsch et al. 1981; Day et al. 1983), and in cavities (Johnston, S. and Carter 1985). In British Columbia, all suspected nest-sites have involved single, large conifers (Guiguet 1956; Harris, R.D. 1971; Savile 1972). Eggs reportedly collected from a burrow on the Queen Charlotte Islands (Darcus 1927) have recently been re-identified as those of the Ancient Murrelet (Kiff 1981). It is generally agreed that Marbled Murrelets use old-growth coniferous forests as primary nesting areas from British Columbia to California.

Eggs: Sealy (1974) determined, by follicular maturation, that nests in British Columbia could contain eggs from 15 May to 31 July. Carter and Sealy (1987) calculated egg-laying, from fledgling dates, to occur as early as 22 April and suggested the breeding season was "protracted in southern British Columbia compared to northern British Columbia." In Alaska, the timing of egg-laying has been recorded from 23 April (Bailey, A.M. 1927) to 13 July (Jewett 1942). In British Columbia, the Marbled Murrelet lays a 1-egg clutch (Drent and Guiguet 1961; Sealy 1972). R.D. Harris (1971) reported 2 flightless chicks, which suggests a clutch size of 2 eggs, but the nest site likely supported more than 1 breeding

Figure 218. *Fledgling Marbled Murrelet found in downtown Chilliwack, 7 July 1987 (RBCM Photo 1242; Ivan Polivka). It was banded and released at Stanley Park, Vancouver.*

pair. The incubation period is about 30 days (Sealy 1974) .

Young: Newly fledged young have been seen at sea from 26 June to 5 October (Carter, H.R. 1984). Calculated dates suggest that young could be found as early as 15 June. Known broods in North America contained a single young. The nestling period is 28 days (Carter, H.R. and Sealy 1987).

REMARKS: The unique preference (among alcids) of the Marbled Murrelet, for nesting in old growth forests south of Alaska has been noted by numerous authors (see Sealy and Carter 1984, D.B. Marshall 1987 and Rodway 1990 for summaries). According to D.B. Marshall (1987), the principal factor affecting continued existence of the species over the southern portion of its range (Oregon and California) is the destruction of old-growth and mature forests (Fig. 219). Some have noted that coastal aggregations of murrelets correspond with coastlines dominated by old-growth forests (Savile 1972; Sowls et al. 1980). Others have suspected that numbers have declined at sea near areas where extensive logging has occurred (Brooks 1926; Pearse 1946; Sowls et al. 1980). Sealy and Carter (1984) note:

> Breeding populations of Marbled Murrelets in southern Georgia Strait and the Strait of Juan de Fuca are smaller (about 1,000 breeding pairs; Wahl et al. 1981) than the breeding population in our smaller census areas on the west coast of Vancouver Island (about 4,230 breeding pairs). In the former area, much forested land has been cleared. The removal of old-growth forest there may have caused a decline in population size but there is inadequate census data to substantiate this.

Conflicts with logging practices and methods of censusing breeding populations are discussed in detail by Sealy and Carter (1984).

Another threat to Marbled Murrelet populations is mortality due to commercial fishing. In a small area of Barkley Sound, H.R. Carter and Sealy (1984) found that 7.8% of the local autumn population drowned in gill-nets set for salmon. The authors recommend avoiding "a small area where foraging Marbled Murrelets aggregate" or at least restricting the fishing there to daylight hours.

Additional information on the feeding ecology, at-sea biology and behaviour, and conservation issues can be found in Sealy (1975c), W.T. Munro and Campbell (1979), J.M. Porter and Sealy (1981), H.R. Carter (1984), and D.B. Marshall (1988).

There are 2 subspecies: *Brachyramphus marmoratus marmoratus* breeds in Canada; *B. m. perdix* breeds in eastern Siberia. The latter race is larger, has a white eye-ring and, in breeding plumage, lacks rufous tones on its upper parts (Harrison, P. 1983).

Figure 219. *Josette Point, 14 July 1977 (R. Wayne Campbell). The destruction of mature forests is perhaps the greatest threat to Marbled Murrelet populations in British Columbia.*

NOTEWORTHY RECORDS

Spring: Coastal - between Chatham Islands and Discovery Island 1 to 30 May 1963-200 to 300; Departure Bay 24 Apr 1968-40 (Crowell and Nehls 1968c); Cultus Lake 11 Apr 1959-6, 4 May 1933-1 (ROM 34.2.27.1); Harrison Lake 28 Apr 1928-14 to 16 (Brooks 1928; RBCM 6167); Deep Cove (Burrard Inlet) 25 Mar 1978-16; Pitt Lake 11 May 1963-2; Gambier Island 3 Apr 1977-56; Qualicum 5 Apr 1976-214, large influx (Dawe 1980); Skookumchuk Narrows 1 Apr 1977-1,800; Quadra Island 28 Apr 1980-400 with 1,000 Common Murres; Cortes Island 1 to 31 Mar 1976-1,700 between Sutil Point and Twin Island; Brooks Bay 6 May 1978-94; Louscoone Inlet 29 May 1977-165; Split Head 29 May 1967-16; Gogit Passage 18 May 1982-292 (Lemon and Rodway 1983); Topping Islands 13 May 1983-245; Kitimat Mission 1 May 1975-16 adults; Wiah Point 14 May 1946-40. **Interior** - No records.

Summer: Coastal - Clover Point 25 Jul 1984-75; Haro Strait 8 Jul 1936-291 (Munro, J.A. and Cowan 1947); Sidney 25 Aug 1952-150 to 200, 25 Aug 1962-140; Nitinat Lake 21 Jun 1984-46 (Carter, H.R. and Sealy 1986); Cree Island to Seabird Rocks 12 Jun 1970-200+ adults, mostly in pairs (Guiguet 1971); Cape Beale 4 Aug 1969-80 adults, 13 immatures (Guiguet 1971); Cultus Lake 14 Jul 1971-3+ adults; Cleland Island 24 Jul 1967-105 (Campbell and Stirling 1968b); Kennedy Lake 19 Jun 1969-7 adults and 1 young (Campbell 1970d); Wickaninnish Bay 20 Jun 1975-320; English Bay 8 Jul 1971-88 including young

(Campbell et al. 1972b); Pitt Lake 11 Jul 1973-2; Great Central Lake 6 Jun 1984-9 on water; Mitlenatch Island to Miracle Beach 21 Jun 1969-150 (Foottit 1969); Checleset Bay 22 Jul 1978-150 feeding with Common Murres; Discovery Passage 21 Jun 1968-265 (Hobson, M. 1976); Garrett Lake 1 Aug 1975-8+; Spring Passage 26 Jun 1982-215 adults; Simmonds Group 21 Jun 1976-77; Spider Island 5 July 1939-1 juvenile female with egg-tooth present and down adherent (Munro, J.A. and Cowan 1947; RBCM 9118). The date (4 July) in J.A. Munro and Cowan is incorrect; Seaforth Channel 21 Jun 1976-70 adults, 5 immatures feeding near herring ball; Lyell Island 6 Jun 1982-222 adults at 1500 hrs; Cumshewa Inlet 12 Jul 1977-268; Gospel Island 20 Jul 1977-123, many young-of-year; Masset Inlet 26 Jul 1947-100 adults, 1 young; Cloak Bay and Parry Passage 21 Jul 1971-400 (Sealy 1975b); Birnie Island 25 Jun 1967-78; Swan Lake (se Meziadin Lake) Jun 1979-1. **Interior** - No records.

Autumn: Interior - No records. **Coastal** - Pearl Harbour 1 Sep 1969-4; Naden Harbour 7 Nov 1974-9; Morning Reef 30 Sep 1969-12; Port Neville 10 Sep 1975-30 to 40; Campbell River (Discovery Passage) 4 Oct 1968-24; Cortes Island 21 Nov 1975-450; Eliza Island 5 Sep 1953-250 (Flahaut and Schultz 1954a); Oyster Bay 1 Sep 1974-50; Egmont 25 Oct 1974-60; Cameron Lake 1 Oct 1981-1; Great Central Lake 23 Sep 1970-5+; Alouette Lake 30 Nov 1981-1; Bedwell Bay 27 Oct 1978-22; Stanley Park (Vancouver) 17 Nov 1973-

30, nearly all in pairs; North Arm (Fraser River) 16 Nov 1947-18; Vargas Island 9 Sep 1972-40+ in small groups along west side; Fulford Harbour 19 Sep 1983-30+; Tsehum Harbour 23 Nov 1978-38; Discovery Island 15 Sep 1962-50; Whiffin Spit 6 Nov 1982-38.

Winter: Interior - No records. **Coastal** - Porpoise Channel 25 Dec 1983-4; Minette Bay 15 Jan 1975-2; Masset Inlet 10 Feb 1983-3; Carmichael Passage 14 Jan 1979-14, 25 Feb 1979-100; Cartwright and Englefield sounds 6 to 10 Feb 1973-16; Cortes Island 15 Dec 1975-1,300 feeding with grebes, Oldsquaws, Buffleheads, and Mew Gulls (Shepard, M.G. 1976b); Egmont 21 Feb 1974-300 (Shepard, M.G. 1974); Bowen and Gambier islands 6 Feb 1921-300 (Munro, J.A. 1921); Sechelt 22 Feb 1987-1,700; Harrison Lake 3 Dec 1926-6 (Stewart, R.M. 1927; RBCM 6162); Cultus Lake 28 Dec 1936-6 (Ricker 1937); Tsawwassen 27 Jan 1975-240 off jetty; Cowichan Lake 7 Jan 1924-12 (Munro, J.A. and Cowan 1947), 24 Dec 1924-8 (Simpson 1925), 27 Dec 1925-24 (Simpson 1926), 27 Dec 1926-30 (Simpson 1927); Bamfield 9 Dec 1976-30; Active Pass 3 Feb 1973-300+; Chain Islands 21 Jan 1983-60.

Christmas Counts: Interior - Not recorded. **Coastal** - Recorded from 21 of 28 localities and on 72% of all counts. Maxima: Ladner 21 Dec 1975-**2,125**, all-time North American high count (Monroe 1976); Vancouver 30 Dec 1963-342; Victoria 22 Dec 1962-294.

Ancient Murrelet
Synthliboramphus antiquus (Gmelin)

ANMU

RANGE: Breeds in western North America from southern Alaska south to northern British Columbia (Queen Charlotte Islands). Winters mainly from the Pribilof and Aleutian islands south to central California. Also occurs in eastern Asia.

STATUS: *Common* to *abundant* spring and autumn migrant on the outer coast including Juan de Fuca Strait; *rare* on the inner coast. *Rare* to *uncommon* in summer on the south coast, *fairly common* to *common* along the northern mainland coast. Locally *very abundant* in late spring and early summer on the Queen Charlotte Islands. *Abundant* to *very abundant* winter visitant off the southern tip of Vancouver Island; *rare* elsewhere on the south coast; *very rare* on the north coast including the Queen Charlotte Islands. *Very rare*, mainly in autumn and winter, in the southern interior. Breeds.

NONBREEDING: The Ancient Murrelet occurs primarily along the coast of the province. In the interior, vagrants have been found in the Okanagan valley from Vaseux Lake north to Vernon and Rawlings Lake, and in the east Kootenay at Cranbrook and Elkford.

It generally avoids protected coastal waters such as inlets and fiords unless a storm forces it there. The Ancient Murrelet is primarily a plankton-feeder, and forages in areas of upwelling and mixing such as surge narrows, channels, and other areas with strong eddies and tidal streams. At sea, its distribution is patchy and poorly understood (Sealy 1972). Within sight of land however, important foraging areas used regularly during the nonbreeding period include Queen Charlotte Strait, Juan de Fuca Strait, Haro Strait, and Active Pass. In the interior, birds have been picked up, usually exhausted, on city streets and highways; occasionally they have been seen on lakes.

Figure 220. Adult Ancient Murrelet photographed at night returning to its burrow on Langara Island, Queen Charlotte Islands, June 1988 (Ervio Sian).

Figure 221. Ancient Murrelet nesting habitat at Langara Island, Queen Charlotte Islands, 16 May 1977 (R. Wayne Campbell).

Ancient Murrelet

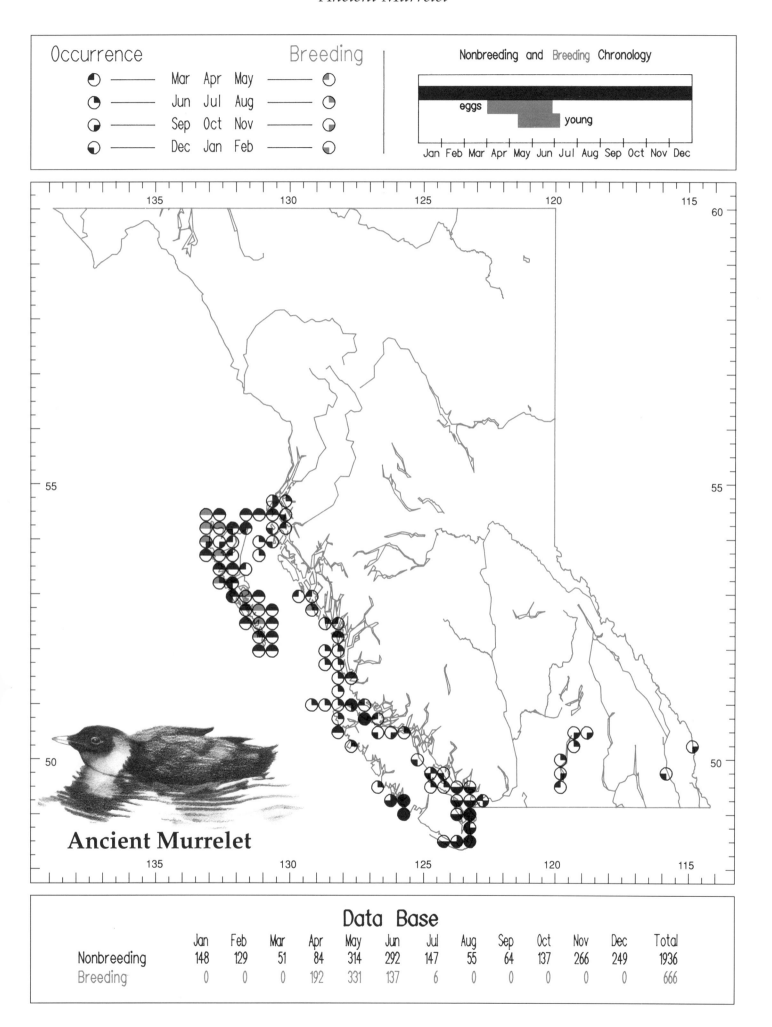

Occurrence   **Breeding**

◑ ——	Mar Apr May	—— ◕
◔ ——	Jun Jul Aug	—— ◔
◔ ——	Sep Oct Nov	—— ◔
◐ ——	Dec Jan Feb	—— ◕

Nonbreeding and Breeding Chronology

eggs

young

Jan Feb Mar Apr May Jun Jul Aug Sep Oct Nov Dec

Ancient Murrelet

Data Base

	Jan	Feb	Mar	Apr	May	Jun	Jul	Aug	Sep	Oct	Nov	Dec	Total
Nonbreeding	148	129	51	84	314	292	147	55	64	137	266	249	1936
Breeding	0	0	0	192	331	137	6	0	0	0	0	0	666

Migration, dispersal and winter distribution of the Ancient Murrelet is poorly understood. Specific information concerning age-classes, routes, numbers, peak movements, and pelagic distribution is lacking. Concentrations of Ancient Murrelets tend to occur on the northern coast from March through July; they are usually associated with breeding colonies. On the south coast, this murrelet is most numerous from September through February.

A spring migration has not been observed along the coast; it has only been indicated by the sudden appearance of large flocks (eg. up to 40,000) near the Queen Charlotte Islands, which suggests that the birds use an offshore route. Flocks of thousands of murrelets occur on regular staging areas close to breeding colonies from late March to early July. Birds have first been seen on nesting slopes in late March (Gaston and Noble 1985) and early April (Sealy 1976).

No other species of alcid begins its dispersal so soon after hatching. In early June and sometimes in late May (Guiguet 1953a), adults with newly hatched young leave colonies on the Queen Charlotte Islands and move westward and northward in Hecate Strait. Between 2 and 6 weeks after hatching, some family groups may be as far south as Vancouver Island (Sealy and Campbell (1979). In July, unaccompanied juveniles are frequently seen in inshore waters, while adult birds are presumably moulting at sea, probably along the continental shelf. At this time, groups are rarely larger than 12 birds in Alaska and occur up to 176 km offshore (Bartonek and Gibson 1972).

In autumn, there is a spectacular influx of Ancient Murrelets into Juan de Fuca Strait, mostly evident in offshore waters from Haro Strait to Port Townsend, Washington. The first migrants may appear in late September, but the main movement occurs in November and December when flocks can number in the thousands, though a few hundred is more common. Most have left this major wintering area by early February. There are only scattered records in winter elsewhere along the coast, and very few aggregations.

Inland wanderings of Ancient Murrelets in western North America have been documented by Munyer (1965) and Verbeek (1966). These writers correlated inland occurrences with low pressure areas over the Pacific Northwest, 1 to 5 days before the birds were actually found. Of the 10 British Columbia inland records, 9 are from 21 August to 20 January, the post-breeding and autumn migration periods. There is also one May record. Three specimens with sex data were females.

BREEDING: The Ancient Murrelet (Fig. 220) breeds mainly on the Queen Charlotte Islands. Small numbers may also nest along adjacent coastal areas. The only definite record, however, is of an incubating adult found on Gander Island (Moore Islands) on 30 May 1970. In most cases, downy young found close to coastal islands away from the Queen Charlotte Islands (e.g. Triangle Island (Scott Islands), UBC 13395 and 13396) do not indicate local breeding but illustrate the species' rapid post-breeding dispersal. Radio tracking studies indicate that Hecate Strait can be crossed by chicks in 24 hours (D. Duncan pers. comm.).

All of the known Ancient Murrelet colonies in British Columbia are on forested islands where the major trees are Sitka spruce, western hemlock and western redcedar (Fig. 221). The Ancient Murrelet nests farther inland than any other colonial alcid in the province so much of their nesting habitat is within stands of western hemlock, western redcedar, and Sitka spruce.

The Ancient Murrelet breeds in 31 colonies on islands around the Queen Charlotte Islands (Figs. 222 and 223). Location, history,

TABLE 16.
Ancient Murrelet: location, history, and size of major colonies in British Columbia.

Location	First Record	Low Survey Results[1]		Year	High Survey Results[1]		Year	Recent Survey Results[1]		Year	Source[2]
North Coast - Colonies > 5000 pairs or nests											
Alder Island	1971	4000	A	1971	14400	At	1985			1985	3,5
Bolkus Islands	1969	500	A	1971	9900	At	1985			1985	3,5,6
Cox Island	1927								E	1981	3,6
Frederick Island	1946	30000	A	1977	68000	At	1980			1980	1,2,3
George Island	1960	7500	A	1977	11600	At	1985			1985	2,3,6
Helgesen Island	1959	150	C	1977	7700	At	1986			1986	1,2,3
Hippa Island	1927	20000	A	1977	40000	At	1983			1983	2,3,4
Kunghit Island E.	1977		S	1977	8800	At	1986			1986	3,6
Langara Island	1910	24000	At	1988	26000	At	1981			1988	1,3,9,10
Lihou Island	1959	6000	At	1986	10000	A	1977			1986	1,2,3
Limestone Island	1971	1500	At	1983	15000	A	1977			1983	2,3,5
Lucy Island	1926								E	1981	1,3
Lyell Island	1976	10000	A	1976	10700	A	1982			1982	2,3,7
Ramsay Island	1971	25	A	1971	18200	At	1984			1984	3,5
Rankine Island	1977	11000	A	1977	26000	At	1984			1984	2,3
Reef Island	1960	500	C	1977	5000	At	1985			1985	2,6,8
Sea Pigeon Island	1960								E	1985	3,6

[1]   A - active burrows; C - nesting confirmed but no count or estimate made; E - colony extinct; S - nesting suspected. All data are estimates unless noted as follows: t - transect estimate.

[2]   1 - Drent and Guiguet 1961; 2 - Campbell and Garrioch 1979; 3 - Rodway et al. In prep.; 4 - Darcus 1930; 5 - Summers 1974; 6 - British Columbia Nest Records Scheme; 7 - Hatter, I. and Bustard 1975; 8 - Gaston and Noble 1985; 9 - Beebe 1960; 10 - Rodway In press.

Figure 222. *Frederick Island, Queen Charlotte Islands, 24 June 1977 (R. Wayne Campbell). About one-quarter of the total breeding population of Ancient Murrelets in British Columbia is found on this island.*

Figure 223. *Ramsay Island, Queen Charlotte Islands, June 1984 (Michael S. Rodway). The high, steep, forested slopes are used by nesting Ancient Murrelets.*

and size of major colonies in the province are given in Table 16. Most of the colonies are along the east coast of Moresby Island but there are 3 large colonies on the west coast of Graham Island, 1 on Lihou Island, and another on Helgesen Island off the northwest coast of Moresby Island. The total population is estimated at 271,500 pairs, which represents 76% of North American and 74% of world populations (Fujimaki 1986; Golovkin 1984; Hasegawa 1984; Melville 1984; Shuntov 1986; United States Department of the Interior 1988; Vyatkin 1986; Watanuki et al. 1986).

Nearly 85,000 pairs are estimated to breed in Alaska. There is a single breeding record for Washington (Hoffman 1924).

Nests: Most burrows are located in moss or bare litter with little shrub cover (Fig. 224); the soil—a loose duff of needles and moss—is held together by fibrous tree roots. Dense thickets of young western hemlock and undisturbed sites within recent blowdowns are also used. The murrelets frequently select an entrance under a root or fallen log, but they will also use hollow stumps, talus slopes, or rocky crevices within the forest. Where grassy areas are used, burrow density is usually much lower than in mossy or bare areas (Lemon and Rodway 1983, 1985b), Reef Island being an exception (A.J. Gaston pers. comm.).

Burrows can be found as far as 500 m from shore and as high as 282 m on the steep slopes of Hippa Island (Lemon and Rodway 1985a). They range from 30 cm to more than 2 m in length. The entrances of very short burrows are frequently concealed with twigs collected by the birds. In the nest chamber, there is often a small nest cup lined with grasses, salal leaves, twigs, and western hemlock cones. The burrows are the same diameter as Cassin's Auklet burrows but can often be distinguished by the less worn appearance of the entrance. In addition, Cassin's Auklet burrow entrances are frequently streaked with white fecal material, whereas droppings are rare at the mouth of Ancient Murrelet burrows. Where droppings do occur they are yellow.

Eggs: Dates for 549 clutches ranged from 1 April (Gaston and Noble 1985) to 17 June, with peak egg-laying occurring during the last 2 weeks of April. The latest clutch initiation was 24 May; theoretically, viable eggs could be found as late as 27 June. Clutch size ranged from 1 to 4 eggs (1E-83, 2E-455, 3E-9, 4E-2) with 83% having 2 eggs. Incubation on Langara Island requires an average of 34.8 days from the laying of the second egg, but the range is 33 to 47 days (Sealy 1972). Gaston and Noble (1985) give a range of 31 to 36 days for Reef Island, with an average of 33.3±2.14 days.

The 2 eggs, which represent 21.9% of the adult weight, take about 14 days to develop (Sealy 1975a). The eggs contain an exceptionally large fat reserve necessary for the production of precocious young. Sealy (1972) concludes that the birds could not produce a second clutch if the first was lost. He also notes that clutches of 3 and 4 eggs are the product of more than 1 female.

The second egg follows the first in 7.3±0.7 days (Sealy 1972) or 8.17±1.53 days (Gaston and Noble 1985), and its arrival often marks the beginning of incubation. In some clutches, however, the eggs are neglected for 2 or 3 days before incubation begins, perhaps helping both eggs to hatch synchronously (Sealy 1984). Hatching may be very slow. Sealy (1972) observed a pair of eggs that took 4 days from the first cracks to actual freedom for the young. In a sample of 18 eggs Gaston and Noble (1985) calculated a hatching time of 6.45±2.51 days. Most young hatch at night.

Young: Dates for 113 broods (in the colony) ranged from 12 May to 7 July with 78% recorded between 27 May and 10 June. Sizes for 88 broods ranged from 1 to 3 young (1Y-12, 2Y-72, 3Y-4) with 82% having 2 young.

The young leave their burrow only 24 to 72 hr after hatching (Fig. 225). The behaviour of chicks at departure varies between colonies. At Forrester Island, Alaska, parents have been heard calling their young to sea (Willett 1915), while Heath (1915) reports that adults actually accompanied chicks to their sea departure. On Langara Island, British Columbia, Sealy (1976) notes that chicks began leaving the colony 30 to 45 minutes before the nightly arrival of adults. On Reef Island, I.L. Jones et al. (1987b) found that parents led their chicks from the burrow for

a short distance before flying to sea. They further state "that the topography of the colony may influence the distance that parents accompany their young."

The Ancient Murrelet is the only alcid known to make extensive use of song (Jones, I.L. 1985; Jones, I.L. et al. 1987a). Each bird has a unique repertoire that elicits a response from its mate and its young. This may be a vital adaptation to taking young to sea where they could easily be lost from sight at night.

The nesting stage ends abruptly with the departure of the young. Nocturnal activity at the colony continues until July, but after the first week of June this activity includes many subadults that will not breed until a later year.

REMARKS: As late as the mid 1920s, Langara Island was the only known Ancient Murrelet colony in British Columbia (Brooks and Swarth 1925). Drent and Guiguet (1961) list 9 colonies in addition to those on Lucy and Cox islands (near Langara Island). Most colonies — about 30 — had been identified by the late 1970s (Campbell and Garrioch 1979), but a previously unreported colony of 5,000 to 10,000 pairs was found on the north side of Annis Point on Kunghit Island in June 1986 (M. Lemon pers. comm.).

The large colony on Langara Island has declined greatly in the last 3 decades. R.W. Nelson and Myres (1976) attribute the decline to biocides or an intrusion of warm water near the British Columbia coast that reduced the food supply of plankton. In addition, M.S. Rodway (pers. comm.) suggests that the accidental introduction of the black rat, and the purposeful introduction of marten may also have contributed to the decline. A program to remove these predators from the island is being instigated.

Sealy (1975c) found that the Ancient Murrelet feeds predominantly on 2 species of euphausiid crustaceans during the early portion of the terrestrial phase of its breeding cycle, and on fish towards the end of the cycle. From March to mid-April the murrelets took *Euphausia pacifica* and from mid-April through July, *Thysanoessa spinifera*. In early June, half of the prey items were Pacific sand lance and shiner perch. Sealy also showed that there were clear differences in foods caught by adults in the early breeding phases and those eaten by fledged juveniles.

See Gaston and Powell (1989) and Gaston et al. (1988) for recent information on the biology of the Ancient Murrelet.

Figure 224. *Ancient Murrelet burrows in moss among fallen trees on Skincuttle Island, Queen Charlotte Islands, 6 July 1977 (R. Wayne Campbell).*

Figure 225. *Ancient Murrelet chicks scampering over beach rocks on Frederick Island to meet parents on the sea, 12 June 1988 (Alan G. Whitney).*

NOTEWORTHY RECORDS

Spring: Coastal - Oak Bay 11 Mar 1979-8; Patricia Bay 26 Mar 1983-2; Active Pass 7 Apr 1984-3 adults; Alouette River (Haney) 11 Apr 1980-1 female (UBC 14178); Cox Bay 11 Apr 1982-1 adult; Port Hardy 25 May 1968-9; Goose Group 30 May 1948-15; 52°24'N, 131°00'W to Huston Bay 26 Mar 1976-6,994 counted from 1800 to 1905 hrs; Rankine Island 31 May 1982-658+ adults and 10 chicks; Juan Perez Sound 14 Mar 1976-1,000 in breeding plumage; Lyell Island 13 May 1982-701 off ne side; Darwin Sound 14 Mar 1976-500; Low and Limestone islands 10 May 1983-1,340 staging; Hippa Passage 28 May 1983-40,000 estimated by telescope; Explorer Bay 11 May 1981-1,072 counted 1 to 3 km offshore from 2210 to 2220 hrs; Parry Passage 30 Mar 1976-32, 1 to 3 May 1966 - in large rafts [thousands] (Campbell 1968h); Rose Spit to Langara Island 12 May 1952-400 to 500. **Interior** - See Extralimital Records.

Summer: Coastal - Victoria 15 to 30 Jul 1984-3+ (Harrington-Tweit and Mattocks 1985); Oak Bay 27 Aug 1929-30 (Bishop 1930); Fleming Island 10 Aug 1968-2 juvenals; 16 km w Cleland Island 15 Jul 1979-1; Florencia Bay 15 Jul 1974-2; Qualicum Beach 13 Aug 1962-4; Cape Lazo 17 Aug 1929-1+ (Bishop 1930); Helmcken Island 21 Jun 1968-4; Clerke Islet 5 Aug 1981-7; Triangle Island (Scott Islands) 21 Jun 1978-10, 2 Jul 1974-2 adults with 1 third-grown downy young; 32 km w Goose Group 13 Jun 1948-8 family groups with newly hatched young (Guiguet 1953a); Rankin Islands 4 Jul 1977-2,000 to 3,000; Moore Islands 25 Jun 1976-2 pairs of adults with 1 half-grown young each; Ramsay Rocks 23 Jun 1971-3,000 (Summers 1974); Hippa Passage 5 Jun 1977-1,840 adults and 1 chick on water at 2300 hrs, 10 Jun 1983-53,000 on water at 0800 hrs; Frederick Island 17 Jun 1981-20,000 to 25,000; Dundas Islands 10 and 23 Jul 1970-20 (Crowell and Nehls 1970d). **Interior** - See Extralimital Records.

Autumn: Interior - See Extralimital Records. **Coastal** - Green Island (Chatham Sound) 13 Sep 1978-2 adults; Naden Harbour 17 Nov 1974-1; Fisherman Bay to Shushartie Bay 12 Sep 1935-5; Port Hardy 3 Sep 1936-2; Doyle Island to Masterman Islands 10 Nov 1950-many small flocks; Sechelt 6 Nov 1983-400 (Campbell 1983a); Point Grey (Vancouver) 16 Nov 1947-2 (UBC 1657, 1659); Sea Lion Rocks 7 Sep 1972-1; Porlier Pass 23 Sep 1983-20; Active Pass 25 Sep 1977-1, 8 Nov 1963-25 (Edwards 1965); Shute Passage 16 Sep 1981-13 adults; Victoria 30 Sep 1972-19 (Tatum 1973); Clover Point 2 Nov 1983-7,000 flying east between 0730 and 0800, 19 Nov 1983-13,000 flying east between 0715 and 0815 hrs, and between 1245 and 1345 hrs.

Winter: Interior - See Extralimital Records. **Coastal** - Prince Rupert 27 Jan 1979-30+; 6 km n Rose Spit 28 Feb 1983-111; Masset Sound 19 Dec 1983-2; Freeman Pass (Porcher Island) 15 Jan 1978-8 (Martin 1978); Port Hardy 2 Jan 1938-6; Mitlenatch Island 22 Dec 1965-24 (Campbell 1965); Irvines Landing 4 Jan 1975-80; Sechelt 18 Dec 1983-33 (Campbell 1983a); Miami Islets 12 Jan 1973-30; Active Pass 15 Feb 1973-500; Houston Passage 7 Dec 1972-37; Haro Strait (Ten Mile Point) 27 Dec 1978-500, 11 Jan 1979-1,250; Oak Bay 8 Feb 1979-1,222; Race Rocks 11 Dec 1975-500.

Christmas Counts: Interior - Not recorded. **Coastal** - Recorded from 10 of 28 localities and on 20% of all counts. Maxima: Victoria 30 Dec 1973-**6,401**, all-time North American high count (Monroe 1974); Sunshine Coast 17 Dec 1983-482; Ladner 29 Dec 1979-77.

Extralimital Records: Interior - Vaseux Lake 26 May 1930-1 (MVZ 101551); Naramata 15 Nov 1975-1 picked up dead (RBCM Photo 559); Okanagan Lake at Peachland 21 Aug 1981-1 with gulls on lake after a heavy storm (Cannings, R.A. et al. 1987); Okanagan Landing 29 Aug 1942-1 female (MVZ 101550); Vernon 19 Nov 1963-1 female found dead (RBCM 18620); Rawlings Lake 26 Oct 1939-1 female (ROM 82595); Cranbrook 7 Dec 1961-1 and 20 Jan 1964-1 (Johnstone, W.B. 1964); 32 km n Cranbrook early winter 1960-1 found dead (Johnstone, W.B. 1964); Elkford 16 Oct 1984-1 (Campbell 1985a; photo published in Rogers, T.H. 1985a).

Cassin's Auklet

Ptychoramphus aleuticus (Pallas)

CAAU

RANGE: Breeds along the west coast of North America from the Aleutian Islands and the Gulf of Alaska south to Baja California. Winters offshore along the Pacific coast, mainly from southern British Columbia to Baja California.

STATUS: *Common* to *abundant* summer visitant, locally *very abundant* in the vicinity of colonies on the west coast of Vancouver Island, Queen Charlotte Strait and the Queen Charlotte Islands; *fairly common* to locally *common* along the northern mainland coast; *very rare* elsewhere. In winter, *casual* on the north coast, including the Queen Charlotte Islands; *uncommon* to *fairly common* off the west coast of Vancouver Island and Juan de Fuca Strait; *casual* in the Strait of Georgia. Breeds.

NONBREEDING: The Cassin's Auklet occurs along most of the outer coast with only scattered records on the inner coastal waters of the Strait of Georgia. It forages in offshore waters more frequently than the other alcids (Wahl 1975) and is only rarely seen close to shore, even near breeding colonies. P.J. Gould et al. (1982) suggest the species congregates along the continental shelf from April through November.

In British Columbia, observations in coastal waters occur most frequently (81%; n=1,113) from March through August (Fig. 226). Autumn and winter records are mostly from southern coastal areas.

Migration to and from the breeding colonies probably occurs mostly offshore and is, therefore, poorly documented. Some evidence suggests that the spring movement begins in late February, peaks in March, and carries into early April. On 1 April 1976 a unique observation was made. M.G. Shepard (pers. comm.) counted 11,259 birds over 2.5 hours from a boat 56 km northwest from Cook Bank (northwest of Cape Scott). The auklets were in 68 groups of up to 900 individuals. Most of the flocks were clustered on either edge of the large submarine trench that separates Vancouver Island and the Queen Charlotte Islands. Few occurred over the centre of the trench or over the shallower areas closer to land. Presumably, oceanic currents were upwelling and carrying food nearer the surface. In autumn, small influxes have been noted offshore from mid-August to mid-September with larger numbers recorded in Juan de Fuca Strait near Victoria in October and November.

Spring flocks tend to be larger than those in autumn. The autumn migration or dispersal is accompanied by a flightless period in which the birds moult all of their primaries (see Payne 1965).

In winter, the Cassin's Auklet has been encountered regularly in small numbers only in Juan de Fuca Strait. Elsewhere in the province, there are only scattered records of individuals in inshore waters; some of these were oiled or starved birds found on beaches.

BREEDING: The Cassin's Auklet breeds along the west coast of Vancouver Island from Sea Bird Rocks to the Scott Islands, near the entrance to Queen Charlotte Sound, locally on the central northern mainland coast, and throughout most of coastal Queen Charlotte Islands.

Figure 226. Immature Cassin's Auklet found alive on Long Beach, Vancouver Island, late July 1967 (R. Wayne Campbell). Each year many recently fledged young are found on west coast beaches from mid-July to mid-August.

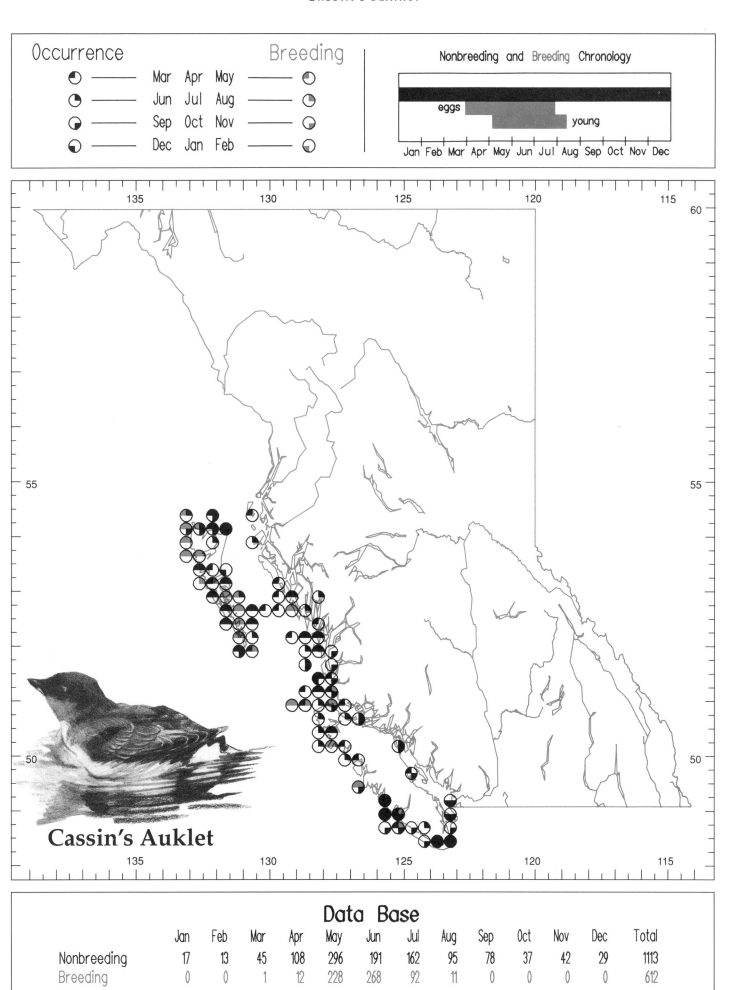

Occurrence / Breeding

	Mar Apr May	
	Jun Jul Aug	
	Sep Oct Nov	
	Dec Jan Feb	

Nonbreeding and Breeding Chronology

eggs / young

Jan Feb Mar Apr May Jun Jul Aug Sep Oct Nov Dec

Cassin's Auklet

Data Base

	Jan	Feb	Mar	Apr	May	Jun	Jul	Aug	Sep	Oct	Nov	Dec	Total
Nonbreeding	17	13	45	108	296	191	162	95	78	37	42	29	1113
Breeding	0	0	1	12	228	268	92	11	0	0	0	0	612

Breeding sites are on islands of varying sizes and heights. Along Vancouver Island and the Kerouard Islands the breeding sites are covered with grasses and shrubs such as salmonberry. Most of the colony sites on the Queen Charlotte Islands have a forest of Sitka spruce, western hemlock, and western redcedar. The understory is often open and mossy; shrubs, when present, include salal, huckleberry, and false azalea. Colonies on forested islands frequently consist of heavily burrowed hummocks close to the sea; they rarely extend far into the forest.

About 80% of the world's Cassin's Auklet breeding population is found in British Columbia. The Scott Group, with over 800,000 breeding pairs, supports 68% of the total British Columbia population of the species. The British Columbia population is estimated to be at least 1,177,000 pairs on about 60 sites, most of which are located around the Queen Charlotte Islands; major colonies in British Columbia are given in Table 17.

The Alaska population is estimated at just over 236,000 pairs, the Washington population at 43,800 pairs (United States Department of the Interior 1988; Speich and Wahl 1989).

Nests: The Cassin's Auklet nests in a variety of situations (Figs. 227 and 228). On Triangle Island and Kerouard Islands, burrows are often intermingled with those of Tufted Puffin and Rhinoceros Auklet, especially where burrows of the larger birds are less densely spaced. Cassin's Auklet avoids tall salmonberry and precipitous slopes. On Triangle Island, preferred sites are covered with short grass, ferns, or forbes at all elevations and

slopes. They are clustered and extend 10 to 15 m into the low salmonberry on the plateau. Patches of saxifrage and fern at the summit of Triangle Island are very densely burrowed. On the west side of the island, where the population is particularly dense, some auklets make burrows just above the tide line, while others tunnel under driftwood.

On the Queen Charlotte Islands, burrows are typically on the perimeters of the islands in grassy or mossy areas (Fig. 228) under Sitka spruce and into the Sitka spruce/western hemlock transition zone. Most burrows are within 30 m of the outer edge of vegetation. They are often among burrows at the seaward edge of Ancient Murrelet and storm-petrel colonies. The copious fecal deposits and the well worn platforms at the entrance of Cassin's Auklet burrows make them easy to distinguish from those of its neighbours. Later in the season, there are often purple deposits of regurgitated food.

Burrows (n=89) ranged from 7 to 12 cm in diameter. Most are from a few centimetres to half a metre below the surface, and according to Drent and Guiguet (1961) vary from 1 to 2.1 m in length. There is a small egg chamber near the end that usually lacks nesting material. There may also be a small side chamber used for defecation, but some birds just use a space behind the nest.

Eggs: Dates for 293 clutches ranged from 4 April to 27 July with 68% recorded between 3 and 25 May. Most egg-laying probably takes place during the latter half of April as data presented are heavily influenced by the periods in which the

---

TABLE 17.
Cassin's Auklet: location, history, and size of major colonies in British Columbia.

Location	First Record	Low Survey Results[1] Year			High Survey Results[1] Year			Recent Survey Results[1] Year		Source[2]
South Coast - Colonies > 5000 nesting pairs										
Beresford Island	1950		C	1950	66000	At	1987		1987	4,8
Buckle Group	1975	300	A	1975	5900	At	1987		1987	2,4,11
Sartine Island	1950		C	1950	376000	At	1987		1987	4,8
Solander Island	1954	200	A	1975	44000	At	1988		1988	1,2,3,11
Triangle Island	1949	100000	A	1975	360000	At	1977		1977	8,9,10
North Coast - Colonies > 5000 nesting pairs										
Anthony Island	1977	24700	At	1985	24700	A	1977		1977	5,12
Byers Islands	1976	7000	A	1976	18800	At	1988		1988	1,11
E. Copper Island	1969	4700	A	1977	10900	At	1985		1985	1,5,11
Frederick Island	1946	60000	A	1977	90000	At	1980		1980	3,4,5
George Island	1977	750	A	1977	5900	At	1985		1985	5,11
Hippa Island	1977	10000	A	1977	12500	At	1983		1983	4,5
Kerouard Islands	1977	22000	A	1977	78000	At	1986		1986	5,12
Langara Island	1926							E	1981	4,7
Lihou Island	1977	1000	A	1977	11200	At	1986		1986	5,12
Marble Island	1961		C	1961	5000	A	1977		1977	1,5
Ramsay Island	1971	7500	A	1977	12900	At	1984		1984	5,6,11
Rankine Islands	1972	5000	A	1977	26000	At	1985		1985	5,6,11
Rock Islet	1977	25	C	1977	5100	At	1986		1986	5,11
Saunders Island	1977	40	C	1977	11000	At	1984	E	1986	5,12
St. James Island	1975				20	A	1977	E	1986	1,5,12

[1] A - active burrows; C - nesting confirmed but no count or estimate made; E - colony extinct. All data are estimates unless noted as follows: t - transect estimate.

[2] 1 - British Columbia Nest Records Scheme; 2 - Campbell 1976a; 3 - Drent and Guiguet 1961; 4 - Rodway et al. In prep.; 5 - Campbell and Garrioch 1979; 6 - Summers 1974; 7 - Young 1930; 8 - Carl et al. 1951; 9 - Vermeer et al. 1976; 10 - Vermeer et al. 1978; 11 - Rodway et al. In prep.; 12 - Rodway et al. 1988; 13 - Rodway et al. 1989.

Figure 227. Cassin's Auklet nesting habitat on the Buckle Group, north of Port Hardy, Vancouver Island, 16 June 1976 (R. Wayne Campbell).

Figure 228. Cassin's Auklet burrows on Rankine Island, Queen Charlotte Islands, 1 June 1984 (Michael S. Rodway).

researchers were active. Calculated dates (see Young) indicate that eggs could be found as early as 29 March. Clutch size ranged from 1 to 2 eggs (1E-289, 2E-4) with 99% having 1 egg (Fig. 229). Clutches of 2 eggs are probably the product of 2 females. Manuwal (1974a) determined the average incubation period to be 37.8 days in California, with a range of 37 to 42 days.

Young: Dates for 314 broods ranged from 5 May to 12 August with 61% recorded between 28 May and 16 June. Fledging has been reported as early as 6 July. Brood size ranged from 1 to 2 young (1Y-311, 2Y-3) with 99% having 1 young (Fig. 230). In dense colonies, burrows intersect and the records of 2 young may represent wanderers. The average length of the nestling period in California is 41.1 days, with a range of 35 to 46 days (Manuwal 1974a). Thoresen (1964) calculated the nestling period to be 44.7 days. Young, once they leave the burrow, are not fed or cared for by the adults and the nightly chorus by the adults ends quite suddenly after the peak period of departure near the end of July.

REMARKS: The Cassin's Auklet has been extensively studied on the Farallon Islands off California (Manuwal 1972, 1979). British Columbia populations, however, have many characteristics different from populations in California. The northern group is migratory, breeds later, is not known to make a second attempt at egg-laying within a year, and birds are a little larger than those of the southern group. Papers of general interest include Manuwal (1974b, 1978) and Speich and Manuwal (1974). In addition, there are 2 papers on the feeding ecology of the Cassin's Auklet in British Columbia by Vermeer (1981) and Vermeer and Cullen (1982).

Figure 229. *Adult Cassin's Auklet with egg in excavated burrow on Gander Island, 30 May 1970 (R. Wayne Campbell). This species is the most numerous breeding seabird in the province and accounts for nearly one-half of the total population.*

Figure 230. *Nestling Cassin's Auklet taken from its burrow on Gander Islet, west of Moore Island off the central mainland coast, 30 May 1970 (R. Wayne Campbell).*

NOTEWORTHY RECORDS

Spring: Coastal - Clover Point 10 May 1976-2; Sooke 17 May 1981-2; Barkley Sound 23 Apr 1982-2; Pine Island (Queen Charlotte Strait) 6 Apr 1977-1 adult, first to arrive on land this year; Solander Island 28 May 1966-15; Kelp Head 23 Mar 1976-1,520 counted between Ruby Rocks and Open Bight from 1209 to 1234 hrs; Triangle Island (Scott Islands) 13 Mar 1976-small groups of 3 to 20 birds always in sight; 51°13'N, 129°00'W to 51°08'N, 128°46'W 1 April 1976-1,379 counted between 1755 and 1840 hrs; 51°23'N, 129°30'W to 51°15'W, 129°00'W 1 April 1976-9,420 counted between 1623 and 1655 hrs; Cape St James 12 Apr 1982-1, first arrival; 8 km e East Copper Island 15 May 1985-420; Huston Bay 26 Mar 1976-100; Shields Bay to Marble Island 30 Mar 1976-50 counted between 1750 and 1745 hrs; Egeria Bay 29 to 30 Mar 1976-15 landed on ship overnight. **Interior** - No records.

Summer: Coastal - Race Rocks 22 Jun 1981-1 adult; Oak Bay 27 July 1979-1; Juan de Fuca Strait 7 Aug 1967-400 counted in a 21 km stretch about 2 km offshore; Pachena Point 7 Aug 1967-385; Tofino 31 July 1971-hundreds seen offshore (Campbell and Shepard 1972); Seymour Narrows 23 Jun 1950-1; Goletas Channel 5 Jul 1987-123 at 0900 hrs; Nahwitti Bar 5 Jul 1987-70+; Langtry Island 26 Jul 1977-50 feeding among young Pacific herring. **Interior** - No records.

Autumn: Interior - No records. **Coastal** - Rose Spit 18 Sep 1971-3; Woodruff Bay 4 Sep 1981-5; Cape St. James 27 Nov 1981-1 found dead; Fitz Hugh Sound 30 Sep 1966-2; Campbell River (Discovery Passage) 22 Oct 1925-2 (RBCM 6199, 6200); Cape Lazo 3 Oct 1958-1; Chesterman Beach 18 Nov 1983-1; s Straight of Georgia 17 Nov 1909-1 (NMC 44210); Bamfield to La Perouse Bank 1 Oct 1977-617 offshore (Shepard 1978); La Perouse Bank 5 Sep 1982-50; Swiftsure Bank 18 Sep 1976-381; sw Jordan River 12 Sep 1982-3; Clover Point 19 Oct 1970-6 (Tatum 1971), 2 Nov 1983-500 in flight east between 0730 and 0800 hrs; Race Rocks 29 Oct 1983-5.

Winter: Interior - No records. **Coastal** - 6 km n Rose Spit 28 Feb 1983-3; Long Beach 23 Dec 1982-2 dead on beach; West Vancouver 3 Dec 1977-1 oiled bird; Barkley Sound 13 Jan 1937-1 (RBCM 6017); Bamfield to La Perouse Bank 13 Feb 1977-2; Active Pass 6 Dec 1979-1; Oak Bay 27 Dec 1953-6, 7 Feb 1954-15.

Christmas Counts: Interior - Not recorded. **Coastal** - Recorded from 4 of 28 localities and on 4% of all counts. Maxima: Victoria 27 Dec 1964-**23**, 17 Dec 1977-**23**, both all-time Canadian high counts (Anderson, R.R. 1976); Sooke 31 Dec 1983-4; Skidegate Inlet 30 Dec 1982-4; Hecate Strait 30 Dec 1980-1.

Rhinoceros Auklet

RHAU

Cerorhinca monocerata (Pallas)

RANGE: Breeds in North America along the Pacific coast from the Bering Sea and Alaska Peninsula south to central California. Winters from southern British Columbia south to Baja California. Also occurs on the northern coast of Asia.

STATUS: *Common* to *abundant* spring and autumn migrant along the outer coast; *rare* in inner coastal waters. Locally *common* to *very abundant* summer visitant along the coast except the Strait of Georgia where it is *uncommon*. In winter, *very rare* on the north coast and on the west coast of Vancouver Island; *rare* in the northern Strait of Georgia, *uncommon* to *fairly common* in the Gulf Islands and Juan de Fuca Strait. Local breeder.

CHANGE IN STATUS: At the time of J.A. Munro and Cowan (1947), the Rhinoceros Auklet was considered a resident species and was known to breed only at 3 sites along the coast. By the late 1950s, another 2 breeding colonies had been discovered (Drent 1961; Drent and Guiguet 1961). Since then, and particularly since the late 1960s, the species has expanded its known breeding range south into Oregon and California (Scott, J.M. et al. 1974). Part of this expansion, however, may have included the re-establishment of former colonies. The number of known active breeding sites in British Columbia increased to at least 30 (Campbell 1976a; Campbell and Garrioch 1979; M.S. Rodway pers. comm.). This change may be due in part to the increasing intensity of recent surveys as well as changing environmental conditions and changes in prey species abundance (Ainley and Lewis 1974).

Figure 231. Adult Rhinoceros Auklet on Cleland Island, August 1974 (R. Wayne Campbell).

Figure 232. Location of part of the Rhinoceros Auklet colony on Anthony Island, Queen Charlotte Islands, May 1988 (R. Wayne Campbell).

Rhinoceros Auklet

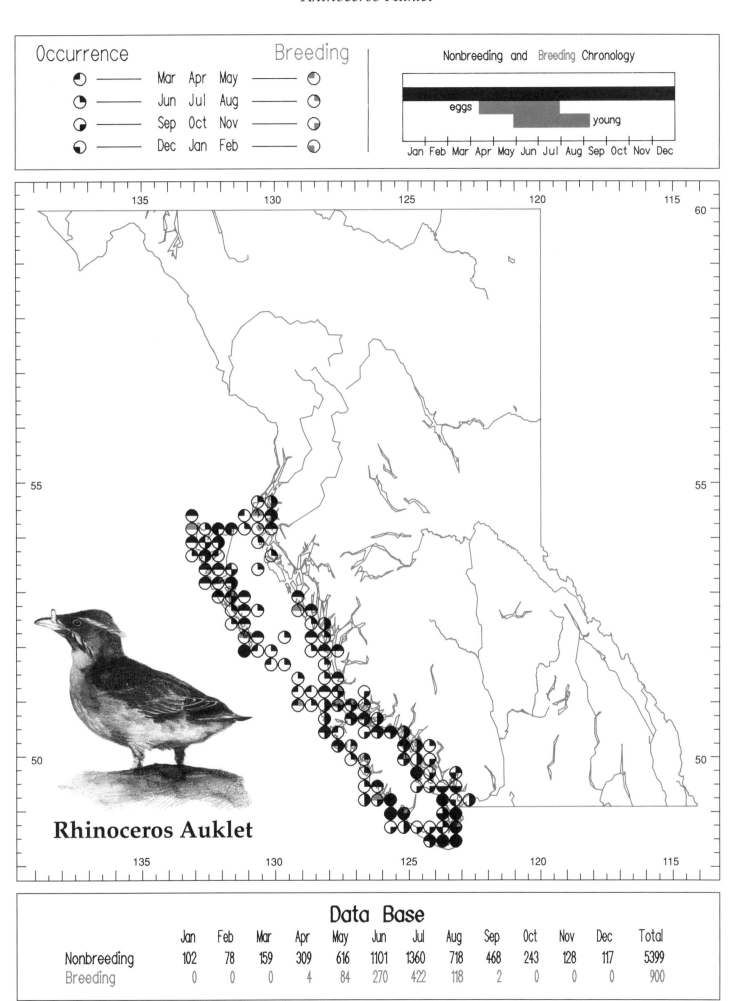

TABLE 18.
Rhinoceros Auklet: location, history, and size of major colonies in British Columbia.

Location	First Record	Colony History Low Survey Results[1] Year		High Survey Results[1] Year		Recent Survey Results[1] Year		Source[2]
South Coast - Colonies > 1000 nests or pairs								
Cleland Island	1961	47 A	1967	2700 A	1982	1000 At	1988	2,13
Pine Island	1907	39500 A	1976	89500 At	1985		1985	3,7,13
Storm Islands	1975	2000 A	1975	72000 At	1987		1987	6,13
Triangle Island	1966	3000 A	1966	22000 At	1984		1984	9,10,13
North Coast - Colonies > 1000 nests or pairs								
Anthony Island	1969	2700 A	1977	13600 At	1985		1985	3,4,11
Byers Islands	1976	1500 A	1976	37900 At	1988		1988	3,13
Helgesen Island	1959			16600 At	1986		1986	11
Kunghit Island	1947	125 A	1947	2500 A	1986		1986	8,12
Langara Island	1915					E	1981	1,5
Lihou Island	1959			2700 At	1986		1986	8,11
Lucy Islands	1907	C	1907	26000 A	1976	21500 At	1983	1,3,8
Moore Islands	1936	250 A	1976	40500 At	1988		1988	3,8,13
Saunders Island	1984			9000 A	1984	E	1986	1
Whitmore Islands	1976	1500 A	1976	12400 At	1988		1988	3,13

[1] A - active burrows; C - nesting confirmed but no count or estimate made; E - colony extinct; . All data are estimates unless noted as follows: t - transect estimate.

[2] 1 - Rodway et al. In prep.; 2 - Campbell and Stirling 1968b; 3 - British Columbia Nest Records Scheme; 4 - Campbell and Garrioch 1979; 5 - Green 1916; 6 - Campbell 1976a; 7 - Rodway and Campbell 1977; 8 - Drent and Guiguet 1961; 9 - Hancock 1970; 10 - Carl et al. 1951; 11 - Rodway et al. 1989; 12 - Rodway et al. 1988; 13 - Rodway In press.

In British Columbia, the increase in the number of new sites and population numbers is well documented at 2 locations. At Triangle Island, off the northern end of Vancouver Island, the Rhinoceros Auklet was not found breeding in 1949 or 1950 during extensive biological surveys (Carl et al. 1951). In 1966, Hancock (1970) estimated 3,000 pairs breeding there; by 1976 the population was estimated at 15,000 pairs (Vermeer 1979); by 1984, 22,000 pairs occupied the colony. At Cleland Island, off the central west coast of Vancouver Island, the Rhinoceros Auklet was first discovered nesting in 1967 (Campbell and Stirling 1968b) despite earlier visits by collectors (Drent and Guiguet 1961). The population was estimated at 25 pairs and occupied an area of about 25 m². In 1969, the population had increased to between 375 and 450 pairs (Hatler et al. 1978) and occupied a much wider area (Summers and Drent 1979); by 1982, 2,700 pairs were breeding on the island.

Today, the breeding population in British Columbia is estimated at 222,800 pairs (Table 18) which represents over 57% of current estimates in North America and 35% of the known world population (Sowls et al. 1978; Sowls et al. 1980; Flint et al. 1984; Golovkin 1984; Hasegawa 1984; Lensink 1984; Wilson, U.W. and Manuwal 1986; Speich and Wahl 1989).

NONBREEDING: The Rhinoceros Auklet is widely distributed along inner and outer coastal areas of the province. It prefers open marine waters but is regularly seen at the mouths of bays and inlets and at the outer limits of estuaries. Only rarely does it occur in inlets, fiords, or estuaries. Favourite foraging and staging areas include channels, banks, and other areas of upwelling. Occasionally, drift logs or other floating debris are used as roosting sites.

Seasonal movements are poorly documented. Spring migration may begin in March and peak in April. Off southern Vancouver Island, a peak movement of birds in May may reflect foraging movements from colonies in northern Washington. The only other large aggregations in spring are associated with breeding colonies farther north.

In summer, large aggregations are usually associated with breeding colonies especially early in the season. The largest congregations occur at the southern end of Queen Charlotte Sound between the large colonies on Pine, Storm, and Triangle islands. Concentrations near Prince Rupert probably come from Lucy and Rachael islands. Birds foraging at the mouth of Clayoquot Sound come from Cleland Island, while the birds off Victoria from May through August, probably come from Protection Island (Washington). Flocks off Tlell and Copper Bay on the east coast of the Queen Charlotte Islands are the most difficult to attribute to a breeding colony. They are more than 110 km from any known breeding site and could be nonbreeding birds.

The autumn movement occurs mostly in September. Post-breeding dispersal is preceded by the congregation of large flocks near the colonies in August. In late August or early September, the auklets undergo a synchronous moult (Wilson, U.W. 1977) and accomplish migration largely by swimming to wintering areas off Oregon and California. Most autumn records consist of small groups scattered throughout coastal waters.

Figure 233. Rhinoceros Auklet nesting habitat on Lucy Island, west of Prince Rupert, 12 May 1977 (Michael S. Rodway).

In winter, single birds and small groups are widely distributed in Juan de Fuca Strait and the southern Strait of Georgia. Elsewhere, only isolated birds are recorded.

The Victoria area is unique in that it is the only area in the province where there are numerous sightings of Rhinoceros Auklets throughout the year. Single birds account for about half of the records between mid-September and the end of March. The other half consists of groups of 2 to 10 birds except in January and February when 10% are in groups of 11 to 20 and another 10% in flocks of 30 to 50. In April and May, most of the birds are in small clusters of pairs rarely exceeding 20 birds, and singles account for 10 to 20% of the sightings. In June, July, and August, when Rhinoceros Auklets are incubating eggs and rearing young, most sightings consist of groups larger than 20. Flocks larger than 150 birds occur about 10% of the time in summer, while singles account for less than 5% of the summer records. Groups of more than 10 are rare (<5%) from the beginning of September until December.

BREEDING: The Rhinoceros Auklet (Fig. 231) breeds from Mandarte Island, off the tip of southern Vancouver Island, north along the west and north coasts of Vancouver Island, Queen Charlotte Strait, locally on the northern mainland coast to Lucy Island (Fig. 233) and on the Queen Charlotte Islands (Fig. 232). There are no colonies in the northern Strait of Georgia, Johnston Strait, or near the mouths of coastal inlets, although Rhinoceros Auklets have been seen landing on Mitlenatch Island in the early 1960s (van Tets 1963). Breeding was only discovered on Mandarte Island in 1985 despite intensive research on the island since the late 1950s. In 1986, 2 abandoned eggs and a dead chick were collected (25 Jun-2 eggs [UBC 2043] and chick [UBC 14653]). By the summer of 1988 at least 10 burrows were counted. In time, the species may spread to occupy larger islands throughout the Strait of Georgia.

Location, history, and size of major colonies in British Columbia are given in Table 18. Colonies on and near Langara Island on the Queen Charlotte Islands and possibly on Lanz and Cox islands in the Scott Islands off northwestern Vancouver Island have disappeared since the turn of the century probably due to the introduction of terrestrial predators such as rats, mink, and raccoons.

Colonies in British Columbia are situated on vegetated islands of 2 to 130 ha in size. On forested islands, they may be established on headlands and can extend up to 180 m inland, but most burrows are located within 100 m of shore. On the Queen Charlotte Islands, Lucy Island, and the islands in Queen Charlotte Sound, there is a forest cover of Sitka spruce, western hemlock, and western redcedar. Triangle and Cleland islands and Seabird Rocks lack trees, but are covered with grasses and dense shrubs, particularly dune wildrye and salmonberry. Smaller plants are frequently worn away by the bird's regular visits and continued excavation during the breeding season. The consequent loss of surface vegetation contributes to erosion on steeper slopes.

There are 35 known breeding locations in British Columbia. Most of the population of 340,000 pairs occurs in just 6 clusters of colonies: Englefield Bay and the Anthony Islands group on the Queen Charlotte Islands, Lucy and Rachael islands in Chatham Sound, the Moore Islands region off the central mainland coast, Pine and Storm islands in Queen Charlotte Strait, and Triangle Island in the Scott Islands.

The Alaska population is estimated at 59,320 pairs and the Washington population at about 30,400 breeding pairs (United States Department of the Interior 1988; Speich and Wahl 1989).

Nests: Most burrows are probably excavated or cleaned out in April, although this activity may start in late March. Burrows occurred on a range of slopes from nearly level to more than 45°.

They ranged from near tideline to more than 180 m inland and 100 m up a hillside. Most entrances were beneath and partially camouflaged by a clump of grass, a log, or a root. Burrows on grassy islands usually ranged from 1 to 2 m in length and were frequently simple tubes or forked only once. Soil on the islands was very friable, held together only by the grass roots. On forested islands, which tend to have deeper and softer soil, burrows frequently reached 4 to 6 m in length, occasionally connected with other burrows, and often had a number of side tunnels. Near the end of the burrow there was usually an egg chamber with fresh soft vegetation such as false lily-of-the-valley, grass, or seaweed. There is normally a separate chamber which the chick can use for defecation. Most active nests had a worn entrance marked by droppings and feathers.

Eggs: Dates for 263 clutches ranged from 24 April to 25 July with 53% recorded between 13 and 30 May. On Cleland Island peak laying occurred between 28 April and 10 May in 1969 (Summers and Drent 1979). Calculated dates (see Young below) indicate that eggs could be found as early as 9 April. Clutch size ranged from 1 to 3 eggs (1E-256, 2E-5, 3E-2) with 97% having a single egg. Reports of more than one egg in a burrow are attributable to dumping by stray females or eggs falling through from other burrows.

Incubation period in Washington averaged 45.1 days with a range of 41 to 49 days, on Destruction Island (Leschner 1976) and 44.9 days with a range of 39 to 52 days, on Protection Island (Wilson, U.W. and Manuwal 1986). In British Columbia (Fig. 234) it averaged 42 days, with a range of 39 to 45 days, on Cleland Island (Summers and Drent 1979). Rhinoceros Auklets quickly desert their eggs if disturbed during incubation.

Young: Dates for 631 broods ranged from 24 May to 5 September with 66% recorded between 30 June and 26 July. The earliest fledging date was 23 July (Summers and Drent 1979). All broods consisted of a single young (Fig. 235).

Fledging periods in Washington averaged 52.6 days, with a range of 42 to 62 days, on Destruction Island (Leschner 1976) and in British Columbia 50.0 days, with a range of 38 to 56 days, on Cleland Island (Summers and Drent 1979).

REMARKS: The breeding biology of the Rhinoceros Auklet was poorly known until Richardson (1961) began studies on Protection Island, Washington. Subsequently, Leschner (1976) and U.W. Wilson (1977) refined and expanded the basic elements in the life cycle of this alcid. In British Columbia, most of the early information was gathered by egg collectors between 1904 and 1948. Drent and Guiguet (1961) summarize all research in the province up to 1960. From the late 1970s onward several papers have appeared on the feeding ecology, reproductive success, and growth of the Rhinoceros Auklet in British Columbia (Vermeer 1979, 1980; Vermeer and Cullen 1979, 1982; Bertram 1988).

There have been 5 band recoveries of Rhinoceros Auklets from British Columbia (Fig. 236), 3 of which are outside the breeding season. All suggest there is a general movement southward, which may be a true migration. In 1983, a flightless chick banded at Lucy Island, near Prince Rupert, on 13 July was recovered during a beached-bird survey on 8 December 1983 near Cambria, California, some 2,200 km south of its hatching site (Kaiser et al. 1984). In the winter of 1984 a bird that hatched on Pine Island was recovered in southern Washington and one from Triangle Island was recovered in California.

U.W. Wilson (1986) shows that Rhinoceros Auklets readily use artificial burrows which may be used for both management and research purposes.

The Rhinoceros Auklet is also known as the Horn-billed Puffin.

Figure 234. Partially exposed incubating Rhinoceros Auklet on Lucy Island, west of Prince Rupert, 8 June 1970 (R. Wayne Campbell).

Figure 235. *Large Rhinoceros Auklet chick found near its burrow on Cleland Island, August 1974 (R. Wayne Campbell).*

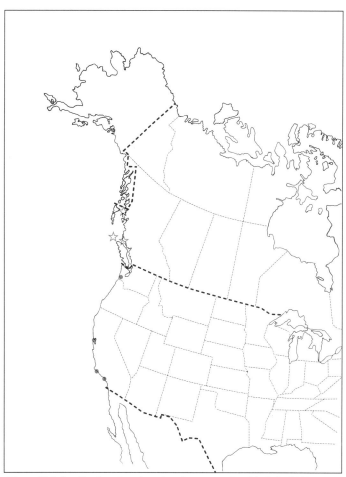

Figure 236. *Banding locations (stars) and recovery sites (circles) of Rhinoceros Auklets associated with British Columbia.*

NOTEWORTHY RECORDS

Spring: Coastal - Race Rocks 21 Mar 1981-17; Victoria 15 Apr 1981-37, 28 May 1984-115; sw Ucluelet 15 May 1977-30; Mitlenatch Island 26 May 1974-7; Solander Island 12 Mar 1976-6, 5 May 1976-187; Hope Island 28 Apr 1939-30 (Munro, J.A. and Cowan 1947); Cape Caution 25 May 1968-76; s Goose Group 22 May 1948-250; Cape St. James 1 Apr 1976-5, 23 Apr 1982-12+; w Anthony Island 21 May 1985-1,900; n Reef Island 2 May 1987-100 to 150; 1.2 km sw Frederick Island 26 May 1952-3,000 to 4,000; Naden Harbour 23 Mar 1976-2; Cape Edenshaw 8 May 1977-105; Cape Knox 30 Mar 1976-1; Ridley Island 28 Mar 1979-6. **Interior** - No records.

Summer: Coastal - Oak Bay 14 Jul 1970-500+; Clover Point 23 Jun 1988-680, in flocks of 5 to 55 counted from 0600 to 0715, 4 Aug 1974-650; Island View Beach 21 Jun 1975-234; Quisitis Point 20 Jun 1975-100; Boundary Bay 10 Aug 1985-1 immature female found dead (UBC 14773); Tofino 14 Jun 1976-250+; Cleland Island 16 Jun 1975-300; Mitlenatch Island 3 Jun 1976-47 adults; 3 km s Hatchett Island 27 Jun 1975-450 feeding with other seabirds; Johnstone Strait 6 Aug 1969-

317; Weynton Passage 28 Jun 1982-122 adults; Pine Island 12 Jul 1975-100 at 2000 hrs, 500 at 2030 hrs, 1,000 at 2100 hrs and 5,000 at 2130 hrs; Smith Sound 6 Jul 1976-3,000+; Fitzhugh Sound 7 Aug 1969-385; Triangle Island (Scott Islands) 6 Jul 1974-1,700 at 2100 hrs; Cape St. James 6 Jul 1979-780; Rose Harbour to Ikeda Bay 5 Jul 1977-2,603 counted from 2000 to 2300 hrs; Langtry Island to Garcier Rocks 10 Aug 1979-1,000; Skedans Island 9 Jun 1985-2,000 to 3,000; Masset Inlet to Naden Harbour 16 Aug 1986-1,500 to 2,500; Chatham Sound 22 Jul 1969-2,300 (Crowell and Nehls 1969c); Langara Island to Masset Harbour 29 Jun 1986-1,350; Port Simpson 22 Jul 1969-2,273. **Interior** - No records.

Autumn: Interior - No records. **Coastal** - Port Simpson 6 Sep 1969-50; Masset Sound 21 Oct 1974-1 in winter plumage; Spiller Channel 23 Sep 1968-1; Cape Scott Park to Quatsino 2 Oct 1935-20; Shushartie 12 Sep 1935-150; Cracroft Islands 3 Oct 1968-5; Maud Island (Campbell River) 19 Sep 1967-25; w Tofino 12 Sep 1970-28; Lighthouse Park (West Vancouver) 25 Sep 1977-2; Gibsons 11 Nov 1986-1; Snake Island 14 Oct 1979-8;

Boundary Bay 3 Nov 1923-1 female (UBC 3091); Bamfield 17 Nov 1979-1; Port Renfrew 21 Sep 1974-27; Fulford Harbour to Swartz Bay 25 Nov 1982-16; Trial Islands 24 Sep 1982-25; Clover Point 14 Nov 1975-28.

Winter: Interior - No records. **Coastal** - 6 km n Rose Spit 28 Feb 1983-2; Cape St. James 22 Dec 1981-1; Hornby Island 31 Jan 1930-1; Long Beach 12 Feb 1983-1 freshly dead on beach; Howe Sound 6 Feb 1921-15 (Munro, J.A. 1921); Burrard Inlet 14 Feb 1975-1; English Bay 31 Dec 1971-1 (Campbell et al. 1972b); Vancouver 4 Dec 1953-1 female (NMC 47839); Horseshoe Bay to Departure Bay 8 Jan 1965-9; Bamfield to La Perouse Bank 13 Feb 1977-2; Oak Bay 27 Dec 1977-15, 11 Feb 1978-50.

Christmas Counts: Interior - Not recorded. **Coastal:** Recorded from 8 of 28 localities and on 14% of all counts. Maxima: Victoria 17 Dec 1977-37, all-time Canadian high count (Anderson, R.R. 1978); Pender Islands 21 Dec 1977-15; Sooke 16 Dec 1984-4.

Tufted Puffin

Fratercula cirrhata (Pallas)

TUPU

RANGE: Breeds along the west coast of North America from northwestern Alaska to northern California. Winters at sea throughout the north Pacific Ocean. Also occurs along the northern Pacific and Bering Sea coasts of Asia.

STATUS: *Uncommon* to *fairly common* summer visitant, becoming *very abundant* locally in the vicinity of breeding colonies on the Queen Charlotte Islands and the west coast of Vancouver Island. *Rare* to locally *uncommon* summer visitant to the northern mainland coast, the Strait of Georgia, and Juan de Fuca Strait. *Casual* in winter on the southern coast of Vancouver Island. Breeds.

NONBREEDING: The Tufted Puffin is widely distributed along the coast. It prefers outer coastal waters, but each year individuals are found scattered in the Strait of Georgia and Juan de Fuca Strait. It visits harbours and bays infrequently.

The Tufted Puffin has been recorded in the province in all months, but most records (93%; n=1,749) are from May through August, the breeding period. About October, the Tufted Puffin disperses to offshore waters and seems to remain there until April. Recent evidence (Harrison, P. 1983) suggests a general pelagic, southward dispersal from breeding colonies. Migration periods are generally unknown. In British Columbia, most birds return to colonies in May and depart in August. Concentrations have not been observed outside of the breeding season.

Figure 237 Adult Tufted Puffin with food, Triangle Island, 18 August 1981 (Richard J. Cannings).

Figure 238. The Kerouard Islands, 3 July 1977 (J. Bristol Foster). Hundreds of Tufted Puffins breed on these grassy islands in the southern Queen Charlotte Islands. They are also a suspected breeding site for Horned Puffins.

Tufted Puffin

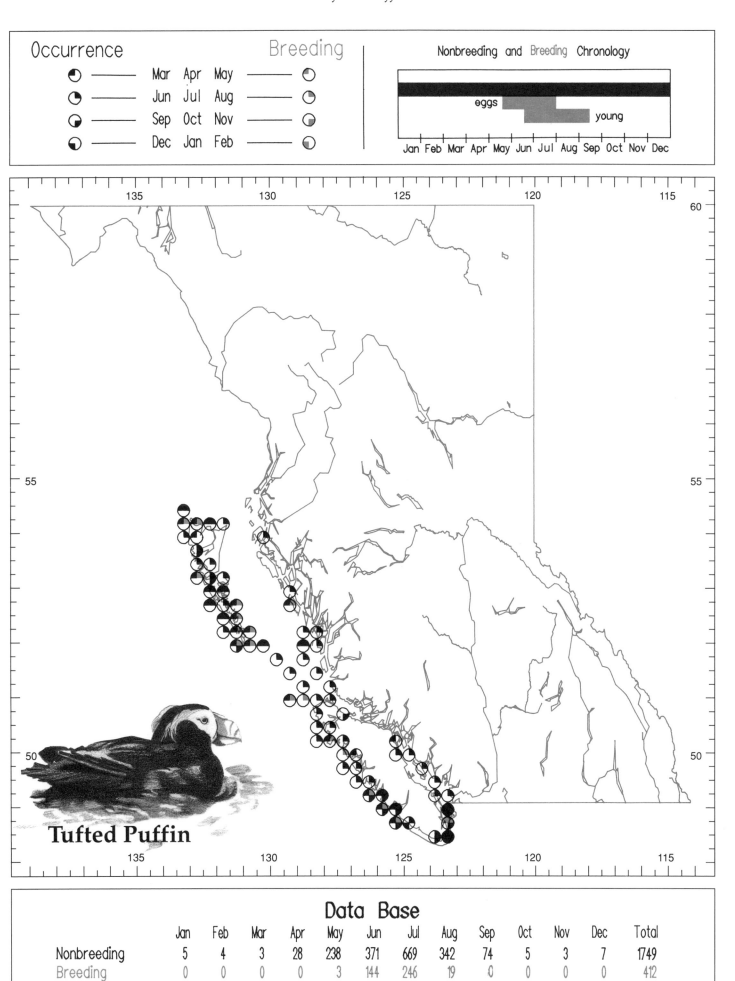

Data Base

	Jan	Feb	Mar	Apr	May	Jun	Jul	Aug	Sep	Oct	Nov	Dec	Total
Nonbreeding	5	4	3	28	238	371	669	342	74	5	3	7	1749
Breeding	0	0	0	0	3	144	246	19	0	0	0	0	412

Tufted Puffin

BREEDING: The Tufted Puffin (Fig. 237) breeds from Mandarte Island north along the west coast of Vancouver Island, locally on the central mainland coast, and throughout much of the Queen Charlotte Islands.

It nests in large colonies, in small groups, and even solitarily on offshore islands. There are no known breeding sites on the mainland and only the colony at Lyman Point on Kunghit Island is located on a headland. The Lyman Point site is also the only colony on an east-facing coast. A few of the breeding islands have trees (Fig. 241) but colony sites tend to be treeless and shrubless (Fig. 238). They are densely covered with grass tussocks including tufted hairgrass and dune wildrye (Fig. 242). Colonies range from 8 to 130 m above sea level.

About 38,365 pairs of Tufted Puffins breed in British Columbia. They occupy 31 sites of which 87% are found on Triangle Island (Fig. 239) and its neighbours in the Scott Islands. This represents about 4% of North American and 3% of world populations (Kaiser and Lemon 1987). Table 19 lists details for major colonies.

The Alaska population is estimated at just over 1,318,000 pairs and the Washington population at just over 11,600 breeding pairs (United States Department of the Interior 1988; Speich and Wahl 1989).

Nests: Most Tufted Puffins nested in burrows, which were simple tubes running horizontally into the ground. Crevices in shoreline rocks were also used where there was a shortage of soil suitable for burrowing (e.g. Mandarte Island - Drent and Guiguet 1961; Moos Islet; Flatrock Islet).

Slopes used for burrowing varied from 10° to 75°, but adults preferred slopes steep enough for takeoff (Fig. 240). Burrow density was higher on shoulders of cliffs/bluffs, when slope behind was minimal. The lengths of burrows ranged from 0.4 to 1.9 m and entrance diameters from 13 to 28 cm. Burrow chambers were usually well lined with dry grasses, feathers, twigs, leaves, and rootlets; a few were unlined.

Eggs: Dates for 237 clutches ranged from 20 May to 31 July with 78% recorded between 20 June and 10 July. Clutch size ranged from 1 to 3 eggs (1E-233, 2E-3, 3E-1) with 98% having 1 egg. Clutches larger than a single egg are probably the product of more than one female. Incubation period is about 46 days (Wehle 1980).

Young: Dates for 172 broods ranged from 9 July to 31 August (adults returning to burrows with fish), with 88% recorded between 11 and 31 July (Lemon et al. 1983). Calculated dates indicate young could be found as early as 20 June and at least as late as 15 September. Brood size ranged from 1 to 2 young (1Y-169, 2Y-2) with 98% having 1 young (Fig. 243). Both broods of 2 young were found in burrows in late August and may represent wandering immatures (see Campbell and Stirling 1968b). Nestling period ranges from 42 to 51 days depending on available food (Vermeer and Cullen 1979).

REMARKS: The Tufted Puffin presents more conservation problems than most of the other alcids. It is diurnal and is more susceptible to desertion when disturbed during breeding (see Pierce and Simons 1986). J.G. King and Sanger (1979) rank it among the most vulnerable to oil pollution. In addition, 18,000 to 40,000 birds drown in drift nets in the Gulf of Alaska each winter (King, W.B. 1984; Ogi 1984), although there is no evidence that British Columbia birds are involved. It also depends on a reliable supply of Pacific sand lance, shortages of which lead to mass starvation of nestlings as happened on Triangle Island in 1976 and 1977 (Vermeer 1978; Vermeer et al. 1979a).

Additional information on the ecology and breeding biology of the Tufted Puffin in Alaska and British Columbia is provided in Amaral (1977), Vermeer (1979), and Wehle (1983).

The Tufted Puffin was formerly placed in the genus *Lunda*.

TABLE 19.

Tufted Puffin: location, history, and size of major colonies in British Columbia.

Location	First Record	Colony History — Low Survey Results[1]	Year	High Survey Results[1]	Year	Recent Survey Results[1]	Year	Source[2]
South Coast - Colonies > 1000 nesting pairs.								
Beresford Island	1950			2100 At	1987		1987	10,11
Sartine Island	1950			6400 At	1987		1987	10,11
Solander Island	1954	C	1954	4000 A	1988		1988	1,2,11
Triangle Island	1909	20000 A	1974	30000 A	1977	24900 At	1982	5,7,8,9
North Coast - Colonies > 100 birds.								
Anthony Island	1971	10 B	1971	190 B	1977	32 B	1986	5,6,13
Kerouard Islands	1958	900 B	1986	1500 P	1977		1986	1,4,13
Kunghit Island	1960	50 B	1960	435 B	1977	323 B	1986	5,12
Langara Island	1920	C	1920	150 B	1947	E	1981	1,3
Marble Island	1961	12 B	1961	350 B	1977		1977	5
St. James Island	1975	100 P	1986	1500 P	1977		1986	4,5,13

[1] A - active nests or burrows; B - breeding birds; C - nesting confirmed but no count or estimate made; E - colony extinct; P - pairs; S - nesting suspected. All data are estimates unless noted as follows: t - transect estimate.

[2] 1 - Drent and Guiguet 1961; 2 - Campbell 1976a; 3 - Rodway et al. In prep.; 4 - Campbell and Garrioch 1979; 5 - British Columbia Nest Records Scheme; 6 - Summers 1974; 7 - Vermeer 1978; 8 - Vermeer et al. 1979a; 9 - Lemon and Rodway 1983; 10 - Carl et al 1951; 11 - Rodway In press; 12 - Rodway et al. 1988; 13 - Rodway et al. 1989.

Figure 239. *Tufted Puffin colony site on Triangle Island, July 1982 (Michael S. Rodway).*

Figure 240. *Tufted Puffin nesting slopes on "Puffin Rock", Triangle Island, July 1982 (Michael S. Rodway).*

Figure 241. *Marble Island, Queen Charlotte Islands, 19 July 1977 (R. Wayne Campbell). Tufted Puffins breed on the steep, grassy slopes near the top of the cliffs.*

Figure 242. *Rudolf Drent checking Tufted Puffin burrows on Wells Rocks off the northern mainland coast, 1 June 1970 (R. Wayne Campbell). In 1988, the colony was abandoned due to the loss of burrowing soil caused by erosion.*

Figure 243. *Fledgling Tufted Puffin at Solander Island off the west coast of Vancouver Island, 14 August 1981 (R. Wayne Campbell).*

Tufted Puffin

NOTEWORTHY RECORDS

Spring: Coastal - Clover Point 13 Mar 1972-2 (Tatum 1971); Trial Islands 26 May 1953-12 in flight; Saanich 17 May 1982-4; Clayoquot Sound 18 May 1907-1 adult male (NMC 3503); Ganges Harbour 2 May 1976-1 adult; Cleland Island 20 Apr 1982-3 adults, 19 May 1982-23; Discovery Passage 29 Apr 1966-1; Solander Island 28 May 1966-750; Triangle Island (Scott Islands) 19 May 1976-100 circling island; Cape St. James 24 Apr 1982-100+ arrived; Treat Bay 28 May 1977-14; Naden Harbour 8 Apr 1975-12 inside harbour; Langara Island 24 Apr 1915-100, first arrival (Green 1916); 13 May 1947-150. **Interior** - No records.

Summer: Coastal - Race Rocks 21 Jul 1984-9, 12 Aug 1977-9; Chain Islets 22 Jun 1984-5 adults; Mandarte Island 9 and 10 Jul 1960-5, 21 Jul 1927-15 pairs estimated (Munro, J.A. 1929b); Finlayson Arm 7 Jul 1924-1 female (RBCM 4777); Saturna Island 8 Aug 1971-1 (Tatum 1972); Seabird Rocks 19 Jun 1975-20 to 30 birds feeding in area; Florencia Island 4 Aug 1974-6 adults; Sea Island 3 Jul 1962-1 (Boggs and Boggs 1962d); Snake Island 8 Jun 1976-1 adult; Cleland Island 11 Aug 1975-100 roosting; White Islets 13 Jul 1974-6; Mitlenatch Island 14 Jun 1966-1 adult (Campbell and Kennedy 1966); Triangle Island (Scott Islands) 15 Jul 1984-9,000 in extended loose flocks at 2130, mid-Jul 1986-1,600 in massed flock (Mattocks 1986b); Cape St. James 3 Jul 1977-300 to 400 flying near nesting cliff; Kerouard Islands 10 Jun 1986-900; 2 km w Bella Bella 6 Aug 1977-2 adults; Byers Islands 27 Jun 1976-11 adults; Lyman Point 4 Jul 1977-360+; Marble Island 20 Jun 1977-300 to 400 flying; Kitkatla 10 Aug 1973-some; Rose Spit 30 Jul 1974-8; Cox Island (Langara Island) 8 Jun 1981-26, 6 Jul 1946-40, 27 Jul 1977-37 adults. **Interior** - No records.

Autumn: Interior - No records. **Coastal** - Hippa Island 11 Sep 1983-1; Skidegate 1 Sep 1895-3 (RBCM 31-33); Cape St. James 9 Sep 1981-7, 22 Nov 1978-1; Hardy Bay 11 Oct 1938-1; Long Beach 30 Oct 1982-1 in winter plumage, washed ashore; Bamfield 10 Sep 1977-2 (Shepard, M.G. 1978); La Perouse Bank 3 Sep 1983-4 adults, 1 immature; Island View Beach 20 Sep 1983-2; Ten Mile Point 23 Sep 1951-3; Esquimalt Lagoon 15 Oct 1953-6 off breakwater.

Winter: Interior - No records. **Coastal** - Galiano Island 4 Dec 1971-1; Carmanah Point 5 Jan 1949-1 carcass (Irving 1953); Victoria 8 Feb 1919-1 male (RBCM 16254), 18 Feb 1919-1 male (RBCM 4697), Oak Bay 29 Jan 1954-4 in winter plumage.

Christmas Counts: Interior - Not recorded. **Coastal** - Recorded 3 times: Victoria 21 Dec 1963-1, 2 Jan 1966-**2**, all-time Canadian high count (Anderson, R.R. 1976), 27 Dec 1966-1.

Horned Puffin

HOPU

Fratercula corniculata (Naumann)

RANGE: Breeds from northwestern Alaska south along the coast of Alaska to the Queen Charlotte Islands in British Columbia. Winters in pelagic waters from the Gulf of Alaska south to California. Also occurs on the northern coast of Asia.

STATUS: *Rare* migrant, locally *uncommon* to *fairly common* summer visitant and *casual* in winter along the outer coast. *Casual* in inner coastal areas. Local breeder.

CHANGE IN STATUS: At the time of J.A. Munro and Cowan (1947), the occurrence of the Horned Puffin was hypothetical in British Columbia; published reports all contained incomplete information (see Chamberlain 1887; American Ornithologists' Union 1895; Fannin 1898; Guiguet 1972).

From the late 1940s through the early 1970s observations of Horned Puffins became more frequent, and specimens were collected, which allowed Sealy and Nelson (1973) to consider it a "regular winter and spring visitant, but uncommon summer visitant along the Queen Charlotte Islands." The same authors report 3 records for Vancouver Island. About the same time, Hoffman et al. (1975) describe the species as "a late spring and early summer visitant to the west coast of the United States."

The observation rate continued to increase during the 1970s and 1980s, mostly from the vicinity of the Queen Charlotte Islands. In 1977, breeding was confirmed at 1 site and suspected at 3 others along the coast (Campbell et al. 1979a). At present, the Horned Puffin is regularly encountered in summer along the outer coast, most often in the vicinity of Tufted Puffin colonies. It also appears to be extending its breeding range throughout the Queen Charlotte Islands and along northwestern Vancouver Island.

NONBREEDING: The Horned Puffin is widely distributed in nearshore waters along outer and inner coastal areas. The bird's seasonal distribution offshore is poorly known, but Pitman and Graybill (1985) found it common in February, 185 to 260 km west of San Francisco, and the most abundant seabird 630 to 815 km west of Cape Blanco, Oregon, in May. They saw none within 185 km of the coast.

The Horned Puffin prefers the open marine environment, but has been found in sheltered bays, surge narrows, tidal rips, and channels close to shore. It is usually found singly, occasionally in very small groups, and often mingling with Tufted Puffins and Rhinoceros Auklets near rich feeding grounds such as Cape St. James and Cape Scott. No large groups have been seen in British Columbia but in Alaska the Horned Puffin forages in large flocks along the edge of the continental shelf (Gould, P.J. et al. 1982).

The Horned Puffin has been recorded in the province from 15 February to 29 August and from 1 October to 19 November.

BREEDING: The Horned Puffin is known to breed at only one location in the province: a small unnamed islet off the northwest corner of Anthony Island (Campbell et al. 1979a). On 4 July 1977, a single egg was located in a rock crevice there.

The Horned Puffin likely breeds at 11 additional sites in British Columbia but evidence to date is inconclusive. The concentration of sightings at these sites, including those of adults carrying fish, on Marble Island, Cape St. James, and the Kerouard Islands (see Fig. 238), strongly suggests a breeding population among Tufted Puffins in British Columbia. During 1987, several Horned Puffins were also seen flying near a Tufted Puffin colony at Lyman Point.

On Triangle Island, adults were seen carrying fish in 1975, 1976, and 1982; in 1976, one adult carried fish into a burrow. In addition, there were territorial adults observed in July 1982 (Lemon et al. 1983) and throughout July 1986 (J. Curson and D. Beadle pers. comm.). Eggs or young have not been found. One or more pairs may also breed on Solander Island. Since 1975, single birds have been seen there throughout the summer flying with Tufted Puffins and occasionally landing on the island, but none have been seen entering burrows or carrying fish (Campbell and Summers In press).

The total breeding population in British Columbia is estimated at 25 pairs. In Alaska over 487,200 pairs breed (United States Department of the Interior 1988). None are known to breed in Washington.

REMARKS: Occasionally, Horned Puffins are involved in "wrecks" of seabirds. They are usually associated with winter storms and very large numbers can be washed ashore. The evidence suggests that the birds are unable to feed in the very rough weather and simply starve; neither oil nor pathogens have ever been implicated. One poorly documented wreck occurred in the early 1940s when "windrows" of dead Horned Puffins washed ashore in Henslung and Bruin bays on the Queen Charlotte Islands (Sealy and Nelson 1973). Wrecks have also been described by Gabrielson and Jewett (1970) who reported "hundreds" washed up on Oregon beaches from late December 1932 through mid-February 1933, and Alcorn (1959) who counted 70 dead Horned Puffins along a beach near Westport, Washington. Wrecks may occur more frequently than the literature suggests but go unnoticed because there are so few observers on the outer coasts of British Columbia.

Sealy (1973b) and Amaral (1977) describe the breeding biology, and Wehle (1983) the feeding ecology of the Horned Puffin.

The Atlantic Puffin (*Fratercula arctica*) and Horned Puffin constitute a superspecies.

NOTEWORTHY RECORDS

Spring: Coastal - Oak Bay 11 May 1979-1 in nonbreeding plumage; Triangle Island (Scott Islands) 23 May 1978-4; Cape St. James 18 May 1983-2 to 4; Reef Island 11 May 1985-1; Masset 27 Mar 1987-2; Beal Cove 18 Mar 1971-1 adult female (UMMZ 218021); Gunia Point 7 Apr 1971-2 in winter plumage (Sealy and Nelson 1973); Cox Island (Langara Island) 5 Apr 1971-2 in winter plumage (Sealy and Nelson 1973). **Interior** - No records.

Summer: Coastal - Wickaninnish Bay 20 Jun 1975-1 adult; Seymour Narrows 18 Aug 1957-1 (Sealy and Nelson 1973); Triangle Island (Scott Islands) 6 to 21 Jul 1986-8 to 10, 1 Aug 1977-8 adults; Cape St. James 5 Jul 1975-7 adults on water, 29 Aug 1981-11 together; Sinnett Islets 27 Jun 1976-1 adult; Anthony Island Park 2 Jul 1977-6 adults; Joseph Island 28 Jun 1976-1 adult; Marble Island 19 Jul 1977-5 adults; Pillar Bay 17 Jun 1971-1 feeding in mixed species (Sealy and Nelson 1973); Langara Point 1 Jul 1968-2 in summer plumage (Sealy and Nelson 1973). **Interior** - No records.

Autumn: Interior - No records. **Coastal** - Tow Hill 24 Oct 1982-4; Naden Harbour 1 Oct 1975-1 in winter plumage (Shepard, M.G. 1975d); Little River (Comox) 19 Nov 1930-2.

Winter: Interior - No records. **Coastal** - Rose Spit 24 Feb 1987-1 (UBC 14732); Smythe Point (Skincuttle Inlet) 25 Feb 1978-1 found in high tide line saturated with heavy crude oil; Scott Channel 15 Feb 1971-2 (Sealy and Nelson 1973); Tofino 16 Feb 1980-1 immature found dead on beach.

Christmas Counts: - Not recorded.

Horned Puffin

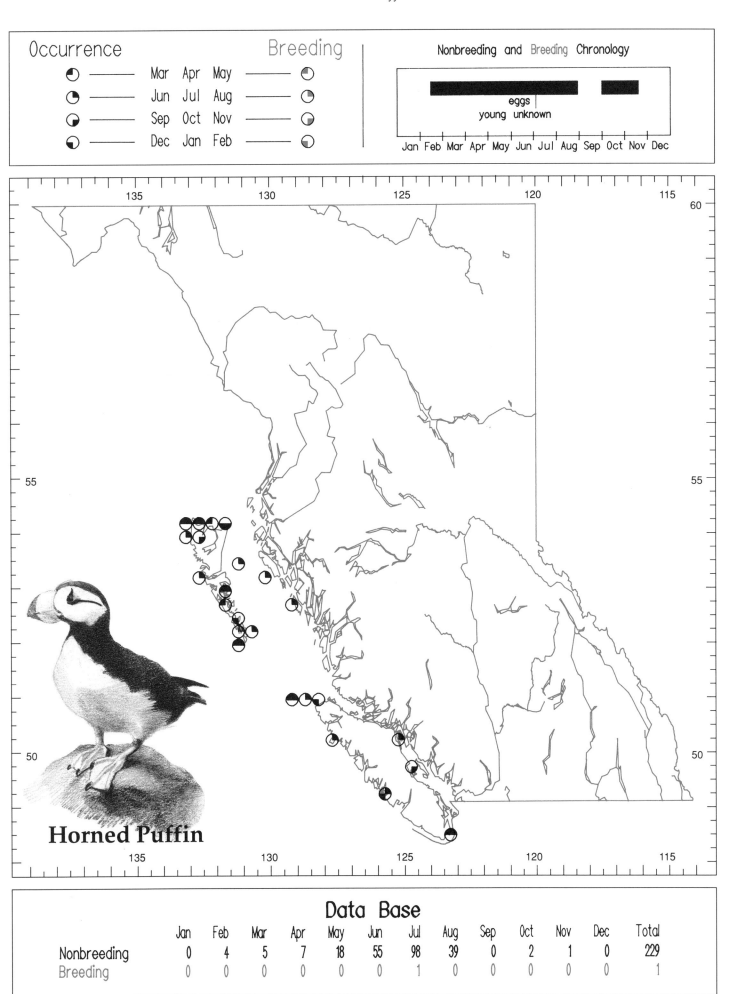

Rock Dove
Columba livia Gmelin

RANGE: In North America, introduced and resident from southern Alaska and across southern Canada south through the United States. Also occurs in Central and South America and the West Indies. Native to the Old World.

STATUS: Introduced. *Uncommon* to *very abundant* local resident on the southern and northern mainland coast; *very rare* and local on the Queen Charlotte Islands. *Rare* to locally *common* in the interior. Breeds.

NONBREEDING: The Rock Dove (Fig. 244) is widely distributed across southern British Columbia. It is more local, and far less numerous, through the central interior, Peace River region, the extreme northwest and the north coast including the Queen Charlotte Islands. It is closely associated with human habitation, frequenting unforested urban and rural areas. It feeds in farm fields, at cattle feedlots and turkey farms, on grain spillage alongside railway tracks and grain elevators, in city parks, along highways, on beaches, and at fast food outlets. It roosts on bridges, city buildings (Fig. 245), barns, silos, wharves, pilings, cliffs, and log booms. The centre of abundance is metropolitan Vancouver. It occurs from sea level to 820 m elevation.

BREEDING: The Rock Dove is probably a local breeder throughout its range in the province but documented breeding has been reported only from the Fraser Lowlands, southeastern Vancouver Island, and Prince Rupert along the coast, and from the Okanagan valley north to Prince George, and in Fort Nelson and Atlin in the interior. The Rock Dove breeds singly or in loose colonies (Table 20) in habitats associated with rural, agricultural, and urban areas, from near sea level to 620 m elevation.

Figure 244. Adult Rock Dove at Reifel Island, Delta, 29 April 1980 (Ervio Sian).

Figure 245. Ledges, windowsills, and roof tops of city buildings in Victoria provide roosting sites for Rock Doves (Grant Hollands).

Rock Dove

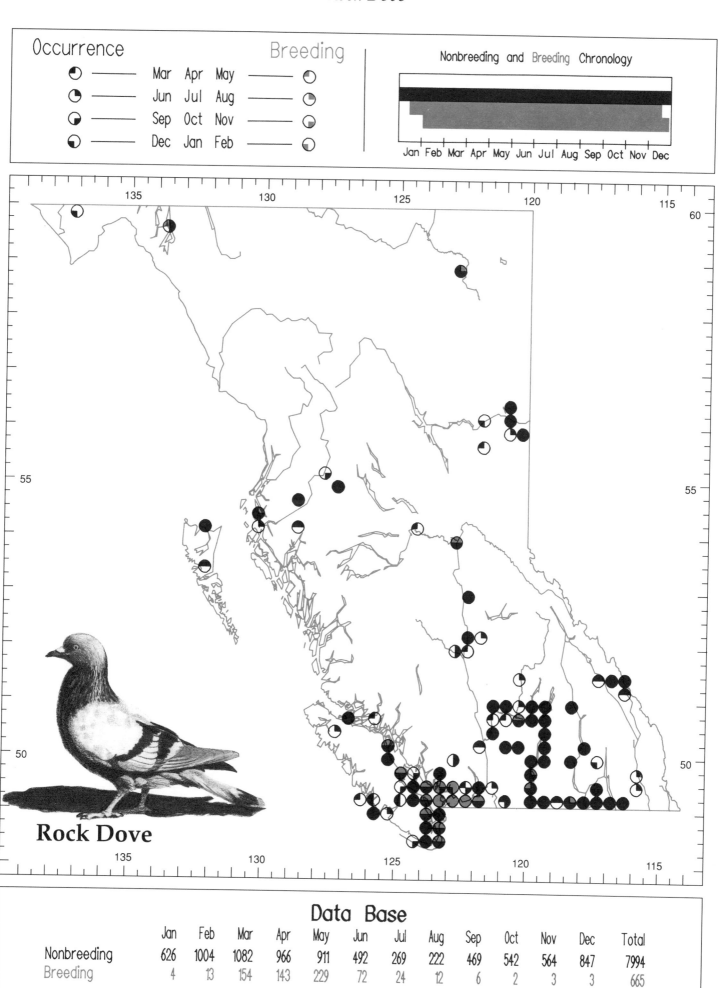

Occurrence   Breeding

	Mar Apr May		
	Jun Jul Aug		
	Sep Oct Nov		
	Dec Jan Feb		

Nonbreeding and Breeding Chronology

Jan Feb Mar Apr May Jun Jul Aug Sep Oct Nov Dec

Rock Dove

Data Base

	Jan	Feb	Mar	Apr	May	Jun	Jul	Aug	Sep	Oct	Nov	Dec	Total
Nonbreeding	626	1004	1082	966	911	492	269	222	469	542	564	847	7994
Breeding	4	13	154	143	229	72	24	12	6	2	3	3	665

Nests: Most nests (64%; n=341) were situated on or in buildings including barns (Fig. 246), silos, grain elevators, hotels, stores, schools, stadiums, and houses. Other nest sites included bridges (20%), wharves and pilings (14%), artificial breakwaters, clay cliffs, and one nest was in a crevice of a Pacific crabapple tree. Most nests (81% of 266) were located on a rafter, beam, ledge, or girder of a building or bridge. Nests were also found under roof eaves, on a light fixture, in a drain pipe, among boulders at the end of a 2-m tunnel, under a rock overhang, and in holes in a clay cliff. Heights of 247 nests ranged from ground level to 30 m with 59% between 3 and 9 m. Nests ranged from no material, where eggs were merely laid on a board, to very neat saucers of grasses (Fig. 246), to messy piles of feces. Most nests (64%; n=214) were composed of feces with various mixtures of grasses, twigs, rope, woodshavings, paper, leaves, and feathers, often lined with twigs or grasses. Other nests were composed of grass only (16%), debris and twigs (13%), sawdust, twigs, or mud. Outside diameters for 23 nests ranged from 12 to 34 cm. Nests were found solitarily and in colonies of up to at least 30 pairs.

Eggs: Dates for 283 clutches ranged from 16 January to 18 December with 63% recorded between 25 March and 15 May. Clutch size ranged from 1 to 4 eggs (1E-84, 2E-188, 3E-7, 4E-4) with 66% having 2 eggs (Fig. 246). Clutches of 3 or 4 eggs may have been the product of 2 females. Incubation period is 17 to 18 days (Lees 1946).

Young: Dates for 137 broods ranged from 4 February to 28 December with 59% between 16 April and 24 May. Brood size ranged from 1 to 3 young (1Y-51, 2Y-83, 3Y-3) with 60% having 2 young (Fig. 247). At least 2 nests produced 4 broods in a single year. Nestling period is 35 to 37 days (Lees 1946).

REMARKS: It is not known when the Rock Dove was introduced into British Columbia but it probably arrived with the first settlers. Even today, its distribution, populations, and other life history information is poorly known. Most villages and cities probably have self-sustaining populations, especially in southern areas.

This familiar bird is considered a pest by many, but control programs have usually failed. In New York, the Buffalo Department of Public Works destroyed over 94,000 birds between 1946 and 1951, "with little apparent effect on their overall abundance" (Beardslee and Mitchell 1965).

The Rock Dove is also known as Common, Domestic, Feral, or Rock Pigeon. All fancy domestic breeds are derived from this species.

Figure 246. Rock Dove nest and eggs in a barn in Agassiz, 6 March 1982 (R. Wayne Campbell).

TABLE 20.
Rock Dove: location, history, and size of major colonies in British Columbia.

Location	First Record	Low Survey Results[1] Year		High Survey Results[1] Year		Recent Survey Results[1] Year	Source[2]
Coastal - Colonies > 10 nests or pairs							
Abbotsford	1982			16	Np 1982	1982	1
Tsawwassen							
Breakwater	1978	4	Np 1978	10-15	P 1981	1981	1
Ferry Terminal	1978			27	Np 1978	1978	1
Vancouver							
Burrard Bridge	1962			26	Np 1963	1963	1

[1]   N - nests; P - pairs. All data are estimates unless noted as follows: p - partial count.

[2]   1 - British Columbia Nest Records Scheme.

Figure 247. Nestling Rock Doves at Chilliwack, 7 March 1982 (R. Wayne Campbell).

NOTEWORTHY RECORDS

Spring: Coastal - Saanich 1 Mar 1982-50; Duncan 26 Apr 1976-43 at grain elevator; Ucluelet 26 Apr 1976-3; Sea and Iona islands 12 Apr 1974-100, 25 Apr 1976-152; Port Neville 16 May 1975-1; Queen Charlotte City 26 Mar 1972-30, introduced feral flock; Prince Rupert 4 Apr 1983-300 in railyards near grain elevator. **Interior** - Grand Forks 13 Apr 1977-25; Penticton 19 May 1974-36; Lytton 20 Mar 1977-6; Nakusp 10 May 1986-12; Kamloops 28 Mar 1978-5; Field 1 Apr 1977-1 (Wade 1977); Chase 20 Jun 1973-20; Doc English Gulch 26 May 1979-12 on rock face, apparently nesting; Quesnel 11 May 1977-23; Prince George 24 Mar 1977-9; Fort St. John 27 Mar 1983-8; Fort Nelson 1 Mar 1975-3; Atlin 21 May 1981-18 (Campbell 1981).

Summer: Coastal - Saanich 19 Jul 1982-100 in flock in farm fields; Bamfield 22 Aug 1976-1; Nanaimo 27 Jul 1967-20; Stanley Park (Vancouver) 19 Aug 1978-70; Alert Bay 9 Aug 1973-50; Masset 5 Jun 1985-1. **Interior** - McIntyre Bluff 25 Jun 1974-7 (Cannings, S.G. 1974); Nelson 5 Aug 1979-4; 150 Mile House 6 Aug 1983-1;

Kamloops 9 Jun 1973-15; Williams Lake 1 Jun 1963-4; Fort St. John 17 Jul 1983-7; Fort Nelson 15 Jun 1975-8; Atlin 6 Jul 1980-3.

Autumn: Interior - Atlin 4 Oct 1980-12; Fort St. John 29 Oct 1983-36 near railyards and grain elevators; Dawson Creek 3 Oct 1982-70; New Hazelton 7 Oct 1982-5; Quesnel 2 Oct 1982-11; Kamloops 26 Sep 1978-9; Nakusp 15 Sep 1984-30; Okanagan Lake (at Penticton) 10 Sep 1978-25; Creston 11 Oct 1975-10. **Coastal** - Prince Rupert 20 Jan 1983-300+ in railway yards near grain elevator; Alert Bay 2 Oct 1968-1; Qualicum Beach 15 Oct 1979-7; Vancouver 24 Oct 1965-900 near bridge and grain elevators; Ucluelet 7 Sep 1973-1; Iona Island 23 Oct 1968-250+ on log booms; Saanich 13 Sep 1982-175, 9 Nov 1978-350 in plowed fields; River Jordan 22 Sep 1984-8.

Winter: Interior - Mile 87.5, Haines Road (Kelsall Lake) winter 1979/1980-1; Fort Nelson 31 Jan 1975-1; Fort St. John 23 Dec 1984-62, highest count (Grunberg 1985b), 20 Feb 1983-25 at grain

elevator; Prince George 21 Jan 1979-3; Williams Lake 2 Jan 1984-41; Revelstoke winter 1982/1983-67 roosting under bridge; South Thompson River 5 Feb 1977-10 carrying nesting material to sites under bridge; Spences Bridge 28 Dec 1976-50; Nakusp 2 Feb 1986-11; Nelson 5 Feb 1977-25; Slocan 25 Jan 1977-2. **Coastal** - Prince Rupert 20 Jan 1983-300+, railway yards near grain elevator; Stanley Park (Vancouver) 29 Dec 1974-160; Vancouver 15 Jan 1968-2,000+ near bridge and grain elevators; Ucluelet 24 Jan 1972-5 (Hatler et al. 1978); Victoria 29 Dec 1980-150.

Christmas Counts: Official counts for the species were first published in 1973. **Interior** - Recorded from 14 of 19 localities and on 60% of all counts. Maxima: Vaseux Lake 23 Dec 1980-526; Vernon 18 Dec 1983-482; Kamloops 15 Dec 1984-270. **Coastal** - Recorded from 20 of 28 localities and on 80% of all counts. Maxima: Vancouver 17 Dec 1978-**15,157**, all-time Canadian high count (Anderson, R.R. 1979); Ladner 29 Dec 1979-2,119; Pitt Meadows 15 Dec 1974-1,942.

Band-tailed Pigeon

Columba fasciata Say

RANGE: Breeds in southeastern Alaska, and from southwestern British Columbia south through the western cordillera of the United States to Mexico, Central America, and South America. Winters from southwestern British Columbia south through the breeding range.

STATUS: *Uncommon* to locally *very abundant* resident on the south coast, including southern Vancouver Island, becoming *uncommon* to locally *very common* transient farther north along the coast. *Rare* visitant in the interior. Breeds.

NONBREEDING: The Band-tailed Pigeon occurs along the coast from southern Vancouver Island and the Fraser Lowlands north to the Queen Charlotte Islands (rarely) and Kitsault. In the interior, it has a sparse but widespread distribution across the southern portion of the province to Sparwood and Mount Robson, becoming scattered throughout the central interior north to Fort St. James and Hazelton. Birds have been observed from sea level to 1,830 m elevation.

During spring migration, the Band-tailed Pigeon frequents railway yards, rail lines, and farmland where it feeds on grain spillage and newly sown grains and peas. It prefers open sites bordered by tall conifers, using the adjacent trees for roosting. Mineral springs and intertidal flats (Fig. 248) are also used and become more important as breeding activity increases. Pigeons usually obtain mineral gravel in the immediate vicinity of shoreline coniferous growth. They move to breeding areas when early fruits become available (March and Sadlier 1972). In late summer, birds may move to higher elevations to feed on ripening fruits. Later, during the autumn movement, they concentrate at mineral springs and gravelling areas as well as farm fields, where many are shot during the hunting season. Birds that remain through the winter frequent both deciduous and coniferous woodlands, favouring open woods and edges where berries and acorns are plentiful. They also occur in residential areas where they are attracted by grains at feeders (Fig. 251) and by horticultural fruits such as holly berries. The winter distribution of the Band-tailed Pigeon appears to coincide with the distribution of Madrone and Garry oak, both favoured winter food trees.

Spring migration begins in late February, and continues through March into April on the south coast, and May farther north. Birds can be found in the interior by late March, but most birds arrive from late April through May or later. Because of their sparse distribution in the interior, movements there are difficult to detect.

The autumn movement on the coast begins in late August and peaks in September. Most birds have left the interior by late September, but some movement can continue through November.

The Band-tailed Pigeon winters in small numbers in the southwest corner of the province with its centre of abundance in the Fraser Lowlands and on the east coast of Vancouver Island from Victoria north to Nanaimo.

Banding returns (Fig. 249) indicate that many birds breeding in British Columbia winter in the Pacific coastal states.

Figure 248. Band-tailed Pigeons picking up calcium from mud flats at Port Moody, 21 July 1979 (Ervio Sian).

Band-tailed Pigeon

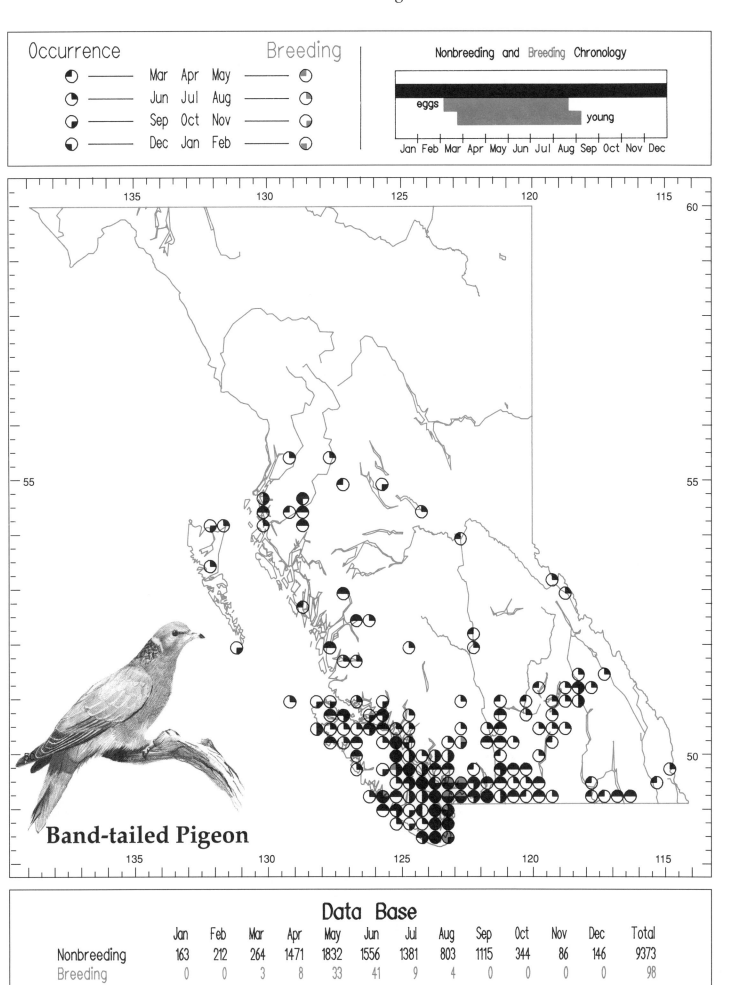

Band-tailed Pigeon

Data Base

	Jan	Feb	Mar	Apr	May	Jun	Jul	Aug	Sep	Oct	Nov	Dec	Total
Nonbreeding	163	212	264	1471	1832	1556	1381	803	1115	344	86	146	9373
Breeding	0	0	3	8	33	41	9	4	0	0	0	0	98

BREEDING: The Band-tailed Pigeon breeds from southern Vancouver Island and the south mainland coast north to Alta Lake and west to Tofino, from near sea level to 760 m elevation. The known breeding range in British Columbia is much reduced from that reported by American Ornithologists' Union (1983) and Godfrey (1986).

It frequents natural and man-associated habitats including edges and openings in mature coniferous, mixed, and deciduous forests, city yards and parks, wooded groves, open bushland, and golf courses. The breeding birds' requirement of calcium for egg production and crop gland function is apparently met through the use of mineral springs and gravelling areas. Activity at these sites peaks about mid-June, coinciding with the pigeons' most intense period of reproductive activity (March and Sadlier 1972).

Nests: Most nests (74%; n=31) were situated in coniferous trees (Fig. 250), including Douglas-fir (33%), western redcedar (15%), Sitka spruce (15%), lodgepole pine, and western hemlock. Others were in deciduous trees (26%), including red alder, Pacific crabapple, birch, and beech. Nests were small, frail, shallow platforms of loose twigs, often so flimsy that the egg could be seen through the nest from below. One nest had sheep's wool in addition to the twigs. Nests were usually located near the end of a horizontal branch. Twenty-nine nests ranged in height from 3 to 15 m with 69% between 3 and 6 m.

Eggs: Dates for 27 clutches ranged from 6 March to 20 August with 51% recorded between 1 and 29 May. Clutch size ranged from 1 to 2 eggs (1E-24, 2E-3). Data from 2 nests in British Columbia suggest that the incubation period is between 16 and 22 days; Goodwin (1967) reports a range of 18 to 20 days.

Young: Dates for 14 broods ranged from 15 April to 10 July with 11 broods recorded between 9 and 23 June. Calculated dates indicate that young could be found as early as 24 March and as late as 7 September. Brood size ranged from 1 to 2 young (1Y-12, 2Y-2) with 86% having 1 young. One brood in British Columbia suggested a nestling period of at least 18 days.

REMARKS: The Band-tailed Pigeon was formerly a summer visitor only to the Gulf Islands, the Fraser Lowlands, and the coast forest biotic area, east to Spuzzum and north to Terrace (Munro, J.A. and Cowan 1947). In addition to the species now being a resident in the southwest corner of the province, it is slowly expanding its range eastward and northward.

See Neff (1947), Silovsky (1969), and March (1971) for additional information on the ecology and biology of the Band-tailed Pigeon in the Pacific Northwest.

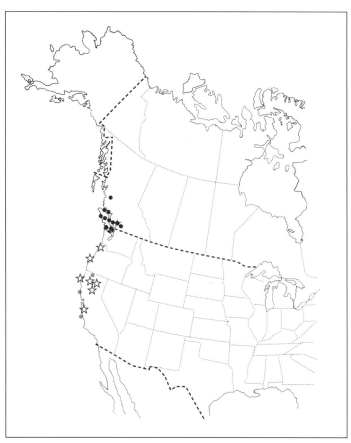

Figure 249. *Banding locations (stars) and recovery sites (circles) of Band-tailed Pigeons associated with British Columbia. Red indicates birds banded in British Columbia; black indicates birds banded elsewhere.*

Figure 250. *Adult Band-tailed Pigeon incubating on twig nest at Oak Bay, Victoria, 10 June 1979 (Mark Nyhof).*

Figure 251. *Band-tailed Pigeons at a feeder near Courtland Flats, Saanich, 7 May 1983 (Tim Zurowski).*

NOTEWORTHY RECORDS

Spring: Coastal - Victoria 14 Mar 1967-200+; Saanich 20 May 1984-1,000 in ploughed field; Tofino 8 Mar 1987-first arrival, 26 Apr 1987-30; Sea Island 17 May 1973-234 feeding in ploughed fields; Cypress Park 29 May 1981-200; Nimpkish River 2 May 1973-10; Adam River 18 and 19 May 1984-141+ feeding on huckleberries in logging slash in 6 flocks of 2 to 50+; Port Hardy 29 Mar 1941-1; Namu 13 Apr 1983-6; Terrace to 64 km w of Terrace 27 May 1977-109 on railway tracks. **Interior** - Osoyoos 26 May 1984-2, 1 found dead; UBC 14429; Yahk 25 Apr 1979-1 graveling on side of highway; Creston 2 May 1981-1; Castlegar 2 to 9 May 1974-1 (RBCM Photo 344); Lytton 25 Apr 1981-2; Westwold 9 Apr 1979-1 at feeder; Lavington 20 May 1972-1 (RBCM Photo 264); Heffley Lake 21 May 1983-1; Greeley 12 May 1983-3; Williams Lake 25 Mar 1979-1; 24 km s Prince George 11 May 1980-1, 14 May 1982-2 adults with juvenile; Smithers 27 May 1979-2.

Summer: Coastal - Victoria 25 Aug 1980-80, 29 Aug 1980-200 feeding on cascara; Saanich 26 Aug 1960-125 in stooked oats; Kennedy Lake 29 Aug 1965-100; Sumas 15 Aug 1966-375+ feeding in fields; Pitt Meadows 4 Jun 1979-100+ in sprouting field; Brem Bay 20 Jul 1951-2,000 in logged area with abundant blackberries; Namu 14 Jun 1981-6; Stuie 15 Aug 1982-3; Queen Charlotte City 4 Jun 1987-6; Lakelse Lake 17 Jun 1977-4, late Jul 1928-some; Tow Hill 28 Jul 1919-1 (Patch 1922); Kitsault 23 and 26 Jul 1980-15. **Interior** - Osoyoos 14 Jun 1976-1 in cherry orchard; Creston Jul 1980-1; Sparwood 29 Jun 1983-1 in newly seeded field; Yale to Boston Bar 21 Jun 1980-100; Spences Bridge to Cache Creek 15 Aug 1966-223; Monashee Mountains 8 Jul 1969-1; Pinaus Lake Jul 1968-1; Sorrento 20 Aug 1970-4 (Stevens et al. 1970); Alkali Lake (Riske Creek) 6 Jun 1969-1; Stuart Lake 15 Jun 1972-1 (Ebel 1973a); Hazelton 1 Jun 1960-12 in small flocks along highway.

Autumn: Interior - Mount Revelstoke National Park 10 Sep 1982-2, 24 Sep 1981-1; Revelstoke 20 Sep 1983-5, last of year; Spuzzum 19 Sep 1934-10 (Munro, J.A. and Cowan 1947). **Coastal** - Stauman Bay (Port Simpson) 7 Sep 1969-125; Masset 4 Nov 1954-1 (RBCM 10701); Cape St. James 15 Oct 1978-7; Port Hardy 8 Oct 1937- last seen; Port Neville 8 Oct 1975-20; Tofino 22 Nov 1986-1; Long Beach 20 Oct 1971-81; Bamfield 1 Sep 1977-30; Vancouver 27 Sep 1979-100+; Saanich 18 Sep 1965-1,000 (Stirling 1966b); Sidney Island 22 Oct 1978-200 feeding on Madrone fruit; Victoria 1 to 4 Sep 1964-600, 20% adults, some shot, feeding on arbutus, wheat, and salal berries; early Oct 1962-1,000 feeding on successful acorn crop (Boggs and Boggs 1963a), 1 Nov 1956-400 feeding on arbutus berries; Metchosin 7 Sep 1959-400.

Winter: Interior - No records. **Coastal** - Cortes Island 12 Feb 1979-20; Little Qualicum River estuary 24 Feb 1978-2 early arrival (Dawe 1980); Nanoose Harbour 18 Feb 1977-1 early arrival (Dawe and Lang 1980); Vancouver 15 Feb 1974-4; Albert Head 5 Feb 1936-2; Victoria Feb 1967-1,000 in one flock (Crowell and Nehls 1967a), 19 Feb 1979-500 in holly trees.

Christmas Counts: Interior - Not recorded. **Coastal** - Recorded from 14 of 28 localities and on 35% of all counts. Maxima: Pender Islands 23 Dec 1978-**449**, all-time Canadian high count (Anderson, R.R. 1979); Victoria 26 Dec 1972-417; Vancouver 26 Dec 1973-110.

Mourning Dove

Zenaida macroura (Linnaeus)

MODO

RANGE: Breeds from southeastern Alaska across southern Canada and throughout the United States. Winters from southern British Columbia and locally from other northern limits of the breeding range south, primarily from northern California east through the central United States, southern Ontario and New England. Also occurs in Mexico, Panama, and the West Indies.

STATUS: *Rare* to *fairly common* migrant and summer visitant to the southern third of the province, including Vancouver Island. *Very rare* transient north of Williams Lake in the interior and central Vancouver Island on the coast, including the Queen Charlotte Islands. *Uncommon* winter visitant to southern portions of the province. Breeds.

NONBREEDING: The Mourning Dove is widely distributed across southern British Columbia, including Vancouver Island, becoming scattered through the northern portions of the province including the Queen Charlotte Islands. It occurs from sea level to 1,070 m elevation.

It frequents agricultural areas, including orchards (Fig. 252), stubble and shrubby fields, and cattle feedlots, as well as weedy areas, road edges, parks, airports, residential areas, and open woods. Roosts have been found in tall black cottonwood trees adjacent to farmland and in ponderosa pine trees on an island.

Early spring migrants are difficult to separate from overwintering birds. Some birds do arrive in March, but most return in mid-April through May. Following breeding, birds become more gregarious and flocks begin to build through

August and September; most have left for southern areas by October. On the coast, wintering Mourning Doves are distributed on southern Vancouver Island and the Fraser Lowlands, with their centre of abundance in the Ladner area. Interior birds winter in the Okanagan valley north to Vernon and, occasionally, in the Shuswap drainage and the west Kootenay and Creston areas; rarely elsewhere. They are most common in the Vernon area, where they frequent cattle feedlots.

Banding returns (Fig. 253) indicate that some birds breeding in British Columbia winter in Nevada and Arizona.

BREEDING: The Mourning Dove (Fig. 255) breeds locally across southern British Columbia including southeastern Vancouver Island and the Fraser Lowlands, east to the Okanagan valley and Kootenays (rarely), and north through the Thompson-Okanagan Plateau and Chilcotin-Cariboo Basin to Prince George in the Nechako Lowlands. It is found from sea level to 880 m elevation. The centre of abundance is the Okanagan valley.

The Mourning Dove breeds most often on or near agricultural land including orchards, where most nests were found, rangeland, pastureland, and farmland. In the interior, other habitats include riparian woodland adjacent to marshes, lakes, and creeks, open ponderosa pine - bunchgrass regions including steep grassy hillsides, and deciduous woodland including trembling aspen and birch groves and black cottonwood bottomland. Coastal habitats include riparian woods adjacent to river dikes, sloughs, and estuarine marsh, deciduous woodlots near agricultural land, and openings in coastal forests including

Figure 252. Apple orchard in the Okanagan valley, May 1972—typical habitat of the Mourning Dove (Stephen R. Cannings).

Mourning Dove

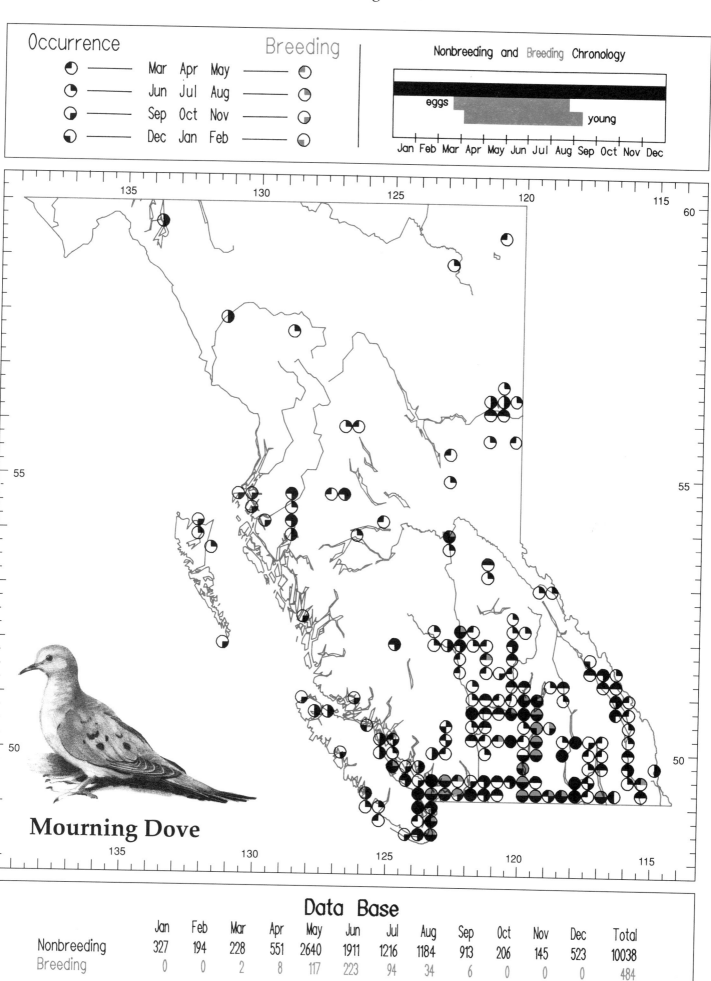

Occurrence — Mar Apr May — **Breeding**
Jun Jul Aug
Sep Oct Nov
Dec Jan Feb

Nonbreeding and Breeding Chronology

eggs / young

Jan Feb Mar Apr May Jun Jul Aug Sep Oct Nov Dec

Mourning Dove

Data Base

	Jan	Feb	Mar	Apr	May	Jun	Jul	Aug	Sep	Oct	Nov	Dec	Total
Nonbreeding	327	194	228	551	2640	1911	1216	1184	913	206	145	523	10038
Breeding	0	0	2	8	117	223	94	34	6	0	0	0	484

logging slashes, burns, and rocky outcrops. Nests were also found in country gardens, cemeteries, parks, and urban residential areas. One nest was found on the edge of an airport road.

Nests: Most nests (48%; n=169) were situated in deciduous trees (36%) and shrubs (12%), including apple (22%), pear, cherry, black cottonwood, birch, hawthorn, Garry oak, red alder, willow (Fig. 255), red-osier dogwood, black greasewood, sagebrush, saskatoon, locust, red elderberry and blackberry The remaining nests were situated on the ground (22%; Fig. 254), in coniferous trees (20%), including ponderosa pine (9%), Douglas-fir, lodgepole pine, Rocky Mountain juniper, and white spruce, and on stumps, fallen logs, and cliffs. One was on a brush pile and one was on a fence. Most tree and shrub nests were located on a horizontal branch, although some were found in crotches. Four nests were found in old American Robin nests, and one was found on a cradle of bark wedged in the crotch of a shrub. Most ground nests (64%) were found sheltered by vegetation. One was found on a cliff ledge under a rock overhang and another in an old Townsend's Solitaire (*Myadestes townsendi*) nest in a gravel bank. Nests (n=188) ranged in height from ground level to 9 m with 85% below 3 m. Most nests were flimsy, shallow platforms of twigs, dried grasses, or weed stems. Ground nests were slight depressions, some lined with grasses, leaves, or needles.

Eggs: Dates for 191 clutches ranged from 22 March to 25 August with 57% recorded between 16 May and 15 June. Egg laying at the coast can begin up to 2 weeks earlier than in the interior. Clutch size ranged from 1 to 4 eggs (1E-22, 2E-165, 3E-2, 4E-2) with 86% having 2 eggs. As many as 3 clutches per bird per year have been reported. Twelve clutches from British Columbia suggest that the incubation period is 14 to 15 days.

Young: Dates for 118 broods ranged from 20 April to 13 September with 53% recorded between 2 and 30 June. Calculated dates indicate that young could be found by 6 April. Brood size ranged from 1 to 2 young (1Y-11, 2Y-107) with 91% having 2 young. The nestling period is 12 to 16 days (Morrison 1969).

REMARKS: Until 1947 there were few winter records for the Mourning Dove in British Columbia (Munro, J.A. and Cowan 1947). An increase in birds wintering in the Okanagan became apparent during the latter half of the 1950s, continued through the 1960s, and peaked in the early 1970s. Winter records on the south coast followed a similar trend beginning in the early 1960s.

R.A. Cannings et al. (1987) suggest that the widespread use of corn silage in the Vernon area may account for the rise in the wintering dove population there.

See Morrison (1969) and Goodwin (1967) for other aspects on the ecology of the Mourning Dove in North America.

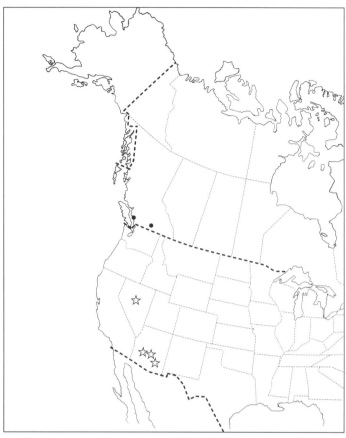

Figure 253. *Banding locations (stars) and recovery sites (circles) of Mourning Doves associated with British Columbia.*

Figure 254. *Mourning Dove ground nest at Oliver, 5 June 1985 (Mark Nyhof).*

Figure 255. *Mourning Dove on nest at Reifel Island, Delta, 2 July 1972 (Ervio Sian).*

NOTEWORTHY RECORDS

Spring: Coastal - Victoria 27 Apr 1981-2; Lulu Island 13 May 1980-85 roosting in cottonwoods; Vedder to Floods 19 Mar 1961-16; Skagit River Park 24 Apr 1971-1; Pitt River 20 May 1968-1; Little Qualicum River 19 Apr 1980-1 on estuary; Cortes Island 16 May 1975-1; Kitimat 17 May 1975-1; Terrace 29 May 1977-1. **Interior** - Richter Pass 3 Apr 1958-1 earliest sighting; Osoyoos 16 May 1971-1+; Creston 18 Mar 1972-1; Penticton 1 Mar 1979-1, first of year; White Lake (Okanagan Falls) 18 May 1974-20; South Slocan 9 May 1973-1, spring arrival; Summerland 28 Mar 1967-1; Balfour 18 Mar 1972-1; Coldstream 11 Apr 1952-1, first of year; Nicola Lake to Merritt 15 Apr 1968-9; Vernon 14 Mar 1965-1, first of year; Numa Creek 23 Apr 1981-1; Williams Lake 14 Mar 1972-1; 24 km s Prince George 27 Apr 1985-1, early date; Quick 26 Apr 1979-1; near Attachie 21 Apr 1984-1, earliest spring record; Helmet (Kwokullie Lake) 18 May 1982-1 female (RBCM 17477).

Summer: Coastal - Millstream 16 Jun 1973-20 in one flock; Saanich 31 Aug 1981-40+ in field; Bamfield 6 Jun 1970-2; Sewall 27 Aug 1981-1; Tlell 29 Aug 1974-1; Terrace 22 Aug 1969-1 (Crowell and Nehls 1970a). **Interior** - Oliver 13 Aug 1968-350 on stubble field, flocks common here until early September (Morrison 1969); Trail 15 Aug 1979-15+; Vaseux Lake May to early Jun 1967-200 roosting in ponderosa pines on Hatfield's Island; Okanagan Lake 24 Aug 1975-55; Wasa 27 Aug 1971-1 (Dawe 1971); Coldstream 2 Aug 1956-60 on stubble field; Columbia Lake 27 Jun 1978-2; Valemount 27 Jul 1973-1; Francois Lake 4 Jun 1977-1; Prince George 7 Jul 1959-22 at airport; Fort St. John to Hudson Hope 2 Aug 1982-5; Telegraph Creek 30 Jul 1962-1 male (NMC 49773); Cold Fish Lake 8 Jul 1952-numerous; Parker Lake (Fort Nelson) 12 Jun 1985-1; Atlin 7 Jul 1935-1 male (RBCM 5899).

Autumn: Interior - Warm Bay Hot Springs 16 Sep 1972-1; Telegraph Creek 6 Nov 1912-1 (RBCM 2622); Fort St. John 7 Nov 1982-1; Round Lake (Smithers) 29 Nov 1987-1; Williams Lake 2 Sep 1978-4 in 1 flock; Kamloops 5 Oct 1965-3; Lavington 14 Oct 1962-200 to 300 in grain fields; Summerland 5 Sep 1972-15, 8 Sep 1972-30, 18 Sep 1972-30, 21 Sep 1972-1, 7 Oct 1965-1; Trail Oct 25 1970-1. **Coastal** - Green Island 18 Sep 1978-1; Prince Rupert 5 Oct 1983-1; Masset 22 Sep 1953-1 female (RBCM 10514); Cape St. James 9 Oct 1977-1, 26 Nov 1981-1; Campbell River (Discovery Passage) 1 Oct 1973-2; Little Qualicum River 31 Oct 1984-1 on estuary; Lennard Island 17 Oct 1976-1; Ladner 20 Nov 1976-120+ in stubble field; Saanich 3 Sep 1985-35, 2 Nov 1974-3.

Winter: Interior - Prince George 21 Dec 1969-7 (Rogers, T.H. 1970b); Williams Lake 26 Dec 1969-2; Blueberry Creek 31 Dec 1974-2; Lillooet 1 Jan 1963-2; Barnhartvale 3 Jan 1977-2; Chase 2 Jan 1976-2; Coldstream 1 Feb 1975-200+, 4 Feb 1953-100; Windermere 25 Dec 1983-1; Lavington 4 Jan 1970-40; Kaleden 21 Jan 1979-42; Castlegar 20 Jan 1975-3; Oliver 29 Dec 1987-52 at cattle feedlot; Creston 1 Jan 1981-35, 4 Jan 1987-51; Osoyoos 10 Jan 1968-40 in orchards; Creston 1 Jan 1981-35, 12 Feb 1987-21. **Coastal** - Sayward 26 Feb 1975-1; Comox 15 Feb 1975-2; Delta 4 Dec 1974-50, 26 Jan 1975-60 in 1 flock; Lulu Island 12 Feb 1980-82; Saanich 14 Dec 1970-20 (Tatum 1971).

Christmas Counts: Interior - Recorded from 7 of 19 localities and on 37% of all counts. Maxima: Vernon 18 Dec 1983-373; Oliver/Osoyoos 26 Dec 1984-57; Vaseux Lake 31 Dec 1976-40. **Coastal** - Recorded from 10 of 28 localities and on 23% of all counts. Maxima: Vancouver 18 Dec 1976-204; Ladner 22 Dec 1973-145; White Rock 22 Dec 1974-54.

Black-billed Cuckoo

Coccyzus erythropthalmus (Wilson)

RANGE: Breeds from Alberta east to Nova Scotia, south to southeastern Wyoming, north-central Texas, northwest Arkansas, southern Ohio, Maryland, northern Alabama and Georgia. Winters in northwestern South America.

STATUS: *Very rare* late spring and summer vagrant in the interior.

CHANGE IN STATUS: The Black-billed Cuckoo was first reported in the province at Okanagan Landing on 22 June 1926, but details of the record are vague and it is not considered by J.A. Munro and Cowan (1947). Thirty-one years later, in May and June 1957, a single bird was heard near Vernon (Gissing 1959). The following year, one was seen and recorded calling near Quesnel (Gissing 1959), which finally documented the bird's occurrence in British Columbia. During the next 28 years, 1 or 2 birds have been found on 16 occasions. There are 2 specimen records.

OCCURRENCE: The Black-billed Cuckoo has been reported in the province from late May to mid-August. It has been found in the Okanagan valley from Osoyoos Lake to Vernon, and in the west and east Kootenays from the Creston area and from Windermere to Revelstoke (Fig. 256). There was one occurrence at Quesnel in the Nechako Lowlands.

Most birds have been found in riparian thickets (e.g. chokecherry, hawthorn, willow) bordering lakes, marshes and irrigation ditches. Most records are of single birds. Some observers have suggested that territorial behaviour was evident in adults occupying sites for several weeks.

All records, listed in chronological order, are as follows:

(1) Okanagan Landing 22 June 1926-1 (probable).
(2) Vernon late May 1957-1 heard in a chokecherry and hawthorn thicket behind house . . . repetitive "cu cu cu cu cu"; and early June 1957-1 heard in thickets near an irrigation ditch (Gissing 1959).
(3) Brisco 8 June to 6 July 1958-1 (Gissing 1959).
(4) Near Quesnel summer 1958-1, call recorded (Gissing 1959).
(5) Trout Creek Point (Summerland) May 1967-1 heard (Cannings, R.A. et al. 1987).
(6) Trout Creek Point 19 July 1968-1 (Cannings, R.A. et al. 1987).
(7) Invermere 28 June 1973-1 (RBCM Photo 300).
(8) Windermere 23 July 1973-1 female found dead (RBCM 12097).
(9) 11 km south of Revelstoke 17 and 24 June 1980-1 calling; and 5 July 1980-2 calling and seen.
(10) 8 km west of Creston (Corn Creek channel) 5 July 1980-1 (Butler, R.W. et al. 1986).
(11) Wye Lake (Vernon) 13 July 1980-2 flew directly overhead (Cannings, R.A. et al. 1987).
(12) Osoyoos Lake 9 and 16 July and 12 August 1981-1 adult in a riparian thicket at the north end.
(13) 16 km south of Revelstoke 10 and 12 July 1982-1 adult.
(14) Morrissey Park 18 August 1984-1 found dead on a road (RBCM 18317; Campbell 1985a).
(15) Red Lake early July 1986-2, documented with field notes.
(16) Osoyoos Lake 12 August 1986-1 adult at the north end.

REMARKS: There are 3 additional records, all lacking convincing details. Single birds were heard at Brisco on 20 June 1986 and Kamloops on 27 June 1982 and one was seen near Tofino on 30 August 1986. Roberson (1980) suggests that birds occurring in British Columbia (and Washington) may be "overshoots beyond the north-central Great Plains woodland breeding areas."

POSTSCRIPT:
(17) Revelstoke 2 July 1988-1 adult near the airport (RBCM Photo 1221).

Figure 256. Wilmer National Wildlife Area, 27 May 1981 (Neil K. Dawe). The riparian thickets along levies in the centre right of the figure are typical Black-billed Cuckoo habitat in the east Kootenay.

Black-billed Cuckoo

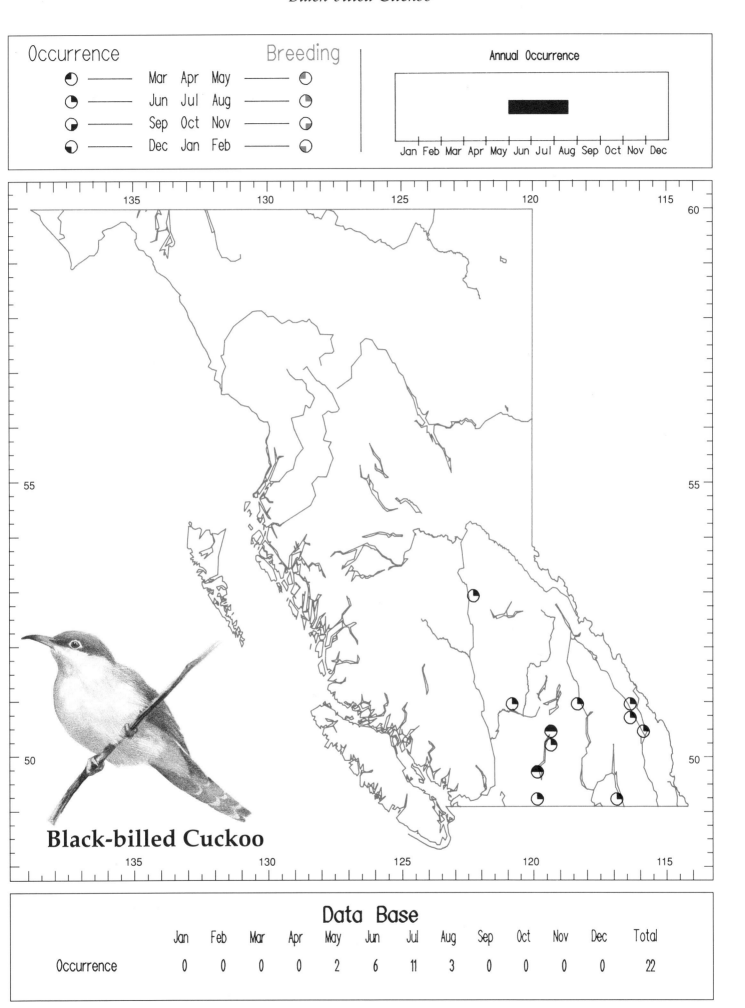

Occurrence | Breeding

	Mar Apr May	
	Jun Jul Aug	
	Sep Oct Nov	
	Dec Jan Feb	

Annual Occurrence

Jan Feb Mar Apr May Jun Jul Aug Sep Oct Nov Dec

Black-billed Cuckoo

Data Base

	Jan	Feb	Mar	Apr	May	Jun	Jul	Aug	Sep	Oct	Nov	Dec	Total
Occurrence	0	0	0	0	2	6	11	3	0	0	0	0	22

Barn Owl

BNOW

Tyto alba (Scopoli)

RANGE: Almost cosmopolitan. In the New World, breeds from extreme southern Canada (southwestern British Columbia and southern Ontario), North Dakota, southern Michigan, and southern New England, south through Central and South America.

STATUS: *Rare* resident on southeastern Vancouver Island north to Nanaimo; *very rare* north to Campbell River and on the Gulf Islands. *Uncommon* resident throughout the Fraser Lowlands to Hope. *Very rare* in the central-southern interior; *accidental* elsewhere. Widespread breeder throughout most of its coastal range.

CHANGE IN STATUS: The Barn Owl was first recorded in British Columbia near the mouth of the Fraser River in 1909 (Brooks 1909b), and was found nesting in the same general area in 1941 (Cowan 1942a). In 1946, it was still known as a resident only on the Fraser River delta, although there was also a single record from Vancouver Island at Duncan (Munro, J.A. and Cowan 1947). During the next 40 years, the Barn Owl spread throughout the Fraser Lowlands to Hope and also became established on southeastern Vancouver Island from Victoria to Nanaimo (Campbell and Campbell 1983). It was first recorded in the interior at Celista in 1949. On 10 June 1966, 3 young were transported from Ladner to Enderby and released there in September. They stayed in the area for 2 weeks, then disappeared. The next occurrence was at Oliver in 1972 (Cannings, S.R. 1972) and in the following 15 years the species has been reported

Figure 257. *Typical nesting and roosting site of the Barn Owl in the Fraser Lowlands (R. Wayne Campbell).*

Figure 258. *Middle Arm of the Fraser River near Westham Island, 17 March 1970 (R. Wayne Campbell). Industrial expansion and urbanization in the Fraser Lowlands threaten old growth fields upon which the Barn Owl depends for foraging.*

Barn Owl

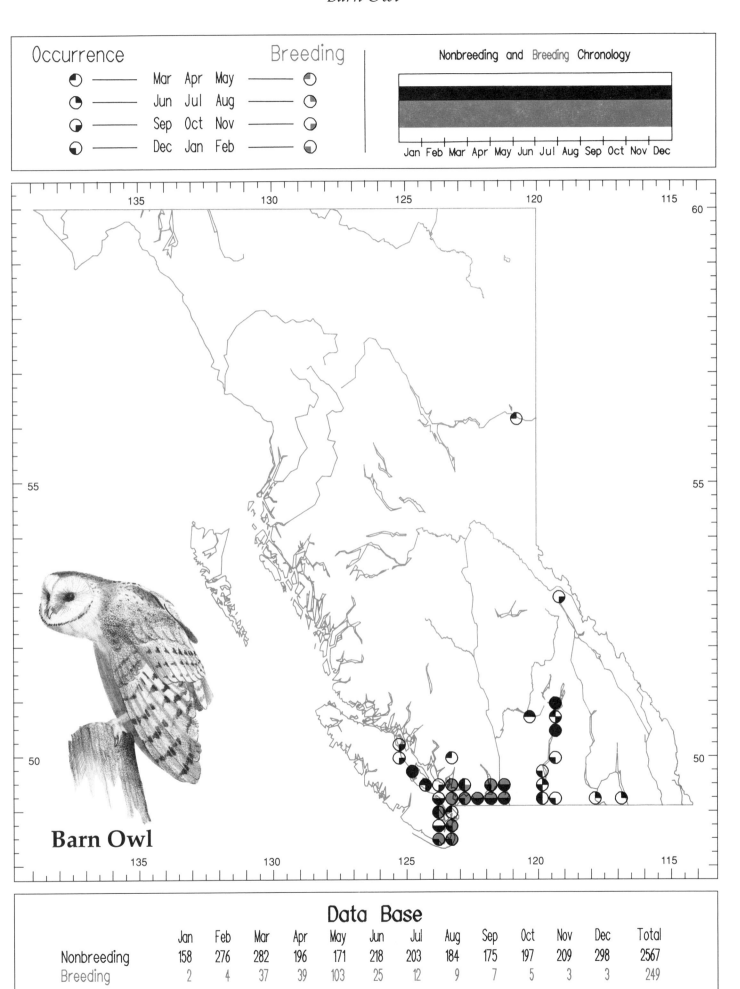

Barn Owl

Data Base

	Jan	Feb	Mar	Apr	May	Jun	Jul	Aug	Sep	Oct	Nov	Dec	Total
Nonbreeding	158	276	282	196	171	218	203	184	175	197	209	298	2567
Breeding	2	4	37	39	103	25	12	9	7	5	3	3	249

almost annually in the southern interior. With the exception of the extralimital records, the Barn Owl has now been reported as far north in the interior as Shuswap Lake. There are no interior breeding records.

As human populations continue to expand and agricultural lands are replaced by urban developments (Fig. 258), the Barn Owl is destined to decrease in numbers. W.C. Weber (1980) states that "barn owl populations are almost certainly declining, and the trend is likely to continue." Campbell and Campbell (1983) report that during an 11-year nest survey on the coast "it was the general feeling of land-owners that Barn Owls were seen less often in recent years."

NONBREEDING: The Barn Owl is distributed on the coast along southeastern Vancouver Island (Sooke to Campbell River), the southern Gulf Islands, and on the mainland coast from Sechelt through the Fraser Lowlands to Hope. There is also one record from Brackendale. In the interior, it has occurred throughout the Okanagan valley from Osoyoos north to Shuswap Lake, and west to Kamloops. There is one record from the West Kootenay at Trail, one from Creston, one from the Rocky Mountains near Valemount, and one from near Fort St. John.

The Barn Owl prefers open country associated with agricultural areas, but also frequents grasslands, river bottom meadows, and, infrequently, cities and residential areas. On Vancouver Island, it frequents riparian woods and edges of mixed woodlands. It roosts, sometimes communally, in man-made structures such as barns, silos, sheds, and nest boxes.

The Barn Owl occurs at low elevations on the coast (below 61 m), but has been found at 460 m in the interior.

On the coast, the Barn Owl is relatively sedentary. Populations fluctuate greatly with microtine population cycles. Of 73 band recoveries from birds banded between 1962 and 1975, 19 were from within 34 km of the banding site. The farthest recovery was of a nestling banded in Richmond on 4 April 1970 and found in Nanaimo, 65 km to the west, on 11 December 1978.

BREEDING: The Barn Owl breeds on southern Vancouver Island from Sooke to Ladysmith, and in the Fraser Lowlands from Vancouver and Reifel Island east throughout the Fraser River valley to Hope. It nests solitarily, mostly in association with agricultural areas. A few breed along edges of open woodlands and, less frequently, in cities. Barn Owls may breed throughout the year, depending on vole numbers. Although British Columbia is at the northern end of the bird's North American range, populations here are among the densest on the continent. Results of an 11-year survey of 2,642 barns throughout the owl's British Columbia range revealed 232 nests and 443 roosting birds, with a total population of 907 birds. Of those, 21 nests and 12 roosting birds were on Vancouver Island. The total breeding population probably ranges between 250 and 275 pairs, with an estimated total population (including nonbreeders) of 1,000 birds (Campbell and Campbell 1983).

Nests: Most nests (93%; n=221) were situated in man-made structures which included old wooden barns (71%; Fig. 257), wooden silos, new wooden barns, concrete silos, metal silos, church spires, airport hangars, apartment buildings, water towers, bridges, and nest boxes. Fifteen nests were found in natural sites including tree cavities (10 nests), cliffs, and hawk nests. Most nests (51%) were positioned on wooden platforms high in the barn. Others were located on wooden floors, ledges, in natural cavities, among hay bales, in nest boxes, attics, hawk nests and on open apartment balconies. Heights of 88 nests ranged from 1.2 to 34.2 m, with 59% recorded between 9.3 and 17.1 m. Nests were usually loose collections of old and new pellets (Fig. 259), occasionally including a few feathers and some straw. Some were without materials. Seven nests ranged from 0.2 to 0.4 m in outside diameter and 3 to 9 cm in height.

Eggs: Eggs have been recorded in every month of the year, with most egg-laying (74% of 84 clutches) recorded between 7 March and 3 May. Clutch size ranged from 1 to 12 eggs (1E-6, 2E-6, 3E-11, 4E-21, 5E-13, 6E-11, 7E-6, 8E-4, 9E-3, 10E-2, 12E-1), with

54% having 3 to 5 eggs. Incubation period is 30 to 34 days (Wallace, G.J. 1948; Godfrey 1986).

Young: Nestlings (Fig. 260) have been reported every month of the year, with most (50% of 154 broods) recorded between 26 April and 2 June. Brood size ranged from 1 to 9 young (1Y-16, 2Y-23, 3Y-34, 4Y-34, 5Y-29, 6Y-11, 7Y-5, 8Y-1, 9Y-1), with 63% having 3 to 5 young. Fledging period is about 60 days (Bunn et al. 1982). The Barn Owl is a prolific breeder during years of high vole populations. The same pair (banded) was reported to have successfully raised 3 consecutive broods in a 15-month period in Ladner in 1978.

REMARKS: The successful invasion and establishment of Barn Owls in southwestern British Columbia is the result of the mild winters, excellent nesting and roosting sites, and an abundant prey base (Campbell 1983e). The Barn Owl feeds mainly on small mammals. An analysis of 11,787 pellets collected from 1941 to 1981 showed that small mammals accounted for 98% of all prey items (Campbell et al. 1987); the vole, *Microtus townsendii*, accounted for 73%. During that 40-year period the proportion of *M. townsendii* ranged annually from 63.3% to 84.5% of the total diet.

Reported cause of death for 185 birds was: unknown (34%), highway vehicles (21%), starvation (12%), shooting (10%), nestling mortality, predation by Great Horned Owl and domestic cat, parasites, nest site collapse, barbed-wire fence, and drowning.

The Barn Owl appears on the "Blue List" from 1972 to 1981 and was delisted to a species of "special concern" in 1982 and 1986 (Tate 1986). Arbib (1979) and Tate (1981) mention that there is a general concern that Barn Owl populations are declining and its range is contracting. The species does, however, respond well to nest box programs (Marti et al. 1979; Tate 1986).

Also known as the Common Barn-Owl.

Figure 259. Barn Owl nest and eggs at Delta showing fresh pellets and prey (Microtus townsendii) ringing the clutch, 7 May 1970 (R. Wayne Campbell).

Figure 260. *Barn Owl brood at Pitt Meadows, 11 May 1976 (R. Wayne Campbell). Note differences in the developmental stages of the young.*

NOTEWORTHY RECORDS

Spring: Coastal - Sea Island 2 Mar 1974-4 on fence posts; Ladner 7 Apr 1909-1 male (RBCM 1734 - Brooks 1909b); Sumas Prairie 2 Mar 1959-2 in aerial display; Chilliwack 11 Mar 1929-1 (RBCM 6331); Qualicum River 10 Mar 1978-1, 17 May 1980-1; Brackendale 13 May 1985-1; Campbell River 7 May 1963-1 roosting in garage. **Interior** - Kamloops 19 Mar 1980-1 adult; Enderby 22 Apr 1985-1 female (RBCM 18449).

Summer: Coastal - Saanich 23 Jul 1983-2, 26 Jun 1985-2; Galiano Island late Aug to 11 Sep 1983-3 at north end; Little Qualicum River delta 26 Jul 1975-1 (Dawe 1976), 15 Aug 1979-1; Courtenay 4 Jul 1963-1. **Interior** - Creston 12 Jul 1983-1 adult; Trail 3 Jun 1982-1 (Campbell 1982c); Penticton 12 Jun 1972-1; Armstrong 19 Jun to Sep 1982-1 (RBCM Photo 806); Kamloops 25 Jun 1983-1;

Celista 21 Aug 1966-1 (RBCM 18133).

Autumn: Interior - Celista 20 Nov 1949 to 25 Feb 1950-1, 15 Nov 1951 to 19 Feb 1952-1; e Swan Lake (Vernon) 24 Oct 1977-1 (RBCM Photo 489), 15 Nov 1983-1 (RBCM 18128); Kelowna 16 Sep 1984-1 male (UBC 14528); Osoyoos Lake autumn 1982-2. **Coastal** - Comox 11 Nov 1961-1; Little Qualicum River delta 18 Oct 1978-1 (Dawe 1980), 12 Sep to 15 Oct 1979-1, 8 to 14 Oct 1981-1; Iona Island 10 Oct 1977-5; Sea Island 18 Oct 1974-4 hunting; Duncan 20 Nov 1942-1 female (ROM 82252); Sooke 25 Nov 1983-1; Trial Islands 24 Oct 1983-1.

Winter: Interior - Celista 8 Dec 1950-1 (Schnider et al. 1971); Sorrento 20 Feb 1972-2; Kelowna 1 Dec 1983-1; Tugulnuit Lake 8 Jan 1972-1

(Cannings, S.R. 1972); Osoyoos Lake 31 Jan 1982-; Osoyoos 28 Dec 1987-1. **Coastal** - Comox 10 Feb 1979-1 (RBCM 17293); Nanaimo early Feb 1947-1; Cowichan Bay 12 Feb 1974-1; Sea Island 16 Dec 1979-7; Westham Island 2 Feb 1985-5; Deroche 18 Feb 1978-2; Duncan 7 Dec 1978-1; Pender Islands 18 Dec 1965-1;

Christmas Counts: Interior - Not recorded. **Coastal** - Recorded from 9 of 28 localities and on 27% of all counts. Maxima: Vancouver 18 Dec 1977-**49**, all-time Canadian high count (Anderson, R.R. 1978); Ladner 27 Dec 1982-16; White Rock 2 Jan 1982-7.

Extralimital Records: Interior - 5 km s Fort St. John May 1983-1 (Campbell 1985b); Valemount 10 Nov 1977-1 adult.

Flammulated Owl

Otus flammeolus (Kaup)

FLOW

RANGE: Breeds from central-southern British Columbia south through the western cordillera into Mexico. Winters in Mexico and Guatemala.

STATUS: *Uncommon* summer visitant in the Okanagan valley and Thompson Basin. *Accidental* in the east Kootenay. Breeds.

NONBREEDING: The Flammulated Owl has been recorded in extreme central southern British Columbia south of 51° N latitude, from Eagle Hill and McQueen Lake south locally through the Okanagan valley. There is one confirmed record for the east Kootenay region (see Van Tighem and Gyug 1983; Howie 1987).

The Flammulated Owl appears to be restricted to mountainous and valley side areas within the interior Douglas-fir biogeoclimatic zone where Douglas-fir is the dominant climax species and ponderosa pine is a seral species (see Tisdale and McLean 1957). Surveys by Howie and Ritcey (1987) ". . . confirm a preference for forest in excess of 100 years of age, and the highest densities of owls occurred in age classes of 140 to 200+ years with many veteran trees." Flammulated Owls have been found between 375 and 1250 m elevation.

It has been recorded in the province from 24 April to 22 October. Most spring migrants arrive by mid-May. In autumn, most have departed by early September. Migration corridors, if present, are unknown.

BREEDING: The Flammulated Owl breeds locally in the Thompson-Okanagan Plateau region along valley sides of the Northern Thompson Upland and Thompson Basin, and throughout the Okanagan valley. Nests have been found between 610 and 1,210 m elevation.

Breeding habitat consists of well-spaced Douglas-firs of varying ages, generally containing thick clumps of young trees with some ponderosa pines. The general appearance is like parkland; the understory is very open, consisting largely of pinegrass, bluebunch wheatgrass, birch-leaved spirea, and isolated larger shrubs such as saskatoon.

Slope and aspect varies considerably but slopes are generally moderate to steep (up to 37°) and are often dissected by streams and gullies.

Nests: Most nests (10 of 16) were in natural sites including Douglas-fir snags and dead ponderosa pines. Many were in old woodpecker nest cavities, usually those made by Northern Flickers. All but one nest had a single opening. Six were found in wooden nest boxes. One nest tree had a diameter at breast height of 55 cm. Nest heights ranged from 1.5 to 13.5 m.

Eggs: Dates for 6 clutches ranged from 31 May to 23 July. Calculated dates indicate eggs could be found as early as 24 April (see Young). Howie (1987) gives the period 13 May to 28 June as the initial cavity occupancy by adults and the main egg-laying period as 1 June to 2 July. Sizes for 6 clutches ranged from 1 to 4 eggs (1E-1, 2E-4, 4E-1). Incubation period is about 22 days

(Reynolds and Linkhart 1987b).

Young: Dates for 10 broods ranged from 26 May to 15 August. Two brood records are significant because they represent unusually early breeding: Adams River 28 May 1958-4 downy young; Pritchard 26 May 1962-4 downy young about a week old. Calculated dates indicate hatching could occur from at least 15 May to 25 July and fledging from at least 6 June to 16 August. Sizes for 9 broods ranged from 1 to 4 young (1Y-4, 2Y-2, 4Y-3). Fledging period ranges from 22 to 24 days (Reynolds and Linkhart 1987b).

REMARKS: Historically, the Flammulated Owl has been considered very rare in British Columbia. It was first recorded in the province on 22 October 1901 (not November 1902 as reported by Brooks 1909a), when an adult female was found dead on the beach of Okanagan Lake at Penticton. During the next 75 years there were only 3 additional records: a bird collected near Kamloops on 11 August 1935 (Williams, M.Y. and Spencer 1942), a fledgling found near Summerland in 1947 (Cannings, R.A. 1974), and a nest discovered west of Penticton on 12 June 1962 (Atkinson 1963). As a result, this diminutive owl was considered by Godfrey (1966) as a "very rare and local breeder in southern British Columbia."

Serious attempts by naturalists to locate birds began in 1977 (Cannings, R.J. et al. 1978) and over the next 10 years Howie (1987; pers. comm.) reports that a minimum of 116 birds was found, including adults, nestlings, and fledged young. Populations are difficult to estimate because the Flammulated Owl is not evenly distributed throughout its range in the province. The most productive linear route near Kamloops produced 16 singing males over 10 km. R.R. Howie (1987) further states that "during 1984 and 1985 when the most intensive survey work was being carried out, it is likely that 25-30 pairs of owls were present in the vicinity of Kamloops, Kelowna and Penticton."

Howie (1987) proposes a status of "Threatened" for this species in British Columbia.

A winter record of a single bird at Penticton on 24 December 1965 (see Rogers, T.H. 1966b) is considered invalid. In addition, there are 3 unconfirmed sight records from the vicinity of Radium, which suggest that the Flammulated Owl may be a rare summer visitant in suitable habitat in the lower reaches of the southern Rocky Mountain Trench.

See Goggans (1986) and Reynolds and Linkhart (1987a, 1987b) for additional information on habitat requirements and nesting biology of the Flammulated Owl.

POSTSCRIPT: Two or three Flammulated Owls were heard calling at Loon Lake, north of Cache Creek on 11 June 1988 (Campbell 1988c). In June 1989, an adult was found in a cavity 12 m up in a trembling aspen, southwest of Cache Creek. Breeding was suspected but not confirmed. These records extend their known range north and west.

NOTEWORTHY RECORDS

Spring: Coastal - No records. **Interior** - Km 12, Camp McKinney Road 20 May 1987-2 hooting; Penticton 4 May 1981-1; Mac's (Madeline) Lake (Penticton) 11 May 1979-2; Bald Range Creek 30 May 1984-3; Lac Du Bois (Kamloops) 28 May 1984-3.

Summer: Coastal - No records. **Interior** - Vaseux Lake 1 Jun 1984-1; Apex Mountain (Okanagan Falls) 12 Jun 1962-1 (RBCM 17703); McLean Creek (Okanagan Falls) 20 Jul 1980-1 adult (RBCM Photo 843); Mac's (Madeline) Lake 2 Jun 1978-2 heard; Trout Creek Point (Summerland) 23 Aug 1947-1 juvenile (RBCM Photo 317); Bald Range Creek 11 Aug 1984-2; Whiskers Hill 9 Jul 1984-1; Eagle Hill (Kamloops Lake) 9 Jul 1984-2; Lac Du Bois (Kamloops) 11 Aug 1935-1 male (RBCM 14704); Paul Lake 21 Jul 1983-1 pair (RBCM Photo 869); Mount Wheeler 16 Jun 1983-8 adults counted along 10 km route, 20 Jul 1987-2.

Autumn: Interior - Pinantan Lake 14 Sep 1983-1 captured alive and later died; Windermere Lake 15 Sep 1977-1 male found dead along highway (RBCM 15940); Penticton 22 Oct 1901-1 female washed up on beach on Okanagan Lake (MVZ 101670). **Coastal** - No records.

Winter: No records.

Flammulated Owl

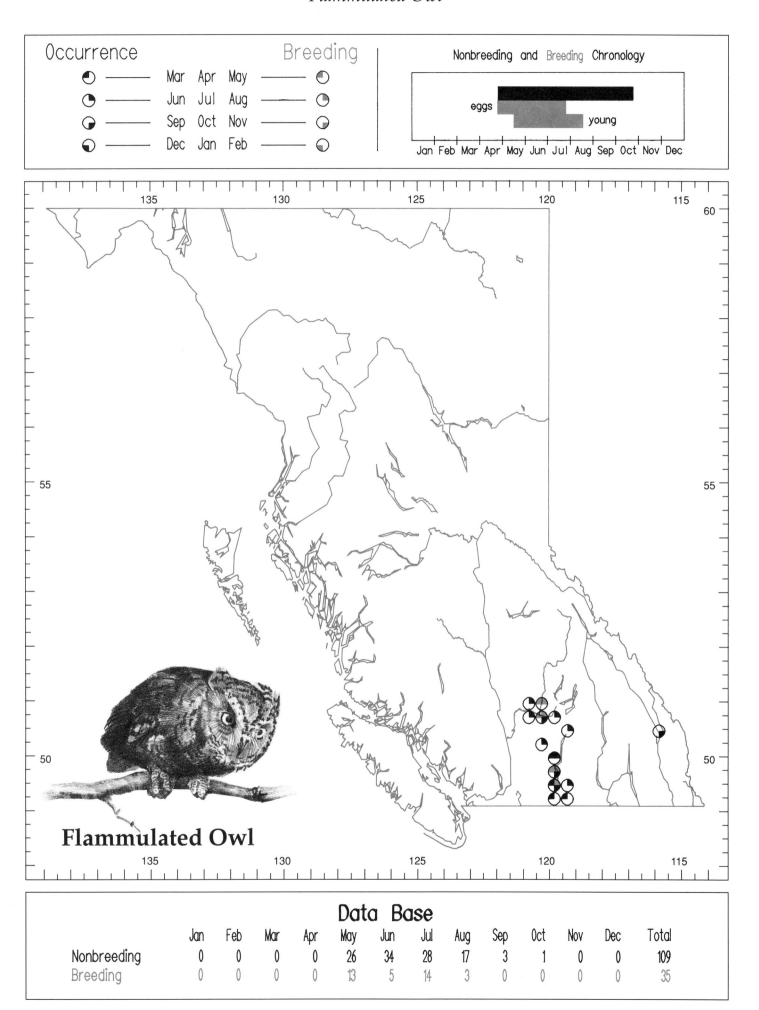

Occurrence — **Breeding**

	Mar Apr May	
Jun Jul Aug	
Sep Oct Nov	
Dec Jan Feb	

Nonbreeding and Breeding Chronology

eggs

young

Jan Feb Mar Apr May Jun Jul Aug Sep Oct Nov Dec

Data Base

	Jan	Feb	Mar	Apr	May	Jun	Jul	Aug	Sep	Oct	Nov	Dec	Total
Nonbreeding	0	0	0	0	26	34	28	17	3	1	0	0	109
Breeding	0	0	0	0	13	5	14	3	0	0	0	0	35

Western Screech-Owl
Otus kennicottii (Elliot)

WSOW

RANGE: Resident from southeastern Alaska south along the coast to Baja California; in the interior from southern British Columbia south through Idaho, Utah, New Mexico, southeastern Colorado, and western Texas to southeastern Coahuila and Mexico City.

STATUS: *Uncommon* to *fairly common* resident on the south coast including Vancouver Island. *Rare* to *uncommon* resident on the northern mainland coast. Absent from the Queen Charlotte Islands. *Rare* to *uncommon* local resident in the central-southern interior; *very rare* in the west and east Kootenays. Breeds.

NONBREEDING: The Western Screech-Owl occurs year round on Vancouver Island and on the adjacent mainland coast throughout the Fraser Lowlands to Hope. It probably also occurs as a resident along the northern mainland coast, west of the Coast Ranges, north to at least Terrace. In the interior, it is a local resident below 600 m elevation from Adams Lake and Shuswap Lake south through the Okanagan valley. Elsewhere, it is very rarely encountered.

The Western Screech-Owl is essentially non-migratory. On the coast, it is found in all woodland habitats, but it prefers mixed deciduous/coniferous forests, usually near a source of water. In the interior, most birds are found in deciduous woodlands along lakeshores and streams. It roosts in tree cavities, nest boxes, buildings, trees, vines, and crevices in cliffs.

Hooting has been recorded every month on the coast but begins in earnest in February; in the interior, hooting begins in early March.

BREEDING: The Western Screech-Owl breeds on southern and eastern Vancouver Island, the Gulf Islands, and the adjacent mainland coast, including the Fraser Lowlands to Chilliwack, north to Kitimat, including coastal islands (e.g. the Goose Group; Guiguet 1949). In the interior, it is known to breed only in the southern Okanagan valley.

This owl nests in open deciduous and coniferous woods and riparian habitats including rivers, creeks, marshes, bogs, lakes, and large ponds. In urban and residential areas it frequents orchards, parks, and gardens. Most nests were situated near water and none were found above 540 m elevation.

Much of the information that follows is the result of nest box programs.

Nests: Most nests (87%; n=62) were situated in wooden nest boxes (61%) and natural cavities (26%) of black cottonwood, red alder, Douglas-fir, western redcedar and western hemlock. All nest tree diameters were greater than 25 cm at breast height. Other nests (13%) were in cavities excavated by Pileated Woodpeckers and Northern Flickers.

Heights for 43 nests ranged from 1.2 to 12.2 m, with 65% recorded between 3.0 and 4.6 m. Depths of 3 tree cavities ranged from 30 to 36 cm; diameters of 2 entrance holes were 15 cm each. Nest materials were usually absent, but a few contained sparse collections of wood chips, feathers, moss, and mammal fur.

Eggs: Dates for 49 clutches ranged from 17 March to 31 May, with 53% recorded between 9 and 21 April. Sizes for 51 clutches ranged from 1 to 5 eggs (1E-4, 2E-20, 3E-17, 4E-9, 5E-1) with 73% having 2 or 3 eggs. Incubation period is probably similar to that of *O. asio* which has variously been reported within range of 21 to 30 days (Bent 1938) but averages 26 days (Sherman 1911).

Young: Dates for 53 broods ranged from 19 April to 21 August, with 51% recorded between 8 May and 3 June. Sizes for 46 broods ranged from 1 to 5 young (1Y-11, 2Y-16, 3Y-13, 4Y-5, 5Y-1), with 63% having 2 or 3 young. Fledging period, also for *O. asio*, ranges from 35 to 42 days (Bent 1938).

REMARKS: There are several unconfirmed sightings and records of birds heard on the Queen Charlotte Islands. None are convincing, including a published occurrence by Patch (1922) who states ". . . believe I heard [at Tow Hill] . . . in woods bordering muskeg." Godfrey (1986) shows the range of the Western Screech-Owl extending north in the interior "rarely" to the Vanderhoof region (see Taverner 1919), however we are unaware of any interior records with convincing details north of Adams Lake.

The taxonomy of screech owls in North and Middle America remains confused. The American Ornithologists' Union (1957) lists 18 subspecies of screech-owls in North America. The Western Screech-Owl was formerly considered part of the Screech Owl *(Otus asio)* complex (American Ornithologists' Union 1957), but was separated from the eastern species on the basis of differences in vocalizations and behaviour as an "incipient species" (Marshall, J.T. 1967; American Ornithologists' Union 1983). Hekstra (1982) describes the subspecies of all North American *Otus* .

The Western Screech-Owl is also known as Kennicotts' Screech-Owl.

NOTEWORTHY RECORDS

Spring: Coastal - Langford 13 Mar 1982-3; Saanich 5 May 1984-3; Ucluelet 5 Mar 1974-1 found dead; Pender Harbour 12 Mar 1979-2; Point Atkinson 12 Mar 1971-6 (Campbell et al. 1972b); Qualicum Beach 1 Mar 1980-3; Port Hardy 8 Mar 1951-2 females collected; Quatsino 10 Mar 1936-2 males (MVZ 101658-59); Princess Royal Island 19 May 1936-1 male (MCZ 282514). **Interior** - Okanagan Falls 16 Apr 1979-2; Boston Bar 20 May 1978-3; Adams Lake 21 May 1984-1.

Summer: Coastal - Victoria 16 Aug 1980-3; Turtle Island 1 Jun 1972-3 (Hatler et al. 1978); Kennedy Lake (Ucluelet) 2 Jun 1978-1; Alice Lake (Cheakamus River) 30 Jul 1971-5; Port Hardy 27 Aug 1935-3; Stuie 18 Jul 1938-1 male (NMC 28769); Goose Group 28 to 30 Jun 1948-1 male and 3 females (RBCM 1983, 1985, 9846-47); Pitt Island 21 Aug 1939-1. **Interior** - Nelson summer 1971-2; Okanagan Landing 6 Aug 1913-2; Ashcroft 25 Jun 1895-1 female (ANSP 46934); Anstey Arm 25 Jun 1963-1.

Autumn: Interior - Shuswap Lake 2 Sep 1970-1; Ashcroft 28 Sep 1895-1 male (ANSP 46933); Vernon 10 Oct 1970-2 traffic-killed; Wardner 21 Oct 1941-1 (Johnstone, W.B. 1949). **Coastal** - Deep Creek (Terrace) 19 Nov 1985-1 (RBCM Photo 1061); Port Neville 13 Sep 1975-1 found dead; Texada Island 19 and 20 Aug 1985-2; Hornby Island 18 Oct 1978-3; Ucluelet 25 Oct 1977-1; Duncan 5 Oct 1974-2; Victoria 5 Oct 1980-3; Sooke 15 Sep 1984-3.

Winter: Interior - Cranbrook 28 Dec 1912-1 (Munro, J.A. and Cowan 1947); Summerland 28 Dec to 6 Jan 1966-1; Penticton 7 Feb 1979-2; Osoyoos 24 Dec 1987-1 roosting in nest box.

Coastal - Terrace 12 Feb 1947-1 male (RBCM 9997); Prince Rupert 1 Feb 1981-1 found dead on railway track; Quatsino Sound 17 Feb 1930-1 (RBCM 5041); Egmont 6 Feb 1976-2; Vancouver 4 Jan 1971-4 (Campbell et al. 1972b); Pachena Point 10 Jan 1975-1 roosting in lighthouse; Caycuse River 7 Jan 1983-1 (RBCM 18146); Victoria 9 Feb 1986-6; Chatham Islands and Discovery Island 20 Dec 1970 and 1 Jan 1971-6 to 8 calling.

Christmas Counts: Interior - Recorded from 2 of 19 localities and on 3% of all counts. Maxima: Vernon 23 Dec 1979-1 and 27 Dec 1981-1; Oliver/Osoyoos 28 Dec 1981-1. **Coastal** - Recorded from 12 of 28 localities and on 25% of all counts. Maxima: Victoria 20 Dec 1980-12; Pender Island 22 Dec 1970-7; Vancouver 27 Dec 1970-6.

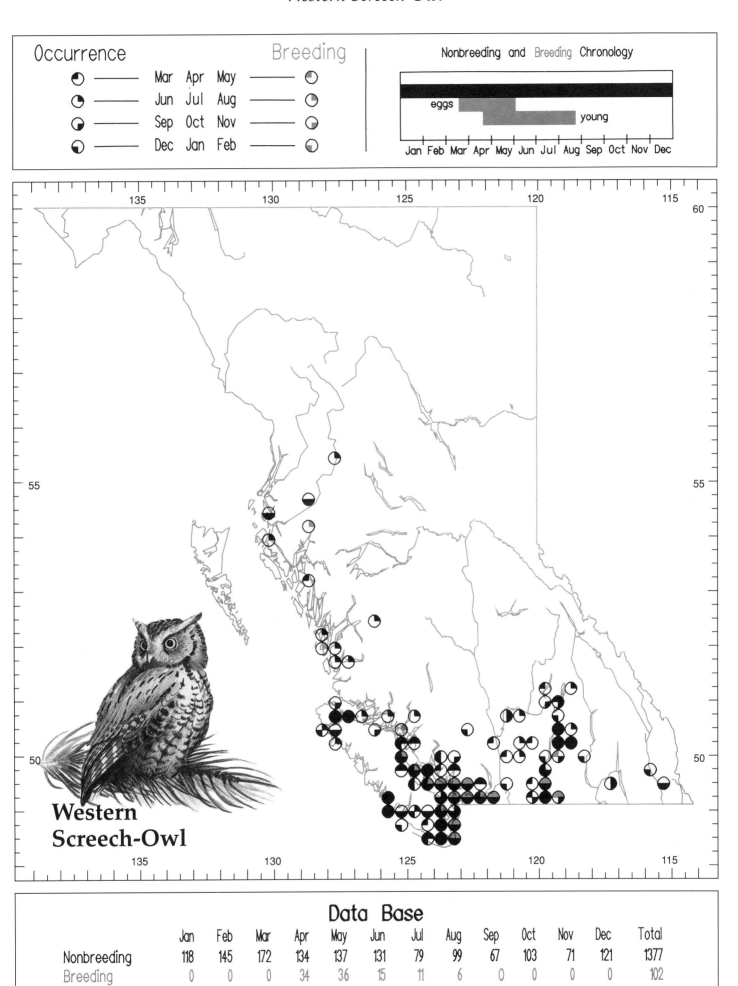

Western Screech-Owl

Occurrence / Breeding

	Mar Apr May	
	Jun Jul Aug	
	Sep Oct Nov	
	Dec Jan Feb	

Nonbreeding and Breeding Chronology

eggs | young

Jan Feb Mar Apr May Jun Jul Aug Sep Oct Nov Dec

Data Base

	Jan	Feb	Mar	Apr	May	Jun	Jul	Aug	Sep	Oct	Nov	Dec	Total
Nonbreeding	118	145	172	134	137	131	79	99	67	103	71	121	1377
Breeding	0	0	0	34	36	15	11	6	0	0	0	0	102

Great Horned Owl

GHOW

Bubo virginianus (Gmelin)

RANGE: Breeds from the northern limit of trees in North America south throughout North, Central, and South America.

STATUS: *Uncommon* resident throughout the province, except in the Queen Charlotte Islands, where it is *casual*. Widespread breeder.

NONBREEDING: The Great Horned Owl is a versatile, usually solitary species which is found in a wide variety of habitats throughout the province. There are 2 records for the Queen Charlotte Islands. Generally, populations appear to decrease northward through the province, and it is less common at higher elevations. It has been recorded from sea level to 2,040 m elevation.

The Great Horned Owl is found in all types of timbered areas. It also frequents river valleys, lakeshores, agricultural and residential areas, swamps, fresh, brackish and marine marshes, and estuaries. Occasionally, it is found in cities, especially near golf courses or parks with adjacent woodlots.

In British Columbia, the Great Horned Owl is considered nonmigratory, but dispersal and wandering does occur, especially during severe winters and shortages in food supply. For example, during the winter of 1926-27 a tremendous invasion of Great Horned Owls occurred on the south coast. During the 5-month period from October 1926 to January 1927, 287 Great Horned Owls were brought into Victoria taxidermists and sporting goods stores (Munro, J.A. 1928, 1929a). It is also one of the most numerous "found dead" or "road-killed" raptors in the province. On the extreme south mainland coast, D.J. Wilson (pers. comm.) reported that, in 1982 and 1983, it was the second most common raptor (behind Barn Owl) brought in dead to the Wildlife Branch office in Surrey.

BREEDING: The Great Horned Owl breeds throughout the province except on the Queen Charlotte Islands, almost anywhere there are groups of small and large trees. It may be found in dense forests, open woodlands bordering lakes and marshes, and along fence rows. It also breeds in holes and crevices in cliffs, clay banks, and man-made structures. Nests have been found from sea level to 1,220 m elevation.

Nests: Most nests (98%; n=97) were situated in natural sites, including coniferous or deciduous woods (75%), and cliffs (20%). In wooded areas, most (89%; n=75) were open tree nests, 8% were in the top of broken snags, and 3% were in large tree cavities. Nineteen nests were situated in crevices and cavities in rock cliffs and clay banks. In addition, 2 nests were found on metal bridges, and 1 was situated on the ground.

Of the 75 tree nests, 57% were in coniferous trees including Douglas-fir (37%), white spruce (12%), ponderosa pine, grand fir, western redcedar, and Norway spruce. The remaining tree nests were found in deciduous trees including black cottonwood (21%), trembling aspen (9%), red alder, paper birch, and willow.

Open tree nests of the Great Horned Owl were generally in old nests of other large birds or among parasitic vegetative growths. Nests of other birds (n=47) included Red-tailed Hawk (43%), American and Northwestern crows (*Corvus brachyrhynchos* and *C. caurinus*; 19%), Great Blue Heron (11%), Bald Eagle (8%), Common Raven (*Corvus corax*; 6% - all in cliffs), Cooper's Hawk, and Northern Goshawk. Three nests were found among witch's broom. All but 7 nests were positioned in the crotches of branches next to the trunk.

Heights for 67 tree nests ranged from 1.5 to 34 m, with 54% recorded between 7.6 and 14 m.

Eggs: Dates for 38 clutches ranged from 15 February to 20 May, with 50% recorded between 24 February and 18 March. Sizes for 35 clutches ranged from 1 to 4 eggs (1E-3, 2E-25, 3E-5, 4E-2), with 71% having 2 eggs. Incubation periods for 3 clutches in British Columbia ranged from 30 to 32 days which is within the range reported by Gilkey et al. (1944).

Young: Dates for 203 broods ranged from 23 March to 10 September, with 51% recorded between 20 April and 1 June. Brood size ranged from 1 to 4 young (1Y-64, 2Y-110, 3Y-26, 4Y-3) with 54% having 2 young. Fledging period is 31 to 35 days but young do not fly well until 63 to 70 days (Harrison, C. 1978).

REMARKS: Three of the ten North American subspecies of the Great Horned Owl are found in British Columbia. *Bubo virginianus subarcticus* breeds in the Peace Lowlands, *B. v. lagophonus* in the interior, and *B. v. saturatus* along the coast. See Godfrey (1986) for additional information on descriptions of the races and taxonomic relationships.

NOTEWORTHY RECORDS

Spring: Coastal - Campbell River (Langley) 10 Apr 1971-3; North Vancouver 12 Mar 1964-3; Alta Lake 17 Jun 1924-3 calling; Miracle Beach Park 19 Mar 1986-2. **Interior** - Bridesville 1 May 1980-5 adults; Vernon 28 Mar 1982-3, 18 May 1969-3; Kamloops 29 Mar 1979-5 adults along Knouff Road; Boundary Lake (Goodlow) 14 Apr 1983-2.

Summer: Coastal - Victoria 10 Jun 1984-3 adults calling on Munn Road; Surrey 14 Jul 1981-4; Campbell River (Discovery Passage) 9 Jun 1965-3 adults; Prince Rupert 14 Jun 1978-3. **Interior** - McCuddy Creek 9 Jun 1922-several; Williams Lake 16 Jul 1980-3; Stum Lake 25 Aug 1975-3; Dease Lake 28 Jun 1962-1 hooting, 8 Aug 1962-6; Fort Nelson 26 Jun 1982-6; Atlin 23 Jun 1978-4 adults.

Autumn: Interior - J.A. Munro (1929a) reports numbers of birds taken for bounty from autumn to early winter 1928 for 8 locations as follows: Smithers-6, Prince George-49, Quesnel-103, Kamloops-100, Vernon-24, Merritt-141, Nelson-17, and Penticton-63. Other records are: Ellison Park 3 Sep 1979-3; Sparwood 18 Oct 1983-3. Vaseux Lake 30 Nov 1932-4; Madden Lake (Oliver) 1 Oct 1981-3. **Coastal** - Kitimat 8 Sep 1978-2 adults; Port Hardy 4 Sep 1939-2; Tofino 11 Nov 1952-2; Vancouver 14 Oct 1962-4; Victoria 6 Nov 1963-3.

Winter: Interior - Fort Nelson 10 Feb 1986-1; Fort St. John 23 Dec 1984-1; Invermere 8 Feb 1986-1. **Coastal** - Westham Island 23 Dec 1972-3; Grice Bay 18 Feb 1985 -1; Central Saanich 20 Jan 1983-4;

Metchosin 18 Jan 1984-4 adults.

Christmas Counts: Interior - Recorded from 9 of 19 localities and on 30% of all counts. Maxima: Vernon 16 Dec 1984-7; Oliver/Osoyoos 29 Dec 1983-3; Vaseux Lake 23 Dec 1979-3; Penticton 26 Dec 1978-2. **Coastal** - Recorded from 13 of 28 localities and on 29% of all counts. Maxima: Ladner 23 Dec 1984-8; 4 additional count areas with 4 birds each as follows: Pitt Meadows 30 Dec 1984; Vancouver 18 Dec 1983 and 16 Dec 1984; Victoria 21 Dec 1963, 18 Dec 1976 and 19 Dec 1981; Duncan 20 Dec 1980.

Extralimital Records: Coastal - Tlell 19 and 20 May 1960-1 heard, 17 Nov 1968-1 seen.

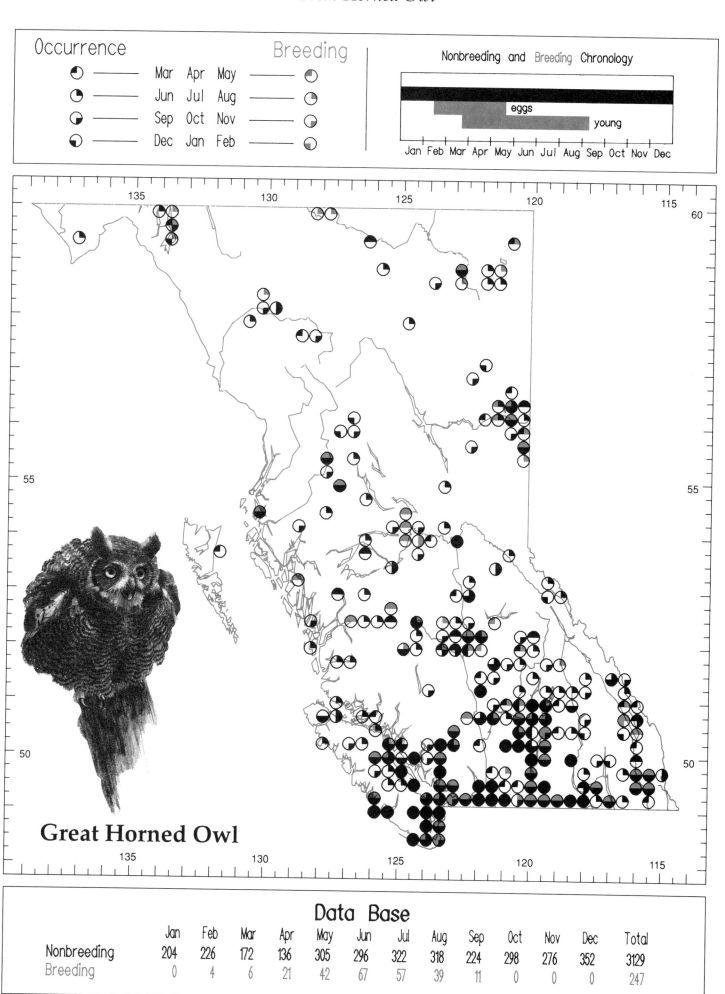

Great Horned Owl

Occurrence

	Breeding
◑ ——— Mar Apr May ——— ◑	
◕ ——— Jun Jul Aug ——— ◔	
◔ ——— Sep Oct Nov ——— ◔	
◕ ——— Dec Jan Feb ——— ◕	

Nonbreeding and Breeding Chronology

eggs

young

Jan Feb Mar Apr May Jun Jul Aug Sep Oct Nov Dec

Data Base

	Jan	Feb	Mar	Apr	May	Jun	Jul	Aug	Sep	Oct	Nov	Dec	Total
Nonbreeding	204	226	172	136	305	296	322	318	224	298	276	352	3129
Breeding	0	4	6	21	42	67	57	39	11	0	0	0	247

Snowy Owl
Nyctea scandiaca (Linnaeus)

SNOW

RANGE: Circumpolar. Breeds in arctic tundras of the world. Winters within breeding range and south to central Europe, central Asia, and the northern United States; occasionally south to the central United States during years of periodic irruptions.

STATUS: *Rare* to *fairly common* but irregular winter visitant on the coast; *rare* to *uncommon* in the interior. During years of irruptions, can be *very common* on the extreme southwest mainland coast, *fairly common* in the northern interior and *uncommon* in the southern interior.

OCCURRENCE: The Snowy Owl has been reported from widespread locations along the coast; southern Vancouver Island and the Fraser River delta are areas of abundance during invasion years. There it frequents log-covered beaches, offshore barren islands, bare rocky headlands, sand dunes, and man-made structures such as jetties, log booms, and wharves. In urban areas, it has been found in airports (Fig. 261), parks, marshes, garbage dumps, and school yards; in agricultural areas, fence posts are favourite perch sites.

In the interior it is widely distributed across the southern half of the province, with a scattered distribution in northern areas. The open country of the Peace Lowlands near Fort St. John and the northern Okanagan valley near Vernon are principal wintering areas. Habitats there include grasslands, lake shores, marshes, and alpine meadows to at least 1,830 m elevation. Residential and urban areas are visited infrequently.

The Snowy Owl is most abundant along the coast where 60% of all records have been obtained. In the interior, one is unlikely to see more than 4 or 5 birds from a single vantage point, while on the Fraser River delta, up to 20 birds have been seen.

Since J.A. Munro and Cowan (1947), the Snowy Owl has been recorded every year. On the coast, it has been seen from 13 September (Sea Island) to 12 May (Ladner). In the northern interior, it has occurred from 29 October (Fort St. John) to 19 May (Fort Nelson), and in the southern interior from 31 October (Williams Lake) to 5 May (Vernon).

Snowy Owl incursions into the Pacific Northwest are irregular and vary considerably in magnitude. Notable irruptions have been documented in the winters of 1889-90, 1896-97, 1908-09, 1916-17, 1917-18 (Jewett et al. 1953), 1945-46 (Gross 1947), 1950-51 (Hudson and Yocom 1954), 1953-54, 1957-58, 1963-64, 1966-67 (Hanson 1971), 1973-74, 1977-78, and 1984-85 (Christmas Bird Counts).

REMARKS: One significant band recovery indicates that some British Columbia birds come from the north coast of Alaska: a bird banded on 28 November 1972 in Ladner was recovered near Barrow, Alaska, on 29 April 1973.

It is well known that the winter diet of the Snowy Owl in southern interior locations of other parts of North America is mainly composed of mice and voles (see Boxall 1980; James 1980). However, recent food habit studies on the Pacific coast suggest that birds comprise the main component of Snowy Owl diets there. Campbell and MacColl (1978) analysed Snowy Owl pellets obtained near Victoria and found them to be composed entirely of bird remains, mainly Horned Grebe and Bufflehead. On the Fraser River delta, A.J. Kennedy et al. (1982) showed that birds, mainly waterfowl, also comprise most of the winter diet (97% frequency, 99.8% biomass).

Figure 261. *Snowy Owl winter roost site at the Victoria International Airport, February 1981 (Mark Nyhof).*

NOTEWORTHY RECORDS

Spring: Coastal - Central Saanich 5 Apr 1964-1 male (RBCM 11274); Nanaimo 15 Apr 1910-2 males (NMC 1027, 4027); Boundary Bay 9 Mar 1985-11, 23 Mar 1985-3; Ladner 12 May 1974-1; Delta 16 Mar 1974-16; Sea Island 16 Mar 1974-12, 6 May 1967-1 (Anderson, E. 1967b); Mount Burnaby 2 May 1985-1; Mitlenatch Island 27 Apr and 7 May 1978-1 (McFetridge and Kirbyson 1978). **Interior** - Penticton 3 May 1974-1 (Cannings, S.G. 1974); Vernon 5 May 1974-2; (latest record-Rogers, T.H. 1974c); Knutsford 11 Mar 1979-2; Tatla Lake 5 Mar 1979-1; Alexis Creek 5 Mar 1979-1; Fort St. John 14 Mar 1983-4; Cecil Lake 5 Apr 1981-1; Fort Nelson 19 May 1974-1 (Erskine and Davidson 1976); Horseranch Range 16 Mar 1982-1 in alpine; Chilkat Pass 3 Apr 1983-1 (Grunberg 1983b).

Summer: No records.

Autumn: Interior - Fort St. John 27 Nov 1983-5; Williams Lake 3 Nov 1973-1; Crowfoot Mountain 7 Nov 1982-1 at 1,830 m; Adams Lake (Shuswap) 16 Nov 1970-1 (Schnider et al. 1971); Lake Windermere 22 Nov 1983-1; Kelowna 23 Nov 1911-1 attacked by adult male Prairie Falcon; Okanagan Landing 21 Nov 1929-1. **Coastal** - Triple Islands 1 Nov 1950-1 (Odlum 1952); Tow Hill 11 Nov 1973-2 on beach; Tlell 31 Oct 1971-1; Port Hardy 16 Nov 1950-2+; Shelter Point 11 Nov 1973-2; Sea Island 13 Sep 1971-1; Iona Island 8 Nov 1969-11; Boundary Bay 18 Nov 1973-33 along foreshore (Crowell and Nehls 1974a), 26 Nov 1980-6 along foreshore; Radar Hill 10 Nov 1973-2; Carmanah Point 25 Nov 1950-several (Irving 1953); Victoria 22 to 29 Oct 1946-3+; Victoria area 18 Nov 1973-13 on offshore islands (Crowell and Nehls 1974a); Chain Island 24 Oct 1978-3.

Winter: Interior - Fort St. John 21 Jan 1984-7, 5 Feb 1983-9; Baldonnel 12 Dec 1981-2; Vernon 2 Jan 1967-2, 10 Feb 1919-3 (Munro, J.A. and Cowan 1947), 6 Dec 1970-4, 4 Dec 1973-2; Wasa 4 Dec 1942-1 male (RBCM 11212); Cranbrook 4 Dec 1942-1 (Munro, J.A. and Cowan 1947); Trail 10 Dec 1973-1. **Coastal** - Masset 5 Dec 1950-7+; Queen Charlotte City 7 Dec 1971-1; Ocean Falls 18 Dec 1977-1; Cape St. James 8 Jan 1978-1; Comox 15 Jan 1979-8 on airport; Tofino 28 Dec 1973-3; Delta 6 Dec 1973-14, 18 Jan 1978-14, 21 Jan 1979-10; Westham Island to Tsawwassen 9 Feb 1974-15; Central Saanich 27 Dec 1973-5, 30 Jan 1974-6; Victoria 26 Dec 1973-4 on golf course; Race Rocks 3 Dec 1966-7.

Christmas Counts: Interior - Recorded from 3 of 19 localities and on 3% of all counts. Maxima: North Pine 20 Dec 1983-2; Vernon 16 Dec 1984-1; Kamloops 15 Dec 1984-1. **Coastal** - Recorded from 10 of 28 localities and on 15% of all total counts. Maxima: Ladner 22 Dec 1973-107, all-time North American high count (Monroe 1974); Vancouver 26 Dec 1973-27; White Rock 30 Dec 1973-14.

Snowy Owl

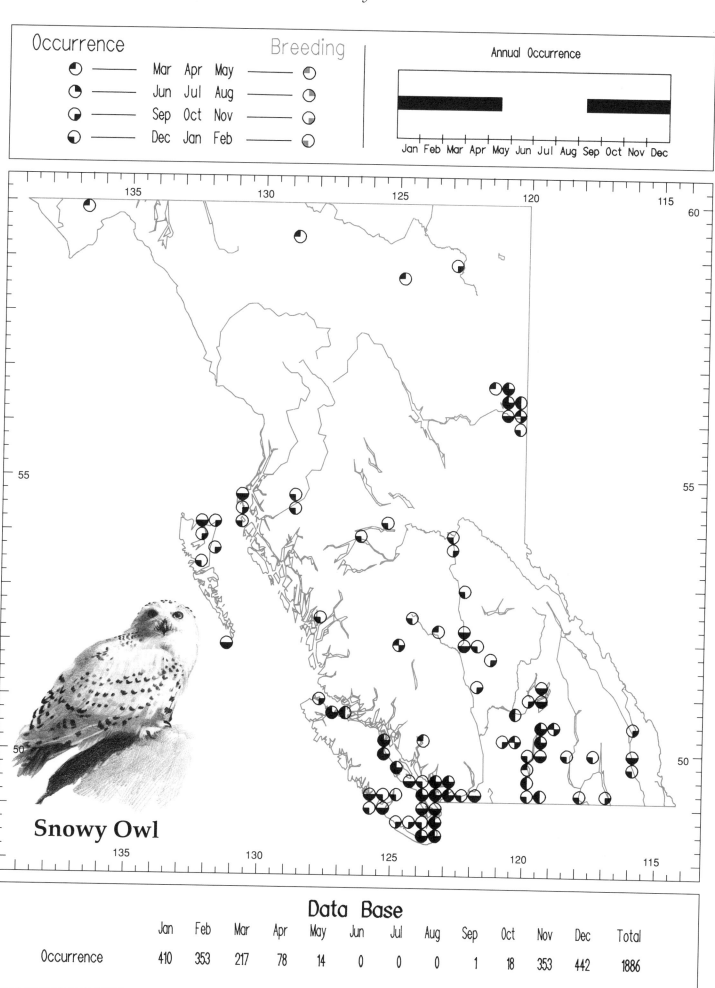

Occurrence

Breeding

	Mar	Apr	May	
	Jun	Jul	Aug	
	Sep	Oct	Nov	
	Dec	Jan	Feb	

Annual Occurrence

Jan Feb Mar Apr May Jun Jul Aug Sep Oct Nov Dec

Snowy Owl

Data Base

	Jan	Feb	Mar	Apr	May	Jun	Jul	Aug	Sep	Oct	Nov	Dec	Total
Occurrence	410	353	217	78	14	0	0	0	1	18	353	442	1886

Northern Hawk Owl

NHOW

Surnia ulula (Linnaeus)

RANGE: Holarctic. Breeds in the northern coniferous forest belt, north to the tree limit, across Eurasia and North America. Winters in the breeding range and farther south; in North America, south to southern Canada and the northern United States.

STATUS: *Uncommon* resident in the northern interior, probably local and *rare* resident at higher elevations in the southern interior. Also irregular transient and *very rare* winter visitant in the south. *Casual* on the northern mainland coast, *very rare* on the southwest coast including southern Vancouver Island. Breeds.

NONBREEDING: The Northern Hawk Owl (Fig. 262) is widely dis-tributed throughout the interior of the province to at least 2,650 m elevation. It is rarely found at the coast. It is primarily a northern species, commonest north of 56°N latitude, and inhabits open coniferous and mixed coniferous-deciduous woodlands. It also frequents forest edges, logging clearings, second-growth woodlands, muskegs, and swamps. It is a solitary species seen mostly during the nonbreeding season when it perches atop trees, usually adjacent to clearings. The Northern Hawk Owl hunts in burns, clear cuts, scrubby fields, lake shores, along highways and roads, and in other clearings. On the coast, most reports were from rural areas with shrubby and cultivated fields and nearby power poles and trees for perch sites.

Outside of family groups, there are no records of more than 2 individuals (probably pairs), from any single location at a time. The open country of the Peace Lowlands may support a substantial wintering population. On 11 December 1982, 6 different birds were counted along 30 km of the Upper Cache Road northwest of Fort St. John. This influx may have been due in part to winter weather conditions and rodent numbers.

In British Columbia the Northern Hawk Owl does not migrate regularly, but it wanders irregularly from breeding areas in autumn and winter. Some of that movement may be altitudinal. Occasionally, the appearance of large numbers in the south occurs during severe winters and shortages in food supplies (Bent 1938; Smith, D.A. 1970).

Extreme dates for the south coast are 26 September (Victoria) and 12 March (Beach Grove).

BREEDING: The Northern Hawk Owl breeds throughout the interior of the province from Manning Park and Moyie River to just north of Chilkat Pass. Nests and recently fledged young have been found between 550 and 1,830 m elevation.

Very little is known about the distribution, habitat require-ments, and breeding biology of the Northern Hawk Owl in British Columbia. Of the 16 breeding records, only 3 represent actual nests; the others are of flightless young.

Nesting habitats included fairly open coniferous and mixed

forests of white spruce, Engelmann spruce, subalpine fir, trembling aspen, birch, and mountain hemlock. In Alaska, Meehan and Ritchie (1982) found that hawk owls preferred open-canopied forests (20% to 60% canopy cover). Some nested at the forest edge, and 2 nests were found near tree line.

Nests: Nests (n=3) were situated in a hole in a dead tree, in the top of a broken-off tree trunk, and in a cavity near the top of a broken-off spruce tree. Heights were recorded as 4.6, 6.1, and 18.3 m respectively.

Eggs: Nests containing eggs have not been found in British Columbia; calculated dates (see Young below) indicate that eggs could be found from 23 April through 31 May. In north-central Alberta, E.T. Jones (1987) found this species on nesting territory in mid-March, while egg-laying began about mid-April. Incubation period is 25 to 29 days (Leinonen 1978; Godfrey 1986).

Young: Dates for 13 broods ranged from 13 June to 9 August; calculated dates indicated that young could be found as early as the last week of May. Sizes for 12 broods ranged from 1 to 5 young (1Y-2, 2Y-6, 3Y-2, 4Y-1, 5Y-1). Fledging period is 21 to 28 days (Huhtala et al. 1987).

REMARKS: See R.J. Clark et al. (1978) for literature on the Northern Hawk Owl in Eurasia.

Formerly known as Hawk Owl and Northern Hawk-Owl.

Figure 262. *Northern Hawk Owl at Pitt Meadows, 20 January 1985 (Tim Zurowski).*

NOTEWORTHY RECORDS

Spring: Coastal - Beach Grove 12 Mar 1982-1; Pitt Meadows 1 Mar 1985-1. **Interior** - Midway 26 Apr 1905-1; Creston Mar 1978-1 (RBCM Photo 948); Riske Creek 8 Mar 1981-2; Lac la Hache 15 Mar 1960-1; 40 km n Wonowon 2 and 3 Apr 1986-2.

Summer: Coastal - Garibaldi Park 8 Aug 1981-1 at 1,675 m. **Interior** - Manning Park Jul 1980-3; Boundary Lake (Creston) 30 Jun 1978-1 (RBCM 16432); Meachen Creek 3 Jul 1975-1; Windermere 24 to 31 Aug 1944-1 (Carl and Hardy 1945); Shuswap Lake 13 Aug 1978-3; Riske Creek 13 Jul 1982-1 young female killed on road (RBCM 17712), 1 adult nearby; Pouce Coupe 9 Jun 1953-3 (NMC 47853-55); Nig Creek 26 Jun 1922-2 (Williams, M.Y. 1933b); Tanzilla Butte 26 Jul 1962-2 (NMC 49783-84).

Autumn: Interior - Chilkat Pass 21 Oct 1981-1; Rolla 9 Oct 1977-2; Nilkitkwa Lake 15 and 16 Sep 1980-2, 14 Nov 1978-2; Kleena Kleene 23 Oct 1956-1 (Paul 1959); Parson 30 Oct 1948-1 female (RBCM 11199); Creston Sep 1968-1 (Butler et al. 1986); Windy Joe Mountain 14 Sep 1973-1 (Belton 1973). **Coastal** - Kitsault 23 and 24 Sep 1980-1, 24 to 28 Nov 1979-1; Diamond Head 5 Oct 1980-1; Comox 21 Sep 1925-1 male (RBCM 12972) 20 Oct 1926-1 female (RBCM 6303); Alberni Oct 1926-1 shot (Munro, J.A. 1928); Sumas 15 Nov 1894-1 male (MCZ 247131); Pitt Meadows 29 Nov 1980 to 4 Feb 1981-1 (RBCM Photo 773), 25 Nov 1985 to 1 Mar 1986-1 (RBCM Photo 1002; Fig. 262); Goldstream Lake 22 Nov 1962-1; Victoria 26 Sep 1951-1 (Anonymous 1951), Oct 1894-1 female (RBCM 1751).

Winter: Interior - Fort St. John 20 Feb 1983-2; Farrell Creek (Peace River) 16 Jan 1983-4 counted in 6 km; Prince George 22 Feb to 9 Jun 1970-2 (Boggs and Boggs 1963b); Kleena Kleene 14 Feb 1968-1; Lillian Lake (Invermere) 2 Feb 1982-1; Nakusp 31 Jan 1983-1 (Rogers, T.H. 1983b); Fraser 8 Jan 1981-1; Manning Park 28 Dec 1978-1. **Coastal** - Maroon Creek (32 km n Terrace) 1 Dec 1977-1; Victoria 10 Dec 1974-1 (Crowell and Nehls 1974b), 30 Jan 1897-1 male (MCZ 247125); Sumas 4 Dec 1904-1 male (MCZ 300835).

Christmas Counts: Interior - Recorded from 7 of 19 localities and on 8% of all counts. Maxima: Lake Windermere 27 Dec 1981-2; Quesnel 24 Dec 1981-2. All other counts of single birds. **Coastal** - Recorded twice: Pitt Meadows 27 Dec 1980-1 and 30 Dec 1984-1.

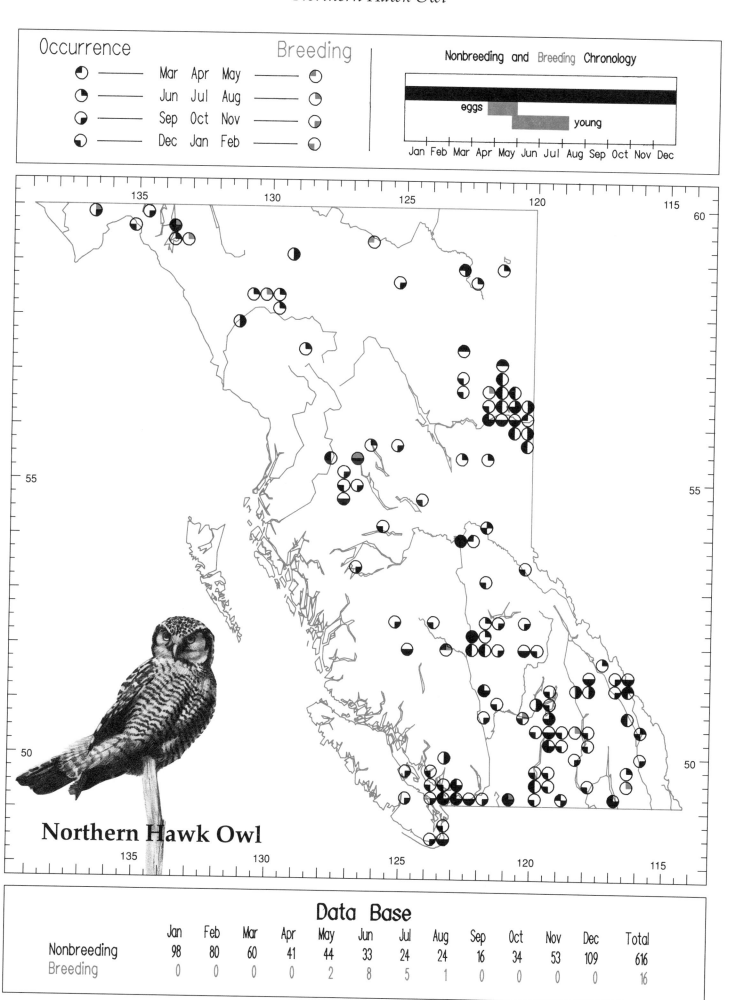

Occurrence

Breeding

Mar Apr May
Jun Jul Aug
Sep Oct Nov
Dec Jan Feb

Nonbreeding and Breeding Chronology

eggs
young

Jan Feb Mar Apr May Jun Jul Aug Sep Oct Nov Dec

Northern Hawk Owl

Data Base

	Jan	Feb	Mar	Apr	May	Jun	Jul	Aug	Sep	Oct	Nov	Dec	Total
Nonbreeding	98	80	60	41	44	33	24	24	16	34	53	109	616
Breeding	0	0	0	0	2	8	5	1	0	0	0	0	16

Northern Pygmy-Owl
Glaucidium gnoma Wagler

RANGE: Primarily resident from southeastern Alaska, central British Columbia, and southwestern Alberta south through the western cordillera to Guatemala.

STATUS: *Uncommon* resident across the province, including Vancouver Island, south of the Chilcotin-Cariboo Basin. *Rare* along the northern mainland coast and in the central interior. *Very rare* in the northwest interior.

NONBREEDING: The Northern Pygmy-Owl is widely distributed in northwestern and southern British Columbia, but resident populations appear restricted to the southern portions of the province. It is absent from the Queen Charlotte Islands and far northeastern British Columbia.

This tiny, diurnal owl prefers the edges of open coniferous forests or mixed woodlands. It has been recorded in logged areas, orchards, riparian thickets, damp and dry meadows, farmlands, river and lake shores, vacant city lots, parks, cemeteries, and residential areas. It occurs from sea level to at least 1,710 m elevation.

Most records (64%) are from the late autumn and winter periods when pygmy-owls move from forested mountains to lower elevations where they are more visible. The movement is most noticeable in the interior and is usually underway by late October and early November. It probably includes both a vertical movement and a general southward dispersal. The return movement probably occurs in mid-to-late February. Winter incursions are irregular, unpredictable events (see Munro, J.A. 1921). Nearly 95% of all records are of single birds.

BREEDING: The Northern Pygmy-Owl breeds along eastern Vancouver Island and the adjacent mainland coast and in the interior from the vicinity of Williams Lake south through the Okanagan valley. It probably also breeds in the Kootenays, but evidence is lacking. It nests in mixed coniferous woodlands (e.g. Douglas-fir, western redcedar, western hemlock, ponderosa pine, lodgepole pine, and western larch), often on steep hillsides, precipitous talus slopes, or steep ravines not far from water. Nests were reported from 490 to 1,220 m elevation.

Nests: Only 5 nests have been discovered in the province. All were in old woodpecker holes in coniferous trees (Fig. 263) including Douglas-fir (3 nests), western hemlock and western larch. Nest heights ranged from 3 to 18 m. Measurements for one nest were: entrance diameter, 3.8 cm; depth, 20.3 cm; and diameter of nest chamber, 14 cm. All nests contained wood chips, probably from woodpecker activity; one nest was lined with fine strips of western redcedar bark.

Eggs: Only 3 nests with eggs have been reported. Egg dates included 24 and 27 April (Frost 1972) and 15 May. Calculated dates indicate that eggs could be found from mid-April through mid-June. Clutch sizes were 1, 5, and 7 eggs. Incubation period is about 28 days (Harrison, C. 1978; Godfrey 1986).

Young: Dates for 11 broods ranged from 9 June to 25 August, the latter date representing a brood of fledged young. Brood size ranged from 1 to 7 young (1Y-5, 2Y-1, 3Y-1, 5Y-2, 7Y-2), with 6 broods having 1 or 2 young. Fledging period is 29 to 32 days (Harrison, C. 1978).

REMARKS: Three races are listed for British Columbia (American Ornithologists' Union 1957). *Glaucidium gnoma grinnelli* occurs along the western mainland of British Columbia, *G. g. californicum* occurs in the northern interior, and *G. g. swarthi* is restricted to Vancouver Island. J.A. Munro and Cowan (1947) examined 100 specimens and suggest that *grinnelli* and *swarthi* are synonymous. Godfrey (1986) mentions the disagreement on the subspecies and nomenclature and suggests that an examination of critical material from Alaska, British Columbia, and Washington is needed.

The Northern Pygmy-Owl was formerly known as Pygmy Owl.

Figure 263. *Northern Pygmy-Owl nest (near the top of the largest tree in the figure) at Rock Creek, southwest of Greenwood, 8 June 1984 (Mark Nyhof).*

NOTEWORTHY RECORDS

Spring: Coastal - Tofino 28 May 1931-1 male (UBC 5603); Chilliwack River 29 Mar 1985-2; Yale 8 Mar 1964-2; Brooks Peninsula 9 May 1978-2. **Interior** - Okanagan Landing 9 Mar 1912-2; Toby Creek (Invermere) 6 Apr 1982-3; Leanchoil Marsh (Kootenay National Park) 7 Apr 1976-2; Driftwood Lake Apr 1941-2 (Stanwell-Fletcher and Stanwell-Fletcher 1943); Wapta Lake 10 May 1976-2+ (Wade 1977).

Summer: Coastal - Forbidden Plateau 30 Jul 1962-2 (Boggs and Boggs 1962d); Patterson Lake (w Campbell River) 9 Aug 1976-2; Dean River 16 Jul 1939-1 female (NMC 29075). **Interior** - Keremeos 28 Jun 1928-1 male (NMC 22684); Scotch Creek 28 Jun 1963-2, 7 Aug 1963-2; Bowron River 14 and 15 Aug 1961-2 (Ritcey and Verbeek 1961); Meziadin Lake 30 Aug 1977-2; Cullivan Creek 6 Aug 1959-1 attacked by 2 Olive-sided Flycatchers.

Autumn: Interior - Atlin 16 Sep 1931-1 (Swarth 1936); Fort St. John 20 Oct 1984-1, first Peace River area record (Campbell 1985a); Tetana Lake 5 Oct 1937-1 male (RBCM 7837); Summit Lake (Mount Averil) 15 Oct 1983-7+; Hidden Lake (e Vernon) 30 Oct 1962-2+; Peter Hope Lake 19 Oct 1976-3; South Slocan 22 Nov 1981-2; Penticton 15 Sep 1980-3; Creston 3 and 5 Sep 1949-2 (Munro, J.A. 1958a); Lightning Lake 31 Oct 1970-2+. **Coastal** - Terrace 19 Oct 1947-1 adult male (ROM 86862); Cape Scott 17 Sep 1935-1 adult male (NMC 26069); Campbell River (Discovery Passage) Oct 1982-2; Rubble Creek 24 Sep 1983-2; Hope 18 Nov 1968-2; Chilliwack 26 Nov 1977-2; Kennedy River 10 Oct 1983-2.

Winter: Interior - 35 km w Prince George 21 Jan 1979-2; Williams Lake 30 Dec 1977-4; Ottertail 18 and 19 Feb 1977-6 (Wade 1977); Salmon Arm 3 Jan 1971-2; Nakusp 29 Jan 1977-2; Vernon 2 Feb 1966-2+; South Slocan 3 Jan 1982-2; Raspberry/Robson 23 Jan 1977-2; Skaha Lake 29 Dec 1977-2. **Coastal** - Port Moody 9 Jan 1897-3; Cypress Park 12 Jan 1981-2.

Christmas Counts: Interior - Recorded from 10 of 19 localities and on 48% of all counts. Maxima: Vernon 26 Dec 1977-17, all-time Canadian high count (Anderson, R.R. 1978); Penticton 27 Dec 1983-10; Oliver/Osoyoos 28 Dec 1981-8. **Coastal** - Recorded from 10 of 28 localities and on 10% of all counts. Maxima: Vancouver 18 Dec 1977-4 , 16 Dec 1984-4; Squamish 1 Jan 1985-4; Pitt Meadows 27 Dec 1976-3; Kitimat 15 Dec 1974-2; Sunshine Coast 15 Dec 1984-2.

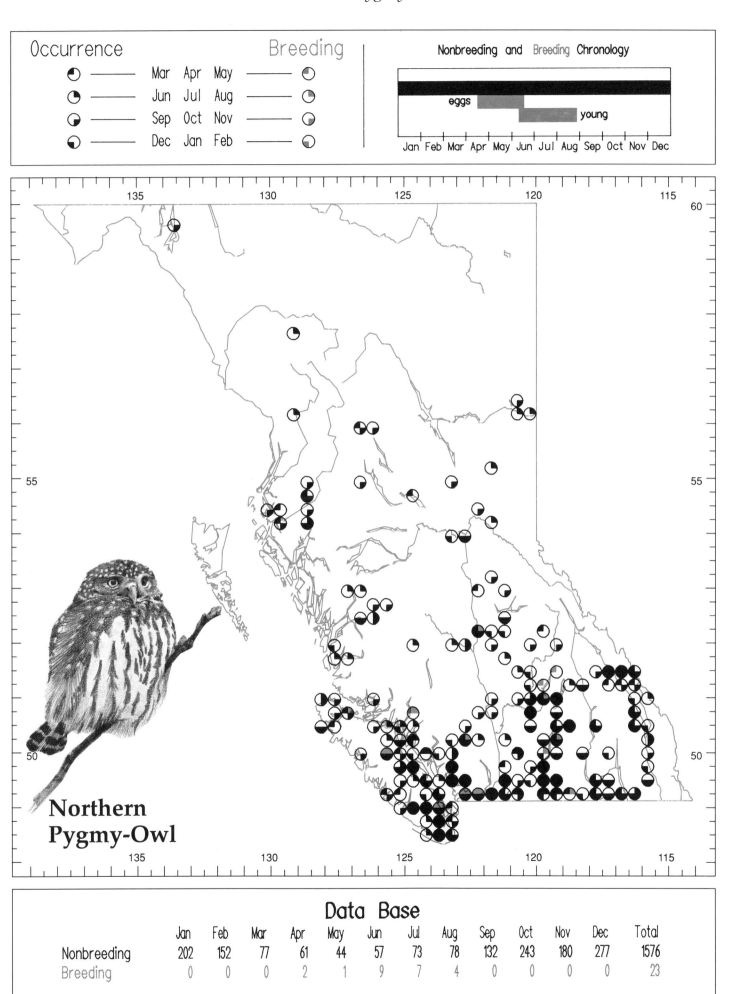

Occurrence   Breeding

Nonbreeding and Breeding Chronology

		Mar	Apr	May		
		Jun	Jul	Aug		
		Sep	Oct	Nov		
		Dec	Jan	Feb		

eggs   young

Jan Feb Mar Apr May Jun Jul Aug Sep Oct Nov Dec

**Northern
Pygmy-Owl**

Data Base

	Jan	Feb	Mar	Apr	May	Jun	Jul	Aug	Sep	Oct	Nov	Dec	Total
Nonbreeding	202	152	77	61	44	57	73	78	132	243	180	277	1576
Breeding	0	0	0	2	1	9	7	4	0	0	0	0	23

Burrowing Owl
Athene cunicularia (Molina)

RANGE: Breeds from central-southern British Columbia and southern Alberta, Saskatchewan, and Manitoba, south through the western and midwestern United States into Central and South America. Resident in central and southern Florida. Migrates from northern parts of the breeding range in winter.

STATUS: *Very rare* to *rare* local summer visitant in the Thompson-Okanagan Plateau; *casual* in winter. Formerly *very rare* resident, now *very rare* winter visitant to the Fraser River delta. *Casual* elsewhere, including southeastern Vancouver Island, the Chilcotin-Cariboo Basin, and the Kootenay Trench. Breeds.

NONBREEDING: The Burrowing Owl (Fig. 264) occurs mainly in the south Thompson and Okanagan basins in the interior, and on the Fraser River delta on the extreme south mainland coast. In the interior, it has wandered north to Beaver valley (west of Horsefly) and has occurred in the east Kootenay from Ta Ta Creek south to Humberton. Records for Vancouver Island and the Fraser Lowlands probably represent the dispersal of birds breeding on the Fraser River delta.

The Burrowing Owl frequents open, short-grass areas of agricultural lands, airports, golf courses, jetties, spits, and coastal sand dunes littered with logs. It has been found roosting in hollow logs, culverts, piles of discarded lumber, and old wooden barns.

Migrants usually arrive in March and depart in September.

BREEDING: The Burrowing Owl breeds in the central-souther interior from the vicinity of Kamloops south through th Okanagan and southern Similkameen valleys. On the coast, breeds locally on the Fraser River delta.

In the interior, it frequents open areas of short-grass, forbs and sagebrush usually with gentle rolling hills, on benchlands plains, rangelands, and valley bottoms. On the coast, open, shor grass, reclaimed agricultural land is inhabited. Nests have bee found from 2 m below sea level on the coast to 425 m elevation i the interior.

Nests: Nests were situated in both natural and man-mad sites, including burrows of the yellow-bellied marmot (4 nests), badger hole, a striped skunk den, a Belted Kingfisher burrow, natural crevice in the side of a railway embankment, and an ol drain pipe. One nest burrow that was opened had a windin tunnel about 3 m long and 0.6 m below the ground. The nes chamber was lined with dry horse droppings, straw, short plan stalks, and assorted bits of cardboard. Where abandoned burrow are not available, and where areas of relatively deep, sandy soi with breaks in the root mat exist, the owls have been successful i constructing their own burrows (R.C. Lincoln pers. comm.).

Eggs: Dates for 5 clutches ranged from 6 May to 24 May. I the interior, eggs collected in late May were all well-incubated indicating that egg-laying there probably begins in late April an early May. On the coast, calculated dates from estimated ages c

Figure 264. Burrowing Owl at Iona Island, Richmond, 7 January 1973 (RBCM Photo 246; Ervio Sian).

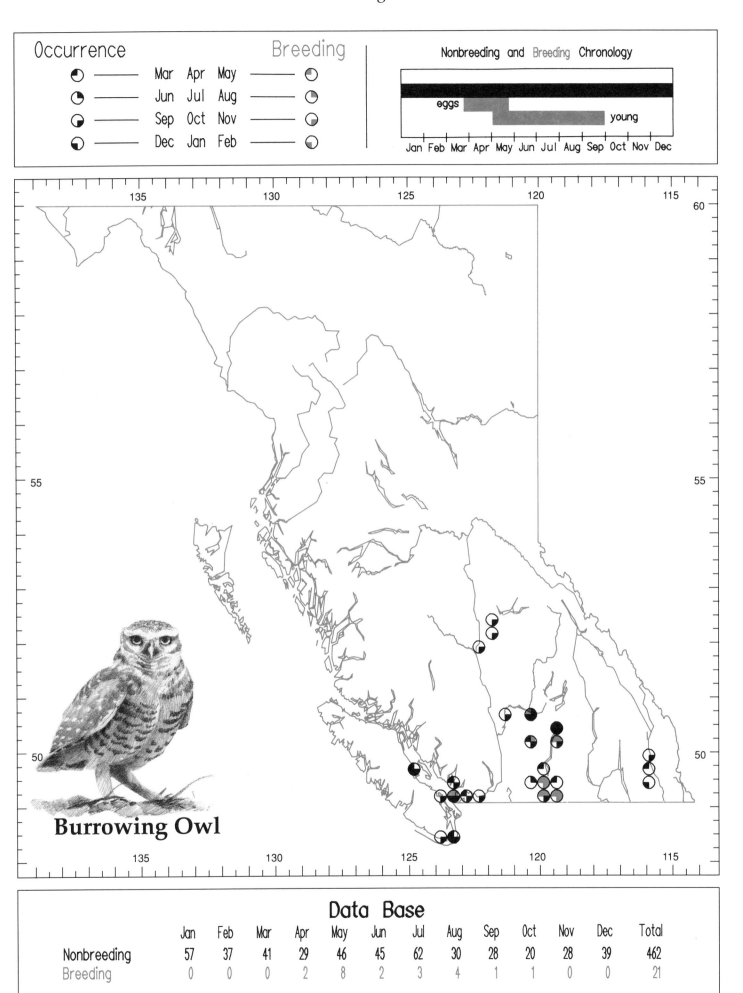

Occurrence

	Mar Apr May	
	Jun Jul Aug	
	Sep Oct Nov	
	Dec Jan Feb	

Breeding

Nonbreeding and Breeding Chronology

eggs

young

Jan Feb Mar Apr May Jun Jul Aug Sep Oct Nov Dec

Burrowing Owl

Data Base

	Jan	Feb	Mar	Apr	May	Jun	Jul	Aug	Sep	Oct	Nov	Dec	Total
Nonbreeding	57	37	41	29	46	45	62	30	28	20	28	39	462
Breeding	0	0	0	2	8	2	3	4	1	1	0	0	21

nestlings indicate that egg-laying may start in late March. Clutch size ranged from 6 to 10 eggs (6E-1, 8E-2, 10E-2). Incubation period is about 21 days (Bent 1938).

Young: Dates for 12 broods ranged from 4 May (coast) and 8 June (interior) to 1 October (interior), with 6 broods recorded between 25 June and 6 August. Brood size ranged from 1 to 6 young (1Y-1, 2Y-2, 3Y-1, 4Y-4, 5Y-3, 6Y-1), with 7 broods having 4 or 5 young (Fig. 265). In British Columbia, young have been reported as flying for the first time "27 days after they first came out of the burrow" (Cannings, R.A. et al. 1987).

REMARKS: Small colonies of Burrowing Owls, up to 6 pairs, were present in grasslands and sagebrush plains of the central-southern interior of the province at the turn of the century (Venables 1909). The last concentration, 4 pairs, was reported near Oliver in 1925 (Munro, J.A. and Cowan 1947). During the next 60 years or so, numbers dwindled, partly due to the development of benchlands and river bottoms for agriculture and human settlements, coupled with the disappearance of burrowing mammals, principally badgers. Burrowing Owls are at the northern limit of their range in British Columbia, a situation where fluctuations in numbers of a species are not unusual. Since the 1940s, evidence of breeding has been reported from only 4 areas: Chopaka in the lower Similkameen valley (1943), Okanagan Landing (occupied more or less continuously until 1963 - Cannings, R.A. et al. 1987), West Bench (1970 - Cannings, S.R. 1972), and east of Douglas Lake (1979).

On the coast, on Lulu Island in the Fraser River delta, 1 or 2 pairs nested most years from 1939 through 1976. Recently (1984), 1 or 2 birds have been seen near the Boundary Bay airport, suggesting the small breeding population has not been extirpated.

Following the success of using artificial nest burrows for Burrowing Owls in California (see Collins and Landry 1977), the provincial Wildlife Branch released 21 Burrowing Owls (Fig. 266) in the grasslands of the central-southern interior in 1983 and 1984 in an attempt to re-establish populations in British Columbia (Ritcey 1985). Thirty-two artificial burrows were installed in the Thompson Basin and Southern Thompson Upland regions. Details of the introduction are summarized by Murphy (1984). In addition, 10 adult and 38 young owls, obtained from eastern Washington were released in the southern Okanagan valley in 1985 following habitat enhancements that included the installation of 58 artificial burrows (Lincoln 1986). Two pairs of birds, all banded, returned to the Okanagan release site in 1986 (Fig. 267) and raised 1 owlet each (R.C. Lincoln pers. comm.).

Another 10 immatures were released at Cache Creek, 6 on 8 August 1985 and 4 on 14 August 1986. In total, 9 artificial burrows were constructed. At least 1 owl remained at the release site throughout the year in 1986 and 1987.

Wedgewood (1978), subsequently reported in Howie (1980), reports 2 possible breeding records for the Burrowing Owl: a pair at Creston, circa 1965, and at Wardner, circa 1972. We could not confirm these reports and have excluded them from the account; observers in those areas should be alert to the possibility that Burrowing Owls occur and may occasionally breed there. Wedgewood (1978) also mentions 2 records from Revelstoke from the 1970s, another from Roosville in 1967, and one from the "West Kootenay" circa 1969. These records also remain unconfirmed.

The Burrowing Owl appears on the "Blue List" from 1972 to 1981 but was delisted to a species of "special concern" in 1982 and 1986 (Tate 1986).

Formerly placed in the monotypic genus *Speotyto*.

POSTSCRIPT: On 27 July 1988, 2 adults and 7 young were seen at the Cache Creek release site indicating successful breeding (D. Low pers. comm.).

Figure 265. Flightless Burrowing Owls at nest entrance, West Bench, Penticton, 21 July 1970 (RBCM Photo 110; Richard J. Cannings).

Figure 266.*Biologist Bob Lincoln with Marsha Radke releasing an adult Burrowing Owl in a reconstructed burrow near Osoyoos Lake in the southern Okanagan valley (William Radke).*

Figure 267. *Juvenile Burrowing Owl (note band) which was fledged at release site near Osoyoos Lake, mid-summer 1985 (British Columbia Ministry of Environment).*

NOTEWORTHY RECORDS

Spring: Coastal - Victoria 20 Apr 1975-1; Roberts Bank 17 to 22 Mar 1981-1 on jetty; Delta 22 Mar 1981-1 (RBCM Photo 692); Iona Island 25 Mar 1972-1; Sea Island 10 Mar 1973-1; Comox 23 Mar 1927-1 (Pearse 1931). **Interior** - Osoyoos 15 Mar 1986-1 male; Wycliffe 15 Apr 1984-1; Okanagan Landing 8 Mar 1963-1; Penticton 1 Apr 1986-1 hit store sign and died, 28 Apr 1970-2, first record for several years (Rogers, T.H. 1970c), Douglas Lake (Quilchena) 22 Mar 1982-1 (Campbell 1982b).

Summer: Coastal - Boundary Bay 7 Jun 1984-1; Vancouver 30 Aug 1979-1 on university golf course. **Interior** - Douglas Lake (Quilchena) 13 Jun 1969-1; Swan Lake (Vernon) 21 Jul 1976-1.

Autumn: Interior - s Williams Lake 22 Oct 1984-1; Beaver Lake (48 km ne Williams Lake) 11 Sep 1948-1 (Jobin 1952c; NMC 47862); Alkali Lake (Cariboo) 20 Nov 1943-1 (NMC 47863); Knutsford 7 Nov 1986-1; Ashcroft 2 Sept 1984-1; Vernon 24 and 26 Oct 1987-1; Minnie Lake 30 Nov 1983-1; Ta Ta Creek 26 Oct 1943-1 (Munro , J.A. and Cowan 1947) and 30 Oct 1939-1; West Bench 19 Sep 1970-4 immatures; Richter Pass 15 Sep 1947-1 (Campbell and Meugens 1971). **Coastal** - Comox Nov 1939-1; Matsqui 14 Nov 1944-1 male (AUMU 0.38112); Sea Island 23 Oct 1964-1 adult banded; Ladner 19 Oct 1952-1 male (UBC 2687); Canoe Passage (Ladner) 6 Nov 1966-1; Crescent Beach (Boundary Bay) 1 Oct 1948-1; Boundary Bay 12 Nov 1962 to 3 Mar 1963-1 (Boggs and Boggs 1963a); Roberts Bank 22 Nov 1980-1 (RBCM Photo 669); Snake Island Nov 1943-1 (Munro, J.A. and Cowan 1947); Oak Bay 13 Sep 1949-1 found dead on golf course, 16 Nov 1949-1 on golf course; Race Rocks 14 Oct 1976-1.

Winter: Interior - Kamloops 1 Dec 1987-1; Swan Lake (Vernon) 15 Dec 1963-1; east Kootenay 16 Jan 1940-1 (RBCM 11203). **Coastal** - Comox 11 Dec 1936-1 male (MVZ 82185), winter 1953-1 (Flahaut 1953b) Dec 1963-1 (Stirling 1972b); Iona Island 6 Dec 1971 to 28 Mar 1972-1 (RBCM Photo 189), 7 Dec 1972 to 1 Apr 1973-1 (RBCM Photo 246; Fig. 264); Boundary Bay 12 Dec 1984 to 14 Jan 1985-1 at airport, Beach Grove 2 Nov 1987-1, 22 to 25 Dec 1987-1; Oak Bay 12 Jan 1949-1; Victoria 13 Sep 1949-1 (RBCM 9887); Trial Islands 8 Jan 1927-1 female (ROM 83064).

Christmas Counts: Interior - Not recorded. **Coastal** - Recorded once: Comox 28 Dec 1963-1, all-time Canadian high count (Anderson, R.R. 1976).

Spotted Owl

SPOW

Strix occidentalis (Xántus de Vesey)

RANGE: Resident along the Pacific coast from extreme southwestern British Columbia to southern California; and in the mountains of southern Colorado and southern Utah south through eastern Arizona, New Mexico and extreme western Texas south to central Mexico.

STATUS: *Rare*, local resident on the extreme south mainland coast. Breeds.

NONBREEDING: The Spotted Owl is known to occur from the vicinity of Lillooet Lake south to Vancouver and east to Spuzzum and Manning Park. It is a non-migratory, secretive, nocturnal species that inhabits dense, coniferous, old-growth forests (over 200 years old) in mountainous areas. Preferred habitat in British Columbia is Douglas-fir or Douglas-fir - western hemlock forests with variable amounts of western redcedar and amabilis fir. A few observations were from young forests (about 80 years old) but some old-growth trees were present in those stands as well. It has been recorded from 245 to 1,190 m elevation.

J.A. Munro and Cowan (1947) list 6 records for the province and consider the Spotted Owl "an uncommon resident in coniferous forests in the southern part of the Coast Forest Biotic Area." The status today has not changed appreciably, except that total numbers have probably decreased somewhat due to loss of habitat, primarily from logging.

In a 1983 status report, E.C. Campbell and Campbell (1984) indicate a growing concern for the species because of the lack of records since the mid-1970s. As a result, surveys were undertaken in 1985, 1986, and 1987 to determine the status of the Spotted Owl in British Columbia (Forsman and Dunbar 1985; Forsman and Booth 1986; Hetherington et al. 1987). Spotted Owls were located at 6 sites in southwestern British Columbia in 1985, 3 additional sites in 1986, and in 1987, 2 singles and 3 pairs of previously unknown birds were found. The number of Spotted Owl responses to taped calls per km of survey transect was, however, very low: 0.03 in 1985 and 0.018 in 1986 Forsman et al. (1977). Of immediate concern is the possible displacement of the Spotted Owl by an invading and expanding population of Barred Owls (q.v.).

BREEDING: The Spotted Owl probably breeds throughout its range in the province, but nesting has been confirmed only in the vicinity of Garibaldi and Manning parks. There are 3 records with convincing details:

On 28 July 1962, 2 recently fledged young were found with adults in Manning Park (Smith, C.C. 1963). The young "... were able to fly but were a little awkward in regaining a perch. They had downy feathers on their heads and breasts . . ." The habitat was mixed coniferous forest composed of mature western hemlock, western redcedar, Douglas-fir, Engelmann spruce, and grand fir, with little underbrush.

The second nest was discovered when loggers felled a "very high" western redcedar 24 km west of Alta Lake on 29 May 1963. The nest cavity contained 3 young estimated to be 4 to 5 weeks old (A. Best pers. comm.).

On 6 June 1986, a third nest was located near Lillooet Lake. A female was seen carrying a mouse into the nest cavity. On 4 July, a fledged owlet and an adult female were present.

Another pair may have nested in the vicinity of Huntingdon, but the evidence is circumstantial. Laing (1942) only mentions that the collected the male "of a nesting pair."

Details used to prepare the bar graph for breeding chronology on the accompanying map were obtained from Forsman et al. (1984) and may not strictly apply to British Columbia.

REMARKS: Two published records, both for the northeastern vicinity of the Strait of Georgia, are not convincing and have been excluded. Laing (1942) reports that "weird calls of this owl were heard several times" at Horseshoe Lake, 13 km north of the Stillwater region in July 1936. In the same summer, he reports that an owl "called every evening from the mountain side above Kenzie Lake" (Leask Lake).

The Spotted Owl has become a species of concern throughout its range in the Pacific Northwest and in California (see select papers in Gutierrez and Carey 1985; Dixon and Juelson 1987; Simberloff 1987; Salwasser 1987). It also appears on the "Blue List" from 1980 to 1986 (Tate 1986). Most biologists agree that the Spotted Owl is dependent on old-growth forests for the maintenance of healthy populations. On average, between 800 and 1,000 ha of old-growth forest are required by a pair of Spotted Owls (Carey 1985).

The British Columbia population should not be considered in isolation; wildlife managers should continue to work with wildlife agencies in the United States as well as provincial forest and land managers to establish Spotted Owl Habitat Areas in British Columbia. Management of old-growth forests in the Pacific Northwest of the United States has evolved from rapid conversion of the stands through logging to the grudging acceptance of the need to retain the special habitat for species such as the Spotted Owl (Lee 1985). This must also happen in British Columbia if the Spotted Owl is to remain a part of the avifauna of Canada.

During the 1970s, the Spotted Owl became the most intensively studied owl in North America. Those interested in the basic biology and methods of field study of the Spotted Owl should consult Forsman (1983) and Forsman et al. (1984). In addition, a bibliography of North American literature has been compiled by Campbell et al. (1984).

NOTEWORTHY RECORDS

Spring: Coastal - 8.7 km west Allison Pass 15 Apr 1985-2 males, 16 May 1962-1 (Smith, C.C. 1963), 18 May 1986-1 male; Skagit River 18 Apr 1985-1 male; McNaught Creek 11 May 1986-1 male, 13 May 1986-1 male; Huntingdon 31 May 1927-1 male (NMC 22470); Chehalis Lake 8 Apr 1985-1 male; Hope 17 May 1986-1, road kill; Lillooet Lake 2 Apr 1985-1 female, 14 Apr 1985-1 pair. **Interior** - No records.

Summer: Coastal - Manning Park 7 Jun 1962-1 and 29 Jul 1962-2 (Smith, C.C. 1963), 16 Jul 1967-1; McNaught Creek 20 Jun 1922-1 (NMC 18357; Thacker and Thacker 1923); Klesilkwa River 24 Jun 1916-1 male (NMC 11594; Munro, J.A. 1918); Nepopekum Creek 13 Aug 1986-1 male; Hope 20 Jun 1940-1 male (UBC 5618); West Vancouver Jul

1925-1 (Cumming 1932); Spuzzum 7 Aug 1940-1 female (MVZ 82187); Alpha Lake (near Garibaldi Park) 17 Jul 1946-1 (Racey 1948); Alta Lake summer 1943-1 (Racey 1944). **Interior** - No records.

Autumn: Interior - No records. **Coastal** - Squamish Sep or Oct 1978-1 female (MC A-470); Yale 25 Nov 1986-1 found dead near train tracks; 39 km e Hope 9 Nov 1947-1 female (ROM 81750); Hope Oct 1947-1 found dead, 5 Nov 1929-1 (MVZ 101801), 25 Nov 1919-1 Male (AMNH 754216); West Vancouver 14 Nov 1946-1 collected; Capilano River watershed (North Vancouver) 3 and 5 Sep 1986-1 female; Seymour River watershed (North Vancouver) 16 Oct 1986-1 pair; Greendrop Lake 17 Oct 1987-2; Vancouver Sep

1947-1 found sitting on the road at corner of Granville and Hastings Streets with a Rock Dove in its talons ... later photographed (RBCM Photo 259) and released in Stanley Park; Vedder Crossing Oct 1939-1 female (RBCM 8841); Manning Park 2 Sep 1948-1 (Edwards 1949).

Winter: Interior - No records. **Coastal** - Cheakamus River 12 Dec 1943-1 female (UBC 5617; Racey 1944) - remains of Gray Jay in its stomach; Hope 13 Feb 1939-1 male (NMC 28964); Chilliwack 26 Jan 1909-1 female (MVZ 101802; Brooks 1909b); Skagit valley 4 Dec 1933-1 (NMC 25713).

Christmas Counts: Not recorded.

Spotted Owl

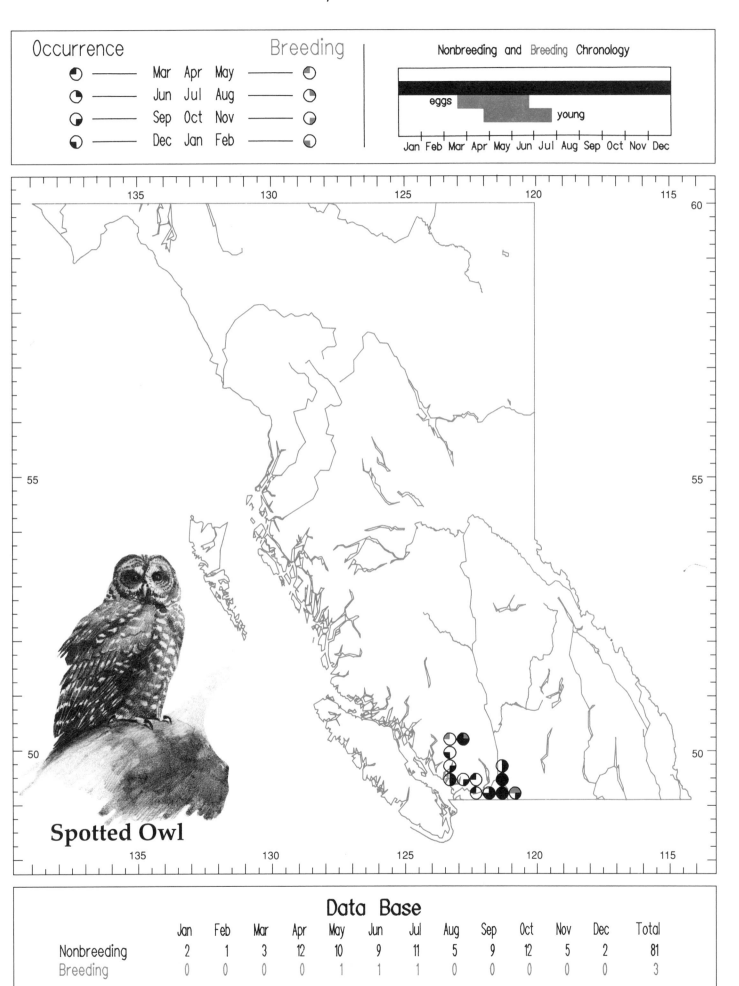

Occurrence Breeding

◗ ——	Mar Apr May	—— ◐
◔ ——	Jun Jul Aug	—— ◔
◕ ——	Sep Oct Nov	—— ◔
◑ ——	Dec Jan Feb	—— ◓

Nonbreeding and Breeding Chronology

eggs

young

Jan Feb Mar Apr May Jun Jul Aug Sep Oct Nov Dec

Spotted Owl

Data Base

	Jan	Feb	Mar	Apr	May	Jun	Jul	Aug	Sep	Oct	Nov	Dec	Total
Nonbreeding	2	1	3	12	10	9	11	5	9	12	5	2	81
Breeding	0	0	0	0	1	1	1	0	0	0	0	0	3

Barred Owl

BAOW

Strix varia Barton

RANGE: Resident from British Columbia across central Canada to New Brunswick and Nova Scotia, southward throughout the eastern United States to Florida and Texas and recently in the western United States from Washington to northern California. Also occurs in Mexico, western Guatemala, and Honduras.

STATUS: *Rare* to *uncommon* resident on southeastern Vancouver Island, the Gulf Islands, the adjacent mainland coast including the Fraser lowlands and the interior south of Prince George. Elsewhere, *rare* to *uncommon*. Widespread breeder.

CHANGE IN STATUS: The Barred Owl was just beginning to expand its range into British Columbia about the time of J.A. Munro and Cowan (1947). They considered it a "rare inhabitant of the Boreal Forest Biotic Area" on the basis of 2 records: Rand (1944) collected a specimen at Liard Crossing (= Liard River) in August 1943, and in April 1946 a nest containing 2 young was discovered at Hazeltine Creek in the southern Nechako Lowlands.

During the 39 years since its arrival, the Barred Owl has slowly extended its range southward and westward and has become established in the central and southeastern portions of the province as well as on the coast. Their southward movement through the boreal forests is summarized by J. Grant (1966b).

The Barred Owl was first observed on the coast at Surrey on 11 October 1966; 3 years later, on 26 November 1969, it was reported at Victoria (Stirling 1970). The coastal invasion has been impressive, as records for the following periods indicate: 1966-70 - 3 records, 1971-75 - 25 records (see Campbell 1973b), 1976-80 - 47 records and 1981-85 - 118 records. The first coastal breeding record was from Cortes Island in July 1975. In 1986 it was found breeding in the Fraser Lowlands near Langley (Ryder 1986).

The Barred Owl has continued its range expansion southward along the Pacific coast of the United States (Taylor, A.L. and Forsman 1976).

NONBREEDING: The Barred Owl is widely distributed in eastern and southern British Columbia. There is only one record for the northwestern portion of the province. It is primarily a bird of deep forests, preferring mixed coniferous woodlands (spruces, subalpine fir, western hemlock, lodgepole pine, western redcedar), but is also found in mixed coniferous and deciduous woodlands and, less frequently, in pure deciduous stands (e.g. alders, black cottonwood, maples). In the vicinity of farmlands, cities, and residential areas, it has been seen in riparian thickets, on railroad bridges, house awnings, ornamental trees, fence rows, television aerials, apartment balconies, and trees in parks, school yards, cemeteries, and along busy streets. It has been reported from sea level to 1,250 m elevation.

In northern areas, it is suspected that many Barred Owls move southward during the late autumn and winter, while in southern areas, it is essentially a sedentary species. There are no reports of communal roosting, and nearly 85% of all records are of single birds.

BREEDING: The Barred Owl breeds on the coast from southern Vancouver Island east to Langley and Manning Park and north to Prince Rupert and Terrace. In the interior, it breeds in the southeast from Rock Creek (Kettle River) north to McBride, and generally eastward to the Alberta boundary.

It inhabits coniferous forests (e.g. Douglas-fir - lodgepole pine, Douglas-fir - western redcedar, and spruce - lodgepole pine) and coniferous-deciduous woodlands (e.g. western redcedar, Douglas-fir, western hemlock, and black cottonwood), usually near water, including lake shores, swamps, creek valleys, and river bottomlands.

Nests and recently fledged young have been recorded from 90 to 1,100 m elevation.

Nests: Only 8 nests have been found, all in trees. Four were positioned in the hollowed-out tops of the dead portions of Douglas-firs; the others were in natural cavities in living and dead black cottonwoods. Nest heights ranged from 6 to 30 m. No materials were added to the nests, although wood chips, probably from the nest stump, lined one nest.

Eggs: The only record is a nest with 2 eggs found on 24 April 1946 (Munro, J.A. and Cowan 1947). Calculated dates from estimated ages of broods indicate that eggs could be found from late March through mid-May. Clutch sizes of at least 3 or 4 are likely (see brood sizes below). Incubation period is between 21 and 28 days (Bent 1938).

Young: Dates for 40 broods ranged from late April (exact date not reported) through 19 August, with 55% recorded between 25 May and 26 June. Broods size ranged from 1 to 4 young (1Y-10, 2Y-20, 3Y-6, 4Y-4), with 50% having 2 young. Fledging period is about 42 days (Bent 1938).

REMARKS: The recent southward expansion of the Barred Owl has created a range overlap with the Spotted Owl. A.L. Taylor and Forsman (1976) express concern: "It seems doubtful that two species so similar in general food habits and habitat requirements could coexist in the same areas for long, but this relationship remains to be investigated." See R.J. Clark et al. (1978) for recent literature on the Barred Owl in North America.

NOTEWORTHY RECORDS

Spring: Coastal - Sooke 12 May 1984-2; Lake Cowichan 26 Mar to 4 Apr 1982-3; Skagit valley 4 Apr 1985-2 males; Skagit River 28 Mar 1981-2; Nanaimo 15 Apr 1982-2; University Hill 21 Mar 1986-2; Vancouver 12 Apr 1986-2; Swordgrass Lake 19 to 21 May 1978-1. **Interior** - Cherryville 1 to 30 Apr 1968-2 (Rogers, T.H. 1968a); Hidden Lake (w Enderby) 26 May 1964-3 (Grant, J. 1966b); Tranquille River 20 Mar 1982-3; Kootenay National Park 19 May 1983-1; Wells Gray Park 21 May 1958-2 (Edwards and Ritcey 1967); Taylor 25 Mar 1985-1, 10 May 1983-2; Fort Nelson 14 May 1986-1.

Summer: Coastal - Saanich 5 Jul 1984-3; Surrey 19 Jun 1976-1; Vancouver 28 Aug 1982-1; Mount Seymour (North Vancouver) early Jun 1978-1; Cortes Island 27 Jul 1975-1 (RBCM Photo 444); Lakelse Lake 16 Jul 1977-2 (Shepard, T. 1977). **Interior** - Manning Park 21 Jul 1971-1 (RBCM Photo 432); Kilpoola Lake 18 Jun 1977-1; Salmo 25 Jul 1971-1 found dead; Fauquier 29 Jun 1959-1 (Grant, J. 1966b); Kootenay National Park 27 Aug 1976-2; Riske Creek 11 Jun 1978-2; Mackenzie 11 Jun 1979-1 male (RBCM 17323); Kledo Creek Park 25 Jun 1974-1 (Erskine and Davidson 1976); Liard Hot Springs 12 Aug 1943-1 male (NMC 29473).

Autumn: Interior - Prince George 5 Oct 1951-1 female (NMC 47865); Likely 2 Oct 1949-1 female (NMC 47864); Hemp Creek 18 Nov 1955-2 (Edwards and Ritcey 1967); Nakusp 18 Nov 1977-1; Creston 14 Sep 1982-3 (Rogers, T.H. 1983a). **Coastal** - Terrace 28 Oct 1974-1; Sointula 8 Oct 1981-1; Quadra Island Oct 1979-1 female (RBCM 16489); Courtenay Nov to 10 May 1986-1; Vancouver 13 Nov 1972-1 (RBCM Photo 226); Skagit valley 27 Oct 1979-3; Sooke 5 Nov 1980-1 (RBCM Photo 702).

Winter: Interior - Fort St. John Feb 1981-1 caught in trap; Nechako River (Prince George) 5 Jan 1986-1; Tranquille River 24 Feb 1980-2; Vernon 1 Feb 1980-4; Cherryville late Feb to early Mar 1968-2; Summerland 13 Jan 1972-1 (RBCM Photo 315). **Coastal** - Terrace 18 Feb 1978-1 caught in trap; Sointula 15 Dec 1981-1; Cortes Island 6 and 8 Feb 1975-2; Cranberry Lake 27 Jan 1986-1 (RBCM Photo 1099); Lake Cowichan 14 Feb 1986-2; Saanich 25 Dec 1985-1.

Christmas Counts: Interior - Recorded from 3 of 19 localities and on 7% of all counts. Maxima: Shuswap Lake 3 Jan 1981-2; Vernon 19 Dec 1982-1 and 16 Dec 1984-1; Quesnel 24 Dec 1981-1. **Coastal** - Recorded from 5 of 28 localities and on 2% of all counts. Maxima: Vancouver 18 Dec 1983-2; White Rock 30 Dec 1978-1; Pender Islands 20 Dec 1983-1; Sooke 31 Dec 1983-1; Terrace 26 Dec 1983-1.

Extralimital Records: Interior - Atlin Sep 1980-1

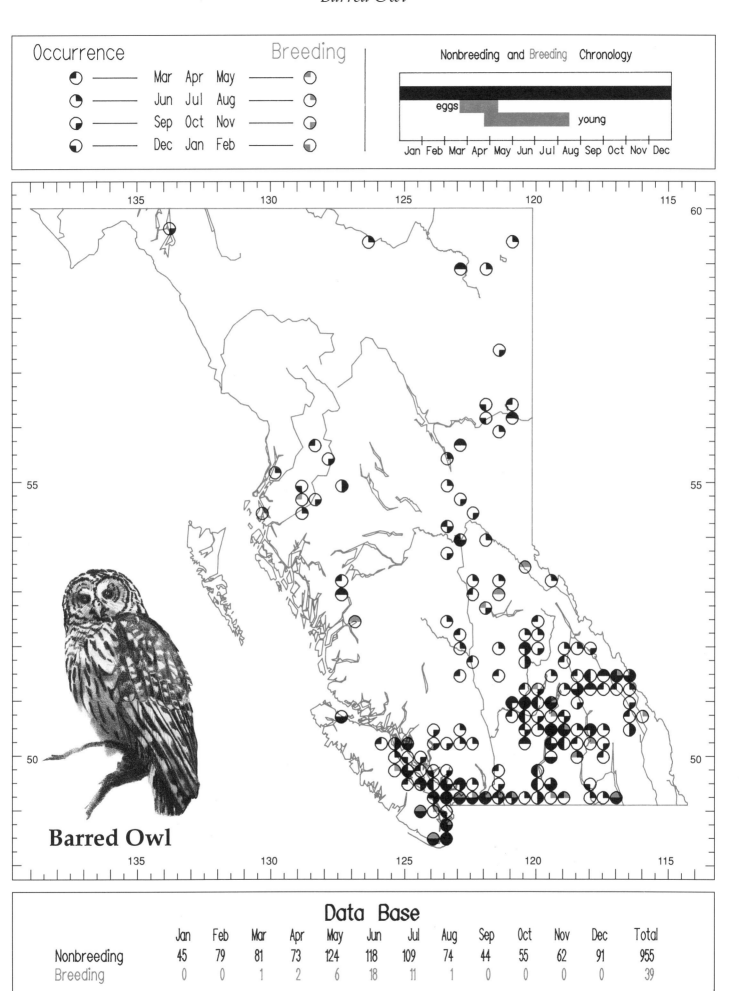

Barred Owl

Mar Apr May
Jun Jul Aug
Sep Oct Nov
Dec Jan Feb

Nonbreeding and Breeding Chronology

eggs   young

Jan Feb Mar Apr May Jun Jul Aug Sep Oct Nov Dec

Data Base

	Jan	Feb	Mar	Apr	May	Jun	Jul	Aug	Sep	Oct	Nov	Dec	Total
Nonbreeding	45	79	81	73	124	118	109	74	44	55	62	91	955
Breeding	0	0	1	2	6	18	11	1	0	0	0	0	39

Great Gray Owl

GGOW

Strix nebulosa Forster

RANGE: Breeds from near tree limit in central Alaska, the Yukon, western Mackenzie, northern Manitoba, and northern Ontario, south to central Saskatchewan, southern Manitoba, northern Minnesota, south-central Ontario, and in the western mountains to central California. Winters within breeding range and irregularly south to the northern United States. Also found in northern Eurasia.

STATUS: An *uncommon* resident in the northern interior and *rare* resident in the southern interior. *Very rare*, but irregular, winter visitant to the extreme south mainland coast; *casual* on Vancouver Island. Breeds.

NONBREEDING: The distribution of the Great Gray Owl in the province is not well known. Despite its large size, this elusive owl is appropriately referred to as "phantom of the northern forests" (Nero 1980). It is most conspicuous during the nonbreeding season when it comes out of the deep woods to perch and hunt along the edges of clearings (Fig. 268), openings, and roadways; over 75% of all records are of nonbreeding birds. The owl appears to be widely distributed in the southern interior and throughout the northeastern corner of the province, but remains extremely rare in the northwestern and coastal regions.

Although edges of pure and mixed coniferous forests ma be preferred, the owl has been found in a wide variety o habitats, including open pastures with trembling aspen grove and some residual Douglas-fir, edges of marshes bordered b open Douglas-fir and poplars, stands of lodgepole pine, area around sedge meadows in subalpine spruce and fir, and logge areas of coniferous forest. In rural areas, it perches on fenc posts, telephone poles and wires, and snags. It occurs to at leas 1,555 m elevation.

The Great Gray Owl is essentially a sedentary species although in winter, occasional irruptions occur into souther areas. Nero (1980) suggests that that behaviour may be due t "high populations of owls, scarcity of food due to low numbers o small mammals and other prey species, icy crusts, or unusuall deep snow." Some first-year birds may also wander grea distances; Nero (1969) reports that a nestling banded in May 196 near Winnipeg, Manitoba was found dead about 5 months late 753 km away in Minnesota.

Large and spectacular incursions of Great Gray Owls, which occur in northeastern North America (see Godfrey 1967; Vicker and Yunick 1979), have not been reported in British Columbia. Th most recent irruption occurred in the winter of 1984-85, when 4 t 6 birds were seen in the Fraser Lowlands and 2 birds appeared o

Figure 268. *Great Gray Owl habitat near Becher's Prairie in the Chilcotin-Cariboo region, 1 June 1973 (Neil K. Dawe).*

Great Gray Owl

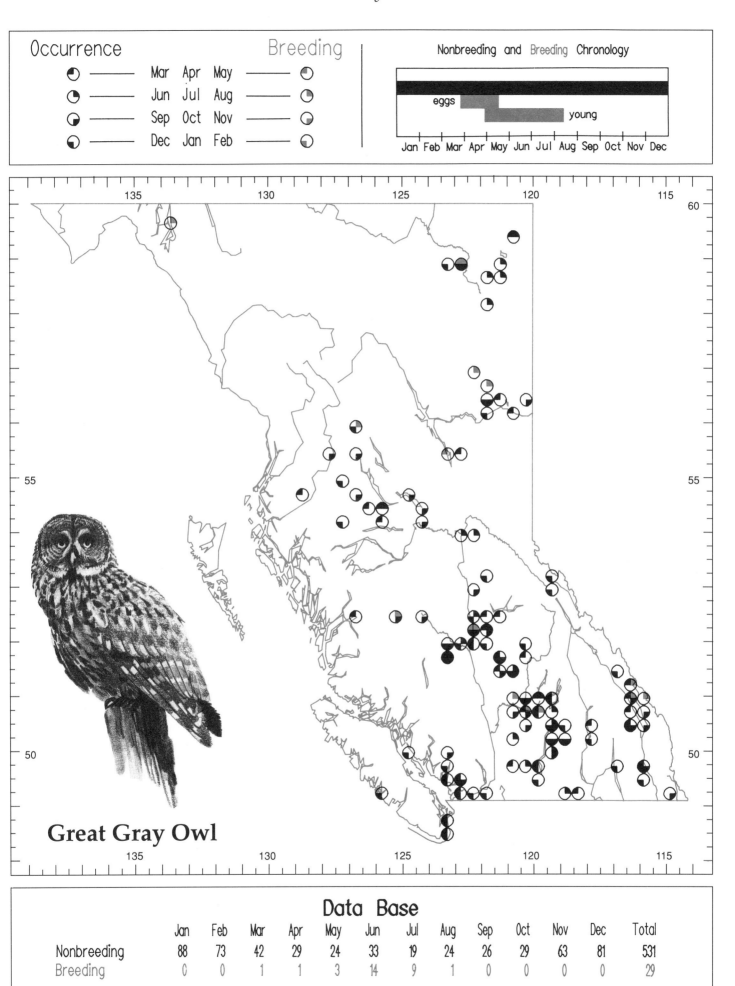

Occurrence / Breeding

◓	—	Mar Apr May	—	◓	
◔	—	Jun Jul Aug	—	◔	
◒	—	Sep Oct Nov	—	◒	
◑	—	Dec Jan Feb	—	◑	

Nonbreeding and Breeding Chronology

eggs   young

Jan Feb Mar Apr May Jun Jul Aug Sep Oct Nov Dec

Data Base

	Jan	Feb	Mar	Apr	May	Jun	Jul	Aug	Sep	Oct	Nov	Dec	Total
Nonbreeding	88	73	42	29	24	33	19	24	26	29	63	81	531
Breeding	0	0	1	1	3	14	9	1	0	0	0	0	29

southern Vancouver Island. This essentially forest-dwelling owl preferred open habitats during this irruption period.

We have 15 records (10 different years) for coastal areas from 1890 to 1985. Extreme dates for southern areas are 27 December (Coquitlam) to 17 April (Langley).

BREEDING: The Great Gray Owl breeds in the vicinity of Brisco and Kamloops in the south interior, northward and eastward to Fort Nelson in the Peace River area. It also probably nests across northern British Columbia to at least Atlin Lake. The lack of information there may be due, in part, to the bird's secretive behaviour. Nests are difficult to find. In Alberta, for example, from 1950 to 1955, Oeming (1955b) "travelled 36,000 miles over every conceivable type of terrain and using every imaginable means of navigation . . . Thousands of trappers, loggers, Indians and other woodspeople were interviewed..." and only 2 nests were discovered. In British Columbia, 1 pair nesting within a few hundred yards of an experienced observer's cabin at Nimpo Lake was not discovered until the young were near fledging.

The Great Gray Owl breeds in coniferous, deciduous, or mixed woodlands (Fig. 269), usually in the vicinity of water, including marshes, lakes, muskegs, wet meadows, and pastures. Vegetative associations included mostly Douglas-fir with patches of trembling aspen, Douglas-fir - lodgepole pine, lodgepole pine - Engelmann spruce, and pure stands of black spruce and Engelmann spruce. Nests and recently fledged young have been found from 900 to 1,220 m elevation.

Nests: Six nests have been found: 2 were in abandoned Northern Goshawk nests in trembling aspens, 2 were in witch's broom in spruce trees, 1 was in an old Red-tailed Hawk nest in a trembling aspen (Fig. 270), and 1 was in an unidentified (probably goshawk) stick nest in a spruce tree. Heights (n=6) ranged from 6 to 15 m, with 3 recorded between 7.6 and 9.1 m. Other than a few feathers, additional nest materials were not reported.

Eggs: Only 1 nest containing eggs was found: Mackenzie 13 April 1973-2 eggs. Clutches of at least 4 eggs, however, must occur (see Young below). When small mammals are plentiful, clutches in Manitoba have contained up to 9 eggs (Nero 1980). Calculated dates indicate that eggs could be found as early as late March, but most egg-laying probably occurs through April. Eggs could be found as late as mid-May. The incubation period is about 30 days, but may vary from 30 to 50 days depending on the size of the clutch and the intervals in which eggs are laid (Nero 1980).

Young: Dates for 21 broods ranged from 1 May to 11 August with 11 broods recorded between 6 June and 3 July. Calculated dates indicate that young could be found as early as the last week of April. Brood size ranged from 1 to 4 young (1Y-2, 2Y-8, 3Y-8, 4Y-3) with 16 broods having 2 or 3 young (Fig. 271). Young begin to leave the nest at 21 to 28 days but do not fly well until 35 days (Nero 1980).

REMARKS: Nero (1980) estimates the North American population of the Great Gray Owl to be "upward of fifty thousand" birds. Oeming (1955a), Pulliainen and Loisa (1977), and Nero (1980) provide additional life history information on this spectacular but little-known species.

Figure 269. Great Gray Owl nesting habitat, 32 km west of Williams Lake, June 1982 (Ervio Sian). Note the nest in the top centre of the figure.

Figure 270. Adult Great Gray Owl with young in what was once a Red-tailed Hawk's nest, 32 km west of Williams Lake, June 1982 (Ervio Sian).

Figure 271. *Nestling Great Gray Owls, 32 km west of Williams Lake, 16 May 1983 (Ervio Sian).*

NOTEWORTHY RECORDS

Spring: Coastal - Langley 17 Apr 1984-1; University Hill 14 Apr 1985-1; Bella Coola 31 Mar 1978-1; Terrace 14 May 1982-1. **Interior** - Midway 30 May 1972-2; Summerland 11 Mar 1974-1 (RBCM Photo 492); Kimberley 6 Apr 1982-1; Invermere 4 Mar 1983-2 (Rogers, T.H. 1983c); 70 Mile House 14 May 1978-1; Williams Lake 23 Mar 1977-2; Fort Nelson 1 Apr 1986-2.

Summer: Coastal - No records. **Interior** - Osprey Lake (Princeton) Aug 1976-2; Merritt 20 Jul 1974-1 (RBCM Photo 421); Hullcar Aug 1946-1 shot (possibly 2 others in vicinity-Grant, J. 1959); Warren Lake 10 Aug 1983-1; Kootenay National Park 11 Aug 1981-1 dead on road; Bald Mountain (Riske Creek) 1 Aug 1981-1; Prince George 10 Jun 1970-2 (Rogers, T.H. 1970d); Nilkitkwa Lake 24 Aug 1975-2.

Autumn: Interior - Nimpo Lake 30 Nov 1977-1; near Greenstone Mountain 4 Oct 1981-2; Blackwell Lake Nov 1980-5; Harris Plateau (Okanagan) 16 Oct 1931-1 female (MVZ 101813); Okanagan Mission 4 Nov 1981-1 (RBCM Photo 741; Campbell 1982a); Cranbrook 18 Nov 1935-1 (Munro, J.A. and Cowan 1947). **Coastal** - No records.

Winter: Interior - Valemount 18 Jan 1977-1 (RBCM 15455); Williams Lake winter 1950/51-3+ (Erskine and Stein 1964); Riske Creek 27 Jan 1982-14 counted in 1 km of road to west, 20 to 30 estimated along road from Bella Coola, 29 Jan 1982-only 6 to 7 along road from Bella Coola to Riske Creek; Buffalo Lake Jan 1977-3; Pritchard 27 Feb 1983-3; White Lake (Okanagan Falls) 18 Feb 1987-1; Moyie 24 Feb 1939-1 (Johnstone, W.B. 1949). **Coastal** - Powell River 8 Feb 1981-1; Jericho Beach 1 Jan 1985-1 (RBCM Photo 992); University Hill 24 Jan to 14 Apr 1985-1; Mount Burnaby 19 Jan to 16 Mar 1985-1 (RBCM Photo 998; UBC 14529); Coquitlam 27 and 28 Dec 1980-1; Pitt Meadows 13 Jan 1985-1 found dead; Maple Ridge 14 to 25 Feb 1974-1 (RBCM Photo 342); Surrey 3 Feb 1962-1; Crescent Beach (Boundary Bay) 23 Jan 1962-1 (RBCM 10797); Chilliwack 7 Dec 1984-1, 14 Jan 1985-1, both road kills; Sumas Jan 1880-1 (Brooks 1917); Aldergrove 26 Jan 1975-1; Pacific Rim National Park Jan to 28 Feb 1985-1; Victoria 12 Feb to 9 Mar 1985-1.

Christmas Counts: Interior - Recorded from 4 of 19 localities and on 4% of all counts. Maxima: Windermere Lake 30 Dec 1984-1; Kamloops 15 Dec 1984-1; Shuswap Lake 3 Jan 1981-1; Smithers 30 Dec 1984-1. **Coastal** - Recorded once: Pitt Meadows 27 Dec 1980-1.

Long-eared Owl

LEOW

Asio otus (Linnaeus)

RANGE: Holarctic. In North America, breeds from central British Columbia, southern Mackenzie, Ontario, and Quebec to California, Texas, Arkansas, and Virginia to northwestern Mexico. Winters from southern Canada south to northern Baja California, Mexico, southern Texas, the Gulf coast and Georgia.

STATUS: *Uncommon* resident, locally in the Thompson-Okanagan Plateau. *Rare* to *very rare* north to Prince George; *very rare* in the east and west Kootenays. *Rare* resident on the extreme south mainland coast, *very rare* along the east coast of Vancouver Island. *Casual* on the northern mainland coast, *accidental* on the Queen Charlotte Islands. Breeds.

NONBREEDING: The Long-eared Owl occurs chiefly throughout the southern third of the province, with its centre of abundance in the Thompson-Okanagan Plateau region. It uses deciduous woodlands, often in mixed and riparian situations adjacent to open country including aspen groves, cottonwood stands, and birch tangles along rivers and creeks, tall willow-thickets bordering marshes, sloughs, and damp meadows, deciduous thickets on islands in lakes, shrub-choked ravines, dry orchards, and hawthorn thickets on dry hillsides. On the coast, favourite sites, including roosts, are single or small clumps of conifers such as western redcedar, western hemlock, and Douglas-fir, but red alders bordering sloughs, walnut groves, black cottonwood - Garry oak groves near creeks, and holly farms are also frequented. The Long-eared Owl occurs mostly below 30 m elevation on the coast and below 915 m in the interior, although Edwards (1949) found 2 birds roosting in a dense clump of subalpine fir in mid-August at 2,135 m in Manning Park.

Large roosting aggregations, often found at other localities in North America, have not been reported in British Columbia. The largest communal roost reported was 6 birds, found in early March in the Okanagan (Cannings, R.A. et al. 1987).

Movements of the Long-eared Owl in the province are unknown. Birds in the northern interior are likely migratory, while those in the extreme south-central interior may be only partially migratory. Seasonal dispersal between habitats may also occur.

BREEDING: The Long-eared Owl breeds in the interior from the Okanagan and Nicola valleys, the Douglas Plateau, and the South Thompson River valley, north to Chilako River and Nulki Lake. The centre of abundance is the Okanagan valley. Small numbers breed infrequently, most recently in 1981, on the extreme south mainland coast: Westham Island, Iona and Sea islands, and Pitt Meadows.

The Long-eared Owl breeds most often in deciduous thickets composed of pure and mixed stands of western birch, willows, trembling aspen, hawthorn, black cottonwood, and occasionally wild cherry and red alder, usually near water. Specific habitats include river bottoms, shores of lakes and ponds, banks of creeks, wet and dry gullies, wet and damp meadows and marshes, and occasionally, dry hillsides. It nests less often in open, deciduous and coniferous stands. Nests have been found from near sea level to 1,020 m elevation.

Nests: Most nests (92%; n=61) were situated in stands of dense deciduous shrubs and trees including western birch (43%), willows (33%), hawthorn, black cottonwood, trembling aspen, red alder, and wild cherry. Coniferous trees (5 nests) included ponderosa pine, Douglas-fir, and spruce. Seventy-five nests were found in the used nests of other species, including American Crow *Corvus brachyrhynchos* (92%), Black-billed Magpie *Pica pica* (4%), and Northwestern Crow *C. caurinus* (4%). Heights of 70 tree nests ranged from 1.4 to 13.7 m, with 50% recorded between 3.6 and 7.6 m. One nest was on the ground.

Eggs: Dates for 66 clutches ranged from 16 March to 11 June, with 50% recorded between 3 and 23 April. Calculated dates indicate that eggs could be found as early as 10 March. Sizes for 68 clutches ranged from 1 to 6 eggs (1E-1, 2E-3, 3E-3, 4E-17, 5E-30, 6E-14), with 90% having 4 to 6 eggs. Incubation period is 25 to 30 days (Harrison, C. 1978).

Young: Dates for 73 broods ranged from 11 April to 2 July, with 52% recorded between 2 and 30 May. After late June, it is unusual to find young in nests; some of these may represent re-nestings. The latest date for recently fledged young was 2 August. Sizes for 69 broods ranged from 1 to 6 young (1Y-5, 2Y-14, 3Y-17, 4Y-13, 5Y-19, 6Y-1), with 71% having 3 to 5 young. Fledging period is 23 to 24 days (Harrison, C. 1978).

REMARKS: T.D. Hooper and Nyhof (1986) studied the food habits of the Long-eared Owl in the southern Okanagan valley from 1981 to 1984. Small mammals comprised 97.0% of all prey and 98.2% of the total biomass. *Microtus* species contributed 51.8% to the total diet and 49.5% to the total biomass. *M. pennsylvanicus* was the most important component in the diet. In total, 10 species of mammals and 5 species of birds were identified.

NOTEWORTHY RECORDS

Spring: Coastal - Victoria 19 Mar 1971-1 (RBCM Photo 164); Mandarte Island 4 Apr 1982-1; Sumas 24 May 1896-1 male (MCZ 247126); Delta 9 May 1985-1; Sea Island 15 Mar 1981-4; Merville 11 May 1934-1 pair (CMNH 115251-52). **Interior** - Creston 28 Mar 1962-2; Penticton 10 Mar 1977-6; Sparwood 2 May 1984-1 (RBCM Photo 1010); Enterprise Mar 1958-1 dead on road (Erskine and Stein 1964); Kleena Kleene 18 May 1961-1 (Paul 1964); Telkwa 19 May 1977-1 dead on road.

Summer: Coastal - Saanich, summer 1957-1 (Clay 1957b); Ladner 3 June 1965-1 (RBCM Photo 42); Comox 26 Aug 1933-1 male (RBCM 13002), 22 Aug 1934-1 male (RBCM 13005); Oyster River 28 Aug 1933-3 (Laing 1935). **Interior** - Manning Park, mid-Aug 1949-2 (Edwards 1949); Castlegar 18 Jul 1968-1; Elko 20 Jun 1953-1 female (NMC 38618); White Lake (Okanagan Falls) 2 Jun 1972-4; Sparwood 29 Jul 1983-2 immatures; Mount Revelstoke National Park 8 Aug 1977-1 dead on road (Woods 1979); Alkali Lake 10 Jul 1978-1, 29 Jul 1956-5 (Erskine and Stein 1964); Moose Lake (Mount Robson Park) 12 Jul 1973-1 dead on road (Cannings, S.G. 1973); Vanderhoof 11 Jul 1948-1 (Munro, J.A. 1955a); Charlie Lake 8 Jun 1985-1 (Campbell 1985d), 3 Jul 1974-2.

Autumn: Interior - Williams Lake 13 Nov 1984-1; Kleena Kleene 14 Sep 1961-1 (Paul 1964); Little Yoho valley 12 Sep 1979-1; Kamloops 21 Oct 1961-2; North Bend 12 Nov 1985-1 hit by train; Sparwood 24 Oct 1983-1; Castlegar 9 Sep 1969-3, 24 Nov 1969-1 dead on road; Vaseux Lake 6 Oct 1963-2. **Coastal** - Hardy Bay 27 Oct 1934-1 female (MVZ 101819); Stanley Park (Vancouver) 5 Nov 1984-1; Langley 5 Nov 1978-2; Chilliwack 4 Oct 1890-1 female (MCZ 244716); Saanich 31 Oct 1978-1, 18 Nov 1983-1; Victoria 5 Nov 1973-1.

Winter: Interior - e Houston 22 Jan 1987-1 found dead; Bowron Lake 1931/32-1 (MCZ 282548); Meldrum Creek 4 Dec 1976-1 dead on road; Walhachin 17 Feb 1982-2 dead on road; Cherry Creek (Kamloops) 23 Jan 1982-2; Pemberton 7 Dec 1936-1 male (UBC 5639); Swan Lake (Vernon) 24 Jan 1965-4; Penticton 20 Dec 1978-1, 2 Jan 1965-1; Castlegar 1 Feb 1970-1; Osoyoos 1 Dec 1970-1 killed by dog. **Coastal** - Comox Dec 1927-1 male (MVZ 101818), 6 Jan 1943-1 male (RBCM 13004); Sea Island 26 Feb 1978-5; Pitt Meadows 20 Jan 1985-1; Westham Island, winter 1970/71-5; Cowichan Bay 25 Jan 1981-1 (RBCM Photo 647); Swan Lake (Saanich) 31 Dec 1980-1; Victoria 9 Dec 1899-1 (Godfrey 1947).

Christmas Counts: Interior - Recorded from 4 of 19 localities and on 10% of all counts. Maxima: Penticton 26 Dec 1978-4; Vernon 26 Dec 1978-1; Vaseux Lake 23 Dec 1984-1; Oliver/Osoyoos 1 on 28 Dec 1981, 29 Dec 1983 and 26 Dec 1984. **Coastal** - Recorded from 5 of 28 localities and on 1% of all counts. Maxima: Ladner 26 Dec 1970-4; Vancouver 20 Dec 1981-3; Pitt Meadows 29 Dec 1973-2; Terrace 2 Jan 1966-2.

Extralimital Records: Coastal - Skidegate 29 Nov 1983-1 (QCIM 161; Sealy and Gessler 1988).

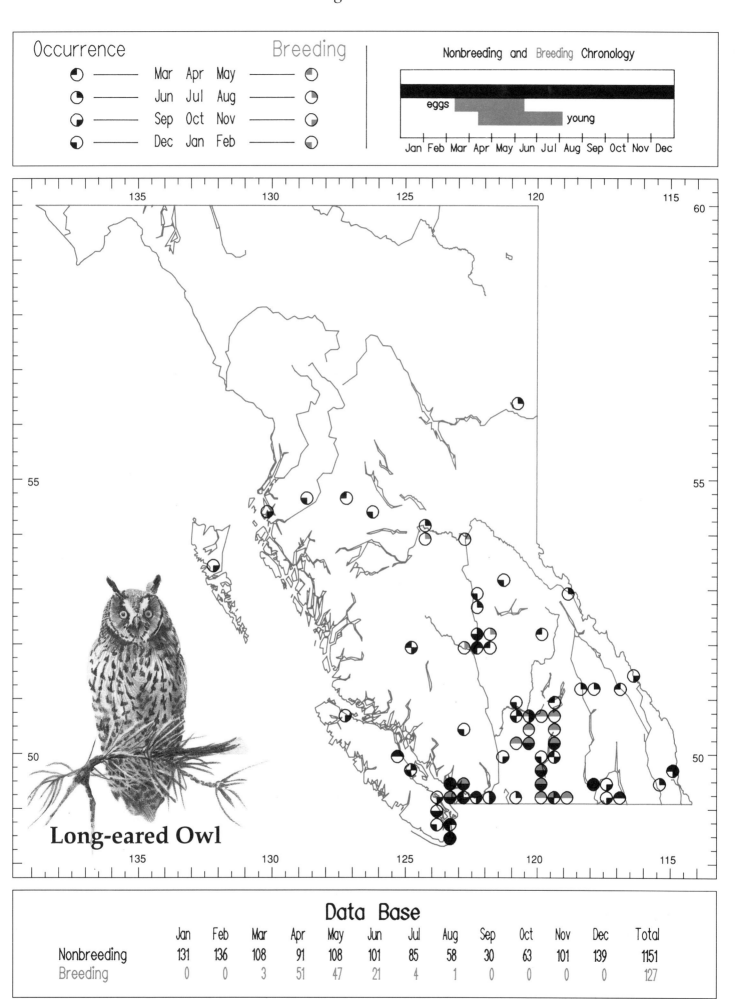

Long-eared Owl

Occurrence

◐ ———	Mar Apr May	——— ◐
◔ ———	Jun Jul Aug	——— ◔
◕ ———	Sep Oct Nov	——— ◕
◓ ———	Dec Jan Feb	——— ◓

Breeding

Nonbreeding and Breeding Chronology

eggs

young

Jan Feb Mar Apr May Jun Jul Aug Sep Oct Nov Dec

Data Base

	Jan	Feb	Mar	Apr	May	Jun	Jul	Aug	Sep	Oct	Nov	Dec	Total
Nonbreeding	131	136	108	91	108	101	85	58	30	63	101	139	1151
Breeding	0	0	3	51	47	21	4	1	0	0	0	0	127

Short-eared Owl
Asio flammeus (Pontoppidan)

SEOW

RANGE: Nearly cosmopolitan. In North America, breeds from Alaska across southern arctic Canada to northern Quebec and Newfoundland south locally to central California, Utah, Kansas, Ohio, and New Jersey. Winters from southern Canada south to California, Texas, and Florida.

STATUS: *Uncommon* spring and autumn migrant throughout the province. *Uncommon* resident on the extreme southwest coast, *rare* resident in the Okanagan valley and *very rare* resident in the Peace Lowlands. *Casual* in winter in the north. Local breeder on the extreme south mainland coast and in the south and central interior.

NONBREEDING: The Short-eared Owl (Fig. 272) is a diurnal, sometimes gregarious species, that occurs in a wide variety of open-country habitats throughout the province, including marshes, swamps, sloughs, estuaries, lakeshores, spits, marine foreshores, beaches, and lagoons, as well as sedge-cranberry fields, sedge-hardhack associations, grasslands, rangelands, and grassy fields (Fig. 273). In addition, it is frequently found in man-made habitats such as airports, golf courses, dykes, and agricultural fields. It has been recorded from sea level to the timberline at 2,165 m elevation.

Migration periods and corridors are not well known, mainly because of the difficulty of separating over-wintering, resident, and migratory populations. In southern areas, records suggest that the spring movement occurs mostly from late March through mid-April and the autumn movement from late October through November.

Figure 272. *Short-eared Owl near Smithers, 28 September 1974 (R. Wayne Campbell).*

Figure 273. *Short-eared Owl nesting habitat on Sea Island, Richmond, 7 May 1970 (R. Wayne Campbell). The rapid loss of old-growth fields in the Fraser River delta threatens the existence of a formerly dense breeding population. Note the nest containing young in the lower right corner of the figure.*

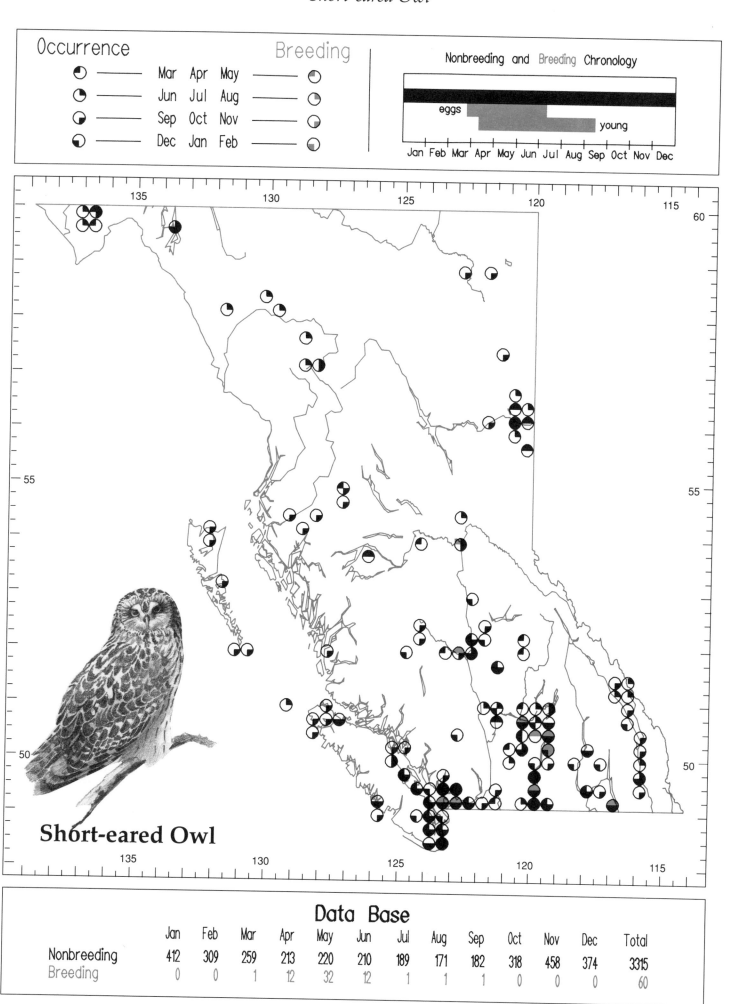

Short-eared Owl

Occurrence / Breeding

Nonbreeding and Breeding Chronology

eggs

young

Jan Feb Mar Apr May Jun Jul Aug Sep Oct Nov Dec

Data Base

	Jan	Feb	Mar	Apr	May	Jun	Jul	Aug	Sep	Oct	Nov	Dec	Total
Nonbreeding	412	309	259	213	220	210	189	171	182	318	458	374	3315
Breeding	0	0	1	12	32	12	1	1	1	0	0	0	60

The Fraser River delta is the main wintering area in British Columbia, with peak numbers of owls occurring in January and February. Of 21 species of raptors censused in the Fraser River delta from January 1975 to May 1980 (Douglas, A. 1984), the Short-eared Owl was the fifth most numerous. During years of high microtine populations, it roosts communally in tall-grass fields and along the lee sides of dykes. Roosts of up to 110 individuals have been located on Sea and Iona islands. Recently, however, wintering numbers of this owl have been quite low, which is cause for concern. Data from Christmas Bird Counts in the Lower Mainland (Fig. 274) show a steady decline in the owl's peak numbers over the past 16 years, a trend that is not likely to change as more and more of the old-field habitat in the Lower Mainland is converted to agricultural, residential, or recreational (e.g. golf courses) uses. M. Tait (pers. comm.) has suggested that, in addition to the loss of owl habitat, competition with the Northern Harrier, a species with a wider niche breadth, may also be playing a role in the decline in owl numbers. In some of Tait's microtine study areas that in the past have supported both owls and harriers, only the Northern Harrier can now be found.

BREEDING: The Short-eared Owl breeds locally in the south and central interior from Creston and the southern Okanagan valley north through the Thompson and Chilcotin-Cariboo basins to Prince George, and on the south mainland coast through the Fraser River delta east to Fort Langley. It is probably more widely distributed than records indicate. However, breeding has not been documented for Vancouver Island, the Gulf Islands, the mainland coast north of Vancouver or the Queen Charlotte Islands. It nests from sea level to at least 975 m elevation.

The Short-eared Owl breeds in open country with short vegetation (Fig. 273), including rangelands, grasslands, near-dry marshes, farmlands, low-arctic tundra, brushy fields, and forest clearings.

Nests: Most nests (44%; n=36) were positioned in shrubby, grass fields adjacent to agricultural areas (Fig. 275); grass heights ranged from 25 to 90 cm. Other sites included airport fields (7), marshes (5), open rangeland (3), sagebrush plains (3), and hayfields (3). Mortality is high when owls select hayfields as nesting sites as nests are often destroyed by farm machinery. All nests were shallow scrapes on the ground, sparsely lined with grasses, leaves, and sometimes a few feathers. Most were

positioned at the bases of grass clumps. Some nests were next to small shrubs or fence posts, and one was located in a willow thicket. Several nests were in open, exposed situations. Two nests were 22 and 32 cm in outside diameter and 4 and 6 cm in height, respectively.

Eggs: Dates for 32 clutches ranged from 24 March to 9 July with 51% recorded between 20 April and 15 May. Sizes for 30 clutches ranged from 1 to 13 eggs (1E-1, 5E-3, 6E-9, 7E-8, 8E-4, 9E-2, 11E-1, 12E-1, 13E-1), with 57% having 6 or 7 eggs (Fig. 276). Incubation periods for 2 nests in British Columbia were 23 and 24 days.

Young: Dates for 29 broods (Fig. 277) ranged from 10 April to 13 Sep-tember, with 15 broods recorded between 29 April and 10 June. The late September date was of "very recently fledged young at Okanagan Landing" (Cannings, R.A. et al. 1987). Sizes for 26 broods ranged from 1 to 8 young (1Y-1, 2Y-2, 3Y-2, 4Y-3, 5Y-9, 6Y-6, 7Y-1, 8Y-2), with 15 broods having 5 or 6 young. Young leave the nest at 12 to 16 days of age (Clark, R.J. 1970) and first fly about 10 to 12 days later.

REMARKS: From 27 January 1964 to 15 May 1967, 426 Short-eared Owls were trapped and banded at the Vancouver International airport as part of a bird control program. Three noteworthy recoveries were: (1) banded 12 August 1964, recovered Grand Coulee, Washington on 17 April 1965; (2) banded 2 September 1964, recovered Palm Dale, California in November 1964; (3) banded 16 September 1964, recovered at Albany, Oregon in March 1966.

The Short-eared Owl appears on the "Blue List" from 1976 to 1986 (Tate 1981, 1986; Tate and Tate 1982), on the basis that populations appear down in North America from 5 areas east of the Central Divide, and greatly down from 3 additional areas including the Middle Pacific Coast region.

See R.J. Clark (1970) for additional details on the life history of the Short-eared Owl.

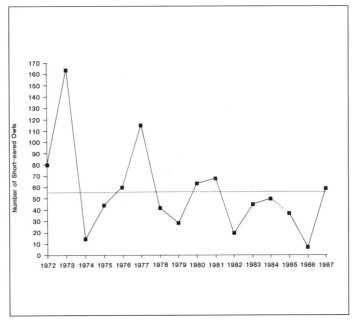

Figure 274. Fluctuations in Short-eared Owl numbers on Christmas Bird Counts in the Lower Mainland for the period 1972 to 1987. Numbers are aggregate totals for the Ladner, Pitt Meadows, Vancouver, and White Rock count areas. The horizontal, dashed line indicates the average numbers observed on these counts over the 16 year period.

Figure 275. Adult Short-eared Owl on nest on Sea Island, Richmond, May 1972 (Ervio Sian).

Figure 276. *Short-eared Owl nest with eggs and recently hatched chicks at Boundary Bay, Delta, 4 April 1970 (Ervio Sian).*

Figure 277. *Short-eared Owl nestlings at Centennial Park, Beach Grove, 2 May 1970 (R. Wayne Campbell). Note the difference in the size of the young, a response to the availability of prey populations.*

NOTEWORTHY RECORDS

Spring: Coastal - Cowichan Bay 19 Mar 1977-3; Iona Island 6 May 1967-10; Ladner 27 Apr 1964-30 counted in 162 ha; Cloverdale 10 Mar 1960-6; Sea Island 10 Mar 1973-14, 25 Mar 1979-20 in roost; Sumas 1 Mar 1977-5; n Fury Bay 21 Apr 1971-1. **Interior** - Castlegar 10 Mar 1974-1; White Lake (Okanagan Falls) 20 Apr 1980-8; Okanagan Landing 9 Apr 1979-4; Vernon 24 Mar 1980-6, 8 May 1973-5; Knutsford 2 Mar 1980-4; Fort St. John 15 Mar 1979-3, 24 Apr 1980-4; Chilkat Pass 13 May 1957-1 (Weeden 1960).

Summer: Coastal - Port Kells 1 Jun 1962-4; Sea Island 10 Jun 1979-6, 13 Jul 1964-33; Iona Island 18 Jul 1970-14; Mitlenatch Island 29 Jul 1965-1 (Campbell and Kennedy 1965); Triangle Island (Scott Islands) 4 Jun 1974-1, 19 Jul 1977-2. **Interior** - Osoyoos Lake 22 Jun 1971-2; Skookumchuk 15 Jun 1976-1; Lac du Bois 25 Jun 1979-2; Marble Canyon (Kootenay National Park) 16 Jul 1970-1 dead (Christman 1970); 45 km n Prince George 17 Jun 1969-1; Grandhaven 15 Jun 1983-1; Stikine River 10 Jul 1962-1 male (NMC 49786); Atlin 5 Jul 1980-1; Chilkat Pass, late Jul 1959-3 (Weeden 1960); Tatshenshini River 19 Jun 1980-1.

Autumn: Interior - Chilkat Pass 20 Oct 1981-1; Fort Nelson 5 Oct 1987-1; sw Kotcho Lake early Nov 1981-1 found dead; Beatton River 19 Oct 1970-1 (RBCM 11683); Taylor 23 Nov 1985-1; Williams Lake 10 Nov 1984-1; Knutsford 2 Sep 1977-5; Vernon 15 Nov 1970-9, 28 Nov 1981-4; Brouse 2 Sep 1977-1 (RBCM Photo 751); Castlegar 11 to 22 Nov 1973-3. **Coastal** - Kitimat 9 Nov 1979-2; Masset 4 Oct 1981-1, 7 Oct 1939-1 female (RBCM 10212); Namu 7 Nov 1980-1; Cape St. James 11 Oct 1978-1; Campbell River 7 Nov 1973-7 hunting on spit; Jericho Beach 22 Oct 1985-3; Sumas 28 Oct 1922-4; Boundary Bay 12 Nov 1962-22; Centennial Park (Delta) 14 Nov 1981-32; Long Beach 3 Nov 1973-5; Crofton 7 Nov 1924-12 (Munro, J.A. and Cowan 1947); Victoria 27 Sep 1939-11 (Munro, J.A. and Cowan 1947); Chain Islands 1 to 3 Nov 1953-3.

Winter: Interior - Atlin Dec 1934-1 (Swarth 1936); Fort St. John 20 Dec 1979-4, 16 Jan 1980-6; Williams Lake 14 Dec 1949-1 male (UBC 5622); Alkali Lake 22 Feb 1970-1; Walhachin 25 Jan 1979-4; Athalmer 26 Dec 1979-1; Stump Lake (Quilchena) 24 Feb 1980-7; Swan Lake (Vernon) 27 Feb 1955-15; Vernon 13 Jan 1980-14; Osoyoos Lake 28 Dec 1973-4, 10 Feb 1974-4. **Coastal** - Quatse River 1 Dec 1980-1 at estuary; Little Qualicum River 12 Feb 1976-1 at estuary (Dawe 1980); Tofino 13 Dec 1978-1; Sea Island 4 Jan 1966-110 in communal roost along dyke, 29 Jan 1978-26 in communal roost, 18 Feb 1967-15 (Anderson 1967b); Centennial Park (Delta) 6 Dec 1981-28 in communal roost, 7 Jan 1981-40; Surrey 26 Jan 1974-12+; Somenos Lake 19 Dec 1971-4; Cowichan Bay 27 Feb 1979-3.

Christmas Counts: Interior - Recorded from 4 of 19 localities and on 10% of all counts. Maxima: Vernon 27 Dec 1981-34; Yoho National Park 18 Dec 1976-3; Oliver/Osoyoos 28 Dec 1981-1; Quesnel 30 Dec 1982-1. **Coastal** - Recorded from 9 of 28 localities and on 37% of all counts. Maxima: Vancouver 18 Dec 1977-**100**, all-time Canadian high count (Anderson, R.R. 1978); Ladner 28 Dec 1980-56; Pitt Meadows 29 Dec 1973-41.

Boreal Owl

BOOW

Aegolius funereus (Linnaeus)

RANGE: Breeds from central Alaska, the Yukon, western Mackenzie, northern Saskatchewan, northern Manitoba, northern Ontario, central Quebec, and southern Labrador south to northern British Columbia, central Alberta, central Saskatchewan, southern Colorado, southern Manitoba, northeastern Minnesota, and east-central Ontario. In winter, occurs south irregularly to the northern United States. Also resident in boreal woodlands across Eurasia.

STATUS: *Rare* resident in the northern interior, and probably a *rare* resident at higher elevations in the southern interior. Irregular, but *very rare* winter visitant to lower elevations in the southern interior. Probably a widespread breeder. *Casual* in autumn and winter west of the Coast Mountains.

NONBREEDING: The Boreal Owl is widespread throughout forested portions of the interior of the province, but remains one of our least-known owls. Preferred habitats in northern areas appear to be stands of white spruce and trembling aspen (Fig. 278), similar to those reported by Meehan and Ritchie (1982) in Alaska. In the Kamloops area, the owl has been found in stands of Engelmann spruce, in the central - southern interior among Douglas-fir - lodgepole pine and subalpine fir - Engelmann spruce - lodgepole pine associations, and in the vicinity of Lillooet Lake in stands of Douglas-fir - western redcedar. In Washington and Colorado, the Boreal Owl occurs at high elevations (1,525 to 3,300 m) in mature Engelmann spruce - subalpine fir forests (Palmer, D.A. 1986; Whelton 1989). Thus, it is likely that the Boreal Owl has been overlooked at higher elevations in the southern interior. It calls early in the season (March to early May), when most high-elevation country is inaccessible. Near Kamloops (Mount Tod), Boreal Owls have been heard calling in mid-March at 1,525 m.

It is considered a sedentary species, but there is some annual altitudinal movement and in severe winters southward irruptions do occur (see Anweiler 1960; Catling 1972).

Over 86% of all records are from the post-breeding season, when the owl becomes slightly more conspicuous. Over 95% of all records are of single birds.

BREEDING: There are only 3 breeding records for British Columbia: 2 of fledged young and 1 of an infertile egg. A fully-fledged young was collected (MVZ 39765) at Flood Glacier on 28 July 1919 (Swarth 1922), and on 3 June 1984, 4 recently fledged young were found huddled together in a stand of spruce trees 40 km nw Wonowon. On 4 May 1988, while checking a nest box at Rabbit Lake, 15 km east of Okanagan Falls, an infertile Boreal Owl egg (UBC 2048) was discovered in a nest that had been used the previous summer (R.J. Cannings pers. comm.). The elevation was 1,500 m. We considered another record (3 young making

begging calls, Yoho National Park, 6 Sept 1979) too late in the season to be included as a breeding location.

Habitat requirements for nesting in British Columbia are unknown. In Alaska, Meehan and Ritchie (1982) found that Boreal Owls nested in a variety of natural and man-made cavities: 4 nests were found in flicker holes, 3 in nest boxes, and 1 in a natural cavity. All but 1 were in closed stands (60% to 100% canopy cover) of deciduous and mixed forests.

The breeding period is also unknown for the province. Calculated dates indicate that, in British Columbia, eggs could be found in April (or earlier) and young could be found from May to about mid-July. The incubation period is 27 days (Godfrey 1986).

REMARKS: Known in the Old World as Tengmalm's Owl.

Figure 278. *Boreal Owl habitat at Charlie Lake, April 1988 (Chris R. Siddle).*

NOTEWORTHY RECORDS

Spring: Coastal - No records. **Interior** - Stagleap Park 28 Mar 1986-1; Vaseux Lake 19 Mar 1985-1 at 300 m elevation (RBCM Photo 1023); Lillooet Lake 3 Apr 1985-pair responded to taped calls; Mount Tod 16 Mar 1982-3 calling; Williams Lake 5 to 26 Apr 1978-1 calling daily; Valemont 29 Mar 1985-1 male (RBCM 19382); Hazelton 11 Mar 1985-1 female (RBCM 18442); Fort Nelson 26 Mar to 3 May 1986-1 (first and last heard calling).

Summer: Coastal - No records. **Interior** - Quiniscoe Lake 6 Jul 1986-1 (RBCM Photo 1127); Kootenay National Park 25 Aug 1983-1; Amiskwi Pass 17 Jun 1976-1 (Wade 1977); 108 Mile Ranch 5 Jul 1980-1; Wonowon 24 and 25 Jun 1984-2; 29 km s Fort Nelson 8 Jul 1987-1; Surprise Lake (Atlin)

17 Jul 1975-1.

Autumn: Interior - Fort St. John Sep 1985-1 flew into balcony door, later released; Fulton Lake 31 Oct 1976-1; Ottertail 27 Nov 1975-1 (Wade 1977); Yoho National Park 6 Sep 1979-1; Whiteswan Lake (Canal Flats) 15 Oct 1984-1; Sparwood Nov 1982-1 (RBCM 17920); Ellis Creek (Penticton) 17 Oct 1987-1 at 1,300 m; Solco Creek 7 Nov 1987-1 at 1,500 m. **Coastal** - Terrace 31 Oct 1984-1; Hope 13 Nov 1914-1 (Brooks and Swarth 1925).

Winter: Interior - Atlin winter 1973-1 in trap; confluence of Black Creek and Beatton River 27 Feb 1984-1 killed in lynx trap (Siddle 1984); Walcott 23 Dec 1986-1 female (RBCM 19381);

Barkerville 1 Jan 1929-1 male (MCZ 282552); 150 Mile House 20 Jan 1985-1; Cherry Creek (Kamloops) 14 Feb 1923-1 (USNM 576196); Okanagan valley 3 Feb 1917-1 male (FMNH 138313); Penticton 27 Dec 1986-2 at 1,000 m, 27 Dec 1987-1 at 1,500 m. **Coastal** - Hope 13 Jan 1946-1 (UBC 4793), 3 Feb 1914-1 (MVZ 101835); Sumas 13 Jan 1903-1 (Brooks 1917).

Christmas Counts: Interior - Recorded twice: Yoho National Park 20 Dec 1975-1; Nakusp 30 Dec 1984-**1**, both all-time Canadian high counts tied with 8 other Canadian localities (Anderson, R.R. 1976, 1978, 1983; Monroe 1984, 1985b). **Coastal** - Not recorded.

Boreal Owl

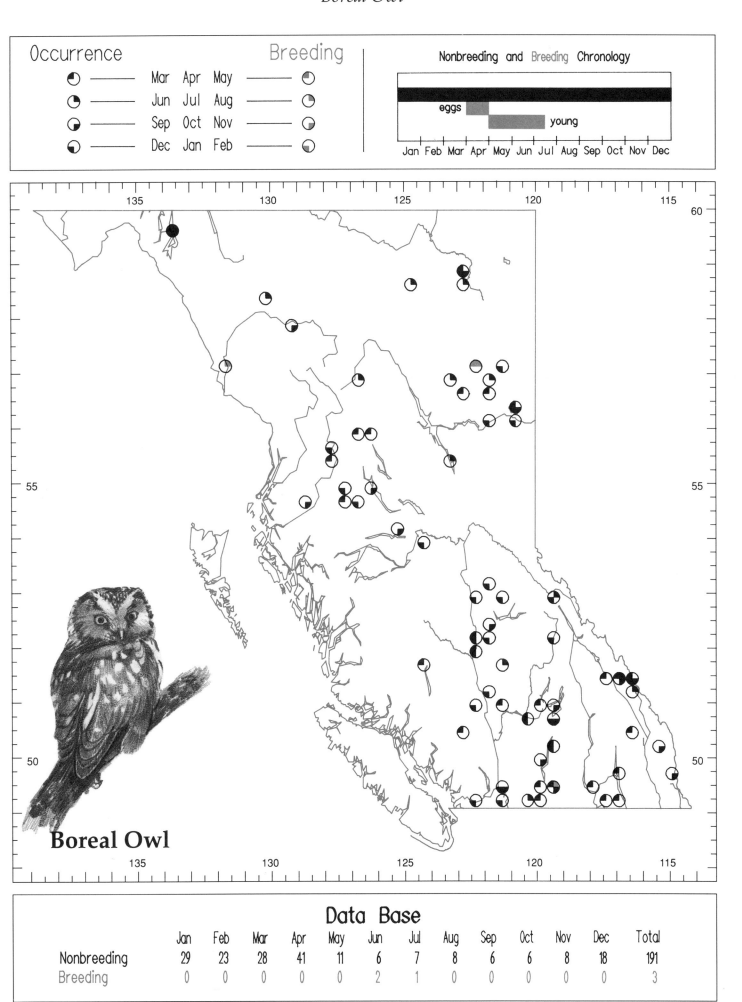

Occurrence

Breeding

	Mar Apr May	
	Jun Jul Aug	
	Sep Oct Nov	
	Dec Jan Feb	

Nonbreeding and Breeding Chronology

eggs

young

Jan Feb Mar Apr May Jun Jul Aug Sep Oct Nov Dec

Boreal Owl

Data Base

	Jan	Feb	Mar	Apr	May	Jun	Jul	Aug	Sep	Oct	Nov	Dec	Total
Nonbreeding	29	23	28	41	11	6	7	8	6	6	8	18	191
Breeding	0	0	0	0	0	2	1	0	0	0	0	0	3

Northern Saw-whet Owl

Aegolius acadicus (Gmelin)

RANGE: Breeds from southern Alaska, central British Columbia to central Ontario, southern Quebec, New Brunswick, and Nova Scotia, south to northern Minnesota, Wisconsin, Michigan, Pennsylvania, and New England and in the western mountains to central Mexico. Winters throughout much of breeding range.

STATUS: *Rare* to *uncommon* resident on the Queen Charlotte Islands, southeastern Vancouver Island, and across interior British Columbia south of 51°N latitude; *rare* to *very rare* summer visitant, and *casual* in winter to the north. *Very rare* along the west coast of Vancouver Island and northern mainland coast. Also, an *uncommon* to *fairly common* local spring and autumn migrant in southern British Columbia. Breeds.

NONBREEDING: The Northern Saw-whet Owl is distributed on the Queen Charlotte Islands, the southern coast including Vancouver Island, and throughout the southern interior. Numbers decrease rapidly north of Prince George in the central interior. Its status along the northern mainland coast is not known.

This species is found in woodlands, dense forests, groves, thickets of pure and mixed coniferous and deciduous trees, and among tall shrubs often in association with lake shores, wet bogs and marshes, hillsides and canyons, city parks, orchards, campgrounds, and wooded residential areas. It occurs from sea level to at least 2,200 m elevation.

Little is known of Northern Saw-whet Owl movements in the province. In southern areas, there is a southward movement evident from mid-October to early November. This movement occurs mostly at night, and has been revealed through banding activities using mist nets over sloughs and creeks, and by annual counts of highway casualties. At times, numbers become locally concentrated.

This owl roosts in dense tangles of branches (e.g. mistletoe, cedar hedges) as well as natural cavities and man-made structures. Individuals have been found roosting in garages, carports, greenhouses, barns, stables, abandoned cabins, airport hangars, and even metal garbage cans.

BREEDING: The Northern Saw-whet Owl breeds on the Queen Charlotte Islands, southeastern Vancouver Island, the southern mainland coast, and in the interior from the Okanagan valley and west Kootenay north to Nulki Lake and locally in the vicinity of Fort St. John. It is found in a variety of woodlands, situated in sparsely-treed rangeland, valleys, canyons, marshes, bogs, parks, and wet and dry thickets. Some mixed vegetative associations include Douglas-fir - ponderosa pine, Engelmann spruce - trembling aspen - lodgepole pine, and black cottonwood - willow. Pure stands of trembling aspen, western larch, and western birch are also used. Frequently, woodlands are in second growth or transitional stages. Nests have been found from sea level to 1,220 m elevation.

Nests: Of 31 nests found, 20 were in natural or animal-created cavities in both coniferous and deciduous trees. Coniferous trees included living and dead western redcedar, Douglas-fir, ponderosa pine, and western larch, while black cottonwood, poplars, trembling aspen, and birches were principal deciduous trees. Seventeen nests were located in woodpecker holes including those of Northern Flicker (11), Pileated Woodpecker (3) and other woodpecker species (3). Three nests were in natural tree cavities, and the remaining eleven were in wooden nest boxes. Some trembling aspen woodland sites ranged from 30 to 40 years old, with nest trees 43 to 56 cm in diameter at breast height. Heights of 21 tree nests ranged from 1.8 to 13.7 m, with 12 between 3.6 and 6 m.

Diameters of 3 nest holes ranged from 5.1 to 8.9 cm, and depths of 4 nests from 30.5 to 61 cm. Most nests contained wood particles and "sawdust" as lining, but a few contained dry grass, mosses, feathers, and pieces of bark.

One nest site was used consecutively from 1960 through 1963, while a nest box used by Flammulated Owls in 1980, 1981, 1986, and 1987 was used by a pair of Northern Saw-whet Owls in 1984.

Eggs: Dates for 27 clutches ranged from 3 March to 1 June with 14 clutches recorded between 20 April and 7 May. Sizes for 26 clutches ranged from 3 to 7 eggs (3E-1, 4E-6, 5E-9, 6E-8, 7E-2), with 65% having 5 or 6 eggs. R.J. Cannings (1987) reports an incubation period of 27 to 29 days (mean 27.3) for 9 nests in the Okanagan valley.

Young: Dates for 47 broods ranged from 7 April to 17 August, with 52% recorded between 25 May and 29 June. After mid-July, most young have fledged, and breeding records are of free-flying young, often in family groups. Brood sizes ranged from 1 to 6 young (1Y-11, 2Y-8, 3Y-9, 4Y-7, 5Y-4, 6Y-8), with 51% having 2 to 4 young. In one nest in British Columbia, the young fledged in 32 days (Cannings, R.A. et al 1987).

REMARKS: Two subspecies are recognized in North America, both of which occur in British Columbia. *Aegolius acadicus brooksi* is endemic to the Queen Charlotte Islands; *A. a. acadicus* is found elsewhere throughout the province.

R.J. Cannings (1987) summarizes the breeding biology of the species in the Okanagan valley.

Formerly known as Saw-whet Owl.

NOTEWORTHY RECORDS

Spring: Coastal - Saanich 26 Apr 1982-1 (RBCM 18238); New Westminster 5 Mar 1954-1 adult female (RBCM 3148); Bamfield 27 Mar 1987-1 calling; Malibu 17 Mar 1981-2; Cape Scott 15 to 19 Apr 1980-2; Hotspring Island 28 Apr 1984-1 calling all night; Spearer Point 8 May 1977-2; Masset Inlet 6 Mar 1980-3. **Interior** - Manning Park 7 Mar 1981-5 calling near sewage treatment plant; Vernon 31 Mar 1979-3; Paul Lake road between Kamloops and Pinantan Lake 5 Mar 1979-21; Heffley Lake road between Heffley Creek and Heffley Lake 7 Mar 1979-23 calling; Heffley Lake to Vinsulla 29 Mar 1979-30 calling; Louis Creek 11 Mar 1980-16 counted between 50°51'N and 119°58'30"W and 51°05'30"N and 120°02'W; Taylor 24 Mar 1986-2, 19 May 1986-2; Telegraph Creek (Stikine River) 9 to 10 Apr 1982-1 (Grunberg 1982).

Summer: Coastal - Bamfield 14 Jul 1979-1; Surrey 1 Jun 1961-4 heard; Sayward Jul 1984-1 male (RBCM 18378); Slim Inlet 6 Jul 1977-1; Ramsay Island 8 Jul 1977-1. **Interior** - Madeline Lake 12 Jul 1979-4; Clearwater Lake (Wells Gray Park) 11 Aug 1975-3; Likely 24 Aug 1953-1 male (NMC 47880); Chilkat Pass 19 Jul 1956-1.

Autumn: Interior - Vanderhoof 8 Oct 1985-1 female (RBCM 19138); Wasa 3 Oct 1925-1 female (USNM 576198); Penticton 11 Nov 1963-2; Osoyoos 17 Nov 1970-2 dead on road. **Coastal** - Hippa Island 17 Sep 1983-2; Green Island 23 Oct 1977-1; Hornby Island 7 Sep 1978-4; Tofino 29 Oct 1981-1; Long Beach 16 Nov 1971-1 (RBCM Photo 214); Westham Island 27 Oct 1969-9 caught in mist nets; Burnaby Lake 1 Nov 1969-4 dead on highway; Victoria 14 to 19 Oct 1950-5 (Guiguet 1950b).

Winter: Interior - Atlin 23 Jan 1932-1 female (RBCM 5884), 20 Feb 1932-1 female (RBCM 5885), 29 Dec 1986-1 (RBCM Photo 1149); Mackenzie 5 Jan 1977-1 caught in trap; Smithers 12 Feb 1977-1 female (RBCM 16042); Burns Lake 2 Feb 1987-2 males caught in traps (RBCM 19379-80); Quesnel winter 1900/1901-1 (Brooks 1901); Williams Lake 16 Dec 1981-1; Kleena Kleene Jan 1965-2 found dead after severe storm; Golden 31 Dec 1963-1 female (RBCM 10792); Cranbrook 13 Jan 1909-1 female (ROM 24-4-14-344). **Coastal** - Kitimat 26 Jan 1980-1; Cape St. James 29 Dec 1978-1; Sea Island 26 Feb 1978-3; Malahat 1 Dec 1950-7.

Christmas Counts: Interior - Recorded from 5 of 19 localities and on 12% of all counts. Maxima: Vernon 26 Dec 1977-2; remaining counts with single birds, Vaseux Lake (4 counts), Shuswap Lake (3 counts), Oliver-Osoyoos (2 counts) and Penticton (1 count). **Coastal** - Recorded from 10 of 28 localities and on 11% of all counts. Maxima: White Rock 2 Jan 1978-10; Vancouver 26 Dec 1961-2 and 18 Dec 1977-2; Victoria 18 Dec 1976-2; Masset 18 Dec 1982-2.

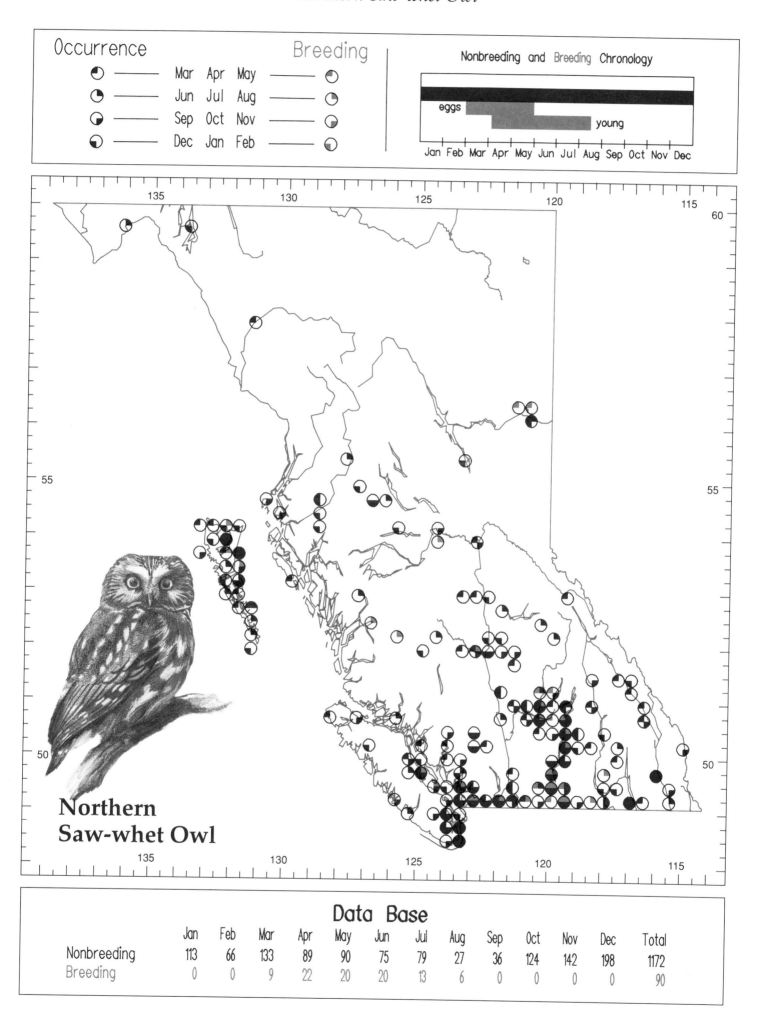

Northern Saw-whet Owl

Occurrence **Breeding**

Mar Apr May
Jun Jul Aug
Sep Oct Nov
Dec Jan Feb

Nonbreeding and Breeding Chronology

eggs   young

Jan Feb Mar Apr May Jun Jul Aug Sep Oct Nov Dec

Data Base

	Jan	Feb	Mar	Apr	May	Jun	Jul	Aug	Sep	Oct	Nov	Dec	Total
Nonbreeding	113	66	133	89	90	75	79	27	36	124	142	198	1172
Breeding	0	0	9	22	20	20	13	6	0	0	0	0	90

389

Common Nighthawk

CONI

Chordeiles minor (Forster)

RANGE: Breeds from the southern Yukon east across most of southern Canada, south to the southern United States, parts of Mexico, and Central America. Winters throughout South America.

STATUS: *Uncommon* to *common* summer visitant throughout most of British Columbia including Vancouver Island; *very rare* west of the Coast Ranges north of Vancouver Island; *accidental* on the Queen Charlotte Islands. *Common* to *abundant* autumn migrant, especially in southern areas; *uncommon* in spring. Breeds.

NONBREEDING: The Common Nighthawk is distributed throughout most of the province. It frequents aerial habitat, usually feeding high in the air, though sometimes low to the ground. It roosts in a variety of open habitats, including coastal sand dunes and beaches, logged and slash-burned areas, farm fields, open ponderosa pine forests, rock outcrops, and flat gravel rooftops of city buildings.

Birds usually arrive between the last week of May and the first week of June. R.A. Cannings et al. (1987) state that birds reported in the Okanagan valley before mid-May are probably Common Poorwills when seen and European Starlings when heard. However, there are several mid-May coastal sightings.

Most observations are of flocks of less than 10 birds, but larger groups are seen sporadically throughout the summer. By mid-August large flocks become more common as birds prepare for their autumn departure (Fig. 279). At this time, spectacular concentrations of Common Nighthawks can be seen in late afternoon and early evening, especially when hawking flying field ants (probably *Lasius* spp. Dawe 1976).

Most have left for their wintering areas by mid-September, although occasionally some linger until October.

Figure 279. *Common Nighthawks hawking field ants over the Little Qualicum River delta, Vancouver Island, 3 September 1975 (Neil K. Dawe).*

Common Nighthawk

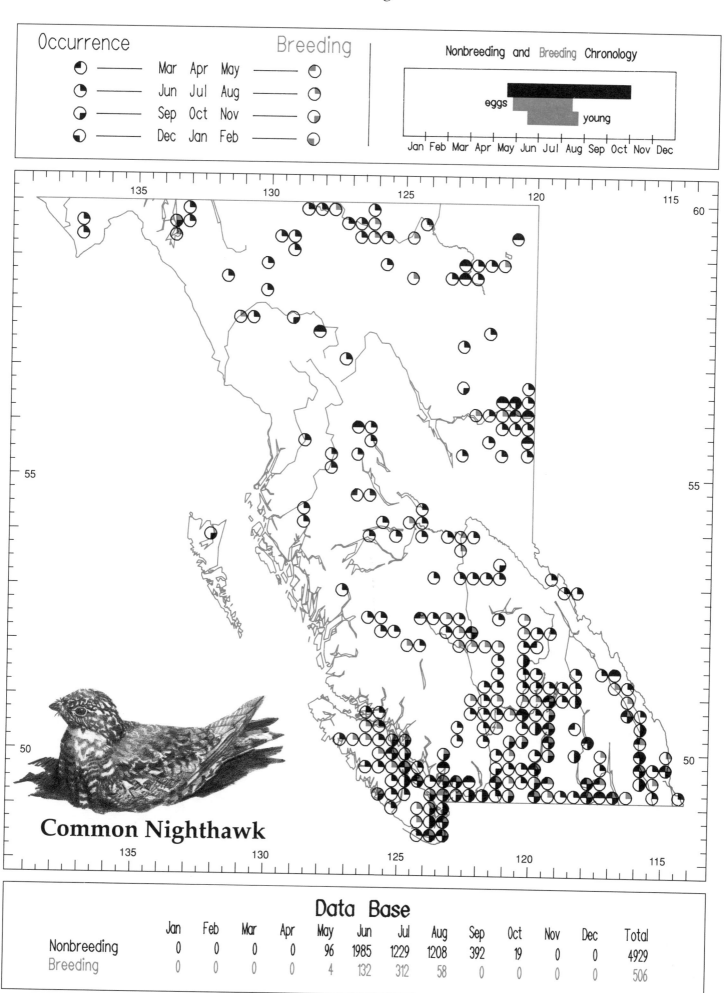

Common Nighthawk

Occurrence

	Mar	Apr	May	
Jun	Jul	Aug	
Sep	Oct	Nov	
Dec	Jan	Feb	

Breeding

Nonbreeding and Breeding Chronology

eggs

young

Jan Feb Mar Apr May Jun Jul Aug Sep Oct Nov Dec

Data Base

	Jan	Feb	Mar	Apr	May	Jun	Jul	Aug	Sep	Oct	Nov	Dec	Total
Nonbreeding	0	0	0	0	96	1985	1229	1208	392	19	0	0	4929
Breeding	0	0	0	0	4	132	312	58	0	0	0	0	506

BREEDING: The Common Nighthawk breeds throughout most of British Columbia. Its centre of abundance is the southern portion of the province, including Vancouver Island, north to approximately 51°N latitude.

Nesting habitats include logged and slash-burned areas of coastal forests, open ponderosa pine forests, the sagebrush and grassland habitat of the dry interior, sand and gravel habitat associated with marine and fluvial beaches, spits, bars, and rocky bluffs or outcroppings. Other breeding habitats used less frequently include farmland, pastureland, old gravel pits and construction sites, openings in regenerating forests, coastal island meadows, and urban areas. It has been reported breeding from sea level to 1,250 m elevation.

Nests: With the exception of 4 nests found on the gravel rooftops of buildings (also see Brigham 1989), all (n=297) were situated on the ground (Fig. 280). No nesting materials, were used. Substrates included gravel, sand, bare rock, wood chips, forest duff, leaves, needles, and, occasionally, living vegetation such as moss, dandelion rosettes, selaginella, and lichens. One nest was found on a rotten log. Occasionally, a slight depression was noted. Nests, usually in the open, were also found near logs, boulders, grass clumps, and shrubs.

Eggs: Dates for 182 clutches ranged from 24 May to 12 August with 55% recorded between 27 June and 12 July. Clutch size ranged from 1 to 4 eggs (1E-18, 2E-159, 3E-4, 4E-1) with 87% having 2 eggs. The 4-egg clutch was probably the product of 2 females. Data from 7 nests in British Columbia suggest that the incubation period is 19 to 20 days. One observer noted that a bird moved eggs from the original nest site to the shade of a grass tuft a short distance away.

Young: Dates for 73 broods (Fig. 281) ranged from 14 June to 20 August with 51% recorded between 17 July and 2 August. Brood size ranged from 1 to 2 young (1Y-14, 2Y-59) with 81% having 2 young. Five broods from British Columbia suggest that the fledging period is about 22 days. The semi-precocial young are often moved from the original nest site shortly after they hatch.

REMARKS: Open areas created by logging activities or fires provide Common Nighthawks with suitable nesting habitat for a number of years depending on the rate of regrowth. Near Chezacut, in the Chilcotin, broods were very common in the 1930s following a forest fire there, but by 1975, with the regrowth of the forests, the birds were no longer common. Nighthawks using a 1952 burn near Campbell River were still using the replanted area in good numbers in 1961. At that time, the regrowth consisted of bracken, small Douglas-fir, willow, and salal.

Regeneration of adjacent forest may also account for the decline in Common Nighthawk numbers in the Greater Vancouver area.

The Common Nighthawk appears on the "Blue List" from 1975 to 1977 and from 1979 to 1981. Tate (1981) notes that "far from being a temporary or cyclic decline, areas from central California to Washington . . . report serious declines." In 1982 it was delisted to a species of special concern (Tate and Tate 1982) with the comment, "Nowhere is it greatly up in numbers." It appears again on the "Blue List" in 1986 based on "widespread declines" (Tate 1986).

Although there are a number of reports of Common Nighthawks in southern areas of the province in late April and early May none are fully documented. Records based on sound are questionable as European Starlings frequently imitate Common Nighthawks.

Figure 280. *Common Nighthawk settling on eggs near Princeton, 29 June 1972 (Ervio Sian).*

Figure 281. Recently hatched Common Nighthawk chick, with the second egg pipping, in a nest near Princeton, 8 July 1972 (Ervio Sian).

NOTEWORTHY RECORDS

Spring: Coastal - Victoria 20 May 1974-1 (Crowell and Nehls 1974c); Sea Island 17 May 1981-1; Pitt Lake 28 May 1966-1; Qualicum Beach 29 May 1976-1; Comox 27 May 1963-1 (Boggs and Boggs 1963c). **Interior** - n Sparwood 20 May 1980-1; Vernon 25 May 1962-1; Cameron Lake 24 May 1981-1; Columbia Lake 20 May 1968-1 (Wilson, M.C. et al. 1972); Nakusp 31 May 1976-1; Roche Lake 24 May 1985-2; Williams Lake 23 May 1958-1 (Erskine and Stein 1964); Tupper Creek 29 May 1938-common (Cowan 1939); Hyland Post 27 May 1976-1; Fort Nelson 28 May 1977-1; Helmet (Kwokullie Lake) 29 May 1982-1.

Summer: Coastal - Victoria 15 Jul 1981-50, 31 Aug 1980-50; Duncan 15 Jul 1972-150; Ladysmith 7 Jul 1983-100; Cassidy 7 Jul 1983-150, 22 Jul 1975-138; Parksville 31 Aug 1965-200; Coombs 14 Jul 1978-110; Little Qualicum River 24 Aug 1974-150 over estuary (Dawe 1976), 25 Aug 1984-200 over estuary; Courtenay 10 Jun 1922-50; Black Creek 28 Aug 1961-600. **Interior** - Osoyoos 19 Aug 1978-150; Trail 19 Aug 1983-100; Wardner 22 Jun 1968-54; Summerland 20 Aug 1970-50; Skookumchuck 19 Jun 1939-63, 22 Aug 1976-250; Stump Lake (Quilchena) 31 Aug 1975-300; Clayhurst 10 Aug 1977-124.

Autumn: Coastal - Melville Island 2 Oct 1967-2; Miracle Beach 3 Sep 1960-167; Comox 14 Sep 1931-1 female (RBCM 13023), 1 Oct 1935-1; Little Qualicum River 3 Sep 1975-76 over estuary (Dawe 1976); Vancouver 11 Oct 1981-1, 14 Oct 1974-1; Saltspring Island 1 Sep 1976-120, 4 Sep 1975-200; Victoria 15 Oct 1955-1; Race Rocks 30 Oct 1969-1. **Interior** - Atlin 6 Sep 1924-1 (Munro, J.A. and Cowan 1947); confluence of McBride-Stikine Rivers 7 Sep 1977-1; Fort St. John 9 Sep 1986-1 (fresh road kill); Indianpoint Lake 7 Sep 1927-1 (MCZ 282555); Upper Chowade River 1 Sep 1975-2; Williams Lake 26 Oct 1981-1 (found in weakened condition and later died); Clearwater 8 Sep 1959-1 (UKMU 38353); Nicola Lake 11 Sep 1984-8; Elk River 19 Sep 1983-1; Penticton 10 Oct 1968-1.

Winter: No records.

Extralimital Records: Sewall 21 Sep 1981-1.

Common Poorwill

Phalaenoptilus nuttallii (Audubon)

COPO

RANGE: Breeds from southern British Columbia and Alberta south through the western United States to central Mexico. Winters from the southern United States to the southern limits of the breeding range.

STATUS: *Uncommon* to *fairly common* local summer visitant to the southern interior. *Casual* west of the Pacific and Cascade ranges, in the Kootenays, and in the Chilcotin-Cariboo Basin. Breeds.

NONBREEDING: The Common Poorwill, the more nocturnal and smaller of British Columbia's 2 goatsuckers, frequents the ponderosa pine - bunchgrass and interior Douglas-fir zones of the southern interior from the Okanagan valley north to the Nicola and Thompson valleys; it is rarely found west of the Coast Ranges, east of Kettle valley, or north of the South Thompson valley. It has been reported from near sea level, but mostly from 300 to 1,500 m elevation.

It favours the open habitat of forested parkland, fields, rangeland, hillsides, and road edges (Fig. 282) where scattered shrubs and grass clumps occur. Daytime roosts are on the ground under shrubs and grasses, and in dune grass clumps. Foraging was most often reported as occurring on or adjacent to unpaved roads.

The Common Poorwill arrives in the Okanagan as early as mid-April, though the main movement appears about mid-May when loose flocks of up to 20 can be found. Most have left for the wintering grounds by mid-September; a few may remain until October.

BREEDING: The Common Poorwill's breeding distribution includes the Okanagan valley from Osoyoos north to Coldstream. It frequents semi-arid, open habitats including ponderosa pine forests, lower level Douglas-fir forests with parkland character, dry pastureland, and rocky sagebrush - bunchgrass hillsides. Breeding has been reported from 330 to 580 m elevation, though birds are regularly found singing at 1,000 m elevation in the south Okanagan.

Nests: All nests (n=8) were found in open areas: on the ground among gravel or pine-needle litter, on a base of flat rocks, or on a rotten log. Four of the nests were in the shelter of a tree, shrub, or overhanging rock. Nesting material, other than the substrate, was not used. Usually, a small depression or hollow was made.

Eggs: Dates for 5 clutches ranged from 16 May to 25 August (RBCM Photo 830). Clutch size for 5 nests was 2 eggs.

Young: Dates for 7 broods ranged from 16 June to 26 July. Calculated dates suggest that nestlings can be found until late August. Sizes of 5 broods ranged from 1 to 2 young (1Y-1, 2Y-4). Common Poorwill young are semi-precocial.

REMARKS: There are 2 possible sightings of the Common Poorwill from Vancouver Island: Victoria 22 September 1979-1; Tugwell Lake 8 June 1985-1. There is also a possible sighting from Yoho National Park, 30 July 1922-1 (Ulke 1923). All lack sufficient details to confirm the observations.

Recent records from the Kootenays suggest a possible expansion of range within the province, and observers there should be alert for the birds' mellow, nocturnal calls.

Previously known as the Poorwill.

Figure 282. *Common Poorwill at Madeline Lake, Penticton, 20 June 1978 (Stephen R. Cannings).*

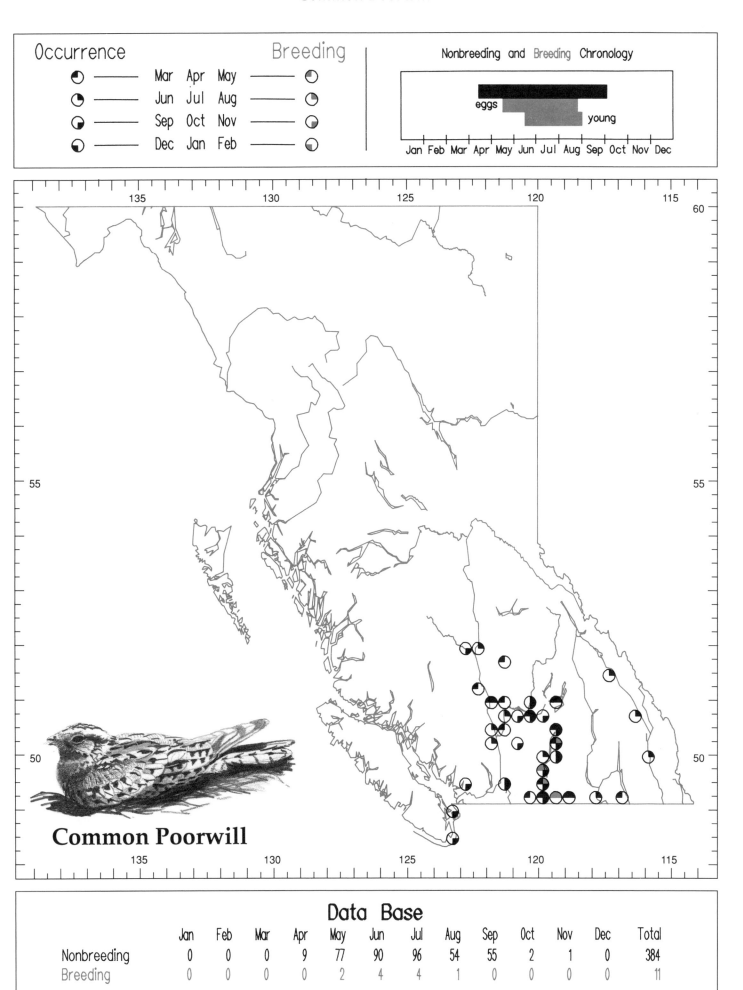

Common Poorwill

Occurrence

Mar Apr May
Jun Jul Aug
Sep Oct Nov
Dec Jan Feb

Breeding

Nonbreeding and Breeding Chronology

eggs

young

Jan Feb Mar Apr May Jun Jul Aug Sep Oct Nov Dec

Data Base

	Jan	Feb	Mar	Apr	May	Jun	Jul	Aug	Sep	Oct	Nov	Dec	Total
Nonbreeding	0	0	0	9	77	90	96	54	55	2	1	0	384
Breeding	0	0	0	0	2	4	4	1	0	0	0	0	11

Black Swift

Cypseloides niger (Gmelin)

BLSW

RANGE: Breeds locally from southeastern Alaska, northwestern and central British Columbia, and southwestern Alberta south through the western United States to southern Mexico, Central America, and the Antilles. Winters in Mexico, Central America, and most of the Greater Antilles.

STATUS: *Fairly common* to *very common* summer visitant on the coast west of the Coast Ranges, including Vancouver Island; at times locally *very abundant*. Absent from the Queen Charlotte Islands. In the interior, *rare* to *uncommon* summer visitant, at times locally *abundant*, south of 56°N latitude. Breeds.

NONBREEDING: The Black Swift is widely distributed across southern British Columbia, including Vancouver Island, from the extreme southern portion of the province north to Prince George and Hazelton. Farther north, it occurs only in the Northern Mountains and Plateaus region to Telegraph Creek; it is absent from the boreal and sub-boreal forests. Its centre of abundance is the southwest coast including the east coast of Vancouver Island from Victoria to Campbell River and the Fraser Lowlands.

The Black Swift frequents aerial habitat from near sea level to the higher elevations of mountain peaks and canyons (2,600 m). During fair weather, the swifts feed at great heights. In overcast or rainy weather, large numbers can often be observed feeding low to the ground.

Spring arrivals can appear in late April, but the main movement occurs from mid-to-late May and occasionally into June. There is a single specimen record for March. Most reports are of flocks of less than 20 birds; however, flocks of hundreds and occasionally thousands have been reported. The larger flocks are usually associated with cloudy or stormy weather. Udvardy (1954) found that the appearance of Black Swifts in the Vancouver area coincided with a cyclone passage. His data suggest that the swifts accumulate from a wide area and not necessarily from close to the area of observation.

The autumn movement, although difficult to ascertain, likely begins in late August and continues through September. Most birds have left the interior by mid-September and the coast by early October. These swifts rarely remain until November.

BREEDING: Godfrey (1986) reports that the Black Swift's breeding distribution in British Columbia includes nearly its entire summer range. While this is likely where suitable habitat occurs, only 2 definite nesting sites have been found: near Clinton (Beebe 1959) and Vernon (Grant, J. 1966a).

Breeding habitats include moist canyon walls and cliff faces, usually in proximity to waterfalls (Fig. 283).

Nests: All nests (n=7) were located on steep canyon walls close to a waterfall. Six of the nests (same site, different years) were located on a shallow ledge under overhanging moss (Fig. 284). Heights of the nests ranged from 3 to 4.5 m. Nests were composed primarily of moss, occasionally with needles or twigs present. One had outer measurements of 14 by 10 cm and was 2 cm deep. In Colorado, Knorr (1961) found that 5 physical-ecological factors determine nesting location: presence of water, high relief, inaccessibility to terrestrial mauraders, darkness, and absence of flyway obstructions near the nest.

Figure 283. *Black Swift nesting habitat near Vernon in the northern Okanagan valley, June 1975 (Ervio Sian). The nest was located on a small ledge below overhanging moss on the cliff face*

Black Swift

Black Swift

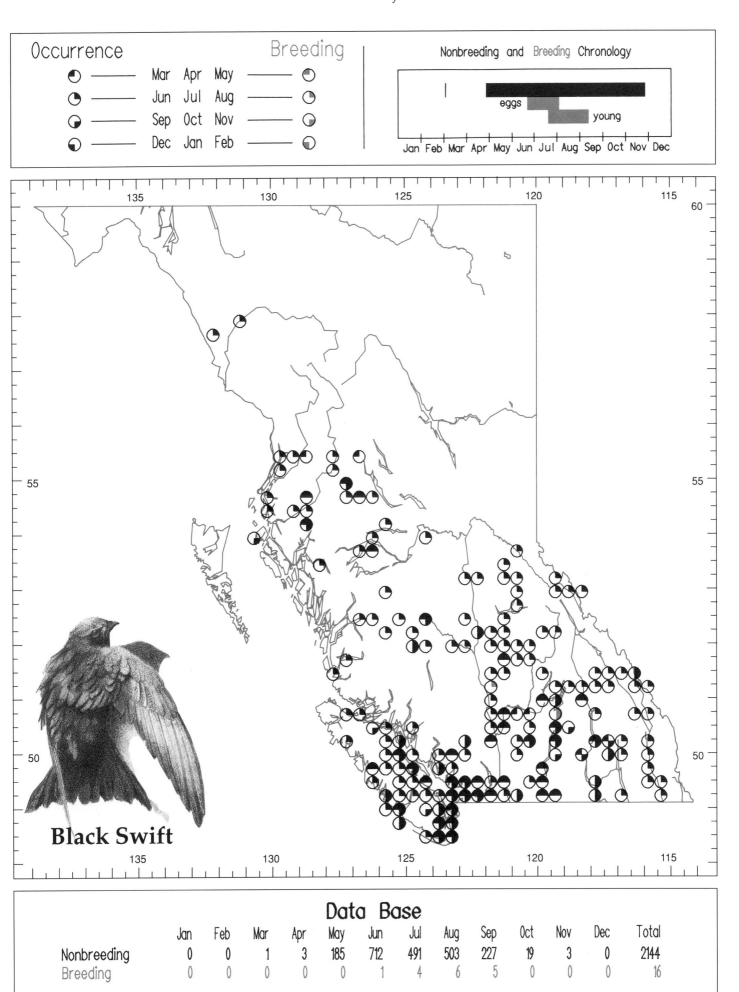

Occurrence / Breeding

Mar Apr May	
Jun Jul Aug	
Sep Oct Nov	
Dec Jan Feb	

Nonbreeding and Breeding Chronology

eggs
young

Jan Feb Mar Apr May Jun Jul Aug Sep Oct Nov Dec

Data Base

	Jan	Feb	Mar	Apr	May	Jun	Jul	Aug	Sep	Oct	Nov	Dec	Total
Nonbreeding	0	0	1	3	185	712	491	503	227	19	3	0	2144
Breeding	0	0	0	0	0	1	4	6	5	0	0	0	16

Eggs: One nest had a single egg on 28 June (Grant, J. 1975). The egg period, on the accompanying map, was calculated from Brooks (1917) and Holroyd and Jalkotzy (1986). Incubation period is unknown.

Young: Dates for 7 broods ranged from 18 July to 10 September. Brood size ranged from 1 to 2 young with 6 broods having 1 young (Figs. 285 and 286). The record of 2 young (Beebe 1959) is extraordinary, as the Black Swift is reported to lay only 1 egg (Harrison, C. 1978; Godfrey 1986); it may have involved 2 nests. The fledging period is about 45 days (Holroyd and Jalkotzy 1986).

REMARKS: Jobin (1955) mentions the location of 2 breeding colonies of the species, but details sufficient to confirm breeding are lacking. The first was on an inaccessible, high cliff at the end of the north arm of Quesnel Lake; the second was on a high cliff about 10 km north of Kleena Kleene. In other areas of North America, the Black Swift does occur in small breeding colonies (Bent 1940). In Kootenay National Park, Black Swifts are frequently observed flying into Marble and Sinclair canyons and over Helmet Falls where they likely nest (Poll et al. 1984). Near Hotsprings Cove on the west coast of Vancouver Island, a swift was observed flying from a cliff face outside a cave. A female, with an egg in its oviduct, collected at Chilliwack on 16 June 1901 (Brooks 1917) and a pair seen copulating in the air over Piercy Creek on 21 June 1974 (M.K. McNicholl pers. comm.) are also noteworthy.

A young Black Swift raised by Beebe (1959) appeared to need extra fluid, and would drink water (or goat's milk) when it was offered until a teaspoonful was consumed. This need for water may partially explain the nest locations. In Johnston Canyon, Alberta, Holroyd and Jalkotzy (1986) found that the Black Swift nested in the coldest part of the canyon; the average maximum temperature was 13.7°C cooler than the adjacent valley, while the average minimum temperature was 2°C warmer. This micro-climate could permit the nestling to become hypothermic, thus saving energy. They also found that the young were fed once or twice each day by each parent, usually at dusk, with Hymenoptera-Formicidae dominating the diet. They concluded

that the nestling stage of the Black Swift is timed so that the young can be fed flying ants that emerge in August and early September—a patchy but abundant food source with a high energy content.

Despite the large flocks of Black Swifts observed throughout the species' summer range, only 2 breeding sites have been confirmed for the province. Undoubtedly, this is due to a number of factors, including its precipitous breeding habitat and its movement far from the breeding area during cyclone passages, at which time it may be away from the nest for days (Udvardy 1954). The breeding distribution and biology of the Black Swift in British Columbia remain for determined and careful observers to reveal.

Figure 284. Black Swift nest with egg on a cliff face near Vernon, late June 1975 (Ervio Sian).

Figure 285. Adult Black Swift (left) feeding a nestling near Vernon, August 1975 (Ervio Sian). British Columbia is the centre of the species' breeding range in Canada.

Figure 286. *Large Black Swift young in nest near Vernon, August 1975 (Ervio Sian).*

NOTEWORTHY RECORDS

Spring: Coastal - Victoria 28 Apr 1968-1 (Crowell and Nehls 1968c); Crescent Beach 29 Apr 1964-6; Port Coquitlam 7 May 1973-7 (Jerema 1973); Vancouver 26 Apr 1953-few (Udvardy 1954), 30 May 1976-300; New Westminster 26 May 1973-200; Qualicum Beach 29 May 1976-174 (Dawe 1980); Piercy Creek 22 May 1972-50, first record; Comox 1 Mar 1925-1 (RBCM 6422). **Interior** - Vaseux Lake 3 May 1965-1; Swan Lake (Vernon) 14 May 1979-60, 18 May 1975-hundreds flying north, 21 May 1984-1,000; 100 Mile House 25 May 1985-3; Nilkitkwa Lake 23 May 1978-6.

Summer: Coastal - Victoria 22 Aug 1959-300; Duncan 8 Jul 1972-186; Vancouver 11 Jun 1952-1,000 (Udvardy 1954), 25 Jun 1975-500, 3 Jul 1964-730; Reifel Island 16 Jun 1973-300; Qualicum Beach 25 Jun 1975-500, 26 Aug 1975-200 (Dawe 1976); Piercy Creek 21 Jun 1974-2 copulating in the air; Campbell River (Discovery Passage) 29 Aug 1975-300; Kitimat 17 Jul 1975-120; Skeena River (w Terrace) 26 Jul 1975-600; Greenville 16 Jun 1981-150. **Interior** - Creston 14 Jun 1978-100; Cranbrook 9 Jun 1938-200; Golden 8 Aug 1951-50; Stump Lake (Quilchena) 24 Jun 1974-200, 31 Aug 1975-270; 100 Mile House 26 Aug 1984-100; Buffalo Lake 14 Aug 1977-100; Telegraph Creek (Stikine River) 12 Jun 1919 (Munro, J.A. and Cowan 1947).

Autumn: Interior - Smithers 3 Oct 1974-9; Williams Lake 6 Sep 1985-100, 3 Oct 1978-17; Chezacut 4 Sep 1933-1 (MCZ 282565); Sorrento 15 Sep 1970-6; Vernon 26 Sep 1972-1; Nicola 8 Sep 1984-1; Nakusp 22 Sep 1984-1 (RBCM 18400); Trail 2 Sep 1980-1. **Coastal** - Kitimat 4 Oct 1974-15, 5 Oct 1974-3 (Hay 1976); Shelter Point 4 Sep 1960-250, 5 Oct 1975-6; Cloverdale 3 Oct 1953-30; Surrey 22 Sep 1972-250; Vancouver 1 Oct 1953-6 (Udvardy 1954), 6 Oct 1976-2; Tofino 22 Sep 1983-10; Crofton 9 and 21 Sep 1972-many thousand after showers (Tatum 1973), 3 Nov 1975-1 (Shepard, M.G. 1976b); Victoria 12 Sep 1984-250, 25 Nov 1954-2 (Flahaut and Schultz 1955).

Winter: No records.

Vaux's Swift
Chaetura vauxi (Townsend)

RANGE: Breeds from southern Alaska, British Columbia, Idaho, and Montana south, mainly confined to coastal ranges, to central California, and discontinuously to Central and South America. Winters from central Mexico south through the breeding range.

STATUS: *Fairly common* to locally *common* summer visitant on the southern coast, including Vancouver Island, becoming *uncommon* to *very rare* farther north along the coast. Not reported from the Queen Charlotte Islands. *Uncommon* to *fairly common* in the Okanagan and Nicola valleys of the southern interior, and in the Kootenays; *very rare* throughout the rest of the province. Breeds.

NONBREEDING: The Vaux's Swift is distributed across most of southern British Columbia, becoming scarce in northern areas. It occurs from the extreme southern portions of the province north along the coast to Alice Arm and through the interior to Hazelton in the west and Mt. Robson Park in the east, rarely farther north. It is absent from the Boreal and Sub-boreal Forests. The centres of abundance include the southern tip of Vancouver Island, the Fraser Lowlands, and the south Okanagan valley.

The Vaux's Swift frequents aerial habitat from near sea level to the higher elevations of interior valleys and coastal mountain peaks (2,100 m). It forages at varying heights, often low over forest openings (logged areas, burns), rivers or lakes (just above the water's surface), and over forest tree tops. It has also been observed in flocks splashing into the water of a lake, perhaps bathing. It roosts in chimneys and hollow trees.

The spring movement begins as early as late March on the coast and mid-April in the interior; however, the major influx begins in May and continues throughout most of the month. Most observations through the summer are of less than 10 birds although occasionally many are seen. Reports of large numbers at lower elevations often coincide with storm fronts. Larger flocks begin to appear in late August as the autumn migration gets underway. Numbers peak in the first and second weeks of September when spectacular flights can often be observed, particularly in the Victoria area. Most have departed by the end of September.

BREEDING: Godfrey (1986) shows the breeding distribution of the Vaux's Swift in British Columbia as occuring throughout most of the bird's summer range. While this is likely, we have convincing breeding records from only 4 southern areas of the province: Bowen Island (Munro, J.A. and Cowan 1947), Nelson, Yale (Munro, J.A. 1918), and Merritt.

All but one of our breeding records with details are from residential areas or on man-made structures from near sea level to 530 m elevation.

Nests: Of 13 nests, 8 were situated in unused chimneys, usually in vacant houses; 1 was found under the roof of a railway water tank (Munro, J.A. 1918); 2 others were in a hollow bigleaf maple. Nests consisted of small twigs or grass stems glued to the inside of the chimney with the bird's saliva. Heights of 7 nests ranged from 3 to 9 m.

Eggs: Dates for 8 clutches ranged from 10 June to 1 July. Sizes for 5 clutches ranged from 4 to 7 eggs (4E-2, 6E-2, 7E-1). Incubation period is 19 days (Baldwin and Zaczkowski 1963).

Young: Dates for 4 broods ranged from 30 June to 7 August. Brood size ranged from 1 to 7 young (1Y-1, 4Y-2, 7Y-1). Fledging period is about 27 days (Baldwin and Zaczkowski 1963).

REMARKS: Jobin (1955) reports finding a small colony of Vaux's Swifts at the north end of Antoine Lake near Horsefly. He notes that the birds were feeding over the lake and flying to and from a small grove of large, dead cottonwoods near the lakeshore. However, evidence to confirm breeding (e.g. nests with eggs or young) is lacking. R.A. Cannings et al. (1987), Belton (1973), Sirk (1972), and a number of other observers mention seeing Vaux's Swifts entering hollow trees or chimneys. Breeding is suspected, but the observations do not include evidence sufficient to confirm breeding. Areas of these observations include Victoria, Manning Park, Nickle Plate Canyon, Monck Park, and the Okanagan valley.

There is much to learn about the breeding distribution and biology of the Vaux's Swift in British Columbia. While their nests are often in hard-to-reach locations, they do not need the precipitous cliff faces used by nesting Black and White-throated swifts. Of the 3, the Vaux's Swift should present the least problem to the amateur or professional ornithologist wishing to fill this gap of knowledge in British Columbia ornithology.

POSTSCRIPT: Tom and Gloria Anderson (pers. comm.) reported the first documented breeding record of the Vaux's Swift for Vancouver Island, 8 km southwest of Duncan. The Swifts were first observed flying in and out of the Anderson's chimney on 15 July 1989. Subsequently, a nest was located 3.6 m down a 30 by 30 cm flue attached to the cinder blocks in a corner. Five young hatched on about 1 August and were seen leaving the nest for the first time on 22 August. The young and the adults flew around during the day, joined by another "family" of swifts, and returned to the nest about 2000 each evening. The swifts were last seen by the Andersons on 7 September. Part of the nest was salvaged and taken to the Canadian Wildlife Service for confirmation. The nest, about "tea cup size," was made primarily of conifer twigs cemented together with the bird's saliva; a few swift feathers also formed part of the nest material.

NOTEWORTHY RECORDS

Spring: Coastal - Victoria 9 and 11 May 1984-200 flew down chimney to roost; Metchosin 1 May 1981-45, 5 May 1974-300, 18 May 1975-150 in thunderstorm; Crescent Beach 27 Mar 1960-30+; Nanaimo 30 Apr 1968-190; Vedder Canal 31 May 1976-100; Vancouver 29 Mar 1979-2, 7 May 1981-250, 25 May 1971-1200 (Campbell et al. 1972b); West Vancouver 5 May 1974-300, 15 May 1983-300 in flocks of 10 to 30 birds migrating east; Courtenay 19 May 1935-100+; Powell River 19 May 1986-hundreds flew down chimney to roost; Kelsey Bay 9 May 1979-75; Khyex River 26 May 1977-10. **Interior** - White Lake (Okanagan Falls) 17 Apr 1976-1; Vaseux Lake 9 May 1981-50; Princeton 10 May 1978-125; Nakusp 5 May 1980-100+; Vernon 19 Apr 1966-2; Revelstoke 23 Apr 1983-10; Alexis Creek 4 May 1981-2; Prince George 30 Apr 1982-2; Peace River 15 May 1975-1 (Penner 1976).

Summer: Coastal - Nanaimo 22 Jul 1975-54; Iona Island 5 Jun 1980-34; Vancouver 18 Jun 1983-300; Glen Valley 5 Jun 1974-150+; Agassiz 28 Aug 1975-80; French Creek 1 Jun 1968-54; Comox 28 Aug 1977-many thousands - flock 3 km wide (Davidson 1979); Kimsquit 25 Jun 1986-250+; Kemano Bay 2 Jul 1975-40; Tseax River (lava beds) 22 Aug 1977-100. **Interior** - Lavington 31 Aug 1980-60; Scotch Creek 25 Aug 1973-200 (Cannings, R.J. 1973); s Kamloops 28 Jun 1975-100+ foraging over lakes in gale-force winds; Revelstoke National Park 2 Jun 1977-149 moving past in 5 min; Horsefly 21 Jul 1954-1 (NMC 47901); Valemount 30 Aug 1956-1 (NMC 41282); Dokdaon Creek 14 Jul 1919 (Munro, J.A. and Cowan 1947); Nass River 8 Jun 1976-30; Basement Creek 8 Jun 1983-1 (Campbell et al. 1983).

Autumn: Interior - Kispiox Valley 3 Sep 1921

(Swarth 1924); Sorrento 11 Sep 1970-60+; Kamloops 17 Sep 1983-50; Monck Park 4 Sep 1977-115; Nakusp 7 Sep 1985-100+; Kelowna 11 Oct 1971-1; Summerland 6 Sep 1962-100+; Richter Pass 21 Sep 1968-3; Creston 14 Sep 1985-6+. **Coastal** - Yeo Island 22 Sep 1968-1; Qualicum Beach 10 Oct 1984-1; Tofino 22 Oct 1985-1; Chilliwack 9 Sep 1982-100, 3 Oct 1981-10; West Vancouver 13 Sep 1981-300; Cypress Park 3 Oct 1982-18; Sumas 19 Sep 1976-200+; River Jordan 13 Sep 1984-980 counted over 52 min, "only small fraction of total flight"; Metchosin 1 and 4 Sep 1964-750, 2 Oct 1981-50; Colwood 9 Sep 1978-120; Coburg Penninsula 18 Sep 1978-1000+ counted over 35 min, continuous flight; Victoria 19 Sep 1959-60, 6 Oct 1972-1 (Crowell and Nehls 1973a), 6 Oct 1973-2.

Winter: No records.

Vaux's Swift

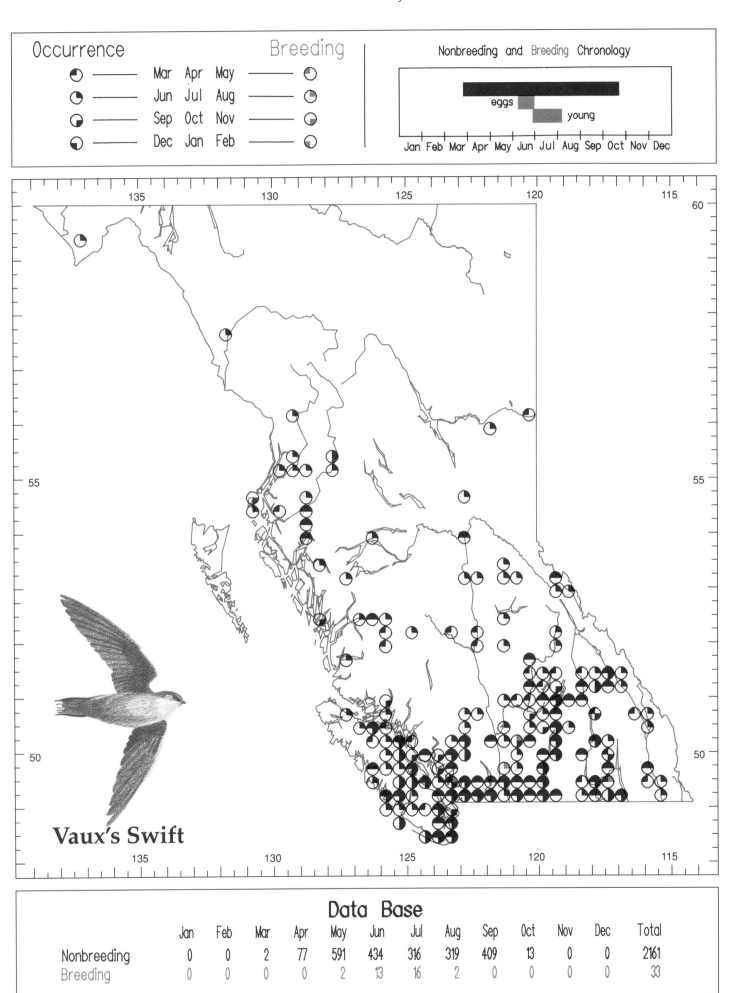

	Jan	Feb	Mar	Apr	May	Jun	Jul	Aug	Sep	Oct	Nov	Dec	Total
Nonbreeding	0	0	2	77	591	434	316	319	409	13	0	0	2161
Breeding	0	0	0	0	2	13	16	2	0	0	0	0	33

White-throated Swift

WTSW

Aeronautes saxatalis (Woodhouse)

RANGE: Breeds from the southern interior of British Columbia east to South Dakota and south in the western cordillera to Honduras. Winters from central California and Arizona south to the limit of the breeding range.

STATUS: *Fairly common* local summer visitant to the southern Okanagan valley becoming locally *rare* in the north Okanagan, the South Thompson River valley and in the Chilcotin-Cariboo Basin. *Casual* in the Kootenays and the Similkameen valley; *accidental* west of the Coast Ranges. Breeds.

NONBREEDING: The White-throated Swift (Fig. 287) is distributed locally throughout the central-southern interior from the southern Okanagan and Similkameen valleys north to Williams Lake, and in 2 locations in the Kootenays. Its centre of abundance is the southern Okanagan valley north to Summerland and Naramata. It frequents aerial habitat, usually associated with dry cliffs and canyons. Like the Vaux's Swift, the White-throated Swift will also skim the surface of lakes while feeding (McNicholl 1975).

Birds arrive in early April with the main movement occurring in the latter part of April and early May. While most observations are of 20 or fewer birds, flocks of up to 50 are not uncommon. Autumn migration begins in late August and larger numbers can be seen at that time; by late September most birds have gone.

BREEDING: The White-throated Swift is known to breed only in the Similkameen valley near Hedley and in the Okanagan valley from Vaseux Lake north to the Naramata area. The breeding centre of abundance appears to be the 20 km stretch from Vaseux Lake to Penticton.

The White-throated Swift breeds in small colonies (Table 21) where steep cliffs, rock bluffs, and canyons are present (Fig. 288), from 300 to 800 m elevation.

Nests: All nests (n=25) were situated on steep cliff faces. Most were inaccessible, tucked in a crack or crevice. One was found on a small ledge below a rock overhang. They ranged in height from 3 to 60 m above the ground with 16% between 3 and 18 m. Materials used to build one nest were grasses, mosses, feathers, and plant down held together by saliva.

Eggs: Dates for 4 clutches ranged from 16 May to 1 July. Clutch size for 1 nest was 3 eggs. Incubation period is unknown (Terres 1980).

Young: Dates for 16 broods ranged from 8 June to 16 August with 9 recorded between 1 and 9 July. Fledging period is unknown (Terres 1980).

Figure 287. White-throated Swift above nesting cliffs at Vaseux Lake in the Okanagan valley (Stephen R. Cannings).

REMARKS: Apparently, the White-throated Swift first bred in British Columbia at Vaseux Lake in 1907 (Brooks 1909a), and has been steadily increasing its range. Since J.A. Munro and Cowan (1947), small, apparent colonies of the White-throated Swift have been found in the Kootenays, the South Thompson River valley (Weber, W.C. 1975) and the Chilcotin-Cariboo Basin. Breeding likely occurs in all these areas, but evidence sufficient to confirm breeding is lacking. Confirmation of breeding is required for all colonies outside the Similkameen and southern Okanagan areas and for many of the colonies within these areas (e.g. Bear Creek Park).

Nest site tenacity seems to be typical of this swift; Dobkin et al. (1986) discuss traditional nest site use by White-throated Swifts in central Nevada and note birds using the same rock outcrop in 1984 where the species was reported nesting 54 years earlier. In the Okanagan, the breeding colony at Vaseux Lake was estimated at 7 pairs in 1917 (Munro, J.A. 1918), and the site is still in use some 70 years later.

We consider hypothetical a record of the White-throated Swift over Point Grey Beach (9 June 1969) reported by McNicholl (1975).

	Colony History				
Location	First Record	Low Survey Results[1] Year	High Survey Results[1] Year	Recent Survey Results[1] Year	Source[2]
Interior - All colonies					
Naramata	1983		Many P 1985	1985	1
Hedley	1975		15-20 P 1975	1975	1
Vaseux Lake	1907	7 P 1917	10-15 P 1968	C 1987	1,2,3

TABLE 21.
White-throated Swift: location, history, and size of major colonies in British Columbia.

[1] C - nesting confirmed but no count or estimate made; P - pairs. All data are estimates.
[2] 1 - British Columbia Nest Records Scheme; 2 - Brooks 1909a; 3 - Cannings, R.A. et al. 1987.

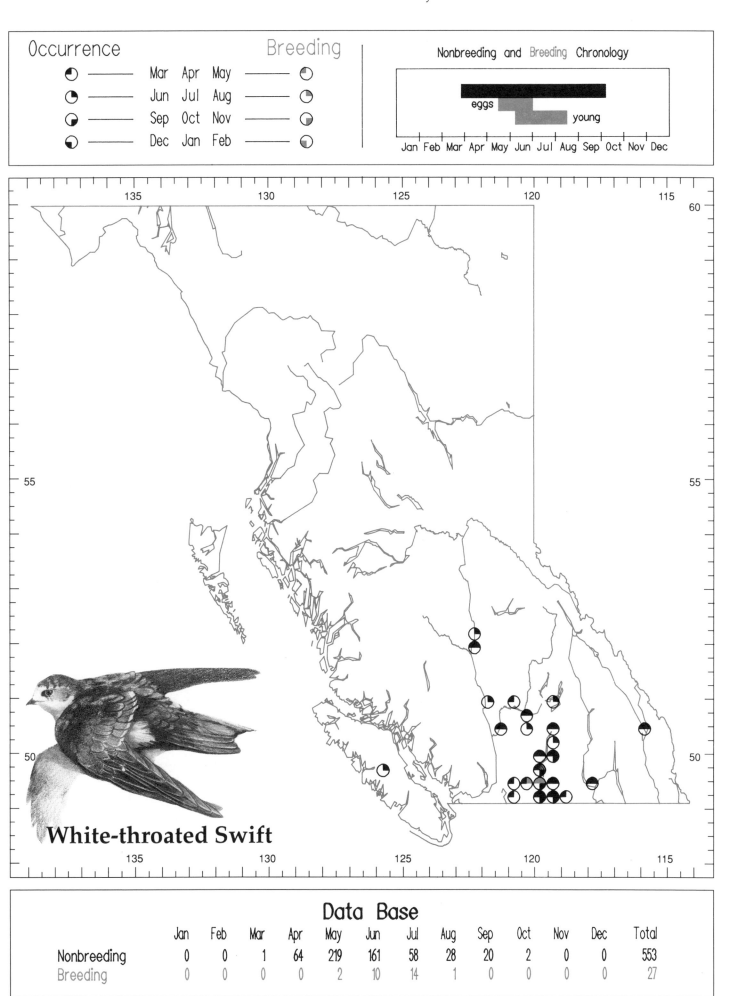

Occurrence

◑	Mar	Apr	May
◔	Jun	Jul	Aug
◕	Sep	Oct	Nov
◕	Dec	Jan	Feb

Breeding

Nonbreeding and Breeding Chronology

eggs
young

Jan Feb Mar Apr May Jun Jul Aug Sep Oct Nov Dec

White-throated Swift

Data Base

	Jan	Feb	Mar	Apr	May	Jun	Jul	Aug	Sep	Oct	Nov	Dec	Total
Nonbreeding	0	0	1	64	219	161	58	28	20	2	0	0	553
Breeding	0	0	0	0	2	10	14	1	0	0	0	0	27

Figure 288. *Nesting site of the White-throated Swift at Vaseux Lake, May 1974 (Stephen R. Cannings).*

NOTEWORTHY RECORDS

Spring: Coastal: No records. **Interior** - Vaseux Lake 26 Mar 1978-6, 10 Apr 1977-40, 24 Apr 1971-50; Robson 13 Apr 1971-1; Castlegar 18 Apr 1969-1; Princeton 17 Apr 1977-10; Summerland 1 Apr 1978-2; Vernon 13 May 1965-1; Dutch Creek 27 May 1981-10; Spences Bridge 31 May 1975-3 (Weber, W.C. 1975); Kamloops 20 Apr 1984-3, 20 May 1986-20; Kamloops Lake 1 May 1983-2; near Riske Creek 21 Apr 1980-6, 8 May 1977-1.

Summer: Coastal: See Extralimital Records.

Interior - Vaseux Lake 3 Jun 1974-40, 20 Jun 1976-40, 28 Jun 1973-50, 26 Aug 1967-100; Robson 6 Jun 1986-20+; Stump Lake (Quilchena) 5 Jul 1963-23; Dutch Creek 6 Jun 1976-8, 22 Jul 1976-12; Armstrong 1 Jun 1961-6; Kamloops 23 Jun 1981-8; Marble Canyon (Pavilion) 5 Jul 1961-50; Riske Creek 6 Jun 1977-6, 13 Jun 1978-4; Williams Lake 26 Jun 1977-5.

Autumn: Interior - Kelowna 9 Sep 1973-2; Summerland 7 Sep 1972-1; Vaseux Lake 24 Sep 1981-150, 25 Sep 1981-50, 6 Oct 1981-10, 7 Oct 1967-1; Gallagher Lake 7 Sep 1977-100. **Coastal:** No records.

Winter: No records.

Extralimital Records: Mt. Colonel Foster 18 and 19 Aug 1974-1 (McNicholl 1975).

Black-chinned Hummingbird

Archilochus alexandri (Bourcier and Mulsant)

BCHU

RANGE: Breeds from central-southern British Columbia and northwestern Montana south to northern Baja California, northwestern Mexico, and Texas. Winters from southwestern California south to southern Mexico.

STATUS: *Very rare* to *uncommon* migrant and summer visitant to the extreme central-southern interior and the Kootenays. *Casual* west of the Pacific and Cascade ranges. Breeds.

CHANGE IN STATUS: J.A. Munro and Cowan (1947) list only 2 records of the Black-chinned Hummingbird and consider it a scarce, nonbreeding summer visitant to extreme southern British Columbia. More recently it has been found on the south coast, in the Kootenays, and north to the Shuswap Lake area and the Thompson Basin. Breeding has now been documented for the Okanagan valley and adults with fledged young have been observed at feeders near Nelson in the west Kootenay.

NONBREEDING: The Black-chinned Hummingbird is locally distributed across extreme southern British Columbia, principally east of the Pacific and Cascade ranges from near sea level to 1,220 m. It occurs in the interior throughout the Okanagan valley and the Shuswap Lake region, north to Little Fort. It is found in the west Kootenay from Trail and South Slocan east to Creston, and in the east Kootenay from Golden south through the Southern Rocky Mountain Trench. On the coast, it has been found only in the Fraser Lowlands. The Black-chinned Hummingbird frequents open riparian woodlands, particularly where deciduous groves occur. It often feeds at sapsucker wells. It is also found in rural and suburban areas such as orchards, parks, and residential sites, where it is attracted to horticultural plants and feeders.

The first Black-chinned Hummingbirds of spring may arrive in late April, but most return in the last 2 weeks of May. Records suggest that males are the first to arrive, followed by females 1 or 2 weeks later. Observations of males decrease after mid-June with only scattered records through to August. Where the males go is unknown; presumably they migrate south. Females and young leave for wintering areas through August; most have departed by the middle of the month. They rarely stay into September.

The centre of abundance is the Okanagan valley. The Black-chinned Hummingbird has been recorded in the interior between 22 April and 30 September and on the coast between 7 May and 25 June.

BREEDING: The Black-chinned Hummingbird breeds in the Okanagan valley north to at least Enderby between 340 and 370 m elevation. It may also nest in the west Kootenay: 2 fledged young, accompanied by adults, were seen at a feeder at Taghum in the summers of 1979 and 1980. All breeding records are from human associated habitats, primarily residential areas and orchards.

Nests: All nests (n=11) were situated in trees (domestic apple and pear, black cottonwood), or shrubs (Virginia creeper, trumpet vine). Nine were located on tree branches; two were in the crotch of a vine. Nests ranged in height from 1 to 7 m with 8 nests between 1 and 2.5 m. They were composed principally of plant down bound together with spider webbing. Occasionally, hair and fine grass were used. One nest had flakes of house paint attached to its outer surface (Cannings, R.A. et al. 1987).

Eggs: Dates for 4 clutches ranged from 2 to 25 June. Calculated dates indicate that eggs could be found as early as 25 May. Clutch size for 4 nests was 2 eggs. Incubation period is 13 to 16 days (Demaree 1970).

Young: Dates for 8 broods ranged from 9 June to 5 August. Brood size ranged from 1 to 2 young (1Y-2, 2Y-6). Fledging period is 21 days (Demaree 1970).

REMARKS: There are 2 additional records for the Vancouver area (Anderson, E. 1967b; Orcutt 1967); both lack supporting documentation and are considered hypothetical.

The distribution, occurrence, and life history of the Black-chinned Hummingbird in British Columbia are poorly known. Stiles (1971) provides helpful hints on field identification, and Baltosser (1987) provides a comprehensive key for in-hand age and sex determination of this species. In addition, all breeding evidence should be fully documented; the most recent breeding record is from 1977.

NOTEWORTHY RECORDS

Spring: Coastal - Agassiz 11 May 1889-1 male (NMC 705); West Vancouver 7 May 1986-1 male (Harris, C. 1987). **Interior** - Oliver 30 May 1951-1 male and 2 females at sapsucker wells; Balfour to Waneta 27 May 1982-7; Trail 22 Apr 1983-1 male; Salmo 17 May 1983-1; Creston 16 May 1971-1, 28 May 1928-1 (Mailliard 1932); Osoyoos 29 May 1907-1 male (MVZ 101962); Vaseux Lake 7 May 1965-1 male; Kimberley 28 May 1949-1 male (Johnstone, W.B. 1949); Lavington 2 May 1976-1 male; Nicholson 23 May 1976-1 male; Little Fort 18 May 1982-1 male.

Summer: Coastal - Strike Lake 10 Jul 1974-1 male (Crowell and Nehls 1974d); Chilliwack 25 Jun 1889-1 male (MVZ 101963); Vancouver 24 Jun 1962-1 at an altitude of 4,000 feet on a trail between Grouse Mountain and Goat Mountain (Boggs and Boggs 1962d). **Interior** - Okanagan Falls 17 May 1969-1 male; Kelowna 5 Jun 1956-1 male (NMC 47910); Lavington 26 Jul 1969-3; Wasa 27 Jun 1977-1 male (Fitz-Gibbon 1977); Tamarack Lake 22 Jul 1976-6; Okanagan Landing 15 Aug 1944-1, last of year; Shuswap Lake Park 14 Jul 1972-3 males at sapsucker wells; Brisco 26

Jun 1976-1 male, 30 Aug 1987-1, last seen; Spillimacheen 28 Jun 1980-1 male; Adams Lake 1 Jul 1963-2 males at sapsucker wells; Golden 18 Jun 1977-1 male.

Autumn: Interior - Cranbrook 30 Sep 1986-1 male hit window (RBCM 19378); Penticton 4 Sep 1973-1 female. **Coastal** - No records.

Winter: No records.

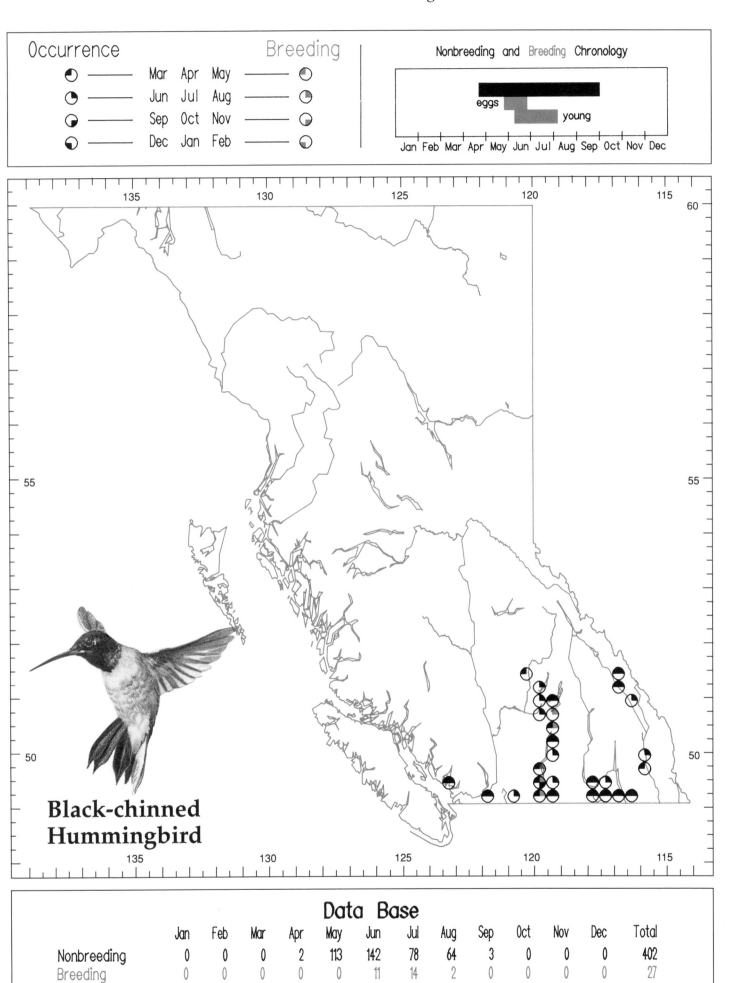

Black-chinned Hummingbird

Occurrence   Breeding

Mar Apr May
Jun Jul Aug
Sep Oct Nov
Dec Jan Feb

Nonbreeding and Breeding Chronology

eggs

young

Jan Feb Mar Apr May Jun Jul Aug Sep Oct Nov Dec

Data Base

	Jan	Feb	Mar	Apr	May	Jun	Jul	Aug	Sep	Oct	Nov	Dec	Total
Nonbreeding	0	0	0	2	113	142	78	64	3	0	0	0	402
Breeding	0	0	0	0	0	11	14	2	0	0	0	0	27

Anna's Hummingbird
Calypte anna (Lesson)

RANGE: Breeds from southwestern British Columbia south along the coast to northwestern Baja California and southern Arizona. Winters from southern British Columbia to central Baja California and east to southern Arizona, southwestern New Mexico (rarely) and northern Mexico; casually north to Alaska.

STATUS: *Rare* to locally *uncommon* resident on the south mainland coast and southern Vancouver Island becoming a *very rare* seasonal visitant north along the mainland coast to Terrace. *Rare* resident in the Okanagan; *very rare* visitant elsewhere in the interior. Breeds.

CHANGE IN STATUS: Since the publication of J.A. Munro and Cowan (1947), who make no mention of the species, the Anna's Hummingbird has established itself as a resident in south-central and southwestern British Columbia, expanding its range north along the coast from California (see Zimmerman 1973).

The species may have appeared in British Columbia as early as 1944. In a letter to the editor of a Victoria newspaper in January 1953, J.O. Clay writes, "a hummingbird was observed here [Victoria] for three winters since 1944 until January 13, 1947 and this season at intervals until January 12." In the 1950s, 18 records of wintering birds are on file, all from southern Vancouver Island, but identification of the wintering birds was not

made until 1958 (Guiguet 1959). The first breeding record was also reported that year. The first record for the mainland coast was from West Vancouver in 1959. Twelve are on file for the 1960s, all but one from the south coast.

Sightings increased dramatically from 1970 to the present; in the Victoria area alone nearly 300 records are on file from 1970 to 1979 and over 400 from 1980 to 1987. The first Okanagan record was on 23 October 1974 at Penticton; on 26 September 1975, the species was reported in Terrace.

NONBREEDING: The Anna's Hummingbird is distributed along the coast from southern Vancouver Island and the lower Fraser River valley, north to Sayward; there are scattered records north to Terrace. It is absent from the Queen Charlotte Islands. In the interior, it is found in the Okanagan and west Kootenay valleys becoming widely scattered farther east to Revelstoke and Golden, and north to Smithers and Prince George. Its centre of abundance is the Greater Victoria area.

Nearly all the British Columbia records for the species are from habitats associated with humans, primarily residential yards and gardens. There is one report of an Anna's Hummingbird landing on a boat about 2 km from shore.

The first observations of the birds in the province were invariably from gardens containing yellow jasmine or fuchsias

Figure 289. Male Anna's Hummingbird at feeder, Hollyhill Place, Victoria, 8 December 1980 (Mark Nyhof).

Anna's Hummingbird

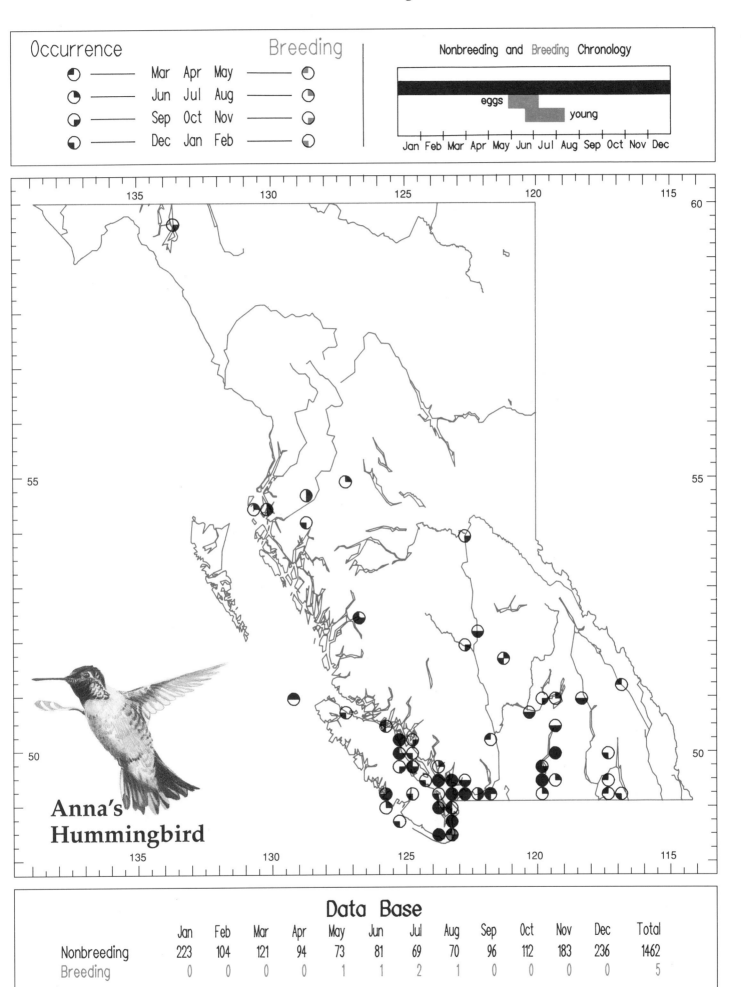

in bloom, but now most reports are of birds at artificial feeders (Fig. 289).

Due to the hummingbird's resident status on the south coast and in the Okanagan valley, and its erratic occurrence elsewhere in the province, migration patterns, if any, are difficult to detect.

BREEDING: There are only 2 indisputable breeding records for British Columbia, both from southern Vancouver Island. On 6 July 1958, a nest containing 2 eggs was found beside the Cowichan River about 13 km south of Duncan (Guiguet 1978). On 26 July, the nest contained 2 unfledged young. It was situated on a western redcedar bough about 1 m above the ground. The second nest, situated on a Douglas-fir bough about 2 m above the ground, was found in Saanich. It contained 2 near-fledged young on 17 June 1984. The nest and young were gone on 19 June. Incubation period is known to be 14 to 19 days and the fledging period is 18 to 23 days (Stiles 1970), so the eggs of this brood may have been laid about 16 May.

Juvenile birds have been reported with adults at feeders throughout the bird's range in the province (see George 1980), but evidence of breeding is only circumstantial.

REMARKS: For a discussion of a recent range expansion of Anna's Hummingbird northward from California, see Zimmerman (1973). Life history information is provided by Stiles (1970) and Johnsgard (1983). Baltosser (1987) provides a comprehensive key for in-hand age and sex determination of the species.

POSTSCRIPT: Details for the following 2 nests, found in a garden in Victoria, were provided by B.R. Gates (pers. comm.). On 29 February 1988, a female Anna's Hummingbird was found on a nest that contained 2 eggs. The nest (Fig. 290) was about 5.5 m from the ground on a limb of a flowering plum tree, 0.75 m from the trunk. On 12 March, both eggs were found on the ground. Nest and eggs were collected (RBCM 2283); incubation was well advanced.

On 12 March 1988, a second nest was located 3.5 m above ground in a sequoia tree, 40 m from the nest above. It contained 2 eggs. The first young hatched 25 March and fledged 14 April; the second (Fig. 291; RBCM Photo 1225) hatched on 26 March and left the nest on 20 April.

This extends the egg period from about 15 February through 6 July and the nestling period from 25 March through 10 August. Females may raise 2 broods (Stiles 1970). See Calder (1974) for a discussion on limiting factors for winter breeding.

Recently, an old record was discovered: on 28 July 1985, a male was seen near Mile 87, Haines Road (Kelsall Lake) in extreme northwestern British Columbia. It was photographed on 11 August (RBCM Photo 1244) and was last seen in late August (L. Goodwin pers. comm.).

Figure 290. *Female Anna's Hummingbird on nest, Uplands, Victoria, 5 March 1988 (Tim Zurowski).*

Figure 291. *Adult female Anna's Hummingbird feeding recently fledged young at Victoria, 20 April 1988 (Ervio Sian).*

NOTEWORTHY RECORDS

Spring: Coastal - Saanich 8 May 1984-6; Ganges 11 Apr 1969-1 male (RBCM 11648); Vancouver Apr 1972-2 (Zimmerman 1973); Whytecliffe 30 Mar 1980-1 pair in courtship; Chilliwack 23 Apr 1983-2 singing males; Comox 20 Mar 1975-1 pair in courtship; Campbell River (Discovery Passage) 11 Apr 1976-2 at feeder; Triangle Island (Scott Islands) 23 May 1978-1 male; 29 May 1974-1 male; Bella Coola 17 Mar 1977-1. **Interior** - Salmo 21 May 1978-1; Penticton 20 Apr 1979-1 male, first of spring; South Slocan 30 May 1984-1 male at feeder; Summerland 27 May 1977-1 (Whitelaw 1977); Kelowna 25 Apr 1977-1 bird wintered, remained until this date; Lytton to Boston Bar 24 May 1964-1 at Blue Lake Resort; Nicholson mid-May 1976-1 male.

Summer: Coastal - Victoria 26 Aug 1958-1 male, first documented record for Canada (Guiguet 1959); Langford 1 to 31 Jul 1984-5; Long Beach 2 Aug 1974-1 (Hatler et al. 1978); West Vancouver 16 Jul 1979-3; Chilliwack 31 Aug 1981-1; Campbell River (Discovery Passage) 9 Jun 1973-1; Triangle Island (Scott Islands) 6 Jul 1974-1 (RBCM Photo 398); Melville Island (Chatham Sound) 3 Jul 1976-1; Prince Rupert 28 Jun 1982-1 (Campbell 1982c); Terrace 11 Jun 1983-1 at feeder (Mattocks et al. 1983). **Interior** - Oliver 11 Aug 1979-2;

Penticton 27 Jul 1980-1; Kelowna 23 Jul 1977-2, adult female with fledged young; 108 Mile House 19 Jun 1980-1; Terrace 9 Jun 1979-1 male (George 1980); Smithers 14 Jun 1983-1, also at feeder each summer from 1982 to 1984.

Autumn: Interior - Prince George 3 Sep 1972-1 male (RBCM Photo 267); Williams Lake 26 Oct 1979-1 at feeder, 3 to 23 Nov 1987-1 male at feeder (Campbell 1988a); Riske Creek 18 Sep 1986-1 at feeder; Revelstoke 15 Nov 1982-1, 23 Nov 1977-1; Kamloops 8 Nov 1985-1; Vernon 20 Nov 1982-1 female (RBCM Photo 652), 1 Nov 1981-1 male (RBCM Photo 742); Kelowna 15 Oct 1976-1 (Whitelaw 1977); Penticton 6 Oct 1978-1 male singing, 28 Oct 1976-1, . **Coastal** - Terrace 26 Sep 1975-1 (Hay 1976); Prince Rupert 3 Oct 1981-1 at feeder; Bella Coola 10 Oct 1975-1 (Shepard, M.G. 1976b); Willow Point 20 Nov 1974-1; Comox 7 Nov 1973-1 male (RBCM Photo 339); Tofino 8 Nov 1983-1 (Campbell 1983d); West Vancouver 8 Nov 1959-1; Langford 22 Sep 1986-4.

Winter: Interior - 100 Mile House mid-Jan 1983-1; Revelstoke 13 Jan 1983-1 male (RBCM 18144); Kamloops 31 Dec 1981-1 at feeder since 31 October; Vernon 3 Dec 1980-1, 3 to 20 Dec 1983-4; Silverton Jan 1978-1 female (RBCM Photo 752);

Okanagan Falls 22 Jan 1980-4 last date seen, here since autumn; Creston 27 Jan 1975-1 at feeder. **Coastal** - Kitimat 12 Dec 1984-1 male at feeder, 19 Dec 1981-1 male (RBCM Photo 790); Bella Coola winter 1976/1977-1 present all winter (for first time) until March, 2 Dec 1980-1 male at feeder, fed every 25 min, temperature -21°C and gale-force winds; Port Hardy 19 Feb 1987-2 males; Comox Jan 1968-1 female (RBCM 11293); Tofino 2 Jan 1981-1 male at feeder; Chilliwack 7 Dec 1980-1 male (RBCM 17127); Vancouver 11 Jan 1971-1 male (RBCM Photo 131); Saanich 15 Feb 1985-4 males, 2 females; Victoria 5 Jan 1974-1 (RBCM Photo 338), 19 Dec 1987-43, bird count.

Christmas Counts: Interior - Recorded from 4 of 19 localities and on 6% of all counts. Maxima: Vernon 18 Dec 1983-2, 27 Dec 1981-1; Kelowna 20 Dec 1981-1; Penticton 27 Dec 1976-1; Vaseux Lake 28 Dec 1974-1, 31 Dec 1975-1. **Coastal** - Recorded from 15 of 28 localities and on 31% of all counts. Maxima: Victoria 15 Dec 1984-24, all-time Canadian high count (Monroe 1985b); Vancouver 16 Dec 1984-16; White Rock 30 Dec 1984-15.

Extralimital Records: Atlin 2 Oct 1980-1 male. Kessel and Gibson (1978) report several records in autumn and winter in southeastern Alaska.

Calliope Hummingbird

Stellula calliope (Gould)

RANGE: Breeds from south-central British Columbia and southwestern Alberta south to northern Baja California and east to western Colorado. Winters in Mexico.

STATUS: *Uncommon* to *fairly common* migrant and summer visitant to the southern interior becoming *uncommon* in the central interior to *very rare* in the Peace Lowlands. *Rare* spring visitant in the Fraser Lowlands; *very rare* on Vancouver Island. Breeds.

NONBREEDING: The Calliope Hummingbird (Fig. 292) is widely distributed throughout the southern interior, north through the Cariboo-Chilcotin to Moricetown, Pine Pass, and Charlie Lake in the Peace River parklands. On the coast, it occurs sporadically through the Fraser Lowlands and on southeastern Vancouver Island. There is a single record for the northern mainland coast. This hummingbird has been reported from sea level to 2,050 m elevation.

The Calliope Hummingbird frequents open forests and forest edges (Fig. 293), subalpine meadows, riparian thickets, canyons, residential gardens, parks, and orchards.

Birds can arrive in early April, but the main movement occurs from the end of April through May. Males arrive first and defend territories usually through May and June (Armstrong 1987). Females arrive 1 or 2 weeks later and begin interacting with territorial males. Males leave their breeding territories after the females begin incubation. In the Okanagan, few adult males are found at low elevations after the end of June; some apparently move south through subalpine meadows (Cannings, R.A. et al. 1987). Adult females and young begin their departure in mid-August and most have gone by the end of the month. Late autumn and winter records are very unusual.

The Calliope Hummingbird has been recorded from 7 April to 13 September. There is an early date reported in the literature of 1 March (Orcutt 1967), but documentation is lacking and we have excluded it from the account.

Figure 292. Male Calliope Hummingbird at Kilpoola Lake, west of Osoyoos, June 1974 (Ervio Sian).

Figure 293. Open, disturbed habitat in the vicinity of Bugaboo Glacier is frequented by Calliope Hummingbirds in the east Kootenay, August 1971 (Neil K. Dawe).

Calliope Hummingbird

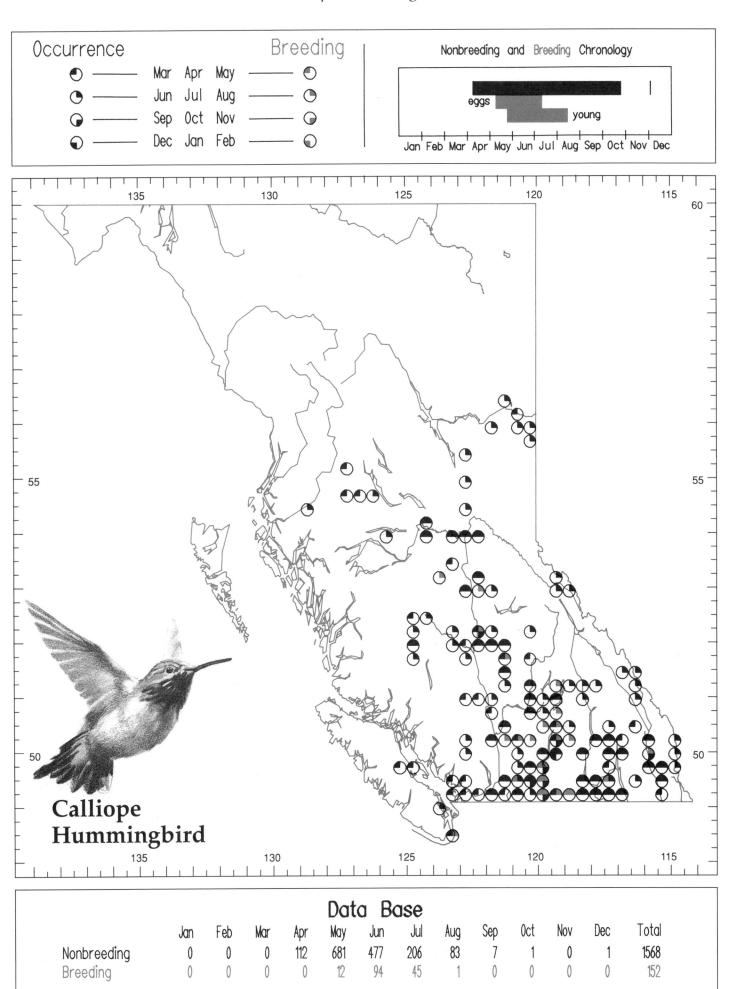

Occurrence · **Breeding**

	Mar Apr May	
	Jun Jul Aug	
	Sep Oct Nov	
	Dec Jan Feb	

Nonbreeding and Breeding Chronology

eggs · young

Jan Feb Mar Apr May Jun Jul Aug Sep Oct Nov Dec

Data Base

	Jan	Feb	Mar	Apr	May	Jun	Jul	Aug	Sep	Oct	Nov	Dec	Total
Nonbreeding	0	0	0	112	681	477	206	83	7	1	0	1	1568
Breeding	0	0	0	0	12	94	45	1	0	0	0	0	152

BREEDING: The Calliope Hummingbird breeds in the interior from the southern portions of the province north through the Thompson-Okanagan and Fraser plateaus to the vicinity of the Nazko Upland. On the coast, it has bred only at Victoria on southern Vancouver Island (RBCM 1848). The breeding centre of abundance is the south Okanagan valley. Nests have been found from near sea level to 1,980 m elevation, although most nests were located above 400 m elevation.

Nests were most often found in gardens, orchards, and the open ponderosa pine - Douglas-fir forests of the central-southern interior. Other habitats included semi-open benchland, open mixed forest, subalpine fir forest adjacent to meadows, wooded pond edges, riparian thickets, and deep canyons near waterfalls and swift water. Pitelka (1942) and Armstrong (1987) note that, generally, there is habitat separation between sexes: females usually nest in wooded situations and males hold territories in more open areas, such as meadows.

Nests: Nests (n=47) were situated in deciduous trees (47%; Fig. 294), including birch (21%), trembling aspen (9%), domestic apple, black cottonwood, poplars, willows, and elm, and in coniferous trees (47%), including Douglas-fir (21%), ponderosa pine (21%), subalpine fir, and spruces. Three nests were found in shrubs, including wild roses and blackberries. Most were positioned on small, horizontal branches, often dead, sheltered under larger branches. Heights of 45 nests ranged from 0.6 to 15 m with 56% between 2 and 4.5 m. Nests were tiny cups, usually composed of moss, fine plant fibers, and spider webs, lined with plant down; the outsides were covered with lichen. Other material included hair, fine grass, bark, bits of dry leaves, and pine and fir needles. In 2 instances, the previous year's nest was rebuilt, a practice which is apparently atypical of hum-

mingbirds, although a similar instance was also noted by Brunton et al. (1979) in Alberta.

Eggs: Dates for 42 clutches ranged from 7 May to 8 July with 51% recorded between 10 and 26 June. Clutch size ranged from 1 to 3 eggs (1E-3, 2E-38, 3E-1) with 93% having 2 eggs. One clutch in British Columbia had an incubation period of 15 days which is within the range reported by Calder (1971).

Young: Dates for 33 broods (Fig. 295) ranged from 29 May to 12 August with 53% of all broods recorded between 21 June and 8 July. Calculated dates indicate that young could be found as early as 22 May. Brood size ranged from 1 to 2 young (1Y-6, 2Y-27) with 82% having 2 young. Three nestling periods in British Columbia ranged from 19 to 22 days.

REMARKS: Two nestlings, collected 31 May 1942 at Cultus Lake (see Munro, J.A. and Cowan 1947) were re-identified as Rufous Hummingbirds.

The Calliope Hummingbird probably nests north to Taylor where a female was seen visiting a nest (contents unknown) on 31 May 1987. It is the smallest bird in British Columbia. Natural food plants include squaw and red-flowering currant, Oregon-grape, gooseberry and honeysuckle (Fig. 296), but most of our feeding records from natural sites were of birds at sapsucker wells in birch trees (Fig. 297). These tiny birds are also attracted to feeders.

A general overview of hummingbird feeding, food flowers, and life history can be found in Grant, K.A. and Grant (1968), Campbell and Hosford (1979), and Johnsgard (1983). Studies of the Calliope Hummingbird have been carried out in the southern Okanagan valley from 1983 to 1985 (see Tamm 1985 and Armstrong 1986).

Figure 294. *Female Calliope Hummingbird on nest at Kilpoola Lake, June 1974 (Ervio Sian).*

Figure 295. *Female Calliope Hummingbird feeding young near Williams Lake, July 1975 (Ervio Sian).*

Figure 296. Male Calliope Hummingbird feeding near Williams Lake, May 1984 (Ervio Sian).

Figure 297. Female Calliope Hummingbird feeding on tree sap at Alexis Creek, July 1983 (Ervio Sian).

NOTEWORTHY RECORDS

Spring: Coastal - Victoria 27 Apr 1984-1 male at feeder; Huntingdon 20 May 1958-1 female (PMNH 71777); Vancouver 23 to 24 Apr 1982-1 male, 16 to 19 May 1986-1 female, 18 May 1929-1 male (RBCM 9500); Maplewood 25 Apr to 2 May 1982-1; Mount Burnaby 9 May 1974-2 (Shepard, M.G. 1975a); Tsolum River near Courtenay 30 Apr to 2 May 1986-pair believed to be nesting. **Interior** - Trail 1 May 1966-1; Lone Pine Hill 4 May 1981-1 male; Okanagan Falls 7 Apr 1976-1 male; Penticton 22 Apr 1978-1 male, first of year, at red-flowering currant; White Lake (Okanagan Falls) 23 May 1968-12; Arawana 9 Apr 1965-1, first of year; Fauquier 23 Apr 1981-1; Winfield 24 Apr 1961-1, first of year; Columbia Lake 23 May 1955-1 male (ROM 73762); Vernon 1 May 1957-1 male, 1 May 1966-1 male; Moha 13 Apr 1968-5, including 3 females; Kleena Kleene 30 May 1961-first males (Paul 1964); 100 Mile House 27 Apr 1977-1; Williams Lake 29 Apr 1978-1 male, 29 Apr 1983-3 males, no females yet; 24 km s Prince George 24 Apr 1983-1 male, 29 Apr 1984-1 male, females arrived about 7 May; Vanderhoof 23 Apr 1983-1 male at feeder, 24 May 1985-1 male (RBCM 18399); Moricetown 26 May 1978-1 male in courtship flight; Fort St. John 23 May 1985-1 female (UBC 14748).

Summer: Coastal - Duncan 10 Jun 1966-1 adult male, window kill; Agassiz late Jul 1892-1 (Saunders 1902); Garibaldi Park 12 Aug 1968-1 feeding at alpine flowers; Lakelse Lake 22 Jul 1976-1. **Interior** - Creston 16 Aug 1982-1, late date; South Slocan 10 Jun 1979-20 to 30 at feeder and in garden; Chauncey Creek 22 Jun 1982-1 male on territory; Wasa 24 Aug 1971-1 (Dawe 1971); Chimney Lake 18 Aug 1977-last date females came to feeder; Chilcotin Lake 7 Jun 1977-1; Williams Lake 1 Jul 1982-10 females, 2 males; Mount Robson Park 17 Jun 1973-1; 32 km e Prince George 17 Jun 1969-1 (NMC 56897); Vanderhoof 1 to 30 Jun 1985-7 at feeders; Topley 22 Jul 1956-1 (NMC 41285); Pine Pass 2 Aug 1965-1 male; Dawson Creek 6 Jul 1986-2 females, 3 Aug 1975-1 male; Moberly Lake 6 Jul 1986-1 male; Mile 63, Alaska Highway 6 Jun 1986-1 adult male.

Autumn: Interior - Williams Lake 3 Sep 1979-1; Skookumchuck 1 Sep 1976-1; Okanagan Landing 2 Sep 1929-1 immature; Summerland 13 Sep 1962-1; Penticton 22 Oct 1976-1; Princeton 5 Sep 1977-2 females. **Coastal** - No records.

Winter: Interior - Kelowna 1 Dec 1968-1 male (Cannings, R.A. et al. 1987). **Coastal** - No records.

Christmas Counts: Not recorded.

Rufous Hummingbird

RUHU

Selasphorus rufus (Gmelin)

RANGE: Breeds from southeastern Alaska, British Columbia and southwestern Alberta south to northwestern California and southern Idaho. Winters in southern Texas and Mexico.

STATUS: *Fairly common* to locally *common* migrant and summer visitant throughout most of the province including Vancouver Island and the Queen Charlotte Islands. *Very rare* summer visitant to the northeastern corner of the province. Breeds.

NONBREEDING: The Rufous Hummingbird is distributed throughout most of British Columbia, becoming sporadic in the northeastern corner of the province. It occurs from sea level to at least 2,260 m elevation.

It frequents a wide variety of habitat types including residential areas, coastal forests and islands, logging slashes and burns, deciduous growths at forest edges, open interior forests, willow swamps, subalpine forests, and alpine meadows.

The first male Rufous Hummingbirds arrive on the south coast in early March, at least 3 weeks earlier than in the interior. Females follow, arriving up to 3 weeks later. The main movement occurs in April on the coast and in May in the interior.

Adult males leave the breeding areas in late June and through July, likely moving to higher elevations where a fresh bloom of wildflowers awaits. Most hummingbirds have left the northern regions by mid-August, the southern interior by September, and the coast by October.

BREEDING: The Rufous Hummingbird breeds throughout most of its summer range in the province, north to at least Dokdaon Creek, excluding the northeastern portion of the province. It breeds from near sea level to 1,830 m elevation.

Nesting habitats include dense mature and second growth coniferous forests, deciduous woods, riparian thickets, swamps and meadows, farmland, pasture edges, orchards, and residential areas such as city yards, parks, gardens, and golf courses.

Nests: Most nests (76%; n=235) were situated in coniferous trees, including western redcedar (27%), Douglas-fir (11%), spruce (Sitka, white, Engelmann), western hemlock, pine (lodgepole, ponderosa), grand fir, Rocky Mountain juniper, and western yew. Nest sites in deciduous trees (16%) included domestic apple, plum, pear, and apricot, birch, red alder, bigleaf maple, arbutus, vine maple, black cottonwood, horse chestnut, holly, trembling aspen, walnut, and oak. Deciduous tree use may be underestimated; Horvath (1964) notes that in summer the crowns of deciduous trees are used by hummingbirds as nest sites, allowing the birds to benefit from the temperature-reducing effects of the

evapotranspiration of the trees. Shrub nest sites (8%) included saskatoon, salal, ocean-spray, salmonberry, and honeysuckle. A few nests were used the previous year; 1 site was used 3 years in succession. Most nests were near the end of a branch. One was found in a cavity left by a rotting branch, one was built on a wind chime on the fourth floor balcony of an apartment (RBCM Photo 935), and one was found on a metal loop over a wharf piling. Most were small neat bowls composed primarily of moss lined with plant down (black cottonwood, willows, cattail). The outsides of the nests were usually covered with lichen attached with spider webbing; one exterior was covered with birch bark. Other materials included hair, fine grasses, plant fibres and bark, needles, feathers, twigs, and leaves. Nests (n=244) ranged in height from 0.5 to 18 m with 85% recorded between 0.5 and 3 m. The diameters of 3 used nests ranged from 3.8 to 6.4 cm; 1 nest was 2.5 cm deep.

Eggs: Dates for 150 clutches ranged from 30 March (RBCM 846) to 10 July, with 52% recorded between 15 May and 14 June. Egg laying at the coast can begin up to 6 weeks earlier than in the interior. Clutch size ranged from 1 to 4 eggs (1E-10, 2E-137, 3E-2, 4E-1) with 90% having 2 eggs. For 7 clutches in British Columbia the incubation period ranged from 15 to 17 days.

Young: Dates for 134 broods ranged from 14 April to 9 August with 53% recorded between 31 May and 2 July. Brood size ranged from 1 to 3 young (1Y-15, 2Y-118, 3Y-1) with 88% having 2 young. The nestling period for 15 nests in British Columbia ranged from 21 to 26 days.

REMARKS: Most winter records for this hummingbird in British Columbia are without adequate data and are from locations where the Anna's Hummingbird winters (see Clay 1947, Irving 1953, Lemon 1958, Boggs and Boggs 1960, Poynter 1960, and Guiguet 1978). One occurrence, verified by colour photographs, was in Victoria on 8 and 9 January 1983: an adult male at a feeder; temperature -2°C, snowing. Other reports have been discounted, including Christmas counts (see Anderson, R.R. 1980, 1982). Observers are encouraged to provide full documentation for sightings of the Rufous Hummingbird for the period December to February.

During the past decade faculty and students at the University of British Columbia have produced a series of important papers on the Rufous Hummingbird, including Gass (1974, 1978, 1979), Gass et al. (1976), and Purdy (1978).

POSTSCRIPT: On 28 February 1988, an adult female Rufous Hummingbird died of cold (UBC 14894) in North Vancouver. This appears to be the second valid winter record .

NOTEWORTHY RECORDS

Spring: Coastal - Chatham Islands 5 May 1983-1 male; Royal Oak (Victoria) 11 Apr 1954-50+ in cherry tree (Flahaut and Schultz 1954b) 11 May 1979-1 male; Saanich 18 Mar 1984-1 male, 8 Apr 1984-1 female, arrival date; Galiano Island 12 Apr 1981-30; Tofino 20 Mar 1980-1 male; Pitt Meadows 29 Mar 1977-1 male; Qualicum Beach 2 Mar 1974-1; Campbell River (Discovery Passage) 25 Mar 1973-1, 28 May 1974-40+ at feeders; Point Neville 22 May 1978-32 at feeders; Port Hardy 29 Mar 1941-1; Namu 30 Mar 1983-2 males, 12 Apr 1983-3 females, arrival; Cape St. James 17 Mar 1978-1, 6 Apr 1982-1, 8 May 1982-3, first female today; Sewall 31 Mar 1984-1 male, 16 Apr 1984-1 first female; Green Island 25 Mar 1966-1 male. **Interior** - Salmo 8 Apr 1977-1; Kinnaird 8 Mar 1969-1; Balfour to Waneta 16 May 1981-69 on bird count; Summerland 18 Apr 1966-1; Revelstoke 23 Apr 1984, first of year; 70 Mile House 24 Mar 1984-1 male; 24 km s Prince George 22 Apr 1983-1 male, 25 Apr 1984-1 male, 5 May 1984-1

female; Vanderhoof 21 Apr 1983-1 male; Quick 26 Apr 1981-1 male; Cecil Lake 9 May 1968-1; Atlin 16 May 1981-1 (Campbell 1981).

Summer: Coastal - Tugwell Lake 3 Jul 1983-60, 10 Jul 1981-61 counted on walk around lake; Victoria 20 Jun 1976-males last seen; Saanich 23 Jun 1978-males last seen; Pacific Rim National Park 8 Jul 1973-adult males gone; Qualicum Beach 10 Jul 1975-adult males gone; Goose Group 12 Jun 1948-1, last record of adult male; Bolkus Islands 6 Jul 1977-10; Sewall 23 Jun 1980-4; Lakelse Lake 17 Jun 1977-8. **Interior** - South Slocan 22 Jun 1979-30 to 40 females and young, males not seen recently; Argenta 3 Aug 1980-8 at 2,130 m elevation; Crowfoot Mountain 9 Aug 1973-1, last sighting; Tatlayoko Lake 5 Aug 1984-4 females, only in alpine meadows at tree line (1,800 m elevation); Williams Lake 11 Jul 1978-1, last male, 4 Aug 1977-1, late date; Isaac Lake 26 Jul 1961-1 female at 2,260 m elevation; Clayhurst 1 Jul 1978-1; Fern

Lake (Kwadacha Wilderness Park) 23 Aug 1983-1 (Cooper and Cooper 1983); Dease Lake 18 Jul 1962-1 male (NMC 49799); Metah Mountain 7 Jul 1977-3 at 1520 m elevation; Atlin 20 Aug 1931-1 (Munro, J.A. and Cowan 1947); Mile 46.5 Haines Road (Kelsall Lake) 21 Jun 1972-1.

Autumn: Interior - Williams Lake 3 Sep 1979-1; Yoho National Park 8 Sep 1976-1 (Wade 1977); Canim Lake 4 Sep 1960-5; Kamloops 10 Sep 1985-1; Kelowna 31 Oct 1968-1; Penticton 18 Sep 1977-1; Salmo 15 Sep 1983-1, last seen. **Coastal** - Sewall 9 Sep 1980-1; Cape St. James 12 Oct 1981-1; Stories Beach 25 Oct 1974-1; Langley 8 Oct 1968-3; Vancouver 10 Oct 1971-1 (Campbell et al. 1972b); Tofino 30 Nov 1978-1; Saanich 30 Nov 1981-1 chased from feeder by an Anna's Hummingbird.

Winter: See Remarks.

Christmas Counts: See Remarks.

Rufous Hummingbird

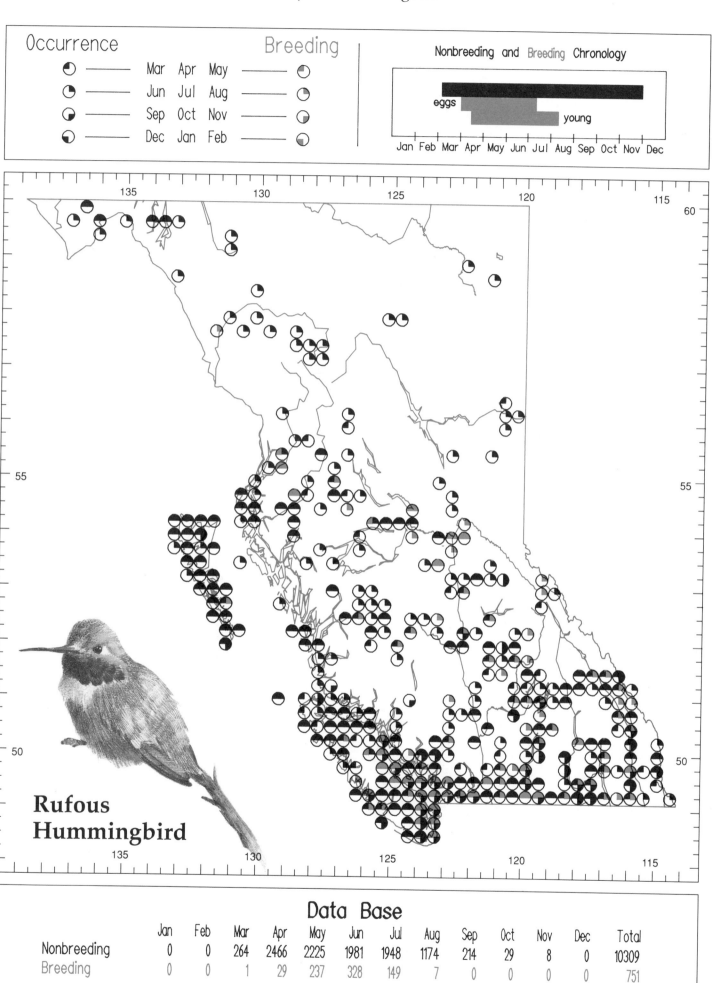

Occurrence

- ◐ ——— Mar Apr May ——— ◑
- ◕ ——— Jun Jul Aug ——— ◔
- ◔ ——— Sep Oct Nov ——— ◑
- ◕ ——— Dec Jan Feb ——— ◐

Breeding

Nonbreeding and Breeding Chronology

eggs

young

Jan Feb Mar Apr May Jun Jul Aug Sep Oct Nov Dec

Rufous Hummingbird

Data Base

	Jan	Feb	Mar	Apr	May	Jun	Jul	Aug	Sep	Oct	Nov	Dec	Total
Nonbreeding	0	0	264	2466	2225	1981	1948	1174	214	29	8	0	10309
Breeding	0	0	1	29	237	328	149	7	0	0	0	0	751

Belted Kingfisher

Ceryle alcyon (Linnaeus)

RANGE: Breeds from western Alaska across forested Canada south to the southern United States. Winters from south coastal Alaska, southern British Columbia, east across the central United States to New England, and south throughout the United States, Middle America, the West Indies, and Bermuda to northern South America and the Galapagos Islands.

STATUS: *Uncommon* migrant and summer visitant throughout the province. In winter, *uncommon* along the coast, *rare* to *uncommon* in the southern interior. Widespread breeder.

NONBREEDING: The Belted Kingfisher (Fig. 299) is distributed throughout British Columbia from sea level to 2,000 m elevation. It frequents a variety of marine, freshwater, and riparian habitats, including rivers (Fig. 300), streams, marshes, lakes, coastal shorelines, lagoons, tidepools, estuaries, beaches, sloughs, beaver ponds, and pools in city parks. Elevated perches such as shrubs, trees, snags, and hydro wires are important habitat components.

Birds can be found in the interior by early March, although the main spring movement occurs through late April, and well into May in northern areas.

The autumn movement begins in late August for the northern populations, and most birds have left the north by early September. The southern populations begin migration in September and the movement continues through mid-October and occasionally into November.

The Belted Kingfisher winters along the coast, including Vancouver Island and the Queen Charlotte Islands. Small numbers winter regularly in southern interior valleys, including the Okanagan, west Kootenay, Creston, and Columbia valleys; rarely elsewhere.

Their numbers, as revealed through weekly counts over one year along a 50 km stretch of the east coast of Vancouver Island (Comox Harbour to Deep Bay; Fig. 298), ranged from a low of 4 in spring to a high of 24 in autumn.

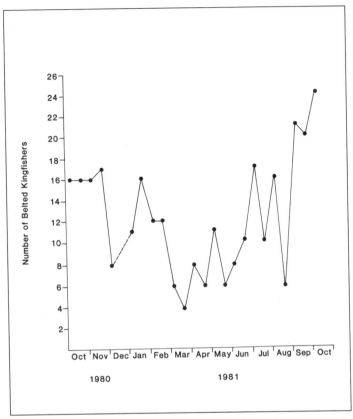

Figure 298. Biweekly counts (averages) of Belted Kingfishers, Comox Harbour to Deep Bay, Vancouver Island, 11 October 1980 to 10 October 1981 (courtesy Canadian Wildlife Service). The dashed line indicates a period when counts were not made.

Figure 299. Adult Belted Kingfisher near Alexis Creek, June 1974 (Ervio Sian).

Belted Kingfisher

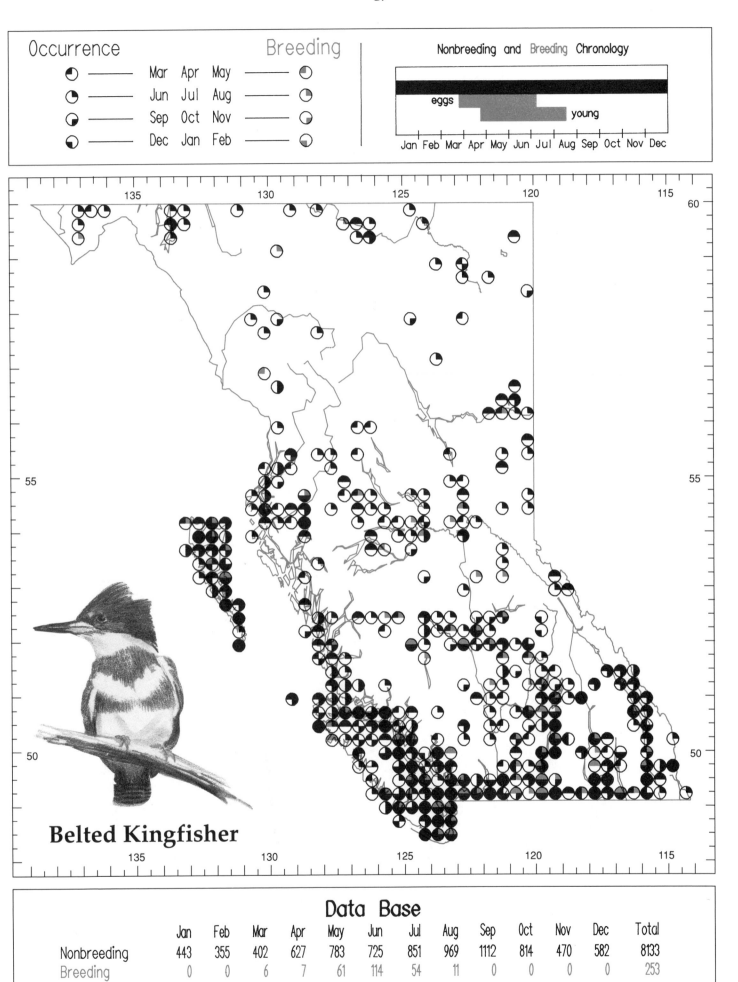

Belted Kingfisher

Data Base

	Jan	Feb	Mar	Apr	May	Jun	Jul	Aug	Sep	Oct	Nov	Dec	Total
Nonbreeding	443	355	402	627	783	725	851	969	1112	814	470	582	8133
Breeding	0	0	6	7	61	114	54	11	0	0	0	0	253

BREEDING: The Belted Kingfisher breeds throughout the province, including Vancouver Island and the Queen Charlotte Islands, wherever breeding sites, in the form of natural or man-made cutbanks, are near foraging areas. Nests have been found from near sea level to 1,370 m elevation.

Nests: Most nests (91%; n=64) were situated in natural or man-made cutbanks including road or railway cutbanks (44%), river and lakeshore banks (31%), and gravel pits. Other nest sites included sawdust piles, soil among overturned tree roots, and one nest was in the wall of a pit silo. Most nests (73%; n=45) were excavated in sand or clay banks. All were located in burrows excavated by the birds. Eggs were usually laid on the bare substrate in an enlarged chamber at the end of the burrow. Occasionally, nests were lined with fish bones, grass stems, plant stems, leaves, or root fibres. Lengths of 22 burrows ranged from 1 to 2.4 m with 14 burrows between 1 and 1.8 m. Heights of 68 nests ranged from 1.2 to 24 m above the base of the bank, with 68% between 1.5 and 6 m. Four entrance hole diameters ranged from 9 to 13 cm. Six nests were located in cutbanks also occupied by Bank Swallow (*Riparia riparia*) or Northern Rough-winged Swallow (*Stelgidopteryx serripennis*) colonies.

Eggs: Dates for 18 clutches ranged from 1 May to 5 July with 9 clutches recorded between 21 May and 7 June. Calculated dates indicate that eggs could be found as early as 23 March. Nests at the coast can have eggs at least one month earlier than those in the interior. Clutch size ranged from 2 to 7 eggs (2E-1, 3E-5, 6E-5, 7E-7) with 12 having 6 or 7 eggs. Incubation period is about 23 to 24 days (Mousely 1938).

Young: Dates for 11 broods (Fig. 301) ranged from 22 April to 14 August. Brood size ranged from 2 to 7 young (2Y-2, 3Y-4, 5Y-2, 6Y-2, 7Y-1). Nestling period is 30 to 35 days (Mousely 1938).

REMARKS: Prose (1985) considered 7 habitat variables in preparing a breeding season habitat suitability index model for the Belted Kingfisher including percent of shoreline subject to severe wave action – no wave action giving the highest index; average water transparency – the clearer the water the higher the index; percent water surface obstruction – zero obstruction preferred; percent of water area that is ≤60 cm in depth; percent riffles – presence (30% to 70%) enhances habitat quality by providing rich food sources, partly a result of the density of invertebrates in riffles; perch availability – at least 1 perch per 25 m of shoreline is optimal; and distance to nearest soil bank from the water's edge – the closer, the higher the suitability.

Figure 300. Pine River west of Chetwynd, 14 July 1969 (Dennis A. Demarchi). Winding waterways with backwaters are used by Belted Kingfishers for foraging.

Figure 301. *Nestling Belted Kingfishers at the entrance of their burrow near Alexis Creek, June 1974 (Ervio Sian).*

NOTEWORTHY RECORDS

Spring: Coastal - Witty's Lagoon 2 Apr 1981-4; Cowichan River 2 Apr 1974-10; Rosewall Creek 30 Apr 1976-16; Comox 20 May 1940-20; Digby Island 13 Apr 1977-5, courtship activities. **Interior** - Okanagan River 23 Mar 1977-2 courting, male fed female small fish; Invermere 28 Mar 1978-1; Okanagan Landing 9 Mar 1926-early spring; Cache Creek 21 Mar 1977-1; Williams Lake 11 Apr 1951-1 (NMC 47922); Prince George 24 Mar 1977-1; Toboggan Lake 7 Apr 1979-2; Bear Flat 4 May 1986-2; Fort Nelson 18 May 1974-1 (Erskine and Davidson 1976); Liard Hot Springs 27 May 1981-1; Atlin 9 May 1981-1.

Summer: Coastal - Witty's Lagoon 6 Jul 1975-11; Nanoose Harbour 23 Jun 1977-3 (Dawe and Lang 1980); Goose Group, June and early Jul 1948-6+ possibly four pairs frequented island; Masset 18 Jul 1982-5 survey. **Interior** - Shuswap Lake Jul 1961-3; Buffalo Lake 15 Jul 1967-3; Williams Lake 14 Jul 1980-4; Tahtsa Lake 12 Aug 1956-7; Alces River 16 Jul 1978-2; near Liard and Beaver Rivers 10 Aug 1977-2.

Autumn: Interior - Atlin 20 Sep 1913-1 (Kermode and Anderson 1914); Liard Hot Springs 6 Sep 1974-1; Fort Nelson early Sep 1974-1 (Erskine and Davidson 1976); Charlie Lake 18 Sep 1982-1; Vanderhoof 21 Sep 1983-1; Tachick Lake 16 Oct 1981-2; Puntzi Lake 22 Oct 1976-1; Mud Creek (Relay Creek) 9 Oct 1982-1; Crowsnest Pass 5 Nov 1983-1. **Coastal** - Kitimat 22 Sep 1974-3; Selwyn and Sewell Inlets 6 Oct 1976-3; Okeover and Theodosia Inlets 12 Nov 1981-4; Little Qualicum River 10 Sep 1975-5 on delta (Dawe 1976); Esquimalt Lagoon 13 Sep 1981-3.

Winter: Interior - Williams Lake 26 Dec 1970-2; Revelstoke 1 to 7 Jan 1983-1; Sorrento to Chase 8 Jan 1971-1; Kamloops 17 Dec 1983-2; n Okanagan Lake 22 Dec 1973-2; Athalmer to Radium 4 Jan 1981-5; Kokanee Park 15 Feb 1979-1; Penticton 21 Dec 1980-1; Creston 27 Dec 1981-2, 13 Feb 1978-1 clocked in flight at 52 km/h. **Coastal** - Prince Rupert 20 Jan 1983-3; Cape St. James 8 Dec 1978-1; Campbell River (Discovery Passage) estuary 1 Feb 1975-4; Widgeon Slough 18 Feb 1972-5; Esquimalt Lagoon 28 Jan 1979-2.

Christmas Counts: Interior - Recorded from 10 of 19 localities and on 51% of all counts. Maxima: Vernon 18 Dec 1983-11; Kelowna 20 Dec 1981-11; Lake Windermere 23 Dec 1979-10; Penticton 27 Dec 1983-9; Vaseux Lake 23 Dec 1982-9. **Coastal** - Recorded from 28 of 28 localities and on 94% of all counts. Maxima: Victoria 17 Dec 1977-**44**, all-time Canadian high count (Anderson, R.R. 1978); Duncan 17 Dec 1977-41; Pender Islands 20 Dec 1975-36, 27 Dec 1980-36.

Lewis' Woodpecker
Melanerpes lewis (Gray)

LEWO

RANGE: Breeds from southern British Columbia and southwestern Alberta south to northern Arizona and south-central California. Winters from southern British Columbia south to northern Mexico.

STATUS: *Uncommon* to *common* migrant and summer visitant to the southern interior. *Very rare* summer visitant to the south coast, including southern Vancouver Island, and in the interior north of 52°N latitude; *casual* in autumn on the Queen Charlotte Islands. *Uncommon* in the Okanagan in winter; *very rare* on the south coast. Breeds.

NONBREEDING: The Lewis' Woodpecker (Fig. 302) is locally distributed across southern British Columbia from Vancouver Island east to the Kootenays and north to the Chilcotin-Cariboo Basin. It wanders irregularly and has been reported as far north as Masset, on the Queen Charlotte Islands, and Takla Lake. It has been reported from near sea level to 1,150 m elevation.

It frequents open forests and bottomland throughout its range including deciduous groves near lakes (Fig. 303) and streams, burns, logged areas, farmland, pastureland, orchards, rural gardens, and urban areas. In winter, birds are usually restricted to residential areas or orchards.

While a few birds remain throughout the year in the Okanagan valley, most are migratory. The main spring movement occurs in the first 2 weeks of May, although some birds arrive in April on the coast and mid-April in the interior. The autumn movement, begins in late summer when large wandering flocks can be seen; it peaks in late August and early September. By the end of September most birds have gone. The Lewis' Woodpecker winters in small numbers in the Okanagan valley with its centre of abundance from Vaseux Lake to Summerland; it rarely winters at the coast. See Hadow (1973) for a useful discussion on the winter ecology.

Figure 302. Lewis' Woodpecker at Vaseux Lake in the Okanagan valley, October 1973 (Ervio Sian).

Figure 303. Lewis' Woodpecker breeding habitat among ponderosa pines (left) on Mount Nkwala looking toward Trout Creek Point in the Okanagan valley, summer 1977 (Robert A. Cannings). The species also breeds and winters on Trout Creek Point among black cottonwoods (right). Nearby orchards provide apples for food in winter.

Lewis' Woodpecker

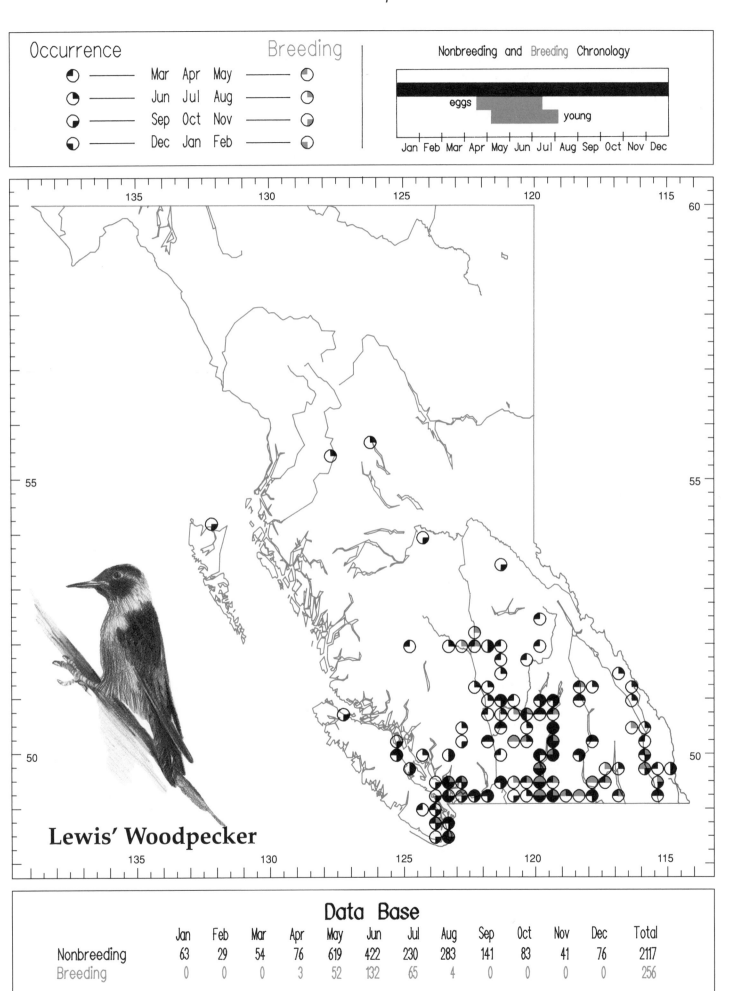

Occurrence | Breeding

◑	——	Mar	Apr	May	—— ◔
◕	——	Jun	Jul	Aug	—— ◔
◔	——	Sep	Oct	Nov	—— ◔
◕	——	Dec	Jan	Feb	—— ◑

Nonbreeding and Breeding Chronology

eggs

young

Jan Feb Mar Apr May Jun Jul Aug Sep Oct Nov Dec

Data Base

	Jan	Feb	Mar	Apr	May	Jun	Jul	Aug	Sep	Oct	Nov	Dec	Total
Nonbreeding	63	29	54	76	619	422	230	283	141	83	41	76	2117
Breeding	0	0	0	3	52	132	65	4	0	0	0	0	256

BREEDING: The Lewis' Woodpecker breeds locally throughout the southern interior of the province from the Similkameen valley east to the Kootenays and north to the Chilcotin-Cariboo Basin. Its centre of abundance is the Okanagan valley.

Breeding habitats include deciduous groves, open ponderosa pine forests (Fig. 303), sage-pine-bunchgrass grassland, farmland, pastureland, orchards, and urban areas, from 275 to 950 m elevation.

Nests: Nests (n=215) were situated primarily in living and dead deciduous (47%) and coniferous (42%) trees. Ponderosa pine (35%; (Fig. 304) and black cottonwood (33%) were the most frequently used nest trees. Eight nests were in power poles; one was in a fence post. Five nests were in trees being used by other nesting species: American Kestrel (1), American Kestrel and Northern Flicker (1), Northern Flicker (1), and European Starling *Sturnus vulgaris* (2). All nests were in cavities (natural or excavated), usually in the main trunk. Nests ranged in height from 1.0 to 30.5 m with most nests (64%; n=212) recorded between 3.5 and 9 m. Five had cavity depths ranging from 46 to 61 cm with a mean of 45 cm. One nest had a cavity diameter of 13 cm. Two had entrance hole diameters of 6 and 8 cm. Nest materials from 6 nests were wood chips from the excavation process.

Eggs: Dates for 69 nests ranged from 16 April to 27 June with 53% recorded between 23 May and 11 June. Calculated dates indicate that eggs could be found as late as 12 July (Fig. 305). Sizes for 30 clutches ranged from 2 to 8 eggs (2E-3, 3E-3, 4E-6, 5E-8, 6E-5, 7E-4, 8E-1) with 63% having 4 to 6 eggs. One clutch from British Columbia had an incubation period of about 15 days.

Young: Dates for 165 broods ranged from 5 May to 3 August with 51% recorded between 12 June and 6 July. Sizes for 28 broods ranged from 1 to 5 young (1Y-2, 2Y-7, 3Y-11, 4Y-7, 5Y-1) with 89% having 2 to 4 young. Two broods from British Columbia suggest a nestling period of 21 to 23 days (see also Terres 1980).

REMARKS: From 1920 to 1940, this woodpecker was an abundant nesting species in the environs of Vancouver, North Vancouver, and southeast Vancouver Island (Cowan 1940a) where logging and forest fires had left an abundance of tall "snags" and standing trunks of giant Douglas-fir, western redcedar, and western hemlock. These were nesting sites and foraging lookouts for the Lewis' Woodpecker. This bird obtained much of its food by hawking insects and from wild and domestic fruit.

After 1940, the cutting of snags for firewood and as a safety requirement of the Forest Service caused a decline in the Lewis' Woodpecker population. On southeastern Vancouver Island, the loss of Garry oak stands probably contributed to the decline in numbers there. The invasion of the European Starling (*Sturnus vulgaris*) beginning in the 1950s may have contributed to further decline because of competition for nest sites (Bock 1950; Weber, W.C. 1980). However, R.A. Cannings et al. 1987 do not think that competition with the European Starling has affected the breeding success or numbers of the Lewis' Woodpecker in the Okanagan valley. They have often observed the woodpecker successfully defending its nest site from starlings.

The most recent nesting records of Lewis' Woodpeckers in the lower Fraser River valley are from Pitt Meadows on 26 June 1963 and from Barnston Island on 13 July 1963.

The Lewis' Woodpecker appears on the "Blue List" for the period 1975 to 1981 on the basis of a decline beginning in the 1960s (Tate 1981). It was transferred to a species of special concern in 1982 (Tate and Tate 1982).

It is often placed in the monotypic genus *Asyndesmus*.

Figure 304. *Adult Lewis' Woodpecker with fruit for young in their nest cavity, near White Lake, west of Okanagan Falls, June 1975 (Ervio Sian).*

Figure 305. *Adult Lewis' Woodpecker with ants for its young at their nest entrance, near White Lake, west of Okanagan Falls, 27 June 1973 (Ervio Sian).*

NOTEWORTHY RECORDS

Spring: Coastal - Victoria 7 Apr 1973-1, 12 May 1984-1; Westham Island 12 May 1982-1; West Vancouver 4 May 1975-1. **Interior** - Osoyoos 3 Mar 1969-1; Creston 8 May 1983-1; Trail 1 May 1965-1; Vaseux Lake 2 May 1974-6; Summerland 18 Mar 1974-6; Vernon 14 May 1967- 1; Kleena Kleene 12 May 1965-1; n 70 Mile House 11 May 1968-2; Clearwater 3 May 1935-1 male (MCZ 282689); Pete Kitchen Lake 11 May 1959-1; Alkali Lake 15 May 1952-1 male (NMC 47938).

Summer: Coastal - Victoria 5 Jun 1982-1, 30 Aug 1953-7; Panama Flats 7 Aug 1959-50; Vancouver 13 Jul 1974-1; North Vancouver 20 Jul 1981-1; Pitt Meadows 1 Jun 1977-1. **Interior** - Vaseux Lake cliffs 26 May 1975-20; White Lake (Okanagan Falls) 10 Aug 1976-42; Summerland 25 Aug 1979-10; Harrop 1 Aug 1977-6; Kamloops 29 Aug 1966-5, 29 Aug 1981-20; Tranquille 26 Aug 1986-22; Clinton 6 Jul 1892-1 male (ANSP 30763);

Hanceville 22 Aug 1978-2; Hazelton 2 Aug 1985-1; Takla Lake last week August 1937-1.

Autumn: Interior - Indianpoint Lake 24 Oct 1929-1 female (MCZ 282687); Nulki Lake 20 Sep 1952-1 female (ROM 83841); Lac la Hache 12 Sep 1978-1; Sorrento 9 Sep 1972-2; Vernon 17 Oct 1955-1; Summerland 13 Sep 1972-5+, 8 Oct 1973-6, 14 Nov 1973-2; Osoyoos 2 Nov 1967-several. **Coastal** - Port Hardy 26 Sep 1939-1, 14 Oct 1935-1; Campbell River (Discovery Passage) 24 Nov 1974-1; Oyster River 7 Sep 1924-1 immature male (UMMZ 55792); Vancouver 30 Nov 1981-1; West Vancouver 29 Sep 1979-11; Duncan 5 Nov 1984-1; Saanich 11 Nov 1982-1; Victoria 12 Sep 1981-1.

Winter: Interior - Oliver 24 Feb 1962-2; Penticton 26 Jan 1974-4; Summerland 5 Dec 1970-5, 12 Dec 1977-2; Oyama 16 Feb 1964-2; Coldstream 26 Dec 1966-1; Kamloops 20 Dec 1987-1. **Coastal** - Sea

Island 2 to 7 Jan 1978-1.

Christmas Counts: Interior - Recorded from 5 of 19 localities and on 20% of all counts. Maxima: Penticton 26 Dec 1974-**25**, all-time Canadian high count (Anderson, R.R. 1976); Oliver/Osoyoos 28 Dec 1981-3; Kelowna 20 Dec 1981-3; Vaseux Lake 28 Dec 1974-2, 31 Dec 1976-2, 23 Dec 1981-2. **Coastal** - Recorded from 4 of 28 localities and on 2% of all counts. Maxima: Victoria 27 Dec 1958-2; Vancouver 28 Dec 1968-1, 26 Dec 1971-1; Nanaimo 31 Dec 1977-1; Pitt Meadows 27 Dec 1983-1.

Extralimital Records: Coastal - Masset 22 Oct 1938-1 (Munro, J.A. and Cowan 1947), 23 Oct 1936-1 female (RBCM 10440), 29 Nov 1949-1 male (RBCM 10439).

Yellow-bellied Sapsucker

YBSA

Sphyrapicus varius (Linnaeus)

RANGE: Breeds from extreme eastern Alaska (Kessel 1986) east across the southern Yukon, southwestern Mackenzie, and most of southern Canada (excepting central and southern British Columbia) to southern Newfoundland, south to the central and eastern United States including eastern North Dakota, Iowa, Illinois, east to Connecticut; also locally in the Appalachians south to Tennessee and North Carolina. Winters from the southern portions of the breeding range south through Texas, the southeastern United States and most of Middle America to the Bahamas, the Antilles, and central Panama.

STATUS: *Uncommon* migrant and summer visitant to the Alberta Plateau, Fort Nelson Lowlands, and Liard Basin; locally *very rare* in the Northern Mountains and Plateaus regions. Breeds.

NONBREEDING: The Yellow-bellied Sapsucker is distributed throughout the northeast corner of the province primarily from Trappers Creek, southeast of Mackenzie, rarely farther south (Vanderhoof and Stoner), north through the Peace Lowlands and the boreal forest to Hyland River Park. It has been reported as far west as Telegraph Creek in the Stikine Plateau. It frequents deciduous groves and the mixed deciduous-coniferous forests of trembling aspen, balsam poplar, birches, and white spruce.

Spring migration can begin by late April, but most birds arrive in early May. Most have left the region by late August, although a few may remain until mid-September.

BREEDING: The Yellow-bellied Sapsucker breeds from the Trappers Creek area in the sub-boreal forest, north through the Peace Lowlands and Boreal Forest region to the Kechika River valley and 42 km north of Kotcho Lake. There is one breeding record from the Stikine River valley. Nests have been found from 380 to 730 m elevation.

Breeding habitat ranges from trembling aspen and balsam poplar stands to disturbed and undisturbed mature trembling aspen forests to mixed bottomland forest of balsam poplar and white spruce. Many nest sites are on the forest edge adjacent to water bodies such as lakes, ponds, marshes (see Fig. 309), and backwater river channels.

Nests: All nests (n=27) were in excavated cavities in deciduous trees including trembling aspen (22), balsam poplar (4), and paper birch. Most of the nest trees were living. Heights of 29 nest cavity entrances ranged from 2.4 to 12.2 m with 15 heights between 3.4 and 6.1 m. Diameters at breast height of 5 nest trees were between 25 and 31 cm.

Eggs: We have one possible egg date: a record of a suspected incubating female on 9 June. Calculated dates indicate that eggs could be found from 30 May to at least 16 June. We have no records of clutch size on file. Incubation period is about 12 to 13 days (Harrison, C. 1978).

Young: Dates for 26 broods ranged from 16 June to 22 July with 15 broods recorded between 24 June and 8 July. Nestlings appear at nest hole at 18 days and fledge at between 25 and 29 days (Harrison, C. 1978).

REMARKS: Until recently (American Ornithologists' Union 1983, 1985), the Yellow-bellied Sapsucker was considered conspecific with the Red-naped (*S. nuchalis*) and the Red-breasted (*S. ruber*) sapsuckers.

There are 2 known areas of contact between *ruber* and *varius* in British Columbia. One is near Telegraph Creek, the other is from Tupper, near Dawson Creek, southwest to Vanderhoof and Stoner. W.E. Godfrey (pers. comm.) conducted fieldwork in the latter area in June 1969; his northernmost active *ruber* nest was 6.5 km south of McLeod Lake. Beyond McLeod Lake he found no sapsuckers until he was 13 km northeast of the junction of Route 39 and the Hart Highway (Trappers Creek) where he found only *varius*. Godfrey noted an abrupt transition from *ruber* to *varius* breeding grounds. Cowan (1939) noted a pair of *ruber* excavating a nest at Tupper Creek while 2.4 m away a pair of *varius* had a nest. In 1974, D.M. Scott et al. (1976) collected 2 birds at Stoner, the female a *varius* and the male intermediate between *varius* and *nuchalis*. At Tacheeda Lake, about 110 km north of Prince George, a *ruber* male and a *varius* female were observed gathering food together and carrying it off in one direction, "presumably to a nest." D.M. Scott et al. (1976) hypothesize that if the range extensions they observed continue, the 3 largely allopatric populations of sapsuckers should come into contact south of Prince George.

Howell (1952, 1953) notes 2 mechanisms that may be isolating the 3 species. First, since males have more red pigmentation than females, they may use the red to recognize other males. N.K. Johnson and Johnson (1985) also suggest that the plumage differences of *S. ruber daggetti* and *S. nuchalis* serve as the principle premating isolating mechanism. Thus a male *nuchalis* might react to a female *ruber* as if it were an intruding male. Of all the mixed pairs Howell studied, the male bird always belonged to the redder of the 2 species. This was also the case in 3 of the 4 records of mixed pairs we have on file. The exception involved a pair collected by W.E. Godfrey (pers. comm.) 40 km north of Prince George; the male was *varius*, the female *ruber*. Secondly, Howell notes an inverse correlation between intensity of pigmentation and migratory tendency. Howell suggests that a *varius* or *nuchalis* arriving on the breeding grounds in areas of contact with *ruber* would already find *ruber* paired. This is supported by our data.

There are at least 12 reports of this species from southern areas across the province. Most lack documentation, but 3 – Victoria and Vancouver on the south coast and Norbury Lake in the east Kootenay – are being investigated further. A useful paper on identifying hybrids between the 3 species of sapsuckers (see Short 1969) is provided by Devillers (1970).

See also Red-breasted Sapsucker and Red-naped Sapsucker.

NOTEWORTHY RECORDS

Spring: Coastal - No records. **Interior** - Tupper Creek 12 May 1938-1 (RBCM 7964); Taylor 10 May 1983-1 first spring arrival, 15 May 1983-6; Hudson Hope 9 May 1968-1; Stoddart Creek (Fort St. John) 26 Apr 1980-1 male; Beatton Park 29 Apr 1984-3 males, first spring arrivals; Fort Nelson 1 May 1986-1; Liard Hotsprings 3 May 1975-1 (Reid 1975); ne Kotcho Lake 26 May 1982-5 chasing each other through forest.

Summer: Coastal - No records. **Interior** - Stoner 14 and 18 Jun 1974-1 female and 1 male collected, the male intermediate between *nuchalis* and *varius* (Scott, D.M. et al. 1976); Vanderhoof 4 Aug 1919-1 male (NMC 13726); 40 km n Prince George 12 Jun 1969-1 male (NMC 56904), with a female *ruber*; s McLeod Lake 3 Jul 1968-1 (Rogers, T.H. 1968b); Trappers Creek 25 Jun 1969-1 (NMC 56906); Tupper Creek 21 Jun 1938-1 (RBCM 7965); Telegraph Creek (Munro, J.A. and Cowan 1947); 50 km s Dease Lake 12 Jul 1962-2, a mated pair with brood patches at nest (NMC 49809-10); Dease Lake 22 Jun 1962-1 (NMC 49808); Fort Nelson 19 Jun 1976-14, breeding bird survey; 48 km ne Elleh 23 Jun 1982-1 (RBCM 17620); Liard River 10 Aug 1943-1 (NMC 29475); 42 km ne Kotcho Lake 10 Jun 1982-2 (RBCM 17670-71).

Autumn: Interior - Muskwa 16 Sep 1943-2 (NMC 29477; Rand 1944); Charlie Lake 12 Sep 1982-4 immatures; Beatton Park 17 Sep 1983-1 immature. **Coastal** - No records.

Winter: No records.

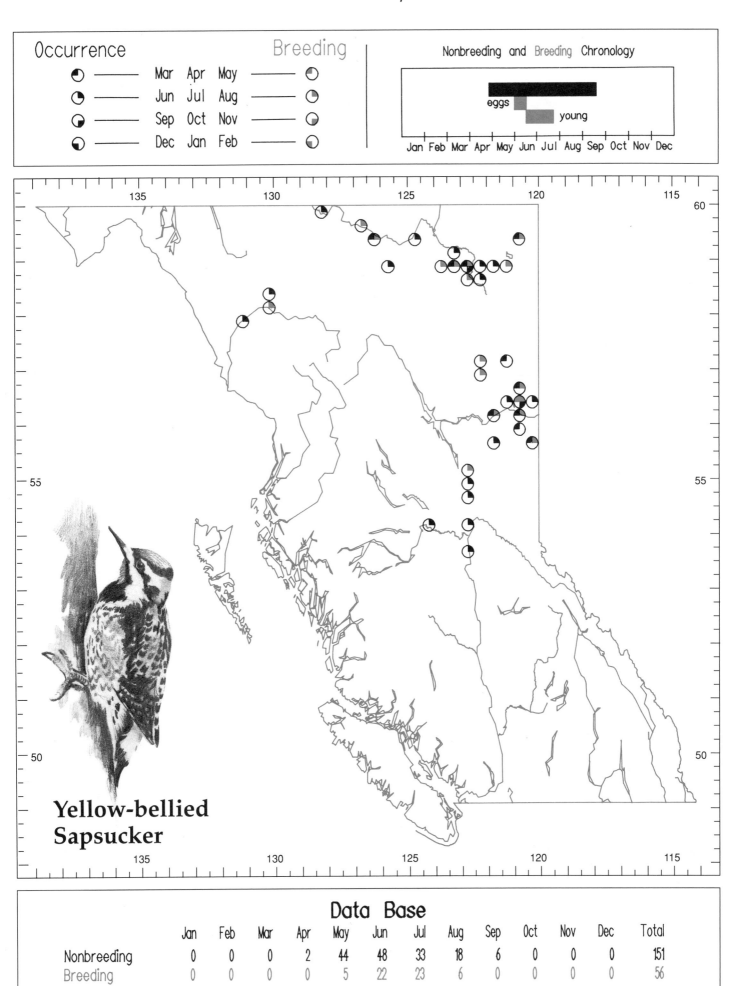

Occurrence

Breeding

◕ ———	Mar Apr May	——— ◑
◔ ———	Jun Jul Aug	——— ◔
◔ ———	Sep Oct Nov	——— ◔
◕ ———	Dec Jan Feb	——— ◑

Nonbreeding and Breeding Chronology

eggs

young

Jan Feb Mar Apr May Jun Jul Aug Sep Oct Nov Dec

Yellow-bellied Sapsucker

Data Base

	Jan	Feb	Mar	Apr	May	Jun	Jul	Aug	Sep	Oct	Nov	Dec	Total
Nonbreeding	0	0	0	2	44	48	33	18	6	0	0	0	151
Breeding	0	0	0	0	5	22	23	6	0	0	0	0	56

Red-naped Sapsucker
Sphyrapicus nuchalis Baird

RNSA

RANGE: Breeds from south central and southeastern British Columbia, southwestern Alberta, and western Montana south to east-central California and east to extreme western Texas. Winters from the southern portion of the breeding range, south to northern Mexico.

STATUS: *Uncommon* to *fairy common* migrant and summer visitant to the south-central and southern interior of the province. *Very rare* vagrant west of the Pacific and Cascade ranges. Breeds.

NONBREEDING: The Red-naped Sapsucker (Fig. 307) is widely distributed across southern British Columbia east of the Pacific and Cascade ranges and north through the Chilcotin-Cariboo Basin and Nechako Plateau, rarely to Nulki Lake in the Nechako Lowlands. It wanders irregularly west of the Pacific and Cascade ranges and has been reported from the Fraser Lowlands and southeastern Vancouver Island.

It frequents a variety of deciduous and mixed woodlands from 300 m (rarely near sea level) to 1,300 m elevation.

The Red-naped Sapsucker can arrive in the interior in late March; however, the main spring movement occurs through April. Autumn migration begins by late August and continues through mid-September, although a few birds may still be found in early October. There are no documented winter records for the Red-naped Sapsucker in the interior of the province, but there are 3 for the coast.

BREEDING: The Red-naped Sapsucker is a widespread breeder across central southern and southeastern British Columbia north to Yoho National Park in the east and through the southern Chilcotin-Cariboo Basin; rarely farther north (Cinema).

It frequents a variety of deciduous and mixed woodlands (Fig. 306) including aspen groves in open ponderosa pine forests, aspen-fir parklands, logged forests where deciduous groves remain, aspen groves in open rangeland, birch groves, and, occasionally, subalpine forest edges and residental gardens, from 300 to 1,280 m elevation.

Nests: Most nests (91%; n=273) were in deciduous trees, including trembling aspen (49%), birches (16%), poplar (14%), black cottonwood, alder, and willow. Coniferous nest trees (6%) included ponderosa pine, Douglas-fir, western larch, and western hemlock. Living trees (73%) were selected more often than dead trees. Keisker (1986) found similar results from her study sites along the North Thompson River. Nest trees were often on the edge of woodlands adjacent to water bodies such as streams, ponds, sloughs, and lakes, or other open areas such as road edges, logging slashes, transmission line rights-of-way, and mountain meadows. Diameters (at breast height) of 27 nest trees ranged from 15 to 64 cm with 63% recorded between 23 and 30 cm. Heights of 284 nests ranged from 0.5 to 22.9 m with 61% recorded between 1.8 and 6.1 m. Eleven cavity depths ranged from 13 to 25 cm with seven depths between 15 and 20 cm. Seven cavity diameters ranged from 10 to 17 cm. Seven entrance holes ranged from 3 to 5 cm in diameter. One sapsucker nest was found in a tree containing active nests of a Pileated Woodpecker, a Northern Flicker, and a European Starling (*Sturnus vulgaris*). Nest materials were usually just the wood chips from the excavation process.

Eggs: Dates for 52 clutches ranged from 6 May to 16 June with 56% recorded between 27 May and 8 June. Calculated dates indicate that eggs could be found as early as 2 May. Sizes for 26 clutches ranged from 2 to 7 eggs (2E-1, 3E-3, 4E-5, 5E-15, 6E-1, 7E-1) with 15 clutches having 5 eggs.

Figure 306. Red-naped Sapsucker breeding habitat in mixed woodland of trembling aspen, willow, and wildrose (left), and a nest location at Hat Creek, near Cache Creek (right), 11 June 1989 (John M. Cooper).

Red-naped Sapsucker

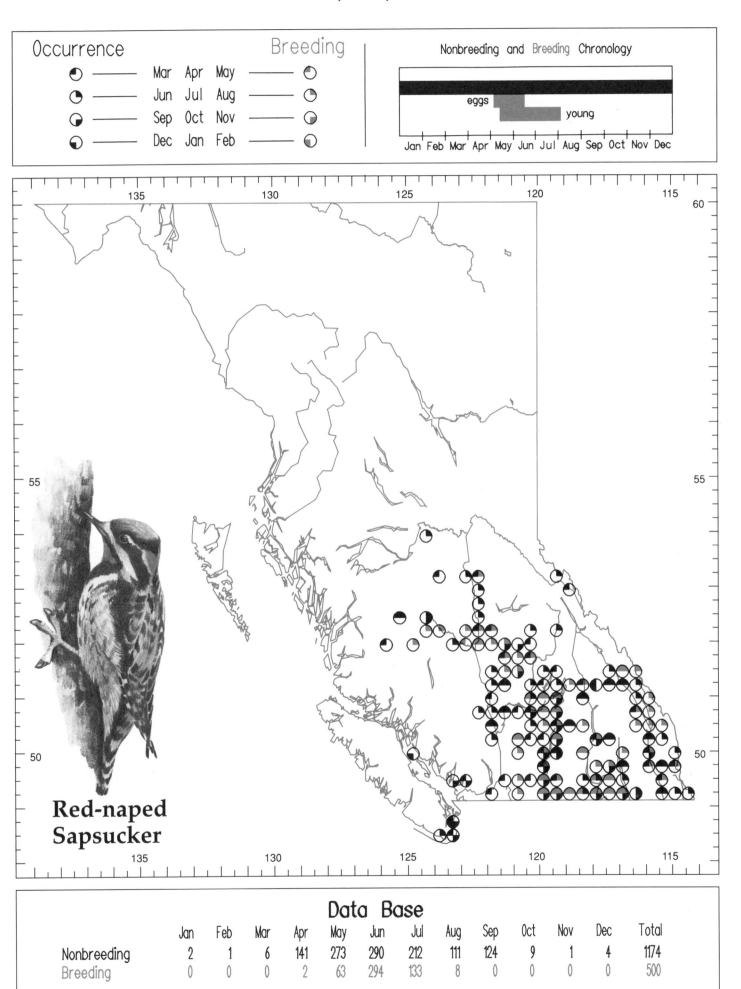

Occurrence

◐	—	Mar Apr May	—	◑
◔	—	Jun Jul Aug	—	◑
◕	—	Sep Oct Nov	—	◑
◕	—	Dec Jan Feb	—	◑

Breeding

Nonbreeding and Breeding Chronology

eggs

young

Jan Feb Mar Apr May Jun Jul Aug Sep Oct Nov Dec

Red-naped Sapsucker

Data Base

	Jan	Feb	Mar	Apr	May	Jun	Jul	Aug	Sep	Oct	Nov	Dec	Total
Nonbreeding	2	1	6	141	273	290	212	111	124	9	1	4	1174
Breeding	0	0	0	2	63	294	133	8	0	0	0	0	500

Young: Dates for 243 broods ranged from 14 May to 4 Aug with 51% recorded between 19 June and 3 July. Sizes for 34 broods ranged from 1 to 6 young (1Y-6, 2Y-6, 3Y-6, 4Y-11, 5Y-3, 6Y-2) with 50% having 3 or 4 young.

REMARKS: In British Columbia, the geographical and biological relationships between the sapsucker species *nuchalis* and *ruber* are confused and dynamic. There are many areas where they meet, nest side by side, and sometimes interbreed.

Along the highway from Hope to Princeton *ruber* predominates on the western slope with *nuchalis* infrequent (Kelleher 1963). In Manning Park, Edwards (1949) found many *ruber* as far east as Copper Creek. There is a nesting record of this species at Tulameen. Only 3 years later, Carl et al. (1952) found *nuchalis* the common species in Manning Park and noted 2 mixed pairs.

S.P. Wetmore (pers. comm.) found only *nuchalis* nesting in the area between Sunday Creek and Merritt from 1983 to 1986.

The major areas of contact between the two species are the Cariboo and Chilcotin regions. Both species occur at 100 Mile House, Kleena Kleene, and Nulki Lake. Howell (1952) found them equally numerous at Kersley, 15 km south of Quesnel but only *ruber* north of there. Twenty years later, Scott et al. (1976) found *nuchalis* 25 km north of Kerseley and outnumbering *ruber* there 6:1.

We have a record of a male *ruber* and female *nuchalis* nesting at Tugwell Creek on Vancouver Island where at least one young was reared, and a mixed pair of *nuchalis* and *ruber* feeding young at Cornwall Mountain, west of Ashcroft.

See also Remarks under Yellow-bellied Sapsucker and Red-breasted Sapsucker.

Figure 307. Red-naped Sapsucker with food for young, 10 km west of Osoyoos, July 1983 (Mark Nyhoff).

Figure 308. Red-breasted Sapsucker breeding habitat at Dudley Marsh near Coombs, Vancouver Island, 15 May 1985 (Neil K. Dawe).

Figure 309. *Yellow-bellied Sapsucker breeding habitat, 65 km east of Fort Nelson, June 1982 (R. Wayne Campbell). Mixed woodlands bordering permanent water bodies, such as marshes, are preferred nesting sites.*

Figure 310. *Red-breasted Sapsucker at Reifel Island, Delta, 20 September 1974 (Neil K. Dawe).*

NOTEWORTHY RECORDS

Spring: Coastal - Saanich 18 Apr 1986-1 male, 19 Apr 1983, 23 Apr 1977-1, 16 May 1974-1; Loon Lake (Maple Ridge) 7 May 1977-1; 3 km n Cultus Lake 7 May 1978-1; Skagit Valley 11 May 1974-1. **Interior** - Osoyoos 24 Apr 1970-1 (RBCM 15125), 1 May 1974-7; Kettle Valley 14 May 1983-2 at 610 m elevation; Lakeview 4 Apr 1984-pair courting; Creston 19 Apr 1941-1 (RBCM 9039); Kilpoola Lake 12 Apr 1969-8; Vaseux Lake 31 Mar 1934-1 (RBCM 9645); Cranbrook 8 Apr 1942-first seen in spring (Munro, J.A. and Cowan 1947); Edgewood 25 Mar 1924-1; Lavington 6 Apr 1969-1; Nakusp 10 Apr 1976-2; Irish Creek (Vernon) 31 Mar 1979-1; Kamloops 25 Apr 1889-1 (NMC 535); Springhouse 18 May 1951-1 (NMC 47946); 100 Mile House 15 Apr 1984-1 male in company of *S. ruber*; Williams Lake 30 Mar 1984-1, 24 Apr 1954-1 (NMC 47940), 28 Apr 1966-6 within 5 km, 6 May 1983-1 male "intermediate between *ruber* and *nuchalis* coming regularly to suet feeder. The

Yellow-bellied [Red-naped] Sapsucker is the usual species seen at Williams Lake"; Anahim Lake 16 May 1932-1 (MCZ 282700); Nazko 22 May 1977-pair; Cottonwood 14 May 1930-1 (MCZ 282692).

Summer: Coastal - Tugwell Creek 11 to 26 Jun 1983-1 female. **Interior** - Manning Park 6 Jul 1945-1 (RBCM 9139); Lytton 5 Jun 1964-2 (NMC 52379-80); Kamloops 30 Jul 1949-1 (UBC 2198); Cayoosh Creek 12 Jul 1980-1; Lillooet 29 Jul 1919-1 (RBCM 2840); Hanceville 26 Aug 1953-1 (RBCM 15686); Clinton 24 Jun 1964-1 (NMC 52384); Wells Grey Park 15 Jun 1962-4 (NMC 50612-15); Blue River 18 Jun 1934-1 (CMNH P115398); Anahim Lake 12 Jun 1932-1 (MCZ 282701); Chezacut 8 Aug 1931-1 (UBC 7470); Nulki Lake 29 Jul 1954-1 (ROM 87012).

Autumn: Interior - Chezacut 12 Sep 1933-2 (MCZ

282704-5); Lac la Hache 21 Sep 1939-1 (ROM 87019); Bridge Lake campsite 7 Sep 1960-5; Lytton 7 Sep 1968-4; Scotch Creek 21 Oct 1964-1; Armstrong Oct 1906-1 (UBC 138); Okanagan Landing 4 Oct 1921-1; Nakusp 6 Sep 1975-1; Kelowna 1 Oct 1975-1; Summerland 8 Oct 1947-1; Penticton 29 Sep 1973-1; Vaseux Lake 26 Sep 1977-1; Waneta 17 Sep 1978-2; Creston 23 Sep 1948-1 (ROM 76725). **Coastal** - Westridge 3 and 5 Sep 1928-1 (RBCM 23083-84) Vancouver 9 Oct 1981-1; North Saanich 22 Sep 1984-1, 13 Oct 1984-1, 4 Nov 1982-1; Victoria 26 Sep 1984-1.

Winter: Interior - No records. **Coastal** - Powell River 23 Dec 1983-1 (RBCM 18510); North Saanich 1 Dec 1983 to 29 Feb 1984-1, 26 Dec 1984-1.

Christmas Counts: Interior - Not recorded (see Cannings, R.A. et al. 1987). **Coastal** - Not recorded.

Red-breasted Sapsucker

Sphyrapicus ruber (Gmelin)

RANGE: Breeds from southeastern Alaska and central and western British Columbia, including Vancouver Island and the Queen Charlotte Islands, south along the coast west of the Cascade Range to central California and the Sierra Nevada, and in the mountains of southern California and southern Nevada. Occurs east of the Cascade Range locally in Oregon, Washington, and British Columbia. Winters throughout the breeding range, except for interior British Columbia, and also in northern Baja California.

STATUS: *Uncommon* resident along the coast including Vancouver and the Queen Charlotte Islands. *Uncommon* to *rare* migrant and summer visitant to the central interior and the northwestern portion of the province. *Very rare* vagrant east of 120°W. *Casual* in winter in the Okanagan valley. Breeds.

NONBREEDING: The Red-breasted Sapsucker (see Fig. 310) is widely distributed along coastal British Columbia and between 52°N and 56°N latitude in the central interior, becoming more localized in the northwestern portion of the province (Telegraph Creek; Haines triangle). In southern British Columbia, it occurs east of the Pacific and Cascade ranges in the Lillooet, Manning Park, and Princeton areas. It wanders occasionally to the Okanagan valley. There is a single record for the Kootenay region. It occurs from sea level to 1,950 m elevation.

This species frequents deciduous and coniferous woodlands from open black cottonwood bottomland, red alder and maple regrowth, and riparian woods to dense, coastal Douglas-fir and western redcedar - western hemlock forests.

Seasonal records indicate that most birds leave southern Vancouver Island by late spring. Equal numbers of seasonal records for the Fraser Lowlands make any movements there difficult to distinguish. Birds can arrive at interior breeding areas by late March; however, the main spring movement occurs through April and into May. Movements from the breeding areas to wintering areas are also difficult to discern, but it is unusual to find Red-breasted Sapsuckers anywhere in the interior after August. Southern Vancouver Island records begin to increase in early September suggesting a return of the birds from their breeding areas.

The centres of winter abundance for the Red-breasted Sapsucker are the east coast of Vancouver Island from Victoria north to Campbell River, and the Fraser Lowlands on the south mainland coast.

BREEDING: The Red-breasted Sapsucker breeds all along the coast of British Columbia; in the interior, it nests across the central portions of the province from Kleena Kleene and Horsefly in the south to Meziadin Lake and Tupper Creek (south of Dawson Creek) in the north. It also breeds on the east slope of the Pacific and Cascade ranges near Manning Park and Tulameen, and in extreme northwestern British Columbia.

It breeds in a wide range of wooded habitats from coniferous forests, including old growth and second growth forests of the coast (see Fig. 308), to lodgepole pine - Douglas-fir forests of the interior. It also uses deciduous and riparian woods and cottonwood bottomland. Other habitats include orchards, power line rights-of-way, and burns. Nests have been found from near sea level to 1,220 m elevation.

Nests: Most nests (65%; n=69) were situated in deciduous trees, including alders (19%), trembling aspen (13%), maples (12%), poplars (10%), black cottonwood, and birches. Coniferous tree nest sites (13%) included hemlock, fir, spruce, and lodgepole pine. Other sites included snags and a power pole. Dead trees (55%) were used more often than living trees. Many nests were on a wooded edge adjacent to a marsh, lake, or other open area. Kelleher (1963) found similar results from his coastal study area. One nest was 2.4 m from an active Yellow-bellied Sapsucker nest. All nests were located in excavated cavities. Heights of 72 nests ranged from 1.8 to 24.3 m with 67% recorded between 3.4 and 9.1 m. The entrance hole diameters of 2 nests were 5 and 10 cm.

Eggs: Dates for 9 clutches ranged from 7 May to 21 June. Calculated dates indicate eggs could be found as early as 25 April. One clutch contained 4 eggs.

Young: Dates for 109 broods ranged from 10 May to 20 July with 51% recorded between 9 June and 28 June. Sizes for 3 broods ranged from 3 to 6 young (3Y-2, 6Y-1). Five nests indicate that the nestling period is at least 22 days.

REMARKS: Both the Red-breasted and Red-naped sapsuckers experience dramatic fluctuations in numbers that appear to influence their distribution and interactions with each other.

See Remarks under Yellow-bellied Sapsucker and Red-naped Sapsucker.

NOTEWORTHY RECORDS

Spring: Coastal - Victoria 14 Mar 1955-1 (RBCM 10169); Lake Cowichan (Marble Bay) 4 Apr 1982-16 in about a 1.5 ha red alder stand; n Qualicum Beach 11 Mar 1977-3; Loon Lake (Maple Ridge) 7 May 1977-6; Gorge Harbour 1 Apr 1976-6; Port Neville 19 Mar 1975-2; Bella Coola 24 Apr 1933-1 (MCZ 282764); Juskatla to Masset 30 May 1985-8+ very common; Naden Harbour 11 May 1977-4, very numerous; Kitimat 23 May 1977-1 (RBCM 16058); Tseax River 28 May 1978-2; Corral Creek on Kispiox Road 17 and 18 May 1981-1. **Interior** - Manning Park 22 Apr 1979-1; Wolfe Lake 3 May 1975-1; Blackwaters Lake 26 May 1916-1 (RBCM 2859); Knot Lake near junction of North Klinaklini River 18 May 1975-1+ "the yellow-bellied [*nuchalis*] form was also seen in the area and crosses between the 2 forms"; 100 Mile House 15 Apr 1984-1 "on lodgepole pine probing for insects, at times side-by-side with Yellow-bellied [*nuchalis*] Sapsucker"; Lac la Hache 7 May 1943-1 (ROM 87022); Williams Lake 25 Apr 1952-1 (NMC 47957); Lonesome Lake 27 Mar 1971-present (Turner, J. 1971); Nulki Lake 15 May 1944-1 (USNM 425041); 24 km s Prince George 18 Apr 1983-2, 9 May 1976-1 (RBCM 15410); Quick 3 Apr 1978-2 males interacting; 2 km s Smithers 29 May 1983-1 (RBCM 17884); Tetana River 23 Apr 1941 (RBCM 8935); Tupper Creek 23 May 1938-2

(RBCM 7971-2); Telegraph Creek 16 to 20 May 1983-1 (Grunberg 1983b).

Summer: Coastal - Stubbs Island 9 Jul 1960-old sign is locally plentiful; Alta Lake 28 Jul 1923-1 (UBC 7462); Klaskish River 13 Aug 1981-1; Banks Island 17 Jun 1970-1; Masset 12 Jul 1987-3. **Interior** - Anarchist Mountain 17 Aug 1928-1; White Lake road (Okanagan Falls) 21 Aug 1965-1; Okanagan Landing 18 Aug 1956-1 (ROM 86960); Lillooet 15 Jun 1964-1 (NMC 52383); e Lillooet Lake 12 Jul 1980-1; Birkenhead Lake Park 10 Jun 1984-1; Antoine Lake 21 Jul 1954-1 (NMC 47959); Spahats Creek 23 and 24 Jun 1971-1; 16 km e Quesnel 12 Jun 1965-1 (UMMZ 209497); Chezacut Lake 19 Jun 1951-1 (RBCM 15680); Nulki Lake 1 Jul 1974-6, both Red-breasted and Red-naped males seen, 30 Jul 1945-1 (USNM 432842); 16 km n Prince George 23 Jun 1949-1 (UBC 2181); New Hazelton 2 Jun 1984-1 (RBCM 18394); Brown's River 26 Jul 1953-2; Buckley Lake 28 Jul 1944-1 (ROM 86961); Towagh Creek 5 Jun 1983-1 (RBCM 17744).

Autumn: Interior - Indianpoint Lake 20 Sep 1929-1 (MCZ 282742); late November to 15 Dec 1968-1 (Rogers, T.H. 1969); Yale 13 Sep 1936-1 (RBCM 6978). **Coastal** - Prince Rupert 23 Nov 1977-1;

Massett 30 Oct 1936-1 (RBCM 10413); Cape Scott 29 Sep 1935-1 (NMC 26286); Port Neville 16 Nov 1975-1; Loon Lake (Maple Ridge) 21 Sep 1975-7; Cypress Bowl 12 Sep 1982-6+ in one group; Swan Lake (Victoria) 6 Sep 1983-1 (RBCM 17882).

Winter: Interior - Naramata 12 Jan 1974-1 (Rogers, T.H. 1974b); Summerland 13 to 20 Dec 1968-1. **Coastal** - Prince Rupert 3 Jan 1982-1; Masset 7 Feb 1937-1 (UMMZ 126876); Cape St. James 29 Dec 1981-1 (RBCM 17669); Tahsis Inlet 29 Jan 1949-1 (Mitchell, G.J. 1959); Victoria 12 Dec 1983-1 (RBCM 17883).

Christmas Counts: Only the Red-breasted Sapsucker has been documented on Christmas Bird Counts in the province, so we have included all official counts under this species (see also Appendix 2). **Interior** - Recorded once: Smithers 19 Dec 1983-2. **Coastal** - Recorded from 21 of 28 localities and on 40% of all counts. Maxima: Vancouver 28 Dec 1968-67, all-time Canadian high count (Anderson, R.R. 1976); Campbell River 31 Dec 1978-19; Pitt Meadows 30 Dec 1978-18.

Extralimital Records: Cranbrook Jul 1940-1 (UMMZ 126886).

Red-breasted Sapsucker

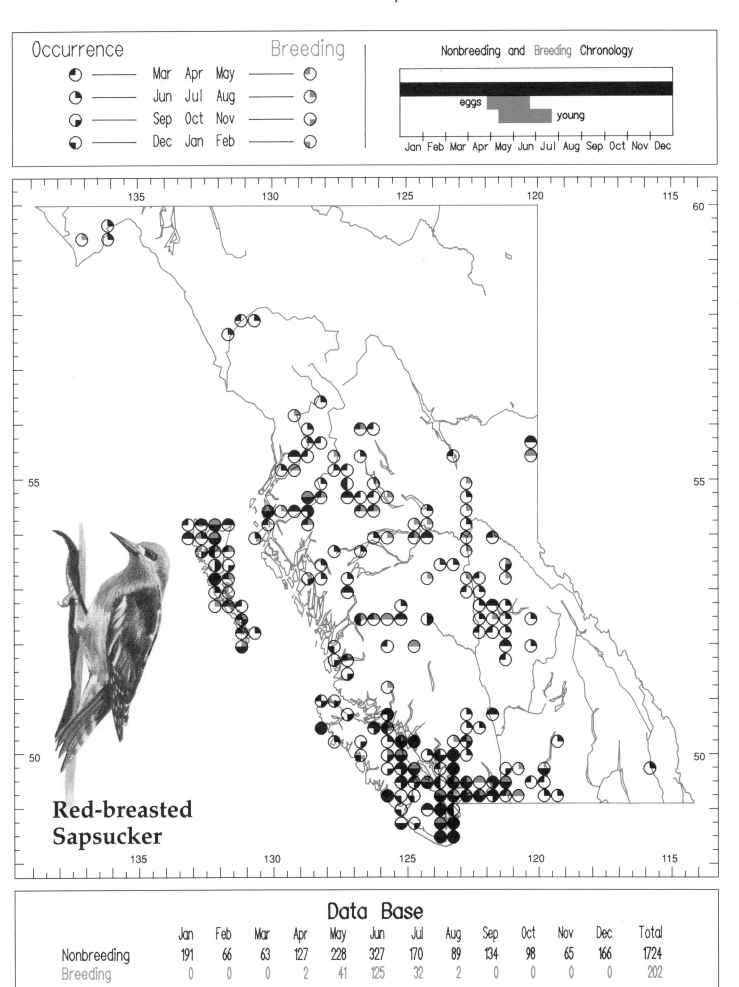

Occurrence / Breeding

Occurrence		Breeding
◔	Mar Apr May	◑
◔	Jun Jul Aug	◕
◕	Sep Oct Nov	◕
◕	Dec Jan Feb	◑

Nonbreeding and Breeding Chronology

eggs — young

Jan Feb Mar Apr May Jun Jul Aug Sep Oct Nov Dec

Red-breasted Sapsucker

Data Base

	Jan	Feb	Mar	Apr	May	Jun	Jul	Aug	Sep	Oct	Nov	Dec	Total
Nonbreeding	191	66	63	127	228	327	170	89	134	98	65	166	1724
Breeding	0	0	0	2	41	125	32	2	0	0	0	0	202

Williamson's Sapsucker

Sphyrapicus thyroideus (Cassin)

WISA

RANGE: Breeds from southeastern British Columbia south to New Mexico. Winters from Arizona to central Mexico.

STATUS: *Uncommon* migrant and summer visitant to the Thompson-Okanagan Plateau and Kootenay Trench regions of the province; absent from the coast. Breeds.

NONBREEDING: The Williamson's Sapsucker is distributed through extreme central - southern British Columbia north to the vicinity of Westwold and formerly in the southern east Kootenay. It frequents montane forests, principally those of the interior Douglas-fir zone. It has occasionally been observed in orchards in the Okanagan valley. It occurs from 310 to 1,425 m elevation.

The sparse data indicate that birds arrive by mid-April. Most have probably left the province by mid-September, although occasionally they can be found as late as mid-October.

BREEDING: The Williamson's Sapsucker breeds at higher elevations throughout the Thompson-Okanagan Plateau from Anarchist Mountain north to the vicinity of Terrace Mountain and Scottie Creek (Cache Creek) and west to the Manning Park and Lytton areas. It formerly bred in the east Kootenay (see Remarks).

It breeds in forested areas at elevations between 850 and 1,300 m, principally the western larch, interior Douglas-fir, and ponderosa pine forests. South of Merritt, birds have been found nesting in groves of trembling aspen.

Nests: Most nests (22 of 28) were located in coniferous trees (Fig. 311) including western larch (12), ponderosa pine (5), Douglas-fir (3), lodgepole pine (1), and Engelmann spruce (1). Five were in trembling aspen and one was in a power pole. All nests were located in excavated cavities. Nests (n=25) ranged in height from 2 to 18 m with 15 between 2 and 6 m.

Eggs: We have only one egg date: 2 June. Calculated dates indicate that eggs could be found from 23 April to 15 June. There are no recorded clutch sizes for the province. Incubation period is 12 to 14 days (Terres 1980).

Young: Dates for 35 broods ranged from 8 May to 15 July with 51% recorded between 13 June and 25 June. There is no information on brood size for the province; nestling period is at least 19 days. Fledging period is 28 to 35 days (Terres 1980).

REMARKS: R.A. Cannings et al. (1987) suggest that the western larch may be a factor limiting the distribution of this woodpecker in the province. However, since 1947, a westward expansion of the species' southern interior range has occurred into areas where the western larch is not very common. The bird is now found with some regularity in Manning Park in lodgepole pine and spruce forests, and we have recent breeding records from near Merritt and Lytton. During forest bird studies south of Merritt, S.P. Wetmore (pers. comm.) found a number of Williamson's Sapsucker nests in habitat largely devoid of western larch. Observers are encouraged to note the habitat occupied by birds they see.

Williamson's Sapsucker was formerly a scarce breeding bird in the extreme southern part of the east Kootenay. The last breeding record there was of young in a nest on 14 May 1938 at Cranbrook (Munro, J.A. and Cowan 1947), and the most recent record was 10 July 1947 at Cranbrook (Johnstone, W.B. 1949).

Crockett and Hadow (1975) studied nest site selection by Williamson's and Red-naped sapsuckers at 3 sites in Colorado and Wyoming. They found that in these areas there were no significant differences between the 2 species in nest site selection; both showed a strong preference for aspen, particularly aspen infected with *Fomes*. There was no larch on their study sites. They also found that nest sites used by *S. thyroideus* were invariably near open ponderosa pine forests, which the birds used for sap and insect foraging. They concluded that, in their study areas, species isolation was not dependent on habitat separation.

Figure 311. *Female Williamson's Sapsucker at a nest entrance with food for young at Cathedral Lakes in Cathedral Park, June 1975 (Ervio Sian).*

NOTEWORTHY RECORDS

Spring: Coastal - No records. **Interior** - Lightning Lake 4 May 1980-1 pair, 6 May 1981-5 adults; 19 km e Allison Pass 15 May 1950-1 male (UBC 2260); Midway 10 Apr 1905-1 male (NMC 3277); Anarchist Mountain 4 Apr 1944-4 (AUMU 0.38164-67), 11 Apr 1933-1 male (RBCM 9646), 18 Apr 1954-1 male (PMNH 71803); Cranbrook 25 Apr 1930-1 pair (NMC 24598-99), 14 May 1938-1 male (RBCM 11090); Aspen Grove 17 May 1986-1 pair; Coldwater River 24 May 1971-1 male.

Summer: Coastal - No records. **Interior** - Anarchist Mountain 4 Jun 1930-4 (ROM 82916-19), Bridesville 30 Aug 1928-2 immatures (RBCM 13100-01); Crooked Lake (Richter Pass) 19 Jun 1963-1 male (Campbell and Meugens 1971); Mount Baker 20 Jun 1943-1 male (Johnstone, W.B. 1949); w Princeton 6 Jun 1977-1 pair; Cranbrook 24 and 25 Jul 1937-2 (RBCM 11089 and 11091), 5 Aug 1919-1 male (ROM 24.4.4.445); Salmon Lake (Westwold) 29 Jul 1985-1 (Rogers, T.H. 1985d).

Autumn: Interior - Kelowna 2 Oct 1987-1; Baldy Mountain (Oliver) 11 Sep 1960-3; Richter Pass 7 Sep 1953-1 (Campbell and Meugens 1971); s Okanagan 18 Oct 1964-1. **Coastal** - No records.

Winter: No records.

Williamson's Sapsucker

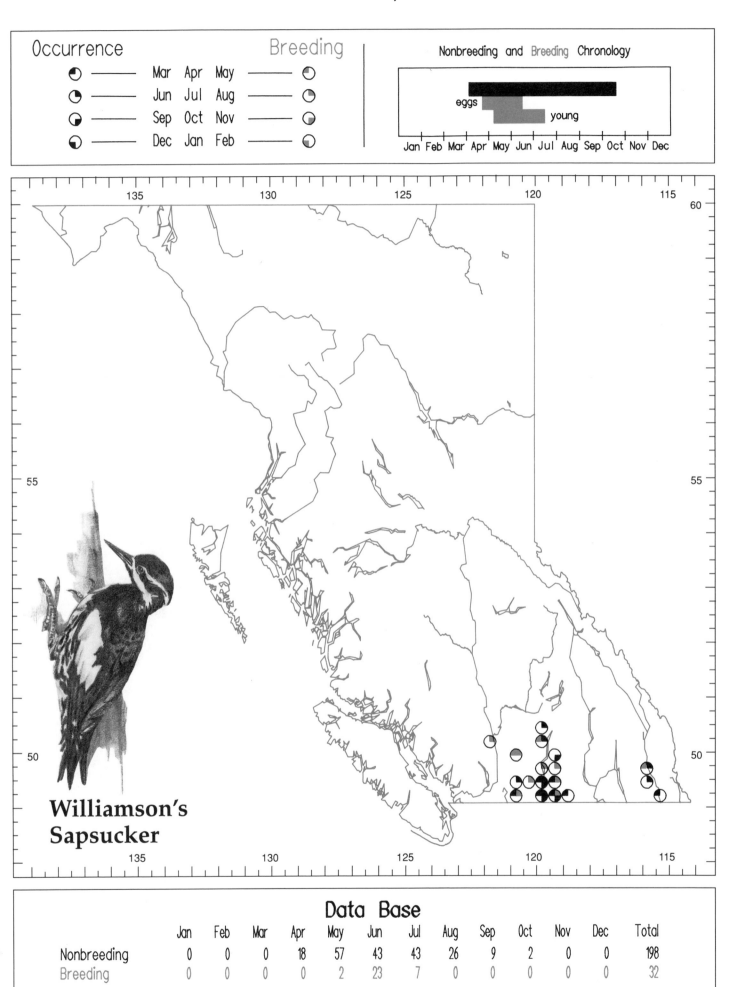

Nonbreeding and Breeding Chronology

eggs

young

Jan Feb Mar Apr May Jun Jul Aug Sep Oct Nov Dec

Williamson's Sapsucker

Data Base

	Jan	Feb	Mar	Apr	May	Jun	Jul	Aug	Sep	Oct	Nov	Dec	Total
Nonbreeding	0	0	0	18	57	43	43	26	9	2	0	0	198
Breeding	0	0	0	0	2	23	7	0	0	0	0	0	32

Downy Woodpecker
Picoides pubescens (Linnaeus)

DOWO

RANGE: Breeds from western Alaska east across most of forested Canada and south to southern California, central Arizona, central New Mexico, central Texas, the Gulf coast and southern Florida. Winters throughout the breeding range.

STATUS: *Rare* to locally *fairly common* resident throughout the province south of 57°N latitude; *very rare* farther north. *Casual* on the Queen Charlotte Islands. Breeds.

NONBREEDING: The Downy Woodpecker is widely distributed across southern British Columbia, including Vancouver Island, becoming sparsely distributed in the northern regions of the province. It is rarely observed on the Queen Charlotte Islands. It occurs from sea level to 1,250 m elevation.

It frequents deciduous and mixed forests, and edges of coniferous forests, including burns and logged areas, as well as riparian thickets, orchards, residential areas, city parks, and gardens.

Winter records north of the Shuswap region are few and suggest that there is a partial withdrawal of northern populations to southern valleys and coastal areas; however, this is yet to be confirmed (see Munro, J.A. and Cowan 1947).

BREEDING: The Downy Woodpecker breeds throughout most of southern British Columbia. On the coast, its breeding distribution includes the extreme south mainland coast and the east coast of Vancouver Island. North of Vancouver Island we have only 3 breeding records; none are from the Queen Charlotte Islands. It nests throughout the interior from the extreme south, north to Tatlow, wherever suitable habitat occurs; there are only 3 nesting records from areas farther north.

The Downy Woodpecker breeds in deciduous forests, groves, bottomland, mixed woods, and riparian thickets as well as forest burns and logged areas. Other habitats include rural and urban parks, gardens, and orchards.

Nests have been found from near sea level to 1,100 m elevation.

Nests: Most nests (57%; n=98) were found in dead trees (Fig. 312); Keisker (1986) found similar results. Deciduous trees (81%) were used far more often than coniferous trees (6%), and included trembling aspen (26%), alders (13%), black cottonwood (12%), Garry oak, birches, willows, and Pacific crabapple. All nests were located in excavated cavities. Heights of 96 nests ranged from 0.9 to 30 m with 54% between 1.8 and 4.6 m. Depths of 4 cavities ranged from 20 to 30 cm. The diameters of 2 entrance holes were 2.5 and 2.9 cm. Nest materials were simply wood chips from the excavation process.

Eggs: Dates for 46 clutches ranged from 2 May to 15 July with 50% recorded between 15 May and 2 June. Sizes for 16 clutches ranged from 4 to 7 eggs (4E-4, 5E-7, 6E-3, 7E-2) with 11 clutches having 4 or 5 eggs. Records for 2 nests suggest that the incubation period is 11 to 13 days; both sexes incubate. A.A. Allen (1928) and Burns (1915) both give an incubation period of 12 days.

Young: Dates for 113 broods ranged from 17 May to 2 Aug with 50% recorded between 3 and 23 June. Sizes for 15 broods ranged from 2 to 5 young (2Y-3, 3Y-10, 4Y-1, 5Y-1) with 10 broods having 3 young. Records of 5 nests indicate the fledging period is 21 to 26 days. Kilham (1962) mentions that nestlings may appear at the nest entrance at the age of 14 days and fledge in 21 to 25 days after hatching. Hadow (1976), however, notes a fledging period of 18 days in Colorado.

REMARKS: Four subspecies of the Downy Woodpecker occur in British Columbia: *P. p. nelsoni, P. p. leucurus, P. p. gairdnerii,* and *P. p. glacialis* (Munro, J.A. and Cowan 1947; Godfrey 1986).

See Hadow (1976) for a discussion of the growth and development of nestling Downy Woodpeckers and how they relate to the nesting strategy of the species.

Figure 312. Male Downy Woodpecker at nest with food, near west Creston, 14 June 1981 (Mark Nyhof).

NOTEWORTHY RECORDS

Spring: Coastal - Victoria 15 Mar 1983-6; Burnaby Lake 3 Mar 1974-5; Campbell River estuary (Discovery Passage) 26 Apr 1975-4; McClinton Creek 25 Apr 1935-1 (Munro, J.A. and Cowan 1947); Langara Island 28 Apr to 3 May 1966-1 (Campbell 1969a); Kitsault 13 to 17 May 1980-1. **Interior** - White Lake (Okanagan Falls) 29 Apr 1978-10+ seen on 5 km walk; Williams Lake 18 Apr 1979-2; Hazelton 20 Mar 1912-1 (CVM 147); n Fort St. John 17 Apr 1977-1 male drumming; Atlin 16 May 1981-1 (Campbell 1981).

Summer: Coastal - Holberg 1 Jul 1978-2; Townsend Island 30 Aug 1938-1 (MCZ 282861); Masset 24 Aug 1920-1 (MVZ 102279). **Interior** - Yoho National Park 27 Aug 1971-1, second record for park (Rogers, T.H. 1972); Mount Robson Park 31 Aug 1973-1 (Cannings, S.G. 1973); Nulki Lake 31 Jul 1954-1 (ROM 87127); Beatton Park 12 Jul 1983-2 immatures; Mile 226, Alaska Highway 17

Jul 1943-1 (Rand 1944); Dease Lake 10 Aug 1962-1 (NMC 49820).

Autumn: Interior - Mile 282 Alaska Highway (s Fort Nelson) 29 Sep 1985-1; Coldfish Lake Sep 1976-1 (Osmond-Jones et al. 1977); Taylor 13 Nov 1982-1; 24 km s Prince George 15 Oct 1975-6 stayed at feeder through to April; Kamloops 5 Oct 1965-4. **Coastal** - Willow Point 20 Sep 1975-2+; Stump Lake (Quilchena) 6 Sep 1971-1; Strawberry Island 26 Nov 1972-5; Port Renfrew 5 Oct 1974-2.

Winter: Interior - Fort Nelson winter 1974/1975-1 (Erskine and Davidson 1976), 4 Jan 1985-1; Alaska Highway n Charlie Lake 11 Dec 1983-1 feeding at garbage dump on trash, -20° C with flurries; Fort St. John 5 Dec 1982-1 at feeder, -22° C; Chetwynd 22 Jan 1982-1, -23° C; Kispiox 24 Jan 1979-1; Williams Lake 2 Jan 1985-14 within

12 km radius of city, Downy:Hairy ratio 1:2, 5 Dec 1952-1 (PMNH 71815); Kamloops 17 Dec 1983-11, 26 Dec 1976-1 feeding on suet at feeder; Revelstoke winter 1982/1983-2 at feeder; Mt. Parker 29 Dec 1987-26 in burn; Creston 6 Jan 1982-7. **Coastal** - Greenville 4 to 14 Jan 1982-2; Bella Coola 11 Jan 1976-2; Cortes Island 11 Feb 1979-1, (Downy:Hairy ratio 1:20); Squamish River 22 Jan 1978-6 (Grass and Grass 1978); Sandhill Creek (Ucluelet) 1 Jan 1974-1; Victoria 16 Feb 1983-4.

Christmas Counts: Interior - Recorded from 17 of 19 localities and on 89% of all counts. Maxima: Vernon 16 Dec 1984-37; Lake Windermere 30 Dec 1983-27; Penticton 27 Dec 1983-24. **Coastal** - Recorded from 21 of 28 localities and on 82% of all counts. Maxima: Victoria 17 Dec 1983-68; White Rock 2 Jan 1978-49; Vancouver 26 Dec 1973-40.

Downy Woodpecker

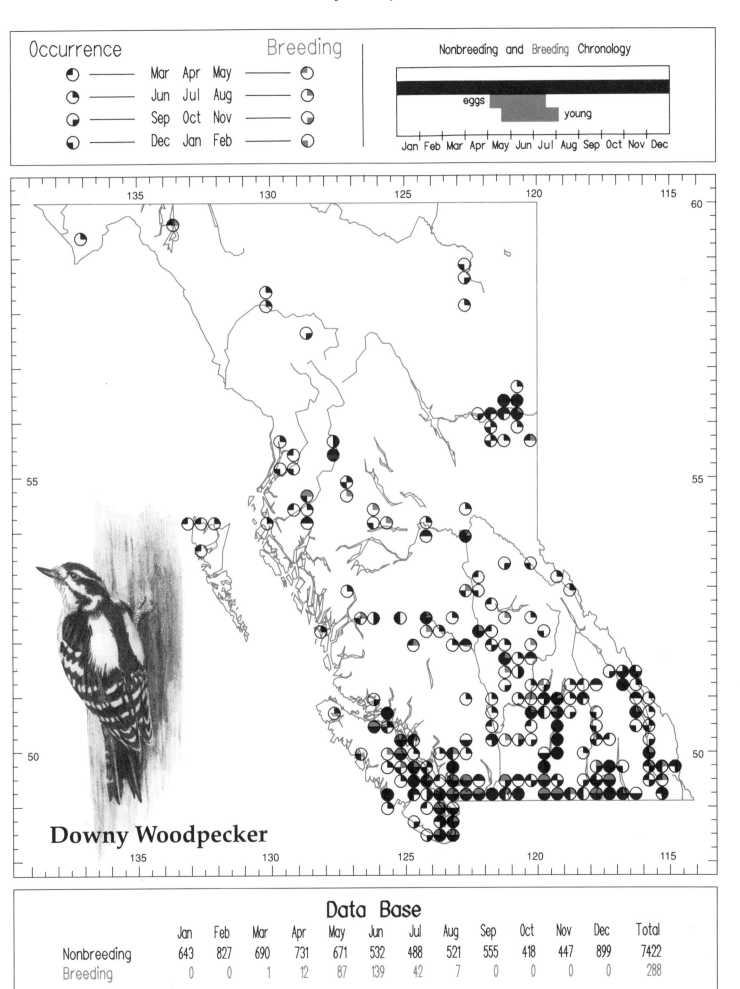

Downy Woodpecker

Data Base	Jan	Feb	Mar	Apr	May	Jun	Jul	Aug	Sep	Oct	Nov	Dec	Total
Nonbreeding	643	827	690	731	671	532	488	521	555	418	447	899	7422
Breeding	0	0	1	12	87	139	42	7	0	0	0	0	288

Hairy Woodpecker

Picoides villosus (Linnaeus)

HAWO

RANGE: Resident from forested Alaska and Canada south to Panama and the Bahamas.

STATUS: *Uncommon* resident throughout most of British Columbia, including Vancouver Island and the Queen Charlotte Islands. *Very rare* in the northwest corner of the province. Breeds.

NONBREEDING: The Hairy Woodpecker has a widespread distribution throughout British Columbia, occurring in all forested zones from near sea level to 1,900 m elevation. Habitats range from mature coniferous forests, where it frequents the edges of openings such as beaver ponds, pastures and meadows, clear cuts, and forest burns, to open ponderosa pine forests, deciduous groves, and mixed woods. In winter, the Hairy Woodpecker may also be found in residential areas where it feeds in horticultural trees and shrubs and at feeders.

Our data suggest some partial vertical migration, with birds moving from higher elevations to valley bottoms or coastal areas during the winter months. There is also some withdrawal of the northern populations over the winter period (Munro, J.A. and Cowan 1947; Cannings, R.A. et al. 1987).

BREEDING: The Hairy Woodpecker breeds throughout the province from near sea level to 1,830 m elevation. It frequents coniferous, deciduous, and mixed forests, often where openings such as meadows, marshes, or burns occur. Most of the breeding records are from coniferous forests, but most of the nest sites are in deciduous trees suggesting that this woodpecker prefers mixed forests or forest edges. Breeding activity can begin up to one month earlier on the south coast than it does in the interior (e.g. young ready to fledge, Pitt Meadows 18 Apr 1981, White Lake (Okanagan Falls) 11 May 1969, Williams Lake 26 May 1972, Fort Nelson 24 May 1975).

Nests: Nests (n=155) were situated in both living (53%) and dead (47%) trees. Of 124 nest trees identified, deciduous trees (69%) were used most often, including trembling aspen (34%), alders (16%), birches (9%), black cottonwood, and big leaf maple. Coniferous nest trees (31%) included Douglas-fir (9%), lodgepole pine (9%), western hemlock, spruces, western larch, western redcedar, and ponderosa pine. Five nests were in fence posts; one was found in a power pole. All nests were in excavated cavities and ranged in height from 0.9 to 38 m with 52% between 1.8 and 6.1 m. The cavity depths of 3 nests ranged from 28 to 31 cm. One nest had a cavity diameter of 11 cm. The entrance hole diameter of 4 nests ranged from 4 to 5 cm. Nest material consisted of wood chips from the excavation process.

Eggs: Dates for 36 clutches ranged from 4 April to 20 June with 53% recorded between 5 May and 19 May. Sizes for 17 clutches ranged from 3 to 5 eggs (3E-3, 4E-10, 5E-4) with 10 clutches having 4 eggs. Observations at one nest indicated that eggs were laid every day; both sexes incubated. Incubation period is 11 to 12 days (Burns 1915).

Young; Dates for 172 broods ranged from 18 April to 22 July with 53% recorded between 24 May and 17 June. Sizes for 10 broods ranged from 2 to 5 young (2Y-1, 3Y-5, 4Y-2, 5Y-1) with 5 broods having 3 young. Records of 4 nests from British Columbia suggest the fledging period is 24 to 27 days.

REMARKS: Six subspecies of the Hairy Woodpecker occur in British Columbia: *P. v. septentrionalis, P. v. monticola, P v. sitkensis* (doubtfully separable from *harrisi* - Godfrey 1986), *P. v. harrisi, P. v. picoideus* (endemic to the Queen Charlotte Islands), and *P. v. orius* (see Munro, J.A. and Cowan 1947; Godfrey 1986).

The Hairy Woodpecker appears on the "Blue List" from 1975 to 1982 (Tate 1981; Tate and Tate 1982). In 1982, it was reported as stable throughout most of its range, but was down in numbers in Washington and Oregon.

NOTEWORTHY RECORDS

Spring: Coastal - McGillivray Slough 17 Apr 1972-5; Thacker Mountain spring 1960/61- abundant (Horvath 1963); n Klaskish River 9 May 1978-2; Cape St. James 16 Apr 1978-2; Delkatla Creek 27 Apr 1979-1; Kitsault 13 to 17 May 1980-5+. **Interior** - Shingle Creek 9 May 1981-4 at old burn; Balfour to Waneta 16 May 1981-12 on bird count; Riske Creek 8 Mar 1981-4; confluence of Fraser and Nechako Rivers 6 Mar 1983-6; Hyland Post 29 May 1976-1 in burn; w Fort Nelson 11 May 1980-2; Liard Hot Springs 27 May 1981-2; Helmet (Kwokullie Lake) 15 May 1982-2.

Summer: Coastal - Pitt Meadows 11 Jul 1971-3 (Campbell et al. 1972b); Langara Island 3 Jul 1946-8+ quite common. **Interior** - Natal Ridge 13 Jun 1984-1; Mount Tatlow 19 Aug 1978-1 in subalpine forest; Chilcotin River (Riske Creek) 23 Aug 1984-1 "third most common resident"; upper Muskwa River 22 Aug 1983-1 (Cooper,

J.M. and Cooper 1983); Telegraph Creek 22 Jun 1919-1 (MVZ 39772); 10 km nw Fort Nelson 12 Jul 1969-1 (UKMU 63968); confluence of Liard and Beaver Rivers 10 Aug 1977-1; Atlin 4 Aug 1931-1 (RBCM 5909); s Basement Creek 9 Jun 1983-1 (Campbell et al. 1983).

Autumn: Interior - Warm Bay Hot Springs 16 Sep 1972-1; Fort St. John 28 Nov 1982-1 at feeder; 24 km s Prince George 14 Oct 1975-6+ "coming to feeder from now until April"; Scotch Creek 22 Sep 1962-4; confluence of Elk River and Michel Creek 10 Oct 1984-3. **Coastal** - Masset 12 Oct 1971-2; Port Neville 2 Sep 1975-4; s Campbell River (Discovery Passage) 1 Sep 1974-3.

Winter: Interior - Atlin 5 Jan 1931-1 (RBCM 5910); Fort Nelson 4 Jan 1985-1; Taylor 29 Jan 1984-2; Williams Lake 2 Jan 1985-25 within 12 km radius of city, 27 Jan 1979-4; 100 Mile House 20

Jan 1979-4 at feeder; Kleena Kleene 16 Jan 1949-1 (Paul 1959); Kamloops 17 Dec 1983-12; Kootenay National Park 9 Feb 1983-1; Revelstoke 26 Jan 1977-1 feeding at dump; Taghum 25 Jan 1979-1 eating suet at feeder; Penticton 27 Dec 1973-13 (Shepard, M.G. 1974); Mt. Parker 29 Dec 1987-47 in burn. **Coastal** - Greenville 4 to 14 Jan 1982-1; Tlell 12 Jan 1972-1; Port Neville 21 Dec 1977-1; confluence of Memekay and Salmon Rivers 25 Feb 1983-2; Victoria 20 Feb 1983-4.

Christmas Counts: Interior - Recorded from 19 of 19 localities and on 94% of all counts. Maxima: Lake Windermere 30 Dec 1984-42; Shuswap Lake 28 Dec 1983-22, 18 Dec 1984-22; Penticton 27 Dec 1983-21. **Coastal** - Recorded from 23 of 28 localities and on 75% of all counts. Maxima: Victoria 27 Dec 1964-35; White Rock 30 Dec 1984-14; Sooke 31 Dec 1983-13.

Hairy Woodpecker

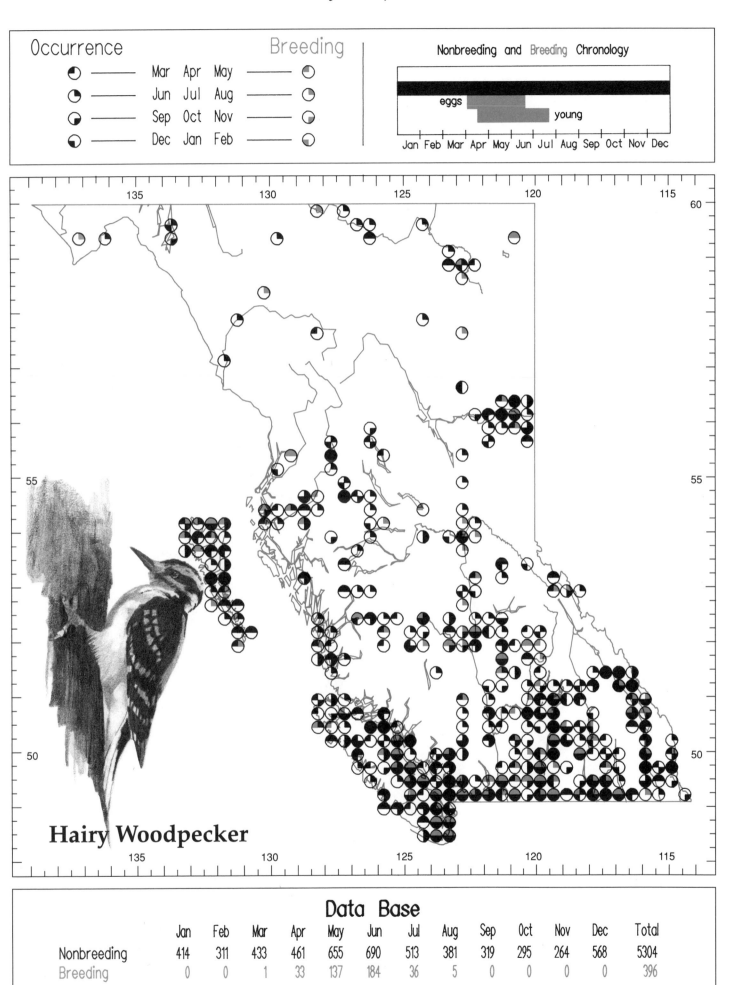

Occurrence　　Breeding

◐ ——————	Mar Apr May	—————— ◔
◔ ——————	Jun Jul Aug	—————— ◔
◔ ——————	Sep Oct Nov	—————— ◑
◕ ——————	Dec Jan Feb	—————— ◔

Nonbreeding and Breeding Chronology

eggs young

Jan Feb Mar Apr May Jun Jul Aug Sep Oct Nov Dec

Data Base

	Jan	Feb	Mar	Apr	May	Jun	Jul	Aug	Sep	Oct	Nov	Dec	Total
Nonbreeding	414	311	433	461	655	690	513	381	319	295	264	568	5304
Breeding	0	0	1	33	137	184	36	5	0	0	0	0	396

White-headed Woodpecker
Picoides albolarvatus (Cassin)

WHWO

RANGE: Resident in the extreme southern interior of British Columbia south through eastern Washington and northern Idaho to southern California and Nevada.

STATUS: *Very rare* resident in the Okanagan valley. *Casual* in the Similkameen valley and east of the Okanagan. Breeds.

NONBREEDING: The White-headed Woodpecker is restricted to the Thompson-Okanagan Plateau and Southern Columbia Mountains regions from Manning Park east to Creston and north to Falkland. It is an irregular summer visitant to the Similkameen valley. Winter distribution includes the Okanagan valley north to at least Naramata; it is casual in winter in the north Okanagan valley (Okanagan Landing) and east of the Okanagan. It has not been reported from the coast.

The White-headed Woodpecker frequents open ponderosa pine and mixed pine - Douglas-fir forests to 760 m elevation as well as Engelmann spruce - lodgepole pine forests to 1,300 m elevation, black cottonwood groves, and residential gardens.

BREEDING: The White-headed Woodpecker nests locally in the Thompson-Okanagan Plateau through the southern Okanagan valley north to Naramata (Fig. 313).

Its breeding habitat is the open ponderosa pine forests from 450 to 600 m elevation.

Nests: Of 7 nests, 5 were situated in ponderosa pine (living and dead), 1 was in a Douglas-fir snag (Cooper, J.K. 1969), and 1 was in a stump. All were located in excavated cavities. Nest heights ranged from 2.5 to 9 m, with 3 between 2.5 and 3 m.

Eggs: One nest was found with 4 fresh eggs on 10 June. Calculated dates indicate that eggs could be found from 15 May to 15 June. Incubation period is about 14 days (Harrison, C. 1978).

Young: Dates for 4 broods ranged from 30 May to 16 July. Fledged broods contained 2 or 3 young (2Y-1; 3Y-2). Fledging period is unknown (Terres 1980).

REMARKS: W.C. Weber and Cannings (1976) mention 2 reports of White-headed Woodpecker sightings for which identification was uncertain: Skihist Park near Lytton, 28 July 1965 and near Bummers Flats, north of Cranbrook (no date). Both are from areas of suitable habitat. There is another possible sighting from just south of Golden: Frances King (pers. comm.) is convinced she saw this bird in autumn, some time during the 1950s, but most details have since been lost.

The White-headed Woodpecker was first reported in British Columbia in 1890; from then until 1950 another 5 observations were reported. J.A. Munro and Cowan (1947) consider the bird casual in the Dry Forest Biotic Area. Observations increased

through the 1950s (15 records), peaking in the 1960s (112 records) and dropping in the 1970s (68 records). Observations through the 1970s remained relatively constant.

Since 1979 we have but 16 records of the White-headed Woodpecker, at least 5 of which are of the same breeding pair. These fluctuations are typical of peripheral species such as the White-headed Woodpecker, which reaches its northern limit of distribution in British Columbia.

Figure 313. *Adult (left) and immature White-headed Woodpecker at Naramata, Okanagan valley, 12 August 1973 (Ervio Sian).*

NOTEWORTHY RECORDS

Spring: Coastal - No records. **Interior** - Manning Park 23 May 1958-1; e Princeton 22 May 1958-1; Cascade 6 Mar 1970-2, 14 May 1971-1; Nine Mile Creek (Anarchist Mountain) 23 May 1966-1; Inkaneep 21 May 1967-1 pair; Mahoney Lake 25 Apr 1965-1; Summerland 14 Mar 1953.

Summer: Coastal - No records. **Interior** - Manning Park late Jun 1970-1; Inkaneep 8 Jul 1967-1 adult male; Gallagher Lake 5 Jun 1974-1 adult female; Fairview 13 Aug 1966-1 feeding on mullein stalks (Weber, W.C. and Cannings 1976); Bromley Creek summer 1972-1; Penticton 5 Jul

1965-1 pair with 2 young; Naramata 2 Jul 1978-3 adults; Carrs 1 Jul 1965-1.

Autumn: Interior - Falkland 7 Oct 1979-1; Kelowna 8 Sep 1975-1, 1 Oct 1971-1 adult; Naramata 20 Sep 1975-1 pair and 2 young; Beaverdell 14 Sep 1986-1; Vaseux Lake 7 Nov 1970-2; Castlegar 23 Nov 1983-1 (Rogers, T.H. 1984a); Richter Pass 15 Oct 1954-1 (Campbell and Meugens 1971); Oliver 3 Sep 1962-1 pair; Anarchist Mountain 9 Oct 1972-1. **Coastal** - No records.

Winter: Interior - Vaseux Lake 1 Jan 1978-1; lower Vaseux Creek 24 Feb 1963-3; Cascade 27 Dec 1970-1, 12 Jan 1971-1; Goat River 16 Jan 1981-1; Keogan Mountain 12 Dec 1965-7; Arawana 30 Dec 1975-5; Okanagan Landing 20 Dec 1911-1 (RBCM 2818). **Coastal** - No records.

Christmas Counts: Interior - Recorded from 2 of 19 localities and on 3% of all counts. Maxima: Vaseux Lake 23 Dec 1984-1, 31 Dec 1975-1, 31 Dec 1977-1, Oliver/Osoyoos 26 Dec 1984-1 all counts are all-time Canadian highs (Anderson, R.R. 1976; Monroe 1985b). **Coastal** - Not recorded.

White-headed Woodpecker

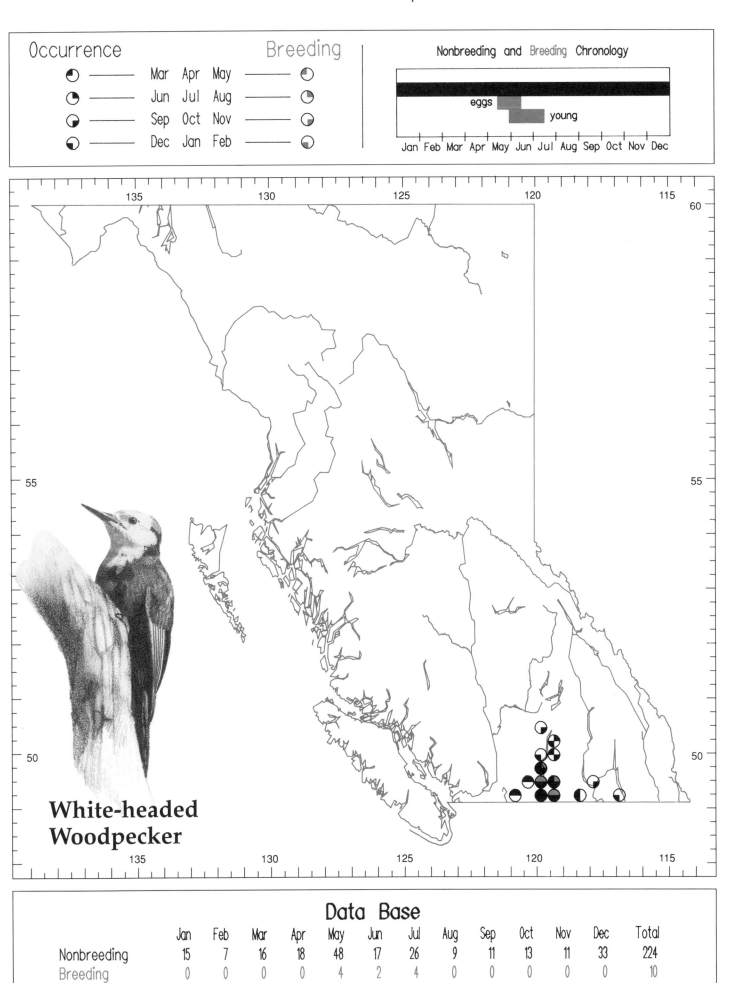

Occurrence

Occurrence		Breeding
◑ ———	Mar Apr May	——— ◑
◵ ———	Jun Jul Aug	——— ◔
◖ ———	Sep Oct Nov	——— ◗
◕ ———	Dec Jan Feb	——— ◒

Nonbreeding and Breeding Chronology

eggs — young

Jan Feb Mar Apr May Jun Jul Aug Sep Oct Nov Dec

White-headed Woodpecker

Data Base

	Jan	Feb	Mar	Apr	May	Jun	Jul	Aug	Sep	Oct	Nov	Dec	Total
Nonbreeding	15	7	16	18	48	17	26	9	11	13	11	33	224
Breeding	0	0	0	0	4	2	4	0	0	0	0	0	10

Three-toed Woodpecker

TTWO

Picoides tridactylus (Linnaeus)

RANGE: Resident locally from Alaska and across much of forested Canada south to southern Oregon and to south central New Mexico, east locally across the northern United States to Maine. Also occurs in Eurasia.

STATUS: *Uncommon* to *rare* resident throughout most of British Columbia. *Very rare* west of the Coast Ranges, including Vancouver Island. Absent from the Queen Charlotte Islands. Breeds.

NONBREEDING: The Three-toed Woodpecker is widely distributed throughout the province east of the Coastal Gap and Pacific and Cascade ranges and only locally along the coast including Vancouver Island. It winters throughout its range.

The Three-toed Woodpecker frequents subalpine, sub-boreal, and boreal forests, and the higher elevations of the interior Douglas-fir and western hemlock forests from 450 to 2,100 m elevation, often near openings made by ponds, lakes, bogs, muskegs, clearcuts, and burns. It occasionally wanders to lower elevations.

BREEDING: The Three-toed Woodpecker breeds throughout most of the province east of the Boundary Ranges, Coastal Gap, and Pacific and Cascade ranges. It nests less frequently on the coastal slope. It probably nests locally in mountains west of Comox on Vancouver Island.

Its breeding habitats include coniferous forests from 520 to 1,690 m elevation, near openings made by burns, clearcuts, ponds, lakes, and bogs. One nest area was a vacant lot within a subdivision.

Nests: With the exception of one nest in a log signpost, all nests (n=63) were located in excavated cavities in both dead and living coniferous (67%, 8 species) and deciduous (25%) trees. Spruce (27%; Engelmann, white, black), lodgepole pine (15%), and trembling aspen (18%) were the most frequently recorded nest trees. Heights of 64 nests ranged from 1 to 24 m with most (58%) between 1 and 4.6 m. Four nests had a cavity depth of 18 to 28 cm. The cavity diameters of 2 nests were 10 and 11 cm. Five had entrance hole diameters of 4 cm.

Eggs: Dates for 12 clutches ranged from 8 May to 13 July. One clutch had 3 eggs and another had 4. Incubation period is about 14 days (Harrison, C. 1978).

Young: Dates for 79 broods ranged from 28 May to 22 July with 51% recorded between 18 and 30 June. Calculated dates indicate that young could be found as early as 22 May. Sizes for 17 broods ranged from 2 to 4 young (2Y-10, 3Y-6, 4Y-1) with 10 broods having 2 young. Data from one nest suggest a nestling period of 18 to 23 days.

REMARKS: There are a number of summer coastal occurrences, and 3 records in particular that suggest the Three-toed Woodpecker may breed more widely at the coast: Mount Washington 19 August 1932-1 (RBCM 13154), juvenile female (see also Laing 1935 and Munro, J.A. and Cowan 1947); a sight record of a pair nesting in a snag near Kitsault 17 to 19 June 1980; and Cypress Park 10 May 1987, a pair excavating nest hole in snag. However, adequate details to confirm coastal breeding are lacking.

The Three-toed Woodpecker is probably more common in British Columbia than our data indicate. R.R. Howie (pers. comm.) believes "this species to be *uncommon* in much of the wetter and boreal habitat in its range." Howie quickly notes that "clearly, their retiring nature and poorly-birded habitat causes a problem in obtaining good quantitative data."

J.A. Munro and Cowan (1947) and Godfrey (1986) report only one subspecies, *P. t. fasciatus*, for British Columbia.

The Three-toed Woodpecker was previously known as the Northern Three-toed Woodpecker.

POSTSCRIPT: On 10 July 1988 a pair of adults was observed feeding 2 or more young in a nest located on the trail to Battleship Lake near Paradise Meadows on Vancouver Island (B.J. Brooks pers. comm.). The nest was 10.7 m from the ground in a dead yellow cedar snag. This constitutes the first confirmed coastal breeding record for Vancouver Island.

NOTEWORTHY RECORDS

Spring: Coastal - Saturna Island 13 Apr 1894-1 male (MCZ 104510), 30 Apr 1894-1 male (MCZ 104509); Cypress Park 10 May 1987-1 pair excavating nest cavity, not completed (Mattocks and Harrington-Tweit 1987a); Wolf Lake 14 May 1934-1 female (CMNH 115565); Helen Mackenzie Lake 19 Apr 1987-1 male. **Interior** - Wulf Creek 20 Apr 1983-1 pair; Canal Flats 11 Apr 1937-1 female (RBCM 11086); Lytton 31 May 1964-1 male (NMC 52408); Shuswap Falls 11 Apr 1918-1 male (AMNH 755559); Enderby 7 May 1956-1 female (UBC 6985); Carpenter Lake (Heffley Creek) 27 May 1987-1; 11 km n Williams Lake 31 Mar 1932-1 female (MCZ 282867); Cottonwood 16 May 1930-1 female (MCZ 282882); Wendle Creek 31 Mar 1981-1; Stoddart Creek 6 Mar 1976-2; Blueberry River 20 May 1922-1 (Williams, M.Y. 1933a); Liard Hot Springs 14 Mar 1975-1 female (Reid 1975); Helmut (Kwokullie Lake) 14 May 1982-1 female.

Summer: Coastal - Cypress Park 10 Jun 1977-1, 27 Jul 1983-1, 28 Jul 1981-2; Seymour Mountain 20 Jul 1984-1 (Harrington-Tweit and Mattocks 1984); Hollyburn Mountain 21 Jul 1984-1 (Harrington-

Tweit and Mattocks 1984); Petgill Lake 6 Aug 1982-1 adult feeding young; Comox 13 Jun 1942-1 male (RBCM 13149), 15 Jun 1932-1 male (Laing 1934); Forbidden Plateau Jul 1961-3 (Boggs and Boggs 1961c), 23 Jul 1976-1; Mount Washington 19 Aug 1932-1 immature female (RBCM 13154); Garibaldi Park 2 Jul 1974-1 male (Thomson, D. 1974), 24 Jul 1983-2 males. **Interior** - Newgate 11 Jun 1953-1 immature male (Godfrey 1955); Shuttle-worth Creek 1 Jun 1984-1; Beaver Lake (New Denver) 7 Aug 1980-4; Trinity Valley 10 Jun 1976-1; Glacier National Park 20 Jun 1983-1 pair; Leonie Lake 9 Jun 1934-1 male (CMNH 115754); Dempsey Lake 15 Aug 1986-1; 42 km n Tatla Lake 18 Jun 1987-2 males, 1 female; Swiftcurrent Creek 15 Aug 1973-1 pair with 2 fledged young; Topley 30 Jul 1956-1 female (NMC 41284); Fort St. John 16 Aug 1986-1; Taylor 21 Aug 1975-2; Muncho Lake 31 Jul 1943-1 male (NMC 29479); Mile 54 Haines Road (s Kelsall Lake) 3 Jul 1980-1 (RBCM 16908).

Autumn: Interior - Atlin 16 Sep 1931-1 (RBCM 5913); Fort Nelson 2 Nov 1984-2; Fort St. John 29 Sep 1983-2; 64 km n Hazelton 12 Sep 1921-1

female (MVZ 42125); Nulki Lake 24 Sep 1953-1 immature female (ROM 85877); Williams Lake 21 Sep 1951-1 (NMC 47986); Kootenay National Park 26 Oct 1981-1; Michel Lake (Elk River) 19 Oct 1984-1 female. **Coastal** - Mount Washington 26 Sep 1981-1 male; Cypress Park 11 Nov 1978-1; Cascade 9 Sep 1891-1 female (MCZ 245600); Victoria 19 Sep 1983-1.

Winter: Interior - Atlin 7 Jan 1932-1 (RBCM 5914); Liard Hot Springs 6 Feb 1975-1 male (Reid 1975); Fort St. John 30 Jan 1983-2, 23 Dec 1985-1; Williams Lake 11 and 12 Jan 1951-2 (NMC 47983, 47985); Penticton 5 Jan 1974-1. **Coastal** - Minette Bay 15 Jan 1975-1; Mount Washington 25 Dec 1987-1 male.

Christmas Counts: Interior - Recorded from 7 of 19 localities and on 18% of all counts. Maxima: Yoho National Park 20 Dec 1975-5; Smithers 19 Dec 1983-4; Vernon 26 Dec 1977-2. **Coastal** - Recorded from 2 of 28 localities and on 1% of all counts. Maxima: Victoria 23 Dec 1961-1; Terrace 26 Dec 1966-1, 26 Dec 1968-1, 26 Dec 1983-1.

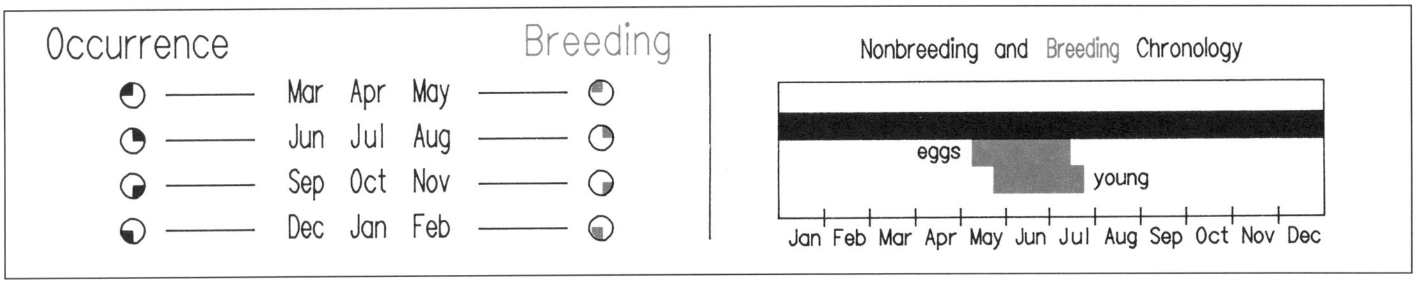
Occurrence
Breeding
Mar Apr May
Jun Jul Aug
Sep Oct Nov
Dec Jan Feb
Nonbreeding and Breeding Chronology
eggs
young
Jan Feb Mar Apr May Jun Jul Aug Sep Oct Nov Dec

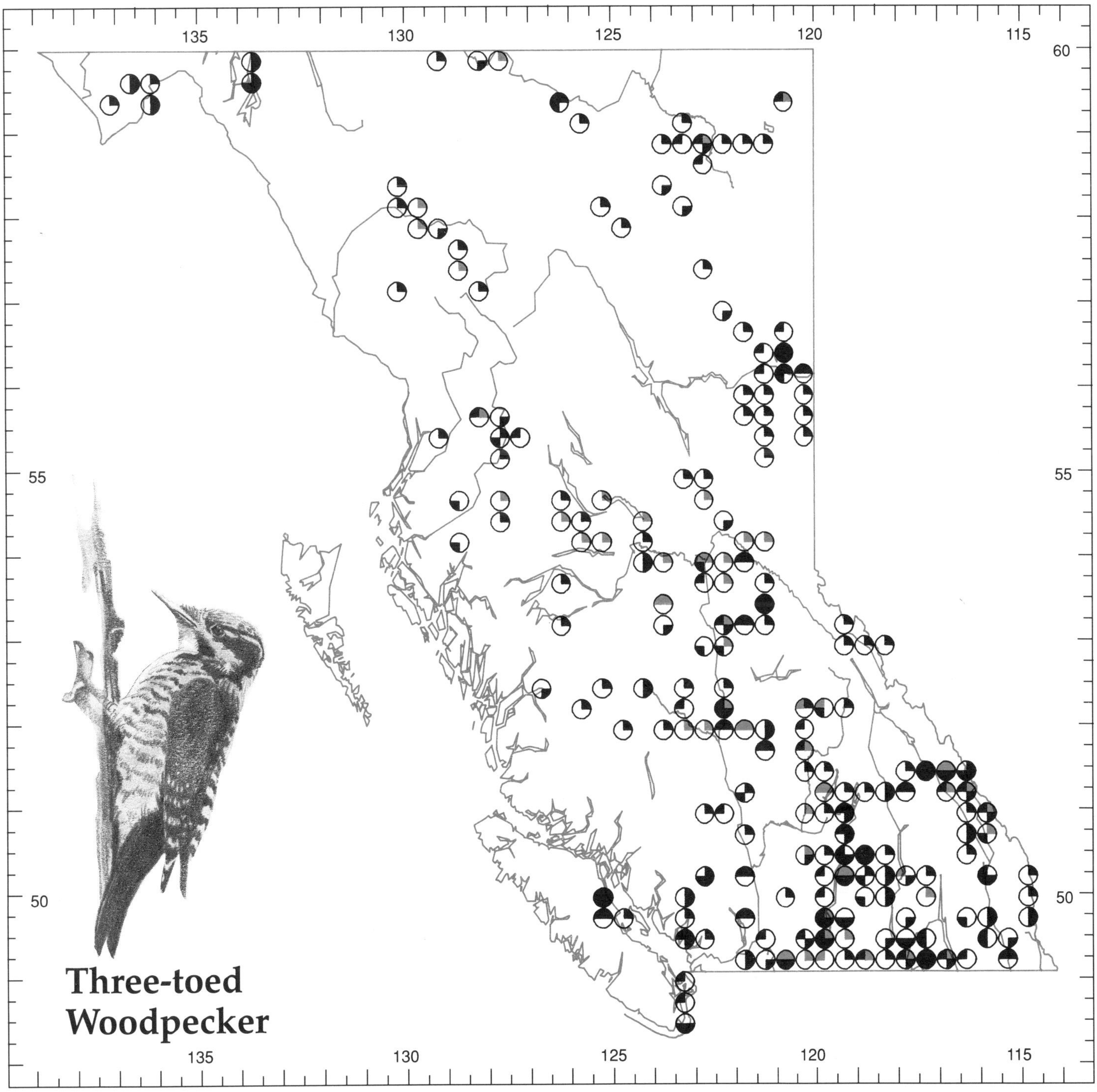
135
130
125
120
115
60
55
50
Three-toed Woodpecker

Data Base

	Jan	Feb	Mar	Apr	May	Jun	Jul	Aug	Sep	Oct	Nov	Dec	Total
Nonbreeding	29	23	26	31	64	145	172	101	53	51	32	44	771
Breeding	0	0	0	0	13	52	21	5	0	0	0	0	91

Black-backed Woodpecker

Picoides arcticus (Swainson)

BBWO

RANGE: Resident locally from Alaska and across much of forested Canada south to central California and east locally through the northernmost United States to Maine.

STATUS: *Rare* to *very rare* resident east of the Coast Ranges. *Casual* west of the Coast Ranges. Breeds.

NONBREEDING: The Black-backed Woodpecker is distributed locally throughout the province, rarely at the coast; it is absent from the Queen Charlotte Islands and Vancouver Island.

It frequents the sub-alpine, sub-boreal, and boreal coniferous forests, and the higher elevations of the interior Douglas-fir and western hemlock forests from 335 to 1,890 m elevation. Occasionally it descends to valley bottoms to feed and nest. Forest burns are favoured habitat. It is also found at lake and pond edges, open bogs, road edges, and residential areas.

The Black-backed Woodpecker is believed to winter throughout its British Columbia range, but winter records are scarce and extend north only to Hazelton (55°N). It wanders south irregularly.

BREEDING: The Black-backed Woodpecker breeds from extreme southern interior British Columbia north to between Beatton and Sikanni Chief rivers (see Williams, M.Y. 1933a; Erskine and Davidson 1976), and likely throughout its nonbreeding range. Its breeding habitat includes coniferous forests from 335 to 1,400 m elevation, often where openings such as burns, logged areas, lake and stream shores, swamps, and bogs occur (Lehnhauser and Murphy 1985).

Nests: With the exception of one nest in a power pole, all nests (n=18) were in living or dead coniferous trees including pines (6), spruces (3), Douglas-fir, western larch, western hemlock, and western redcedar. All were located in excavated cavities, in the main trunk of the tree, often with the bark chipped away from the cavity entrance, and occasionally with the bark scaled off the tree perimeter from the adult's approach (Fig. 314). Heights of 19 nests ranged from 1 to 24 m with 69% between 1 and 3 m. The cavity depth of 1 nest was 30 cm; the entrance hole diameters of 2 nests were 5 and 7 cm.

Eggs: Dates for 3 clutches ranged from 12 May to 11 June. One clutch had 3 eggs and another had 4. Incubation period is about 14 days (Bent 1939).

Young: Dates for 15 broods ranged from 23 May to 7 July with 9 broods recorded between 16 June and 1 July. Sizes for 9 broods ranged from 1 to 3 young (1Y-5, 2Y-2, 3Y-2). Fledging period is unknown (Terres 1980).

REMARKS: This species is possibly more common in British Columbia than our data indicate, probably because of the bird's retiring nature coupled with the limited birding effort in its habitat.

We have one possible observation of the species from the Queen Charlotte Islands (Tlell, 20 July 1974-1 female), and a possible breeding record from Rainbow Lake (Prince Rupert), 24 June 1971 - adults feeding young at cavity entrance. Both records lack sufficient details to confirm identification.

The Black-backed Woodpecker was previously known as the Arctic Woodpecker or Black-backed Three-toed Woodpecker.

Figure 314. Adult Black-backed Woodpecker at nest entrance near Christina Lake, north of Grand Forks, 24 May 1980 (Mark Nyhof).

NOTEWORTHY RECORDS

Spring: Coastal - No records. **Interior -** Manning Park 26 Jul 1945-1 male (RBCM 9137); Newgate 2 May 1930-1 pair (NMC 24607-08); Vaseux Lake 23 May 1922-1 female (MVZ 102361); Canal Flats 11 Apr 1932-1 male (RBCM 11082); Vernon 15 Mar 1961-2 pairs; Carpenter Lake 27 May 1987-1; Gateway 29 May 1919-1 male (MVZ 102354); 103 Mile Lake 5 May 1947-1 pair (Munro, J.A. 1955c); Williams Lake 5 Mar 1952-1 female (NMC 47980); Mokus Creek 30 May 1980-1 male; Halfway River 30 Apr 1978-1 male at mouth; Atlin 11 Mar 1932-1 (RBCM 5915).

Summer: Coastal - Lakelse Lake 4 Jun 1976-1; 8 km n Terrace 22 Jun 1975-1 (Hay 1976); **Interior -** Flathead Valley 26 Jul 1956-1 (NMC 40586); Sirdar 5 Aug 1948-2 (ROM 76726, 83873); Kelowna 19 Jul 1933-1 immature female (ROM 83869); Lytton 8 Jun 1964-1 female (NMC 52405); Vermillion Pass 14 Jul 1973-1 (Scott, G. 1973);

Quesnel 9 Jun 1900-1 male (RBCM 1769); 77 km w Chetwynd 16 to 20 Jun 1969-2 (Webster 1969); Dease Lake 9 Jun 1962-1 female (NMC 49821); 58°57'N 121°33'W 23 Jun 1982-1 male (RBCM 17621); sw junction Alsek and Tatshenshini rivers 8 Jun 1983-1 male (Campbell et al. 1983).

Autumn: Interior - Klappan River 14 Sep 1977-1 male; Cameron River (ne Wonowon) 18 Oct 1978-1 female; Fort St. John 2 Nov 1975-1 female; Tetana Lake 22 Nov 1938-1 female (RBCM 8372); Mount Averil 18 Oct 1983-1; Williams Lake 23 Nov 1951-1 male (RBCM 15694); Lac la Hache 3 Oct 1952-1 male (ROM 83878); Buffalo Lake 1 Sep 1932-1 female (RBCM 11464); Golden 24 Nov 1899-1 female; Cranbrook 18 Sep 1920-1 male (ROM 24.4.14.420); Princeton 30 Sep 1927-1 male (RBCM 13144); Hope 4 Oct 1909-1 (Munro, J.A. and Cowan 1947); Okanagan Landing 1 Oct 1957-1 female (ROM 83871). **Coastal -** Vancouver 1 Oct

1984-1.

Winter: Interior - Hazelton 21 Dec 1911-1 (Munro, J.A. and Cowan 1947); near Quesnel winter 1900/01-1 (Brooks 1901); Williams Lake 24 Dec 1949-1 male (NMC 47976); Daer Creek 19 Jan 1983-1 female; Girard 18 Dec 1952-1 male (UBC 6994); Trinity Valley 3 Jan 1940-1 male (UMMZ 127388); Gold Creek (Cranbrook) 4 Feb 1938-1 (Johnstone, W.B. 1949); Kaleden, 5 Jan 1974-1 male; Sheep Creek (Salmo) 29 Dec 1984-1 male. **Coastal -** No records.

Christmas Counts: Interior - Recorded from 6 of 19 localities and on 8% of all counts. Maxima: Lake Windermere 26 Dec 1982-3; Nakusp 2 Jan 1983-2; Oliver/Osoyoos 29 Dec 1983-1; Penticton 27 Dec 1980-1; Smithers 17 Dec 1977-1; Wells Gray 29 Dec 1984-1. **Coastal -** Not recorded.

Black-backed Woodpecker

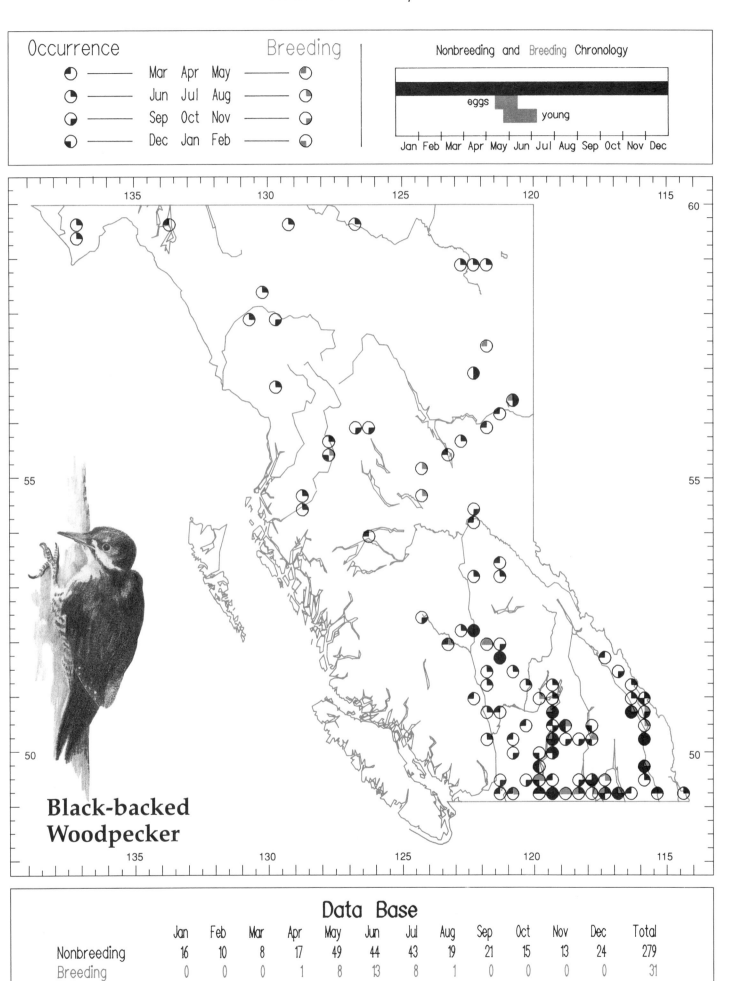

Black-backed Woodpecker

Data Base

	Jan	Feb	Mar	Apr	May	Jun	Jul	Aug	Sep	Oct	Nov	Dec	Total
Nonbreeding	16	10	8	17	49	44	43	19	21	15	13	24	279
Breeding	0	0	0	1	8	13	8	1	0	0	0	0	31

Northern Flicker

NOFL

Colaptes auratus (Linnaeus)

RANGE: Breeds throughout most of North America from the Arctic tree limit to Nicaragua. Winters from southern Canada south through the remainder of the breeding range.

STATUS: *Fairly common* local resident in the southern third of the province including Vancouver Island; *uncommon* resident north to the Queen Charlotte Islands and Prince Rupert on the coast. *Rare* to *uncommon* summer visitant throughout the remainder of the province. Breeds.

NONBREEDING: The Northern Flicker (Fig. 315) is widely distributed in the province. Throughout its nonbreeding range it frequents a variety of open forest types as well as farmland, pastureland, and other open habitats including rural and urban residential areas (Fig. 316). In the latter areas, it can often be found feeding on cultivated fruits and at feeders. One male flicker visited a suet feeder daily throughout -40° C temperatures (Williams Lake, January 1979).

Migration periods are difficult to discern in areas where birds are resident. During spring, the number of observations in certain areas increases from March to May. Birds arrive on their breeding areas in early March in southern areas, and in the latter half of May in the north. Autumn migration appears to begin in late August, peaking by mid-to-late September and continuing through October. In some areas, small loose flocks of more than 10 birds have been reported. During autumn, some of the northern populations move from their breeding areas to southern interior valleys and the coast. Winter distribution of the *cafer* group ("Red-shafted Flicker") includes Vancouver Island east through the Fraser Lowlands, the Okanagan valley, and the Kootenays, with smaller numbers farther north to Williams Lake; rarely to Prince George and Smithers. The majority of the *auratus* group ("Yellow-shafted Flicker") appears to winter outside British Columbia.

Figure 315. Northern Flicker at a feeder in New Westminster, 18 November 1976 (Ervio Sian).

Figure 316. The Northern Flicker forages and nests in this habitat at Campbell River Park, Langley, 15 April 1971 (R. Wayne Campbell).

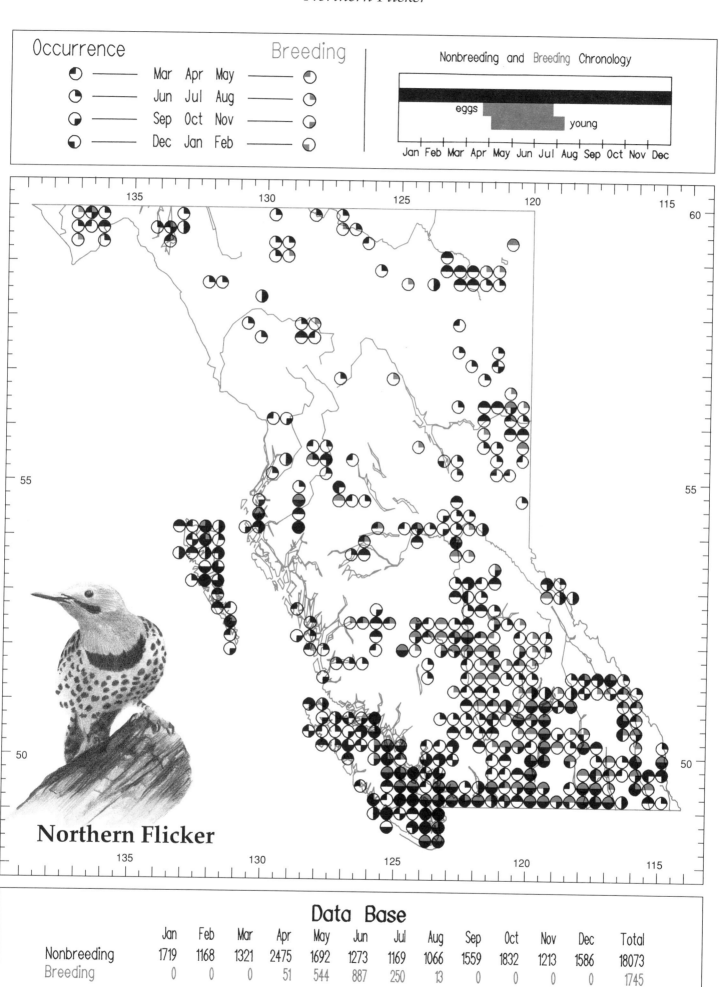

Northern Flicker

Data Base

	Jan	Feb	Mar	Apr	May	Jun	Jul	Aug	Sep	Oct	Nov	Dec	Total
Nonbreeding	1719	1168	1321	2475	1692	1273	1169	1066	1559	1832	1213	1586	18073
Breeding	0	0	0	51	544	887	250	13	0	0	0	0	1745

BREEDING: The Northern Flicker is a widespread breeder throughout most of the province. Breeding habitats include virtually all forested zones in the province from near sea level to 2,100 m. It prefers open habitats (Fig. 317) such as aspen - lodgepole pine parkland, riparian woodland, forest edges, ponderosa pine forests, urban and rural gardens, rangeland, pastureland, orchards, alpine meadow edges, burns, logged areas, and second growth plantations.

Nests: Most nests (90%; n=731) were situated in natural sites, including deciduous (48%; Fig. 318) and coniferous (26%) trees, stumps and snags (16%), and silt or clay cliffs. Man-made sites included nest boxes (4%), fence posts (3%), buildings, power poles, marina breakwater pilings, and a clothesline pole. Of the 543 nest trees identified, the most frequently used species were trembling aspen (38%), lodgepole pine (10%), ponderosa pine (9%), black cottonwood (8%), Douglas-fir (8%), and birches (6%); 67% of the deciduous trees were living, while only 35% of the coniferous trees were alive. In her Orchard Lake study area, Keisker (1986) found that flickers preferred dead trees or the dead tops of live trees. She labelled the Northern Flicker a "weak excavator," noting that the birds generally did not excavate through sound wood but required trees where decay had weakened both sapwood and heartwood. The diameter at breast height (DBH) of 5 coastal nest trees ranged from 25 to 89 cm with a mean of 48 cm; the DBH of 59 interior nest trees ranged from 23 to 91 cm with a mean of 38 cm. These data are supported by Kelleher's (1963) coastal and Keisker's (1986) interior studies. Most nests (94%) were located in excavated cavities, mainly in the main trunk of trees, 26 nests were found in nest boxes, 10 in the walls of abandoned buildings, and 1 in the ventilator of a hospital operating room. Both sexes excavate the cavity (n=2). Heights for 772 nests ranged from ground level to 27 m with most nests (60%) below 3 m. The cavity bottom of a nest in a fencepost was 46 cm below the ground. The cavity depth of 33 nests ranged from 25 to 76 cm with a mean depth of 43 cm. Three cavity diameters ranged from 13 to 25 cm. The diameter of 13 entrance holes ranged from 5 to 13 cm with a mean of 8 cm. Nest material was primarily wood chips from the excavation process.

Eggs: Dates for 258 clutches ranged from 23 April to 10 July with 51% recorded between 19 May and 6 June. Calculated dates suggest nests can have eggs as late as 25 July. In southern areas, where birds are resident, clutch initiation begins up to one month earlier than in northern areas. Sizes for 209 clutches ranged from 1 to 13 eggs (1E-2, 2E-3, 3E-10, 4E-11, 5E-23, 6E-29, 7E-48, 8E-58, 9E-15, 10E-7, 11E-2, 13E-1) with 51% having 7 or 8 eggs. Incubation periods for 17 nests in British Columbia ranged between 11 and 13 days. In 1 nest, 7 eggs hatched over a 6 day period. Eggs are laid 1 per day (n=6); both sexes incubate (n=13).

Young: Dates for 370 broods (Fig. 319) ranged from 4 May to 10 Aug with 51% recorded between 11 and 29 June. Sizes for 187 broods ranged from 1 to 11 young (1Y-2, 2Y-10, 3Y-12, 4Y-21, 5Y-33, 6Y-31, 7Y-49, 8Y-17, 9Y-8, 10Y-3, 11Y-1) with 60% having 5 to 7 young. Data from 26 nests in British Columbia suggest a nestling period of 23 to 27 days. Sherman (1910) notes that nestlings may be seen at the nest hole at 17 to 18 days and leave the cavity at 25 to 28 days.

REMARKS: Both the Yellow-shafted (*auratus*) and Red-shafted (*cafer*) groups of the Northern Flicker occur in British Columbia. The *cafer* group is the more common of the two, ranging throughout most of the province, including Vancouver and the Queen Charlotte Islands, but absent from the northeastern corner. The *cafer* group's centre of abundance is coastal and southern British Columbia. The range of the *auratus* group lies north of a line running approximately from Mount Robson Park in the southeast to Vanderhoof and Francois Lake in the central interior and Stewart in the west. In the Chilcotin-Cariboo Basin, the *cafer* group predominates, but intergrades between the 2 groups are not uncommon (see Erskine 1962).

Previously known as Common Flicker, Yellow-Shafted Flicker, and Red-shafted Flicker.

Figure 317. *R. Wayne Campbell inspecting a Northern Flicker nest in open habitat near Nadahini Creek, Chilkat Pass, July 1980 (Ervio Sian).*

Figure 318. *Northern Flicker at nest tree at Wilgress Lake near Grand Forks, 6 June 1981 (Mark Nyhof).*

Figure 319. *Northern Flicker feeding young at Vaseux Lake, Okanagan valley, 6 June 1981 (Mark Nyhof).*

NOTEWORTHY RECORDS

Spring: Coastal - Klemtu 5 Apr 1976-1. **Interior** - Heffley Lake 1 Apr 1979-15; Kleena Kleene, 20 Mar 1947-1; Alkali Lake 2 Apr 1977-1; 100 Mile House 20 Mar 1984-1; Prince George 26 Mar 1981-7, 29 Mar 1978-4, 31 Mar 1984-1; Vanderhoof 17 Apr 1983-1; Francois Lake 7 Apr 1978-1; Nilkitwa Lake 22 May 1978-2; Tupper Creek 24 Apr 1976-1; Farrell Creek 27 Apr 1980-1; Hudson Hope 18 Apr 1976-1; Cache Creek (Peace River parklands) 14 Apr 1984-1; Hyland Post 27 May 1976-1; Parker Lake (Fort Nelson) 7 May 1978-3; Atlin 16 May 1972-2; Mile 69 Haines Road (Kelsall Lake) 14 May 1977-8.

Summer: Coastal - Port Hardy 16 Jun 1976-1; Georgie Lake 9 Jun 1978-1. **Interior** - Charlie Lake 20 Aug 1975-2; Clarke Lake 28 Aug 1978-1.

Autumn: Interior - Atlin 29 Oct 1985-1; Nig Creek 15 Sep 1984-1; Meziadin Lake 12 Sep 1979-1; Farrell Creek 1 Sep 1979-1; Beatton River Canyon 11 Sep 1983-2, 19 Sep 1982-2; Hazelton 10 Sep 1921-1 (MVZ 42145); Prince George 7 Sep 1982-20; Indian Point Lake 11 Oct 1929-1 (MCZ 282619); 100 Mile House 20 Sep 1976-4; Alkali Lake 26 Oct 1978-1; Kleena Kleene 7 Nov 1948-1; Vaseux Lake 24 Sep 1975-13; Osoyoos 7 Sep 1964-19. **Coastal** - Cape Scott 29 Sep 1935-"influx due to migration"; Boundary Bay 29 Sep 1960-12; Langley 30 Oct 1957-11; Reifel Island 18 Sep 1965-31.

Winter: Interior - Kleena Kleene 10 Dec 1948-1; Williams Lake 2 Jan 1985-7, 3 Jan 1976-10, 26 Dec 1973-11 (flickers recorded every winter from 1968 to 1986 - A. Roberts pers. comm.); Quesnel 30 Dec 1982-1, 30 Dec 1984-1; 1 Prince George 23 Dec 1981, bird at feeder all winter in 1982 and 1984; Smithers 2 Jan 1983-1. **Coastal** - Prince Rupert, 1 Feb 1984-1; Masset 26 Dec 1972-2.

Christmas Counts: Interior - Recorded from 13 of 19 localities and on 74% of all counts. Maxima: Vernon 18 Dec 1983-171; Penticton 27 Dec 1983-161; Oliver/Osoyoos 28 Dec 1981-115. **Coastal** - Recorded from 25 of 28 localities and on 92% of all counts. Maxima: Victoria 21 Dec 1963-**376**, all-time Canadian high for "Red-shafted" form. Anderson, R.R. (1976) incorrectly lists the total at 374; Vancouver 26 Dec 1957-291; Ladner 21 Dec 1975-155.

Pileated Woodpecker
Dryocopus pileatus (Linnaeus)

PIWO

RANGE: Resident across forested Canada and the United States south to California, the Gulf coast and Florida.

STATUS: *Uncommon* to *rare* resident in southern British Columbia, including Vancouver Island, becoming *very rare* throughout the remainder of the province except the northwest portion. Breeds.

NONBREEDING: The Pileated Woodpecker is widely distributed across southern British Columbia becoming sparsely distributed across central British Columbia north through the Peace Lowlands to the northeastern regions of the province. There is only one record from western British Columbia north of 56°N. It frequents forested areas throughout its range from the mature coastal and interior Douglas-fir and western hemlock forests (Fig. 320), including adjacent logged and second growth areas, to the open deciduous and mixed woods of the Chilcotin-Cariboo Basin. In winter, it probes for insects deep within dead trees (Fig. 321) and is often found in residential areas where it feeds on cultivated fruit or suet at feeders. The paucity of winter records north of Williams Lake suggests that most birds leave the northern parts of their range to winter in southern valleys or at the coast. Occasionally, they winter as far north as Fort Nelson. The Pileated Woodpecker has been reported from near sea level to 1,200 m elevation.

BREEDING: The Pileated Woodpecker breeds across southern British Columbia, including Vancouver Island, north on the coast to Bella Coola, and in the interior at least to Vanderhoof (Munro, J.A. 1955a) and Ormond Lake. Erskine and Davidson (1976) report 2 pairs near cavities in the Fort Nelson area; however, details sufficient to confirm breeding are lacking. The Pileated Woodpecker likely breeds throughout its range in the province. It frequents a wide variety of forested habitats from open deciduous forests to dense, mature coniferous stands.

Figure 320. Mixed coniferous forest, Capilano River watershed north of Vancouver, September 1988 (Douglas J. Wilson). The Pileated Woodpecker is resident in mature coniferous forests on the south coast.

Figure 321. Characteristic Pileated Woodpecker probings in dead trees at Qualicum Beach (left), October 1976 (Neil K. Dawe) and Langley (right), April 1972 (Ervio Sian).

Pileated Woodpecker

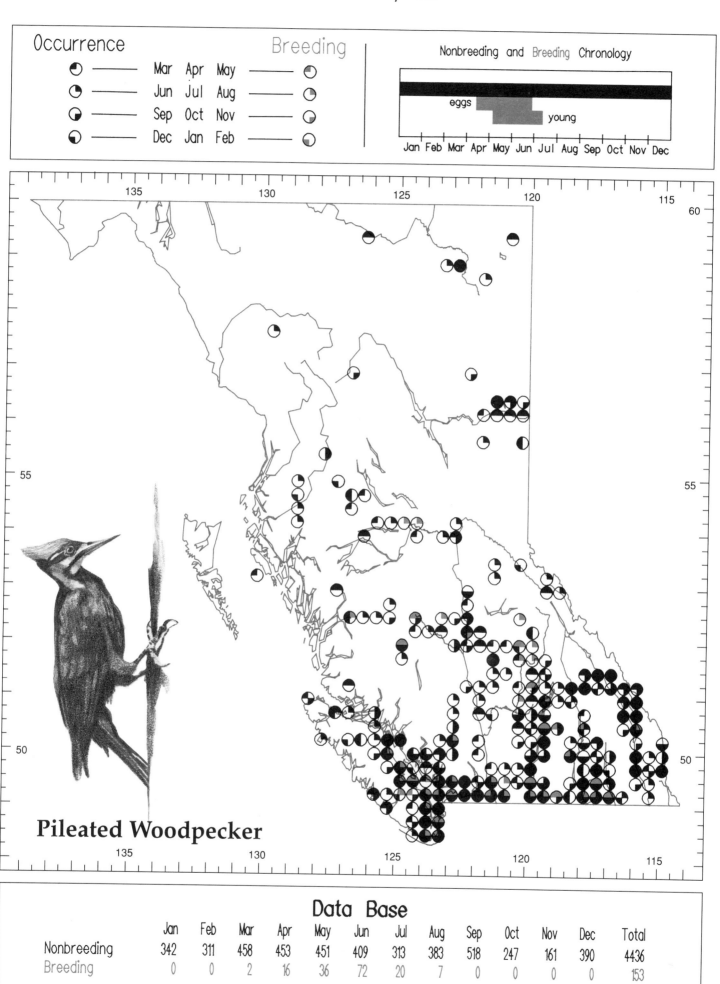

Occurrence / Breeding

Occurrence		Breeding
◐	Mar Apr May	◑
◔	Jun Jul Aug	◕
◕	Sep Oct Nov	◔
◑	Dec Jan Feb	◒

Nonbreeding and Breeding Chronology

eggs — young

Jan Feb Mar Apr May Jun Jul Aug Sep Oct Nov Dec

Pileated Woodpecker

Data Base

	Jan	Feb	Mar	Apr	May	Jun	Jul	Aug	Sep	Oct	Nov	Dec	Total
Nonbreeding	342	311	458	453	451	409	313	383	518	247	161	390	4436
Breeding	0	0	2	16	36	72	20	7	0	0	0	0	153

Nests: Most nests (70%; n=44) were situated in deciduous trees including trembling aspen (32%), black cotton-wood (25%), birches, alders, and maples. Other sites included coniferous trees (18%) and a power pole. Living trees (66%) were used more than dead trees. Similar results were found by Keisker (1986) on her Orchard Lake study area. All nests were located in excavated cavities in the main trunk of the nest tree. Nest materials were primarily the finer wood chips from the excavation process. Heights of 58 nests ranged from 4 to 30 m with 68% between 6.4 and 12.2 m. Depths of 6 cavities ranged from 41 to 66 cm. Diameter of the oval entrance hole (Fig. 322) for 5 nests ranged from 8 by 10 cm to 10 by 15 cm. In Keisker's (1986) study area, Pileated Woodpecker nests were not found in trees with a diameter at breast height (DBH) of less than 25.8 cm; the mean DBH of nest trees on her study site was 40.5 cm (Fig. 323).

Eggs: Dates for 9 clutches ranged from 24 April to 28 June. Calculated dates indicate that eggs could be found as early as 15 April. Clutch size ranged from 2 to 4 eggs (2E-1, 3E-2, 4E-6). One nest record indicated that one egg is laid each day, with incubation by both sexes. Incubation period is 18 days (Hoyt, J.S.Y. 1944).

Young: Dates for 18 broods ranged from 7 May to 12 July with 10 broods recorded between 12 and 27 June (Fig. 324). Brood size ranged from 1 to 5 young (1Y-1, 2Y-7, 3Y-8, 4Y-1, 5Y-1) with 15 broods having 2 or 3 young. Fledging period is 22 to 26 days (Hoyt, J.S.Y. 1944).

REMARKS: The American Ornithologists' Union (1957) reports 2 subspecies for British Columbia: *D. p. picinus* and *D. p. abieticola*. Godfrey (1986) notes that the area of intergradation between the 2 races in the province is not well known.

See Mellen (1987) for a discussion of the Pileated Woodpecker's home range and habitat use in western Oregon, and, S.F. Hoyt (1957) for additional information on its ecology.

Figure 322. Typical oval-shaped nest hole of the Pileated Woodpecker at Wilgress Lake near Grand Forks, 26 May 1980 (Mark Nyhof).

Figure 323. Pileated Woodpecker nesting habitat near Oliver, southern Okanagan valley, 16 June 1989 (Mark Nyhof). This large woodpecker requires trees with a minimum diameter at breast height of 25.8 cm before it can excavate a suitable nest cavity.

Pileated Woodpecker

Figure 324. *Adult female Pileated Woodpecker at nest with young at Wilgress Lake near Grand Forks, 22 June 1981 (Mark Nyhof).*

NOTEWORTHY RECORDS

Spring: Coastal - Thetis Lake 24 Mar 1977-5 during a 14 km walk; Willow Point 15 Mar 1975-5, all on one old maple tree; Cape Scott Park 21 May 1974-1, 15 to 19 Apr 1980-1; Spearer Point 8 May 1977-1. **Interior** - Oliver 18 May 1970-1 (RBCM 15106); Balfour to Waneta 16 May 1981-5 on bird count; South Slocan 4 May 1982-4; 141 Mile House 13 Mar 1950 (RBCM 15698); 24 km e Prince George 21 Apr 1983-1, not seen for a few years; Perow 25 Mar 1977-1; Tupper Creek (Tupper) 29 May 1954-1 (NMC 47935); Farrell Creek (Hudson Hope) 5 May 1979-2 copulating; Fort St. John 8 Mar 1986-2; Fort Nelson 3 Apr 1986-1; Liard Hot Springs 16 May 1975-1 (Reid 1975).

Summer: Coastal - Bamfield 1 Mar 1976-1; MacLean Point (Tofino) 20 May 1987-1 adult; Port Hardy 9 May 1937-4; Kitsumkalum Lake summer 1973-1 (Hay 1976). **Interior** - Waldo 18 Jun 1953-1 (NMC 38633); Loon Lake (Clinton) 4 Jun 1977-1; 59 Mile House (Clinton) 1 Jul 1964-1 (NMC 52374); Witney Lake 13 Jun 1972-1; Prince George 22 Jun 1969-1; Hazelton Jun to Jul 1917-1 (Taverner 1919); Taylor 5 Jul 1986-2; Bear Flat 15 Jun 1986-1; Todagin Lake 9 Jul 1963-1; Evie Lake 2 Aug 1980-1; Liard Hot Springs 8 Aug 1943-1 (Rand 1944).

Autumn: Interior - Fort Nelson 10 Oct 1987-1; Cameron River (Wonowon) 18 Oct 1978-1; Mile 65 Alaska Highway (nw Charlie Lake) 30 Oct 1975-1; Hazelton 22 Sep 1921-1 (MVZ 42140); 24 km e Prince George 14 Sep 1981-1; Corkscrew Creek (Nimpo Lake) 25 Oct 1976-1; Williams Lake 21 Nov 1951-1 (NMC 47932); Big Bar Creek 11 Nov 1974-1; Monte Lake 23 Sep 1978-3; South Slocan 15 Nov 1981-3. **Coastal** - Cape Scott 19 Sep 1935-1; Cortes Island 9 Oct 1977-2; Hornby Island 2 Nov 1980-3; Bowen Island 27 Sep 1964-3; Chesterman Beach 12 Oct 1983-1; Saanich 6 Sep 1983-4.

Winter: Interior - Fort Nelson 21 Dec 1986-1; Bear Flat 19 Feb 1984-1, first winter record (Grunberg 1984b); 20 km se Pouce Coupe 10 Dec 1978-1; Quesnel 26 Feb 1979-1; Williams Lake 2 Jan 1985-9 at suet feeders around city, 29 Dec 1978-1 at suet feeder (numbers wintering in the Cariboo have increased in the last few years - A. Roberts pers. comm.); Wells Gray Park Dec 1952 to Jan 1953-1 seen or heard daily in burn (Ritcey 1953); 100 Mile House 14 Jan 1983-3; Taghum 21 Jan 1979-3; Mt. Parker 29 Dec 1987-15 in burn; Creston 27 Dec 1981-3. **Coastal** - Terrace 21 Dec 1969-2 (Vance 1970); Bella Coola 6 Jan 1976-1; Elk Falls Park 18 Feb 1977-1; Little Qualicum River estuary 21 Jan 1975-2; Saltspring Island 16 Feb 1974-3; Thetis Lake 27 Jan 1959-2.

Christmas Counts: Interior - Recorded from 13 of 19 localities and on 61% of all counts. Maxima: Lake Windermere 30 Dec 1984-20; Shuswap Lake 21 Dec 1982-18; Revelstoke 21 Dec 1983-8. **Coastal** - Recorded from 20 of 28 localities and on 67% of all counts. Maxima: Victoria 27 Dec 1970-22, all-time Canadian high count (Anderson, R.R. 1976); Nanaimo 27 Dec 1976-20; Duncan 14 Dec 1974-19.

Casual, Accidental, Extirpated
and Extinct Species

Eurasian Kestrel

EUKE

Falco tinnunculus Linnaeus

RANGE: Breeds in much of Eurasia to southern Africa, India, China, and Japan. Winters south to the East Indies and the Philippines.

STATUS: *Accidental.*

OCCURRENCE: An immature female was collected (RBCM 15934; Fig. 325) on 10 December 1946 at Alkali Lake, 41 km south of Williams Lake in the Chilcotin-Cariboo region (Campbell 1985f). This is the first Canadian and second North American record.

REMARKS: The only other records from western North America are from the Aleutian Islands, where a bird was observed from 5 to 9 September 1978 and another bird was observed from 2 to 6 October 1978 (Gibson, D.D. 1981). Also, a female was photographed in the Bering Sea 177 km west of Alaska on 12 September 1983 (D.D. Gibson pers. comm.).

The species was formerly known as Kestrel.

Figure 325. Eurasian Kestrel collected at Alkali Lake, 10 December 1946 (RBCM 15934; Andrew Niemann).

Sage Grouse

SAGR

Centrocercus urophasianus (Bonaparte)

RANGE: The distribution of Sage Grouse in North America follows that of the big sagebrush from central Washington, southern Alberta and Saskatchewan south through western North Dakota, south Dakota, Wyoming to southwestern Colorado, Utah, Nevada and eastern California. Where once it was widespread, it is today a local resident throughout its range.

STATUS: *Extirpated.*

REMARKS: The status of the Sage Grouse in British Columbia prior to the 20th century is not well documented. Fannin (1898) suggests that it was "probably accidental" in the vicinity of Osoyoos Lake. Numbers were small and apparently restricted to open, big sagebrush habitats in the extreme southern Okanagan. Fannin (1898) provides the earliest record: "three specimens taken . . . at Osoyoos Lake in October, 1864." In the same year, an unaged male was collected (RBCM 5075; Fig. 326) from the Dewdney Trail. The exact date was not included with the specimen but it was likely one of the three mentioned by Fannin (1898), since Osoyoos Lake was on the Dewdney Trail.

In 1883, 2 birds were killed at Osoyoos (Brooks and Swarth 1925). This record was apparently unknown to Fannin (1898), who also published a comment contained in a letter from C. de B. Green of Osoyoos on 21 May 1896: "I have two most reliable reports of the occurrence of Sage Hens [Sage Grouse] in the

locality." During the next 23 years the birds' status remained unknown. Yocom (1956) mentions that the last Sage Grouse seen near Oliver was shot by a prospector in 1918. This is the final reference to the existence of native populations in the province.

In attempts to re-establish Sage Grouse, the British Columbia Fish and Wildlife Branch obtained 63 birds trapped in mid-August 1958 at Malheur by the Oregon State Game Commission. The grouse were transported to British Columbia on 21 August (Taylor, E.W. 1959). Four birds died in transit, another 2 during release, so the total number released alive was 57 (Anonymous 1958). Most were birds-of-the-year but a few adults were also present. The release site was on the edge of a small pot-hole lake about 3 km north of Richter Lake. The transplant was unsuccessful. According to Carl and Guiguet (1972) none has been reported since 1960.

There were, however, 4 reports during the 1960s, 3 of which may be questionable. Four birds were reported near Osoyoos Lake in 1962, a pair at Osoyoos in early August 1963, and "Sage Hens" sighted several times by a different observer in August 1963 about 1 km north of Osoyoos (Cannings, R.A. et al. 1987). The fourth report is provided by Barkley (1966), who picked up a dead Sage Grouse on the Osoyoos side of Anarchist Mountain on 14 August 1966. This is the last record for the province.

R.A. Cannings et al. (1987) state: "It is possible, but unlikely, that a few stragglers still remain here [Okanagan valley]."

Figure 326. *Male Sage Grouse collected on the Dewdney Trail in 1864 (RBCM 5075; Andrew Niemann).*

Northern Bobwhite

Colinus virginianus (Linnaeus)

NOBO

RANGE: Resident from eastern Wyoming, southern Minnesota, central Michigan, southern Ontario, New York, and Massachusetts south through eastern New Mexico and western Texas to Guatemala, the southeastern United States, and Cuba. Introduced and established in western North America including Washington, Oregon, Idaho, and Montana.

STATUS: Introduced. Status unknown; has bred.

NONBREEDING: The Northern Bobwhite has been introduced several time to British Columbia from shortly after the turn of the century to the early 1980s. Initially, birds were released as hunting stock, but some recent introductions have been for aesthetic reasons, other isolated records are of birds that escaped during their use at dog trials. Introductions have been attempted in 7 general areas of southern British Columbia. The history and present status of the Northern Bobwhite in each area is discussed separately, as follows:

(1) Vancouver Island - First released, although unsuccessfully, on Vancouver Island (numbers and location unknown) in the early 1900s and again in 1922 (Guiguet 1955b). The only recent record is of an unaged and unsexed bird found north of Duncan on 7 February 1982. The origin of bird is unknown.

(2) Gulf Islands - Apparently present on Pender Island in 1882, and disappeared about the turn of the century. Carl and Guiguet (1972) mention, however, that there was no official record of the introduction. In the spring of 1979 several birds were released on Hornby Island by local residents. An adult female was reported on 21 April and 6 May but none were seen thereafter. In early September 1986, 50+ immatures were released on Mount Tuam on Saltspring Island. The present status of these birds is unknown.

(3) Fraser Lowlands - Birds were released in the "lower mainland" shortly after the turn of the century but numbers and locations are not known. The field notes of Kenneth Racey show that small numbers (up to 3 birds seen or heard at one time) survived in the Huntingdon area from 1922 to 1948. A female was collected on 21 October 1934 (UBC 4312). Later, Racey (1945) wrote:

... for many years these birds have nested on this hillside [his Huntingdon ranch], not excepting the present summer [1945]. The number of nesting birds is not known accurately but was probably two. He also documented the last occurrence there, in his field notes].

... all the bobwhite completely vanished during the severe winter of 1947/48. The heavy snow and cold was too much for them. Many were found dead together under snow at hill below large raspberry plantation.

The only other early record of the Northern Bobwhite in the area was supplied by Holdom (1952). Some time in 1924 he saw a "large flock of Bobwhite quail" on a farm near Cloverdale.

Other introductions occurred in the vicinity of the Fraser River delta. In 1967 or 1968, some were released in Ladner and apparently reproduced successfully (Carl and Guiguet 1972). Two coveys were found in December 1969 but none afterward.

In mid-April 1971, 9 Northern Bobwhites (Fig. 327) were released at the George C. Reifel Bird Sanctuary (Westham Island) and another 2 pairs in late April. On 1 May 1971, a single male was seen in North Vancouver, 27 km north of the release site. The last record from the sanctuary area was 18 July 1971 (Campbell et al. 1972b).

The only other records are of single birds seen in Pitt Meadows on 11 and 22 July 1972. These birds were probably escapees from a local game farm (Campbell et al. 1974).

(4) Ashcroft - One hundred and thirty were released there in 1900 (Carl and Guiguet 1972). None survived.

(5) Shuswap - Thirty-two were released in 1905 (Carl and Guiguet 1972). None survived.

(6) Okanagan valley - The history and status there is well documented by R.A. Cannings et al. (1987). From an initial release of 35 birds at the Coldstream Ranch near Vernon in 1907, small numbers became established, but they gradually dwindled (Phillips, J.C. 1928) and were last seen in January 1912 (Munro, J.A. and Cowan 1947).

In Osoyoos, 6 or 8 birds were shot in 1924. They probably came from introductions in Washington state. This is the only record for the area.

There is a report of birds that escaped during dog trials near Vernon "probably about 1974." One was found dead "sometime between 1973 and 1977." The only well-documented record is of a fully-fledged brood of 18 young seen near Vernon on 10 September 1984 (Cannings, R.A. et al. 1987).

(7) Creston - There is one record, in June 1980, of a female with chicks (Butler, R.W. et al. 1986). They may have wandered into British Columbia from northern Idaho where introduced populations exist.

It appears that all attempts to introduce the Northern Bobwhite into British Columbia have been unsuccessful. Some introductions (e.g. Huntingdon) lasted for a quarter of a century before infrequent, severe winters decimated the birds. Crispens (1960) provides important references to other introductions in western North America, notably Washington, Idaho, and Montana. It is possible that in the future, birds from such successful and established introductions there may wander into extreme southern areas of British Columbia.

BREEDING: Racey (1945) indicates that the Northern Bobwhite nested at Huntingdon but he does not give specific details. R.W. Butler et al. (1986) report a female with an undetermined number of chicks in June 1980 at Creston. The only well-documented breeding record is of a fully-fledged brood of 18 young seen near Vernon on 10 September 1984 (Cannings, R.A. et al. 1987). Calculated dates indicate that eggs could be found in British Columbia between late May and June and young between late June and mid-September; the latter date would represent a renesting.

REMARKS: Formerly known as Bobwhite. Also referred to as Common Bobwhite.

Figure 327. *Northern Bobwhite released at the George C. Reifel Bird Sanctuary, Reifel Island, Delta, 15 May 1971 (RBCM Photo 194; Jack Bryan).*

Common Moorhen

Gallinula chloropus (Linnaeus)

RANGE: Breeds in California, Nevada, Arizona, and New Mexico, and from Minnesota, Michigan, southern Ontario, Quebec, Vermont, and New Brunswick (locally) south to Texas, Florida, and the Gulf Coast. Winters mainly from the Gulf States, California, and Arizona southward. Also occurs in the West Indies, Central and South America, Hawaii, and Eurasia.

STATUS: *Accidental.*

OCCURRENCE: An adult frequented the sewage ponds at Iona Island, Richmond, from 26 May to 3 June 1981 (Weber, W.C. 1982). The bird was photographed on 27 May (RBCM Photo 727; Fig. 328).

REMARKS: There are 2 hypothetical records. Parham (1937), in his list of Okanagan birds, states that a Florida Gallinule [Common Moorhen] was reported at Okanagan Falls in August 1937. There are no details and the report was not included in subsequent major publications (Munro, J.A. and Cowan 1947; Godfrey 1966). T.H. Rogers (1981), published a record of a single bird observed at Skookumchuck Prairie near Kimberley on 14 August 1980. Details were very sketchy. This record was not accepted by Godfrey (1986) and we, too, could find no documentation..

The Common Moorhen was previously known as the Common Gallinule.

Figure 328. Common Moorhen at Iona Island, Richmond, 27 May 1981 (RBCM Photo 727; Ervio Sian).

Whooping Crane

WHCR

Grus americana (Linnaeus)

RANGE: Breeds in south-central Mackenzie and adjacent northern Alberta. Winters near the coast of southern Texas and occasionally parts of Louisiana.

STATUS: *Casual* in the interior.

OCCURRENCE: Five reports were examined but only 2 are convincing. In September 1955, a flock of about 30 Whooping Cranes was observed northeast of Fort Nelson. Independently, a helicopter pilot saw 6 at the Fort Nelson airport about the same time.

These observations were submitted to *The Canadian Field-Naturalist* as a note, but were rejected because they were "too controversial." The occurrence is briefly mentioned by Cowan (1955).

On 25 and 26 April 1962, 6 adults were observed at Alexandria, south of Quesnel (Fig. 329). At 0530 on the 25th, the birds rose from open, prairie-like habitat, climbed to a height of about 300 m, and landed about 3 km to the west, calling all the time. The following morning, the cranes had returned to the original area. McNulty (1966), in her book *The Whooping Crane*, states: "In the spring of 1962, the flock of thirty-eight migrated normally, but were met by cold, wet weather in Canada . . . To make matters worse, six adults had been lost and the flock was back to thirty-two birds." It is quite likely the 6 missing cranes were at Alexandria.

REMARKS: We consider the following 4 records hypothetical. From 23 to 25 March 1967, a single bird was observed in a field near Alkali Lake (Roberts, A. 1973). It was described over the telephone to a local, experienced birder, who was confident that the identification was correct.

Nearly a decade later, on 13 August 1976, a single bird was observed flying northwest along Okanagan Lake at Summerland between 450 and 600 m. The bird had ". . . white plumage (adult or subadult), long neck and legs trailing – Sandhill Crane-like – black wing tips covering one-quarter of wing." This record is also considered hypothetical by R.A. Cannings et al. (1987).

The next report, the least convincing, involves two flocks (9 and 17 birds) seen on a clearcut north of Big Lake (150 Mile House) on 11 September 1982 (Campbell 1982c). The last report was of a flock of 4 adults seen flying south over Nita Lake, Kelsey Bay on 10 September 1985. Field notes are on file.

The North American population of Whooping Cranes, prior to the arrival of European settlers, was estimated at 1,400 to 1,500 birds. Numbers declined drastically and since the 1940s the species has been fighting extinction; it has been listed as endangered by the International Council for Bird Preservation (King, W.B. 1981). Recently, however, numbers appear to be slowly increasing. The autumn 1986 migration of 110 birds (E. Kuyt pers. comm.) was one of the most successful in recent years.

See Binkley and Miller (1983) for a discussion of the population characteristics of the Whooping Crane.

Figure 329. Field sketch of 6 adult Whooping Cranes observed at Alexandria, south of Quesnel, on 25 and 26 April 1962 (Glen R. Ryder).

Spotted Redshank

Tringa erythropus (Pallas)

SPRE

RANGE: Breeds in northern Eurasia and winters in southern Eurasia, north Africa, and Indonesia. In western North America, it occurs most often as a fall migrant in the Aleutian and Pribilof islands of Alaska. There are also a few spring records for that area (Kessel and Gibson 1978).

STATUS: *Accidental* in spring, *casual* in autumn on the south mainland coast.

OCCURRENCE: There are 4 records, 1 in spring and 3 in the autumn.

The first 3 records are all from Reifel Island, Delta. On 24 September 1970, a red-legged wader was apparently observed among some dowitchers but was not identified as a Spotted Redshank until 17 October (Campbell et al. 1972a). The bird was photographed on 17 October and 3 November (Fig. 330; RBCM Photo 130) and was last reported on 11 November. Since the first report was unconfirmed, and was not reported until after the discovery on 17 October, we have not considered it (see Roberson 1980; Godfrey 1986). A decade later, a single bird was seen briefly on 29 November 1980 (Hunn and Mattocks 1981a). The only spring record is of single bird present from 1 March to 1 April 1981 (Weber, W.C. 1982). It was photographed on 18 March (RBCM Photo 699).

The only other record comes from Serpentine Fen, Surrey, 23 km east of Reifel Island, where a single bird was present from 9 to 17 October 1982 (Weber, W.C. 1985).

Figure 330. Spotted Redshank at Reifel Island, Delta, 3 November 1970 (RBCM Photo 130; Ervio Sian).

Terek Sandpiper

TESA

Xenus cinereus (Güldenstädt)

RANGE: Breeds from Finland, northern Russia and northern Siberia south to central Russia, Lake Baikal and Anadyrland. Winters from the Persian Gulf, southern Red Sea, southeast Asia, and Hainan south to South Africa, India, East Indies, New Guinea, and Australia. In migration in North America, occurs casually in the western Aleutian Islands and western and south coastal Alaska.

STATUS: *Accidental.*

OCCURRENCE: A single bird was present in the vicinity of Goodridge Peninsula, Sooke, Vancouver Island from 21 July to 6 August 1987. It was photographed on 21 July (RBCM Photo 1159; Fig. 331). This is the first Canadian record.

REMARKS: Goodwill and Goodwill (1988) provide additional details of the record. For a comprehensive review of the species see Cramp (1983).

Figure 331. Terek Sandpiper at Goodridge Peninsula, Sooke, 21 July 1987 (RBCM Photo 1159; Tim Zurowski).

Bristle-thighed Curlew
Numenius tahitiensis (Gmelin)

BTCU

RANGE: Breeds in western Alaska. Winters on islands in the central and south tropical Pacific. It is considered a stray anywhere on the west coast south of Alaska (Roberson 1980).

STATUS: *Casual* on the coast.

OCCURRENCE: Two records. On 31 May 1969, a Bristle-thighed Curlew was collected (RBCM 11610; Fig. 332) at Grant Bay, northwestern Vancouver Island (Richardson 1970).

On 13 and 14 May 1983, a single bird was seen among a flock of Whimbrels at Blackie Spit, northwest of White Rock. The bird was "closely seen and well described" (Mattocks and Hunn 1983b).

REMARKS: There is one additional record (Godfrey 1986) which has recently been re-examined by D.R. Paulson and is now considered hypothetical. On 1 September 1982, a curlew was photographed (RBCM Photo 1058) at Cox Bay, 6 km south of Tofino. Hunn and Mattocks (1983a) report that the photograph shows "the almost unmarked flanks and coarse back splotching which distinguish juvenile Bristle-thighed Curlews from similarly plumaged Whimbrels." Paulson now suggests that the bird could have been a Whimbrel (*N. phaeopus*).

Figure 332. Bristle-thighed Curlew collected at Grant Bay, northwestern Vancouver Island (RBCM 11610; Andrew Niemann).

Far Eastern Curlew
Numenius madagascariensis (Linnaeus)

FECU

RANGE: Breeds in northeast Asia and winters from the Philippines to Australia.

STATUS: *Accidental.*

OCCURRENCE: On 24 September 1984, a single bird was photographed (RBCM Photo 1000; Fig. 333) on the shore of Boundary Bay at the foot of 112th Street, Delta. This constitutes the first record for Canada and the first North American record outside Alaska (Sladen 1966; M.C. Thompson and DeLong 1969; Byrd et al. 1974; Kessel and Gibson 1978; Kragh et al. 1986).

REMARKS: Also known in the Old World as Eastern Curlew.

Figure 333. Far Eastern Curlew at the foot of 112th Street, Delta (Boundary Bay), 24 September 1984 (RBCM Photo 1000; Ervio Sian).

Rufous-necked Stint

RNST

Calidris ruficollis (Pallas)

RANGE: Breeds in northeastern Asia. Winters in eastern Asia, the Philippines, and Australia. In North America it is a migrant on the Bering Sea coasts and islands.

STATUS: *Casual* in summer on the south mainland coast.

OCCURRENCE: Four records. From 24 June to 26 August 1978, there were 3 reports of a single Rufous-necked Stint at Iona Island, Richmond as follows: 24 and 25 June (RBCM Photo 765 on 24 June); 13 to 15 July (RBCM Photo 536 on 14 July) and 25 and 26 August. It is unlikely, given the extremely high turnover rates of migrating "peeps" on the Fraser River delta, (average stay 2 to 3 days), that these records involved the same bird (Campbell 1986c; Mattocks 1986b).

The only other acceptable record is of an adult in partial breeding plumage seen at Iona Island on 3 and 4 July 1986.

REMARKS: There are at least 10 other reported sightings for the Fraser River delta, all with detailed notes, but none is considered conclusive. Two were published as follows: 6 August 1979 (Roberson 1980) and 19 and 25 July 1981 (Harrington-Tweit et al. 1981).

Observers should refer to D.I.M. Wallace (1979) and Veit and Jonsson (1984) for details concerning field identification of this species.

The Rufous-necked Stint was formerly known as the Rufous-necked Sandpiper.

POSTSCRIPT: In 1988, a single bird in breeding plumage was seen by many observers at Iona Island, Richmond, from 26 June to 5 July.

Little Stint
Calidris minuta (Leisler)

RANGE: Breeds from northern Scandinavia east to the New Siberian Islands; winters in Africa and the Indian region. In migration in North America, occurs casually in the western Aleutian Islands, northern and western coastal Alaska, Ontario, New Brunswick, Massachusetts, Delaware, and Bermuda.

STATUS: *Accidental.*

OCCURRENCE: A singe bird, in breeding plumage, was seen at the sewage lagoon at Iona Island by many observers on 21 July 1983. Detailed field notes were compared to major works on stint identification including D.I.M. Wallace (1974, 1979), Roberson (1980), and P.J. Grant (1981).

REMARKS: For a comprehensive review of the Little Stint see Cramp (1983).

POSTSCRIPT: On 10 July 1988 a single bird in full breeding plumage was seen at Boundary Bay (R.J. Cannings pers. comm.). The bird's status should be elevated to *casual.*

Temminck's Stint

Calidris temminckii (Leisler)

RANGE: Breeds in northern Scandinavia, northern Russia, and northern Siberia. Winters in southern Eurasia, Africa, and southeast Asia. In North America it has been recorded in both spring and autumn migrations in western Alaska (Kessel and Gibson 1978) and in autumn in British Columbia.

STATUS: *Accidental.*

OCCURRENCE: A juvenile was observed at Reifel Island, Delta, from 1 to 4 September 1982 and photographed (RBCM Photo 879; Figs. 334 and 335) on 2 September (Kautesk et al. 1983). The photograph was published in the journal of the Vancouver Natural History Society (*Discovery* 11:167) but with an incorrect date of 5 September. Identification was confirmed by D.R. Paulson who compared photographs of the bird with specimens from the Washington State Museum in Seattle (Hunn and Mattocks 1983a).

REMARKS: There are more than 5 other reports from the Fraser River delta, all with detailed notes, all considered unconfirmed pending further review. One was published (Mattocks and Hunn 1981) but later re-examined and refuted (D.R. Paulson pers. comm.): 14 December 1980-1 at Blackie Spit, Crescent Beach, Boundary Bay.

See Veit and Jonsson (1984) for problems concerning identification of the smaller Calidridine sandpipers.

Figure 334. Temminck's Stint at Reifel Island, Delta, 1 September 1982 (RBCM Photo 879; Ervio Sian).

Figure 335. Temminck's Stint with Least Sandpiper at Reifel Island, Delta, 2 September 1982 (RBCM Photo 879; Dennis R. Paulson).

Spoonbill Sandpiper

SBSA

Eurynorhynchus pygmeus (Linnaeus)

RANGE: Breeds in northeastern Siberia, and winters from southeastern China south to Southeast Asia. It is a casual migrant in northwestern Alaska.

STATUS: *Accidental.*

OCCURRENCE: An adult frequented the sewage ponds at Iona Island, Richmond, from 30 July to 3 August 1978. Photographs taken on 2 and 3 August (RBCM Photo 552; Fig. 336) were widely published (e.g. Sauppe et al. 1978). This is the first Canadian and third North American record.

REMARKS: The American Ornithologists' Union (1983, p. 201) incorrectly lists the earliest date as 31 July. The species was formerly referred to as Spoon-bill Sandpiper.

Figure 336. Two photographs of the Spoonbill Sandpiper at Iona Island, Richmond, 31 July 1978 (RBCM Photo 552; Ervio Sian).

Iceland Gull

Larus glaucoides Meyer

ICGU

RANGE: Confined to the North Atlantic Ocean. Breeds on southern Baffin Island and coastal Greenland; occasionally Iceland. Nonbreeding birds are found casually in summer to central southern British Columbia, Saskatchewan, the Great Lakes and New Jersey, and west to northern Alaska. Winters in North America along Atlantic coast from Newfoundland and the Gulf of St. Lawrence south to Virginia, casually on the Pacific coast south to California.

STATUS: *Accidental.*

OCCURRENCE: The Iceland Gull has been positively recorded once in British Columbia: Shuswap Lake 3 Jun 1971-1 (RBCM 11668; Fig. 337).

REMARKS: The Iceland Gull has also been reported from several locations in the Fraser Lowlands and from the Victoria area (e.g. Mattocks 1984; Fix 1984; Hunn and Mattocks 1985; Mattocks 1985a; Mattocks 1985b; Force and Mattocks 1986). It has also been reported on one Christmas Bird Count from Vancouver. While many reports were accompanied by complete field descriptions and, in some cases, photographs (e.g. RBCM Photos 971, 1133) we are not convinced, given the relative abundance of Thayer's Gulls on the south coast, that field identification alone can distinguish an Iceland Gull from some Thayer's Gull individuals.

The subspecies of Iceland Gull likely to occur along coastal British Columbia is "Kumlien's" Gull, *L. g. kumlieni*, which Godfrey (1986) describes as "an extremely unstable subspecies, very few individuals exactly alike." Godfrey (1986) considers the Thayer's Gull conspecific with the Iceland Gull, although the American Ornithologists' Union (1983) treats them as separate species. He notes that in the Thayer's Gull, "individual variation is much more extreme than is generally realized", and he further cautions:

> . . . there is so much individual variation, *even complete overlapping of characters* [italics ours], that some individuals of one race are almost certain to be mistaken for the other. For instance, some (not all) reports of "Kumlien's" Gull occurrence on the west coast may well be based on field observation of pale extremes of "Thayer's" Gull.

Godfrey (1986) lists a specimen record of the Iceland Gull (he refers to it as *L. g. kumlieni*) taken on 14 March 1928 at Departure Bay, Nanaimo. The specimen (ROM 86744), a female, was recently examined by R.D. James. He concluded it was intermediate between *kumlieni* and *thayeri* and suggested calling it *thayeri* with the added note that it is "a very pale bird with some question as to its identity."

P.J. Grant (1982) further discusses the complexities of identifying and ageing this species in different plumages.

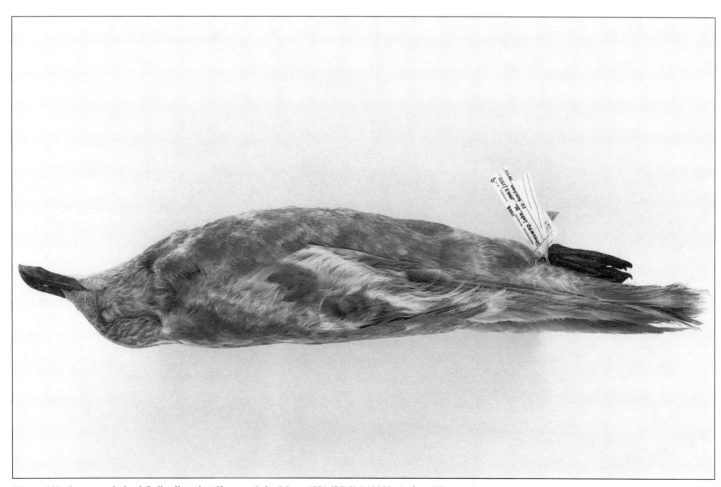

Figure 337. Immature Iceland Gull collected at Shuswap Lake, 3 June 1971 (RBCM 11668; Andrew Niemann).

Slaty-backed Gull
Larus schistisagus Stejneger

SBGU

RANGE: Breeds in northeastern Asia. Winters from the Bering Sea and Kamchatka south to Japan and China. In the past decade it has become a rare visitor to northern and western Alaska (Kessel and Gibson 1978).

STATUS: *Casual* on the south coast.

OCCURRENCE: Two records. On 1 March 1974, a nearly full-plumaged adult was observed at Clover Point, Victoria, and was photographed on 16 mm colour movie film. W.E. Godfrey confirmed the identification by comparing the original film with specimens at the National Museum of Canada. A duplicate copy of the film and an enlargement from a movie frame are on file at the Royal British Columbia Museum (RBCM Photo 340). The enlarged movie frame was published by Roberson (1980). This was the first documented occurrence in Canada.

On 11 and 12 November 1986, an adult was present at Beaver Harbour, near Port Hardy, Vancouver Island (Campbell 1987a; Mattocks and Harrington-Tweit 1987). It was photographed (RBCM Photo 1138; Fig. 338) on 11 November.

REMARKS: Hybrids between *L. schistisagus* and the Herring Gull (*L. argentatus*) have been described.

Figure 338. Slaty-backed Gull at Beaver Cove, Port Hardy, 11 November 1986 (RBCM Photo 1138; Michael Force).

Ross' Gull

ROGU

Rhodostethia rosea (MacGillivray)

RANGE: Breeds in northern Siberia and locally in arctic Canada (northeastern Manitoba). Winter range poorly known, but probably pelagic in open Arctic waters.

STATUS: *Accidental.*

OCCURRENCE: On 27 October 1966, a Ross' Gull was spotted among a flock of Bonaparte's and Mew gulls off Clover Point, Victoria. The event was recorded on 16 mm colour movie film. The bird was rediscovered on 9 November when black and white photographs were obtained (RBCM Photo 136; Fig. 339). One was published on the cover of the *Victoria Naturalist* (Stirling 1967). This was the first record in temperate North America outside the gull's arctic range.

REMARKS: Davidson (1966, p. 22) erroneously reports events occurring on 24 November. See Bledsoe and Sibley (1985) for a discussion of annual and seasonal patterns of vagrancy of the Ross' Gull in subarctic North America through 1984.

Figure 339. Ross' Gull off Clover Point, Victoria, 9 November 1966 (RBCM Photo 136; Ralph Fryer).

Ivory Gull

IVGU

Pagophila eburnea (Phipps)

RANGE: Breeds on islands in Arctic North America and in the Palearctic in northern Greenland, Spitsbergen, Franz Josef Land, northern Novaya Zemlya, and North Land. Winters in North America over northern drift ice and edges of pack-ice casually south on the Pacific coast to southeastern Alaska and British Columbia and along the Atlantic coast to New England; in the Palearctic from southern Greenland, Iceland, the Faeroe Islands, Scandinavia, northern Russia, and northern Siberia south to the Commander Islands.

STATUS: *Casual* in autumn in the interior; *accidental* on the south coast.

OCCURRENCE: Four records. In September 1889, a male Ivory Gull, in first winter plumage, was collected at Dease Lake, northwestern British Columbia (RBCM 1462).

In October 1897, an adult female was collected (RBCM 1463) at Penticton (Brooks 1900). The date on the specimen label reads "November" but R.A. Cannings et al. (1987) determined that the correct month was October. The specimen was prepared as a display mount by Royal British Columbia Museum staff.

A third record, not mentioned by either J.A. Munro and Cowan (1947) or Godfrey (1986), is acceptably documented. On 19 February 1925, an unusual medium-sized gull was seen in Victoria Harbour (Preece 1925a). The gull was "pure white all over without any shading or marking of gray or black; the eye was dark . . . In size it appeared to be slightly larger than the Short-billed Gull [Mew Gull], with which it was sharing the cabin roof." Preece also studied the specimen collected at Penticton and decided that he had, indeed, seen an Ivory Gull.

The most recent record is of an immature observed on the north shore of Logger Bay on Atlin Lake (RBCM Photo 1212; Fig. 341). The bird was present from 15 to 22 November 1987. It seemed starved and, as a result, was quite tame. The gull was fed on fish entrails and meat from early dawn to late dusk throughout its stay.

REMARKS: There has been only one other west coast record south of Alaska: a single bird seen at Gray's Harbor, Washington, 20 December 1975 (Crowell and Nehls 1976).

Adult Ivory Gulls are unmistakable and unlikely to be confused with any other species in the world (Harrison, P. 1983).

POSTSCRIPT: An immature, in first winter plumage, was seen on 30 October and again on 2 November 1988 on the Atnarko River at Stuie (Campbell 1989a). The bird was photographed (RBCM Photo 1228; Fig. 340) feeding on spawned salmon with Glaucous-winged Gulls.

Figure 340. *First winter Ivory Gull, Atnarko River near Stuie, 2 November 1988 (RBCM Photo 1228; Ron Mayo).*

Figure 341. *Immature Ivory Gull at Logger Bay, Atlin Lake, 15 November 1987 (RBCM Photo 1212; Ute and Ed Kirschner).*

Elegant Tern
Sterna elegans Gambel

ELTE

RANGE: Breeds along the Pacific coast from southern California south to central Baja California and from the Gulf of California south to Nayarit, Mexico. Winters south to Chile and Peru and regularly along the north coast of California.

STATUS: *Casual.*

OCCURRENCE: In the autumn of 1983, an unprecedented invasion of Elegant Terns occurred in the Pacific Northwest, attributed to the warm waters of *El Niño* (Hunn and Mattocks 1984). Small flocks of up to 11 birds were reported from 3 general locations in southwestern British Columbia between 21 August and 25 September.

The records are: Boundary Bay, Delta, 21 and 22 August-7, 24 August-4 (RBCM Photo 864; Fig. 342); Active Pass, 1 September-2 with Common Terns; Cadboro Bay, 25 September-2; Clover Point, Victoria, 2 September-1; Esquimalt Lagoon, 23 August-5 and 4 September-2.

REMARKS: See Schaffner (1986) for a discussion of trends in Elegant Tern populations in California.

The Elegant Tern was previously placed in the genus *Thalasseus*.

Figure 342. Four Elegant Terns (note larger size) with Common Terns at Boundary Bay, Delta, 24 August 1983 (RBCM Photo 864; Mark Daly).

Aleutian Tern

ALTE

Sterna aleutica Baird

RANGE: The Aleutian Tern breeds in Alaska along the coasts and offshore islands of the Chukchi and Bering seas as well as on islands off Siberia. It winters at sea.

STATUS: *Casual* on the Queen Charlotte Islands.

OCCURRENCE: Three records. On 30 May 1983, an Aleutian Tern was seen 1 km north of Masset (Hearne and Cooper 1987). On 10 May 1985, a dead Aleutian Tern was found on the beach at Masset, Queen Charlotte Islands (Hearne and Cooper 1987). The specimen (RBCM 18367; Fig. 343) was a female and is the first confirmed North American record outside Alaska.

On 6 June 1987, an adult was seen off Anthony Island, southwest Queen Charlotte Islands (Campbell 1987d).

REMARKS: Sowls et al. (1978) estimate the Alaskan breeding population at 10,000 birds.

POSTSCRIPT: On 25 May 1989, an adult was seen near the entrance to Flamingo Inlet, southwest of Queen Charlotte Islands (A.G. Whitney pers. comm.).

Figure 343. Adult Aleutian Tern found dead at Masset, Queen Charlotte Islands, on 10 May 1985 (RBCM 18367; Andrew Niemann).

Kittlitz's Murrelet

Brachyramphus brevirostris (Vigors)

KIMU

RANGE: Breeds in Alaska from Port Hope (northwestern Alaska) south to the Aleutians and east to Glacier Bay. Winters generally offshore from the Aleutians east to Glacier Bay. Also breeds and winters on northern coast of Asia.

STATUS: *Accidental* on extreme south coast.

OCCURRENCE: A single bird was present around the entrance to Victoria Harbour from 24 November 1985 to 12 April 1986 (Mattocks 1985b; Campbell 1986a). It was photographed on 7 December 1985 (RBCM Photo 1081; Fig. 344), a copy of which appeared on the cover of the January-February 1986 issue of the *Victoria Naturalist.*

Figure 344. Kittlitz's Murrelet in winter plumage, Victoria Harbour, 7 December 1985 (Tim Zurowski).

Xantus' Murrelet

XAMU

Synthliboramphus hypoleucus (Xántus de Vesey)

RANGE: Breeds on islands off southern California and western Baja California. Winters from central California south to southern Baja California.

STATUS: *Accidental.*

OCCURRENCE: On 25 October 1971, an adult female (WSM 26809; Fig. 345) died after colliding with a ship at 51°15'N, 129°58'W, in southern Hecate Strait (Sanger 1973b).

REMARKS: Records off Washington and Oregon (Feinstein 1958; Scott, J.M. et al. 1971; Roberson 1980) suggest the Xantus' Murrelet may occur regularly throughout those areas in late summer or autumn. Its appearance in British Columbia is therefore not unexpected.

The Xantus' Murrelet was formerly referred to as *Endomychura hypoleuca*.

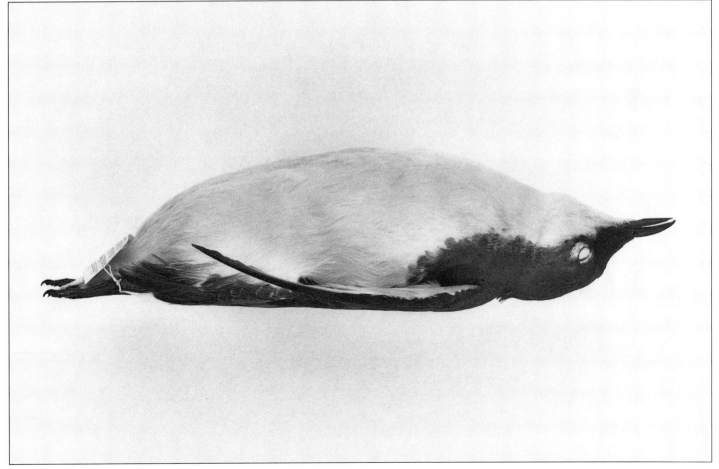

Figure 345. *Adult Xantus' Murrelet found dead in southern Hecate Strait on 25 October 1971 (WSM 26808; Andrew Niemann).*

Crested Auklet

CRAU

Aethia cristatella (Pallas)

RANGE: Breeds on islands in the Bering Sea, along the Aleutian Islands, and in northeastern Asia. Winters from the Bering Sea to Japan.

STATUS: *Accidental.*

OCCURRENCE: During the winter of 1892-93 a Crested Auklet was collected off Kyuquot, north-western Vancouver Island by a seal hunter (Pitman et al. 1983). The specimen (RBCM 11915; Fig. 346 was discovered among a series of skins from Alaska and is the first North American record south of Alaska.

Figure 346. *Crested Auklet collected off Kyuquot, Vancouver Island, during the winter of 1892/1893 (RBCM 11915; Andrew Niemann).*

White-winged Dove

WWDO

Zenaida asiatica (Linnaeus)

RANGE: Breeds in the southwestern United States and south through the Caribbean to central South America. Winters generally in the breeding range; northern birds are migratory. Casual in the Pacific Northwest. Roberson (1980) considers it a vagrant from July to early February in Oregon and Washington.

STATUS: *Accidental.*

OCCURRENCE: In July 1918, 2 White-winged Doves were seen together at French Beach, near Sheringham Point, southern Vancouver Island (Anonymous 1922). One bird was collected (RBCM 4744; Fig. 347) and identified as *Z. a. mearnsi*, the race found in the southwestern United States.

Hunn and Mattocks (1983a) report a single bird seen in Victoria on 18 November 1982. The date is in error, however; the actual sighting was made on 14 November (J.E.V. Goodwill pers. comm.). Although the report corresponds with vagrant patterns for the west coast of North America (Roberson 1980), the possibility of an escapee cannot be ruled out. White-winged Doves are kept in captivity as close as Mercer Island, Puget Sound, Washington.

Figure 347. White-winged Dove collected at French Beach, southern Vancouver Island, July 1918.

Passenger Pigeon

Ectopistes migratorius (Linnaeus)

RANGE: Formerly bred from central Montana, North Dakota, southern Manitoba, and southeastern Canada south to eastern Kansas, Oklahoma, Mississippi, and Georgia. Wintered in southeastern United States (Godfrey 1986).

STATUS: *Extinct.*

OCCURRENCE: One of the earliest references to Passenger Pigeons occurring in British Columbia is provided by Lord (1866). He collected and observed birds in the province, but details concerning the precise locations are in doubt (Munro, J.A. and Cowan 1947). Pearse (1936) reports a previously overlooked reference from *The Northwest Passage by Land - Being a narrative of an expedition from the Atlantic to the Pacific - Undertaken with the view of exploring a route across the continent to British Columbia through British Territory by one of the Northern passes in the Rocky Mountains.* This report states that Passenger Pigeons were found "as far west as the source of the North Thompson [River]" in the summer of 1863. In the spring of 1887, Rhoads (1891) reported "flocks of wild pigeons during travels from California to Vancouver's Island [sic] being most common in Pierce County, Washington." Unfortunately, specific locations were not mentioned, and the possibility that these birds were Band-tailed Pigeons cannot be overlooked.

The only complete specimen extant from British Columbia, however, is one from Chiloweyuck [Chilliwack] Depot, taken on 29 June 1859 (USNM 15993; Duvall 1946). It is this record that led the American Ornithologists' Union (1983) to list the Passenger Pigeon as accidental in British Columbia.

Recently, skeletal elements of the extinct bird were recovered from an archaeological site at Fort D'Epinette, northeastern British Columbia (Williams, J.H. 1978). Six elements [bones] were excavated, that came from 2 birds. This location is the most northerly reported site of occurrence for the Passenger Pigeon in British Columbia. J.H. Williams (1978) suggests that Passenger Pigeons may have been more numerous in the west than previously believed.

REMARKS: The last Passenger Pigeon on the planet died in the Cincinnati Zoological Gardens in 1914. Major factors contributing to its extinction have been summarized by Mershon (1907) and Schorger (1955). These factors mainly involved decrease and destruction of the birds' habitat and mass over-exploitation by man. Brisbin (1968) suggests another theory. The factors that contributed to the sudden onset and rapid rate of mass exploitation, he postulates, are:

> the result of a complex interaction between the ecology of the Passenger Pigeon itself and the ecology and economic development of civilized man on the North American continent. One particularly important aspect of this interaction was the appearance and development of the railroads in the mid 1800s which suddenly connected the mid-western nesting sites with the vast cities of the eastern seaboard, making the marketing of birds economically feasible and profitable.

Recently, however, Blockstein and Tordoff (1985) suggest that because of the bird's ecology and abundance it became an early victim of technology.

Yellow-billed Cuckoo

YBCU

Coccyzus americanus (Linnaeus)

RANGE: Breeds locally in California and from southern Canada (from Alberta east), south to West Indies and Mexico. Winters in South America.

STATUS: *Extirpated.* Formerly an *uncommon* summer visitant to the lower Fraser River valley; *casual* on Vancouver Island.

CHANGE IN STATUS: The distribution and status of the Yellow-billed Cuckoo was poorly documented prior to 1947. The occurrence of the bird was discussed in generalities, with few supporting details. For example, Brooks (1900) mentions that the bird was "becoming more abundant in the coast region every year, probably on account of the invasion of tent caterpillar." At the turn of the century Kermode (1904) lists it as "a regular summer resident in the south-western portions of the Province" and mentions that this cuckoo "breeds on Vancouver Island near Victoria." In the Chilliwack area, Brooks (1917) suggests that the Yellow-billed Cuckoo was a "tolerably common summer resident of late years. Formerly rare." By the 1930s, it was still considered a "scarce summer visitant" in the Vancouver area (Cumming 1932), and it was again listed as "nesting," but without documentation. J.A. Munro and Cowan (1947) list 7 specimen records for the province from 1892 to 1927 but still considered the bird a "scarce summer visitant," even though there had been no records since 1927.

We have located 21 records for the province, 18 of which are supported by specimens.

OCCURRENCE: The Yellow-billed Cuckoo was probably locally distributed in thickets of deciduous vegetation throughout the lower Fraser River valley from Vancouver to Chilliwack, and on Vancouver Island in the vicinity of Victoria. There is one old record for Kamloops (Macoun and Macoun 1909; Bent 1940). It was recorded in the province between 26 May and 29 August. Breeding was never confirmed.

All records, listed in chronological order, are as follows:
(1) Burrard Inlet (Vancouver) May 1881-1 (Macoun and Macoun 1909).
(2) Kamloops June 1882-2 found breeding (Macoun and Macoun 1909). Details to substantiate record not listed.
(3) Victoria June 1887-pair at Skinner swamp (Macoun and Macoun 1909)
(4) Chilliwack 17 July 1887-1 female (MVZ 101645).
(5) Chilliwack 26 May 1888-1 male (ROM 8759).

(6) Chilliwack 28 May 1891-1 female (MCZ 244703).
(7) Chilliwack 4 June 1891-1 female (MCZ 187910).
(8) Victoria July 1892-1 female (RBCM 1757).
(9) Sumas (Abbotsford) 30 May 1896-1 adult female (FMNH 6509).
(10) Victoria June 1896-1 adult female (FMNH 137663).
(11) Victoria 3 July 1896-1 male (RBCM 1756; Fig. 348).
(12) Victoria 16 June 1903-1 female (ROM 69268).
(13) Victoria 28 June 1904-1 female (RBCM 480).
(14) Vancouver 1 August 1913-1 adult female (NMC 47844).
(15) Vedder Mountain 29 August 1921-1 female (UBC 4905).
(16) Marpole (Vancouver) July 1922-2 observed by R.A. Cumming.
(17) Vancouver 9 August 1922-1 male (UBC 4904).
(18) Sumas Prairie 5 August 1923-1 female (ROM 81981).
(19) Vancouver 10 June 1926-1 male (RBCM 6940).
(20) Alouette River (Pitt Meadows) 4 June 1927-1 female (UBC 4903).
(21) Huntingdon 19 June 1927-1 male (RBCM 13029); 1 adult female.

REMARKS: Roberson (1980), after examining recent records from Oregon, Washington, and British Columbia, determined that the Yellow-billed Cuckoo has suffered "catastrophic range reductions on the West Coast." There are only 4 records for Washington from 1934 (Edson 1935) to 1979 (Roberson 1980).

In California, Gaines (1974) has shown that the Yellow-billed Cuckoo is absent where (1) understory vegetation is sparce, (2) water is more than 100 m away, and (3) the vegetation is not sufficiently extensive, at least 300 m in length and 100 m in width. He further states that "destruction of this habitat has so reduced its numbers ... that survival of California's cuckoos is questionable." Laymon and Halterman (1987) discuss management considerations for populations remaining on the west coast of North America.

See Banks (1988) for a recent discussion on the taxonomy of the Yellow-billed Cuckoo.

POSTSCRIPT: On 5 July 1989, an emaciated Yellow-billed Cuckoo was picked up alive after being hit by a car in Victoria. It subsequently died and was given to the provincial museum (RBCM 21620; Richard C. West pers. comm.). This is the first documented occurrence of the species in British Columbia since 1927. The status of the Yellow-billed Cuckoo is now considered *accidental*.

Figure 348. Yellow-billed Cuckoo collected at Victoria on 3 July 1896 (RBCM 1756; Andrew Niemann).

Ruby-throated Hummingbird

RTHU

Archilochus colubris (Linnaeus)

RANGE: Breeds in eastern North America from southern Canada (central Alberta east to Nova Scotia) south to the Gulf states and west in the United States to eastern North Dakota, central Nebraska, central Oklahoma, and east-central Texas. Winters from Mexico south to Costa Rica; rarely north to southern Alabama and southern Florida.

STATUS: *Casual* on the south coast; *accidental* in the Peace Lowlands.

OCCURRENCE: The Ruby-throated Hummingbird has been reported 6 times in the province, but only 4 occurrences are well documented. They are from the Campbell River area on Vancouver Island, the Greater Vancouver area, and the Peace Lowlands. Records are from spring and summer; extreme dates are 28 April and 12 July, both from North Vancouver.

The species was first reported at a nectar feeder in a garden at Stories Beach near Campbell River on 4 May 1977 (Telosky 1977). It was a male and may have arrived in early April but went unnoticed until a month later. It was also seen on 5 and 6 May and photographed (RBCM Photo 626) on 5 May. Unfortunately, the photographs are inconclusive for identification purposes (R.D. James pers. comm.), but the field notes are acceptable. In late May 1978, a male (presumably the same individual) was again seen in the same location (Mattocks and Hunn 1978).

The next 2 records, accompanied by detailed and convincing field notes (Weber, W.C. 1982), are from the Greater Vancouver area. On 28 April 1979, a male was seen in a private garden in North Vancouver and on 12 July 1981 a male was seen along the Yew Lake Trail, Cypress Provincial Park, West Vancouver.

The last acceptable record was of a male seen perched on a telephone wire near Tupper (Peace River) on 12 June 1983 (Campbell 1983c).

REMARKS: There are 2 additional published reports, one of which lacks sufficient detail to document the sighting and is therefore considered hypothetical.

The other record includes an incorrect location. Sometime between 11 and 21 June 1951 a male Ruby-throated Hummingbird was seen near Vanderhoof (Guiguet 1952a). Guiguet reports: "A bright metallic green-backed hummingbird with a full red gorgette was observed at closer range . . . The possibility of a ruby-throat occurring so far off its normal range is small, but the only other explanation for a bird so marked would be that it was an atypically pigmented rufous hummer, an equally remote possibility."

The other report is a sighting of "at least two male Ruby-throated Hummingbirds . . . at feeders with Rufous and Calliopes . . . at Crowsnest Pass, B.C." in the spring of 1983 (Rogers, T.H. 1983c). According to D.F. Fraser (pers. comm.), the sighting actually was made on the Alberta side of the provincial boundary.

Mattocks et al. (1976) and Roberson (1980) list no records of the Ruby-throated Hummingbird for Washington. Gabrielson and Lincoln (1959) report a bird found dead in western Alaska (St. Michael) in 1925. Field identification of female and immature hummingbirds is very difficult. Stiles (1971) provides some helpful advice for identifying west coast hummingbirds. In addition, observers are encouraged to refer to the important paper by Banks and Johnson (1961) on hybrid hummingbirds in North America.

Costa's Hummingbird

COHU

Calypte costae (Bourcier)

RANGE: Breeds mainly in the arid desert regions from central California, southern Nevada and southwestern Utah south to southern Baja California, Sonora, southern Arizona, and southwestern New Mexico. Winters from southern California and southern Arizona south to northwestern Mexico.

STATUS: *Casual* on the extreme south coast; *accidental* in the southern interior.

OCCURRENCE: There are 5 records of adult males, 4 in spring and 1 in summer. A Costa's Hummingbird was observed feeding at a red-flowering currant and a hummingbird feeder in Cadboro Bay, Saanich, from 14 to 17 April 1972. Detailed notes and a coloured painting document the bird's first occurrence in Canada (MacKenzie-Grieve and Tatum 1974).

The second record was from Nanaimo. On 3 July 1984, a bird hit a window and was photographed (RBCM Photo 940; Fig. 350) while it lay stunned on the ground below (Campbell 1984b). Shortly afterward, the hummingbird flew up to a perch and was not seen again.

A third Costa's Hummingbird appeared at a feeder in Pitt Meadows on 17 May 1986 (Mattocks 1986a). Colour photographs of the bird were taken (RBCM Photo 1132). It was not seen again.

In the spring of 1987, 2 Costa's Hummingbirds were reported. One was at a feeder in Lillooet from 17 to 19 May (RBCM Photo 1171), while a second appeared at a Burnaby feeder on 20 May and stayed until 1 June (RBCM Photo 1172; Fig. 349).

REMARKS: Several other sightings have been reported and there are 2 published reports: West Vancouver, 27 December 1973-1 male (Shepard, M.G. 1974) and Whaler Bay (Gabriola Island), 13 and 14 April 1985-1 male (Campbell 1985c). These records are considered hypothetical because no supporting details are given.

Roberson (1980) lists 6 records of males at feeders in western Oregon. There are apparently no records for Washington state.

Figure 349. Male Costa's Hummingbird in urban garden at Burnaby, 31 May 1987 (RBCM Photo 1172; W. Douglas Kragh).

Figure 350. This is the second documented provincial record of the Costa's Hummingbird: Nanaimo, Vancouver Island, 3 July 1984 (RBCM Photo 940; David Thompson).

Red-headed Woodpecker

Melanerpes erythrocephalus (Linnaeus)

RHWO

RANGE: Breeds from southern Canada (Saskatchewan to New Brunswick) south to northern Mexico, central Texas, the Gulf coast, and Florida. Migratory in northern portions of its range. Winters north to Kansas, Ohio, and New Jersey.

STATUS: *Accidental.*

OCCURRENCE: An adult was observed from 11 to 13 July 1965 frequenting roadside deciduous woods 13 km east of Vernon (Grant, J. 1966c). It was photographed (RBCM Photo 207) on 11 July.

Hypothetical Species

HYPOTHETICAL SPECIES

The following 15 species of birds have been reported in various publications and for the following reasons the records are considered questionable.

1. The data on which the record is based are erroneous, cannot be verified, are recorded by a single observer, have been rejected by a regional records committee, or are based on written or photographic evidence that is less than satisfactory.

2. The species' occurrence in the province is believed to be either through escape from captivity or human-aided other than from intentional introduction.

Another 12 species have accompanying detailed field notes on file but all are unpublished or have been reported by only a single observer. They include Black-shouldered Kite (*Elanus caeruleus*), Greater Golden-Plover (*Pluvialis apricaria*), Common Ringed Plover (*Charadrius hiaticula*), Mountain Plover (*Charadrius montanus*), Wood Sandpiper (*Tringa glareola*), Gray-tailed Tattler (*Heteroscelus brevipes*), Great Knot (*Calidris tenuirostris*), American Woodcock (*Scolopax minor*), Lesser Black-backed Gull (*Larus fuscus*), Red-legged Kittiwake (*Rissa brevirostris*), Chimney Swift (*Chaetura pelagica*), and Blue-throated Hummingbird (*Lampornis clemenciae*).

Black Vulture
Coragyps atratus (Bechstein)

A Black Vulture was reported being chased by two Golden Eagles at Keremeos on 3 May 1975. The bird was described as having a short tail and white patches near the ends of the wings; it was flying with deep wing-strokes. Another was observed on 25 June 1981 soaring along a cliff edge about 1 km south of Okanagan Falls (Brunton and Pratt 1986).

However, as R.A. Cannings et al. (1987) mention:

. . . two or more Black Vultures escaped from a zoo in Seattle in the late fall of 1974. They were seen several times around Seattle and then disappeared (D.R. Paulson pers. comm.). The possibility that these sightings, especially the former, involve one of these birds cannot be discounted.

The only other record for western Canada, which is also believed to be an escaped bird, is of one photographed at Kluane Lake, southwestern Yukon, on 2 July 1982 (Grunberg 1984d).

California Condor
Gymnogyps californianus (Shaw)

During his wanderings in British Columbia, Lord (1866) recorded this species at the "mouth of the Fraser River" and mentions that it "seldom visits the interior." Later, Fannin (1891) reports:

In September, 1880, I saw two of these birds at Burrard Inlet. It is more than probable they are accidental here.

The final alleged occurrence was provided by Rhoads (1893a) who states:

Seen on Lulu Island [Fraser River delta] as late as 'three or four years ago' by Mr. W. London. 'None seen since, used to be common.'

The species may have wandered into British Columbia as there are several documented occurrences for coastal Washington (Harris, H. 1941; Jewett et al. 1953). It is even suggested by some writers (e.g. Cooper, J.G. 1860) that the California Condor used to visit the Columbia River in the autumn to gorge on dead salmon. Records for British Columbia, however, remain inconclusive, as they lack supporting documentation.

White-tailed Eagle
Haliaeetus albicilla (Linnaeus)

This species, formerly known as the Gray Sea Eagle, is possibly represented by a specimen. On 18 March 1898, a taxidermist said that an immature male was taken on Vancouver Island, British Columbia (Bishop 1905). The record, however, lacks complete and convincing details, as the location of the specimen is not known.

Red-shouldered Hawk
Buteo lineatus (Gmelin)

This species was reported to have occurred at Burrard Inlet and Fort Simpson (Fannin 1891) and "in the British Columbia Interior" (Rhoads 1893a) but without specific details. Brooks (1917) lists 2 sight records at Chilliwack, but later, Brooks and Swarth (1925) suggest that these records were errors. Another sighting at Hope on 8 June 1948 (Thacker 1948) was not accepted by the American Ornithologists' Union (1957) or by Godfrey (1966).

There are recent records for Oregon and Washington (Roberson 1980).

Northern Hobby
Falco subbuteo Linnaeus

As Godfrey (1986) states:

A well-described observation of one individual apparently of this species near Merritt, in the Nicola valley, British Columbia, on 22 May 1982, is not supported by a photograph.

Common Peafowl
Pavo cristatus Linnaeus

Between 1960 and 1965, 3 Common Peafowl escaped from a private zoo operated in Langford on southern Vancouver Island. Another 5 birds escaped in 1980 and during the next 7 years a small breeding population, of about 25 birds, has become established in a subdivision in the vicinity of Bellamy and Phelps roads in Langford (M. Drew pers. comm.).

To many people, the birds are a source of enjoyment, but to others they are a nuisance. In February 1988, the Capital Regional District agreed to reduce the population to 5 breeding pairs (Hume 1988). The results of that control program, as of April, 1988 are not known.

This species is feral also, on Sidney Island, as a result of a release.

Yellow Rail
Coturnicops noveboracensis (Gmelin)

There are 3 records, 2 involving birds heard and 1 of a bird seen. There are no photographs or specimens, or satisfactory field notes.

The first record was supplied by K. Wood (1964):

... between June 29 and July 9, 1964 ... heard the stone-clicking song of the ... Yellow Rail in the marshy back region of Lake Lillian in the east Kootenay.

Later, in correspondence (16 October 1985), he said:

... it was not a sighting, but a hearing identification. We spent ten days ... on the shore of Lake Lillian and we heard the distinctive tik-tik-tik-tik-tik of the Yellow Rail daily while there. This species used to be quite audible in the Gaetz Lakes bird sanctuary at Red Deer [Alberta] in earlier years, where I did sight it on rare occasions scuttling across the lily pads.

On 26 May 1976, a bird was apparently heard at Somenos Lake on Vancouver Island. The recorder was convinced of the call, having heard and seen the species while living in the Canadian prairies.

The last record is of a single bird "reportedly seen at Corn Creek marsh near Lone Pine Hill [Creston] on 9 August 1979." R.W. Butler et al. (1986) consider the record "unconfirmed."

The Yellow Rail has been found in Washington on the Skagit River (16 November 1935; Ransom 1938) and near Othello (April 1969; Furrer 1974).

POSTSCRIPT: On 10 June 1989 a bird was heard calling at Boundary Lake (Goodlow) for about 5 minutes in the late afternoon. It was not seen, but the distinctive "tik-tik, tik-tik-tik, tik-tik, tik-tik-tik" calls were heard. Subsequent visits failed to find (or hear) the bird (Campbell 1989d).

Black Rail
Laterallus jamaicensis (Gmelin)

On 1 June 1958, 2 "rail" eggs (neither Sora nor Virginia Rail) were discovered in a nest at Spotted Lake, Richter Pass. On a return visit to check the nest contents on 14 June, observers found that cattle had trampled the eggs. Fragments were salvaged and sent to W.E. Godfrey at the National Museum of Canada, but they could not be positively identified. Meugens and Cooper (1962) and Campbell and Meugens (1971) provide additional details about this unconfirmed record.

Piping Plover
Charadrius melodus Ord

On 30 August 1976, 2 birds were reported at Waglisla near Bella Bella on the central mainland coast (Shepard, M.G. 1977a). Although a written field description is on file, it is incomplete, and the record must be considered questionable. In addition, neither Haig (1985) nor Godfrey (1986) have accepted the record.

Little Curlew
Numenius minutus Gould

On 17 July 1983, a single bird was reported with 2 Whimbrels on the mud flats at Blackie Spit, Boundary Bay (Kautesk 1985a). Although subsequent searches were made, the bird was not relocated and positive identification was not confirmed. A Little Curlew was recently observed, however, near Santa Maria, California from 16 September to 14 October 1984 (McCaskie 1985).

The Little Curlew is very similar in appearance to the nearly extinct Eskimo Curlew (*N. borealis*). See Farrand (1977) for details on separating them in the field.

Long-toed Stint
Calidris subminuta (Middendorf)

The Long-toed Stint has been reported from southern coastal areas of the province almost annually since 1981. The earliest record was of an adult seen at Iona Island from 27 June to 1 July 1981 and possibly the same bird was seen again on 30 July (Harrington-Tweit et al. 1981). The following year, a single bird was reported from a small pond at Cordova Spit, Vancouver Island, on 19 and 20 September. Detailed field notes accompanied by a colour painting were submitted with the record. Subsequently they were compared with colour photographs and museum specimens with the conclusion that the bird in question had been a juvenile Least Sandpiper. In addition, there are at least 6 reported sightings from the Fraser River delta, with detailed field notes, which have not been published. Because of its close resemblance to the Least Sandpiper, the Long-toed Stint must remain on the hypothetical list for British Columbia birds until photographs or specimens are obtained. In western Alaska this species has been reported in spring migration betwen 12 May and 13 June, and in autumn migration between 20 July and 25 September (Kessel and Gibson 1978).

Observers are encouraged to study Veit and Jonsson (1984) for assistance with field identification of this small sandpiper.

Parakeet Auklet
Cyclorrhynchus psittacula (Pallas)

On 24 February 1971, 3 single birds, 1 of which came aboard ship, were seen about 24 km southwest of Estevan Point off Vancouver Island (Campbell and Shepard 1973). The sight records are convincing but all were reported by a single observer.

It is likely this species is a regular visitor in winter to waters off the coast of British Columbia. There are several records of beached birds for Washington (Balmer 1935; Parkham 1950) and California (Kenyon 1937) as well as additional sight records of live birds off the west coast of the United States (Roberson 1980).

POSTSCRIPT: In late December 1988, an oil spill off the Washington coast travelled north into British Columbia and for the next month or so contaminated marine birds off Vancouver Island. Fifteen Parakeet Auklets were found washed ashore on beaches. See Addenda for details.

Least Auklet
Aethia pusilla (Pallas)

The American Ornithologists' Union (1910) includes the British Columbia coast in the winter range of this species, presumably based on the ambiguous record published by Rhoads (1893b) for the Puget Sound area. The only published occurrence of Least Auklets in British Columbia was reported by Darcus (1930) as follows:

. . . observed in pairs off the coast of Langara Island in April [1927]. No doubt it winters in these waters as I have found it doing so on the west coast of Vancouver Island.

The records may be valid, because other small alcids, such as the Marbled Murrelet, Ancient Murrelet, and Cassin's Auklet, which may be confused with Least Auklets, were also mentioned by Darcus. However, because specific details are lacking, the species remains hypothetical.

There are no records in western North America outside its breeding range in western Alaska.

Ringed Turtle-Dove
Streptopelia risoria (Linnaeus)

There are at least 12 records of free-flying birds from scattered locations across southern areas of the province. Two are documented: Westham Island 16 May 1971-1 (Campbell et al. 1972b); Cranbrook 27 December 1986-1 at feeder (RBCM Photo 1177).

Although the Ringed Turtle-Dove was introduced and has established feral populations in southern California (American Ornithologists' Union 1983) all records in British Columbia are probably locally escaped cagebirds.

Allen's Hummingbird
Selasphorus sasin (Lesson)

For many years, species of *Selasphorus* hummingbirds, suspected of being the Allen's Hummingbird, have been reported in the province (see Fannin 1898, Saunders 1902, Brooks 1903, Kermode 1904, Crowell and Nehls 1971b, Tatum 1972, and Guiguet 1978). The identification of these birds has not yet been established beyond doubt.

Godfrey (1986) includes the Allen's Hummingbird on the Hypothetical List despite photographic evidence of a male in Victoria in Spring, 1971. After examining the photograph he stated "[it] does not eliminate the possibility of confusion with the very similar Rufous Hummingbird."

APPENDICES

APPENDIX 1

Migration Chronology

In the following table, dates are given for regular spring and/or autumn migrants in 3 coastal and 8 interior locations in the province. The data for composing the migration dates were obtained from published literature as well as field notebooks of birders. Periods of records vary with area as follows: Victoria (1969-1985), Vancouver (1968-1986), Masset (1980-1986), Okanagan (1897-1986), Nakusp (1975-1986), Radium (1979-1986), Kamloops (1978-1986), Williams Lake (1958-1986), Prince George (1981-1986), Fort St. John (1980-1986), and Fort Nelson (1975-1986). Dates for peak movements (Fig. 351) are generally given as ranges. A single date indicates a calculated average for all records. Localities and dates were deleted if information was incomplete.

Each species generally falls into 1 of 3 categories: summer visitant, winter visitant, or passage migrant. Earliest arrival, latest departure, and peak movement dates are given for each "season." A completed matrix for each category is as follows:

	SPRING			AUTUMN		
	Early Arrival	Late Departure	Peak Movement	Early Arrival	Late Departure	Peak Movement
Summer Visitant	X	—	X	—	X	X
Winter Visitant	—	X	X	X	—	X
Passage Migrant	X	X	X	X	X	X

Figure 351. *Migrating shorebirds, mostly dowitchers, resting during autumn migration on Westham Island, south of Vancouver, 10 October 1969 (R. Wayne Campbell).*

	SPRING			AUTUMN		
	Early Arrival	Late Departure	Peak Movement	Early Arrival	Late Departure	Peak Movement
Turkey Vulture						
Victoria	7 Feb	—	late Mar	—	26 Nov	21 Sep-3 Oct
Vancouver	8 Mar	—	10 Apr	—	19 Nov	25 Sep
Okanagan	27 Feb	—	—	—	—	early Sep
Kamloops	6 May	—	—	—	8 Nov	—
Osprey						
Victoria	3 Mar	—	late Mar	—	31 Oct	Sep
Vancouver	21 Feb	—	31 Mar	—	18 Nov	9 Oct
Okanagan	27 Mar	—	15 Apr	—	—	late Sep
Nakusp	1 Apr	—	—	—	22 Sep	—
Radium	19 Mar	—	—	—	16 Sep	—
Kamloops	14 Apr	—	20-25 Apr	—	20 Sep	2-10 Sep
Williams Lake	—	—	3-18 Apr	—	—	mid-Sep
Prince George	17 Apr	—	—	—	21 Sep	—
Bald Eagle						
Kamloops	1 Feb	—	3 Mar-10 Apr	—	30 Nov	—
Williams Lake	29 Feb	—	Apr	—	—	—
Prince George	17 Mar	—	—	—	8 Dec	—
Fort Nelson	13 Apr	—	—	—	6 Oct	—
Northern Harrier						
Victoria	—	21 May	Apr	16 Jul	—	mid-Sep
Vancouver	—	—	17 Apr	—	—	30 Sep
Okanagan	—	—	Apr	Aug	—	early Oct
Nakusp	20 Apr	—	—	16 Aug	31 Oct	—
Kamloops	20 Mar	—	3-22 Apr	10 Aug	30 Nov	15 Sep-15 Oct
Williams Lake	—	—	16 Mar-20 Apr	—	—	Oct-Nov
Prince George	28 Mar	—	—	—	—	—
Fort St. John	31 Mar	—	15-27 Apr	—	6 Nov	10-20 Sep
Fort Nelson	15 Apr	—	—	—	4 Oct	—
Sharp-shinned Hawk						
Victoria	—	—	Apr	—	—	Sep
Vancouver	10 Apr	—	15 Apr	3 Aug	—	22 Sep
Okanagan	early Apr	—	late Apr-early May	5 Aug	—	late Aug-early Sep
Nakusp	11 Apr	—	—	—	16 Sep	—
Kamloops	4 Apr	—	5-25 Apr	—	10 Oct	10-25 Sep
Williams Lake	—	—	13-18 Apr	—	—	19-23 Sep
Fort St. John	14 Apr	—	—	—	18 Oct	20 Aug-10 Sep
Fort Nelson	19 Apr	—	—	—	16 Sep	—
Cooper's Hawk						
Victoria	—	—	Mar	—	—	Sep-Oct
Vancouver	—	—	15 Apr	—	—	23 Sep
Okanagan	—	—	late Apr	late Aug	—	early Sep
Kamloops	1 Mar	—	15-30 Apr	4 Sep	20 Oct	—
Swainson's Hawk						
Victoria	7 Mar	28 May	—	6 Sep	30 Oct	—
Okanagan	25 Mar	—	early May	early Aug	—	late Aug
Kamloops	25 Apr	—	2-10 May	—	20 Sep	1-3 Sep

Migration Chronology

	SPRING			AUTUMN		
	Early Arrival	Late Departure	Peak Movement	Early Arrival	Late Departure	Peak Movement
Red-tailed Hawk						
Okanagan	12 Mar	—	early Apr	late Aug	—	mid-Sep
Nakusp	1 Mar	—	—	5 Sep	31 Oct	15-30 Sep
Radium	29 Mar	—	5-12 Apr	—	30 Nov	—
Kamloops	1 Mar	—	15 Mar-15 Apr	25 Aug	30 Nov	15 Sep-5 Oct
Williams Lake	—	—	15 Mar-30 Apr	—	—	Oct-Nov
Prince George	17 Mar	—	—	21 Sep	—	—
Fort St. John	29 Mar	—	10-24 Apr	9 Sep	31 Oct	10-20 Sep
Fort Nelson	12 Apr	—	18-25 Apr	9 Sep	24 Oct	15 Sep-15 Oct
Rough-legged Hawk						
Victoria	—	18 Apr	—	22 Sep	—	Oct
Vancouver	—	22 May	4 Apr	18 Aug	—	8 Nov
Okanagan	—	—	—	18 Sep	28 Oct	late Oct
Radium	—	—	—	8 Sep	9 Oct	—
Kamloops	—	24 May	5-25 Apr	29 Sep	—	20 Oct-15 Nov
Williams Lake	—	—	4 Apr	—	—	1-2 Nov
Prince George	1 Apr	—	—	21 Sep	—	—
Fort St. John	31 Mar	—	5-20 Apr	—	—	5-27 Oct
Fort Nelson	19 Apr	18 Jun	—	8 Oct	—	—
Golden Eagle						
Victoria	—	—	Mar-Apr	—	—	Oct
Okanagan	—	—	early May	—	—	early Oct
Kamloops	1 Mar	—	1-15 Mar	—	30 Nov	—
Fort St. John	28 Mar	—	—	—	—	—
Fort Nelson	3 Apr	—	—	—	15 Nov	—
American Kestrel						
Victoria	—	—	Apr	—	—	Sep
Vancouver	—	—	25 Apr	—	—	14 Sep
Okanagan	—	—	early May	—	—	early Sep
Nakusp	15 Feb	—	16 Apr-15 May	—	21 Nov	10-25 Sep
Radium	2 Apr	—	—	—	15 Oct	—
Kamloops	15 Mar	—	20 Apr-15 May	—	1 Nov	1-15 Sep
Williams Lake	1 Mar	—	30 Mar-27 Apr	—	—	25 Sep-18 Nov
Fort St. John	3 Apr	—	18-28 Apr	—	20 Oct	2-11 Sep
Fort Nelson	18 Apr	—	6-17 May	—	28 Sep	—
Merlin						
Victoria	—	—	Apr	—	—	Sep
Vancouver	—	25 May	4 May	3 Aug	—	17 Aug
Okanagan	—	—	—	—	—	late Sep
Nakusp	2 Mar	—	—	1 Sep	11 Oct	—
Kamloops	15 Feb	—	—	4 Aug	31 Oct	1-20 Sep
Prince George	9 Apr	—	—	—	29 Oct	—
Fort St. John	26 Feb	—	27 Apr 12 May 26 Aug	29 Oct	15 Aug-5 Sep	—
Fort Nelson	20 Apr	—	—	—	27 Sep	—
Peregrine Falcon						
Victoria	—	—	Mar-Apr	—	—	Sep-Oct
Kamloops	15 Feb	—	1-20 Apr	15 Sep	—	—
Fort St. John	21 Apr	—	—	—	5 Oct	—
Gyrfalcon						
Victoria	—	22 Apr	—	11 Oct	—	—
Vancouver	—	20 Apr	—	6 Sep	—	—
Kamloops	—	4 Apr	—	3 Nov	—	—

| | SPRING | | | AUTUMN | | |
	Early Arrival	Late Departure	Peak Movement	Early Arrival	Late Departure	Peak Movement
Prairie Falcon						
Kamloops	1 Mar	—	—	—	25 Nov	—
Virginia Rail						
Okanagan	—	—	Apr-May	—	—	Sep-Oct
Kamloops	7 May	—	—	—	11 Oct	—
Sora						
Victoria	11 Apr	—	early May	—	27 Nov	—
Vancouver	12 Mar	—	20 Apr	—	13 Oct	17 Sep
Okanagan	18 Apr	—	—	—	—	Sep-Oct
Nakusp	30 Apr	—	—	—	26 Sep	—
Radium	30 Apr	—	—	—	—	—
Kamloops	4 May	—	—	—	20 Sep	—
Williams Lake	—	—	15-30 Apr	—	—	—
Fort St. John	28 Apr	—	—	—	18 Sep	—
Fort Nelson	11 Mar	—	—	—	31 Aug	—
American Coot						
Victoria	—	—	Apr	—	—	early Oct
Vancouver	—	—	23 Apr	—	—	6 Oct
Masset	21 Mar	24 May	—	27 Sep	—	—
Okanagan	—	—	late Mar-Apr	—	—	Sep-Oct
Nakusp	31 Mar	—	10 Apr-16 May	—	21 Nov	1-25 Sep
Radium	4 Apr	—	25 Apr-5 May	31 Aug	—	14 Sep-14 Oct
Kamloops	4 Mar	—	10-25 Apr	—	1 Dec	—
Williams Lake	16 Mar	—	5Apr	—	—	Oct-early Nov
Fort St. John	10 Apr	—	10-16 May	—	27 Oct	—
Sandhill Crane						
Victoria	1 Apr	29 May	—	31 Aug	26 Nov	—
Vancouver	1 Mar	—	8 Apr	—	21 Nov	26 Sep
Masset	8 Apr	—	22 Apr	—	—	—
Okanagan	10 Mar	—	18-25 Apr	early Aug	—	late Sep-early Oct
Kamloops	18 Mar	16 May	20-28 Apr	15 Aug	25 Nov	15 Sep-15 Oct
Williams Lake	20 Mar	—	15-30 Apr	—	—	13-18 Sep
Prince George	—	—	4 May	—	—	—
Fort St. John	25 Apr	—	—	9 Sep	2 Oct	16 Sep
Fort Nelson	25 Apr	19 May	25 Apr-4 May	20 Aug	16 Oct	2-22 Sep
Black-bellied Plover						
Victoria	—	4 Jun	20 Apr	12 Jun	—	Sep
Vancouver	—	—	25 Apr	—	—	9 Sep
Masset	17 Apr	22 May	20-27 Apr	Sep	—	—
Okanagan	—	—	—	9 Sep	—	22-24 Sep
Nakusp	—	—	—	9 Aug	10 Oct	10-25 Sep
Kamloops	—	—	—	5 Sep	19 Oct	25-30 Sep
Fort St. John	11 May	6 Jun	17 May-3 Jun	18 Sep	21 Oct	—
Fort Nelson	—	—	—	16 Sep	8 Oct	—

Migration Chronology

	SPRING			AUTUMN		
	Early Arrival	Late Departure	Peak Movement	Early Arrival	Late Departure	Peak Movement
Lesser Golden-Plover						
Vancouver	31 Mar	30 May	27 Apr	15 Aug	14 Nov	19 Sep
Masset	1 Apr	16 Jun	25 Apr-10 May	Sep	9 Nov	—
Okanagan	—	—	—	9 Sep	—	22-24 Sep
Nakusp	—	—	—	7 Sep	18 Oct	10-25 Sep
Kamloops	—	—	—	7 Sep	2 Nov	25-30 Sep
Fort St. John	8 May	19 May	8-19 May	8 Sep	2 Oct	9-16 Sep
Fort Nelson	15 May	19 May	—	16 Sep	6 Oct	17-26 Sep
Semipalmated Plover						
Victoria	10 Apr	23 May	3-13 May	4 Jul	23 Oct	16 Jul-4 Sep
Vancouver	1 Apr	—	4 May	—	11 Nov	3 Aug
Masset	18 Apr	—	22 Apr-10 May	—	11 Aug	—
Okanagan	—	—	—	20 Jul	—	early Sep
Kamloops	3 May	15 May	12 May	4 Aug	21 Sep	26 Aug-20 Sep
Williams Lake	30 Apr	22 May	—	—	—	4 Sep
Prince George	2 Apr	—	—	4 Aug	14 Sep	
Fort St. John	26 Apr	9 May	5-26 May	24 Jun	21 Sep	11-28 Jul (adult) 28 Aug-10 Sep (juv)
Fort Nelson	14 May	—	—	26 Aug	—	—
Killdeer						
Vancouver	—	—	—	—	—	30 Aug
Okanagan	17 Feb	—	—	—	—	—
Nakusp	6 Mar	—	1-25 Apr	—	21 Nov	6-25 Sep
Radium	25 Feb	—	—	—	26 Oct	—
Kamloops	20 Feb	—	15-30 Mar	—	1 Dec	20 Aug-10 Sep
Williams Lake	14 Feb	—	5 Mar-2 Apr	—	—	Oct-Nov
Prince George	17 Mar	—	—	29 Oct	—	—
Fort St. John	1 Apr	—	25-30 Apr	—	19 Oct	—
Fort Nelson	26 Apr	—	—	—	31 Aug	—
Greater Yellowlegs						
Victoria	—	27 May	12 Apr-12 May 9 Jun	—	5 Jul-25 Aug	
Vancouver	—	—	17 Apr	—	—	11 Sep
Masset	27 Mar	2 Jun	15-25 Apr	5 Jul	11 Nov	—
Okanagan	23 Mar	21 May	15 Apr	—	—	—
Nakusp	11 Apr	10 May	—	14 Aug	7 Sep	—
Radium	24 Apr	1 May	—	—	30 Aug	—
Kamloops	6 Apr	—	6-15 Apr	21 Jul	4 Oct	15-30 Aug
Williams Lake	—	—	10-27 Apr	—	—	9 Jul-31 Aug
Fort St. John	10 Apr	—	19-26 Apr	25 Aug	19 Sep	—
Fort Nelson	27 Apr	—	6-8 May	16 Aug	26 Aug	—
Lesser Yellowlegs						
Victoria	13 Apr	30 May	—	29 Jun	24 Nov	8-28 Aug
Vancouver	2 Apr	—	8 May	29 Jun	28 Nov	1 Sep
Masset	30 Mar	25 May	29 Apr-2 May	1 Jul	10 Oct	mid-Aug
Okanagan	28 Apr	13 May	—	7 Jul	26 Oct	Aug
Nakusp	7 May	14 May	—	7 Aug	17 Sep	—
Radium	13 May	—	—	—	30 Aug	—
Kamloops	15 Apr	15 May	15-20 Apr	21 Jul	4 Oct	15-30 Aug
Williams Lake	—	—	6-29 May	14 Jul	15 Oct	Aug
Prince George	27 Apr	—	—	—	5 Oct	—
Fort St. John	18 Apr	—	28 Apr-10 May	—	21 Oct	—
Fort Nelson	26 Apr	—	6-8 May	—	26 Aug	—

	SPRING			AUTUMN		
	Early Arrival	Late Departure	Peak Movement	Early Arrival	Late Departure	Peak Movement
Solitary Sandpiper						
Victoria	22 Apr	1 Jun	—	27 Jun	28 Sep	—
Vancouver	20 Apr	19 May	7 May	1 Jul	27 Sep	24 Aug
Okanagan	28 Apr	16 May	mid-May	—	—	mid-Aug
Nakusp	30 Apr	15 May	—	28 Jul	7 Sep	—
Radium	15 May	—	—	—	19 Aug	—
Kamloops	2 May	3 Jul	—	3 Aug	15 Sep	15 Aug-5 Sep
Williams Lake	1 May	18 May	—	23 Jul	13 Sep	15-27 Aug
Prince George	1 Apr	—	4 May	—	14 Sep	—
Fort St. John	26 Apr	—	6-14 May	12 Jul	20 Sep	Aug
Fort Nelson	11 May	19 May	—	31 Jul	5 Sep	—
Wandering Tattler						
Victoria	24 Apr	2 Jun	9-19 May	23 Jun	29 Oct	19 Jul-30 Aug
Vancouver	—	—	—	22 Jul	9 Oct	7 Sep
Spotted Sandpiper						
Victoria	—	—	May	—	—	Aug-Sep
Vancouver	24 Apr	—	21 May	—	11 Nov	1 Sep
Masset	23 May	—	18 Jun	—	—	—
Okanagan	19 Apr	—	mid-May	—	—	mid-Aug
Nakusp	9 May	—	—	29 Aug	25 Sep	—
Radium	12 May	—	—	—	25 Aug	—
Kamloops	7 May	—	—	15 Aug	30 Sep	—
Williams Lake	30 Apr	—	May	23 Aug	28 Sep	late Aug
Fort St. John	7 May	—	—	—	28 Sep	—
Fort Nelson	7 May	—	—	31 Jul	4 Sep	15-25 Aug
Whimbrel						
Victoria	15 Apr	18 Jun	1-26 May	3 Jul	21 Nov	Jul-Aug
Vancouver	5 Apr	—	6 May	29 Jun	18 Nov	25 Jul
Fort St. John	25 May	28 May	—	—	—	—
Fort Nelson	13 May	—	—	4 Jul	—	—
Long-billed Curlew						
Vancouver	1 Mar	23 May	28 Apr	14 Aug	25 Oct	—
Okanagan	3 Mar	—	early Apr	—	29 Oct	mid-Jul
Radium	4 Apr	—	15-30 Apr	—	—	—
Kamloops	27 Mar	—	6-20 Apr	—	5 Aug	—
Hudsonian Godwit						
Victoria	11 May	12 May	—	4 Sep	8 Sep	—
Vancouver	—	—	—	9 Aug	11 Oct	late Aug-early Sep
Fort St. John	29 Apr	25 May	early May	14 Jul	11 Sep	—
Marbled Godwit						
Victoria	28 Apr	16 May	—	7 Jul	19 Oct	—
Vancouver	19 Apr	8 May	—	1 Aug	26 Oct	—
Masset	24 Apr	6 May	—	—	—	—

Migration Chronology

	SPRING			AUTUMN		
	Early Arrival	Late Departure	Peak Movement	Early Arrival	Late Departure	Peak Movement
Ruddy Turnstone						
Victoria	21 Apr	26 May	4-13 May	1 Jul	21 Nov	18-31 Jul
Vancouver	12 Apr	31 May	8 May	12 Jul	7 Sep	11 Aug
Okanagan	—	—	—	23 Aug	14 Sep	—
Fort St. John	—	—	—	23 Aug	9 Sep	—
Black Turnstone						
Victoria	—	7 Jun	1 Apr-4 May	17 Jun	—	Jul-Aug
Vancouver	—	12 May	23 Apr	14 Jul	—	11 Sep
Surfbird						
Victoria	—	12 May	25 Apr-4 May	23 Jun	—	22 Jul-29 Aug
Vancouver	—	30 Apr	2 Apr	18 Jul	—	25 Sep
Red Knot						
Victoria	17 Apr	8 May	—	15 Jul	17 Nov	—
Vancouver	18 Apr	23 May	12 May	11 Aug	27 Oct	25 Aug
Sanderling						
Victoria	—	9 Jun	15 Apr-15 May	4 Jul	—	Sep
Vancouver	—	1 Jun	25 Apr	27 Jun	—	20 Aug
Okanagan	23 May	7 Jun	—	25 Jul	—	Aug
Williams Lake	—	—	—	14 Jul	—	4-24 Sep
Fort St. John	24 May	30 May	—	28 Aug	22 Sep	—
Semipalmated Sandpiper						
Victoria	23 Apr	25 May	—	3 Jul	14 Oct	7 Jul-17 Aug
Vancouver	29 Apr	2 Jun	13 May	20 Jun	12 Oct	17 Jul
Masset	—	—	—	5 Jul	—	
Okanagan	13 May	16 May	—	15 Jul	—	Aug
Kamloops	—	—	—	20 Aug	9 Sep	6-9 Sep
Prince George	—	—	—	4 Aug	6 Sep	—
Fort St. John	30 Apr	10 Jun	22-26 May	14 Jul	16 Sep	mid-Jul
Western Sandpiper						
Victoria	22 Mar	3 Jun	21 Apr-9 May	10 Jun	25 Nov	5 Jul-31 Aug
Vancouver	22 Mar	2 Jun	2 May	20 Jun	29 Nov	11 Jul
Masset	16 Apr	25 May	1-3 May	17 Jun	3 Nov	4 Jul-22 Aug
Okanagan	28 Apr	24 May	—	late Jul	—	7-14 Aug
Nakusp	—	—	—	8 Aug	6 Sep	—
Kamloops	22 Apr	14 May	—	10 Jul	26 Sep	5-30 Aug
Williams Lake	—	—	10 May	—	—	23 Aug-9 Sep
Fort St. John	22 May	29 May	—	24 Aug	16 Sep	—
Fort Nelson	—	—	—	10 Aug	—	—
Least Sandpiper						
Victoria	11 Mar	30 May	27 Apr-11 May	4 Jul	26 Sep	Aug
Vancouver	30 Mar	2 Jun	4 May	19 Jun	26 Nov	18 Aug
Masset	26 Mar	—	29 Apr-1 May	—	29 Nov	mid-Jul
Okanagan	26 Apr	28 May	mid-May	3 Jul	17 Aug	early Jul
Kamloops	25 Apr	15 May	1-3 May	3 Jul	26 Sep	10 Aug-3 Sep
Williams Lake	—	—	30 Apr-11 May	—	—	4 Jul-31 Aug
Fort St. John	26 Apr	4 Jun	24-26 May	2 Sep	16 Sep	15 Jul (adults) 15-20 Aug (juv.)
Fort Nelson	7 May	19 May	—	—	16 Aug	—

	SPRING			AUTUMN		
	Early Arrival	Late Departure	Peak Movement	Early Arrival	Late Departure	Peak Movement
White-rumped Sandpiper						
Fort St. John	18 May	12 Jun	25 May-5 Jun	—	—	—
Baird's Sandpiper						
Victoria	14 Apr	12 May	27 Apr-1 May	4 Jul	26 Sep	Aug
Vancouver	28 Mar	24 May	8 May	21 Jun	18 Nov	24 Aug
Okanagan	21 Apr	—	early May	7 Jul	—	21 Aug
Kamloops	14 Apr	15 May	1 May	10 Jul	21 Sep	20 Aug-5 Sep
Fort St. John	23 Apr	2 Jun	14-25 May	2 Jul	21 Oct	12-15 Jul (adults) 10-20 Aug (juv.)
Fort Nelson	14 May	17 May	—	—	3 Sep	—
Pectoral Sandpiper						
Victoria	29 Apr	23 May	—	4 Jul	15 Nov	Sep
Vancouver	27 Apr	24 May	19 May	20 Jun	17 Nov	24 Sep
Masset	3 May	28 May	11-18 May	27 Jul	10 Nov	late Sep
Okanagan	12 May	31 May	—	6 Jul	6 Nov	Sep
Nakusp	—	—	—	6 Sep	26 Oct	—
Kamloops	—	—	—	25 Jul	19 Oct	15-25 Sep
Williams Lake	—	—	12 May	—	—	29 Aug-9 Sep
Fort St. John	2 May	2 Jun	10-15 May 24-28 May	9 Jul	31 Oct	14 Jul (adults) 15 Aug-15 Sep (juv.)
Fort Nelson	—	—	—	16 Aug	22 Sep	—
Sharp-tailed Sandpiper						
Victoria	—	—	—	7 Sep	6 Nov	—
Vancouver	—	—	—	22 Jul	10 Nov	4 Oct
Masset	—	—	—	3 Sep	17 Nov	—
Okanagan	—	—	—	12 Sep	—	—
Kamloops	—	—	—	20 Sep	21 Sep	—
Fort St. John	—	—	—	9 Sep	8 Oct	—
Rock Sandpiper						
Victoria	—	11 May	15 Apr-6 May	7 Oct	—	15 Oct-30 Nov
Vancouver	—	5 May	17 Apr	9 Oct	—	21 Oct
Dunlin						
Victoria	—	29 May	15 Apr-15 May	3 Jul	—	Oct
Vancouver	—	—	19 Apr	—	—	20 Oct
Masset	—	6 Jun	21 Apr-3 May	14 Jul	—	—
Okanagan	5 Apr	16 May	—	—	25 Nov	—
Kamloops	4 Mar	1 May	22-25 Apr	—	25 Nov	—
Fort St. John	23 Apr	4 May	—	17 Jul	16 Oct	—
Stilt Sandpiper						
Victoria	27 May	29 May	—	2 Aug	16 Oct	13 Aug-27 Sep
Vancouver	20 May	20 Jun	—	3 Aug	25 Oct	29 Aug
Okanagan	—	—	—	—	25 Sep	late Aug
Kamloops	—	—	—	20 Aug	10 Sep	20 Aug
Fort St. John	23 May	9 Jun	26-30 May	7 Jul	22 Sep	14-17 Jul (adults) 17 Aug-5 Sep (juv.)
Buff-breasted Sandpiper						
Vancouver	—	—	—	7 Jul	8 Oct	late Aug-early Sep

Migration Chronology

	SPRING			AUTUMN		
	Early Arrival	Late Departure	Peak Movement	Early Arrival	Late Departure	Peak Movement
Ruff						
Vancouver	—	—	—	26 Jun	23 Oct	mid-Aug-mid-Sep
Short-billed Dowitcher						
Victoria	28 Mar	26 May	19 Apr-3 May	11 Jun	29 Nov	4 Jul-25 Sep
Vancouver	3 Apr	18 May	23 Apr	—	27 Oct	30 Aug
Masset	18 Apr	17 May	29-30 Apr	5 Jul	27 Sep	17-22 Jul
Okanagan	7 May	—	—	5 Aug	—	—
Fort St. John	9 May	25 May	—	29 Jun	27 Sep	—
Long-billed Dowitcher						
Victoria	14 Apr	29 May	14 Apr-12 May	29 Jun	27 Nov	4 Aug-24 Oct
Vancouver	—	—	16 May	—	—	12 Oct
Masset	9 Apr	25 May	21-29 Apr	1 Jul	—	31 Jul-12 Sep
Okanagan	13 May	19 May	—	30 Jul	31 Oct	Sep-early Oct
Kamloops	3 May	30 May	12-15 May	23 Jul	21 Oct	20 Sep-5 Oct
Williams Lake	—	—	5-15 May	24 Jun	12 Oct	19 Jul-1 Oct
Fort St. John	2 May	3 Jun	10-25 May	5 Jul	27 Oct	15-20 Jul (adults) 1-15 Sep (juv.)
Common Snipe						
Victoria	—	—	Apr	—	—	Oct
Vancouver	—	—	14 Apr	—	—	12 Oct
Okanagan	—	—	—	—	—	Sep-Oct
Nakusp	5 Apr	—	—	—	7 Nov	—
Radium	5 Apr	—	—	—	28 Oct	—
Kamloops	28 Mar	—	20 Apr	—	—	1-30 Sep
Fort St. John	20 Apr	—	22 Apr-6 May	—	20 Oct	—
Fort Nelson	26 Apr	—	—	—	15 Aug	—
Wilson's Phalarope						
Victoria	6 May	—	—	—	5 Sep	—
Vancouver	27 Apr	—	21 May	—	29 Sep	14 Aug
Okanagan	3 May	—	—	—	11 Sep	late Aug
Kamloops	4 May	—	15 May	—	30 Aug	15-20 Aug
Williams Lake	—	—	8-20 May	—	—	20 Aug
Fort St. John	3 May	—	24-28 May	—	25 Aug	—
Red-necked Phalarope						
Victoria	1 May	25 May	—	26 Jun	25 Nov	10 Aug-16 Sep
Vancouver	—	—	—	24 Jun	3 Oct	23 Aug
Okanagan	25 Apr	—	19-25 May	28 Jul	27 Oct	early Sep
Radium	12 May	—	—	—	23 Aug	—
Kamloops	22 May	—	20-24 May	4 Aug	3 Oct	10-20 Sep
Fort St. John	14 May	—	17-28 May	21 Aug	19 Sep	late Aug
Red Phalarope						
Victoria	—	—	—	12 Aug	11 Dec	1-15 Nov
Pomarine Jaeger						
Victoria	12 May	31 May	—	17 Jul	26 Sep	—
Parasitic Jaeger						
Victoria	1 May	1 Jun	—	28 Jul	21 Nov	10 Sep-10 Oct
Vancouver	9 May	2 Jun	—	15 Aug	13 Nov	2 Oct

	SPRING			AUTUMN		
	Early Arrival	Late Departure	Peak Movement	Early Arrival	Late Departure	Peak Movement
Long-tailed Jaeger						
Victoria	—	—	—	4 Aug	20 Oct	—
Okanagan	—	—	—	30 Aug	18 Sep	—
Radium	—	—	—	18 Sep	29 Sep	—
Franklin's Gull						
Victoria	2 May	27 May	—	6 Jul	9 Nov	Sep
Vancouver	—	—	—	3 Jul	24 Nov	5 Sep
Okanagan	18 May	26 May	—	3 Aug	19 Sep	—
Fort St. John	25 Apr	29 May	—	27 Aug	26 Oct	—
Bonaparte's Gull						
Victoria	—	—	1 Apr-15 May	—	—	1 Sep-15 Dec
Vancouver	—	—	3 May	—	—	19 Sep-16 Dec
Okanagan	24 Apr	—	29 Apr-2 May	20 Jul	—	—
Nakusp	28 Apr	—	18 Apr-10 May	—	23 Oct	1-15 Sep
Radium	—	—	—	31 Aug	26 Oct	—
Kamloops	2 May	—	2-10 May	3 Aug	10 Nov	—
Williams Lake	15 Apr	—	6-18 May	—	—	20-23 Aug
Prince George	28 Apr	—	4-6 May	—	—	—
Fort St. John	2 May	—	6-17 May	15 Jul	31 Oct	17-22 Jul (adults) 18-28 Aug (juv.)
Fort Nelson	7 May	—	13-25 May	8 Aug	4 Sep	—
Heermann's Gull						
Victoria	2 May	26 Jun	—	17 Jul	30 Nov	13 Sep-29 Oct
Vancouver	—	—	—	28 Aug	27 Nov	24 Oct
Mew Gull						
Vancouver	—	—	5 May	—	—	7 Oct
Okanagan	—	—	—	—	—	late Aug-early Sep
Kamloops	10 May	—	10-15 May	—	9 Nov	—
Fort St. John	25 Apr	—	1-15 May	—	12 Oct	13-27 Aug
Ring-billed Gull						
Victoria	—	—	—	—	—	Jul-Sep
Vancouver	—	—	6 May	—	—	6 Sep
Okanagan	late Feb	—	late Mar-Apr	late Jul	—	late Oct
Nakusp	5 Apr	—	—	—	19 Sep	—
Kamloops	1 Mar	30 May	—	20 Jul	—	1-30 Sep
Fort St. John	24 Apr	18 May	—	21 Aug	13 Oct	—
California Gull						
Victoria	—	—	Mar-Apr	—	—	Jul-Sep
Vancouver	—	—	22 Apr	—	—	23 Aug
Okanagan	17 Mar	—	mid-Apr	late Jul	—	Sep-early Nov
Nakusp	4 Mar	—	—	—	21 Oct	20 Aug-20 Sep
Kamloops	8 Mar	—	15-20 Mar	—	5 Dec	1-15 Nov

Migration Chronology

	SPRING			AUTUMN		
	Early Arrival	Late Departure	Peak Movement	Early Arrival	Late Departure	Peak Movement
Herring Gull						
Victoria	—	4 Jun	—	20 Jul	—	15-30 Sep
Vancouver	—	26 May	—	20 Aug	—	Sep
Okanagan	mid-Mar	—	Apr	—	—	Sep-Oct
Nakusp	—	—	—	15 Aug	22 Nov	1-30 Sep
Kamloops	25 Feb	15 May	2-9 Apr	4 Aug	20 Dec	1-20 Nov
Williams Lake	27 Mar	—	6 Apr-7 May	—	—	—
Prince George	20 Apr	—	—	—	1 Nov	—
Fort St. John	19 Apr	—	4-11 May	—	31 Oct	—
Fort Nelson	1 May	—	8-14 May	—	14 Sep	—
Thayer's Gull						
Victoria	—	22 May	—	19 Aug	—	15-30 Sep
Vancouver	—	24 May	30 Apr	18 Aug	—	11 Oct
Western Gull						
Vancouver	—	21 May	—	30 Aug	—	—
Glaucous Gull						
Victoria	—	11 May	—	3 Sep	—	Nov
Vancouver	—	17 May	—	6 Sep	—	—
Caspian Tern						
Victoria	19 Apr	—	28 May-10 Jul	—	22 Sep	—
Vancouver	12 Apr	—	20 May	—	12 Oct	—
Common Tern						
Victoria	20 Apr	8 Jun	6-27 May	24 Jun	28 Nov	25 Aug-16 Oct
Vancouver	12 Apr	31 May	10 May	21 Jul	2 Nov	1 Sep
Okanagan	6 May	—	21-31 May	8 Aug	24 Oct	Sep
Kamloops	5 May	10 May	—	11 Aug	9 Oct	3-10 Sep
Williams Lake	30 Apr	—	—	20 Jun	—	24 Aug-4 Sep
Fort St. John	24 May	10 Jun	late May	24 Aug	8 Sep	—
Arctic Tern						
Victoria	—	—	—	20 Jul	18 Oct	—
Vancouver	—	—	—	13 Jul	14 Oct	6 Sep
Fort St. John	21 May	18 Jun	21 May-3 Jun	—	24 Aug	—
Black Tern						
Vancouver	17 Apr	—	late May	—	17 Aug	—
Okanagan	9 May	—	late May	—	—	Aug
Kamloops	9 May	26 May	20-24 May	—	10 Sep	—
Williams Lake	10 May	—	17-27 May	—	1 Sep	late Aug
Fort St. John	16 May	—	22 May-3 Jun	—	16 Sep	—
Fort Nelson	26 May	12 Jun	—	31 Jul	3 Aug	—
Common Murre						
Victoria	—	—	Apr	—	—	Sep
Vancouver	—	—	12 May	—	—	1 Nov
Ancient Murrelet						
Victoria	—	26 Apr	—	15 Jul	—	Nov
Vancouver	—	6 Mar	—	15 Sep	—	2 Nov

	SPRING			AUTUMN		
	Early Arrival	Late Departure	Peak Movement	Early Arrival	Late Departure	Peak Movement
Tufted Puffin						
Victoria	2 May	—	—	—	20 Sep	—
Band-tailed Pigeon						
Vancouver	—	—	19 Apr	—	—	1 Oct
Mourning Dove						
Victoria	6 Apr	—	May	—	30 Nov	Sep
Nakusp	2 May	—	5 May-20 Jun	—	—	—
Radium	23 Apr	—	10-20 May	—	—	—
Kamloops	20 Apr	—	—	—	30 Nov	28 Aug-15 Sep
Williams Lake	14 Mar	—	3-30 May	—	—	—
Fort St. John	21 Apr	14 May	—	16 Sep	7 Nov	—
Flammulated Owl						
Okanagan	4 May	—	—	—	22 Oct	—
Kamloops	18 May	—	18-25 May	—	15 Sep	28 Aug-10 Sep
Snowy Owl						
Victoria	—	20 Apr	—	17 Oct	—	—
Vancouver	—	12 May	21 Mar	13 Oct	—	16 Nov
Okanagan	—	5 May	—	21 Nov	—	—
Radium	—	—	—	22 Nov	25 Nov	—
Kamloops	—	12 Mar	—	8 Oct	—	—
Williams Lake	—	—	—	3 Nov	29 Dec	—
Fort St. John	—	18 Apr	—	29 Oct	—	—
Fort Nelson	—	29 May	—	16 Oct	—	—
Northern Hawk Owl						
Okanagan	—	21 Mar	—	13 Oct	—	Nov
Burrowing Owl						
Okanagan	8 Mar	—	Apr	—	1 Oct	Sep
Kamloops	10 Mar	—	—	—	7 Nov	—
Long-eared Owl						
Kamloops	—	—	9-15 Apr	—	—	12-30 Sep
Short-eared Owl						
Victoria	—	27 Apr	—	26 Aug	—	Oct-Nov
Vancouver	—	—	20 Mar	—	—	21 Oct
Okanagan	—	—	Mar-Apr	—	—	Nov
Radium	—	—	—	5 Oct	25 Nov	—
Fort Nelson	—	—	—	3 Nov	23 Nov	—
Northern Saw-whet Owl						
Okanagan	—	—	—	—	—	late Oct-early Nov
Kamloops	17 Feb	—	12-25 Mar	—	—	1-15 Oct

Migration Chronology

	SPRING			AUTUMN		
	Early Arrival	Late Departure	Peak Movement	Early Arrival	Late Departure	Peak Movement
Common Nighthawk						
Victoria	6 May	—	1-16 Jun	—	15 Oct	Sep
Vancouver	17 May	—	early Jun	—	14 Oct	25 Aug
Okanagan	25 May	—	—	—	10 Oct	late Aug
Nakusp	24 May	—	1-20 Jun	—	16 Sep	20 Aug-10 Sep
Radium	20 May	—	1-7 Jun	—	15 Sep	—
Kamloops	30 May	—	1-10 Jun	—	8 Sep	15-30 Aug
Williams Lake	22 May	—	1-9 Jun	—	26 Oct	22 Aug
Fort St. John	25 May	—	—	—	9 Sep	—
Fort Nelson	25 May	—	—	—	4 Aug	—
Common Poorwill						
Okanagan	14 Apr	—	—	—	3 Oct	7-14 Sep
Kamloops	7 May	—	15-25 May	—	20 Sep	5-15 Sep
Black Swift						
Victoria	28 Apr	—	15-30 May	—	25 Nov	Sep
Vancouver	26 Apr	—	26 May	—	13 Oct	mid-Sep
Okanagan	3 May	—	late May	—	26 Sep	20 Aug-10 Sep
Nakusp	24 May	—	11-30 Jun	—	22 Sep	24 Aug-10 Sep
Kamloops	1 Jun	—	—	—	7 Sep	—
Williams Lake	—	—	—	—	3 Oct	14-29 Aug
Vaux's Swift						
Victoria	5 Apr	—	May	—	13 Oct	Sep
Vancouver	29 Mar	—	14 May	—	17 Oct	17 Sep
Okanagan	17 Apr	—	mid-May	—	11 Oct	30 Aug-6 Sep
Nakusp	21 Apr	—	1-31 May	—	15 Sep	1-15 Sep
Kamloops	20 Apr	—	—	—	30 Sep	15-30 Sep
White-throated Swift						
Okanagan	26 Mar	—	early May	—	7 Oct	26 Aug-15 Sep
Black-chinned Hummingbird						
Okanagan	2 May	—	late May	—	4 Sep	early Aug
Calliope Hummingbird						
Vancouver	23 Apr	19 May	11 May	—	—	—
Okanagan	7 Apr	—	late Apr-May	—	22 Oct	Aug
Nakusp	1 May	21 May	—	—	—	—
Kamloops	18 Apr	—	20-30 Apr	—	—	—
Williams Lake	19 Apr	—	2-28 May	—	3 Sep	—
Rufous Hummingbird						
Victoria	4 Mar	—	late Mar-early Apr	—	17 Oct	late Aug-early Sep
Vancouver	10 Mar	—	17 Apr	—	10 Oct	—
Okanagan	16 Apr	—	May	—	31 Oct	Aug
Nakusp	20 Apr	—	1-20 May	—	4 Sep	—
Radium	29 Apr	—	—	—	28 Sep	—
Kamloops	18 Apr	—	1-10 May	—	15 Sep	—
Williams Lake	23 Apr	—	1-22 May	—	14 Sep	11 Jul-5 Aug
Prince George	22 Apr	—	—	—	16 Sep	—

	SPRING			AUTUMN		
	Early Arrival	Late Departure	Peak Movement	Early Arrival	Late Departure	Peak Movement
Belted Kingfisher						
Okanagan	—	—	late Apr-early May	—	—	Sep-early Oct
Radium	6 May	—	20-24 May	—	13 Oct	—
Kamloops	5 Apr	—	15-30 Apr	—	15 Nov	—
Prince George	26 Feb	—	—	—	1 Nov	—
Fort St. John	27 Apr	—	—	—	18 Sep	—
Fort Nelson	27 Apr	—	—	—	early Sep	—
Lewis' Woodpecker						
Victoria	7 Apr	5 Jun	—	12 Sep	11 Nov	—
Vancouver	28 Apr	21 May	—	27 Sep	30 Nov	—
Okanagan	17 Apr	—	early May	—	—	23 Aug-7 Sep
Kamloops	30 Apr	—	—	—	10 Sep	28 Aug-6 Sep
Williams Lake	—	—	2-12 May	—	—	29 Aug-3 Sep
Yellow-bellied Sapsucker						
Fort St. John	26 Apr	—	3-5 May	—	17 Sep	—
Fort Nelson	1 May	—	—	—	16 Sep	—
Red-naped Sapsucker						
Okanagan	31 Mar	—	29 Apr-6 May	—	8 Oct	late Aug-early Sep
Nakusp	5 Apr	—	20 Apr-10 May	—	22 Sep	—
Radium	26 Apr	—	—	—	9 Sep	—
Kamloops	1 Apr	—	25 Apr-7 May	—	20 Sep	1-7 Sep
Williams Lake	30 Mar	—	5-16 Apr	—	—	—
Williamson's Sapsucker						
Okanagan	late Mar	—	early Apr	—	18 Oct	early Sep
Northern Flicker						
Vancouver	—	—	10 Apr	—	—	18 Oct
Okanagan	—	—	7-14 Apr	—	—	Oct
Kamloops	1 Mar	—	15-30 Apr	—	15 Nov	10-20 Sep
Williams Lake	9 Mar	—	early Apr	—	—	—
Fort St. John	14 Apr	—	5-15 May	—	29 Sep	25-31 Aug
Fort Nelson	26 Apr	—	—	—	16 Sep	15 Sep

APPENDIX 2

Summary of Christmas Bird Counts in British Columbia: 1957 through 1984

The following tables summarize, by species, the Christmas Bird Count data for Diurnal Birds of Prey through Woodpeckers in British Columbia. Only official Christmas Bird Counts, as published in *Audubon Field Notes* and *American Birds* from 1957 through 1984 have been used (Fig. 352). Highest provincial, interior, and coastal totals are the highest sums for all official counts in the province within a given count period. "Count locality" refers to the most recent name under which that count has been published. The time span of count activity for a particular location is shown under "Count years"; discontinuities can be determined by comparing "Count years" with "Total counts." "Frequency of occurrence" indicates the percentage of the counts in a locality on which a species has been recorded. The general abundance of the species over the count periods is shown by the range of values in the last 3 columns. The highest and lowest numbers recorded are given. An asterisk following a "High" number indicates that some caution is required in interpreting the data. Refer to the respective species account or to the note at the end of that species' entry in the table. The median

has been chosen as an indicator of the "usual" value when the species does occur. It is the middle value of the data set and will lie closer to the low value when a species frequently occurs in small numbers and closer to the high value when a species rarely occurs in small numbers. In a symmetrically distributed data set the median is an unbiased and consistent estimate of the mean (Zar 1974). Counts of zero have not been used as the "Low" value but they can be determined using the values under "Frequency of occurrence" and "Total count."

For example, there is only an 8 percent chance of seeing a Turkey Vulture on the Ladner Christmas Bird Count and the probability that this is an accurate estimate of the chance of seeing the bird is high because there is a long history of counts on which to base that estimate. Similarly, you are not likely to see a bird every year and 3 would be exceptional.

See Figure 177 in Volume I for location of official Christmas Bird Counts and Table 6 in Volume I for the number of counts in each locality.

Figure 352. *Birdwatchers from the Bulkley Valley Naturalists club on the official 1983 Smithers Christmas Bird Count (courtesy Rosamund Pojar).*

Turkey Vulture

Highest provincial total: 4 (1968)
Highest interior total: 1 (1982)
Highest coastal total: 4 (1968)

Count locality	Count years	Total counts	Frequency of occurrence (%)	Range of total counts when species occurred		
				Low	Median	High
Interior						
Penticton	1974-1984	9	11			1
Coastal						
Duncan	1970-1984	15	7			1
Ladner	1957-1984	26	8	1		3
Pender Islands	1964-1984	19	5			2
Vancouver	1957-1984	28	11	1	1	4
White Rock	1971-1984	14	7			1

Osprey

Highest provincial total: 4 (1978)
Highest interior total: Not recorded
Highest coastal total : 4 (1978)

Count locality	Count years	Total counts	Frequency of occurrence (%)	Range of total counts when species occurred		
				Low	Median	High
Coastal						
Chilliwack	1972-1984	11	9			1
Comox	1961-1984	23	9	1		1
Deep Bay	1975-1984	10	10			3
Terrace	1963-1984	20	5			1
White Rock	1971-1984	14	7			1

Bald Eagle

Highest provincial total: 2,846 (1983)
Highest interior total: 63 (1983)
Highest coastal total: 2,783 (1983)

Count locality	Count years	Total counts	Frequency of occurrence (%)	Range of total counts when species occurred		
				Low	Median	High
Interior						
Cranbrook	1984	1	100			1
Fauquier	1984	1	100			1
Kamloops	1984	1	100			3
Kelowna	1981	1	100			3
Lake Windermere	1979-1984	6	100	2	5	7
Nakusp	1979-1984	6	50	1	1	1
Oliver/Osoyoos	1979-1984	6	100	1	4	8
Penticton	1974-1984	9	89	1	7	15
Quesnel	1981-1984	4	25			1
Revelstoke	1981-1984	4	75	1	2	3
Shuswap Lake	1972-1984	13	85	1	5	23
Smithers	1977-1984	8	100	1	5	6
Vaseux Lake	1974-1984	11	100	1	4	7
Vernon	1975-1984	10	100	3	6	13
Coastal						
Bella Bella	1976	1	100			19
Campbell River	1972-1984	13	100	9	54	75
Chilliwack	1972-1984	11	100	5	27	134
Comox	1961-1984	23	100	2	44	180
Deep Bay	1975-1984	10	100	67	273	424
Dewdney	1967	1	100			11
Duncan	1970-1984	15	100	3	63	96
Hecate Strait	1980	1	100			9
Kitimat	1974-1984	7	100	2	12	21
Ladner	1957-1984	26	85	2	6	96
Masset	1982-1984	3	100	20	39	52
Nanaimo	1963-1984	19	100	1	5	86
North Saanich	1960	1	100			4
Pender Islands	1964-1984	19	100	5	37	117
Pitt Meadows	1972-1984	13	92	2	10	77
Port Alberni	1975	1	100			19
Port Clements	1984	1	100			13
Prince Rupert	1980-1984	5	100	26	37	60
Sayward	1973-1984	12	100	3	10	25
Skidegate Inlet	1982-1984	3	100	38	51	65
Sooke	1983-1984	2	100	11		18
Squamish	1980-1984	5	100	131	271	1,396
Sunshine Coast	1979-1984	6	100	14	32	71
Terrace	1963-1984	20	90	1	5	26
Vancouver	1957-1984	28	100	1	13	88
Victoria	1958-1984	27	100	2	11	48
White Rock	1971-1984	14	79	1	6	16

Northern Harrier

Highest provincial total: 261 (1981)
Highest interior total: 58 (1981)
Highest coastal total: 242 (1977)

Count locality	Count years	Total counts	Frequency of occurrence (%)	Range of total counts when species occurred		
				Low	Median	High
Interior						
Kamloops	1984	1	100			1
Kelowna	1981	1	100			8
Lake Windermere	1979-1984	6	33	2		4
Oliver/Osoyoos	1979-1984	6	100	1	13	16
Penticton	1974-1984	9	67	1	1	7
Shuswap Lake	1972-1984	13	8			1
Vaseux Lake	1974-1984	11	36	1	2	2
Vernon	1975-1984	10	90	1	9	27
Coastal						
Chilliwack	1972-1984	11	73	1	9	12
Comox	1961-1984	23	30	1	1	3
Duncan	1970-1984	15	100	1	2	6
Ladner	1957-1984	26	92	2	61	135
Nanaimo	1963-1984	19	68	1	3	5
Pitt Meadows	1972-1984	13	92	10	29	55
Sayward	1973-1984	12	8			1
Skidegate Inlet	1982-1984	3	33			1
Surrey	1960-1966	7	14			1
Terrace	1963-1984	20	5			1
Vancouver	1957-1984	28	96	2	10	34
Victoria	1958-1984	27	22	1	1	2
White Rock	1971-1984	14	100	3	19	34

Sharp-shinned Hawk

Highest provincial total: 90 (1983)
Highest interior total: 28 (1983)
Highest coastal total: 62 (1983)

Count locality	Count years	Total counts	Frequency of occurrence (%)	Range of total counts when species occurred		
				Low	Median	High
Interior						
Kamloops	1984	1	100			2
Kelowna	1981	1	100			1
Oliver/Osoyoos	1979-1984	6	83	1	2	3
Penticton	1974-1984	9	67	1	4	14
Shuswap Lake	1972-1984	13	15	1		1
Smithers	1977-1984	8	13			1
Vaseux Lake	1974-1984	11	73	1	1	5
Vernon	1975-1984	10	90	1	3	7
Coastal						
Campbell River	1972-1984	13	77	1	2	4
Chilliwack	1972-1984	11	64	1	2	8
Comox	1961-1984	23	70	1	2	6
Deep Bay	1975-1984	10	50	1	1	3
Dewdney	1967	1	100			1
Duncan	1970-1984	15	47	1	2	6
Kitimat	1974-1984	7	29	1		1
Ladner	1957-1984	26	92	1	5	13
Masset	1982-1984	3	100	1	1	1
Nanaimo	1963-1984	19	53	1	3	6
North Saanich	1960	1	100			5
Pender Islands	1964-1984	19	68	1	1	5
Pitt Meadows	1972-1984	13	92	1	5	7
Port Alberni	1975	1	100			1
Sayward	1973-1984	12	17	1		1
Skidegate Inlet	1982-1984	3	100	1	1	2
Sooke	1983-1984	2	100	4		9
Squamish	1980-1984	5	20			1
Sunshine Coast	1979-1984	6	83	1	2	3
Surrey	1960-1966	7	43	1	1	1
Terrace	1963-1984	20	30	1	2	3
Vancouver	1957-1984	28	100	1	8	24
Victoria	1958-1984	27	100	2	9	16
White Rock	1971-1984	14	100	1	4	8

Cooper's Hawk

Highest provincial total: 89 (1983)
Highest interior total: 15 (1983)
Highest coastal total: 74 (1983)

Count locality	Count years	Total counts	Frequency of occurrence (%)	Range of total counts when species occurred		
				Low	Median	High
Interior						
Kamloops	1984	1	100			2
Kelowna	1981	1	100			1
Nakusp	1979-1984	6	50	1	1	1
Oliver/Osoyoos	1979-1984	6	83	1	3	6
Penticton	1974-1984	9	100	1	2	5
Quesnel	1981-1984	4	25			1
Shuswap Lake	1972-1984	13	15	1		1
Vaseux Lake	1974-1984	11	91	1	2	6
Vernon	1975-1984	10	80	1	3	8
Coastal						
Campbell River	1972-1984	13	46	1	1	2
Chilliwack	1972-1984	11	91	1	1	8
Comox	1961-1984	23	65	1	2	5
Deep Bay	1975-1984	10	60	1	2	7
Duncan	1970-1984	15	93	1	4	9
Ladner	1957-1984	26	92	1	4	11
Nanaimo	1963-1984	19	74	1	2	6
North Saanich	1960	1	100			1
Pender Islands	1964-1984	19	53	1	2	4
Pitt Meadows	1972-1984	13	92	1	3	7
Sooke	1983-1984	2	100	4		5
Squamish	1980-1984	5	60	1	1	2
Sunshine Coast	1979-1984	6	33	1		1
Surrey	1960-1966	7	14			1
Terrace	1963-1984	20	15	1	1	1
Vancouver	1957-1984	28	93	1	5	11
Victoria	1958-1984	27	100	1	8	21
White Rock	1971-1984	14	93	1	4	10

Northern Goshawk

Highest provincial total: 30 (1983)
Highest interior total: 23 (1983)
Highest coastal total: 9 (1984)

Count locality	Count years	Total counts	Frequency of occurrence (%)	Range of total counts when species occurred		
				Low	Median	High
Interior						
Fauquier	1984	1	100			1
Kelowna	1981	1	100			2
Lake Windermere	1979-1984	6	33			2
Nakusp	1979-1984	6	50	1		1
Oliver/Osoyoos	1979-1984	6	83	1	1	1
Penticton	1974-1984	9	78	1	1	5
Quesnel	1981-1984	4	25	1	5	8
Shuswap Lake	1972-1984	13	15			1
Smithers	1977-1984	8	63	1		2
Vaseux Lake	1974-1984	11	55	1	2	4
Vernon	1975-1984	10	90	1	1	4
				1	2	4
Coastal						
Campbell River	1972-1984	13	8			2
Chilliwack	1972-1984	11	9			1
Comox	1961-1984	23	17	1	1	1
Duncan	1970-1984	15	27	1	1	2
Kitimat	1974-1984	7	29	1		1
Ladner	1957-1984	26	27	1	1	2
Nanaimo	1963-1984	19	21	1	1	1
Pender Islands	1964-1984	19	5			1
Pitt Meadows	1972-1984	13	38	1	1	3
Port Alberni	1975	1	100			1
Sayward	1973-1984	12	25	1	1	1
Sooke	1983-1984	2	50			1
Squamish	1980-1984	5	20			1
Terrace	1963-1984	20	10	1		2
Vancouver	1957-1984	28	50	1	1	3
Victoria	1958-1984	27	22	1	1	2
White Rock	1971-1984	14	29	1	1	2

Swainson's Hawk

Highest provincial total: 2 (1977,78,79)
Highest interior total: Not recorded
Highest coastal total: 2 (1977,78,79)

Count locality	Count years	Total counts	Frequency of occurrence (%)	Range of total counts when species occurred		
				Low	Median	High
Coastal						
Deep Bay	1975-1984	10	10			1*
Pitt Meadows	1972-1984	13	23	1	1	1*
White Rock	1971-1984	14	21	1	1	1*

Red-tailed Hawk

Highest provincial total: 472 (1984)
Highest interior total: 62 (1983)
Highest coastal total: 436 (1984)

Count locality	Count years	Total counts	Frequency of occurrence (%)	Low	Median	High
Interior						
Kamloops	1984	1	100			1
Kelowna	1981	1	100			6
Lake Windermere	1979-1984	6	17			1
Nakusp	1979-1984	6	17			1
Oliver/Osoyoos	1979-1984	6	83	1	4	8
Penticton	1974-1984	9	89	2	5	15
Revelstoke	1981-1984	4	25			1
Shuswap Lake	1972-1984	13	38	1	1	1
Vaseux Lake	1974-1984	11	55	1	2	5
Vernon	1975-1984	10	100	3	8	35
Coastal						
Campbell River	1972-1984	13	77	1	3	6
Chilliwack	1972-1984	11	100	3	27	35
Comox	1961-1984	23	87	1	4	17
Deep Bay	1975-1984	10	70	1	2	9
Dewdney	1967	1	100			4
Duncan	1970-1984	15	100	4	10	21
Kitimat	1974-1984	7	14			1
Ladner	1957-1984	26	96	3	46	130
Masset	1982-1984	3	33			1
Nanaimo	1963-1984	19	84	1	5	11
Pender Islands	1964-1984	19	84	1	4	7
Pitt Meadows	1972-1984	13	100	19	60	80
Port Alberni	1975	1	100			4
Port Clements	1984	1	100			1
Prince Rupert	1980-1984	5	20			1
Sayward	1973-1984	12	92	1	1	4
Skidegate Inlet	1982-1984	3	67	1		1
Sooke	1983-1984	2	100	6		11
Squamish	1980-1984	5	100	2	2	8
Sunshine Coast	1979-1984	6	100	1	9	58
Vancouver	1957-1984	28	96	1	22	63
Victoria	1958-1984	27	100	4	19	43
White Rock	1971-1984	14	100	15	38	63

Rough-legged Hawk

Highest provincial total: 132 (1977)
Highest interior total: 37 (1983)
Highest coastal total: 124 (1977)

Count locality	Count years	Total counts	Frequency of occurrence (%)	Range of total counts when species occurred		
				Low	Median	High
Interior						
Kamloops	1984	1	100			3
Lake Windermere	1979-1984	6	17			1
Oliver/Osoyoos	1979-1984	6	67	1	4	6
Penticton	1974-1984	9	33	1	1	2
Smithers	1977-1984	8	13			1
Vaseux Lake	1974-1984	11	18	1		1
Vernon	1975-1984	10	100	2	16	31
Coastal						
Chilliwack	1972-1984	11	27	1	1	2
Ladner	1957-1984	26	92	1	14	72
North Saanich	1960	1	100			1
Pender Islands	1964-1984	19	5			13
Pitt Meadows	1972-1984	13	85	4	9	25
Terrace	1963-1984	20	10	1		1
Vancouver	1957-1984	28	89	1	9	39
Victoria	1958-1984	27	15	1	1	11
White Rock	1971-1984	14	86	2	9	32

Golden Eagle

Highest provincial total: 25 (1979)
Highest interior total: 19 (1979)
Highest coastal total: 8 (1978)

Count locality	Count years	Total counts	Frequency of occurrence (%)	Range of total counts when species occurred		
				Low	Median	High
Interior						
Kamloops	1984	1	100			1
Kelowna	1981	1	100			1
Lake Windermere	1979-1984	6	33	1		1
Oliver/Osoyoos	1979-1984	6	83	1	3	5
Penticton	1974-1984	9	56	1	1	3
Shuswap Lake	1972-1984	13	8			1
Smithers	1977-1984	8	13			1
Vaseux Lake	1974-1984	11	91	1	4	11
Vernon	1975-1984	10	100	2	3	6
Coastal						
Chilliwack	1972-1984	11	9			1
Comox	1961-1984	23	4			1
Duncan	1970-1984	15	27	1	1	2
Ladner	1957-1984	26	4			1
Nanaimo	1963-1984	19	11	1		1
Pender Islands	1964-1984	19	5			1
Pitt Meadows	1972-1984	13	31	1	1	1
Prince Rupert	1980-1984	5	20			1
Sooke	1983-1984	2	50			1
Vancouver	1957-1984	28	18	1	1	1
Victoria	1958-1984	27	37	1	2	4
White Rock	1971-1984	14	21	1	2	2

American Kestrel

Highest provincial total: 68 (1983)
Highest interior total: 47 (1983)
Highest coastal total: 23 (1963)

Count locality	Count years	Total counts	Frequency of occurrence (%)	Range of total counts when species occurred		
				Low	Median	High
Interior						
Kelowna	1981	1	100			18
Nakusp	1979-1984	6	17			1
Oliver/Osoyoos	1979-1984	6	100	1	3	7
Penticton	1974-1984	9	78	2	4	7
Quesnel	1981-1984	4	25			1
Shuswap Lake	1972-1984	13	31	1	1	2
Smithers	1977-1984	8	13			1
Vaseux Lake	1974-1984	11	73	1	1	3
Vernon	1975-1984	10	100	4	16	31
Coastal						
Campbell River	1972-1984	13	23	1	1	1
Chilliwack	1972-1984	11	73	1	2	5
Comox	1961-1984	23	30	1	1	2
Deep Bay	1975-1984	10	10			1
Dewdney	1967	1	100			6
Duncan	1970-1984	15	73	1	1	3
Ladner	1957-1984	26	81	1	3	12
Masset	1982-1984	3	33			1
Nanaimo	1963-1984	19	21	1	1	1
Pender Islands	1964-1984	19	21	1	1	2
Pitt Meadows	1972-1984	13	62	1	2	3
Port Alberni	1975	1	100			1
Sayward	1973-1984	12	8			1
Sooke	1983-1984	2	100	1		1
Sunshine Coast	1979-1984	6	50	1	1	1
Surrey	1960-1966	7	29	1		1
Terrace	1963-1984	20	5			1
Vancouver	1957-1984	28	89	1	3	10
Victoria	1958-1984	27	85	1	2	8
White Rock	1971-1984	14	64	1	3	8

Merlin

Highest provincial total: 64 (1984)
Highest interior total: 16 (1983)
Highest coastal total: 50 (1984)

Count locality	Count years	Total counts	Frequency of occurrence (%)	Range of total counts when species occurred		
				Low	Median	High
Interior						
Kelowna	1981	1	100			1
Oliver/Osoyoos	1979-1984	6	50	1	1	2
Penticton	1974-1984	9	100	1	2	8
Shuswap Lake	1972-1984	13	31	1	1	1
Vaseux Lake	1974-1984	11	9			4
Vernon	1975-1984	10	90	1	4	8
Yoho National Park	1975-1984	5	40	1		1
Coastal						
Campbell River	1972-1984	13	92	1	1	3
Chilliwack	1972-1984	11	55	1	2	4
Comox	1961-1984	23	48	1	2	4
Deep Bay	1975-1984	10	50	1	1	3
Duncan	1970-1984	15	60	1	2	5
Kitimat	1974-1984	7	14			1
Ladner	1957-1984	26	85	1	4	9
Nanaimo	1963-1984	19	68	1	1	5
Pender Islands	1964-1984	19	32	1	2	4
Pitt Meadows	1972-1984	13	54	1	2	3
Sayward	1973-1984	12	8			1
Sooke	1983-1984	2	100	2		7
Squamish	1980-1984	5	40	2		2
Sunshine Coast	1979-1984	6	50	2	2	3
Terrace	1963-1984	20	15	1	1	2
Vancouver	1957-1984	28	93	1	5	13
Victoria	1958-1984	27	96	1	3	6
White Rock	1971-1984	14	64	1	1	3

Peregrine Falcon

Highest provincial total: 29 (1984)
Highest interior total: 1 (1976,1984)
Highest coastal total: 28 (1984)

Count locality	Count years	Total counts	Frequency of occurrence (%)	Range of total counts when species occurred		
				Low	Median	High
Interior						
Kamloops	1984	1	100			1
Vernon	1975-1984	10	10			1
Coastal						
Campbell River	1972-1984	13	15	1		1
Chilliwack	1972-1984	11	27	1	1	2
Comox	1961-1984	23	30	1	1	2
Duncan	1970-1984	15	93	1	2	3
Kitimat	1974-1984	7	14			1
Ladner	1957-1984	26	92	1	2	7
Masset	1982-1984	3	67	1		3
Nanaimo	1963-1984	19	32	1	1	2
North Saanich	1960	1	100			2
Pender Islands	1964-1984	19	32	1	1	2
Pitt Meadows	1972-1984	13	38	1	1	1
Port Alberni	1975	1	100			1
Port Clements	1984	1	100			2
Skidegate Inlet	1982-1984	3	67	1		3
Sooke	1983-1984	2	100	1		1
Squamish	1980-1984	5	20			1
Sunshine Coast	1979-1984	6	17			1
Vancouver	1957-1984	28	82	1	2	7
Victoria	1958-1984	27	81	1	2	7
White Rock	1971-1984	14	43	1	1	1

Gyrfalcon

Highest provincial total: 7 (1981)
Highest interior total: 2 (1981)
Highest coastal total: 5 (1981)

Count locality	Count years	Total counts	Frequency of occurrence (%)	Range of total counts when species occurred		
				Low	Median	High
Interior						
Quesnel	1981-1984	4	25			1
Vernon	1975-1984	10	40	1	1	1
Coastal						
Ladner	1957-1984	26	35	1	1	2
Pitt Meadows	1972-1984	13	8			1
Vancouver	1957-1984	28	14	1	1	1
Victoria	1958-1984	27	19	1	1	2

Prairie Falcon

Highest provincial total: 3 (1981)
Highest interior total: 3 (1981)
Highest coastal total: Not recorded

Count locality	Count years	Total counts	Frequency of occurrence (%)	Range of total counts when species occurred		
				Low	Median	High
Interior						
Oliver/Osoyoos	1979-1984	6	50	1	1	1
Penticton	1974-1984	9	11			1
Vaseux Lake	1974-1984	11	9			1
Vernon	1975-1984	10	30	1	1	1

Gray Partridge

Highest provincial total: 106 (1980)
Highest interior total: 106 (1980)
Highest coastal total:17 (1960)

Count locality	Count years	Total counts	Frequency of occurrence (%)	Range of total counts when species occurred		
				Low	Median	High
Interior						
Oliver/Osoyoos	1979-1984	6	17			24
Penticton	1974-1984	9	44	4	6	8
Vaseux Lake	1974-1984	11	9			5
Vernon	1975-1984	10	100	10	51	100
Coastal						
Ladner	1957-1984	26	12	10	10	14
North Saanich	1960	1	100			7

Chukar

Highest provincial total: 241 (1983)
Highest interior total: 241 (1983)
Highest coastal total: 1 (1978)

Count locality	Count years	Total counts	Frequency of occurrence (%)	Range of total counts when species occurred		
				Low	Median	High
Interior						
Kamloops	1984	1	100			31
Oliver/Osoyoos	1979-1984	6	100	15	48	193
Penticton	1974-1984	9	89	1	13	28
Vaseux Lake	1974-1984	11	91	2	27	118
Coastal						
Deep Bay	1975-1984	10	10			1

Ring-necked Pheasant

Highest provincial total: 1,040 (1975)
Highest interior total: 511 (1983)
Highest coastal total: 707 (1975)

Count locality	Count years	Total counts	Frequency of occurrence (%)	Range of total counts when species occurred		
				Low	Median	High
Interior						
Kelowna	1981	1	100			37
Oliver/Osoyoos	1979-1984	6	100	5	45	71
Penticton	1974-1984	9	100	22	48	87
Shuswap Lake	1972-1984	13	15	1		1
Vaseux Lake	1974-1984	11	100	1	9	19
Vernon	1975-1984	10	100	93	302	371
Coastal						
Campbell River	1972-1984	13	8			1
Chilliwack	1972-1984	11	36	1	1	4
Comox	1961-1984	23	87	1	10	41
Deep Bay	1975-1984	10	70	1	2	9
Duncan	1970-1984	15	100	2	14	30
Ladner	1957-1984	26	96	39	133	256
Nanaimo	1963-1984	19	84	3	11	32
North Saanich	1960	1	100			26
Pender Islands	1964-1984	19	58	1	2	14
Pitt Meadows	1972-1984	13	100	13	27	115
Port Alberni	1975	1	100			30
Sayward	1973-1984	12	8			2
Surrey	1960-1966	7	43	2	3	20
Vancouver	1957-1984	28	100	11	72	208
Victoria	1958-1984	27	100	14	46	93
White Rock	1971-1984	14	100	11	46	79

Spruce Grouse

Highest provincial total: 3 (1980)
Highest interior total: 3 (1980)
Highest coastal total: 1 (1973)

Count locality	Count years	Total counts	Frequency of occurrence (%)	Range of total counts when species occurred		
				Low	Median	High
Interior						
Fort St.John	1975-1978	4	25			1
Lake Windermere	1979-1984	6	50	1	1	2
Shuswap Lake	1972-1984	13	15	1		1
Smithers	1977-1984	8	13			1
Yoho National Park	1975-1984	5	20			1
Coastal						
Terrace	1963-1984	20	5			1

Blue Grouse

Highest provincial total: 20 (1982)
Highest interior total: 18 (1982)
Highest coastal total: 6 (1975)

Count locality	Count years	Total counts	Frequency of occurrence (%)	Range of total counts when species occurred		
				Low	Median	High
Interior						
Lake Windermere	1979-1984	6	17			4
Oliver/Osoyoos	1979-1984	6	33	1		1
Penticton	1974-1984	9	78	1	3	3
Shuswap Lake	1972-1984	13	8			1
Smithers	1977-1984	8	50	1	2	6
Vaseux Lake	1974-1984	11	9			2
Vernon	1975-1984	10	50	1	3	13
Coastal						
Chilliwack	1972-1984	11	18	1		1
Comox	1961-1984	23	4			1
Duncan	1970-1984	15	27	1	2	2
Pender Islands	1964-1984	19	53	1	2	2
Pitt Meadows	1972-1984	13	8			1
Squamish	1980-1984	5	20			3
Vancouver	1957-1984	28	18	1	1	2
Victoria	1958-1984	27	30	1	1	3

Willow Ptarmigan

Highest provincial total: 2 (1982)
Highest interior total: 2 (1982)
Highest coastal total: Not recorded

Count locality	Count years	Total counts	Frequency of occurrence (%)	Range of total counts when species occurred		
				Low	Median	High
Interior						
Smithers	1977-1984	8	25	1		2

Rock Ptarmigan

Highest provincial total: 3 (1978)
Highest interior total: 3 (1978)
Highest coastal total: Not recorded

Count locality	Count years	Total counts	Frequency of occurrence (%)	Range of total counts when species occurred		
				Low	Median	High
Interior						
Smithers	1977-1984	8	13			3

White-tailed Ptarmigan

Highest provincial total: 19 (1983)
Highest interior total: 19 (1983)
Highest coastal total: Not recorded

Count locality	Count years	Total counts	Frequency of occurrence (%)	Range of total counts when species occurred		
				Low	Median	High
Interior						
Smithers	1977-1984	8	25	2		19
Yoho National Park	1975-1984	5	20			4

Ruffed Grouse

Highest provincial total: 99 (1979)
Highest interior total: 47 (1979)
Highest coastal total: 84 (1975)

Count locality	Count years	Total counts	Frequency of occurrence (%)	Range of total counts when species occurred		
				Low	Median	High
Interior						
Fort St.John	1975-1978	4	25			6
Kamloops	1984	1	100			1
Lake Windermere	1979-1984	6	67	1	3	3
Nakusp	1979-1984	6	83	1	1	4
Oliver/Osoyoos	1979-1984	6	50	1	5	8
Penticton	1974-1984	9	78	1	4	9
Revelstoke	1981-1984	4	25			1
Shuswap Lake	1972-1984	13	92	1	4	11
Smithers	1977-1984	8	88	7	19	31
Vaseux Lake	1974-1984	11	64	1	2	5
Vernon	1975-1984	10	90	2	9	15
Wells Gray	1984	1	100			2
Yoho National Park	1975-1984	5	20			2
Coastal						
Campbell River	1972-1984	13	92	1	5	14
Chilliwack	1972-1984	11	82	1	2	5
Comox	1961-1984	23	78	1	4	11
Deep Bay	1975-1984	10	90	1	2	5
Dewdney	1967	1	100			1
Duncan	1970-1984	15	100	1	6	16
Ladner	1957-1984	26	62	1	3	12
Nanaimo	1963-1984	19	74	1	2	5
North Saanich	1960	1	100			1
Pender Islands	1964-1984	19	32	1	2	3
Pitt Meadows	1972-1984	13	100	1	3	20
Port Alberni	1975	1	100			15
Sayward	1973-1984	12	25	1	1	1
Sooke	1983-1984	2	50			1
Squamish	1980-1984	5	80	1	2	5
Sunshine Coast	1979-1984	6	83	1	1	3
Terrace	1963-1984	20	35	1	3	5
Vancouver	1957-1984	28	79	1	4	10
Victoria	1958-1984	27	70	1	2	10
White Rock	1971-1984	14	100	1	5	11

Sharp-tailed Grouse

Highest provincial total: 2 (1975,76,77)
Highest interior total: 2 (1975,76,77)
Highest coastal total: Not recorded

Count locality	Count years	Total counts	Frequency of occurrence (%)	Range of total counts when species occurred		
				Low	Median	High
Interior						
Fort St.John	1975-1978	4	75	2	2	2

Wild Turkey

Highest provincial total: 1 (1976,77)
Highest interior total: 1 (1976,77)
Highest coastal total: Not recorded

Count locality	Count years	Total counts	Frequency of occurrence (%)	Range of total counts when species occurred		
				Low	Median	High
Interior						
Penticton	1974-1984	9	22	1		1

California Quail

Highest provincial total: 2,973 (1983)
Highest interior total: 2,662 (1981)
Highest coastal total: 615 (1968)

Count locality	Count years	Total counts	Frequency of occurrence (%)	Range of total counts when species occurred		
				Low	Median	High
Interior						
Kelowna	1981	1	100			145
Oliver/Osoyoos	1979-1984	6	100	105	601	1,339
Penticton	1974-1984	9	100	485	834	1,114
Vaseux Lake	1974-1984	11	100	167	352	800
Vernon	1975-1984	10	100	12	61	116
Coastal						
Comox	1961-1984	23	78	1	20	70
Deep Bay	1975-1984	10	10			1
Duncan	1970-1984	15	93	4	62	119
Ladner	1957-1984	26	65	1	13	81
Nanaimo	1963-1984	19	26	1	8	20
North Saanich	1960	1	100			113
Pender Islands	1964-1984	19	32	2	7	32
Sooke	1983-1984	2	100	43		103
Victoria	1958-1984	27	100	111	226	584

Mountain Quail

Highest provincial total: 9 (1963)
Highest interior total: Not recorded
Highest coastal total: 9 (1963)

Count locality	Count years	Total counts	Frequency of occurrence (%)	Range of total counts when species occurred		
				Low	Median	High
Coastal						
Victoria	1958-1984	27	11	2	5	9

Virginia Rail

Highest provincial total: 69 (1984)
Highest interior total: 8 (1983)
Highest coastal total: 65 (1984)

Count locality	Count years	Total counts	Frequency of occurrence (%)	Range of total counts when species occurred		
				Low	Median	High
Interior						
Penticton	1974-1984	9	56	1	1	4
Vaseux Lake	1974-1984	11	45	1	3	6
Vernon	1975-1984	10	10			1
Coastal						
Duncan	1970-1984	15	53	1	1	2
Ladner	1957-1984	26	27	1	2	7
Nanaimo	1963-1984	19	26	1	2	5
Pender Islands	1964-1984	19	11	1		1
Pitt Meadows	1972-1984	13	31	1	1	2
Port Alberni	1975	1	100			1
Sooke	1983-1984	2	50			3
Squamish	1980-1984	5	40	1		1
Vancouver	1957-1984	28	54	1	4	39
Victoria	1958-1984	27	56	1	2	14
White Rock	1971-1984	14	14	1		2

Sora

Highest provincial total: 3 (1974)
Highest interior total: 1 (1980)
Highest coastal total: 3 (1974)

Count locality	Count years	Total counts	Frequency of occurrence (%)	Range of total counts when species occurred		
				Low	Median	High
Interior						
Penticton	1974-1984	9	11			1
Coastal						
Ladner	1957-1984	26	8	1		2
Nanaimo	1963-1984	19	5			1
Vancouver	1957-1984	28	14	1	1	1

American Coot

Highest provincial total: 14,314 (1975)
Highest interior total: 12,256 (1975)
Highest coastal total: 3,719 (1976)

Count locality	Count years	Total counts	Frequency of occurrence (%)	Range of total counts when species occurred		
				Low	Median	High
Interior						
Kelowna	1981	1	100			2,011
Lake Windermere	1979-1984	6	67	1	3	20
Nakusp	1979-1984	6	50	1	2	3
Oliver/Osoyoos	1979-1984	6	100	100	444	999
Penticton	1974-1984	9	100	953	2,905	7,103
Shuswap Lake	1972-1984	13	46	2	60	160
Vaseux Lake	1974-1984	11	100	105	321	3,434
Vernon	1975-1984	10	100	830	2,029	5,823
Coastal						
Campbell River	1972-1984	13	23	1	2	3
Chilliwack	1972-1984	11	100	38	78	106
Comox	1961-1984	23	96	1	18	88
Deep Bay	1975-1984	10	90	1	4	66
Duncan	1970-1984	15	100	67	507	963
Ladner	1957-1984	26	96	6	329	760
Masset	1982-1984	3	100	1	3	8
Nanaimo	1963-1984	19	100	1	46	155
North Saanich	1960	1	100			169
Pender Islands	1964-1984	19	21	1	5	36
Pitt Meadows	1972-1984	13	92	5	78	556
Port Alberni	1975	1	100			50
Prince Rupert	1980-1984	5	40	1		1
Sooke	1983-1984	2	50			4
Sunshine Coast	1979-1984	6	100	20	30	39
Surrey	1960-1966	7	57	1	4	8
Vancouver	1957-1984	28	100	220	765	1,886
Victoria	1958-1984	27	100	149	654	1,672
White Rock	1971-1984	14	93	1	29	89

Sandhill Crane

Highest provincial total: 4 (1980)
Highest interior total: Not recorded
Highest coastal total: 4 (1980)

Count locality	Count years	Total counts	Frequency of occurrence (%)	Range of total counts when species occurred		
				Low	Median	High
Coastal						
Chilliwack	1972-1984	11	9			1
Comox	1961-1984	23	4			1
Ladner	1957-1984	26	8	2		4
Victoria	1958-1984	27	4			1

Black-bellied Plover

Highest provincial total: 978 (1981)
Highest interior total: Not recorded
Highest coastal total: 978 (1981)

Count locality	Count years	Total counts	Frequency of occurrence (%)	Range of total counts when species occurred		
				Low	Median	High
Coastal						
Campbell River	1972-1984	13	62	1	25	40
Comox	1961-1984	23	57	2	14	194
Deep Bay	1975-1984	10	40	3	12	19
Duncan	1970-1984	15	40	1	5	8
Ladner	1957-1984	26	92	2	110	727
Masset	1982-1984	3	33			7
Nanaimo	1963-1984	19	42	1	5	19
Pender Islands	1964-1984	19	5			13
Sooke	1983-1984	2	100	5		12
Sunshine Coast	1979-1984	6	50	1	1	4
Vancouver	1957-1984	28	68	2	28	151
Victoria	1958-1984	27	96	4	67	266
White Rock	1971-1984	14	36	3	38	75

Lesser Golden-Plover

Highest provincial total: 19 (1974)
Highest interior total: Not recorded
Highest coastal total: 19 (1974)

Count locality	Count years	Total counts	Frequency of occurrence (%)	Range of total counts when species occurred		
				Low	Median	High
Coastal						
Comox	1961-1984	23	4			19
Ladner	1957-1984	26	4			2

Semipalmated Plover

Highest provincial total: 1 (1974,76,77,81)
Highest interior total: Not recorded
Highest coastal total: 1 (1974,76,77,81)

Count locality	Count years	Total counts	Frequency of occurrence (%)	Range of total counts when species occurred		
				Low	Median	High
Coastal						
Campbell River	1972-1984	13	8			1
Comox	1961-1984	23	4			1
Deep Bay	1975-1984	10	10			1
Ladner	1957-1984	26	4			1

Killdeer

Highest provincial total: 1,160 (1976)
Highest interior total: 29 (1976)
Highest coastal total: 1,131 (1976)

Count locality	Count years	Total counts	Frequency of occurrence (%)	Range of total counts when species occurred		
				Low	Median	High
Interior						
Kamloops	1984	1	100			1
Kelowna	1981	1	100			6
Lake Windermere	1979-1984	6	50	1	2	3
Nakusp	1979-1984	6	33	1		1
Oliver/Osoyoos	1979-1984	6	50	1	2	5
Penticton	1974-1984	9	56	1	2	18
Shuswap Lake	1972-1984	13	31	2	4	10
Vaseux Lake	1974-1984	11	36	1	5	5
Vernon	1975-1984	10	70	1	4	12
Coastal						
Bella Bella	1976	1	100			1
Campbell River	1972-1984	13	100	1	8	50
Chilliwack	1972-1984	11	73	1	5	33
Comox	1961-1984	23	96	1	36	78
Deep Bay	1975-1984	10	100	4	37	59
Duncan	1970-1984	15	100	4	28	227
Kitimat	1974-1984	7	29	1		1
Ladner	1957-1984	26	100	13	78	411
Masset	1982-1984	3	100	28	38	38
Nanaimo	1963-1984	19	95	3	22	69
North Saanich	1960	1	100			24
Pender Islands	1964-1984	19	58	1	8	17
Pitt Meadows	1972-1984	13	92	2	13	52
Port Alberni	1975	1	100			83
Prince Rupert	1980-1984	5	80	2	6	7
Sayward	1973-1984	12	67	2	7	20
Skidegate Inlet	1982-1984	3	67	8		14
Sooke	1983-1984	2	100	47		54
Squamish	1980-1984	5	80	1	5	5
Sunshine Coast	1979-1984	6	83	8	20	23
Surrey	1960-1966	7	57	3	12	15
Vancouver	1957-1984	28	100	23	79	227
Victoria	1958-1984	27	100	37	196	375
White Rock	1971-1984	14	86	1	45	140

Black Oystercatcher

Highest provincial total: 404 (1983)
Highest interior total: Not recorded
Highest coastal total: 404 (1983)

Count locality	Count years	Total counts	Frequency of occurrence (%)	Range of total counts when species occurred		
				Low	Median	High
Coastal						
Deep Bay	1975-1984	10	100	3	17	29
Duncan	1970-1984	15	13	1		4
Hecate Strait	1980	1	100			5
Ladner	1957-1984	26	4			14
Masset	1982-1984	3	67	64		140
Nanaimo	1963-1984	19	79	1	10	60
Pender Islands	1964-1984	19	63	3	7	27
Prince Rupert	1980-1984	5	40	19		31
Skidegate Inlet	1982-1984	3	100	71	119	123
Sooke	1983-1984	2	100	21		72
Sunshine Coast	1979-1984	6	100	5	11	43
Vancouver	1957-1984	28	4			1
Victoria	1958-1984	27	100	17	38	96

Greater Yellowlegs

Highest provincial total: 80 (1982)
Highest interior total: Not recorded
Highest coastal total: 80 (1982)

Count locality	Count years	Total counts	Frequency of occurrence (%)	Range of total counts when species occurred		
				Low	Median	High
Coastal						
Comox	1961-1984	23	26	1	1	7
Deep Bay	1975-1984	10	100	2	7	29
Duncan	1970-1984	15	7			1
Ladner	1957-1984	26	50	1	3	16
Nanaimo	1963-1984	19	16	1	1	2
North Saanich	1960	1	100			15
Vancouver	1957-1984	28	32	1	2	28
Victoria	1958-1984	27	96	3	32	70
White Rock	1971-1984	14	36	1	2	9

Lesser Yellowlegs

Highest provincial total: 8 (1969)
Highest interior total: Not recorded
Highest coastal total: 8 (1969)

Count locality	Count years	Total counts	Frequency of occurrence (%)	Range of total counts when species occurred		
				Low	Median	High
Coastal						
Comox	1961-1984	23	4			2
Vancouver	1957-1984	28	7	1		7
Victoria	1958-1984	27	12	1	1	2

Willet

Highest provincial total: 2 (1973)
Highest interior total: Not recorded
Highest coastal total: 2 (1973)

Count locality	Count years	Total counts	Frequency of occurrence (%)	Range of total counts when species occurred		
				Low	Median	High
Coastal						
White Rock	1971-1984	14	7			2

Wandering Tattler

Highest provincial total: 1 (1963)
Highest interior total: Not recorded
Highest coastal total: 1 (1963)

Count locality	Count years	Total counts	Frequency of occurrence (%)	Range of total counts when species occurred		
				Low	Median	High
Coastal						
Vancouver	1957-1984	28	4			1

Spotted Sandpiper

Highest provincial total: 11 (1983)
Highest interior total: Not recorded
Highest coastal total: 11 (1983)

Count locality	Count years	Total counts	Frequency of occurrence (%)	Range of total counts when species occurred		
				Low	Median	High
Coastal						
Campbell River	1972-1984	13	15	1		1
Comox	1961-1984	23	13	1	1	6
Deep Bay	1975-1984	10	10			3
Duncan	1970-1984	15	30	1	1	2
Ladner	1957-1984	26	4			1
Nanaimo	1963-1984	19	11	1		2
Pitt Meadows	1972-1984	13	15	1		2
Port Alberni	1975	1	100			3
Sooke	1983-1984	2	100	2		2
Squamish	1980-1984	5	20			1
Vancouver	1957-1984	28	50	1	1	4
Victoria	1958-1984	27	48	1	1	3
White Rock	1971-1984	14	7			1

Whimbrel

Highest provincial total: 6 (1961)
Highest interior total: Not recorded
Highest coastal total: 6 (1961)

Count locality	Count years	Total counts	Frequency of occurrence (%)	Range of total counts when species occurred		
				Low	Median	High
Coastal						
Victoria	1958-1984	27	30	1	2	6

Long-billed Curlew

Highest provincial total: 1 (1979)
Highest interior total: Not recorded
Highest coastal total: 1 (1979)

Count locality	Count years	Total counts	Frequency of occurrence (%)	Range of total counts when species occurred		
				Low	Median	High
Coastal						
Ladner	1957-1984	26	4			1

Ruddy Turnstone

Highest provincial total: 5 (1983)
Highest interior total: Not recorded
Highest coastal total: 5 (1983)

Count locality	Count years	Total counts	Frequency of occurrence (%)	Range of total counts when species occurred		
				Low	Median	High
Coastal						
Comox	1961-1984	23	4			1
Ladner	1957-1984	26	12	1	1	1
Nanaimo	1963-1984	19	5			1
Skidegate Inlet	1982-1984	3	33			4
Vancouver	1957-1984	28	18	1	1	1
White Rock	1971-1984	14	7			1

Black Turnstone

Highest provincial total: 4,261 (1982)
Highest interior total: Not recorded
Highest coastal total: 4,261 (1982)

Count locality	Count years	Total counts	Frequency of occurrence (%)	Range of total counts when species occurred		
				Low	Median	High
Coastal						
Bella Bella	1976	1	100			9
Campbell River	1972-1984	13	92	1	13	65
Comox	1961-1984	23	83	2	94	3,560
Deep Bay	1975-1984	10	100	84	206	605
Duncan	1970-1984	15	93	2	12	163
Ladner	1957-1984	26	81	1	30	92
Masset	1982-1984	3	100	37	41	51
Nanaimo	1963-1984	19	89	3	31	262
North Saanich	1960	1	100			23
Pender Islands	1964-1984	19	68	2	12	177
Pitt Meadows	1972-1984	13	8			1
Port Clements	1984	1	100			8
Prince Rupert	1980-1984	5	80	20	63	125
Skidegate Inlet	1982-1984	3	100	31	55	825
Sooke	1983-1984	2	100	79		94
Sunshine Coast	1979-1984	6	100	18	36	148
Vancouver	1957-1984	28	100	6	75	262
Victoria	1958-1984	27	100	54	141	374
White Rock	1971-1984	14	50	2	10	18

Surfbird

Highest provincial total: 380 (1983)
Highest interior total: Not recorded
Highest coastal total: 380 (1983)

Count locality	Count years	Total counts	Frequency of occurrence (%)	Range of total counts when species occurred		
				Low	Median	High
Coastal						
Bella Bella	1976	1	100			4
Comox	1961-1984	23	9	1		7
Nanaimo	1963-1984	19	58	1	104	343
Pender Islands	1964-1984	19	16	1	2	55
Skidegate Inlet	1982-1984	3	33			2
Sooke	1983-1984	2	100	2		18
Sunshine Coast	1979-1984	6	83	16	130	172
Vancouver	1957-1984	28	29	1	6	68
Victoria	1958-1984	27	93	1	10	70

Sanderling

Highest provincial total: 1,276 (1983)
Highest interior total: Not recorded
Highest coastal total: 1,276 (1983)

Count locality	Count years	Total counts	Frequency of occurrence (%)	Range of total counts when species occurred		
				Low	Median	High
Coastal						
Campbell River	1972-1984	13	15	4		30
Comox	1961-1984	23	91	1	25	216
Deep Bay	1975-1984	10	60	2	39	230
Duncan	1970-1984	15	7			1
Ladner	1957-1984	26	92	17	145	436
Masset	1982-1984	3	100	107	525	587
Nanaimo	1963-1984	19	5			1
Pender Islands	1964-1984	19	5			4
Sayward	1973-1984	12	33	1	16	80
Skidegate Inlet	1982-1984	3	100	3	42	76
Surrey	1960-1966	7	29	17		22
Vancouver	1957-1984	28	96	32	139	514
Victoria	1958-1984	27	81	1	12	67
White Rock	1971-1984	14	36	1	9	28

Western Sandpiper

Highest provincial total: 39 (1983)
Highest interior total: Not recorded
Highest coastal total: 39 (1983)

Count locality	Count years	Total counts	Frequency of occurrence (%)	Range of total counts when species occurred		
				Low	Median	High
Coastal						
Comox	1961-1984	23	9	2		13
Deep Bay	1975-1984	10	10			1
Ladner	1957-1984	26	12	1	2	11
Pitt Meadows	1972-1984	13	15	2		4
Sayward	1973-1984	12	8			6
Surrey	1960-1966	7	14			5
Vancouver	1957-1984	28	29	1	5	26
Victoria	1958-1984	27	7	2		3
White Rock	1971-1984	14	64	1	3	33

Least Sandpiper

Highest provincial total: 13 (1971)
Highest interior total: Not recorded
Highest coastal total: 13 (1971)

Count locality	Count years	Total counts	Frequency of occurrence (%)	Range of total counts when species occurred		
				Low	Median	High
Coastal						
Ladner	1957-1984	26	4			8
Masset	1982-1984	3	67	1		3
Vancouver	1957-1984	28	4			13
Victoria	1958-1984	27	7	1		1
White Rock	1971-1984	14	7			6

Pectoral Sandpiper

Highest provincial total: 3 (1978)
Highest interior total: Not recorded
Highest coastal total: 3 (1978)

Count locality	Count years	Total counts	Frequency of occurrence (%)	Range of total counts when species occurred		
				Low	Median	High
Coastal						
Nanaimo	1963-1984	19	5			3
Vancouver	1957-1984	28	4			1

Rock Sandpiper

Highest provincial total: 188 (1983)
Highest interior total: Not recorded
Highest coastal total: 188 (1983)

Count locality	Count years	Total counts	Frequency of occurrence (%)	Range of total counts when species occurred		
				Low	Median	High
Coastal						
Masset	1982-1984	3	100	1	1	14
Nanaimo	1963-1984	19	16	2	6	11
Pender Islands	1964-1984	19	5			1
Port Clements	1984	1	100			5
Skidegate Inlet	1982-1984	3	100	15	121	161
Sooke	1983-1984	2	50			10
Sunshine Coast	1979-1984	6	83	1	4	52
Vancouver	1957-1984	28	25	1	5	12
Victoria	1958-1984	27	89	1	23	57

Dunlin

Highest provincial total: 57,790 (1978)
Highest interior total: Not recorded
Highest coastal total: 57,790 (1978)

Count locality	Count years	Total counts	Frequency of occurrence (%)	Range of total counts when species occurred		
				Low	Median	High
Coastal						
Campbell River	1972-1984	13	38	2	38	125
Comox	1961-1984	23	96	3	546	3,046
Deep Bay	1975-1984	10	100	102	554	1,035
Duncan	1970-1984	15	100	16	346	758
Kitimat	1974-1984	7	29	20		50
Ladner	1957-1984	26	100	2,689	21,919	45,575
Masset	1982-1984	3	100	257	329	399
Nanaimo	1963-1984	19	68	2	95	446
North Saanich	1960	1	100			57
Pender Islands	1964-1984	19	11	8		20
Pitt Meadows	1972-1984	13	92	26	300	900
Port Clements	1984	1	100			211
Skidegate Inlet	1982-1984	3	100	142	551	560
Sooke	1983-1984	2	100	2		40
Surrey	1960-1966	7	100	60	300	909
Vancouver	1957-1984	28	100	300	2,905	27,525
Victoria	1958-1984	27	100	24	130	966
White Rock	1971-1984	14	100	449	6,091	22,391

Short-billed Dowitcher

Highest provincial total: 68 (1969)
Highest interior total: Not recorded
Highest coastal total: 68 (1969)

Count locality	Count years	Total counts	Frequency of occurrence (%)	Range of total counts when species occurred		
				Low	Median	High
Coastal						
Duncan	1970-1984	15	7			5*
Ladner	1957-1984	26	4			12*
Vancouver	1957-1984	28	7	4		68*

Long-billed Dowitcher

Highest provincial total: 691 (1975)
Highest interior total: Not recorded
Highest coastal total: 691 (1975)

Count locality	Count years	Total counts	Frequency of occurrence (%)	Range of total counts when species occurred		
				Low	Median	High
Coastal						
Deep Bay	1975-1984	10	10			2
Duncan	1970-1984	15	13	2		4
Ladner	1957-1984	26	35	1	8	683
Masset	1982-1984	3	67	2		10
Pitt Meadows	1972-1984	13	23	10	10	15
Sooke	1983-1984	2	50			1
Vancouver	1957-1984	28	42	1	16	82
Victoria	1958-1984	27	22	1	4	17
White Rock	1971-1984	14	43	6	16	113

Common Snipe

Highest provincial total: 319 (1981)
Highest interior total: 18 (1982)
Highest coastal total: 302 (1981)

Count locality	Count years	Total counts	Frequency of occurrence (%)	Range of total counts when species occurred		
				Low	Median	High
Interior						
Nakusp	1979-1984	6	83	1	1	9
Oliver/Osoyoos	1979-1984	6	50	1	2	6
Penticton	1974-1984	9	78	2	4	5
Shuswap Lake	1972-1984	13	38	1	1	2
Vaseux Lake	1974-1984	11	55	1	2	4
Vernon	1975-1984	10	90	1	4	8
Coastal						
Bella Bella	1976	1	100			4
Campbell River	1972-1984	13	85	1	3	8
Chilliwack	1972-1984	11	18	1		1
Comox	1961-1984	23	52	1	3	23
Deep Bay	1975-1984	10	30	1	4	12
Duncan	1970-1984	15	100	4	12	77
Kitimat	1974-1984	7	57	1	1	2
Ladner	1957-1984	26	100	1	20	127
Masset	1982-1984	3	100	2	19	20
Nanaimo	1963-1984	19	84	1	4	35
North Saanich	1960	1	100			4
Pender Islands	1964-1984	19	21	1	8	16
Pitt Meadows	1972-1984	13	69	1	7	24
Port Alberni	1975	1	100			59
Prince Rupert	1980-1984	5	60	1	1	4
Sayward	1973-1984	12	17	1		1
Skidegate Inlet	1982-1984	3	33			1
Squamish	1980-1984	5	60	4	5	32
Surrey	1960-1966	7	29	3		8
Terrace	1963-1984	20	5			2
Vancouver	1957-1984	28	100	2	52	151
Victoria	1958-1984	27	100	5	42	115
White Rock	1971-1984	14	93	1	5	48

Red Phalarope

Highest provincial total: 8 (1979)
Highest interior total: Not recorded
Highest coastal total: 8 (1979)

Count locality	Count years	Total counts	Frequency of occurrence (%)	Range of total counts when species occurred		
				Low	Median	High
Coastal						
Victoria	1958-1984	27	4			8

Parasitic Jaeger

Highest provincial total: 1 (1977)
Highest interior total: Not recorded
Highest coastal total: 1 (1977)

Count locality	Count years	Total counts	Frequency of occurrence (%)	Range of total counts when species occurred		
				Low	Median	High
Coastal						
White Rock	1971-1984	14	7			1

Franklin's Gull

Highest provincial total: 1 (1969,70)
Highest interior total: Not recorded
Highest coastal total: 1 (1969,70)

Count locality	Count years	Total counts	Frequency of occurrence (%)	Range of total counts when species occurred		
				Low	Median	High
Coastal						
Duncan	1970-1984	15	7			1
Vancouver	1957-1984	28	4			1

Little Gull

Highest provincial total: 1 (1972)
Highest interior total: Not recorded
Highest coastal total: 1 (1972)

Count locality	Count years	Total counts	Frequency of occurrence (%)	Range of total counts when species occurred		
				Low	Median	High
Coastal						
Vancouver	1957-1984	28	4			1

Bonaparte's Gull

Highest provincial total: 5,072 (1977)
Highest interior total: Not recorded
Highest coastal total: 5,072 (1977)

Count locality	Count years	Total counts	Frequency of occurrence (%)	Range of total counts when species occurred		
				Low	Median	High
Coastal						
Campbell River	1972-1984	13	31	1	4	15
Comox	1961-1984	23	13	2	9	21
Deep Bay	1975-1984	10	10			1
Duncan	1970-1984	15	40	1	3	22
Kitimat	1974-1984	7	14			1
Ladner	1957-1984	26	65	1	4	1,053
Nanaimo	1963-1984	19	21	1	39	175
Pender Islands	1964-1984	19	37	1	4	40
Squamish	1980-1984	5	20			4
Sunshine Coast	1979-1984	6	67	2	3	32
Surrey	1960-1966	7	14			6
Vancouver	1957-1984	28	100	2	40	380
Victoria	1958-1984	27	63	1	55	5,004
White Rock	1971-1984	14	21	1	1	205

Heermann's Gull

Highest provincial total: 5 (1982)
Highest interior total: Not recorded
Highest coastal total: 5 (1982)

Count locality	Count years	Total counts	Frequency of occurrence (%)	Range of total counts when species occurred		
				Low	Median	High
Coastal						
Duncan	1970-1984	15	7			1
Pender Islands	1964-1984	19	5			4
Sunshine Coast	1979-1984	6	17			1
Victoria	1958-1984	27	7	1		1

Mew Gull

Highest provincial total: 26,117 (1974)
Highest interior total:2 (1983)
Highest coastal total: 26,116 (1974)

Count locality	Count years	Total counts	Frequency of occurrence (%)	Range of total counts when species occurred		
				Low	Median	High
Interior						
Oliver/Osoyoos	1979-1984	6	17			1
Penticton	1974-1984	9	11			1
Vernon	1975-1984	10	20	1		2
Coastal						
Campbell River	1972-1984	13	100	53	250	3,225
Chilliwack	1972-1984	11	73	1	20	524
Comox	1961-1984	23	100	6	286	812
Deep Bay	1975-1984	10	100	76	185	285
Dewdney	1967	1	100			589
Duncan	1970-1984	15	100	210	1,954	3,814
Kitimat	1974-1984	7	86	20	56	176
Ladner	1957-1984	26	100	327	1,315	7,243
Masset	1982-1984	3	100	22	55	62
Nanaimo	1963-1984	19	100	15	186	578
North Saanich	1960	1	100			215
Pender Islands	1964-1984	19	84	1	64	365
Pitt Meadows	1972-1984	13	100	4	371	1,928
Port Alberni	1975	1	100			342
Port Clements	1984	1	100			2
Prince Rupert	1980-1984	5	80	16	48	141
Sayward	1973-1984	12	100	7	27	1,147
Skidegate Inlet	1982-1984	3	100	22	23	30
Sooke	1983-1984	2	100	261		277
Squamish	1980-1984	5	100	35	81	1,034
Sunshine Coast	1979-1984	6	100	74	203	312
Surrey	1960-1966	7	86	40	81	500
Vancouver	1957-1984	28	100	1,590	4,155	9,741
Victoria	1958-1984	27	100	677	2,988	16,375
White Rock	1971-1984	14	100	40	446	1,564

Ring-billed Gull

Highest provincial total: 396 (1982)
Highest interior total: 316 (1981)
Highest coastal total: 331 (1980)

Count locality	Count years	Total counts	Frequency of occurrence (%)	Range of total counts when species occurred		
				Low	Median	High
Interior						
Kelowna	1981	1	100			195
Oliver/Osoyoos	1979-1984	6	67	1	3	14
Penticton	1974-1984	9	100	17	43	106
Revelstoke	1981-1984	4	50	1		2
Shuswap Lake	1972-1984	13	8			2
Vaseux Lake	1974-1984	11	55	1	3	9
Vernon	1975-1984	10	80	1	6	26
Coastal						
Campbell River	1972-1984	13	23	1	1	20
Chilliwack	1972-1984	11	18	1		5
Comox	1961-1984	23	30	1	6	93
Deep Bay	1975-1984	10	30	1	2	3
Duncan	1970-1984	15	80	1	4	16
Ladner	1957-1984	26	73	3	11	178
Masset	1982-1984	3	33			1
Nanaimo	1963-1984	19	16	1	1	4
Pitt Meadows	1972-1984	13	31	1	11	25
Sayward	1973-1984	12	8			3
Skidegate Inlet	1982-1984	3	67	1		1
Sunshine Coast	1979-1984	6	17			2
Surrey	1960-1966	7	43	1	2	3
Vancouver	1957-1984	28	79	2	23	210
Victoria	1958-1984	27	22	1	1	113
White Rock	1971-1984	14	93	2	25	254

California Gull

Highest provincial total: 149 (1984)
Highest interior total: 51 (1984)
Highest coastal total: 98 (1984)

Count locality	Count years	Total counts	Frequency of occurrence (%)	Range of total counts when species occurred		
				Low	Median	High
Interior						
Kelowna	1981	1	100			4
Nakusp	1979-1984	6	50	2	7	11
Oliver/Osoyoos	1979-1984	6	67	1	1	5
Penticton	1974-1984	9	100	3	9	40
Revelstoke	1981-1984	4	25			3
Vaseux Lake	1974-1984	11	82	1	1	7
Coastal						
Campbell River	1972-1984	13	23	2	3	5
Comox	1961-1984	23	17	1	6	10
Deep Bay	1975-1984	10	20	1		2
Duncan	1970-1984	15	13	1		2
Ladner	1957-1984	26	38	1	2	16
Nanaimo	1963-1984	19	11	1		5
Pitt Meadows	1972-1984	13	8			2
Sayward	1973-1984	12	17	1		2
Vancouver	1957-1984	28	82	1	5	92
Victoria	1958-1984	27	52	1	5	74
White Rock	1971-1984	14	14	1		2

Herring Gull

Highest provincial total: 2,607 (1974)
Highest interior total: 219 (1982)
Highest coastal total: 2,593 (1974)

Count locality	Count years	Total counts	Frequency of occurrence (%)	Range of total counts when species occurred		
				Low	Median	High
Interior						
Kamloops	1984	1	100			2
Kelowna	1981	1	100			138
Nakusp	1979-1984	6	17			2
Oliver/Osoyoos	1979-1984	6	100	1	3	18
Penticton	1974-1984	9	100	5	13	75
Revelstoke	1981-1984	4	75	13	29	37
Shuswap Lake	1972-1984	13	62	1	2	39
Vaseux Lake	1974-1984	11	82	1	2	8
Vernon	1975-1984	10	100	3	8	91
Coastal						
Bella Bella	1976	1	100			16
Campbell River	1973-1984	12	100	5	31	299
Chilliwack	1973-1984	10	90	1	15	589
Comox	1973-1984	12	100	4	80	273
Deep Bay	1975-1984	10	100	3	32	76
Duncan	1973-1984	12	100	1	63	136
Hecate Strait	1980	1	100			3
Kitimat	1974-1984	7	57	1	2	10
Ladner	1973-1984	12	100	6	129	1,016
Masset	1982-1984	3	67	26		88
Nanaimo	1973-1984	12	92	1	7	75
Pender Islands	1973-1984	12	92	2	34	128
Pitt Meadows	1973-1984	12	58	11	126	1,028
Port Alberni	1975	1	100			531
Prince Rupert	1980-1984	5	100	1	17	127
Sayward	1973-1984	12	50	1	3	4
Skidegate Inlet	1982-1984	3	100	4	23	49
Sooke	1983-1984	2	100	1		3
Squamish	1980-1984	5	60	1	2	2
Sunshine Coast	1979-1984	6	50	3	154	193
Terrace	1973-1984	12	25	3	4	7
Vancouver	1973-1984	12	92	8	25	1,066
Victoria	1973-1984	12	100	1	34	288
White Rock	1973-1984	12	100	1	78	432

Note: Prior to 1973, Thayer's Gull and Herring Gull were not separated on the coast, so the analysis of coastal counts only includes counts after that year. The highest coastal total for the combined species before 1973 was 8,646 in 1963.

Christmas Bird Counts

Thayer's Gull

Highest provincial total: 3,122 (1984)
Highest interior total: Not recorded
Highest coastal total: 3,122 (1984)

Count locality	Count years	Total counts	Frequency of occurrence (%)	Range of total counts when species occurred		
				Low	Median	High
Coastal						
Campbell River	1973-1984	12	67	1	35	194
Chilliwack	1973-1984	10	40	1	6	112
Comox	1973-1984	12	58	2	4	32
Deep Bay	1975-1984	10	70	1	4	327
Duncan	1973-1984	12	83	1	8	51
Hecate Strait	1980	1	100			83
Kitimat	1974-1984	7	14			6
Ladner	1973-1984	12	100	62	424	924
Masset	1982-1984	3	100	20	21	99
Nanaimo	1973-1984	12	50	1	4	612
Pender Islands	1973-1984	12	92	1	180	1,433
Pitt Meadows	1973-1984	12	67	1	23	117
Port Clements	1984	1	100			1
Prince Rupert	1980-1984	5	20			3
Skidegate Inlet	1982-1984	3	100	1	22	126
Sooke	1983-1984	2	100	10		11
Squamish	1980-1984	5	100	6	35	195
Sunshine Coast	1979-1984	6	67	13	44	93
Vancouver	1973-1984	12	92	45	770	1,220
Victoria	1973-1984	12	100	4	143	1,000
White Rock	1973-1984	12	100	4	22	462

Note: Before 1973 Thayer's Gull was not separated from Herring Gull.

Iceland Gull

Highest provincial total: 1 (1984)
Highest interior total: Not recorded
Highest coastal total: 1 (1984)

Count locality	Count years	Total counts	Frequency of occurrence (%)	Range of total counts when species occurred		
				Low	Median	High
Coastal						
Vancouver	1957-1984	28	4			1*

Western Gull

Highest provincial total: 13 (1984)
Highest interior total: Not recorded
Highest coastal total: 13 (1984)

Count locality	Count years	Total counts	Frequency of occurrence (%)	Range of total counts when species occurred		
				Low	Median	High
Coastal						
Comox	1961-1984	23	4			2
Deep Bay	1975-1984	10	10			3
Ladner	1957-1984	26	31	1	1	6
Masset	1982-1984	3	67	1		3
Pender Islands	1964-1984	19	5			5
Pitt Meadows	1972-1984	13	8			1
Skidegate Inlet	1982-1984	3	33			1
Sooke	1983-1984	2	100	1		2
Vancouver	1957-1984	28	39	1	2	5
Victoria	1958-1984	27	56	1	2	7
White Rock	1971-1984	14	29	1	1	2

Glaucous-winged Gull

Highest provincial total: 104,150 (1980)
Highest interior total:2 (1979)
Highest coastal total: 104,150 (1980)

Count locality	Count years	Total counts	Frequency of occurrence (%)	Range of total counts when species occurred Low	Median	High
Interior						
Kelowna	1981	1	100			2
Penticton	1974-1984	9	11			1
Shuswap Lake	1972-1984	13	8			1
Coastal						
Bella Bella	1976	1	100			272
Campbell River	1972-1984	13	100	633	1,579	11,103
Chilliwack	1972-1984	11	100	145	2,197	6,184
Comox	1961-1984	23	100	190	1,812	6,550
Deep Bay	1975-1984	10	100	663	1,119	2,291
Dewdney	1967	1	100			296
Duncan	1970-1984	15	100	317	875	1,821
Hecate Strait	1980	1	100			379
Kitimat	1974-1984	7	86	180	1,337	2,300
Ladner	1957-1984	26	100	760	19,750	44,832
Masset	1982-1984	3	100	92	163	206
Nanaimo	1963-1984	19	100	174	3,260	6,755
North Saanich	1960	1	100			926
Pender Islands	1964-1984	19	95	189	623	1,270
Pitt Meadows	1972-1984	13	100	500	1,894	9,984
Port Alberni	1975	1	100			973
Port Clements	1984	1	100			68
Prince Rupert	1980-1984	5	80	871	2,458	2,520
Sayward	1973-1984	12	100	9	85	342
Skidegate Inlet	1982-1984	3	100	117	327	550
Sooke	1983-1984	2	100	1,341		1,826
Squamish	1980-1984	5	100	1,136	1,961	3,139
Sunshine Coast	1979-1984	6	100	202	888	1,014
Surrey	1960-1966	7	100	76	350	769
Terrace	1963-1984	20	45	1	21	257
Vancouver	1957-1984	28	100	7,112	12,176	35,442
Victoria	1958-1984	27	100	2,641	6,946	14,943
White Rock	1971-1984	14	100	746	2,046	13,387

Glaucous Gull

Highest provincial total: 17 (1984)
Highest interior total:4 (1974)
Highest coastal total: 16 (1984)

Count locality	Count years	Total counts	Frequency of occurrence (%)	Range of total counts when species occurred		
				Low	Median	High
Interior						
Penticton	1974-1984	9	44	1	1	4
Shuswap Lake	1972-1984	13	8			2
Vernon	1975-1984	10	30	1	1	1
Coastal						
Campbell River	1972-1984	13	15	1		1
Comox	1961-1984	23	30	1	1	2
Deep Bay	1975-1984	10	10			1
Duncan	1970-1984	15	20	1	1	1
Ladner	1957-1984	26	58	1	4	6
Pitt Meadows	1972-1984	13	15	1		1
Prince Rupert	1980-1984	5	20			1
Skidegate Inlet	1982-1984	3	33			3
Sooke	1983-1984	2	100	1		1
Squamish	1980-1984	5	20			1
Terrace	1963-1984	20	10	1		1
Vancouver	1957-1984	28	32	1	1	3
Victoria	1958-1984	27	41	1	2	4
White Rock	1971-1984	14	14	1		2

Black-legged Kittiwake

Highest provincial total: 4 (1982)
Highest interior total: Not recorded
Highest coastal total: 4 (1982)

Count locality	Count years	Total counts	Frequency of occurrence (%)	Range of total counts when species occurred		
				Low	Median	High
Coastal						
Nanaimo	1963-1984	19	5			1
Victoria	1958-1984	27	11	1	1	3

Sabine's Gull

Highest provincial total: 1 (1963)
Highest interior total: Not recorded
Highest coastal total: 1 (1963)

Count locality	Count years	Total counts	Frequency of occurrence (%)	Range of total counts when species occurred		
				Low	Median	High
Coastal						
Victoria	1958-1984	27	4			1

Common Tern

Highest provincial total: 5 (1961)
Highest interior total: Not recorded
Highest coastal total: 5 (1961)

Count locality	Count years	Total counts	Frequency of occurrence (%)	Range of total counts when species occurred		
				Low	Median	High
Coastal						
Surrey	1960-1966	7	14			5

Common Murre

Highest provincial total: 8,542 (1973)
Highest interior total: Not recorded
Highest coastal total: 8,542 (1973)

Count locality	Count years	Total counts	Frequency of occurrence (%)	Range of total counts when species occurred		
				Low	Median	High
Coastal						
Bella Bella	1976	1	100			39
Campbell River	1972-1984	13	100	2	1,155	7,518
Comox	1961-1984	23	100	2	21	220
Deep Bay	1975-1984	10	100	14	62	168
Duncan	1970-1984	15	87	1	11	111
Hecate Strait	1980	1	100			163
Kitimat	1974-1984	7	43	1	4	5
Ladner	1957-1984	26	100	1	142	313
Masset	1982-1984	3	100	3	19	20
Nanaimo	1963-1984	19	89	1	29	571
North Saanich	1960	1	100			9
Pender Islands	1964-1984	19	95	6	117	592
Port Clements	1984	1	100			1
Prince Rupert	1980-1984	5	100	2	4	7
Sayward	1973-1984	12	67	4	32	200
Skidegate Inlet	1982-1984	3	100	60	138	143
Sooke	1983-1984	2	100	715		1,935
Squamish	1980-1984	5	60	2	2	2
Sunshine Coast	1979-1984	6	67	5	9	12
Vancouver	1957-1984	28	96	1	31	270
Victoria	1958-1984	27	100	3	188	7,831
White Rock	1971-1984	14	14	1		2

Thick-billed Murre

Highest provincial total: 1 (1982)
Highest interior total: Not recorded
Highest coastal total: 1 (1982)

Count locality	Count years	Total counts	Frequency of occurrence (%)	Range of total counts when species occurred		
				Low	Median	High
Coastal						
Masset	1982-1984	3	33			1

Pigeon Guillemot

Highest provincial total: 299 (1973)
Highest interior total: Not recorded
Highest coastal total: 299 (1973)

Count locality	Count years	Total counts	Frequency of occurrence (%)	Range of total counts when species occurred		
				Low	Median	High
Coastal						
Bella Bella	1976	1	100			1
Campbell River	1972-1984	13	85	1	5	13
Comox	1961-1984	23	91	1	3	14
Deep Bay	1975-1984	10	90	1	6	11
Duncan	1970-1984	15	93	1	2	13
Hecate Strait	1980	1	100			14
Ladner	1957-1984	26	96	1	11	38
Masset	1982-1984	3	67	5		9
Nanaimo	1963-1984	19	63	1	5	50
North Saanich	1960	1	100			25
Pender Islands	1964-1984	19	79	1	9	17
Sayward	1973-1984	12	8			4
Skidegate Inlet	1982-1984	3	67	1		1
Sooke	1983-1984	2	100	4		27
Sunshine Coast	1979-1984	6	50	1	2	5
Vancouver	1957-1984	28	92	1	8	75
Victoria	1958-1984	27	100	13	44	260
White Rock	1971-1984	14	43	1	3	11

Marbled Murrelet

Highest provincial total: 2,359 (1975)
Highest interior total: Not recorded
Highest coastal total: 2,359 (1975)

Count locality	Count years	Total counts	Frequency of occurrence (%)	Range of total counts when species occurred		
				Low	Median	High
Coastal						
Bella Bella	1976	1	100			24
Campbell River	1972-1984	13	69	1	8	39
Comox	1961-1984	23	87	1	7	28
Deep Bay	1975-1984	10	100	2	5	15
Duncan	1970-1984	15	100	2	26	117
Hecate Strait	1980	1	100			6
Kitimat	1974-1984	7	43	1	2	17
Ladner	1957-1984	26	92	1	21	2,125
Masset	1982-1984	3	33			2
Nanaimo	1963-1984	19	95	4	15	72
North Saanich	1960	1	100			10
Pender Islands	1964-1984	19	100	2	26	104
Prince Rupert	1980-1984	5	60	2	4	7
Sayward	1973-1984	12	58	1	8	15
Skidegate Inlet	1982-1984	3	100	2	2	7
Sooke	1983-1984	2	100	26		30
Squamish	1980-1984	5	100	23	46	199
Sunshine Coast	1979-1984	6	100	12	61	92
Vancouver	1957-1984	28	100	5	77	342
Victoria	1958-1984	27	100	4	29	294
White Rock	1971-1984	14	71	1	3	45

Ancient Murrelet

Highest provincial total: 6,401 (1973)
Highest interior total: Not recorded
Highest coastal total: 6,401 (1973)

Count locality	Count years	Total counts	Frequency of occurrence (%)	Range of total counts when species occurred		
				Low	Median	High
Coastal						
Ladner	1957-1984	26	35	1	9	77
Masset	1982-1984	3	33			2
Nanaimo	1963-1984	19	5			54
North Saanich	1960	1	100			1
Pender Islands	1964-1984	19	37	2	2	11
Skidegate Inlet	1982-1984	3	33			1
Sooke	1983-1984	2	100	2		7
Sunshine Coast	1979-1984	6	33	33		482
Vancouver	1957-1984	28	43	1	6	31
Victoria	1958-1984	27	85	4	185	6,401

Cassin's Auklet

Highest provincial total: 23 (1964,77)
Highest interior total: Not recorded
Highest coastal total: 23 (1964,77)

Count locality	Count years	Total counts	Frequency of occurrence (%)	Range of total counts when species occurred		
				Low	Median	High
Coastal						
Hecate Strait	1980	1	100			1
Skidegate Inlet	1982-1984	3	33			4
Sooke	1983-1984	2	50			4
Victoria	1958-1984	27	33	1	2	23

Rhinoceros Auklet

Highest provincial total: 55 (1977)
Highest interior total: Not recorded
Highest coastal total: 55 (1977)

Count locality	Count years	Total counts	Frequency of occurrence (%)	Range of total counts when species occurred		
				Low	Median	High
Coastal						
Duncan	1970-1984	15	7			1
Ladner	1957-1984	26	4			1
Nanaimo	1963-1984	19	16	1	1	2
North Saanich	1960	1	100			2
Pender Islands	1964-1984	19	42	1	2	15
Sooke	1983-1984	2	100	3		4
Vancouver	1957-1984	28	7	1		2
Victoria	1958-1984	27	81	1	2	37

Tufted Puffin

Highest provincial total: 2 (1965)
Highest interior total: Not recorded
Highest coastal total: 2 (1965)

Count locality	Count years	Total counts	Frequency of occurrence (%)	Range of total counts when species occurred		
				Low	Median	High
Coastal						
Victoria	1958-1984	27	11	1	1	2

Rock Dove

Highest provincial total: 20,266 (1978)
Highest interior total: 676 (1983)
Highest coastal total: 19,795 (1978)

Count locality	Count years	Total counts	Frequency of occurrence (%)	Range of total counts when species occurred		
				Low	Median	High
Interior						
Cranbrook	1984	1	100			15
Kamloops	1984	1	100			270
Kelowna	1981	1	100			70
Nakusp	1979-1984	6	17			14
North Pine	1983-1984	2	50			63
Oliver/Osoyoos	1979-1984	6	100	8	91	129
Penticton	1974-1984	9	100	12	44	111
Quesnel	1981-1984	4	100	22	54	56
Revelstoke	1981-1984	4	100	1	14	67
Shuswap Lake	1973-1984	12	23	5		19
Smithers	1977-1984	8	38	3	25	37
Vaseux Lake	1974-1984	11	91	3	16	526
Vernon	1975-1984	10	100	64	230	482
Yoho National Park	1975-1981	5	40	1		1
Coastal						
Campbell River	1973-1984	12	100	17	50	155
Chilliwack	1977-1984	8	100	210	580	722
Comox	1973-1984	12	100	80	240	368
Deep Bay	1975-1984	10	90	1	17	23
Duncan	1973-1984	12	100	48	118	182
Hecate Strait	1980	1	100			7
Ladner	1973-1984	12	100	603	971	2,119
Masset	1982-1984	3	33			6
Nanaimo	1973-1984	12	100	32	183	319
Pender Islands	1973-1984	12	33	1	16	18
Pitt Meadows	1973-1984	12	100	431	1,074	1,942
Prince Rupert	1980-1984	5	100	55	363	1,013
Sayward	1973-1984	12	8			1
Sooke	1983-1984	2	100	19		19
Squamish	1980-1984	5	100	24	27	54
Sunshine Coast	1979-1984	6	100	22	72	111
Terrace	1973-1984	12	75	3	11	27
Vancouver	1973-1984	12	100	4,039	8,027	15,157
Victoria	1973-1984	12	100	171	566	1,062
White Rock	1973-1984	12	100	232	447	935

Note: Rock Doves were not part of the official Christmas Bird Count records until 1973.

Band-tailed Pigeon

Highest provincial total: 1,136 (1984)
Highest interior total: Not recorded
Highest coastal total: 1,136 (1984)

Count locality	Count years	Total counts	Frequency of occurrence (%)	Range of total counts when species occurred		
				Low	Median	High
Coastal						
Campbell River	1972-1984	13	8			1
Chilliwack	1972-1984	11	9			28
Comox	1961-1984	23	13	4	5	16
Duncan	1970-1984	15	30	2	3	83
Ladner	1957-1984	26	19	2	3	15
Nanaimo	1963-1984	19	63	2	54	105
Pender Islands	1964-1984	19	53	1	3	449
Pitt Meadows	1972-1984	13	38	1	3	31
Sooke	1983-1984	2	50			1
Sunshine Coast	1979-1984	6	33	2		28
Terrace	1963-1984	20	15	1	5	10
Vancouver	1957-1984	28	75	1	17	110
Victoria	1958-1984	27	89	1	42	417
White Rock	1971-1984	14	64	1	3	13

Mourning Dove

Highest provincial total: 504 (1976)
Highest interior total: 450 (1983)
Highest coastal total: 258 (1976)

Count locality	Count years	Total counts	Frequency of occurrence (%)	Range of total counts when species occurred		
				Low	Median	High
Interior						
Kelowna	1981	1	100			32
Nakusp	1979-1984	6	17			1
Oliver/Osoyoos	1979-1984	6	83	4	38	57
Penticton	1974-1984	9	100	1	6	29
Shuswap Lake	1972-1984	13	8			1
Vaseux Lake	1974-1984	11	73	2	28	40
Vernon	1975-1984	10	100	55	180	373
Coastal						
Chilliwack	1972-1984	11	36	1	2	3
Comox	1961-1984	23	39	1	2	7
Deep Bay	1975-1984	10	10			9
Duncan	1970-1984	15	7			1
Ladner	1957-1984	26	73	1	27	145
Pitt Meadows	1972-1984	13	15	1		5
Sayward	1973-1984	12	8			1
Vancouver	1957-1984	28	39	1	3	204
Victoria	1958-1984	27	26	1	5	37
White Rock	1971-1984	14	86	1	9	54

Barn Owl

Highest provincial total: 63 (1977)
Highest interior total: Not recorded
Highest coastal total: 63 (1977)

Count locality	Count years	Total counts	Frequency of occurrence (%)	Range of total counts when species occurred		
				Low	Median	High
Coastal						
Chilliwack	1972-1984	11	18	1		1
Comox	1961-1984	23	4			1
Duncan	1970-1984	15	67	1	2	5
Ladner	1957-1984	26	73	1	5	16
Pender Islands	1964-1984	19	11	1		1
Pitt Meadows	1972-1984	13	46	1	3	3
Vancouver	1957-1984	28	61	1	3	49
Victoria	1958-1984	27	33	1	1	2
White Rock	1971-1984	14	93	1	3	7

Western Screech-Owl

Highest provincial total: 20 (1976)
Highest interior total: 2 (1981)
Highest coastal total: 20 (1976)

Count locality	Count years	Total counts	Frequency of occurrence (%)	Range of total counts when species occurred		
				Low	Median	High
Interior						
Oliver/Osoyoos	1979-1984	6	17			1
Vernon	1975-1984	10	20	1		1
Coastal						
Campbell River	1972-1984	13	8			3
Comox	1961-1984	23	9	1		1
Deep Bay	1975-1984	10	30	1	1	2
Duncan	1970-1984	15	40	1	2	3
Ladner	1957-1984	26	4			1
Nanaimo	1963-1984	19	21	1	1	4
Pender Islands	1964-1984	19	74	1	3	7
Pitt Meadows	1972-1984	13	15	1		3
Sunshine Coast	1979-1984	6	17			2
Vancouver	1957-1984	28	39	1	1	6
Victoria	1958-1984	27	96	1	2	12
White Rock	1971-1984	14	14	1		2

Great Horned Owl

Highest provincial total: 40 (1984)
Highest interior total: 14 (1984)
Highest coastal total: 26 (1984)

Count locality	Count years	Total counts	Frequency of occurrence (%)	Range of total counts when species occurred		
				Low	Median	High
Interior						
Cranbrook	1984	1	100			1
Lake Windermere	1979-1984	6	17			1
North Pine	1983-1984	2	50			1
Oliver/Osoyoos	1979-1984	6	83	1	2	3
Penticton	1974-1984	9	67	1	1	2
Revelstoke	1981-1984	4	25			1
Smithers	1977-1984	8	13			1
Vaseux Lake	1974-1984	11	27	1	1	3
Vernon	1975-1984	10	90	1	3	7
Coastal						
Chilliwack	1972-1984	11	9			1
Comox	1961-1984	23	13	1	1	1
Duncan	1970-1984	15	60	1	1	4
Ladner	1957-1984	26	42	1	2	8
Nanaimo	1963-1984	19	5			1
Pender Islands	1964-1984	19	11	1		2
Pitt Meadows	1972-1984	13	62	1	2	4
Sooke	1983-1984	2	50			2
Squamish	1980-1984	5	20			1
Sunshine Coast	1979-1984	6	33	1		1
Vancouver	1957-1984	28	75	1	1	4
Victoria	1958-1984	27	67	1	2	4
White Rock	1971-1984	14	50	1	1	3

Snowy Owl

Highest provincial total: 164 (1973)
Highest interior total: 2 (1983,84)
Highest coastal total: 164 (1973)

Count locality	Count years	Total counts	Frequency of occurrence (%)	Range of total counts when species occurred		
				Low	Median	High
Interior						
Kamloops	1984	1	100			1
North Pine	1983-1984	2	50			2
Vernon	1975-1984	10	10			1
Coastal						
Campbell River	1972-1984	13	8			1
Comox	1961-1984	23	22	1	2	5
Ladner	1957-1984	26	65	1	6	107
Nanaimo	1963-1984	19	5			1
Skidegate Inlet	1982-1984	3	33			1
Surrey	1960-1966	7	14			5
Terrace	1963-1984	20	5			1
Vancouver	1957-1984	28	39	1	3	27
Victoria	1958-1984	27	11	3	6	13
White Rock	1971-1984	14	21	1	2	14

Christmas Bird Counts

Northern Hawk Owl

Highest provincial total: 5 (1981)
Highest interior total: 5 (1981)
Highest coastal total: 1 (1980,84)

Count locality	Count years	Total counts	Frequency of occurrence (%)	Range of total counts when species occurred		
				Low	Median	High
Interior						
Lake Windermere	1979-1984	6	17			2
Nakusp	1979-1984	6	17			1
Oliver/Osoyoos	1979-1984	6	17			1
Penticton	1974-1984	9	11			1
Quesnel	1981-1984	4	25			2
Smithers	1977-1984	8	13			1
Vernon	1975-1984	10	20	1		1
Coastal						
Pitt Meadows	1972-1984	13	15	1		1

Northern Pygmy-Owl

Highest provincial total: 37 (1984)
Highest interior total: 25 (1977,84)
Highest coastal total: 12 (1984)

Count locality	Count years	Total counts	Frequency of occurrence (%)	Range of total counts when species occurred		
				Low	Median	High
Interior						
Fauquier	1984	1	100			1
Lake Windermere	1979-1984	6	67	1	2	3
Nakusp	1979-1984	6	33	1		2
Oliver/Osoyoos	1979-1984	6	67	2	5	8
Penticton	1974-1984	9	78	1	3	10
Revelstoke	1981-1984	4	50	2		4
Shuswap Lake	1972-1984	13	54	1	2	3
Smithers	1977-1984	8	25	1		1
Vaseux Lake	1974-1984	11	73	1	4	6
Vernon	1975-1984	10	70	1	2	17
Coastal						
Chilliwack	1972-1984	11	9			1
Comox	1961-1984	23	9	1		1
Kitimat	1974-1984	7	29	1		2
Nanaimo	1963-1984	19	11	1		1
Pitt Meadows	1972-1984	13	23	1	1	3
Squamish	1980-1984	5	80	1	3	4
Sunshine Coast	1979-1984	6	17			2
Terrace	1963-1984	20	15	1	1	1
Vancouver	1957-1984	28	32	1	2	4
Victoria	1958-1984	27	4			1

Burrowing Owl

Highest provincial total: 1 (1963)
Highest interior total: Not recorded
Highest coastal total: 1 (1963)

Count locality	Count years	Total counts	Frequency of occurrence (%)	Range of total counts when species occurred		
				Low	Median	High
Coastal						
Comox	1961-1984	23	4			1

Barred Owl

Highest provincial total: 5 (1983)
Highest interior total: 2 (1980)
Highest coastal total: 5 (1983)

Count locality	Count years	Total counts	Frequency of occurrence (%)	Range of total counts when species occurred		
				Low	Median	High
Interior						
Quesnel	1981-1984	4	25			1
Shuswap Lake	1972-1984	13	31	1	1	2
Vernon	1975-1984	10	20	1		1
Coastal						
Pender Islands	1964-1984	19	5			1
Sooke	1983-1984	2	50			1
Terrace	1963-1984	20	5			1
Vancouver	1957-1984	28	11	1	1	2
White Rock	1971-1984	14	7			1

Great Gray Owl

Highest provincial total: 3 (1984)
Highest interior total: 3 (1984)
Highest coastal total: 1 (1980)

Count locality	Count years	Total counts	Frequency of occurrence (%)	Range of total counts when species occurred		
				Low	Median	High
Interior						
Kamloops	1984	1	100			1
Lake Windermere	1979-1984	6	17			1
Shuswap Lake	1972-1984	13	8			1
Smithers	1977-1984	8	13			1
Coastal						
Pitt Meadows	1972-1984	13	8			1

Long-eared Owl

Highest provincial total:6 (1978)
Highest interior total: 5 (1978)
Highest coastal total: 4 (1970)

Count locality	Count years	Total counts	Frequency of occurrence (%)	Range of total counts when species occurred		
				Low	Median	High
Interior						
Oliver/Osoyoos	1979-1984	6	50	1	1	1
Penticton	1974-1984	9	44	1	2	4
Vaseux Lake	1974-1984	11	9			1
Vernon	1975-1984	10	10			1
Coastal						
Ladner	1957-1984	26	15	1	1	4
Pitt Meadows	1972-1984	13	8			2
Terrace	1963-1984	20	5			2
Vancouver	1957-1984	28	29	1	1	3
White Rock	1971-1984	14	7			1

Short-eared Owl

Highest provincial total: 170 (1973)
Highest interior total: 35 (1981)
Highest coastal total: 170 (1973)

Count locality	Count years	Total counts	Frequency of occurrence (%)	Range of total counts when species occurred		
				Low	Median	High
Interior						
Oliver/Osoyoos	1979-1984	6	17			1
Quesnel	1981-1984	4	25			1
Vernon	1975-1984	10	60	1	3	34
Yoho National Park	1975-1984	5	20			3
Coastal						
Duncan	1970-1984	15	40	1	2	3
Ladner	1957-1984	26	96	2	19	56
Nanaimo	1963-1984	19	68	1	2	5
North Saanich	1960	1	100			2
Pitt Meadows	1972-1984	13	85	1	2	41
Surrey	1960-1966	7	14			1
Vancouver	1957-1984	28	100	1	11	100
Victoria	1958-1984	27	37	1	1	2
White Rock	1971-1984	14	93	1	6	34

Boreal Owl

Highest provincial total: 1 (1975,84)
Highest interior total: 1 (1975,84)
Highest coastal total: Not recorded

Count locality	Count years	Total counts	Frequency of occurrence (%)	Range of total counts when species occurred		
				Low	Median	High
Interior						
Nakusp	1979-1984	6	17			1
Yoho National Park	1975-1984	5	20			1

Northern Saw-whet Owl

Highest provincial total: 16 (1977)
Highest interior total: 3 (1977,82)
Highest coastal total: 13 (1977)

Count locality	Count years	Total counts	Frequency of occurrence (%)	Range of total counts when species occurred		
				Low	Median	High
Interior						
Oliver/Osoyoos	1979-1984	6	33	1		1
Penticton	1974-1984	9	11			1
Shuswap Lake	1972-1984	13	23	1	1	1
Vaseux Lake	1974-1984	11	36	1	1	1
Vernon	1975-1984	10	10			2
Coastal						
Ladner	1957-1984	26	15	1	1	1
Masset	1982-1984	3	67	1		2
Nanaimo	1963-1984	19	5			1
Pender Islands	1964-1984	19	5			1
Pitt Meadows	1972-1984	13	23	1	1	1
Sooke	1983-1984	2	50			1
Squamish	1980-1984	5	20			1
Vancouver	1957-1984	28	29	1	1	2
Victoria	1958-1984	27	22	1	1	2
White Rock	1971-1984	14	29	1	2	10

Anna's Hummingbird

Highest provincial total: 71 (1984)
Highest interior total: 2 (1981,83)
Highest coastal total: 71 (1984)

Count locality	Count years	Total counts	Frequency of occurrence (%)	Range of total counts when species occurred		
				Low	Median	High
Interior						
Kelowna	1981	1	100			1
Penticton	1974-1984	9	11			1
Vaseux Lake	1974-1984	11	18	1		1
Vernon	1975-1984	10	20	1		2
Coastal						
Campbell River	1972-1984	13	85	2	4	9
Chilliwack	1972-1984	11	9			2
Comox	1961-1984	23	26	1	2	4
Duncan	1970-1984	15	67	1	1	3
Kitimat	1974-1984	7	14			1
Nanaimo	1963-1984	19	58	1	3	5
Pender Islands	1964-1984	19	5			1
Pitt Meadows	1972-1984	13	31	1	2	3
Port Alberni	1975	1	100			5
Sayward	1973-1984	12	8			1
Sooke	1983-1984	2	100	2		2
Sunshine Coast	1979-1984	6	100	2	3	5
Vancouver	1957-1984	28	50	1	6	16
Victoria	1958-1984	27	52	1	8	24
White Rock	1971-1984	14	50	3	7	15

Rufous Hummingbird

Highest provincial total: 1 (1961,66,79,81)
Highest interior total: Not recorded
Highest coastal total: 1 (1961,66,79,81)

Count locality	Count years	Total counts	Frequency of occurrence (%)	Range of total counts when species occurred		
				Low	Median	High
Coastal						
Sunshine Coast	1979-1984	6	17			1*
Victoria	1958-1984	27	11	1	1	1*

Belted Kingfisher

Highest provincial total: 298 (1983)
Highest interior total: 38 (1981)
Highest coastal total: 266 (1983)

Count locality	Count years	Total counts	Frequency of occurrence (%)	Range of total counts when species occurred		
				Low	Median	High
Interior						
Kelowna	1981	1	100			11
Lake Windermere	1979-1984	6	67	2	9	10
Nakusp	1979-1984	6	17			1
Oliver/Osoyoos	1979-1984	6	100	1	4	6
Penticton	1974-1984	9	100	4	5	9
Revelstoke	1981-1984	4	50	2		3
Shuswap Lake	1972-1984	13	31	1	1	2
Smithers	1977-1984	8	13			1
Vaseux Lake	1974-1984	11	91	1	4	9
Vernon	1975-1984	10	100	1	5	11
Coastal						
Bella Bella	1976	1	100			5
Campbell River	1972-1984	13	100	3	10	19
Chilliwack	1972-1984	11	100	1	5	9
Comox	1961-1984	23	100	1	11	21
Deep Bay	1975-1984	10	100	4	10	21
Dewdney	1967	1	100			1
Duncan	1970-1984	15	100	1	16	41
Hecate Strait	1980	1	100			1
Kitimat	1974-1984	7	86	1	2	4
Ladner	1957-1984	26	92	1	6	10
Masset	1982-1984	3	100	3	10	13
Nanaimo	1963-1984	19	100	1	10	22
North Saanich	1960	1	100			12
Pender Islands	1964-1984	19	100	1	18	36
Pitt Meadows	1972-1984	13	92	3	9	13
Port Alberni	1975	1	100			12
Port Clements	1984	1	100			5
Prince Rupert	1980-1984	5	100	5	8	9
Sayward	1973-1984	12	100	1	4	7
Skidegate Inlet	1982-1984	3	100	5	12	16
Sooke	1983-1984	2	100	19		24
Squamish	1980-1984	5	100	1	6	7
Sunshine Coast	1979-1984	6	100	4	9	15
Surrey	1960-1966	7	86	1	3	3
Terrace	1963-1984	20	30	1	2	3
Vancouver	1957-1984	28	100	2	11	20
Victoria	1958-1984	27	100	13	23	44
White Rock	1971-1984	14	100	1	8	16

Lewis' Woodpecker

Highest provincial total: 27 (1974)
Highest interior total: 27 (1974)
Highest coastal total: 2 (1958)

Count locality	Count years	Total counts	Frequency of occurrence (%)	Range of total counts when species occurred		
				Low	Median	High
Interior						
Kelowna	1981	1	100			3
Oliver/Osoyoos	1979-1984	6	67	1	1	3
Penticton	1974-1984	9	100	4	7	25
Vaseux Lake	1974-1984	11	27	2	2	2
Vernon	1975-1984	10	20	1		1
Coastal						
Nanaimo	1963-1984	19	5			1
Pitt Meadows	1972-1984	13	8			1
Vancouver	1957-1984	28	7	1		1
Victoria	1958-1984	27	11	1	1	2

Red-breasted Sapsucker

Highest provincial total: 74 (1968)
Highest interior total:2 (1983)
Highest coastal total: 74 (1968)

Count locality	Count years	Total counts	Frequency of occurrence (%)	Range of total counts when species occurred		
				Low	Median	High
Interior						
Penticton	1974-1984	9	11			2*
Smithers	1977-1984	8	25	1		2
Vaseux Lake	1974-1984	11	9			1*
Coastal						
Campbell River	1972-1984	13	46	1	4	19
Comox	1961-1984	23	30	1	1	2
Deep Bay	1975-1984	10	30	1	3	3
Duncan	1970-1984	15	47	1	2	5
Ladner	1957-1984	26	42	1	2	10
Masset	1982-1984	3	33			1
Nanaimo	1963-1984	19	26	1	2	10
Pender Islands	1964-1984	19	32	1	1	2
Pitt Meadows	1972-1984	13	46	1	2	18
Port Alberni	1975	1	100			1
Prince Rupert	1980-1984	5	20			2
Sayward	1973-1984	12	17	1		2
Skidegate Inlet	1982-1984	3	33			1
Sooke	1983-1984	2	50			8
Squamish	1980-1984	5	40	2		4
Sunshine Coast	1979-1984	6	50	1	2	4
Surrey	1960-1966	7	14			1
Terrace	1963-1984	20	5			1
Vancouver	1957-1984	28	100	1	3	67
Victoria	1958-1984	27	63	1	1	12
White Rock	1971-1984	14	57	1	2	14

Note: Of the *Sphyrapicus* complex, only the Red-breasted Sapsucker has been documented on Christmas Bird Counts in British Columbia. Both the Penticton and Vaseux Lake counts, however, lack documentation (Cannings, R.A. et al. 1987). Because only the Red-breasted Sapsucker is known to occur in winter in the Okanagan valley (Cannings, R.A. et al. 1987), we have placed those counts here.

Downy Woodpecker

Highest provincial total: 412 (1984)
Highest interior total: 174 (1984)
Highest coastal total: 262 (1983)

Count locality	Count years	Total counts	Frequency of occurrence (%)	Range of total counts when species occurred		
				Low	Median	High
Interior						
Cranbrook	1984	1	100			6
Fort St.John	1975-1978	4	75	1	2	4
Kamloops	1984	1	100			6
Kelowna	1981	1	100			5
Lake Windermere	1979-1984	6	100	7	21	27
Nakusp	1979-1984	6	100	1	4	6
North Pine	1983-1984	2	50			2
Oliver/Osoyoos	1979-1984	6	100	2	13	18
Penticton	1974-1984	9	100	2	11	24
Quesnel	1981-1984	4	50	1		7
Revelstoke	1981-1984	4	75	2	4	4
Shuswap Lake	1972-1984	13	100	4	9	17
Smithers	1977-1984	8	100	5	10	18
Vaseux Lake	1974-1984	11	91	1	4	12
Vernon	1975-1984	10	100	5	18	37
Wells Gray	1984	1	100			1
Yoho National Park	1975-1984	5	60	1	2	5
Coastal						
Campbell River	1972-1984	13	92	1	6	12
Chilliwack	1972-1984	11	100	2	7	30
Comox	1961-1984	23	96	1	10	18
Deep Bay	1975-1984	10	60	1	2	3
Dewdney	1967	1	100			4
Duncan	1970-1984	15	100	4	16	25
Ladner	1957-1984	26	96	3	20	37
Nanaimo	1963-1984	19	74	1	6	10
North Saanich	1960	1	100			9
Pender Islands	1964-1984	19	89	1	2	6
Pitt Meadows	1972-1984	13	100	2	13	27
Port Alberni	1975	1	100			6
Sayward	1973-1984	12	67	1	2	4
Sooke	1983-1984	2	100	6		17
Squamish	1980-1984	5	100	1	5	16
Sunshine Coast	1979-1984	6	33	2		7
Surrey	1960-1966	7	71	1	4	6
Terrace	1963-1984	20	55	1	1	4
Vancouver	1957-1984	28	100	5	17	40
Victoria	1958-1984	27	100	3	25	68
White Rock	1971-1984	14	100	10	21	49

Hairy Woodpecker

Highest provincial total: 258 (1984)
Highest interior total: 163 (1984)
Highest coastal total: 122 (1983)

Count locality	Count years	Total counts	Frequency of occurrence (%)	Range of total counts when species occurred		
				Low	Median	High
Interior						
Cranbrook	1984	1	100			7
Fauquier	1984	1	100			2
Fort St.John	1975-1978	4	75	1	1	2
Kamloops	1984	1	100			7
Kelowna	1981	1	100			7
Lake Windermere	1979-1984	6	100	6	23	42
Mackenzie	1982	1	100			1
Nakusp	1979-1984	6	100	1	5	7
North Pine	1983-1984	2	50			2
Oliver/Osoyoos	1979-1984	6	100	1	5	6
Penticton	1974-1984	9	100	4	13	21
Quesnel	1981-1984	4	100	1	2	7
Revelstoke	1981-1984	4	75	2	3	3
Shuswap Lake	1972-1984	13	92	1	12	22
Smithers1977-	1984	8	88	4	12	15
Vaseux Lake	1974-1984	11	100	2	3	9
Vernon1975-	1984	10	100	4	8	19
Wells Gray	1984	1	100			5
Yoho National Park	1975-1984	5	80	1	3	4
Coastal						
Campbell River	1972-1984	13	100	1	4	6
Chilliwack	1972-1984	11	82	1	2	3
Comox	1961-1984	23	91	1	5	11
Deep Bay	1975-1984	10	100	1	3	8
Duncan	1970-1984	15	93	2	5	8
Kitimat	1974-1984	7	29	1		1
Ladner	1957-1984	26	50	1	1	4
Masset	1982-1984	3	67	1		2
Nanaimo	1963-1984	19	68	1	5	8
North Saanich	1960	1	100			3
Pender Islands	1964-1984	19	58	1	2	6
Pitt Meadows	1972-1984	13	85	1	5	7
Port Alberni	1975	1	100			5
Port Clements	1984	1	100			1
Sayward	1973-1984	12	58	1	2	5
Skidegate Inlet	1982-1984	3	33			4
Sooke	1983-1984	2	100	1		13
Squamish	1980-1984	5	80	1	5	8
Sunshine Coast	1979-1984	6	67	1	3	7
Terrace	1963-1984	20	80	1	2	6
Vancouver	1957-1984	28	93	1	4	9
Victoria	1958-1984	27	100	1	6	35
White Rock	1971-1984	14	93	2	7	14

White-headed Woodpecker

Highest provincial total: 2 (1984)
Highest interior total: 2 (1984)
Highest coastal total: Not recorded

Count locality	Count years	Total counts	Frequency of occurrence (%)	Range of total counts when species occurred		
				Low	Median	High
Interior						
Oliver/Osoyoos	1979-1984	6	17			1
Vaseux Lake	1974-1984	11	18	1		1

Three-toed Woodpecker

Highest provincial total: 15 (1983)
Highest interior total: 14 (1983)
Highest coastal total: 1 (1961,66,68,83)

Count locality	Count years	Total counts	Frequency of occurrence (%)	Range of total counts when species occurred		
				Low	Median	High
Interior						
Penticton	1974-1984	9	22	1		1
Quesnel	1981-1984	4	25			1
Shuswap Lake	1972-1984	13	8			1
Smithers	1977-1984	8	38	1	1	4
Vaseux Lake	1974-1984	11	9			1
Vernon	1975-1984	10	50	1	1	2
Yoho National Park	1975-1984	5	80	1	3	5
Coastal						
Terrace	1963-1984	20	15	1	1	1
Victoria	1958-1984	27	4			1

Black-backed Woodpecker

Highest provincial total: 5 (1982)
Highest interior total: 5 (1982)
Highest coastal total: Not recorded

Count locality	Count years	Total counts	Frequency of occurrence (%)	Range of total counts when species occurred		
				Low	Median	High
Interior						
Lake Windermere	1979-1984	6	33	1		3
Nakusp	1979-1984	6	33	1		2
Oliver/Osoyoos	1979-1984	6	17			1
Penticton	1974-1984	9	11			1
Smithers	1977-1984	8	13			1
Wells Gray	1984	1	100			1

Northern Flicker

Highest provincial total: 1,384 (1983)
Highest interior total: 563 (1981)
Highest coastal total: 901 (1975)

Count locality	Count years	Total counts	Frequency of occurrence (%)	Range of total counts when species occurred		
				Low	Median	High
Interior						
Fauquier	1984	1	100			3
Kamloops	1984	1	100			19
Kelowna	1981	1	100			88
Lake Windermere	1979-1984	6	100	4	13	28
Nakusp	1979-1984	6	100	1	9	14
Oliver/Osoyoos	1979-1984	6	100	26	82	115
Penticton	1974-1984	9	100	68	134	161
Quesnel	1981-1984	4	50	1		1
Revelstoke	1981-1984	4	100	7	13	13
Shuswap Lake	1972-1984	13	92	1	12	26
Smithers	1977-1984	8	13			1
Vaseux Lake	1974-1984	11	100	9	30	54
Vernon	1975-1984	10	100	93	110	171
Coastal						
Campbell River	1972-1984	13	100	4	20	39
Chilliwack	1972-1984	11	100	13	32	69
Comox	1961-1984	23	100	3	43	77
Deep Bay	1975-1984	10	100	5	14	23
Dewdney	1967	1	100			7
Duncan	1970-1984	15	100	7	31	69
Kitimat	1974-1984	7	29	1		1
Ladner	1957-1984	26	100	3	73	155
Masset	1982-1984	3	100	4	6	7
Nanaimo	1963-1984	19	100	5	44	67
North Saanich	1960	1	100			56
Pender Islands	1964-1984	19	100	11	27	53
Pitt Meadows	1972-1984	13	100	17	38	65
Port Alberni	1975	1	100			22
Prince Rupert	1980-1984	5	80	1	1	2
Sayward	1973-1984	12	75	1	3	7
Skidegate Inlet	1982-1984	3	100	4	7	8
Sooke	1983-1984	2	100	74		103
Squamish	1980-1984	5	100	3	5	9
Sunshine Coast	1979-1984	6	100	4	12	16
Surrey	1960-1966	7	100	3	10	17
Terrace	1963-1984	20	50	1	2	4
Vancouver	1957-1984	28	100	48	100	291
Victoria	1958-1984	27	100	44	181	374
White Rock	1971-1984	14	100	30	64	125

Pileated Woodpecker

Highest provincial total: 112 (1984)
Highest interior total: 50 (1984)
Highest coastal total: 77 (1976)

Count locality	Count years	Total counts	Frequency of occurrence (%)	Range of total counts when species occurred		
				Low	Median	High
Interior						
Fauquier	1984	1	100			4
Kamloops	1984	1	100			2
Kelowna	1981	1	100			2
Lake Windermere	1979-1984	6	100	6	10	20
Nakusp	1979-1984	6	67	1	2	2
Oliver/Osoyoos	1979-1984	6	33	1		2
Penticton	1974-1984	9	78	1	1	2
Quesnel	1981-1984	4	25			2
Revelstoke	1981-1984	4	100	2	4	8
Shuswap Lake	1972-1984	13	92	1	5	18
Smithers	1977-1984	8	75	1	1	2
Vaseux Lake	1974-1984	11	36	1	1	2
Vernon	1975-1984	10	80	1	5	7
Coastal						
Campbell River	1972-1984	13	92	1	2	5
Chilliwack	1972-1984	11	18	1		1
Comox	1961-1984	23	78	1	4	10
Deep Bay	1975-1984	10	100	1	3	9
Duncan	1970-1984	15	100	2	7	19
Kitimat	1974-1984	7	14			1
Ladner	1957-1984	26	62	1	2	6
Nanaimo	1963-1984	19	79	1	6	20
North Saanich	1960	1	100			2
Pender Islands	1964-1984	19	89	1	5	9
Pitt Meadows	1972-1984	13	85	1	3	7
Port Alberni	1975	1	100			2
Sooke	1983-1984	2	100	4		7
Squamish	1980-1984	5	40	2		3
Sunshine Coast	1979-1984	6	83	1	3	4
Surrey	1960-1966	7	29	1		3
Terrace	1963-1984	20	5			2
Vancouver	1957-1984	28	93	1	3	12
Victoria	1958-1984	27	100	1	5	22
White Rock	1971-1984	14	93	2	8	12

APPENDIX 3

Contributors

Abbey, E.
Abbey, J.
Ablitt, Sheila
Ackerman, Andy
Ackroyd, Gayle
Ackroyd, John
Acton, Tim
Adair, E.M.
Adalman, Steven
Adams, Barbara
Adams, Bob
Adams, Brenda
Adams, Elsie
Adams, Errol
Adams, J.
Adams, Kaye
Adams, Mark
Adams, Mike
Adams, W.
Adamson, Anne
Ainscough, H.M.
Aitchison, Cathy
Akerlund, W.
Aldcroft, David S.
Alderman, E.S.
Alderson, G.W.
Aldridge, Alex
Alexander, A.G.
Alexander, A.M.
Alexander, Linda
Alexander, M.E.
Alexander, T.R.
Alger, Dave
Allan, B.
Allan, Jean
Allen, Charles
Allen, Donald
Allen, Dorothy
Allen, Marty
Allen, Roy
Allies, Kelly
Allies, Wendy J.
Allies, Wilson F.
Allison, Barney
Almond, H.
Alton, R.R
Alway, J.H.
Ambridge, Dave
Amedro, Matt J.
Amos, Ralph
Amundsen, Adeline
Amys, Necia
Amys, Philip
Anderson, B.
Anderson, C.H.
Anderson, Dale
Anderson, Dix
Anderson, E.A.
Anderson, Errol M.
Anderson, F.
Anderson, Gail
Anderson, Gary
Anderson, Gerald

Anderson, Gladys
Anderson, J.S.
Anderson, J.W.
Anderson, Jerry
Anderson, John
Anderson, K.
Anderson, L.
Anderson, R.R.
Anderson, T.M.
Anderson, Tony L.
Anderson, Walter
Anderson, William A.
Anderson, William J.
Andre, Jean
Andrews, Betty
Andrews, N.
Angell, N.
Angermeyer, Katie
Angle, Edith
Angle, Neil
Angus, J.
Angus, Robert
Anker, B.
Ansell, Gerry
Ansell, Wendy
Antifeau, Ted
Antoniazzi, Cathy
Appleton, Frank
Arcese, Peter
Arlt, E.
Armstead, Carol
Armstead, Rex
Armstrong, Malcolm C.
Armstrong, Marie
Armstrong, P.
Armstrong, W.
Arnet, Dorothy
Arnet, Douglas
Arnet, Edward
Arnold, Genevieve
Arter, J.
Arvey, D.
Ashcroft, Greg
Asher, Dale
Asher, Richard C.
Ashmore, Margaret
Askevold, R.
Asplin, Heather
Assaly, Robin
Atkins, Allan
Atkins, M.
Atkinson, Chris
Atkinson, Knute
Atkinson, Pat
Atkinson, R.N.
Atkinson, R.W.
Auhold, Brad
Austin, Dorothy
Austin, June
Austring, Ruth
Axhorn, Denise
Axhorn, Peter
Ayers, Helen

Babcock, A.
Bach, Ernie
Bach, R.
Bachi, Albert
Bachi, Heidi
Backs, Mel
Backs, Rose
Bader, W.A.
Badgley, E.
Baechler, Marilyn
Bailey, Anne C.
Bailey, Norma
Bailey, Paul
Bailey, S.
Baillie, Steve
Bain, J.
Baine, Stan
Baird, Robin
Baker, Alan
Baker, Betty
Baker, Bob
Baker, D.
Baker, Eric
Baker, G.
Baker, Margaret
Baker, Phillip
Baker, Robert L.
Baker, Stanley W.F.
Baker, Teresa
Bakkom, W.
Baldwin, James
Ballard, John T.
Ballin, Peter
Bamford, Ted
Bampton, Chris
Bandy, P.J.
Banks, Douglas
Bantom, Audrey
Banwell, June
Barclay, Grace
Barclay, H.
Bard, Fred
Barker, I.
Barkley, William D.
Barkwill, W.
Barlow, Jon C.
Barnard, Anthony E.
Barnes, Helen
Barnes, Jack
Barnes, John
Barnes, Raymond
Barnes, Verna
Barnett, Henry
Barnett, Ian
Barnett, Jennifer M.
Barnett, Judy
Barr, Andy
Barr, Barry
Barr, Kenneth
Barr, R.A.
Barraclough, Dave
Barraclough, Edward
Barraclough, Mary

Barrard, Tony
Barrett, Grace
Bartholomew, K.
Bartkow, Virginia
Bartlett, Les
Barvis, Marg
Bashan, Berton
Bastaja, Dan S.
Bateman, Robert
Bates, Bob
Bates, Catherine
Bates, Ernie
Bates, Marjorie
Bates, T.H.
Bates, Tom
Bath, Fermine
Batt, Edna
Bauder, Kris
Bauer, H.E.
Baumbrough, Harold
Baumbrough, John
Baumbrough, June
Bavin, Helen
Bavin, Ryan
Bavington, B.
Bawtree, K.
Baylor, G.
Bazett, Stephen J.
Beacham, E. Derek
Beachem, Al
Beadle, David
Beak, Alice
Beals, Alice
Beam, B.
Beardmore, Roger
Beauchesne, Moira
Beaudet, Sheila
Beaulieu, Joanne
Beaulieu, Michelle
Beaumont, Art
Beaumont, Barbara
Beaven, N.
Bech, Paul
Bechett, K.R.
Bechler, Marilyn
Beck, J.E.
Beck, R.E.
Becker, Phyllis
Beckett, K. Ray
Beckner, D.
Beebe, Frank L.
Beedle, Mac
Begg, Barbara
Beise, Kathleen
Bekhuys, Timothy J.
Bell, Alistair
Bell, Barbara
Bell, Brian
Bell, Dick
Bell, Eileen
Bell, Ernie
Bell, Faith
Bell, Grace

Bell, H.M.
Bell, Hedley
Bell, Jacques
Bell, Karina
Bell, Katie
Bell, Kevin M.
Bell, W.
Bellevance, Anne
Bellis, Charles
Belsom, Betty
Belsom, June
Belsom, Sid
Belton, Desmond E.J.
Bendell, James F.
Bender, Fred
Beninger, P.
Benmore, B.
Bennett, Barry
Bennett, Bruce
Bennett, Gerry
Bennett, Herb
Bennett, Mary
Bennie, Fred
Bennie, Winnifred
Benoit, James
Benson, M.
Bentley, Caroline L.
Bentley, Mike
Benton, Bill
Benton, Fran
Benton, Julie
Benton, Marian
Benton, Roger
Benyon, E.
Bergen, M.
Berger, Alan
Bergerud, A.T.
Berry, Ron
Bertram, Douglas F.
Berukoff, P.
Best, Alan
Best, Ken
Best, Robin
Best, S.
Best, Ted
Bettison, L.J.
Betts, Mike
Bevan, Jan
Bewick, Mary
Beynon, Ed
Beynon, J.
Biel, Jim
Bigelow, E.
Bigelow, V.
Biggar, James
Biggin-Pound, J.
Bigley, Dick
Bijdemast, Edie
Billie, Tonio
Billings, Ray R.
Bilodau, B.
Bingham, Dan S.
Bingham, Peter
Bird, Fred
Bird, Jackie
Bird, W.
Birkel, Anne
Birkett, Wilma
Birney, C.E.
Bishop, Charlie
Bishop, James

Bishop, Jean
Bishop, L.
Black, Tom
Blackbourne, S.
Blais, Dan
Blake, Joe
Blanchard, Harriet
Bland, Trudy
Blankendaal, Cor
Blattner, Hans
Blaylock, S.G.
Bloem, Gerard
Blokker, P.F.
Blomgren, Bemgt
Blood, Donald A.
Bloom, F.C.
Blouw, Marjon
Blow, Barbara
Boag, D.A.
Boas, Charles
Boas, F.
Bode, Miles
Bodman, Geoff
Bogewold, Gwen
Boggs, Bob
Boggs, Elsie
Bolen, Loren
Bolton, Doris
Bomford, Charles
Bomford, H.
Bomford, Ted
Bonar, Richard L.
Boney, R.
Bonner, Vera
Boone, J.A.
Boot, Lance
Boot, Leslie
Booth, Barry
Booth, J.H.
Borrelly, Maurice
Bortnik, Shelly
Bosomworth, Myrna
Boston, R.E.
Boulton, G.
Bouman, Dan
Bourne, Jean
Bourne, Neil
Boutillier, Norma
Boux, J.
Bowden, Sheila
Bowden, Wallie
Bowe, L.
Bowen, Dan
Bowen, Edna
Bowers, Bonny
Bowers, David
Bowers, Deborah
Bowes, Stanley
Bowford, Ted
Bowling, Jack
Boyce, Kenneth C.
Boyd, W. Sean
Boye, J.C.
Boyle, Brad L.
Boyle, Larry
Bracewell, Dorothy
Bracewell, Vince
Brade, Robert
Bradford, Mike
Bradford, Sherry
Bradley, Arlene

Bradley, Dorothy M.
Bradley, M.
Bradley, Robert M.
Bradley, S.F.
Bradshaw, Jeff
Brand, Trudy
Brandie, G.
Brandon, Jean
Brandon, Jimmy
Brandt, Charles A.E.
Braun, Abe
Braun, Ralph
Bray, R.
Brayshaw, Chris
Breadon, James
Breault, Andre
Breen, Peter
Breitkreutz, A.R.
Brett, Roland J.
Brewer, David
Brewster, Bill
Brewster, N.
Briant, Pat
Briault, Peg
Bricknell, Peter
Briggs, Gwen
Briggs, Tom R.
Brigham, R. Mark
Britton, G.A.
Broadland, Ken R.
Broadley, Tom
Brock, Hugh
Brock, Lyle
Brodorson, Malfdan
Brokenshire, Betty
Bromley, Robert G.
Bronsch, Harold
Brook, M.
Brook, Nigel
Brook, S.
Brooke, Elizabeth
Brooke, Mavis
Brooke, Robert C.
Brooke, William
Brooks, A.A.
Brooks, Allan C.
Brooks, Betty J.
Brooks, D.
Brooks, E.S.
Brooks, J.A.
Brooks, Jocie M.
Brooks, Robert
Brooks, Vi
Broomfield, G.A.
Broomfield, J.F.
Brown, Andrew
Brown, Bedford B.
Brown, Bill
Brown, Bob
Brown, Debbie
Brown, Dennis
Brown, Dorothy
Brown, Doug
Brown, Eileen
Brown, G.L.
Brown, Gladys
Brown, Gordon
Brown, Janet
Brown, Margaret
Brown, Marian
Brown, Michael

Brown, Mildred
Brown, Paul
Brown, R.P.
Brown, Rory
Brown, Shawn
Brown, Susan J.
Brown, Thomas H.
Brown, Valerie
Brown, William M.
Browne-Clayton, Pat
Browning, R.W.
Brownlow, Harry
Brownsword, F.
Bruce, Dan
Bruce, Rosemary
Brucker, Maury
Brunham, C.
Brunham, G.
Brunt, Kim
Brunton, Daniel F.
Bruton, J.W.
Bryan, Anthea
Bryan, C.
Bryan, Jim
Bryden, Colleen
Bryden, Jim
Bryson, Greg
Buch, Nancy E.
Buchanan, Don
Buchanan, Melda
Buchanan, S.
Buck, E.
Buck, Jim
Buckingham, R.
Buckle, Evelyn
Buckle, Neil
Buckles, Jack
Budzinski, Luz
Buffam, Frank
Buhler, Andy
Buhler, Marilyn
Buhler, R.A.
Buker, Ian
Bull, John
Bull, P.
Bull, S.
Bullard, Collin
Bullen, Bev
Bullock, G.F.
Bultug, Helen
Bumpus, Ruth
Bunnell, Fred L.
Burbidge, Jim
Burbidge, Joan
Burger, Alan
Burgerjon, Joop
Burgerjon, Miep
Burgess, Joe
Burgess, Tom E.
Burgess, W.
Burne, C.S.
Burnett, Stella
Burnett, Terry
Burnette, Peter
Burns, Andrew
Burns, C.
Burns, J.E.
Burrell, Linda
Burroughs, A.O.
Burroughs, Betty
Burroughs, Bill

Contributors

Burroughs, May
Burton, Clyde H.
Busch, Fred
Bush, Dave
Bush, Gary
Bush, Gordon
Bushman, Ortrude
Bustard, David
Butler, Bruce
Butler, Elinor
Butler, Greg
Butler, Jim
Butler, Michelle
Butler, Richard
Butler, Robert W.
Butler, Sharon
Butt, Colin
Butters, Dan
Butterworth, David
Buys, Hans
Byatt, A.
Byatt, Steve
Bye, Dana
Bylie, Bill
Byrd, Vernon
Cachet, Klaus
Caldwell, Kit
Calef, George
Calladine, John
Callender, Graham
Callin, Elmer
Calvert, Gilbert
Calvert, Joy
Calvert, Lissa
Cameron, Arlene
Cameron, D.
Cameron, Fred
Cameron, I.
Cameron, Jim
Cameron, Mavis
Cameron, Sharon
Camfferman, Dean
Camp, Frank E.
Campbell, Barbara
Campbell, Barry
Campbell, Betty
Campbell, Carol
Campbell, D. Sean
Campbell, D. Wayne
Campbell, David
Campbell, Eileen C.
Campbell, J.V.
Campbell, Larry
Campbell, Lorne
Campbell, Lucile
Campbell, Marcile
Campbell, Mildred W.
Campbell, R. Wayne
Campbell, Robert L.
Campbell, Tessa N.
Camsell, M.
Cannings, E.J.
Cannings, Jean
Cannings, Richard J.
Cannings, Robert A.
Cannings, Stephen R.
Cannings, Sydney G.
Cannon, Violet E.
Cape, Barbara
Cape, Myrtle
Capes, Phil

Carpenter, L.
Caravetta, I.
Caravetta, Joe
Carcasson, Robert H.
Cardinal, K.
Cardwell, Sarah
Carefoot, T.H.
Carey, Betty
Carey, Neil
Carl, G. Clifford
Carl, Jennifer
Carl, Ruth
Carleton, J.
Carlisle, Susan
Carlson, Barbara E.
Carlson, Gary R.
Carlson, J.S.
Carmichael, Agnes
Carmody, Michael
Carper, Larry
Carr, Daniel
Carr, Elsie
Carr, Ian
Carr, Jan
Carruthers, Donald
Carson, Andy
Carson, Betty
Carson, Don
Carson, Kevin
Carson, Trudy
Carson, Walter
Carter, Bruce
Carter, Harry R.
Cartwright, Joan
Cartwright, John
Cartwright, Maureen
Caskey, Marlene
Casperson, Audrey
Casperson, R.
Casperson, Susan
Cassidy, Alice
Castagner, Lynn
Catchpole, Rob
Cathcart, M.
Catt, Danny
Cavenaugh, Brian
Cavers, Beth
Cawley, Nettie-Jean
Cehak, K.F.
Cerrenzia, Bob
Chaddock, Arnold
Chalmers, Graham
Chalmers, Hubert
Chalmers, Orville
Chambers, M.
Chan, Brian
Chandler, Art
Chandy, Rosalind
Chapman, Betty-Ann
Chapman, David P.
Chapman, F.
Chapman, Sharon
Charbonneau, Alan
Charbonneau, D.
Charles, Walter
Charlton, A.
Charters, D.
Chartier, A.
Chartier, B.
Chase, Dave
Chase, J.D.

Chatwin, R.
Cherney, Gordon
Chester, S.
Chesterfield, Norman
Child, Ken N.
Chisholm, B.R.
Christie, A.E.
Christie, H.C.
Christie, Norma
Christmas, M.J.
Chrysler, Judy
Chudyk, M.
Chudyk, W.
Chungranes, Vi
Church, Mike
Churchill, Betty
Churchill, Brian P.
Churchill, Bryon
Churchill, Harold
Chutter, Myke J.
Chutter, W.
Chwojka, Amy
Clague, Alexis
Clague, John
Clapham, Paul
Clapp, B.E.
Clapperton, D.
Clark, Alan M.
Clark, Colin
Clark, David
Clark, Frank C.
Clark, H.G.
Clark, Heather
Clark, Martin
Clark, Mary
Clark, Mike
Clark, Murray
Clarke, B.
Clarke, D.
Clarke, Edward
Clarke, I.
Clarke, M.
Clarke, Paul
Clarke, R.
Clarke, S.
Clarke, Vivian
Clarkson, Norman
Clarkson, Ron
Clarkson, Rosemary
Clayton, Gerry
Clayton, Margaret
Clegg, Dick
Clibbon, Brooke
Cline, Bev
Clough, A.
Clulow, George
Cnossen, Andy
Cnossen, Jenny
Coates, Dave
Cober, A.
Code, D.
Coderre, Elaine
Coe, Colin
Coffin, Ed
Cohen, Robin
Colby, C.H.
Colby, Gwen
Colby, Norris A.
Coldham, Frank
Coldwell, Barry
Cole, Joan

Collard, Paul
Collicut, Lorne
Colling, Richard
Collings, Brande
Collins, Henry A.
Collins, Jack M.
Collins, Mary
Collins, Peter
Collins, R.H.W.
Collins, Tom
Collinson, Shiela
Coltman, A.W.
Coltman, M.A.
Comer, John
Comfort, David
Como, G.
Condrashoff, S.F.
Congreve, W.M.
Conner, C.F.
Conti, Barbara
Conway, Kay
Cook, Ann
Cook, C.
Cook, F. Stanley
Cook, R.A.
Cook, Vernon
Cooke, F.
Coombes, Tom
Cooper, Albert
Cooper, Aziza
Cooper, Bunny
Cooper, Carrie
Cooper, Daphne
Cooper, Dave
Cooper, Dianne L.P.
Cooper, Dick
Cooper, Dorothy
Cooper, Dwane
Cooper, Heather
Cooper, Henry
Cooper, John K.
Cooper, John M.
Cooper, Louise
Cooper, Richard
Cooper, S.
Cooper, Walter
Coopland, Peter
Copeland, F.G.
Copping, Edna N.
Copping, Harold
Copping, R.P.
Corbet, Lew
Corbett, A.
Corbett, J.N.
Corderi, Merrilly
Corey, D.
Corey, James
Cormack, F.
Corman, J.
Cornall, F.A.
Corner, John
Cornish, Willa
Cornwall, Sonia
Corrance, Ian
Corrigan, Anne
Corry, M.
Cortez, Pascal
Cossentine, C.
Cossentine, E.R.
Costanzo, Brenda
Coste, S.

Côte, Serge
Cotton, Ray
Coulson, Evi
Coulson, Mel
Coulter, Annie
Coulter, Bob
Coulter, Eric
Coulter, Pat
Counsell, Eric
Counsell, Jean
Coutts, H.
Cowal, Doug
Cowan, Walt
Cowie, John T.
Cowley, Cliff
Cowlin, Charles
Cowlin, Sybil
Cox, Bryan
Cox, Les
Cox, Stephen
Cox, Terry
Coyle, R.L.
Crabbe, Joan
Crabtree, Tom
Crack, David T.
Craig, Gordon
Craig, Jean
Craig, Muriel
Craig, Noel
Crampton, Heather
Craven, Ruth
Crawford, Dosie
Crawford, Scott
Crichlow, E.
Crins, William J.
Critch, Marion
Critchlow, P.R.
Croft, Phil
Crook, Heather
Crook, W.D.
Cross, Janet
Cross, Mark
Crossman, E.
Crowe, Jim
Crowther, Marjorie
Crowthers, O.
Crystal, Bill
Cullen, L.
Cuming, Jean
Cumming, June
Cumming, Sue
Cunningham, Albert
Cunningham, Don
Cunningham, John
Cunningham, Marge
Cupp, Keith
Curran, Frances
Currie, H.H.
Currie, James
Curson, Jon
Curtain, Fred
Curtis, D.
Cuthbert, James
Cuthbert, Ross
Cutler, Herky
Dafoe, Eric
Dafoe, Peggy
Dahl, Kelly
Dahlke, Anna M.
Dale, Betty
Dale, Jack

Dale-Johnson, V.
Daloise, Richard
Daly, Carol
Daly, Eugene
Daly, Mark K.
Dance, Patti
Daniels, Wes
Danlock, Tye
Darby, Nancy
Darling, Jim
Darnall, Ruth A.
Darney, Judy
Darney, Mike
Dascon, D.
Dates, Steve
Daughty, Harry
Davenport, George
David, Art
Davidson, Albert R.
Davidson, Douglas
Davidson, Eleanor
Davidson, Gary S.
Davidson, Gordon
Davidson, Harry
Davidson, Marie
Davidson, Mary
Davidson, P.W.
Davidson, Peter J.
Davidson, Sarah
Davidson, Terry
Davies, A.R.
Davies, Bill
Davies, Brian
Davies, David
Davies, Doris
Davies, Dorothy
Davies, J.
Davies, Jennifer
Davies, K.
Davies, Lloyd
Davies, Rick G.
Davies, Roy
Davies, Thomas R.
Davis, D.G.
Davis, Ed
Davis, Edna
Davis, John
Davis, Lyndis
Davis, Margaret
Davis, Martin
Davis, S.K.
Dawdrey, Ernie
Dawe, George G.
Dawe, Jordan T.
Dawe, Karen E.
Dawe, Lynn R.
Dawe, Neil K.
Dawson, Jim
Dawson, John
Dawson, Rick
Day, Betty
Day, Colleen
Day, F.
De Burg, H.
De Jong, Westman M.M.
DeAngeles, Milo
DeBourdais, Lorraine
DeGeus, Nell
DeWitt, Art
DeWitt, Louis
Deagle, George

Deakin, D.
Deakin, Ronald
Dean, Anna
Dean, O.S.
Deanna, M.
Deas, Alec
Debent, Anne
de Boon, Arnold
de Boon, Frank
Decamp, Gwen
Decker, Dick
Demarchi, Raymond
Denis, David
Denison, R.A.
Dephyffer, John
Deptford, Vera
Dergthorson, F.
De Rousie, D.
Dery, E.
Desbrosse, Alain
Desrochers, Barbara
Devereux, Stan
Deveson, Bert
Dewitt, Larry
Diack, George
Diakow, Brent
Diakow, Joan
Diakow, Thor M.
Diakow, Wayne
Dibb, Allan
Dicer, Pam
Dick, Asher
Dick, Clarence
Dick, Gary M.
Dick, John
Dick, Pauline
Dickens, H.B.
Dickenson, Frances
Dickenson, George
Dickson, B.
Dickson, Doug
Dickson, Elaine
Dickson, J.
Dickson, Peter
Dickson, W.M.
Diduck, Dorothy
Diederichs, Ron
Diggle, Paul
Dilabio, Bruce
Dillabough, Cecil A.
Dillabough, Eileen D.
Din, Nasar A.
Dingman, Frank
Dingman, Helen
Dinsdale, Graham
Dinse, David
Dion, C.
Dionne, Suzie
Dirkson, Bob
Dirkson, Irene
Dirom, C.
Disney, John
Dites, G.
Dixon, J.
Dobson, Carrie
Dobson, David
Dobson, Donald
Dobson, Fred W.
Dobson, Ken
Dobson, Una
Dobson, Wendy K.

Dohan, Nancie J.
Dolan, Ethel
Donald, J.
Donald, Stephen
Donald, Tom
Donaldson, D.
Donaldson, Ed
Dooley, Brent
Dooley, Robert A.
Dorfer, M.
Dorst, Adrian
Dorst, Suzanne
Doubleday, Jody
Doubleday, Michael
Dougan, Harold
Dougan, Ida
Doughton, B.
Douglas, Aileen C.
Douglas, John
Douglas, Paul
Douglas, Quinn
Douglas, Sheila
Dow, Chris
Dow, Douglas D.
Dow, Margaret A.
Dowding, Bill
Dowling, D.B.
Downey, Phyl
Doyle, D.D.
Drabit, Aaron
Draper, Sid
Drent, Rudolf H.
Drew, Betty
Drew, Bill
Drew, Miles
Drewbrook, Robert
Drexel, Darrel
Drinnal, Warren
Drought, Brian
Duchastel, Andrea
Duchastel, Tom
Duffus, Al
Dumond, F.A.
Dumont, Floyd
Dunbar, David
Dunbar, Lu
Duncan, Adrian
Duncan, David
Duncan, Fred
Duncan, Lyn
Dundas, Bob
Dunham, C.
Dunlop, Florence
Dunn, J.
Dunn, Michael
Dunn, Pat
Dunn, Valerie
Dunning, Jesse
Dupilka, Allan
Dupilka, Becky
Durand, Chips
Durell, Linda
Durkee, Art
Dutton, Marilyn
Dwyer, D.
Dyck, E.
Dyer, Bob
Dyer, Michael
Eadie, John
Earl, Gordon T.
Eastman, Donald S.

Contributors

Ebel, G.R.A.
Ebel, John
Ebel, Roy
Eberts, Tony
Eccles, Brian
Eckman, R.
Eddy, G.
Eddy, Harold
Eddy, Lorrie
Eddy, Mike
Eddy, Robbie
Ede, H.
Eden, Don R.
Edenshaw, Jaalen
Edenshaw, Jenny
Edgar, Joshua
Edge, J.
Edgell, Michael C.R.
Edie, Alan
Edward, Anne
Edwards, Barry
Edwards, Dan
Edwards, Eddie
Edwards, Fred
Edwards, George
Edwards, Glen
Edwards, O.A.
Edwards, R. Yorke
Edwards, Yvonne
Egely, Mary E.
Egg, C.W.
Egger, K.
Ehman, Gerry
Eisenmann, E.
Eisser, Doug
Eldridge, George
Eldridge, Ros
Elias, Mel
Ellames, Peggy
Ellingsen, Carl
Ellingsen, David
Elliot, D.W.
Elliot, E.
Elliot, J.A.
Elliot, Jim
Elliot, Peter
Elliot, Ritchie
Elliott, Gillian H.
Elliott, John
Elliott, Peter W.
Ellis, Barbara
Ellis, David V.
Ellis, David W.
Ellis, Rick
Ellis, Steve
Ellis, W.C.
Ellison, Maurice
Elmore, D.T.
Elphinstone, D.
Elsasser, Doug
Elston, Alice L.
Elston, Suzanne M.
Embleton, Nonie
Embleton, Tony
Emery, Chuck
Emery, Robert
Emes, J.
Emmaneel, Klaus
Emory, B.
Emrich, Ralph W.
Enderwick, Peter

Endicott, O.R.
Endwick, Peter D.
Eng, Marvin
England, Lindie
England, Phillip
Englestonft, Chreistan
Erasmus, G.
Erasmus, J.
Ericksen, J.R.
Erickson, Harriette
Erickson, Ron
Erickson, Wayne
Ernest, L.
Ernest, W.
Ernst, Rick
Erskine, Anthony J.
Escott, Christopher J.
Escott, Ralph W.
Eshleman, Valerie Ann
Esouloff, Lorna
Esralson, Lloyd
Estock, Trudy
Etzkorn, J.
Evans, Chuck
Evans, Darcy
Evans, Dave
Evans, Grant
Evans, Jack
Evans, Joan
Evans, Marie
Evans, Theodore
Evans, Tim
Everette, Valene
Ewart, Anna
Exworthy, R. June
Faasse, Tambrey
Faigin, Sybill
Fair, Brent
Fair, Joan
Fairbairn, Steve
Fairhurst, P.
Fairley, J.
Fairley, K.
Fairweather, Noreen
Fallis, Dave
Fallis, Mary
Fallis, Mike
Falls, J. Bruce
Famer, H.
Farley, Ted
Farmer, Joanna
Farr, Anthea
Fawcett, Ian
Fawcett, S.
Fedoruk, Alan
Fedoruk, Andrew
Feick, Jenny
Feltner, Ben
Feltner, L.
Fenwick, A.A.
Ferrario, Giovanni
Ferris, Jeanne
Ferris, Ken
Fieldgate, W.
Fields, Norman
Filgate, Harry
Finch, Joanna
Finch, Terry
Findlater, Jane
Findley, Finola
Finegan, Rory

Fink, J.
Finlay, B.
Finley, Becky
Finzel, J.E.
Fish, Gordon
Fisher, D. Ross
Fisher, Dean
Fisher, J.G.
Fisher, Len
Fisher, Martin
Fisher, R.
Fitch, John
Fitz-Gibbon, Joyce
Fitzpatrick, Erma
Fitzpatrick, Irmie
Fitzpatrick, John
Fitzpatrick, Michael
Fitzpatrick, Walter J.
Flahaut, Martha
Flaherty, Marg
Fleck, E.
Flellow, Len
Fleming, K.J.
Fletcher, B.B.
Fletcher, Ross
Fletcher, Russell
Flett, J.A.
Fleury, Norman
Flowerdew, G.
Floyd, Randy
Foessler, Lorraine
Fohr, Brian
Folbegg, Joyce
Fontaine, J.
Fontaine, L.
Fontaine, Marlene
Fooks, A.
Fooks, H.A.
Foote, R.
Foottit, Michael K.
Foottit, Robert G.
Forbes, Bob
Forbes, Joe
Forbes, L. Scott
Forbes, Robert
Forbes, Susan
Forbes, Ted
Force, Michael
Ford, A.H.
Ford, Bruce S.
Ford, John
Ford, Ron
Ford, Victor
Ford, William
Foreman, Barbara
Forer, Barry
Forman, Barry
Fornataro, Mark
Forrest, Margaret
Forrester, Shelly
Forryan, Doreen
Forsman, Eric D.
Forster, Mary
Forster, Nancy
Forsyth, Evelyn
Fortin, Shawn
Forty, T.
Foskett, Ann
Foskett, Dudley
Foss, Ray
Foster, A.

Foster, B.
Foster, Eric
Foster, G.G.
Foster, Ian
Foster, J. Bristol
Foster, Jack W.
Foster, M.
Foubister, M.
Foulser, Art
Fowle, D.
Fowle, J.T.
Fowler, Fran
Fowler, Scott
Fox, J.
Fox, L.
Fox, Rosemary
Fox, S.D.
Foxall, Roger
Fram, Roland
Francis, Brian
Francis, G.
Frank, Floyd
Frank, P.
Franken, John P.
Franklin, D.H.
Franklin, June
Franklin, R.
Franko, G.
Fraser, A.
Fraser, Bill
Fraser, David F.
Fraser, Douglas P.
Fraser, Joan
Fraser, Kitsy
Fraser, M.A.
Fraser, Nancy
Fraser, Tom A.
Fraser, William
Frazer, Evelyn
Frazer, Frank
Frederick, Bruce G.
Freebairn, Tom
French, Brigitte
Freshwater, N.G.
Frew, Gordon
Frewin, M.
Friberg, Sherrie
Fricke, Patricia
Fried, S.
Friedli, E.
Friend, G.B.
Friesz, Ron
Friis, Laura K.
Frisby, Alan
Froese, Dave
Froese, Susan
Froimovitch, Mark J.
Frost, Bud
Frost, D. Lorne
Frost, M.L.
Fry, B.
Fry, Kathleen
Fryer, Ralph
Fuhr, Brian L.
Fuhrer, Hans
Fujino, Ken K.
Fulton, Murrey
Funk, Phyllis
Furniss, O.C.
Fusco, L.
Futur, G.

Fyall, Gerrie
Fyles, J.
Fynn, Sonia
Gabreau, Martin
Gadsen, Ron
Gage, Kim
Gainer, Bob
Gak, Janice
Gak, Marc
Galbraith, Florence
Galbraith, J. Douglas
Gale, Alf
Galicz, George
Galliford, J.
Galloway, Phyllis
Galt, Betty
Gamble, Eleanor
Gammer, A.
Ganguin, Reiner
Gardiner, Mark
Gardner, Gerry
Gardner, Ivan
Gardner, Joe
Gardner, Penny
Gardner, W.E.
Gariett, C.
Garlick, Ella
Garneau, Larry
Garnier, Donald
Garnier, Hattie
Garrioch, Hans
Garrioch, Heather M.
Gaskin, Jeff
Gasser, Ellen
Gaston, Anthony J.
Gates, Bryan R.
Gates, Conrad
Gaunt, Sean
Gawn, Mark
Gaze, D.
Gebauer, Martin
Gee, Andrea
Geernaert, Karen
Geernaert, T.O.
Geeroms, Darryn
Gehlert, R.E.
Gehlin, Phil
Geist, V.
George, D.V.
George, H.E.
George, Val
Gerow, Dave
Gerow, Helen
Gibbard, Fern
Gibbard, H.J.
Gibbard, Les A.
Gibbard, P.
Gibbard, Robert T.
Gibbard, Violet
Gibbon, Robert
Gibbons, Bob
Gibbons, Jeanette
Gibbons, Terry
Gibbons, Tim
Gibbs, Andrew E.
Gibbs, Nicholas
Gibbs, Richard E.
Gibson, A.
Gibson, Carlen
Gibson, Daniel D.
Gibson, D.E.

Gibson, G.G.
Gibson, Ian
Gibson, Kenneth
Gibson, Kevin
Gibson, Pete
Gieson, Cyril
Gifford, Bruce
Gifford, Janet
Gilbert, Frank
Gilbert, Laura
Giles, Lorna
Gill, Cathy
Gill, Leslie
Gillard, Margaret
Gilles, A.S.
Gilles, Cathy
Gillespie, Grahame
Gillies, Barry
Gillingham, Michael
Gillis, W.M.
Gilmour, Bill
Giovanella, Carlo
Girard, Mark
Gissing, A.
Gladstone, B.
Glasgow, Nancy
Glazier, Bob
Glenny, Jim
Glide, Margaret
Glover, Bev
Gobbett, M.
Goble, Edie
Goble, Jim
Godau, Helmut
Goddard, Peter
Godfrey, Dudley
Godfrey, Monica
Godfrey, W. Earl
Godin, Tom
Godkin, Sharon
Godlien, Pat
Goff, A.
Goff, D.
Goff, H.
Gold, G.R.
Gold, P.
Goldberg, Kim
Golden, Linda
Golden, Sandy
Gonzales, B.
Good, Ed
Goodacre, Brian W.
Goodall, Kay
Goodwill, J.E. Victor
Goodwill, Margaret E.
Goodwin, Kent
Goodwin, Lance
Goodwin, Mark
Goodwin, Ruth
Goold, Joan
Goossen, J. Paul
Gorden, John
Gordon, Amelia
Gordon, Bruce
Gordon, Janette
Gordon, John
Gordon, K.
Gordon, Ruth
Gordon, Sheila
Gorman, Wyn
Gorog, K.

Gorsuch, C.V.
Gosling, A.G.
Gosling, Gordon D.
Goudie, Douglas M.
Gough, C.F.
Gould, Glen
Gould, Lenny
Gould, Lorne
Gould, T.C.
Goulet, Louise
Goward, Trevor
Goysuch, C.
Grabowski, Tony J.
Grady, Glen
Graenager, Earl
Graf, Ronald P.
Graham, David
Graham, Elaine
Graham, J. Douglas
Graham, Jim
Graham, Sheila
Graham, Walter
Granger, Ted
Grant, James
Grant, Peg
Grant, Robert
Grant-Duff, Adrian
Grass, Al
Grass, Jude F.
Gray, Alex
Gray, Chris
Gray, David
Gray, Dennis
Gray, Jim
Gray, N.
Gray, Ron
Gray, Tom
Greber, W.
Green, A.
Green, C. De B.
Green, Daphne
Green, David M.
Green, T.R.
Green, William
Greene, R.K.
Greener, Karl
Greenfield, Tony
Gregory, Ann
Gregory, M.S.
Gregory, Patrick T.
Gregson, Jack
Grenager, Earl
Grewer, D.
Grierson, John
Griffin, Mark
Griffin, R.V.
Griffiths, Pele
Grigg, Garry J.
Griggs, Tamar
Grinnel, Dick
Groenveld, Anna
Gronau, Christian W.
Gronau, Steffi G.
Gross, A.
Grossman, Eric
Grotage, Loyd
Grove, Sarah
Gruener, Karl
Grunberg, Helmut
Guernsey, Vera
Guest, Catherine

Guest, Harold
Guiguet, Charles J.
Guiguet, M.L.
Guiguet, Suzanne M.
Guillon, Frank E.
Guinet, Allan
Guinet, Frances
Guinet, Lynn
Guinet, Victor
Gully, P.
Gunther, Jack
Guppy, A.G.
Guppy, G.A.
Gurr, Ray
Gustafson, Barbara
Gustafson, Richard
Guthrie, David
Guthrie, Don
Guthrie, Jim
Gwilliam, John
Gyug, Les
Haas, Norma
Haavik, Andre
Haavik, Colleen
Haavik, Steven
Hack, F.W.
Hackett, John
Hackett, Kathy
Hackett, Shannon
Haddow, W.
Haegart, John
Haering, Penny
Hagen, Barry
Hagen, Betty
Hagen, Catherine
Hagen, Patricia
Haggart, Lee
Haggert, Leona
Hagmeier, E.M.
Hahn, Rick J.
Haig-Brown, Roderick
Halasz, Gabor
Hale, Hilda L.
Hales, D.
Halfnights, B.
Hall, Brian
Hall, D.
Hall, E.R.S.
Hall, J.
Hall, Ken
Hall, W.A.
Halladay, D. Raymond
Halliday, Erik
Halliday, R.L.
Halliday, Valerie
Halverson, Larry
Halz, Gabbro
Hamel, Peter J.
Hames, A.M.
Hames, Michael
Hamilton, Anthony N.
Hamilton, Daphne
Hamilton, Dulcie
Hamilton, John
Hamilton, K.
Hamilton, Marla
Hamilton, Richard
Hamilton, W.
Hammell, Terry
Hammill, Sally
Hammond, D.

Hammond, Elsie
Hammond, Jo
Hammond, Vi
Hanceville, Dorothy
Handford, Paul
Handley, Catherine
Handley, L.
Hann, Paddy
Hannam, May
Hansen, J.
Hansen, Marilyn
Hansen, Ruth
Hansen, Stanley
Hansen, Vicky
Hanson, David
Hanson, Don
Hanson, L.
Hanson, Wayne G.
Hansvall, Erling
Hansvall, Louise
Haraldson, T.
Haras, Moreen
Haras, W.
Harcombe, Andrew P.
Harcombe, Rick
Hardie, David
Harding, Martha
Harding, Rob
Hardley, C.
Hards, Jennifer
Hardstaff, Lynn
Hardwick, S.
Hardy, Bill
Hardy, Chuck
Hardy, David
Hardy, Duncan
Hardy, G.A.
Hardy, Phyllis
Hardy, W.
Harestad, Alton S.
Hargrave, A. Nairn
Hark, F.W.
Harlock, F.
Harlow, Susan
Harman, Barry C.
Harms, W.
Harper, Charles
Harper, Don
Harper, Fred E.
Harper, John
Harper, Lynn
Harrington, R.F.
Harris, A.E.
Harris, B.J.
Harris, Brian S.
Harris, Chris
Harris, Christopher G.
Harris, Elizabeth
Harris, G.J.
Harris, Margaret
Harris, Nancy
Harris, P.
Harris, R.P.
Harris, Robert D.
Harris, Ron
Harris, Ross E.
Harrison, John
Harrison, Julian D.
Harrison, Linda
Harrison, William
Hart, A.M.

Hart, Carole
Hart, E.H.
Hart, F. Gordon
Hart, J.G.
Hart, J.S.
Hart, Kit
Hart, Lauren
Hart, Mark
Hart, Ted
Hartland, D.
Hartland, G.
Hartman, F.
Hartman, G.
Hartman, Harold
Hartman, Mary
Hartt, E.A.
Hartwick, E. Brian
Harvard, Peggy
Harvey, Merle
Harvey, Richard
Harvey, Virginnia
Harwell, W.
Haslam, Cathy
Hassell, Sharon
Hatfield, John
Hatler, David F.
Hatler, Mareca
Hatler, Mary Eta
Hatter, D.
Hatter, I.
Hatter, James
Haughan, Linda
Haun, Ariel
Hauser, Pearl
Haven, Stoner
Hawes, David B.
Hawes, David M.
Hawes, James
Hawes, Myrnal A.L.
Hawken, J.
Hawken, M.
Hawkey, G.
Hawkins, J.
Hawksley, Janet
Haworth, Kent
Hay, E.A.
Hay, Heather
Hay, Robert B.
Hayden, M.A.
Hayes, Eric
Hayes, Lauren
Hayes, Maryann
Hayes, Richard
Haylock, Cliff
Haylock, Linda
Hayman, Gus
Hayman, Tom
Haynes, Muriel
Hayton, B.
Hayton, M.
Hazelwood, Grant W.
Heakes, Todd
Healey, John
Healy, Michael
Hearn, David
Hearn, Dorothy
Hearn, Ed
Hearn, O.
Hearne, Georgina
Hearne, Margo E.
Heathman, R.L.

Hebert, Daryl
Hedley, A.F.
Heintz, Gretta
Helleiner, Fred
Helset, R.
Henderson, Bryan A.
Henderson, Martha
Henderson, Michael
Henderson, Nolan
Henderson, Nonie
Henderson, Otto
Henderson, Phil
Henderson, Valerie
Hendra, Isabel
Hendricks, Allan
Hendricks, Gus
Henkins, Harmon
Henn, Keith
Hennan, Ed G.
Hennig, Karla
Henning, E.E.
Henning, Mrs. E.E.
Henry, G.
Henry, John
Henry, Margaret
Henson, Colen
Henson, Gary
Henson, P.
Henson, Simon
Herbert, B.
Herbert, William S.
Herbison, B.
Heriot, Joan E.
Herr, G.R.
Hervieux, Margot
Herzig, R.J.
Hesse, Hilde
Hesse, Werner H.
Hetherington, Anne E.
Hett, M.
Hettis, Rob
Hewson, C.A.
Heybrock, Bill
Heyland, J.B.
Heywood, J.
Hickson, Cathie
Higginson, T.
Highe, Barbara
Highe, Donald
Hill, B.
Hill, Dorothy
Hill, L.
Hill, Mark
Hill, P.
Hill, Robert
Hill, Roy
Hillaby, Bruce
Hillard, R.W.
Hillier, George
Hilligan, D.
Hilligan, S.
Hillis, Nancy
Hilton, Jim
Hinckle, David
Hind-Smith, John
Hindson, Mr.
Hindson, Mrs.
Hines, Garfield
Hinton, J.L.
Hippen, H.
Hirschbolz, Heinz

Hirschbolz, Marlene
Hirst, Stanley
Hitchmough, John
Hlady, Debbie
Hoar, Carol
Hoar, N.J.
Hoar, Rick J.
Hoar, Robin
Hoar, W.
Hobeck, Erika
Hobson, Alan
Hobson, Cam
Hobson, J. Fred
Hobson, James
Hobson, Kerry
Hobson, Mark
Hobson, Marie
Hobson, Shirley
Hochachka, W.
Hocker, Pat
Hocking, Jack
Hocking, Jennifer H.
Hodgins, Betty
Hodson, C.
Hodson, Keith
Hoek, Jane
Hogarth, L.
Hogg, Edward
Hogg, Lori
Holden, D.
Holdom, Canon M.W.
Holland, David
Holland, M.
Holland, R.H.
Holland, Stephen
Hollands, Grant R.
Hollands, J.
Hollington, Jack
Hollington, Madge
Holloway, Lawrence
Holm, Margaret
Holman, John H.
Holman, M.
Holman, P.J.
Holmes, Brian
Holmes, George
Holmes, J.
Holmes, Ken
Holmes, Marc
Holmes, Norman
Holmes, Philip
Holms, Maureen
Holohan, Stewart
Holroyd, Geoff
Holsworth, W.N.
Holt, Beryl H.
Holt, John C.
Hood, Terry
Hook, R.
Hooke, J.
Hooper, Bob
Hooper, Daryl
Hooper, Gordon N.
Hooper, Gwennie
Hooper, Joan
Hooper, Mary
Hooper, Ronald
Hooper, Tracey D.
Hooper, Win
Hope, Herbert
Hopkins, Kay

Hopkins, Vera
Hopkinson, Bubsie
Hopp, Diane
Horn, Dorothy
Horn, J.C.
Horncastle, G.S.
Horne, L.
Horner, N.
Horvath, Otto
Horwood, Brenda
Horwood, Dennis
Hosford, Harold
Hosie, S.
Hosman, P.
Hotchkiss, C.T.
Houlhen, M.
House, H.B.
Houston, Bob
Houston, C.
Houston, G.F.
Houston, M.L.
Houston, R.
Howaldt, Jorg
Howard, B.
Howard, Maureen
Howard, R.G.
Howden, Patrick F.
Howe, Ann
Howe, N.I.
Howe, R.S.
Howe, Robert W.
Howell, Steven N.G.
Howes, Anne
Howie, Gordon
Howie, Richard R.
Howie, Thomas
Howland, E.R.
Howlett, Bruce
Howsam, Judy
Hoyer, G.A.
Hudson, Janet
Huett, Jim
Huett, Patsy
Huggard, Dave
Huggett, Colin
Hughes, Brenda
Hughes, Wm. M.
Hume, Alison
Humeniuk, Natalie
Humphries, Dianne
Hunley, W.
Hunn, Eugene
Hunt, Bob
Hunt, George
Hunt, Robert
Hunter, Bill
Hunter, Elizabeth
Hunter, Gary
Hunter, Joan
Hunter, John
Hunter, Paul
Hunter, Rodger
Hunter, T.
Huntington, Mary E.
Huppler-Poliak, Amy
Hurst, T.
Hustead, Eileen
Hustead, Jack
Hustead, Lynn
Hutchinson, Bob
Hutchinson, Neil

Huxley, Bill
Huxley, Mae
Hyatt, Ron
Hyde, A.S.
Hyde, Eric
Hyde, Frank
Hyde, George
Hyslop, Joyce
Ibera, Carlos
Iden, Bill
Iden, Margaret
Idu, Terry
Ikona, Katherina
Ikona, Richard
Ingles, Joan
Inglis, Rolli
Inkster, C.
Innes, Douglas W.
Innes, Marian
Innes, Martin
Ireland, John
Ireland, Teresa
Irons, Byron
Irvine, Bob
Irvine, Elsie
Irvine, Jean
Irving, Bruce K.
Irving, E. Bruce
Irving, Lyn
Irving, Peggy
Irwin, Alan
Irwin, Barbara
Irwin, Bob
Irwin, Jack
Irwin, Joel
Irwin, Kate
Irwin, Ki
Iverson, J.
Jack, Ian
Jacklin, Isabel
Jackson, Andrew
Jackson, Anne
Jackson, George
Jackson, J.
Jackson, Mary F.
Jacobs, A.E.
Jacobs, Karen
Jacobson, Tom
Jacobson, W.
Jacques, Art
Jacques, Tommy
Jakimchuk, R.D.
James, David
James, Eleanor E.
James, Jennie
James, Paul C.
James, Ross D.
James, Ted
James-Veitch, E.A.
Jamieson, Glen
Jamieson, Jean
Jamieson, Mrs. Glen
Jamison, Eric
Jamison, Margaret
Janelle, Yvan
Janes, Russell W.
Janyk, Barry
Janz, Douglas W.
Jaques, Tim
Jarvie, I.
Jay, K.

Jeal, Margaret
Jeal, Mary
Jean, Cheryl
Jeffrey, R.
Jellett, Jim
Jellicoe, Janice
Jenkerson, Douglas
Jenkins, Eric
Jenkins, Jane E.
Jenkins, Lynn J.
Jenkins, Mildred
Jenkins, Pam
Jenkins, Ron L.
Jenne, M.
Jennings, Gerald
Jennings, Iris
Jensen, B.A.
Jensen, Dale
Jensen, Eve
Jenson, Loraine
Jentsch, Carl
Jerema, Michael
Jerema, Richard S.
Jeroschewitz, Valerie
Jessop, P.
Johns, N.
Johnson, Albert
Johnson, Ann
Johnson, Daryl
Johnson, Donald A.
Johnson, Fran
Johnson, G.
Johnson, H.
Johnson, K.F.
Johnson, P.
Johnson, Sam
Johnson, Sigrid
Johnson, Stephen R.
Johnson, Terry
Johnson, Vern
Johnston, Aleda
Johnston, Dale
Johnston, David W.
Johnston, Dean
Johnston, Holly
Johnston, Jean
Johnston, Joan
Johnston, Larry
Johnston, Nancy
Johnston, Paul
Johnston, Richard
Johnston, Scott
Johnston, Stuart
Johnston, W.
Johnstone, Cecil
Joly, Stephen
Jones, Aaron
Jones, Ann
Jones, Dave
Jones, Don
Jones, Edgar T.
Jones, G.
Jones, Ian
Jones, Kate
Jones, Keith R.
Jones, Ken
Jones, Lindsay E.
Jones, Mike
Jones, Mildred
Jones, Peter
Jones, Robert D.

Jones, Ruth
Jones, Valerie
Jones, Wayne
Jones, William
Jorgensen, Mike
Joyce, Russ
Junck, Chris
Jury, Douglas
Jyrkkanen, Jorma
Kaiser, Dieter
Kaiser, Gary W.
Kaisner, George
Kalman, D.
Kalman, John
Kalmbach, Beverly
Kalmbach, Richard
Kantrim, Desi
Karger, Fritz
Karpuk, Allan
Karpuk, Betty
Karran, P.
Karst, Carl
Karup, Anthony
Karup, L.
Kashin, G.L.
Kautesk, Brian
Kay, A.T.
Kay, Ian
Keddie, Grant
Kedgh, Ruth
Keding, K.H.H.
Keith, Anthony
Keith, David
Keith, Mabel
Keith, Margaret
Keizer, Jasper
Kelleher, K.E.
Kellerhals, Heather
Kellerhals, Rolf
Kelley, Errol
Kelley, Janice
Kelly, Colleen
Kelly, Ethel
Kelly, Fran
Kelly, J.
Kelly, Mary
Kelly, Sean
Kelsey, Lee E.
Kembel, Vern
Kemmett, Dorothy
Kendall, Dean
Kendall, Frank
Kennah, J.
Kennedy, Archie
Kennedy, Bruce
Kennedy, D.M.
Kennedy, Ian D.
Kennedy, Kathryn
Kennedy, Ken
Kennedy, Kevin
Kennedy, Marilyn
Kennedy, R.
Kenner, Gail
Kenner, Rex
Kennett, Dorothy
Kenset, Sandra
Keogh, Ruth
Keranen, Eric
Kergin, A.J.
Kerr, Elspeth M.
Kerr, Frank

Kerr, M.
Kerr, T.
Kershaw, M.
Kidd, J.I.
Kidder, E.L.
Kihm, Ruth
Killough, Harry
Kime, Doris
Kime, Frank
Kimpton, Jerry
Kindrachuk, Sonia
King, Avery
King, David G.
King, Derek
King, Don
King, Frances
King, Freeman
King, H.
King, James
King, Jean
King, Joan
King, Peter
King, Rod
King, Wayne
Kingswood, S.
Kinsey, Sandra
Kippin, Ethel
Kippin, J.W.C.
Kirbyson, John
Kirchner, Lothar
Kirkpatrick, F.
Kirkvold, Sherry
Kirschner, Ed
Kirschner, Ute
Kirychk, Walter
Kitson, Alan R.
Klassen, Barry
Klein, Kathy
Kline, C.R.
Kline, Kelly
Knapton, Richard W.
Knecht, Ernie
Knezevich, Gladys
Knezevich, John
Knight, Pat
Knight, Richard
Knowles, Anne
Knowles, David
Knowles, Ken
Knowles, Les
Knowles, Peter
Knowlson, Bill
Koch, Dorothy
Koch, Linda
Koechl, Rick
Koenig, D.F.
Kolstertan, A.
Konkin, Lorne
Kool, Richard
Koonts, Ralph
Koop, Frank
Kormski, Henry
Kormski, Mae
Koth, Edgar
Kowalczyk, L.W.
Kragh, Heather
Kragh, W. Douglas
Krahe, Rolf G.
Krebs, C.
Krebs, John R.
Kremsater, Laurie

Kremsater, Terry
Kribs, J.
Kroek, Jake
Kronlund, A.R.
Krown, Daronne
Krueger, Nancy
Krul, Jane
Kuipers, C.
Kuipers, S.
Kukan, Barbara
Kuntz, Christine
Kuschmin, A.M.
Kuyt, Ernie
Kyle, Brian
L'Ecuyer, Sylvia
Laberge, Frank
Lacey, E.
Lacey, M.
Lacey, P.
Lacon, H.R.
Ladbury, Joan
Laeser, Lynne
Lafave, L.D.
Lafontaine, J.D.
Laforme, George
Laforme, Margaret
Laishey, D.
Lalonde, Maurice
Lamb, Evelyn
Lamb, Helen
Lamb, J.
Lambert, Marilyn A.
Lambert, Phil
Lambert, Wendy
Lambin, Xavier
Lamond, Barry
Lamond, Bill
Lamont, Peter
Lamoureux, E.
Lancaster, R.
Lance, A.N.
Lanchester, Frank
Land, J.
Landry, Gaetan
Lane, Dale
Lane, David
Lane, L.P.
Lane, Les
Lang, Ken
Lang, Sylvia D.
Langdale-Smith, R.
Langer, Ann
Langevin, Arnica
Langevin, Kathy
Langevin, Marlene
Langin, H.
Langley, Lin
Lanko, Joyce
Lansdell, Jane
Lansdowne, Edith
Lansdowne, J. Fenwick
Larkey, J.
Laserre, L.
Lau, Alfred
Laub, Fred
Law, D.
Law, George
Law, Laird
Lawrason, M.G.
Lawrence, Alysoun
Lawrence, Arlene

Lawrence, David
Lawrence, Donald
Lawrence, Gary
Lawrence, Howard
Lawrence, Joanne
Lawrence, Kathleen
Lawrence, Susan
Lawrence, Theresa
Lawrenson, Lee
Laws, Ann
Lawson, Doreen
Lawson, E.H.
Lawson, John
Lawson, Steve
Lay, A.M.
Lay, Dan W.
Lay, R.
LeBaron, Ama
LeBaron, Robert
LeBourdais, Lorraine
Leach, Barry D.
Leadem, Carol
Leadem, Tim
Leaky, Mrs.
Leckie, C.P.
Leckie, Robert
Lecky, B.M.
Lee, Joyce
Lee, Martin C.
Lee, Tom
Lee, Wally
Lees, Sybil
Legate, Gail
Legg, K.
Legg, Peter
Lehman, Paul
Leighton, Douglas A.
Leinor, R.
LeJeune, John
Lellis, C.
Lemke, B.J.
Lemon, Enid K.
Lemon, Moira
Lenfesty, Jack
Lepin, Lynne
Leslie, Edna
Lester, Jody
Lester, Robert
Leveson-Gower, Heather
Levey, Don
Levey, Edith
Levy, E.
Lewall, B.C.
Lewall, Nel
Lewis, David E.
Lewis, J.M.
Lewis, J.P.
Lewis, Lee
Lewis, Moray
Liboiron, Sonia
Light, L.
Lightle, Bob
Lilcox, Joan
Lima, Steven
Lincoln, Arthur
Lincoln, Neville
Lincoln, Robert
Lindsay, G.
Lindstrom, Carl
Lindstrom, Dick
Lines, Mary

Lines, Molly
Lissel, H.
Lisson, R.A.
Little, Bill
Little, Bonnie
Little, Brian
Little, Bruce
Little, R.S.
Little, Robert W.
Littlejohn, David
Littler, Leona
Living, Len
Lloyd, Bob
Lloyd, E.
Lloyd, Helen
Lloyd, Kevin
Lloyd-Walters, J.G.
Loan, D.
Lockhart, D.
Lockhart, Roy
Lodge, Terry
Loewan, David
Lofroth, Eric C.
Loftus, Linda J.
Logan, Douglas B.
Logan, Vernon
Long, Ken
Long, W.S.
Lopatecki, L.
Lopatecki, M.
Lorimer, J.
Lothian, Betty
Lott, Joan
Lott, Tom
Louise, Mary
Love, R.
Lovett, Nancy
Low, Bill
Low, Dave
Lubbers, I.
Luck, Alan
Luck, Brian E.
Luckock, Brian
Lucuik, George
Lukinchuk, Al
Lunam, Betty
Lunam, Jim
Lundell, D.
Lunn, Jerry
Luscher, Robert E.
Luton, Tony
Lutz, Hope
Lutz, Larry
Luz, Fritz X.
Luz, Michael
Lynott, Mary
Lyon, Allan M.
Lyons, C.P.
MacAdam, G.
MacBean, Eric
MacColl, M.C.
MacColl, M.D.
MacDonald, Alan B.
MacDonald, Alex
MacDonald, Bruce A.
MacDonald, Carrie
MacDonald, Doris
MacDonald, Eloise
MacDonald, Greg
MacDonald, Heather
MacDonald, Ian

MacDonald, Lorne
MacDonald, Mary Louise
MacDonald, Murray
MacDonald, Ross G.
MacDonald, S.D.
MacDougall, S.
MacFarlane, Nathalie
MacFarlane, S.
MacGillivray, Alice
MacHutchon, Grant
MacIntosh, Jim
MacKay, D.
MacKay, J.R.
MacKay, Naomi
MacKay, Violet
MacKenzie, Hue
MacKenzie, Jo Ann
MacKenzie, Roddy
MacLeod, Adrian
MacNaughton, C.
MacNaughton, Nancy
MacPhee, Darcy
MacPherson, Bill
MacPherson, F.
MacPherson, Peggy
MacTavish, Bruce
Macartney, J.M.
Macartney, M.
Macher, Marlene
Mack, Eva
Mack, Jim W.
Mack, Mary
Mackay, Ronald H.
Mackenzie-Grieve, Margaret
Mackenzie-Grieve, Rob
Mackie, A.C.
Maclean, Neil
Madsen, Katy
Madsen, Kim
Magee, Elda
Mageorsen, F.
Maginnis, D.
Mahoney, Brian
Mahoney, N.A.
Maitland, Victoria
Major, Jack
Malins, Daphne
Mallet, Leo
Mallory, Enid
Mallory, Gord
Maloff, Diana
Malone, M.
Malyae, Jim
Manly, Betts
Mantle, P.
Manuwal, David A.
March, E.
Marchant, Chris
Marcus, Norman
Mark, David M.
Mark, Murray
Mark, Thomas C.
Marsh, V.
Marshall, Brian
Marshall, Chad
Marshall, Gordon
Marshall, Maureen
Marshall, Rick
Marshall, Sandy
Marshall, Sherwood B.
Marshall, Wayne

Marshall, Wendy
Marshall, William
Marsman, Peter
Martel, Paul
Martell, Andre
Martell, Arthur M.
Martell, Hugh
Martell, Sue
Marten, Malcolm
Martin, Dale
Martin, David
Martin, Elfreda
Martin, Evan
Martin, Gary
Martin, Joan
Martin, Karen
Martin, Malcolm
Martin, Nancy
Martin, Patrick W.
Martin, Peter
Martin, Rae
Marty, K.
Mason, Alfred
Mason, Byron
Mason, George
Mason, Gwen
Mason, Red
Mason, Robert
Massam, G.
Masters, Grant
Masters, Ruth
Mathews, E.C.
Mathews, Gary
Mathews, Herb
Mathews, Rosemary
Mattews, Dave
Matthews, F.
Matthews, W.H.
Mauer, Bud
Mauer, Freda
Maulton, Robert
Maurer, April
Maurer, Frank
Maurer, Mary C.
Maxey, M.
Maxie, Tom
Maxted, Diane
May, Doug
May, Jim
May, Nancy
May, Val
Mayall, June
Mayall, Ken
Maynard, A.H.
Maynard, Edith
Maynard, Ken
Maynes, Dennis
Mayo, Ron
McAlary, Eric
McAlary, F.
McAlary, Lois
McAllister, Nancy
McAllister, Pamela
McAllister, Pat
McAllister, Peter B.
McBain, Dona
McBryde, Trevor
McCall, Stephen
McCallion, Bonnie
McCallion, Russell
McCamant, T.

McCammon, B.M.
McCammon, James W.
McCann, Dorothy
McCann, Mike
McCarten, Michael
McCaskie, Guy
McCaughran, D.A.
McClarnon, J.
McClarnon, S.
McClellam, M.
McColl, Bill
McConnell, Steve D.
McCord, B.
McCord, D.
McCormick, J.
McCrory, Wayne
McCuaig, Georgina
McCurdy, Dave
McDaniel, Caroline
McDevitt, D.C.
McDiarmid, Ray
McDonald, D.
McDouglas, J.
McEachern, J.A.
McEallion, Bonnie
McFarland, David E.
McFarlane, Nancy
McFeat, Marjorie
McFeat, Mark
McFetridge, Jerry
McGavin, Rosemarie
McGibbon, Jane
McGill, Allan S.
McGillis, Joe
McGillivray, W. Bruce
McGinnis, Ed
McGowam, Mary
McGregor, Ian
McGregor, Jo
McGregor, K.
McGregor, Robert
McGrenere, Barbara
McGrenere, Mike
McGrenere, Rob
McGuingle, Terry
McHaffie-Gow, Bertha
McHughs, William M.
McIlwain, Rick
McInnes, G.R.
McInnes, J.D.
McInnis, Nelson
McIntosh, Audrey
McIntosh, Dave
McIntosh, John D.
McIntosh, Lorne D.
McIntosh, M.
McIntosh, W.
McIntyre, Betty
McIntyre, Mary
McIntyre, Walt
McIntyre, William E.
McIvor, Don
McKay, George M.
McKay, P.
McKay, R.H.
McKay, W.A.
McKee, Mike
McKelvey, Richard W.
McKenzie, A.
McKenzie, Dawson
McKerron, Alison

McKie, Mike
McKim, Christine S.
McKinnon, Audrey
McKinnon, Betty
McKinnon, Bill
McKinnon, Joe
McLardy, R.
McLaren, Art
McLaren, Bill
McLaren, Faith
McLaren, I.
McLaren, Karen
McLaren, Margaret
McLaren, Muriel
McLaren, Peter
McLaren, W.D.
McLaren, W.E.
McLary, Eric
McLaughlin, John
McLaughlin, Donna
McLaughlin, Ronald T.
McLaurin, Lee
McLean, A.
McLean, Carina
McLean, Leslie
McLeish, Isobel
McLennan, Ken P.
McLennon, Betty
McLeod, Alan
McLeod, April
McLeod, Erin
McLeod, Frances
McLeod, J.B.
McLintock, B.J.
McMackin, Edward
McMahon, John
McMehan, Fred
McMillan, Daryl
McMillan, Jack
McMillan, Jean
McMillan, Susan
McMullen, Kathy
McMullen, R.D.
McNab, Randy
McNall, Faye
McNall, Michael C.E.
McNaughton, Ernie
McNaughton, J.
McNaughton, Peter
McNeely, Dick
McNeil, I.G.
McNichol, Keith
McNicholl, G.
McNicholl, Martin K.
McPhee, Don
McPherson, Frances
McQuillan, Susan
McQuinn, Betty
McRay, Martha
McRuer, Sandy
McTaggart-Cowan, Ian
McTaggart-Cowan, Joyce
McTavish, Al
McTeer, Wilma
McWhirter, J.L.
McWilliams, Anita
Meadowcroft, Neil F.
Mechie, D.
Meiklejohn, Barbara
Meiklejohn, J.M.
Meiklejohn, Michael

Contributors

Meiklejohn, Teresa
Melbourne, M.C.
Melderis, Martin
Mellett, Mary
Mennel, B.
Mennel, Tuke
Menzies, Charles R.
Mercer, G.
Mercer, Joseph
Mercer, Marie
Mercer, Michael
Mercer, Robert
Mercereau, Lorne
Meredith, C.B.
Merideth-Jones, Winnifred
Merilees, William J.
Merkens, Markus
Merlies, Bob
Merriman, J.D.
Mesley, Victor
Meteer, A.
Meteer, W.A.
Meugens, Arthur L.
Meunier, Maurice
Meyer, Angie
Meyer, Bonnie
Meyer, G.
Meyer, H.
Meyer, Roger
Meyer, Ron
Meyers, Anika
Michael, Paige
Michael, Peter
Middlemass, A.D.
Middleton, H.
Miles, Doris
Miles, Jack
Miles, Keith
Millar, Steve
Miller, Bob
Miller, Doris
Miller, Dusty
Miller, George
Miller, Harold
Miller, Hettie
Miller, Joan
Miller, Josie
Miller, June
Miller, Kate
Miller, Linda
Miller, Lynn
Miller, M.
Miller, M.D.
Miller, Michael
Miller, Ruby
Miller, Stella
Miller, Steve
Milligan, D.
Milligan, Tony
Mills, A.
Mills, Eric L.
Mills, Marjorie
Mills, Maureen
Millward, Peter J.
Miln, H.
Milne, G.
Milne, R.
Milne, W.
Milnes, Lynne
Mitchell, George J.
Mitchell, J.

Mitchell, Marjorie
Mitchell, Nora
Mitchell, Paul
Mitchell, R.P.
Mitchell, Steve
Mitchell, W.
Mitchell-Banks, B.
Miyamoto, Susie
Mock, B.
Mock, Ralph
Mogensen, Faye
Mollet, L.
Mollet, M.
Molnar, Les
Molyneux, Betty
Monahan, Hugh
Moncton, P.M.
Mondey, Dave
Montador, Marian
Montague, P.
Monteith, W.B.
Montgomery, Gill
Montgomery, Pat
Moody, Anne I.
Moody, Ed
Moody, Robert
Mooney, Steve
Moore, Dwight D.
Moore, Huber
Moore, Keith
Moore, Lynn
Moore, Marion
Moore, R.A.
Moore, Richard
Moore, Trudy
Moores, Glen W.
Moores, Judith A.
Moorhead, Maeve
Morberg, Don
Mordy, J.P.B.
Morehen, C.W.
Morford, Bob
Morford, W.R.
Morgan, Barry
Morgan, Harold
Morgan, Jane
Morgan, Jeff
Morgan, Joan
Morgan, Ken
Morgan, M.P.
Morgan, Richard
Morganson, Faye
Morgenstern, Bruce
Morgenstern, Pearl
Morhan, Sue
Morin, Bill
Morley, Bill
Morley, Wayne
Morrell, Mike
Morris, Bill
Morris, G.
Morris, Mary C.
Morris, Mary J.
Morris, P.L.
Morris, William A.
Morrison, D.
Morrison, Jeff
Morrison, Karen
Morrison, Ken P.
Morrison, Terry
Morse, Ann

Morse, F.
Mortimer, John
Morton, Keith
Morton, Norma
Morton, Paul
Mosedale, M.
Mosedale, W.
Moss, L.
Moss, Patricia
Mossip, David
Mosveen, Norman
Mottishaw, B.
Mouat, I.
Mouat, S.
Mould, Alice
Mould, Frank
Moursey, Lee
Mowat, D.
Moyle, Diane
Moyle, Gail
Moyle, Ken
Moyls, B.
Muellers, Angela
Muffley, B.
Muir, Alexander
Muir, Allister
Muir, K.S.
Muirhead, Nancy
Muirhead, R.C.
Mullen, Karen
Mulligan, Pat
Mumford, Mary
Munn, A.
Munn, D.
Munn, R.
Munro, Beth
Munro, David A.
Munro, Deane
Munro, Edward
Munro, I.H.
Munro, Kathleen
Munro, Patricia
Munro, W.H.
Munro, William T.
Munson, T.
Murphy, Diane
Murphy, Pam
Murphy, Tim
Murr, Norman
Murray, Jim
Musfelt, V.
Myers, Helen
Myers, Roger
Myers, Shawn
Myers, Steve J.
Myres, Linda
Myres, M. Timothy
Nagel, R.A.
Nagorsen, David
Nairne, Charlie
Nancarrow, P.
Naomi, Anna
Napper, E.
Narod, Mary
Nash, Harry
Nash, Joyce
Nealis, Jonathan
Nealis, V.G.
Nebel, Isabel
Neiderlich, Wolf
Neilsen, Christian E.

Neilson, D.
Neilson, Winnifred
Neily, Wayne
Neish, Jim
Nelson, Erin
Nelson, Jim
Nelson, Judy
Nelson, Marge
Nelson, R. Wayne
Nelson, W. Lyon
Nero, Robert W.
Netbay, A.
Netting, Anthony
Neuls, Karl
Newall, Linda
Newberry, P.
Newell, David S.
Newell, Gail
Newell, George
Newell, Ted
Newman, J.
Newman, Roy
Newman, Wendy B.
Newson, Marion
Newson, Verna
Newton, Amy D.
Newton, Betty
Newton, E. Faye
Newton, Kevin S.
Newton, Kyla R.
Newton, M.I.
Newton, Rose
Newton, Sean
Nichol, R.H.
Nicholls, S.
Nichols, Alan
Nickel, Ellison
Nickel, Tom
Nicol, Adeline
Nicol, Karen
Nicolai, Brian
Nicholson, Cindy
Nielsen, C.E.
Nielsen, R.B.
Niemann, F.
Nishi, Geri
Nivison, C.
Nixon, Wendy
Nobel, D.
Noble, Leigh
Noble, Malcolm
Noble, R.W.
Noel, Doug
Noel, Phyllis
Noel, Russel
Nomme, K.
Norman, Alex
Norsworthy, Marge
North, Elizabeth
North, Ernie
North, Lois
Norton, Gloria
Nott, Phil R.
Nowosad, June
Nunwieler, Conrad
Nurmeste, Alan
Nuttall, J.K.
Nuttall, Pat
Nuttall, Brian
Nyberg, Brian
Nye, Doris F.

Nygren, Edward L.
Nygren, P.
Nyhof, Mark
O'Brian, Derek
O'Connor, David
O'Neil, Betty
O'Neill, Mike
O'Neill, Myrtle
O'Neill, W.R.
Oakley, Darryl
Oakley, Karen
Obana, J.
Oberg, Evelyn
Oberg, Nanny
Odear, Bob
Odion, D.
Odlum, D.G.
Odlum, Gordon C.
Ogilvie, H.
Ogilvie, Robert
Oguss, Emily
Ohanjanian, Penny
Oke, Dennis
Oko, Hilda
Oldaker, R. Frank
Oldfield, Mike
Oliphant, Bill
Oliver, Chris
Oliver, Joyce
Oliver, Lyle
Oliver, Marg
Oliver, Roy
Olmstead, J.
Olsen, Brent
Olsen, Carl
Olsen, H.I.
Olson, Daniel
Ommundson, P.
Orcut, Lowell
Orman, Linda
Orser, Ray
Osborn, Bill
Osborn, June
Osborne, C.
Osman, C.D.
Osmond-Jones, E.J.
Ostrom, Nancy
Otway, Bill
Ouellet, Henri
Overhoff, Nettie
Overstall, Richard
Pageot, Madeleine
Paget, John
Paget, Trine
Paille, Gerry
Paine, F.
Paine, Roger
Palfreyman, Gail
Palmateer, Calvor
Palmer, Greg
Palmer, Katherine
Palmer, Ken
Palmer, Mary
Palmer, Naida
Palmer, Ray
Palmer, Walter
Paquette, Maggie
Parham, H.J.
Parish, Pat
Parker, Bill
Parker, Delbert N.

Parker, Jess
Parkin, David
Parkin, Joan
Parkin, Tom W.
Parks, Lorraine
Parks, W.
Parlee, Richard
Parry, John
Parsons, Bob
Parsons, D.K.
Parsons, Evelyn
Parsons, L.
Parsons, Ron
Parsons, S.
Partington, Geoffrey W.
Paseika, Marilyn
Passmore, R.
Pastrick, Bobbie
Pastrick, Mary
Pastrick, Trudy
Paterson, Aurora
Paterson, Lyn
Paterson, Stan
Patey, W.
Patt, Diane
Patt, Roy
Patten, Ray
Pattenaude, Mary
Pattenden, B.
Patterson, Alec
Patterson, Ernie
Patterson, Gerry
Patterson, James
Patterson, Jane
Patterson, Joyce
Patterson, Lloyd
Patterson, Wilma
Pattinson, C.
Pattison, Lyn
Pattison, Stan
Paul, Anna
Paul, C.R.
Paul, Frank
Paul, Mary
Paul, W.A.B.
Paull, G.W.
Paulson, Dennis R.
Pavlick, Leon
Pawless, Irene I.
Payne, D.E.
Peach, Derek
Peake, Arthur
Peake, Fred
Pearce, David
Pearce, Ed
Pearce, Gordon
Pearce, Marguerite
Pearce, T.
Pearkes, Marg
Pearlstone, Paul
Pearse, Theed
Pearse, Tony
Pearson, A.M.
Pearson, G.A.
Pearson, Vi
Pearson, Winifred
Peatt, Alan D.
Peck, Jess
Peden, Alex E.
Pedersen, Vibeke
Pedley, David

Pedley, Lynne
Peers, Betty-Lou
Pegler, Moreen
Pelham, H.
Pelper, John A.
Pendergast, Bruce
Pendray, C.H.
Penker, Linden
Penker, Robin
Penker, Sandy
Penker, Wilfred
Perez, Mario
Perkins, Ann
Perkins, H.C.
Perreault, Henry
Perrin, David
Perrin, Jacob
Perrin, Janne
Perrin, Murielle
Perrin, Peter W.
Perrin, Roland
Perrin, Tim
Perrone, Mike
Perry, Audrey
Perry, Jim
Person, Everett
Petapiece, V.
Peters, Iris A.
Peters, Sheila
Peters, Vi
Peters, Wilbur
Petersen, Claus
Peterson, Bruce R.
Peterson, Dan
Peterson, Don
Peterson, Ernie
Peterson, Faye
Peterson, Gretchen
Peterson, Larry
Peterson, Les
Peterson, P.
Petley, Pat
Petrar, Brian J.
Petrar, Heidi
Peve, Armand
Peyton, Leonard J.
Phelps, Dave E.
Phillip, Connie
Phillip, John
Phillipedes, George
Phillips, Pat
Phillips, Roy W.
Phipps, Barbara
Phipps, Bill
Phyall, Doug
Pick, Paula
Pickens, Len C.
Pickens, Lola
Pickering, V.
Picman, Jaraslov
Piddington, Phyllis
Pielou, Chris
Pienze, J.
Pike, Gordon
Pike, P.C.
Pikula, Flo
Pilconis, Lorie
Pilkey, Ron
Pillsbury, R.W.
Pinch, Brian
Pinette, Tom

Pirnke, Mike
Pitt, Marg
Pitt, Rae
Pitt-Brook, David
Piuze, Jean
Plath, Tom
Platt, M.
Pleckaitis, Harold
Pletzer, Laurie
Plewes, Heather
Plowden-Wardlaw, J.
Po, Catherine
Pocklington, Bill
Poff, Carol
Poggenmiller, G.
Poile, Irene
Poirier, Evelyn
Pojar, Jim
Pojar, Rosamond
Polivka, Ivan
Poll, Dave
Pollard, Lynn
Pollock, Harold
Polsom, Jacob
Polson, John E.
Polson, Melissa
Pooley, R.H.
Pope, Arthur
Porcher, Alf
Port, Bert
Port, Sue
Porter, Bill
Porter, Julie
Porter, Marian
Porter, Steve
Postey, W.
Potsepp, Ted
Potts, E.
Potts, George
Potts, Marc
Poulsom, J.
Powell, David
Powell, Derek
Powell, Douglas
Powell, Joe L.
Powell, Joyce
Power, Damian
Power, M.
Power, Rosemary
Powers, Gerry
Poynter, G. Allen
Poynter, Helen
Pratt, F.C.
Pratt, T.
Pratt, W.J.
Precious, Norman
Prehara, Bea
Prentice, Jim
Preston, Al
Preston, John
Preston, Margaret
Preston, W.B.
Prestwich, T. Alex
Previer, Jim
Price, A.T.
Price, Maureen
Price, Michael
Price, Neil
Price, Richard
Prier, Jim
Prince, Shirley

Contributors

Prior, Roy
Pritchard, Bill
Pritchard, K.
Prokop, Randy
Proverbs, M.P.D.
Provo, Brian
Pryce, Colin
Pullman, K.
Puls, Judy
Punnett, Walter
Purches, Sandi
Purdy, Bob
Purdy, Jim
Purdy, Margaret
Purdy, Robert O.
Purssell, Norman
Purssell, W.
Quadvelieg, R.
Quayle, Jim
Quijano, Gina
Quirk, John
Quirk, Shirley
Rack, Kurt
Rack, Marilyn
Rae, William S.
Raible, L.
Raincock, M.
Rainville, Claire
Ralph, C.J.
Ralph, J.
Ramsay, B.
Ramsay, J.H.
Ramsay, Jamie
Ramsay, Leah
Ramsay, R.L.
Ramsay, Terri A.
Ramsdin, Bernice
Ramsey, Helen
Ramsey, Keith
Rankin, Cynthia
Rankin, Leo J.
Ransom, P.
Ransom, W.
Ranson, J. Philip
Rathbone, Phil
Rathbone, Sandy
Rathbone, Tony
Rattray, Jim
Rauch, F.
Ray, N.
Raymond, Gilbert
Raynor, C.
Read, Gloria
Realton, Clare
Realton, Jim
Redhead, Bob
Redhead, P.C.
Reed, Austin
Reed, Bob
Reed, Joyce Hagerbaumer
Reed, Ruth
Reedamon, Martin
Reeson, David
Reeve, Jeff
Reeve, Meredith
Regan, Howard
Reid, Chris
Reid, Clifford R.
Reid, Emerson
Reid, Ken
Reid, Lyle

Reid, Mary
Reid, Patrick
Reid, T.C.
Reider, C.
Reifel, George H.
Reimchen, Tom E.
Reimer, Al
Reiter, Jean
Reiter, John
Rekert, Gladys
Rekert, Harry
Rekert, Tony
Rempel, Dan
Rempel, Mary
Renfrey, G.
Renner, J.
Renouf, Ed M.
Rentmeester, Tony
Rephin, Steve E.
Retfalvi, Laszlo
Reusch, Randy
Reynolds, John
Reynolds, R.W.
Reynolds, Rob
Reynolds, Sheila
Rhama, Ann
Rhynas, K.
Rhynas, P.
Rice, Desmond
Rice, Louise
Richards, Dave
Richards, Keith
Richardson, Frank
Richmond, Mary
Richter, F.M.
Rick, Pamela
Ricker, William E.
Ridsdale, Doreen
Riedman, Martin
Riedman, Sophie
Riley, J.H.
Rissling, Jim P.
Ritcey, Clara
Ritcey, David
Ritcey, Ralph W.
Ritchie, Dave
Ritchie, M.
Ritz, C.W.
Ritz, W.
Roach, Anthony J.
Roberson, Don
Roberts, Ann
Roberts, Anna
Roberts, Dave
Roberts, Don
Roberts, G.
Roberts, Hanna
Roberts, Leila G.
Roberts, Naomi
Roberts, Phyllis
Roberts, Stan
Roberts, Syd
Roberts, William
Robertson, Betty
Robertson, Bob
Robertson, Brian
Robertson, Dorothy
Robertson, Fiona
Robertson, Ian
Robertson, J.F.
Robertson, Kelly

Robertson, L.
Robertson, R.M.
Robertson, Steven
Robertson, Strilan
Robertson, Terry
Robinson, Al
Robinson, Brian
Robinson, D.J.
Robinson, France
Robinson, G.
Robinson, Harold
Robinson, James I.
Robinson, Jack
Robinson, Joan
Robinson, Lois
Robinson, Ray
Robinson, Robin D.
Robinson, Ron
Robinson, Steve H.
Robinson, V.
Robinson, Wilma F.
Robitaille, Mary
Rocchini, R.
Roch, A.J.
Rock, Christopher
Rock, Kurt
Rock, Marilyn
Rockwell, Diane
Rockwell, I. Laurie
Roddick, M.
Rodgers, Ed
Rodgers, John
Rodway, Joy A.
Rodway, Michael S.
Roe, Earl
Roe, Elizabeth
Roe, Nicholas A.
Roe, Rick
Roemer, Hans
Rogan, M.L.
Roger, Benton
Rogers, B.W.
Rogers, Dale
Rogers, G.B.
Rogers, J.V.
Rogers, Jean
Rogers, Len
Rogers, Pat
Rogers, Paul
Rogers, Ray
Rogers, Ruth J.
Rogers, T.H.
Rogers, Victor
Rollins, Adrian
Rollins, Daphne P.
Rollins, P.
Rooklin, Lynda
Rose, Paul
Rosen, Carl
Ross, Alex
Ross, Barbara
Ross, D.A.
Ross, D.R.
Ross, F.
Ross, Gail
Ross, Graham
Ross, Joel
Ross, Lena
Ross, Martin
Ross, R.
Ross, Sandra

Rossiter, Doreen
Rote, Betty
Rottacher, B.
Routledge, Adele
Routledge, Dave
Routledge, Harold
Routledge, Maureen
Row, Earl
Roysum, Wayne
Ruckles, Phyllis A.
Ruckles, Gwen
Rudy, F.
Rungren, Peggy
Runyan, Bruce
Runyan, Craig
Rushton, Charles E.
Russell, Fraser
Russell, G.
Russell, Judy
Russell, L.S.
Russell, Noel
Russell, William
Russell, Yvonne
Rutherglen, Ted
Ryberg, Max
Ryder, Angie
Ryder, Dave
Ryder, Glen R.
Ryder, June
Ryder, P.
Ryder, R.A.
Ryder, Sue
Rye, Darrell
Ryff, Alan J.
Ryga, G.
Safir, Ann
Salal, J.
Salisbury, Dan
Samper, Cristian
Sampson, Phil
Sanders, Areta
Sanders, Jeffrey R.
Sanderson, Elaine
Sandwell, Robert
Sanford, Frank
Sanftleben, Peggy
Sargeant, L.E.
Sargeant, D.E.
Sarles, Jack G.
Sarles, John
Sarles, Rosamond
Sarlund, Barb
Sarlund, Lee
Sars, Karel
Sather, Mike
Satterfield, Joy
Satterfield, Ronald
Satterly, Jack
Sattman, R.
Saunders, Betty
Saunders, E.
Saunders, James
Saunders, Jane
Saunders, Jean
Saunders, Noel
Sauppe, Barry
Savale, Bill
Savard, Jean-Pierre L.
Sawade, Ron
Saxon, Greg
Scheer, Robert

Schell, Ed
Schick, W. Jack
Schmidt, Chris
Schmidt, Dennis
Schnider, Robert W.
Schoceten, Lorna
Schoceten, Madelen
Schoen, Ellen
Scholes, David
Schouten, Madelon
Schreck, J.M.
Schueler, Fred
Schultz, Zella M.
Schutz, Allan C.
Schutz, Phyllis
Schwab, B.
Schwab, Francis E.
Schwabl, Hubert
Scott, A.W.
Scott, Brian
Scott, Greg
Scott, Irving
Scott, Pat
Scott, W.E.
Scott-Mason, F.
Scott-Moncrieff, R.
Scotter, George
Screeton, Edward
Screeton, Roberta
Scruton, Andrew
Scruton, Colin
Scruton, David
Scruton, Joan
Seaborne, Jean
Seaborne, K.T.
Seabrook, Marie
Sealy, Spencer G.
Searing, Gary F.
Seaton, B.
Sedgewick, Barb
Sedgewick, Don
Seel, K.E.
Seggie, Mike
Seidel, D.C.
Sekhon, Kelly
Selby, R.C.
Self, Brian
Seliciki, Daphne
Selley, C.
Sendall, Bill
Sendall, Kelly
Seon, G.E.
Septer, Dirk
Sewell, Richard
Sewell, Roslyn
Sexsmith, Bob
Sexsmith, Sheila
Shaddick, Stan
Shamlock, Margaret
Shandler, B.
Shaneman, John
Shank, Howard
Shank, I.C.
Shank, M.
Sharp, Al
Sharp, Thelma
Shatwell, Alan
Shatwell, Rosemary
Shatwell, Una
Shaver, Gerry
Shaver, Jim

Shaw, Dorothy
Shaw, Eric
Shaw, Janice
Shaw, Rick
Shaw, Sandy
Shea, Josh
Shea, Judy
Sheard, C.
Shearer, B.
Shearman, S.
Shears, Ken
Sheehan, Brian R.
Sheehan, Michael W.
Sheer, B.
Shelford, J.C.
Shelford, Neil
Shenan, Frank
Shennon, F.
Shepard, Bettie
Shepard, Bob
Shepard, Chris D.
Shepard, J.
Shepard, Mark F.
Shepard, Michael G.
Shepard, Teresa E.
Shepard, V.
Shepherd, P.E.K.
Sheppard, R.F.
Sheppard, Stephen R.J.
Sheppy, J.
Shera, W.P.
Sherman, D.K.
Sherman, E.
Sherman, F.A.
Sherman, S.
Sherman, T.K.
Sherrif, Douglas
Sherrington, Peter
Shervill, Daniel
Sherwood, John
Shields, Joan
Shields, Ken
Shields, Tom
Shillaker, F.M.
Shinkawa, Anthony
Shireman, Tim
Short, Steve
Shorter, Harry
Shouldice, Wayne
Shriever, P.
Shunter, M.
Shutz, A.C.
Sian, Ervio
Siddle, Chris D.
Siddle, Sonja
Sieburth, H.G.
Sigsworth, Bill
Sigsworth, Jack
Sigsworth, Joan
Silver, D.
Silver, Rod
Silvey, Joe
Sim, Sybil
Simmon, Earl
Simmons, P.A.
Simmons, Stephen
Simon, David
Simon, Winnifred
Simonson, Tim
Simpson, Craig
Simpson, Don

Simpson, Fred A.
Simpson, George
Simpson, Ken
Simpson, L.
Simpson, Sam
Sims, J.
Sing, Edward C.
Sing, Kay
Sirk, George P.
Sirk, Lauren
Sirois, Jacques
Sironen, Sandra
Sismey, E.
Skapski, Kornel
Skapski, Viola
Skoba, Rosamond
Skoba, W. Fred
Skriletz, Jeff
Skwarok, Denise J.
Slack, Jack
Slack, Sharon
Slater, J.R.
Slater, M.E.
Slavens, R.D.
Sleeman, Ken
Slessor, Norman
Slingerland, Richard
Sloan, Bill
Sloan, Irene
Sloan, John
Slocom, M.
Slocombe, Jean
Slocombe, June
Slocombe, Linda
Slocombe, Scott
Sluggett, G.
Slupianek, B.
Smart, Gail
Smedley, C.
Smedley, Lydia
Smirl, Robert J.
Smith, Andrew
Smith, Arthur
Smith, Barney
Smith, Bernice
Smith, Beverly
Smith, Brad
Smith, Brian
Smith, Bruce
Smith, Cyril
Smith, D. Wayne
Smith, D.A.
Smith, D.J.
Smith, Daryl
Smith, Dave W.
Smith, Dean
Smith, Douglas H.
Smith, Elizabeth
Smith, Evan
Smith, Eve
Smith, George
Smith, Gertrude
Smith, Glen E.
Smith, Gordon
Smith, I.C.
Smith, Ian D.
Smith, James N.M.
Smith, Jason
Smith, Jeremy
Smith, Joseph
Smith, Karen M.

Smith, Karl
Smith, Kay
Smith, Larry
Smith, Lorraine C.
Smith, Norman
Smith, Nini
Smith, Pat
Smith, Raymond
Smith, Richard C.
Smith, Risa
Smith, Roger
Smith, Susan M.
Smith, T.G.
Smith, Terry
Smith, W.G.
Smither, J.J.
Smithson, Barry
Smyly, John
Smyly, Noreen
Smyth, Jonathan
Smythe, G.A.
Snee, Margaret E.
Snow, Derek
Snow, P.
Snyder, Andy
Snyder, Beth C.
Snye, Terry
Soadvent, Ralph
Soberg, D.
Solberg, H.A.
Solecki, D.
Soleckie, Daphne
Solf, J.D.
Solly, Grace
Somerford, M.
Somerville, Alison
Sopuck, Leonard
Sorapure, Peter
Sothcott, C.
Soules, Keith
Soulsby, Gladys
Sousby, H.W.S.
Soutar, D.
Souther, Barb
Souther, J.
Southerland, Grahame
Sowden, Margaret J.
Spalding, D.J.
Spalding, David A.E.
Spalding, H.
Spanier, T.
Sparks, Frank
Sparks, Tony
Sparling, D.B.
Spaulding, Anne
Spaulding, D.
Speechly, Win
Specht, Marlene
Speich, Steve M.
Spence, Chris
Spence, Doris
Spence, Gordon
Spenst, Del
Spenst, Sandy
Spicer, Chris
Spicer, Jean
Spiers, Carole
Spiers, L.T.
Spitman, Bernie
Spitman, Prue
Springett, B.

Contributors

Stace-Smith, Tine
Stacey, Pam
Stachera, Stan
Stafford, B.
Stainer, B.
Stainer, John
Staines, G.
Stalker, W.J.
Stanley, Ann
Stanley, Denis
Stanley, Doris
Stanley, G.
Stanley, S.O.
Stark, J.P.
Steeds, Rita
Steel, D.
Steele, Billie
Steele, Doris W.
Steele, John
Steele, Rita
Steele, Tony
Steele, William
Steen, Ardell
Steeves, Jack
Steeves, John
Stein, David
Stein, R.C.
Steinke, Wally
Stelfox, H.A.
Stent, Peter
Stephen, J.A.
Stephenson, A.B.
Stephenson, J.
Stephenson, Marylee
Stepniewski, Andrew M.
Sterling, Tom
Stevens, Irene
Stevens, John
Stevens, Tom
Stevenson, B.
Stevenson, D.G.H.
Steward, G.E.
Stewart, Andy C.
Stewart, Ann
Stewart, Dave
Stewart, E. Ann
Stewart, Geoff E.
Stewart, Harold
Stewart, Lilian
Stewart, T.D.
Sties, Jack
Stinson, Jackie
Stirling, Andrew
Stirling, David
Stirling, Ian D.
Stirling, Ruth
Stiven, A.E.
Stockdale, T.D.
Stockman, William
Stocks, F.
Stone, Jack
Stoneberg, R.
Stoney, Frank
Stopne, Adrianne
Storey, Katherine
Straight, L.
Straith, Bob
Straley, Gerald
Stratton, M.B.
Stream, Lee
Street, Hazel

Street, Janet
Street, Jim
Strickland, Al
Strickland, William
Strikwerda, Fred
Stroctman, Anita
Strom, G.
Strube, Becky
Stuart-Stubbs, Basil
Stubbe, Eileen F.
Stubley, Ken
Stuible, Shirley
Stushnoff, Brian G.
Sugden, Ben A.
Sugden, J.
Sugden, L.
Suggitt, B.
Suggitt, L.
Sullivan, B.
Sullivan, R.D.
Sullivan, Sibohan
Sullivan, Terry
Summers, J.D.
Summers, Kenneth R.
Summerville, Valeri
Sunderland, Graham
Sundquist, Lance
Sundstrom, J.
Sundstrom, V.
Surkan, David
Suterbach, Bob
Sutherland, Bob
Sutherland, Doreen
Suttill, D.E.H.
Suttill, Dennis L.
Suttill, Kaye
Sutton, Britt
Sutton, Derek
Sutton, Dorothy
Sutton, Kathy
Sutton, William
Svoboda, Emily
Svoboda, John Jr.
Swanson, Harold
Swindle, Pat
Switzer, Bob
Switzer, Jim
Symon, Margaret
Symons, P.E.K.
Symons, P.W.
T'Amboline, D.
Tabak, John
Tagles, Robin
Tainter, S.L.
Tait, Doreen
Tait, J.D.
Tait, Mary
Takacs, J.
Takishita, Faith
Tamasi, J.
Tamke, Vern
Tansky, J.E.
Tarr, Hugh
Tarr, Tom
Tate, Mary Ann
Tatum, Jeremy B.
Taylor, B.W.
Taylor, Bill
Taylor, Carrie
Taylor, Clark
Taylor, Cynthia

Taylor, Darwin
Taylor, Dudley
Taylor, M. Elizabeth
Taylor, Ernie W.
Taylor, Gary
Taylor, George
Taylor, Gwen
Taylor, Jim
Taylor, John D.
Taylor, John S.
Taylor, Keith G.
Taylor, Ken
Taylor, Leah
Taylor, Lucinda
Taylor, Marty
Taylor, Mary
Taylor, Petty
Taylor, Philip S.
Taylor, Roger
Taylor, Ron
Taylor, Ruth
Taylor, Sid
Taylor, Simon
Taylor, Stirling
Taylor, Traff
Taylor, W.L.
Teal, Aileen
Teichroe, Peter
Telosky, B.M.
Telosky, Howard A.
Templemann, D.
Tennant, Walt
Teske, Irene
Thacker, B.M.
Thacker, George
Thacker, T.L.
Thatcher, D.J.
Thomas, Vincent
Thompson, Al
Thompson, Anne
Thompson, Antony B.
Thompson, David
Thompson, Diana
Thompson, Gary
Thompson, George
Thompson, Jean
Thompson, John
Thompson, Ken
Thompson, Marlene
Thompson, Peter
Thompson, Ron D.
Thomsen, Kurt
Thomson, Brenda
Thomson, Chuck
Thomson, David
Thomson, George
Thomson, Glen
Thomson, H.
Thomson, John
Thomson, Robert
Thorgeirson, Jack
Thornber, R.
Thornburgh, J.
Thorne, B.
Thorne, Debby
Thorne, E.
Thorne, Frank
Thorne, G.
Thorne, Walter
Thornton, Ed
Thornton, Meredith

Ticard, E.G.
Tidmus, Rene
Tiernan, John
Till, Madeline
Timmins, Moira
Tingley, S.
Tinney, Art
Tinney, Jean
Tipper, G.K.
Tisdale, Rod
Tivel, Tracey
Tnasky, A.
Todd, Jack
Todd, Terese
Toft, Lowes
Toftdahl, Kjeld
Tomlinson, Mike
Tompa, Frank
Tonge, Peter
Tonge, Win
Toochin, John
Toochin, Mike
Tootell, Barbara
Tootell, Bert
Tosh, B.
Touzeau, K.
Tow, P.H.
Towers, Ruth
Traicheff, George
Trefry, Colin
Trefry, Sharon
Tremblay, Ellen
Trembley, Wayne
Tremewen, Charles
Trenholme, Neil S.
Trent, Robert
Trevitt, John
Trotter, Brenda
Trotter, Charles A.
Tsang, Larry
Tucker, G.W.
Tuffy, B.
Tull, C. Eric
Tuomaala, Eileen
Turcotte, Jean-Pierre
Turcotte, Yves
Turnbull, A.D.
Turnbull, Douglas
Turnbull, G.J.
Turnbull, Rochelle
Turnbull, W.G.
Turner, Charles
Turner, Frank
Turner, Margaret
Turney, Laurence
Tutt, Jim
Tyson, Danny
Udvardy, Miklos D.F.
Uliet, Bob
Underhill, J.E.
Upshall, Muriel
Upton, Ross
Urban, Judy
Usher, Robyn
Vaida, Tom
Vaillancourt, Andre
Valenda, Lon J.
Valentin, W.J.
Vallee, Anne
Van Blaricom, E.W.
Van Damme, Linda

Van De Vlassaker, J.
Van Den Berg, Duanne
Van Den Berg, Kees
Van Der Gulick, L.
Van Der Gulick, R.
Van Der Pol, Hank
Van Der Raay, Brigitta M.
Van Driel, Lenard
Van Drimmelen, Ben
Van Egmond, John
Van Herwaarden, Tina
Van Kerkoerle, Anneke
Van Kerkoerle, Peter
Van Meecuven,
Van Meel, Rosie
Van Oosdam, Jay
Van Strien, Jack
Van Tets, Gerard F.
Van Thienen, F.J.
Van Tighem, Kevin J.
Van Tine, Leo
Vance, Horace R.
Vandenburg, K.
Vanderburg, D.
Vandergucht, Matthew
Vanderlinde, Jost
Vanderpol, Hank
Vanhove, John
Vanson, John
Varger, Fritz
Vaudry, A.
Veale, David
Vedova, Dan
Venables, E.P.
Verbeek, Nicolaas A.M.
Verbrugge, William
Vereeken, Irene
Verner, J.
Vicker, Sue
Vickers, A.
Vickery, Keith
Vickery, Sue
Viken, Aubrey J.
Villenueve, Claudette
Vipond, Clare
Visentin, Paul
Vogel, Bill
Vold, Cecily
Von Sacken, Angela
Von Shuckmann, Sylvia
Voous, Karel H.
Vooys, J.
Vulgaris, Sam
Vyse, Alan
Vyse, Frances
Vyse, Rachel
Waddell, E.
Waddell, James B.
Wade, Carson
Wade, Keith
Wadsworth, Gordon
Wahl, Terrence R.
Waibler, Stephen F.
Wainwright, Margaret
Wainwright, Mary
Waite, Jean
Waite, Leon
Waite, Ronald
Wakefield, K. Stuart
Wakelam, Richard
Wakelam, William

Walburger, Bill
Waldon, A.G.
Waldon, Robert
Walens, Stanley
Walker, Andrew
Walker, Bruce
Walker, Frank
Walker, H.D.
Walker, Ian
Walker, J.
Walker, M.D.
Walker, Ronald P.
Walker-Taylor, Gwen
Walkley, Doug
Wallace, Brenda
Wallace, Jane
Wallace, Kurt
Wallach, Elizabeth
Wallden, John
Waller, Lillian
Walsh, Bob
Walsh, D.
Walsh, J.
Walsh, L.
Walton, C.
Walton, E.M.
Walton, John
Walton, Kenneth
Walton, Marge
Walton, Mark
Walton, Robert
Wampler, Ed
Wanderer, J.
Ward, Goldpan
Ward, Greg
Ward, H.
Ward, John G.
Ward, L.W.
Ward, Peter R.B.
Ward, Rick
Ward, S.C.
Ward-Harris, E.D.
Ward-Harris, Jane
Warde, Martha
Ware, Marie
Wareing, Jane
Warham, Bill
Warham, Mildred
Warhurton, S.
Warkentin, W.
Warren, H.O.
Warren, Keith
Warren, Morgan
Warren, W.H.
Waterhouse, Louise
Waterhouse, Michaela J.
Waterman, A.
Waterman, Flora
Waterman, K.
Waters, G.Ross
Watkins, Al
Watkins, Gord
Watmough, D.
Watson, G.D.
Watson, Jane
Watson, Lorraine
Watson, Margaret
Watson, Peg
Watson, Philip R.
Watt, Alison M.E.
Watts, Brad F.

Watts, Emily
Watts, Marilyn
Watts, Sid
Wayne, Margaret
Webb, A.
Webb, Dick
Webb, J.
Webb, Keith
Webb, Richard C.
Webb, Robert
Webb, Scott
Webb, Suzanne
Webber, Bernard
Webber, Christine
Webber, Christopher
Webber, Jeremy
Weber, K.
Weber, Robin A.
Weber, Wayne C.
Weber, Wendy
Webster, B.
Webster, J. Dan
Webster, Marg
Weeden, Don
Weeden, Linda
Weeden, R.B.
Wege, Rita
Weiler, O.J.
Weins, Andy
Weir, F.B.
Weismiller, Dianne
Weismiller, Teresa
Welch, Dave
Welch, R.
Welland, R.
Wellborn, Jean
Wellborn, Roy
Wells, G.
Wellwood, Ron
Weninger, Margery
Wershler, Deborah
Wershler, Peter
Wershler, Roy M.
Wessel, J.C.O.
West, Al
West, Mark
West, Nancy
West, Rick
Westcott, D.
Westerborg, Betty
Westhaver, Stan
Westheuser, H.
Westman, M. Marja de J.
Weston, Danny
Weston, Inez
Weston, Jim
Weston, Tom
Wetmore, Stephen P.
Wetmore, T.
Whalen, Paul
Whebell, Yvonne M.
Whellams, Neil
Whipps, Olga
White, Al
White, Andy
White, Betty
White, D.L.
White, Eric R.
White, Graham
White, John
White, Ken

White, Mildred V.
White, P.
White, Sheila
White, Ted
Whiteaves, J.F.
Whitecross, Wally
Whitehead, Phil E.
Whitehead, George
Whitelaw, D.W.
Whitelaw, Virginia R.
Whitfield, Judy
Whiting, David
Whitley, Wendy
Whitman, D.
Whitman, S.D.
Whitney, Alan G.
Whitney, Irene E.
Whitney, R.
Whittaker, Andrew
Whittaker, Jean
Whittaker, Michael
Whittington, Bruce
Whittington, Margaret
Whittington, Mary
Whyte, C.
Whyte, M.
Whyte, Peter
Wick, A.L.
Widdowson, T.
Wideski, Tony
Wiebe, Karen L.
Wier, Josette
Wieringa, D.
Wieringa, L.
Wiggins, Ira L.
Wiggs, A.J.
Wight, G.
Wigmore, Ruth
Wilcox, Vi
Wilding-Davies, Michelle
Wilding-Davies, Peter
Wilford, Kathy
Wilkes, Brian
Wilkes, Myrtle
Wilkes, Ralph
Wilkie, Dale
Wilkie, R.
Wilkinson, Doug
Wilkinson, George
Wilkinson, Henry
Wilkinson, Margaret
Wilkowski, Joe
Will, John
William, Jean
Williams, Anthony
Williams, Donna R.
Williams, Dorothy
Williams, Eldred
Williams, Geoff
Williams, George
Williams, Jack E.
Williams, Joan E.
Williams, Kerry
Williams, Laidlaw
Williams, Laurel
Williams, Margaret
Williams, Mark
Williams, Marlene
Williams, Murray
Williams, Nancy
Williams, P. Ray

Williams, P.H.
Williams, Raechelle
Williams, Ray
Williams, Robert
Williams, Ronald
Williams, Sarah
Williams, Seiriol
Williamson, Susan
Willies, Gordon
Willies, Karen
Willies, Peter
Willis, Karen
Willis, Les
Willox, Mavis E.
Wilson, Anthony
Wilson, Bill
Wilson, Dan
Wilson, Daryll
Wilson, Don
Wilson, Douglas J.
Wilson, Eilbeck B.
Wilson, Eunice
Wilson, Heather
Wilson, Jim A.
Wilson, Jim C.
Wilson, Kerry
Wilson, Mary
Wilson, Robert
Wilson, Roslyn
Wilson, Ruby
Wilson, S.E.
Wilson, V.
Wilson, W.G.
Winchester, Neville
Winson, J.W.
Winstone, Mary
Wintemute, Ben P.
Winterbottom, J.M.
Wise, Betty
Wishlow, Bill
Wisnia, Lynn
Wisselink, A.
Withers, Lois
Witte, Marion
Wittrin, Martin P.
Wolfe, Michael
Wolterson-Strauss, Anna J.
Wong, Kent
Wood, Anne
Wood, C. Edward
Wood, Chauncey
Wood, Daryl
Wood, Douglas
Wood, E.D.
Wood, F.H.
Wood, J.
Wood, Peter
Wood, R.
Wood, Sarah
Woodcock, Don
Woodcock, Joe
Woodcock, Mike
Woods, G.
Woods, John G.
Woods, Marcia E.
Woods, Susan M.
Woodworth, Freda
Woodworth, John
Wooldridge, Chris E.
Wooldridge, Donald R.
Woolgar, David

Woolgar, Pam
Wootton, A.
Workman, Bob
Wrenshall, Anne
Wright, Dan
Wright, Eileen
Wright, G.W.
Wright, James
Wright, Ken
Wright, Lois
Wright, Richard T.
Wrigley, Bill
Wydman, Roy
Wye, Doris
Wylie, Bill
Wysong, Dennis
Yak, John
Yardley, C.
Yaunk, Hans
Yellowlees, Jean
Yellowlees, Lou A.
Yellowlees, Mary
Yellowlees, Robin
Yewchan, Karl
Yorke, Paul
Youds, J.
Younger, Dave
Youngson, Danny
Youngson, Margie
Youwe, A..
Zamluk, Joan
Zeck, Hal
Zeeman, T.
Zeral, Martin
Zettergreen, Barry
Zielinski, Anne
Zieroth, Dale
Zimmerman, Ella
Zinkan, Betty
Zinkan, Ted
Zolinski, Ed
Zoyetz, Cynthia
Zroback, Bill
Zroback, Ki
Zurowski, Tim
Zwickel, Fred C.

REFERENCES CITED

REFERENCES CITED

Originally the nonpasserine component of *Birds of British Columbia* was prepared as one volume with two parts, both relying on a common bibliography. During the editorial phase, however, each book evolved as a self contained volume, primarily for the convenience of the reader. Due to time constraints in the publication process we chose to include the entire list of references with each volume knowing that repetition occurs.

Citations of unpublished material contain a reference to the two-volume *A Bibliography of British Columbia Ornithology* (Campbell et al. 1979b, 1988). Copies of the papers cited in this publication are on file at the Royal British Columbia Museum.

Ainley, D.G. 1976. The occurrence of seabirds in the coastal region of California. Western Birds 7:33-68.

_____. 1980. Geographic variation in Leach's Storm-Petrel. Auk 97:837-853.

Ainley, D.G. and T.J. Lewis. 1974. The history of Farallon Island marine bird populations, 1854-1972. Condor 76:432-446.

Ainley, D.G. and B. Manolis. 1979. Occurrence and distribution of the Mottled Petrel. Western Birds 10:113-123.

Aitchison, N.W. 1972. The Pigeon Guillemot, *Cepphus columba*: breeding biology and brood size. B.Sc. Thesis, University of British Columbia, Vancouver. 25 pp.

Alcorn, G.D. 1958. Nesting of the Caspian Tern in Gray's Harbor, Washington. Murrelet 39:19-20.

_____. 1959. Puffins on the south Gray's Harbor beaches. Murrelet 40:21.

Aldrich, J.W. and H. Friedmann. 1943. A revision of the Ruffed Grouse. Condor 45:85-103.

Allen, A.A. 1928. Downy Woodpecker story. Bird-Lore 30:415-424.

Allen, J.N. 1980. The ecology and behavior of the Long-billed Curlew in southeast Washington. Wildlife Monographs 73:1-67.

Amaral, M.J. 1977. A comparative breeding biology of the Tufted and Horned Puffin in the Barren Islands, Alaska. M.S. Thesis, University of Washington, Seattle. 98 pp.

American Ornithologists' Union. 1895. Check-list of North American birds, 2nd edition. E.W. Wheeler Press, New York. 372 pp.

_____. 1910. Check-list of North American birds, 3rd edition. American Ornithologists' Union, New York. 430 pp.

_____. 1931. Check-list of North American birds, 4th edition. Lancaster, Pennsylvania. 526 pp.

_____. 1957. Check-list of North American birds, 5th edition. Lord Baltimore Press, Inc., Baltimore, Maryland. 691 pp.

_____. 1973. Thirty-second supplement to the American Ornithologists' Union Check-list of North American birds. Auk 90:411-419.

_____. 1983. Check-list of North American birds, 6th edition. Allen Press, Inc., Lawrence, Kansas. 877 pp.

_____. 1984. Report of meeting of the committee on classification and nomenclature. Auk 101:348.

_____. 1985. Thirty-fifth supplement to the American Ornithologists' Union Check-list of North American birds. Auk 102:680-686.

_____. 1987. Thirty-sixth supplement to the American Ornithologists' Union Check-list of North American birds. Auk 104:591-596.

_____. 1989. Thirty-seventh supplement to the American Ornithological' Union Check-list of North American birds. Auk 106:532-538.

Ammann, G.A. 1957. The prairie grouse of Michigan. Michigan Department of Conservation Technical Bulletin, Lansing.

Anderson, C.M., D.G. Roseneau, B.J. Walton, and P. Bente. 1988. New evidence of a peregrine migration on the west coast of North America. Pages 507-516 *in* T.J. Cade, J.H. Enderson, C.G. Thelander, and C.M. White (editors). Peregrine Falcon populations - their management and recovery. The Peregrine Fund, Inc., Boise, Idaho.

Anderson, D.R. and C.J. Henny. 1972. Population ecology of the Mallard: I. A review of previous studies and the distribution and migration from breeding areas. United States Department of the Interior, Fish and Wildlife Service Resource Publication 105, Washington, D.C. 166 pp.

Anderson, D.R., P.A. Skaptason, K.G. Fahey, and C.J. Henny. 1974. Population ecology of the Mallard: III. Bibliography of published research and management findings. United States Department of the Interior, Fish and Wildlife Service Resource Publication 119, Washington, D.C. 46 pp.

Anderson, D.W. and I.T. Anderson. 1976. Distribution and status of Brown Pelicans in the California current. American Birds 30:3-12.

Anderson, E. 1967a. Commensal feeding of gull and peregrine. Blue Jay 25:72.

_____. 1967b. The intermediates are busy birders. Vancouver Natural History Society News 135:9-10.

Anderson, E.A. 1972. Unusual behavior of a male Mute Swan. Federation of British Columbia Naturalists Newsletter 10:4.

Anderson, E.M. 1914. Report on birds collected and observed during April, May and June 1913 in the Okanagan Valley, from Okanagan Landing south to Osoyoos Lake. Pages G7-G16 *in* Report of the Provincial Museum of Natural History for the year 1913, Victoria, British Columbia.

_____. 1915. Report of E.M.Anderson on Atlin expedition, 1914. Pages F7-F17 *in* Report of the Provincial Museum of Natural History for the year 1914, Victoria, British Columbia.

Anderson, M. 1976. Ecology of Long-tailed Jaegers. Journal of Animal Ecology 45:537-559.

Anderson, R.R. 1976. Summary of all-time highest counts of individuals for Canada. American Birds 30:645-648.

_____. 1977. Summary of highest counts of individuals for Canada. American Birds 31:916-918.

_____. 1978. Summary of highest counts of individuals for Canada. American Birds 32:931-933.

_____. 1979. Summary of highest counts of individuals for Canada. American Birds 33:708-709.

_____. 1980. Summary of highest counts of individuals for Canada. American Birds 34:708-710.

_____. 1981. Summary of highest counts of individuals for Canada. American Birds 35:763-765.

_____. 1982. Summary of highest counts of individuals for Canada. American Birds 36:784-786.

_____. 1983. Summary of highest counts of individuals for Canada. American Birds 37:797-799.

Annas, R.M. and R. Coupe (editors). 1979. Biogeoclimatic zones and subzones of the Cariboo forest region, British Columbia Ministry of Forests, Victoria. 103 pp.

Anonymous. 1922. Ornithology. Page 11 *in* Provincial Museum of Natural History Report for the year 1921, Victoria, British Columbia.

_____. 1947. Bird note. Victoria Naturalist 4:20.

_____. 1951. Hawk Owl (*Surnia ulula*). Victoria Naturalist 8:9.

_____. 1958. We get Sage Grouse from Oregon. Wildlife Review 2:30.

_____. 1970. Rare Bird ... short life. Daily Colonist, 23 September, Victoria, British Columbia.

_____. 1972. Little Gull rare sight. Victoria Daily Colonist, 2 November, p. 48.

_____. 1978a. Chilean Willy? Campbell River Upper Islander Newspaper, 6 September.

_____. 1978b. A rare catch. Victoria Times Newspaper, 7 November.

_____. 1984. North American management plan for Trumpeter Swans (draft of July 1984). United States Fish and Wildlife Service, Washington, D.C. and Canadian Wildlife Service, Ottawa, Ontario. 62 pp.

_____. 1985. Gazetteer of Canada-British Columbia. Canada Department of Energy, Mines, and Resources, Surveys and Mapping Branch, Ottawa, Ontario. 281 pp.

_____. 1986. The North American Trumpeter Swan survey-1985. United States Fish and Wildlife Service - Migratory Bird Management Office report. Portland, Oregon. 9 pp.

_____. 1987. Creston Valley Wildlife Management Area Annual Newsletter, 1986-1987. Creston, British Columbia. 6 pp.

_____. 1987a. Goshawk banding results (1980-1986). Western Foundation for Raptor Conservation News 1:6-8.

_____. 1988. Lazy Osprey fathers fail to bring home the goods. Simon Fraser Week 40(11):2.

Anthony A.W. 1896. The Black-vented Shearwater (*Puffinus opisthomelas*). Auk 13:222-228.

Anthony, R. 1970. Ecology and reproduction of California Quail in southeastern Washington. Condor 72:276-287.

Anthony, R.G., R.L. Knight, G.T. Allen, B.R. McClelland, and J.J. Hodges. 1982. Habitat use by nesting and roosting Bald Eagles in the Pacific Northwest. Transactions of the North American Wildlife and Natural Resources Conference 47:332-342.

Antifeau, T. 1977. Carpenter Lake folio inventory: wildlife and range condition, summer 1977. British Columbia Fish and Wildlife Branch Unpublished Report, Kamloops. 134 pp. (Bibliography 2170).

Anweiler, G. 1960. The Boreal Owl influx. Blue Jay 10:61-63.

Appelby, R.H., S.C. Madge, and K. Mullarney. 1986. Identification of divers in immature and winter plumages. British Birds 79:365-391.

Arbib, R. 1975. The blue list for 1976. American Birds 29:1067-1072.

_____. 1979. The blue list for 1980. American Birds 33:830-835.

Armstrong, D.P. 1986. Some aspects of the economics of territoriality in North American hummingbirds. M.Sc. Thesis, University of British Columbia, Vancouver. 108 pp.

_____. 1987. Economics of breeding territoriality in male Calliope Hummingbirds. Auk 104:242-253.

Ashmole, N.P. 1963. The regulation of numbers of tropical oceanic birds. Ibis 103:458-473.

_____. 1971. Seabird ecology and the marine environment. Pages 223-286 *in* D.S.Farner and J.R. King (editors). Avian Biology, Volume 1. Academic Press, New York.

Atkinson, R.N. 1963. Flammulated Owl nesting in British Columbia. Canadian Field-Naturalist 77:59-60.

Austin, J.E. and L.H. Frederickson. 1986. Moult of female Lesser Scaup immediately following breeding. Auk 103:293-298.

Bailey, A.M. 1927. Notes on the birds of southeastern Alaska. Auk 44:1-23.

_____. 1948. Birds of arctic Alaska. Colorado Museum of Natural History Popular Series No. 8:1-317.

Bailey, P.F. 1977. The breeding biology of the Black Tern (*Chlidonias niger surinamensis* Gmelin). M.Sc. Thesis, University of Wisconsin, Oshkosh. 67 pp.

Bailey, R.G. 1980. Descriptions of the ecoregions of the United States. United States Department of Agriculture Miscellaneous Publications No.1391, Washington, D.C. 77 pp.

_____. 1983. Delineation of ecosystem regions. Environmental Management 7:365-373.

Bailey, R.G. and H.C. Hogg. 1986. A world ecoregions map for resource reporting. Environmental Conservation 13:195-202.

Baillie, J.L. 1963. Three bird immigrants from the Old World. Transactions of the Royal Canadian Institute 34:95-105.

_____. 1969. In memoriam: James Alexander Munro. Auk 86:624-630.

Baird, S. 1858a. Birds. *in* Reports of explorations and surveys to ascertain the most practicable and economical route for a railroad from the Mississippi River to the Pacific Ocean. Volume 2, Part 2. Washington, D.C.

Baird, S.F. 1858b. Reports of explorations and surveys for a railroad route to the Pacific ocean. Volume 9 (Part 2):1-1005.

Baldridge, A. and J.B. Crowell. 1966. The fall migration - northern Pacific coast region. Audubon Field Notes 20:81-86.

Baldwin, P.H. and N.K. Zaczkowski. 1963. Breeding biology of the Vaux Swift. Condor 65:400-406.

Balmer, A. 1935. Some new state records at Westport, Washington. Murrelet 16:16.

Baltosser, W.H. 1987. Age, species, and sex determination of four North American hummingbirds. North American Bird Bander 12:151-166.

Baltz, D.M. and G.V. Morejohn. 1977. Food habits and niche overlap of seabirds wintering on Monterey Bay, California. Auk 94:526-543.

Bang, B.G. 1966. The olfactory apparatus of tubenosed birds. Acta Anatomica 65:391-415.

Banko, W.E. 1960. The Trumpeter Swan: its history, habits and populations in the United States. North American Fauna No. 63, Washington, D.C. 214 pp.

Banks, R.C. 1986. Subspecies of the Glaucous Gull, *Larus hyperboreus* (Aves: Charadriiformes). Proceedings of the Biological Society of Washington 99:149-159.

_____. 1988. Geographic variation in the Yellow-billed Cuckoo. Condor 90:473-477.

Banks, R.C. and N.K. Johnson. 1961. A review of North American hybrid hummingbirds. Condor 63:3-28.

Barkley, W.D. 1966. Shuswap Lake nature house - 1966 season report. British Columbia Parks Branch Unpublished Report, Victoria. 15 pp. (Bibliography 2197).

Barnard, A.E. 1973. Occurrence of Black Brant moulting in Boundary Bay, British Columbia. Murrelet 54:12-13.

Barnston, G. 1861. Recollections of the swans and geese of Hudson Bay. Canadian Naturalist and Geologist 6:334.

Barry, T.W. 1968. Observations on natural mortality and native use of eider ducks along the Beaufort Sea coast. Canadian Field-Naturalist 82:140-144.

Barth, E.K. 1968. The circumpolar systematics of *Larus argentatus* and *Larus fuscus* with special reference to the Norwegian populations. Nytt Magasin Zoologi 15:1-50.

Bartle, J.A. 1968. Observations on the breeding habits of Pycroft's Petrel. Notornis 15:70-99.

Bartonek, J.C. and D.D. Gibson. 1972. Summer distribution of pelagic birds in Bristol Bay, Alaska. Condor 74:416-422.

Bauer, R.D. 1979. Historical and status report of the Tule White-fronted Goose. Pages 44-55 *in* R.L. Jarvis and J.C. Bartonek (editors). Management and Biology of Pacific Flyway Geese. A symposium sponsored by the Northwest Section, The Wildlife Society, 16 February 1979, Portland, Oregon. Oregon State University Book Store, Inc., Corvallis.

Beardslee, C.S. and H.D. Mitchell. 1965. Birds of the Niagara Frontier Region. Bulletin of the Buffalo Society of Natural Science 22:1-478.

Beckett, R. 1971. European Grey Partridge (*Perdix perdix* L.). Victoria Naturalist 28:34-35.

Beebe, F.L. 1959. A nesting record of a Black Swift. Murrelet 40:9-10.

_____. 1960. The marine peregrines of the northwest Pacific coast. Condor 62:145-189.

_____. 1965. The known status of the Peregrine Falcon in British Columbia. Pages 53-60 *in* J.J. Hickey (editor). Peregrine Falcon populations: their biology and decline. University of Wisconsin Press, Madison.

_____. 1974. Field studies of the Falconiformes of British Columbia. British Columbia Provincial Museum Occasional Paper No.17, Victoria. 163 pp.

Behle, W.H. and W.A. Goates. 1957. Breeding biology of the California Gull. Condor 59:235-246.

Bell, K.M. 1973. Birds of Tahsis, Vancouver Island (September, 1967 to July, 1973). British Columbia Provincial Museum Unpublished Report, Victoria. 5 pp. (Bibliography 2210).

_____. 1975. Fall flocking and migration. British Columbia Parks Branch Unpublished Report, Victoria. 9 pp. (Bibliography 2211).

Bellrose, F.C. 1955. Housing for Wood Ducks. Illinois Natural History Survey Circular 45, Urbana. 48 pp.

_____. 1976. Ducks, geese, and swans of North America. Stackpole Books, Harrisburg, Pennsylvania. 540 pp.

Belton, D. 1973. Park naturalists' report, Manning Provincial Park. British Columbia Parks Branch Unpublished Report, Victoria. 33 pp. (Bibliography 2223).

Bendell, J.F. 1955. Age, breeding behavior and migration of sooty grouse, *Dendragapus obscurus fuliginosus* (Ridgway). Transactions of the North American Wildlife Conference 20:367-381.

Bendell, J.F. and F.C. Zwickel. 1984. A survey of the biology, ecology, abundance, and distribution of the Blue Grouse (Genus *Dendragapus*). Pages 163-192 *in* P.J. Hudson and T.W.I. Lovel (editors). Third International Grouse Symposium, York University, Toronto, Ontario.

Bendire, C.E. 1882. Malheur Lake, Oregon. Ornithologist and Oologist 7:137-138.

Bengtson, S.-A. 1966. Field studies on the Harlequin Duck in Iceland. Wildfowl Trust Annual Report 17:79-94.

Bennie, W. 1979. Common Loon's nest with three eggs. Federation of British Columbia Naturalists Newsletter 17(4):4.

Bent, A.C. 1919. Life histories of North American diving birds. United States National Museum Bulletin No.107, Washington, D.C. 239 pp.

_____. 1922. Life histories of North American petrels, pelicans and their allies. United States National Museum Bulletin No.121, Washington, D.C. 343 pp.

_____. 1923. Life histories of North American wildfowl. Part 1. United States National Museum Bulletin No. 126, Washington, D.C. 244 pp.

_____. 1925. Life histories of North American wildfowl. Part 2. United States National Museum Bulletin No.130, Washington, D.C. 314 pp.

_____. 1926. Life histories of North American marsh birds. United States National Museum Bulletin No. 135, Washington, D.C. 392 pp.

_____.1927. Life histories of North American shorebirds. Part 1. United States National Museum Bulletin No.142, Washington, D.C. 420 pp.

_____. 1932. Life histories of North American gallinaceous birds. United States National Museum Bulletin No. 162, Washington, D.C. 490 pp.

_____. 1938. Life histories of North American birds of prey. Orders Falconiformes and Strigiformes. United States National Museum Bulletin No. 170, Washington, D.C. 482 pp.

_____. 1939. Life histories of North American Woodpeckers. United States National Museum Bulletin No. 174, Washington, D.C. 334 pp.

_____. 1940. Life histories of North American cuckoos, goatsuckers, hummingbirds, and their allies. United States National Museum Bulletin No. 176, Washington, D.C. 506 pp.

Bergerud, A.T. and H.D. Hemus. 1975. An experimental study of the behavior of Blue Grouse (*Dendragapus obscurus*). 1. Differences between the founders from three populations. Canadian Journal of Zoology 53:1222-1237.

Bertram, D.F. 1988. The provisioning of nestlings by parent Rhinoceros Auklets (*Cerorhinca monocerata*). M.Sc. Thesis, Simon Fraser University, Burnaby, British Columbia. 100 pp.

Bertram, D.F. and G.W. Kaiser, 1988. Monitoring growth and diet of nesting Rhinoceros Auklets to guage prey availability. Canadian Wildlife Service Technical Report Series No. 48, Delta, British Columbia, 45 pp.

Beurling, G. 1978. On patting a penguin. Vancouver Sun Newspaper, 19 August.

Bicknell, F.T. 1914. California Brown Pelican in British Columbia. Condor 16:92.

Binford, L.C. and J.V. Remsen. 1974. Identification of the Yellow-billed Loon (*Gavia adamsii*). Western Birds 5:111-126.

Binford, L.C., B.G. Elliott, and S.W. Singer. 1975. Discovery of a nest and the downy young of the Marbled Murrelet. Wilson Bulletin 87:303-319.

Binkley, C.S. and R.S. Miller. 1983. Population characteristics of the Whooping Crane, *Grus americanus*. Canadian Journal of Zoology 61:2768-2776.

Birkhead, M.E. and C.M. Perrens. 1986. The Mute Swan. Christopher Helm Publishers Ltd., London, England. 157 pp.

Bishop, L.B. 1905. The Gray Sea Eagle (*Haliaeetus albicilla*) in British Columbia. Auk 22:79-80.

_____. 1930. An Ancient Murrelet in the inside passage. Murrelet 11:19.

Blake, E.R. 1977. Manual of Neotropical birds (Volume 1). University of Chicago Press, Chicago, Illinois. 674 pp.

Blakiston, T.W. 1861-1862. On birds collected and observed in the interior of British North America. Ibis, October, 1861, pp. 314-320; January, 1862, pp. 3-10.

_____. 1863. On the birds of the interior of British North America. Ibis, January, pp. 39-87; April, pp. 121-155.

Bledsoe, A.H. and D. Sibley. 1985. Patterns of vagrancy of Ross' Gull. American Birds 39:219-227.

Blockstein, D.E. and H.B. Tordoff. 1985. Gone forever - a contemporary look at the extinction of the Passenger Pigeon. American Birds 39:845-851.

Blokpoel, H., P.J. Blancher, and P.M. Fetterolf. 1985. On the plumage of nesting Ring-billed Gulls of different ages. Journal of Field Ornithology 56:113-124.

Blomquist, S. 1983. Bibliography of the Genus *Phalaropus*. Ottenby Bird Observatory, Degerhamn, Sweden. 27 pp.

Blood, D.A. 1976. Migratory bird use of the Ladysmith-Chemainus area, winter 1974-75. Canadian Wildlife Service Unpublished Report, Delta, British Columbia. 64 pp. (Bibliography 2282).

Blood, D.A. and G.W. Smith. 1967. Report on the status of waterfowl hunting in the Tofino area. British Columbia Fish and Wildlife Branch Unpublished Report, Nanaimo. 9 pp.

Bock, C.E. 1970. The ecology and behavior of the Lewis', Woodpecker (*Asyndesmus lewisi*). University of California Publications in Zoology 92:1-100.

Boersma, P.D. 1986. Body temperature, torpor, and growth in chicks of Fork-tailed Storm-Petrels (*Oceanodroma furcata*). Physiological Zoology 59:10-19.

Boersma, P.D., N.T. Wheelwright, M.K. Nerini, and E.S. Wheelwright. 1980. The breeding biology of the Fork-tailed Storm-Petrel (*Oceanodroma furcata*). Auk 97:268-282.

Boggs, B. and E. Boggs. 1960. The winter season - northern Pacific coast region. Audubon Field Notes 14:334-336.

_____. and _____. 1961a. The winter season - northern Pacific coast region. Audubon Field Notes 15:352-353.

_____. and _____. 1961b. The spring migration - northern Pacific coast region. Audubon Field Notes 15:433-434.

_____. and _____. 1961c. The nesting season - northern Pacific coast region. Audubon Field Notes 15:487-489.

_____. and _____. 1962a. The fall migration - northern Pacific coast region. Audubon Field Notes 16:67-69.

_____. and _____. 1962b. The winter season - northern Pacific coast region. Audubon Field Notes 16:357-359.

_____. and _____. 1962c. The spring migration - northern Pacific coast region. Audubon Field Notes 16:440-442.

_____. and _____. 1962d. The nesting season - northern Pacific coast region. Audubon Field Notes 16:500-502.

_____. and _____. 1963a. The fall migration - northern Pacific coast region. Audubon Field Notes 17:58-61.

_____. and _____. 1963b. The winter season - northern Pacific coast region. Audubon Field Notes 17:351-353.

_____. and _____. 1963c. The nesting season - northern Pacific coast region. Audubon Field Notes 17:478-480.

_____. and _____. 1964. Sight record of Short-tailed Albatross. Murrelet 45:48.

Boise, C.M. 1977. Breeding biology of the Lesser Sandhill Crane *Grus canadensis* (L.) on the Yukon-Kuskokwim Delta. M.S. Thesis, University of Alaska, Fairbanks. 74 pp.

Bolen, E.G. and M.K. Rylander. 1983. Whistling-ducks: Zoogeography, ecology, anatomy. Special Publications The Museum Texas Tech University No.20, Lubbock, Texas. 67pp.

Bonar, R.L. 1978a. Summary of terrestrial biology program - Revelstoke project - first annual report March, 1977 - March, 1978. British Columbia Hydro and Power Authority Unpublished Report, Vancouver. 11 pp. (Bibliography 2312).

_____. 1978b. Summary of terrestrial biology program - Revelstoke project - 2nd annual report , 1978. British Columbia Hydro and Power Authority Unpublished Report, Vancouver. 118 pp. (Bibliography 2313).

Bourne, W.R.P. and T.J. Dixon. 1975. Observations of seabirds 1970-1972. Sea Swallow 24:65-88.

Boxall, P. 1980. Ecology of wintering Snowy Owls. M.Sc. Thesis, University of Calgary, Calgary, Alberta. 213 pp.

Boyd, H. and L.S. Maltby. 1979. The Brant of the western Queen Elizabeth Islands, N.W.T. Pages 5-21 *in* R.L. Jarvis and J.C. Bartonek (editors). Management and Biology of Pacific Flyway Geese. Oregon State University Book Stores, Corvallis.

Bradley, D.M. 1959. Birds and mammals seen at the V.N.H.S. camp, Cosen's Bay, Kalamalka Lake, north Okanagan, July 4-14, 1958. Bulletin of the Vancouver Natural History Society 108:3-4.

Branson, N.J.B.A., E.D. Ponting, and C.D.T. Minton. 1978. Turnstone migration in Britain and Europe. Bird Study 25:181-187.

Braun, C.E. 1969. Population dynamics, habitat and movements of white-tailed ptarmigan in Colorado. Ph.D. Thesis, Colorado State University, Fort Collins. 189 pp.

_____. 1980. Alpine bird communities of western North America: implications for management and research. Pages 280-291 *in* R.M. DeGraff and M.G. Tilghman (compilers). Workshop Proceedings, Management of western forests and grasslands for non-game birds. United States Department of Agriculture, Forest Service General Technical Report INT-86.

_____. 1984. Biological investigations of White-tailed Ptarmigan in Colorado, U.S.A. - A review. Pages 131-147 *in* P.J. Hudson and T.W.I. Lovel (editors). Third International Grouse Symposium, World Pheasant Association, York University, Toronto, Ontario.

Braun, C.E., J.H. Enderson, C.J. Henny, H. Meng, and A.G. Nye. 1977. Conservation committee report on falconry: effects on raptor populations and management in North America. Wilson Bulletin 89:360-369.

Breault, A.M. 1988. Productivity and distribution of Great Blue Heron colonies in the Strait of Georgia. Canadian Wildlife Service Unpublished Report, Delta, British Columbia. 59 pp.

Breault, A.M., K.M. Cheng, and J-P.L. Savard. 1988. Distribution and abundance of Eared Grebes (*Podiceps nigricollis*) in British Columbia. Canadian Wildlife Service Technical Report Series No.51, Delta, British Columbia. 87 pp.

Breckenridge, W.J. 1935. An ecological study of some Minnesota Marsh Hawks. Condor 37:268-276.

_____. 1956. Nesting study of Wood Ducks. Journal of Wildlife Management 20:16-21.

Briggs, K.T. and E.W. Chu. 1986. Sooty Shearwaters off California: distribution, abundance, and habitat use. Condor 88:355-364.

Brigham, R.M. 1989. Roost and nest sites of Common Nighthawks: are gravel roots important? Condor 91:722-724.

Brisbin, I.L. 1968. The Passenger Pigeon: a study in the ecology of extinction. Modern Game Breeding 4:13-20.

British Columbia Ministry of Forests. 1988. Biogeoclimatic zones of British Columbia 1988. British Columbia Ministry of Forests, Victoria. Map.

Britton, D. 1980. Identification of Sharp-tailed Sandpipers. British Birds 73:333-345.

Brooke, R.K. 1978. The *Catharacta* Skuas (Aves: Laridae) occurring in south African waters. Durban Museum Novitates 11:295-308.

Brooks, A. 1900. Notes on some of the birds of British Columbia. Auk 17:104-107.

_____. 1901. Notes on the winter birds of the Cariboo district, B.C. Ottawa Naturalist 15:152-154.

_____. 1903. Notes on the birds of the Cariboo district, British Columbia. Auk 20:277-284.

_____. 1909a. Some notes on the birds of Okanagan, British Columbia. Auk 26:60-63.

_____. 1909b. Three records for British Columbia. Auk 26:313-314.

_____. 1912. Some British Columbia records. Auk 29:252-253.

_____. 1917. Birds of the Chilliwack district, B.C. Auk 34:28-50.

_____. 1918. Brief notes on the prevalence of certain birds in British Columbia. Canadian Field-Naturalist 31:139-141.

_____. 1920. Notes on the Limicolae of southern British Columbia. Condor 22:26-32.

_____. 1921. A twelve month with the shorebirds. Condor 23:151-156.

_____. 1923a. Notes on the birds of Porcher Island, B.C. Auk 40:217-224.

_____. 1923b. Some recent records for British Columbia. Auk 40:700-701.

_____. 1923c. A comment on the alleged occurrence of *Mesophoyx intermedia* in North America. Condor 25:180-181.

_____. 1926. Scarcity of the Marbled Murrelet. Murrelet 7:39.

_____. 1927. Notes on Swarth's report on a collection of birds and mammals from the Atlin region. Condor 29:112-114.

_____. 1928. Does the Marbled Murrelet nest inland? Murrelet 9:68.

_____. 1930. In memoriam: Charles de Blois Green. Condor 32:9-11.

_____. 1932. The occurrence of the Falcated Duck (*Eunetta falcata*) in Okanagan, British Columbia. Murrelet 13:92.

_____. 1937. Pacific Golden Plover and Curlew Sandpiper on the Pacific Coast of North America. Condor 39:176-177.

_____. 1942. Additions to the distributional list of the birds of British Columbia. Condor 44:33-34.

Brooks, A. and H.S. Swarth. 1925. A distributional list of the birds of British Columbia. Pacific Coast Avifauna No.17, Berkeley, California. 158 pp.

Brown, B. 1985. Sidney man loses old-gull friend. Victoria Times-Colonist, 24 August:A1-A2.

Brown, P.W. 1977. Breeding biology of the White-winged Scoter (*Melanitta fusca*). M.Sc. Thesis, Iowa State University, Ames. 46 pp.

Browne, P.W.P. 1958. The field identification of Baird's and Semipalmated Sandpipers. British Birds 51:81.

Browning, M.R. 1977. Interbreeding members of the *Sphyrapicus varius* group (Aves: Picidae) in Oregon. Bulletin of the Southern California Academy of Science 76:38-41.

Bruce, A.M., R.J. Anderson, and G.T. Allen. 1982. Observations of Golden Eagles nesting in western Washington. Raptor Research 16:132-134.

Brunton, D.F. and T. Pratt. 1986. Sightings of a Black-throated Sparrow, *Amphispiza bilineata*, and a Black Vulture, *Coragyps atratus atratus*, in British Columbia. Canadian Field-Naturalist 100:256-257.

Brunton, D.F., S. Andrews, and D.G. Paton. 1979. Nesting of the Calliope Hummingbird in Kananaskis Provincial Park, Alberta. Canadian Field-Naturalist 93:449-451.

Buchanan, J.B. 1988a. Migration and winter populations of Greater Yellowlegs, *Tringa melanoleuca*, in western Washington. Canadian Field-Naturalist 102: 611-616.

_____. 1988b. North American Merlin populations: an analysis using Christmas Bird Count data. American Birds 42:1178-1180.

Buffam, F. 1966. Wickaninnish Provincial Park summer report 1966. British Columbia Parks Branch Unpublished Report, Victoria. 14 pp. (Bibliography 2389).

Bull, J. 1963. On leg color in immature jaegers. Linnaean Newsletter 17: April.

_____. 1974. Birds of New York state. Doubleday/Natural History Press, Garden City, New York. 655 pp.

Bump, G., R.B. Darrow, F.C. Edminster, and W.F. Grissey. 1947. The Ruffed Grouse - life history, propagation, management. New York State Conservation Department, Buffalo. 915 pp.

Bunn, D.S., A.B. Warburton and R.D.S. Wilson. 1982. The Barn Owl. Buteo Books, Vermillion, South Dakota. 264 pp.

Bunnell, F.L. and R.G. Williams. 1980. Subspecies and diversity - The spice of life or prophet of doom. Pages 246-259 *in* R. Stace-Smith, L. Johns, and P. Joslin (editors). Proceedings of the Symposium on Threatened and Endangered Species and Habitats in British Columbia and the Yukon. British Columbia Ministry of Environment, Victoria.

Bunnell, F.L., D. Dunbar, L. Koza, and G. Ryder. 1981. Effects of disturbance on the productivity and numbers of White Pelicans in British Columbia - observations and models. Colonial Waterbirds 4:2-11.

Bunni, M.K. 1959. The Killdeer, *Charadrius v. vociferus* Linnaeus, in the breeding season: ecology, behaviour, and the development of homoiothermism. PhD. Thesis, University of Michigan, Ann Arbor.

Burgess, T.E. 1970. Foods and habitat of four Anatinids wintering on the Fraser delta tidal marshes. M.Sc. Thesis, University of British Columbia, Vancouver. 124 pp.

Burn, D.M. and J.R. Mather. 1974. The White-billed Diver in Britain. British Birds 67:258-296.

Burnes, J. 1978. Penguins seen around north end of island. Vancouver Sun Newspaper, 12 August.

Burns, F.L. 1915. Comparative periods of deposition and incubation of some North American birds. Wilson Bulletin 27:275-286.

Burr, I.W. 1967. King Eider (*Somateria spectabilis*) in the San Juans. Murrelet 48:7.

Burton, B.A. 1977. Some aspects of the ecology of Lesser Snow Geese wintering on the Fraser River estuary. M.Sc. Thesis, University of British Columbia, Vancouver. 173 pp.

Burton, J. and R. McNeil. 1976. Age determination of six species of North American shorebirds. Bird-Banding 47:201-209.

Butler, J.R. and G.D. Fenton. 1986. Bird watchers at Point Pelee National Park, Canada: their characteristics and activities, with special consideration to their social and resource impacts. Paper presented at First National Symposium on Social Science in Resource Management, Oregon State University, Corvallis, May 12-16.

Butler, R.W. 1973. Mitlenatch Island Nature Park - 1973 summer report. British Columbia Parks Branch Unpublished Report. Victoria. 41 pp. (Bibliography 2408).

_____. 1989. Breeding ecology and population trends of the Great Blue Heron *Ardea herodias fannini*, in the Strait of Georgia, British Columbia. Pages 112-117 *in* K. Vermeer and R.W. Butler (editors). The ecology and status of marine and shoreline birds in the Strait of Georgia, British Columbia. Canadian Wildlife Service Special Publication, Ottawa, Ontario.

Butler, R.W. and S. Butler. 1976. Naturalists' summer report, Mitlenatch Island (May 19-August 30, 1976). British Columbia Parks Branch Unpublished Report, Victoria. 9 pp. (Bibliography 2409).

Butler, R.W. and R.W. Campbell. 1987. The birds of the Fraser River delta: populations, ecology, and international significance. Canadian Wildlife Service Occasional Paper No.65, Ottawa, Ontario. 73 pp.

Butler, R.W. and J.W. Kirbyson. 1979. Oyster predation by the Black Oystercatcher in British Columbia. Condor 81:433-435.

Butler, R.W. and J.-P.L. Savard. 1985. Monitoring of the spring migration of waterbirds throughout British Columbia: a pilot study. Canadian Wildlife Service Unpublished Report, Delta, British Columbia. 13 pp.

Butler, R.W., N.A.M. Verbeek, and R.G. Foottit. 1980. Mortality and dispersal of the Glaucous-winged Gulls of southern British Columbia. Canadian Field-Naturalist 94:315-320.

Butler, R.W., B.G. Stushnoff, and E. McMackin. 1986. The birds of the Creston valley and southeastern British Columbia. Canadian Wildlife Service Occasional Paper No. 58, Ottawa, Ontario. 37 pp.

Butler, R.W., G.W. Kaiser, and G.E.J. Smith. 1987. Migration chronology, length of stay, sex ratio, and weight of Western Sandpipers (*Calidris mauri*) on the south coast of British Columbia. Journal of Field Ornithology 58:103-111.

Byrd, G.V., D.D. Gibson, and D.L. Johnson. 1974. The birds of Adak Island, Alaska. Condor 76:288-300.

Cade, T.J. 1955. Variation of the Common Rough-legged Hawk in North America. Condor 57:313-346.

_____. 1960. Ecology of the peregrine and Gyrfalcon population in Alaska. University of California Publications in Zoology 63:151-290.

Calder, J.A. and R.L. Taylor. 1968. Flora of the Queen Charlotte Islands, Part 1. Systematics of the vascular plants. Canada Department of Agriculture Research Branch Agriculture Monograph 4(1), Ottawa. 659 pp.

Calder, W.A. 1971. Temperature relationships and nesting of Calliope Hummingbird. Condor 73:314-321.

_____.1974. The thermal and radiant environment of a winter hummingbird nest . Condor 76: 268-273.

Call, M.W. 1978. Nesting habitats and surveying techniques for common western raptors. United States Department of the Interior Bureau of Land Management Technical Note TN-316, Washington, D.C. 115 pp.

Callin, E. 1962. Winter bird counts. Blue Jay 20:38.

Campbell, E.C. and R.W. Campbell. 1983. Status report on the Common Barn-Owl (*Tyto alba*) in Canada - 1982. Committee on the Status of Endangered Wildlife in Canada Report, Canadian Nature Federation, Ottawa, Ontario. 71 pp. (Bibliography 2428).

_____. and _____. 1984. Status report on the Spotted Owl (*Strix occidentalis caurina*) in Canada - 1983. Committee on the Status of Endangered Wildlife in Canada Report, Canadian Nature Federation, Ottawa, Ontario. 62 pp. (Bibliography 2429).

Campbell R.W. 1965. Mitlenatch Island Nature Park, December 19-22, 1965. British Columbia Parks Branch Unpublished Report, Victoria. 8 pp. (Bibliography 2501).

_____. 1966. On Black Oystercatchers "catching" oysters. Victoria Naturalist 23:26.

_____. 1967. Common Teals wintering in southwestern British Columbia. Murrelet 48:27.

_____. 1968a. Notes on a twenty-year-old Glaucous-winged Gull. Bird-Banding 39:226-227.

_____. 1968b. Status of breeding Herring Gulls at Bridge Lake, British Columbia, from 1933 to 1963. Canadian Field-Naturalist 82:217-219.

_____. 1968c. Two records of the Ruddy Duck nesting at Vancouver, British Columbia. Canadian Field-Naturalist 82:220-221.

_____. 1968d. Long-tailed Jaegers sighted at Vancouver, British Columbia. Murrelet 49:6.

_____. 1968e. Occurrence and nesting of the Black Oystercatcher near Vancouver, British Columbia. Murrelet 49:11.

_____. 1968f. A sight record of the Emperor Goose at White Rock, British Columbia. Murrelet 49:14.

_____. 1968g. Alexandrian rat predation on Ancient Murrelet eggs. Murrelet 49:38.

_____. 1968h. Capturing Ancient Murrelets by night-lighting. Blue Jay 26:90-91.

_____. 1969a. Spring bird observations on Langara Island, British Columbia. Blue Jay 27:155-159.

_____. 1969b. Occurrence and nesting of Wilson's Phalaropes at Vancouver, British Columbia. Condor 71:434.

_____. 1970a. The Sabine's Gull in southwestern British Columbia. Canadian Field-Naturalist 84:310-311.

_____. 1970b. Occurrence and nesting of Black Terns in southwestern British Columbia. Condor 72:500.

_____. 1970c. The White Pelican in southwestern British Columbia. Murrelet 51:18-19.

_____. 1970d. Recent information on nesting colonies of Mew Gulls on Kennedy Lake, Vancouver Island, British Columbia. Syesis 3:5-14.

_____. 1971a. First Canadian specimen of New Zealand Shearwater. Canadian Field-Naturalist 85:329-330.

_____. 1971b. Steller's Eider photographed near Campbell River, British Columbia. Canadian Field-Naturalist 85:330-331.

_____. 1971c. Status of the Caspian Tern in British Columbia. Syesis 4:185-189.

_____. 1972a. Coastal records of the Long-billed Curlew for British Columbia. Canadian Field-Naturalist 86:167-168.

_____. 1972b. Summary of selected winter bird counts in British Columbia. Vancouver Natural History Society Discovery 1:2-5.

_____. 1972c. The American Avocet (*Recurvirostra americana*) in British Columbia. Syesis 5:173-178.

_____. 1972d. The Green Heron in British Columbia. Syesis 5:235-247.

_____. 1973a. The seventy-third Christmas bird count - Vancouver, B.C. American Birds 27:182-183.

_____. 1973b. Coastal records of the Barred Owl for British Columbia. Murrelet 54:25.

_____. 1974. British Columbia roadside raptor census - southern British Columbia, September 11-15, 1973. British Columbia Provincial Museum Unpublished Report, Victoria. 5 pp. (Bibliography 2435).

_____. 1975a. Longevity record of a Glaucous-winged Gull. Bird-Banding 46:166.

_____. 1975b. Seabird colonies in Skidegate Inlet, Queen Charlotte Islands, British Columbia. Syesis 8:355-361.

_____. 1975c. Marginal habitat used by Glaucous-winged Gulls for nesting. Syesis 8:393.

_____. 1976a. Sea-bird colonies of Vancouver Island area. British Columbia Provincial Museum, Victoria. Map. (Bibliography 1989).

_____. 1976b. Sea-birds breeding on the Canadian West Coast. Pages 39-65 in H. Hosford (editor). Selected papers from the Fifth Annual Conference of the Canadian Nature Federation, Victoria, British Columbia, June 12/16, 1975. Canadian Nature Federation Special Publication No.5 and British Columbia Museum Heritage Record No. 1.

_____. 1977a. Checklist of British Columbia birds (to June 1977). British Columbia Provincial Museum, Victoria. Leaflet. (Bibliography 1990).

_____. 1977b. Use of man-made structures as nest sites by Pigeon Guillemots. Canadian Field-Naturalist 91:193-194.

_____. 1977c. Seabird colonies in Masset and Juskatla Inlets, Queen Charlotte Islands, British Columbia. British Columbia Provincial Museum Unpublished Report, Victoria. 5 pp. (Bibliography 1771).

_____. 1978a. British Columbia roadside raptor census, Vancouver to Smithers, May 17-18, 1978. British Columbia Provincial Museum Unpublished Report, Victoria. 9 pp. (Bibliography 2436).

_____. 1978b. Census of Herring, California and Ring-billed gulls nesting on Whiskey Island, Okanagan Lake. British Columbia Provincial Museum Unpublished Report, Victoria. 3 pp. (Bibliography 2438).

_____. 1978c. Assessment of Boundary Lake as a provincial ecological reserve for breeding marsh birds. British Columbia Museum Unpublished Report, Victoria. 5 pp. (Bibliography 2440).

_____ 1978d. Census of waterbirds nesting at Cecil Lake, British Columbia. British Columbia Provincial Museum Unpublished Report, Victoria. 10 pp. (Bibliography 2441).

_____ 1979. Proposal for an ecological reserve at "McQueen's Slough", Dawson Creek area, British Columbia. British Columbia Provincial Museum Unpublished Report, Victoria. 6 pp.

_____. 1980. Charlie Guiguet retires. B.C. Naturalist 18(1):7.

_____. 1981. Spring migrants observed 16-21 May 1981 at Atlin British Columbia. British Columbia Provincial Museum Unpublished Report, Victoria. 7 pp. (Bibliography 2447).

_____. 1981a. List of species and subspecies of British Columbia birds (through September 1981). British Columbia Provincial Museum Unpublished Report Victoria. 19 pp. (Bibliography 2448).

_____. 1982a. Wildlife atlases progress report. B.C. Naturalist 20(2):8-10.

_____. 1982b. Wildlife atlases progress report - spring 1982. B.C. Naturalist 20(3):6-8.

_____. 1982c. Wildlife atlases progress report - summer 1982. B.C. Naturalist 20(4):5-7.

_____. 1983a. Wildlife atlases progress report. B.C. Naturalist 21(1):4-5.

_____. 1983b. Wildlife atlases progress report - winter 1982-83. B.C. Naturalist 21(2):4-5.

_____. 1983c. Wildlife atlases progress report - spring-summer 1983. B.C. Naturalist 21(3):4-6.

_____. 1983d. Wildlife atlases progress report - fall 1983. B.C. Naturalist 21(4):4-6.

_____. 1983e. Feeding ecology of the Common Barn-Owl in North America. M.Sc. Thesis, University of Washington, Seattle. 87 pp.

_____. 1983f. Census of Double-crested and Pelagic cormorants breeding on Chain Islets Ecological Reserve - August 1983. British Columbia Provincial Museum Unpublished Report Victoria. 7 pp (Bibliography 2456).

_____. 1984a. Wildlife atlases progress report - winter 1983-1984. B.C. Naturalist 22(2):6-7.

_____. 1984b. Wildlife atlases progress report - fall 1984. B.C. Naturalist 22(4):6-7, 19.

_____. 1984c. Checklist of British Columbia birds (to May 1984). British Columbia Provincial Museum, Victoria. Leaflet. (Bibliography 2458).

_____. 1985a. Wildlife atlases progress report - winter 1984-1985. B.C. Naturalist 23(1):6-7.

_____. 1985b. Wildlife atlases progress report - spring 1985. B.C. Naturalist 23(2):6-7.

_____. 1985c. Wildlife atlases progress report - summer 1985. B.C. Naturalist 23(3):6-7.

_____. 1985d. Wildlife atlases progress report - fall 1985. B.C. Naturalist 23(4):6-9.

_____. 1985e. Census of birds nesting on Ellis Island, Fraser Lake, British Columbia, in 1985. British Columbia Provincial Museum Unpublished Report, Victoria. 2 pp.

_____. 1985f. First record of the Eurasian Kestrel for Canada. Condor 87:294.

_____. 1986a. Wildlife atlases progress report - spring 1986. B.C. Naturalist 24(2):6-7.

_____. 1986b. Violet Gibbard retires as nest program coordinator. B.C. Naturalist 24(2):7.

_____. 1986c. Wildlife atlases progress report - summer 1986. B.C. Naturalist 24(3):6-7.

_____. 1986d. Wildlife atlases progress report - autumn 1986. B.C. Naturalist 24(4):6-7.

_____. 1986e. Birds and mammals observed during a cruise of Moresby Island, Queen Charlotte Islands, 11-20 May 1986. British Columbia Provincial Museum Unpublished Report, Victoria. 10 pp.

_____. 1986f. Birds and mammals observed during a cruise of Moresby Island, Queen Charlotte Islands, 9-19 June 1986. British Columbia Provincial Museum Unpublished Report, Victoria. 16 pp.

_____. 1986g. List of British Columbia birds. Pages 9-29 *in* Higher vertebrates of British Columbia. British Columbia Provincial Museum, Victoria.

_____. 1987a. British Columbia wildlife - winter report 1986-87. B.C. Naturalist 25(1):6-7.

_____. 1987b. Birds and mammals observed during a cruise of Moresby Island, Queen Charlotte Islands, 9-18 May 1987. British Columbia Provincial Museum Unpublished Report, Victoria. 9 pp.

_____. 1987c. British Columbia wildlife - spring report 1987. B.C. Naturalist 25(2):6-7.

_____. 1987d. British Columbia wildlife - summer report 1987. B.C. Naturalist 25(3):6-7.

_____. 1987e. British Columbia wildlife - autumn report 1987. B.C. Naturalist 25(4):6-7.

_____. 1988a. British Columbia wildlife - winter report 1987-88. B.C. Naturalist 26(1):6-7.

_____. 1988b. British Columbia wildlife - spring report 1988. B.C. Naturalist 26(2):6-7.

_____. 1988c. British Columbia wildlife - summer report 1988. B.C. Naturalist 26(4):6-7.

_____. 1988d. Checklist of British Columbia birds (to June 1988). Royal British Columbia Museum, Victoria.

_____. 1989a. British Columbia wildlife - autumn report 1988. B.C. Naturalist 27(1):6-7.

_____. 1989b. Checklist of British Columbia birds (to June 1989). Federation of British Columbia Naturalists, Vancouver. Leaflet.

_____. 1989c. British Columbia wildlife - winter report 1988-1989. B.C. Naturalist 27(2):6-7.

_____. 1989d. British Columbia wildlife - spring report 1989. B.C. Naturalist 27(3): 6-8.

Campbell, R.W. and W.J. Anderson. 1972. Black-necked Stilt, new for British Columbia. Canadian Field-Naturalist 86:296.

Campbell, R.W. and R.G. Foottit. 1972. The Franklin's Gull in British Columbia. Syesis 5:99-106.

Campbell, R.W. and H.M. Garrioch. 1978a. Report on the Herring Gull colony on Ellis Island, Fraser Lake, British Columbia. British Columbia Provincial Museum Unpublished Report, Victoria. 9 pp. (Bibliography 1950).

_____. and _____. 1978b. Waterbirds nesting on south Westwick Lake, British Columbia - June, 1978. British Columbia Provincial Museum Unpublished Report, Victoria. 8 pp. (Bibliography 2481).

_____. and _____. 1979. Sea-bird colonies of the Queen Charlotte Islands. British Columbia Provincial Museum, Victoria. Map. (Bibliography 2482).

Campbell, R.W. and V. Gibbard. 1973. British Columbia nest records scheme - eighteenth annual report, 1972. Federation of British Columbia Naturalists Newsletter 11(1):3-5.

_____. and _____. 1981. British Columbia nest record scheme 1979/80. B.C. Naturalist 19(2):7-10.

_____. and _____. 1984. B.C. nest records scheme - twentieth annual report - 1983. B.C. Naturalist 22:9-11.

_____. and _____. 1986. British Columbia nest records scheme - thirtieth annual report - 1985. B.C. Naturalist 24(1):14, 16-17.

Campbell, R.W. and P.T. Gregory. 1976. The Buff-breasted Sandpiper in British Columbia, with notes on its migration in North America. Syesis 9:123-130.

Campbell, R.W. and A.P. Harcombe. 1985. Wildlife habitat handbooks for British Columbia: standard taxonomic list and codes of amphibians, reptiles, birds, and mammals. British Columbia Ministry of Forest Wildlife Habitat Research WHR-20, British Columbia Ministry of Environment Wildlife Report R-11, Victoria. 86 pp.

Campbell R.W. and H. Hosford. 1979. Attracting and feeding birds in British Columbia. British Columbia Provincial Museum Methods Manual No. 7, Victoria. 31 pp.

Campbell, R.W. and K. Kennedy. 1965. An annotated list of birds of Mitlenatch Island, June 23-August 27, 1965. British Columbia Parks Branch Unpublished Report, Victoria. 13 pp. (Bibliography 2492).

_____. and _____. 1966. Mitlenatch Island Nature Park summer report, 1966. British Columbia Parks Branch Unpublished Report, Victoria. 172 pp. (Bibliography 2493).

Campbell, R.W. and R.E. Luscher. 1972. Semi-palmated Plover breeding at Vancouver, British Columbia. Murrelet 53:11-12.

Campbell, R.W. and M.D. MacColl. 1978. Winter foods of Snowy Owls in southwestern British Columbia. Journal of Wildlife Management 42:190-192.

Campbell, R.W. and M.C.E. McNall. 1982. Field report of the Provincial Museum expedition to the vicinity of Kotcho Lake, northeastern British Columbia, June 11-July 9, 1982. British Columbia Provincial Museum Unpublished Report, Victoria. 307 pp. (Bibliography 2495).

Campbell, R.W. and A.L. Meugens. 1971. The summer birds of Richter Pass, British Columbia. Syesis 4:93-123.

Campbell, R.W. and M.G. Shepard. 1971. Summary of spring and fall pelagic birding trips from Tofino, British Columbia. Vancouver Natural History Society Discovery 150:13-16.

_____. and _____. 1972. Summary of 1971 offshore birding trips. Vancouver Natural History Society Discovery 1:7-8.

_____. and _____. 1973. Laysan Albatross, Scaled Petrel, Parakeet Auklet: additions to the list of Canadian birds. Canadian Field-Naturalist 87:179-180.

Campbell, R.W. and D. Stirling. 1968a. Notes on the vertebrate fauna associated with a Brandt's Cormorant colony in British Columbia. Murrelet 49:7-9.

_____ . and _____. 1968b. Notes on the natural history of Cleland Island, British Columbia, with emphasis on the breeding bird fauna. Pages 25-43 in Provincial Museum of Natural History and Anthropology Report for the Year 1967, Victoria, British Columbia.

_____. and _____. 1971. A photoduplicate file for British Columbia vertebrate records. Syesis 4:217-222.

Campbell, R.W. and K.R. Summers. In press. Vertebrates of the Brooks Peninsula, British Columbia. Royal British Columbia Museum Heritage Record.

Campbell, R.W. and B.M. Van Der Raay. 1981. Winter distribution and population dynamics of Bald Eagles in south-western mainland British Columbia. British Columbia Provincial Museum Unpublished Report, Victoria. 29 pp. (Bibliography 2498).

Campbell, R.W. and W.C. Weber. 1976. Occurrence and status of the Tufted Duck in British Columbia. Syesis 9:25-30.

_____ . and _____. 1977. The Cattle Egret in British Columbia. Canadian Field-Naturalist 91:87-88.

Campbell, R.W., M.G. Shepard, and R.H. Drent. 1972a. Status of birds in the Vancouver area in 1970. Syesis 5:137-167.

Campbell, R.W., M.G. Shepard, and W.C. Weber. 1972b. Vancouver birds in 1971. Vancouver Natural History Society Special Publication, Vancouver, British Columbia. 88 pp.

Campbell, R.W., M.G. Shepard, B.A. Macdonald, and W.C. Weber. 1974. Vancouver birds in 1972. Vancouver Natural History Society Special Publication, Vancouver, British Columbia. 96 pp.

Campbell, R.W., J.G. Ward, and M.G. Shepard. 1975. A new Common Murre colony in British Columbia. Canadian Field-Naturalist 89:244-248.

Campbell, R.W., M.A. Paul, M.S. Rodway, and H.R. Carter. 1977. Tree-nesting Peregrine Falcons in British Columbia. Condor 79:500-501.

Campbell, R.W., H.R. Carter, and S.G. Sealy. 1979a. Nesting of Horned Puffins in British Columbia. Canadian Field-Naturalist 93:84-86.

Campbell, R.W., H.R. Carter, C.D. Shepard, and C.J. Guiguet. 1979b. A bibliography of British Columbia ornithology: volume 1. British Columbia Provincial Museum Heritage Record No. 7, Victoria. 185 pp.

Campbell, R.W., R.J. Cannings, S.G. Cannings, and R.A. Cannings. 1979c. A proposal for an ecological reserve at Rock Lake, Becher's Prairie, British Columbia. British Columbia, Provincial Museum Unpublished Report, Victoria. 9 pp. (Bibliography 2474).

Campbell, R.W., J.M. Cooper, and M.C.E. McNall. 1983. Field report of the Provincial Museum expedition in the vicinity of Haines Triangle, northwestern British Columbia, May 27-July 4, 1983. British Columbia Provincial Museum Unpublished Report, Victoria. 351 pp. (Bibliography 2477).

Campbell, R.W., E.D. Forsman, and B.M. Van Der Raay. 1984. An annotated bibliography of literature on the Spotted Owl. British Columbia Ministry of Forests Land Management Report No. 24, Victoria. 115 pp.

Campbell, R.W., B.M. Van Der Raay, I. Robertson, and B.J. Petrar. 1985. Spring and summer distribution, status, and nesting ecology of the Arctic Loon, *Gavia arctica*, in interior British Columbia. Canadian Field-Naturalist 99:337-342.

Campbell, R.W., D.A. Manuwal, and A.S. Harestad. 1987. Food habits of the Common Barn-Owl in British Columbia. Canadian Journal of Zoology 65:578-586.

Campbell, R.W., T.D. Hooper, and N.K. Dawe. 1988. A bibliography of British Columbia ornithology: volume 2. Royal British Columbia Museum Heritage Record No.19 , Victoria. 591 pp.

Canada Department of Fisheries and Environment. 1978. Groundfish and herring resources. Canada Department of Fisheries and Environment Protection Service Map No.4, Ottawa, Ontario.

Canaris, A.G. 1950. Sight record of American Egret in eastern Washington. Murrelet 31:46.

Canning, D.J. and S.G. Herman. 1983. Gadwall breeding range expansion into western Washington. Murrelet 64:27-31.

Cannings, R.A. 1974. Another record of the Flammulated Owl in Canada. Canadian Field-Naturalist 88:234-235.

_____. 1975a. Natural history report: Cape Scott Park. British Columbia Parks Branch Unpublished Report, Victoria. 80 pp. (Bibliography 2552).

_____. 1975b. The Parasitic Jaeger in the British Columbia interior. Syesis 8:395-396.

Cannings, R.A., R.J. Cannings, and S.G. Cannings. 1987. Birds of the Okanagan Valley, British Columbia. Royal British Columbia Museum, Victoria. 420 pp.

Cannings, R.J. 1973. Shuswap birds, 1973 - annotated list. British Columbia Parks Branch Unpublished Report, Victoria. 15 pp. (Bibliography 2528).

_____. 1987. The breeding biology of Northern Saw-whet Owls in southern British Columbia. Pages 193-198 in R.W. Nero, R.J. Clark, R.J. Knapton, and R.H. Hamre (editors). Biology and Conservation of Northern Forest Owls: Symposium Proceedings. 1987 Feb. 3-7; Winnipeg, Manitoba. United States Department of Agriculture, Forest Service General Technical Report RM-142, Fort Collins Colorado. 309 pp.

_____. 1989. A Common Black-headed Gull: second Vancouver record. Vancouver Natural History Society Discovery 18: 14-15.

Cannings, R.J., B. Fredericks, and A. Stepniewski. 1974. Year-end hike: 1974 - Tonquin area - Mt. Robson Park. British Columbia Parks Branch Unpublished Report, Victoria. 5 pp. (Bibliography 2542).

Cannings, R.J., S.R. Cannings, J.M. Cannings, and G.P. Sirk. 1978. Successful breeding of the Flammulated Owl in British Columbia. Murrelet 59:74-75.

Cannings, S.G. 1973. Mount Robson vertebrate report, 1973. British Columbia Parks Branch Unpublied Report, Victoria. 18 pp. (Bibliography 2558).

_____. 1974. South Okanagan bird report - summer 1974. British Columbia Parks Branch Unpublished Report, Victoria. 27 pp. (Bibliography 2559).

Cannings, S.R. 1972. Some bird records from the Okanagan valley. Vancouver Natural History Society Discovery 1:37.

Carey, A.B. 1985. A summary of the scientific basis for Spotted Owl management. Pages 100-114 in R.J. Gutierrez and A.B. Carey (editors). Ecology and management of the Spotted Owl in the Pacific Northwest. United States Department of Agriculture, Forest Service General Technical Report PNW-185, Portland, Oregon.

Carl, G.C. 1942. Another record of the King Eider in British Columbia. Murrelet 23:62.

_____. 1959. In memoriam - James Alexander Munro. Murrelet 40:17-18.

Carl, G.C. and C.J. Guiguet. 1972. Alien animals in British Columbia. British Columbia Provincial Museum Handbook No.14, Victoria. 103 pp.

Carl, G.C. and G.A. Hardy. 1945. Flora and fauna of the Paradise Mine area, British Columbia. Pages 13-38 in Provincial Museum of Natural History and Anthropology Report for the year 1944, Victoria, British Columbia.

Carl, G.C., C.J. Guiguet, and G.H. Hardy. 1951. Biology of the Scott Island Group, British Columbia. Pages B21-B63 in Provincial Museum of Natural History and Anthropology Report for the year 1950, Victoria, British Columbia.

_____, _____, and _____. 1952. A natural history survey of the Manning Park area, British Columbia. British Columbia Provincial Museum Occasional Paper No.9, Victoria. 130 pp.

Carson, T. and J. Howsam. 1978. A study of waterfowl in relation to spawning herring at Ganges Harbour and Captain's Passage, British Columbia. British Columbia Provincial Museum Unpublished Report, Victoria. 39 pp. (Bibliography 1925).

Carter, B.C. 1958. The American Goldeneye in central New Brunswick. Canadian Wildlife Service Wildlife Management Bulletin (Series 2) No.9, Ottawa, Ontario. 47 pp.

Carter, H.R. 1984. At-sea biology of the Marbled Murrelet (*Brachyramphus marmoratus*) in Barkley Sound, British Columbia. M.Sc. Thesis, University of Manitoba, Winnipeg. 143 pp.

Carter, H.R., and S.G. Sealy. 1984. Marbled Murrelet (*Brachyramphus marmoratus*) mortality and a gill-net fishery in Barkley Sound, British Columbia. Pages 212-220 in D.N. Nettleship, G.A. Sanger and P.F. Springer (editors). Marine birds: their feeding ecology and commercial fisheries relationships. Canadian Wildlife Service Special Publication. Ottawa, Ontario.

_____. and _____. 1986. Year-round use of coastal lakes by Marbled Murrelets. Condor 88:473-477.

_____. and _____. 1987. Inland records of downy young and fledgling Marbled Murrelets in North America. Murrelet 68:58-63.

Carter, H.R., K.A. Hobson, and S.G. Sealy. 1984. Colony-site selection by Pelagic Cormorants (*Phalacrocorax pelagicus*) in Barkley Sound, British Columbia. Colonial Waterbirds 7:25-34.

Caspell, B., A. Danvers, J. Hutchinson, P. Ostrander, D. Pringle, and D. Udey. 1979. Field report of fall migration of waterbirds in the Columbia Valley, 1979. Canadian Wildlife Service Unpublished Report, Delta, British Columbia. 28 pp.

Cassidy, A.L.E.V. 1983. Winter ecology of Bald Eagles at Qualicum River estuary, British Columbia. B.Sc. Thesis, University of Victoria, Victoria, British Columbia. 34 pp.

Catling, P.M. 1972. A study of the Boreal Owl in southern Ontario, with particular reference to the irruption of 1968-69. Canadian Field-Naturalist 86:223-232.

Centennial Wildlife Society of British Columbia. 1987. Our Wildlife Heritage: 100 Years of Wildlife Management. Centennial Wildlife Society of British Columbia, Victoria, 192 pp.

Chamberlain, M. 1887. Catalogue of Canadian birds with notes on the distribution of the species. St. John, New Brunswick. 143 pp.

Chamberlain, M.L. 1977. Observations on Red-necked Grebe nesting in Michigan. Wilson Bulletin 89:32-46.

Chaniot, G.E. 1966. Another California specimen of *Pluvialis dominica fulva*. Condor 68:212.

Chapman, B.-A., J.P. Goossen, and I. Ohanjanian. 1985. Occurrences of Black-necked Stilts, *Himantopus mexicanus*, in Western Canada. Canadian Field-Naturalist 99:254-257.

Chapman, F.M. 1890. On a collection of birds made by Mr. Clark P. Streator in British Columbia, with field notes by the collector. Bulletin of the American Museum of Natural History 3:123-158.

Chapman, J.A., C.J. Henny, and H.M. Wight. 1969. The status, population dynamics, and harvest of the Dusky Canada Goose. Wildlife Monographs 18:1-48.

Chapman, J.D. 1952. The climate of British Columbia. Paper presented to the Fifth British Columbia Natural Resources Conference, University of British Columbia, Vancouver, February 27th, 1952. 47 pp.

Chapman-Mosher, B.-A. 1986. Factors influencing reproductive success and nesting strategies in Black Terns. M.Sc. Thesis, Simon Fraser University, Burnaby, British Columbia. 154 pp.

Chilton, G. and S.G. Sealy. 1987. Species roles in mixed-species feeding flocks of seabirds. Journal of Field Ornithology 58:456-463.

Choate, T.S. 1963. Habitat and population dynamics of White-tailed Ptarmigan in Montana. Journal of Wildlife Management 27:684-699.

Christensen, G.C. 1970. The Chukar Partridge - Its introduction, life history, and management. Nevada Department of Fish and Game Biological Bulletin No. 4, Reno. 82 pp.

Christman, M.J. 1969. Bird sightings in Kootenay National Park. Parks Canada Unpublished Report, Radium Hotsprings, British Columbia. 14 pp. (Bibliography 2591).

_____. 1970. Occurrence of birds on the Vermilion Pass burn, Kootenay National Park. Parks Canada Unpublished Report, Radium Hotsprings, British Columbia. 51 pp. (Bibliography 2592).

Chu, E.W. 1984. Sooty Shearwaters off California: diet and energy gain. Pages 64-71 in D.N. Nettleship, G.A. Sanger and P.F. Springer (editors). Marine birds: their feeding ecology and commercial fisheries relationships. Proceedings of the Pacific Seabird Group Symposium, Seattle, Washington, 6-8 January 1982. Canadian Wildlife Service Special Publication. Ottawa, Ontario.

Clague, J.J. 1981. Late quaternary geology and geochronology of British Columbia. Part 2: summary and discussion of radio-carbon-dated quaternary history. Geological Survey of Canada Paper 80-35, Ottawa, Ontario. 41pp.

Clark, R.J. 1970. A field study of the Short-eared Owl (*Asio flammeus* Pontoppidan) in North America. Ph.D. Thesis, Cornell University, Ithaca, New York. 209 pp.

Clark, R.J., D.G. Smith and L.H. Kelso. 1978. Working bibliography of owls of the world. National Wildlife Federation Scientific and Technical Series No.1, Washington, D.C. 319 pp.

Clark, W.S. 1983. The field identification of North American eagles. American Birds 37:822-826.

Clay, J.O. 1946. Western Willet seen at Victoria, British Columbia. Murrelet 27:13.

_____. 1947. Note on a hummingbird. Victoria Naturalist 3:105.

_____. 1950. Christmas bird count. Victoria Naturalist 6:88-89.

_____. 1955. Christmas bird census, 1954 - Victoria, British Columbia. Canadian Field-Naturalist 69:58.

_____. 1955a. Birds seen out of season. Victoria Naturalist 11:100-101.

_____. 1957a. Christmas bird census, 1956 - Victoria, British Columbia. Canadian Field-Naturalist 71:28.

_____. 1957b. Some interesting birds. Victoria Naturalist 14:73-75.

Coffey, B.B. 1948. Post-juvenal migration of herons. Bird-Banding 19:1-5.

Cogswell, H.L. 1977. Water birds of California. University of California Press, Berkeley. 399 pp.

Collins, C.T. and R.E. Landry. 1977. Artificial nest burrows for Burrowing Owls. North American Bird-Bander 2:151-154.

Conant, B. 1988. Alaska productivity surveys of geese, swans and Brant - 1987. United States Fish and Wildlife Service Report, Juneau, Alaska. 26 pp.

Connors, P.G. 1983. Taxonomy, distribution, and evolution of golden plovers (Pluvialis dominica and Pluvialis fulva). Auk 100:607-620.

Conover, M.R. and G.G. Chasko. 1985. Nuisance Canada Goose problems in the eastern United States. Wildlife Society Bulletin 13:228-233.

Cook, F.R. and D. Muir. 1984. The Committee on the Status of Endangered Wildlife in Canada (COSEWIC): history and progress. Canadian Field-Naturalist 98:63-70.

Cook, F.S. 1947. Notes on some fall and winter birds of the Queen Charlotte Islands, British Columbia. Canadian Field-Naturalist 61:131-133.

Cooke, W.W. 1915. Distribution and migration of North American gulls and their allies. United States Department of Agriculture Bulletin No. 292, Washington, D.C. 70 pp.

Cooper, J.G. 1860. Report upon the birds collected on the survey. Land birds. Chapter 1. United States Pacific Rail Road Exploration and Survey 12 (Book 2. Zoology) 3:140-226.

Cooper, J.K. 1969. First breeding record of the White-headed Woodpecker for Canada. Canadian Field-Naturalist 83:276-277.

Cooper, J.M. 1983. Recent occurrences of the American Avocet in British Columbia. Murrelet 64:47-48.

Cooper, J.M. 1987. Notes on the vertebrates of Delkatla Inlet, Queen Charlotte Islands, 2 May-15 August 1987. Royal British Columbia Museum Unpublished Report, Victoria 185 pp.

Cooper, J.M. and M. Adams. 1979. The birds and mammals of Kwadacha Wilderness Park, August 13-September 8, 1979. British Columbia Provincial Museum Unpublished Report, Victoria. 10 pp. (Bibliography 2687).

Cooper, J.M. and D.L.P. Cooper. 1983. A second report on the summer vertebrates of the Fern Lake area of Kwadacha Wilderness Park. British Columbia Provincial Museum Unpublished Report, Victoria. 7 pp. (Bibliography 2688).

Corkran, C.C. 1988. Status and potential for breeding of the Common Loon in the Pacific Northwest. Pages 107-116; in P.I.V. Strong (editor). Papers from the 1987 Conference on Common Loon Research and Management. North American Loon Fund, Meredith, New Hampshire.

Cottam, C., J.J. Lynch and A.L. Nelson. 1944. Food habits and management of American sea brant. Journal of Wildlife Management 8:36-56.

Council of Biology Editors, Committee on Form and Style. 1972. CBE style manual. Third edition. American Institute of Biological Sciences, Washington, D.C. 297 pp.

Cowan, I.McT. 1939. The vertebrate fauna of the Peace River district of British Columbia. British Columbia Provincial Museum Occasional Paper No.1, Victoria. 102 pp.

_____. 1939a. The White-tailed Ptarmigan of Vancouver Island. Condor 41:82-83.

_____. 1940. Bird records from British Columbia. Murrelet 20:69-70.

_____. 1940a. Winter occurrence of summer birds on Vancouver Island, British Columbia. Condor 42:213-214.

_____. 1942a. Food habits of the Barn Owl in British Columbia. Murrelet 23:48-53.

_____. 1942b. Economic status of the pheasant on the cultivated lands of the Okanagan Valley, B.C. Pages 49-62 in Annual Report of the British Columbia Provincial Game Commission for 1942, Victoria.

_____. 1955. The Whooping Crane. Bulletin of the Vancouver Natural History Society 95:2-3.

_____. 1987. Science and the conservation of wildlife in British Columbia. Pages 85-106 in Our Wildlife Heritage: 100 years of Wildlife Management. The Centennial Wildlife Society of British Columbia, Victoria. 192 pp.

Cowan, I.McT. and C.J. Guiguet. 1965. The mammals of British Columbia. British Columbia Provincial Museum Handbook No. 11, Victoria. 414 pp.

Cowan, I.McT. and J.A. Munro. 1944. Birds and mammals of Revelstoke National Park. Canadian Alpine Journal 29:100-121; 237-256.

Cramp, S. (editor). 1983. Handbook of the birds of Europe, the Middle East and North Africa: The birds of the western Palearctic, Volume III - waders to gulls. Oxford University Press, Oxford, England. 913 pp.

Craven, S.R. 1981. The Canada Goose (Branta canadensis) - an annotated bibliography. United States Department of the Interior, Fish and Wildlife Service Special Scientific Report - Wildlife No.231, Washington, D.C. 66 pp.

Cringan, A.T. 1957. Notes on the biology of the Red-necked Grebe in western Ontario. Canadian Field-Naturalist 71:72-73.

Crispens, C.G. 1960. Quails and partridges of North America - a bibliography. University of Washington Press, Seattle. 125 pp.

Crockett, A.B. and H.H. Hadow. 1975. Nest site selection by Williamson and Red-naped sapsuckers. Condor 77:365-368.

Cronau, J.P., R.G.M. Goede, and E. Nieboer. 1986. A new character for age determination in the Bar-tailed Godwit Limosa lapponica. Ringing and Migration 7:135-138.

Crowell, J.B. and H.B. Nehls. 1966a. The fall migration - northern Pacific coast region. Audubon Field Notes 20:449-453.

_____. and _____. 1966b. The spring migration - northern Pacific coast region. Audubon Field Notes 20:539-542.

_____. and _____. 1966c. The nesting season - northern Pacific coast region. Audubon Field Notes 20:591-595.

_____. and _____. 1967a. The winter season - northern Pacific coast region. Audubon Field Notes 21:448-452.

_____. and _____. 1967b. The spring migration - northern Pacific coast region. Audubon Field Notes 21:532-535.

_____. and _____. 1967c. The nesting season - northern Pacific coast region. Audubon Field Notes 21:596-600.

_____. and _____. 1968a. The fall migration - northern Pacific coast region. Audubon Field Notes 22:78-83.

_____. and _____. 1968b. The winter season - northern Pacific coast region. Audubon Field Notes 22:468-472.

_____ and _____. 1968c. The spring migration - northern Pacific coast region. Audubon Field Notes 22:567-571.

_____. and _____. 1968d. The nesting season - northern Pacific coast region. Audubon Field Notes 22:638-642.

_____. and _____. 1969a. The winter season - northern Pacific coast region. Audubon Field Notes 23:508-513.

_____. and _____. 1969b. The spring migration - northern Pacific coast region. Audubon Field Notes 23:615-619.

_____. and _____. 1969c. The nesting season - northern Pacific coast region. Audubon Field Notes 23:684-688.

_____. and _____. 1970a. The fall migration - northern Pacific coast region. Audubon Field Notes 24:82-88.

_____. and _____. 1970b. The winter season - northern Pacific coast region. Audubon Field Notes 24:530-533.

_____. and _____. 1970c. The spring migration - northern Pacific coast region. Audubon Field Notes 24:635-638.

_____. and _____. 1970d. The nesting season - northern Pacific coast region. Audubon Field Notes 24:708-711.

_____. and _____. 1971a. The winter season - northern Pacific coast region. Audubon Field Notes 25:614-619.

_____. and _____. 1971b. The spring migration - northern Pacific coast region. Audubon Field Notes 25:787-793.

_____. and _____. 1972a. The fall migration - northern Pacific coast region. American Birds 26:107-111.

_____. and _____. 1972b. The winter season - northern Pacific coast region. American Birds 26:644-648.

_____. and _____. 1972c. The nesting season - northern Pacific coast region. American Birds 26:893-897.

_____. and _____. 1972d. The spring migration - northern Pacific coast region. American Birds 26:797-801.

_____. and _____. 1973a. The fall migration - northern Pacific coast region. American Birds 27:105-110.

_____. and _____. 1973b. The winter season - northern Pacific coast region. American Birds 27:652-656.

_____. and _____. 1973c. The spring migration - northern Pacific coast region. American Birds 27:809-812.

_____. and _____. 1973d. The nesting season - northern Pacific coast region. American Birds 27:908-911.

_____. and _____. 1974a. The fall migration - northern Pacific coast region. American Birds 28:93-98.

_____. and _____. 1974b. The winter season - northern Pacific coast region. American Birds 28:679-684.

_____. and _____. 1974c. The spring migration - northern Pacific coast region. American Birds 28:840-845.

_____. and _____. 1974d. The nesting season - northern Pacific coast region. American Birds 28:938-943.

_____. and _____. 1975a. The fall migration - northern Pacific coast region. American Birds 29:105-112.

_____. and _____. 1975b. The spring migration - northern Pacific coast region. American Birds 29:897-902.

_____. and _____. 1976. The winter season - northern Pacific coast region. American Birds 30:755-760.

_____. and _____. 1977a. The fall migration - northern Pacific coast region. American Birds 31:212-216.

_____. and _____. 1977b. Spring migration - northern Pacific coast region. American Birds 31:1037-1041.

Crowley, J.M. 1967. Biogeography. Canadian Geographer 11:312-326.

Cumming, R.A. 1924. Pectoral Sandpiper eating seeds. Migrant 2:15. (Bibliography 1936).

_____. 1926. Vancouver notes. Migrant 3:43-44. (Bibliography 1944).

_____. 1931. Some birds observed in the Queen Charlotte Islands, British Columbia. Murrelet 11:15-17.

_____. 1932. Birds of the Vancouver district, British Columbia. Murrelet 13:1-15.

_____. 1935. Rock Ptarmigan at Vancouver, British Columbia. Murrelet 16:39.

Curtin, F. 1978. Rare penguins sighted off Vancouver Island. Vancouver Province Newspaper, 16 August.

Cushing, J.E. 1941. Notes on the feeding habits of two species of hawks. Condor 43:70-71.

Cuthbert, J.T. 1972. Port Hardy airport eagle study - final report for period October 28-December 3, 1972. L.G.L. Ltd. Environmental Research Associates Unpublished Report, Toronto, Ontario. 67 pp. (Bibliography 2751).

Dane, C.W. 1966. Some aspects of breeding biology of the Blue-winged Teal. Auk 83:389-402.

Darcus, S.J. 1927. Discovery of the nest of the Marbled Murrelet (*Brachyramphus marmoratus*) in the Queen Charlotte Islands, British Columbia. Canadian Field-Naturalist 41:197-199.

_____. 1930. Notes on birds of the northern part of the Queen Charlotte Islands in 1927. Canadian Field-Naturalist 44:45-49.

_____. 1930a. Status of Canada Geese on the Vaseux Lake bird sanctuary, British Columbia. Canadian Field-Naturalist 44:21-22.

_____. 1935. Christmas bird census, 1934 - Summerland, Okanagan Lake, British Columbia. Canadian Field-Naturalist 49:44.

Darwin, L.H. 1916. First and second annual reports of the chief game warden to the governor of the state of Washington, June 12, 1913 to February 28, 1915. Olympia, Washington. 58 pp.

_____. 1918. Third and fourth reports of the state game warden to the governor of the state of Washington, March 1, 1915 to February 28, 1917. Olympia, Washington. 78 pp.

Davidson, A.R. 1963. An annotated list of the birds of southern Vancouver Island. Victoria Natural History Society Mimeo Report, Victoria, British Columbia. 23 pp. (Bibliography 306).

_____. 1965. Victoria Natural History Society bird report - 1964. Victoria Natural History Society Mimeo Report, Victoria, British Columbia. 12 pp. (Bibliography 1249).

_____. 1966. Annotated list of birds of southern Vancouver Island. Victoria Natural History Society, Victoria, British Columbia. 23 pp. (Bibliography 306).

_____. 1979. Unusual sighting in the Comox valley. Victoria Naturalist 35:77.

Davies, R.G. 1973. Demography and behaviour of Ruffed Grouse in British Columbia. M.Sc. Thesis, University of Victoria, Victoria, British Columbia. 86 pp.

_____. 1978. Status of swans wintering on Vancouver Island between 1971 and 1977. British Columbia Fish and Wildlife Branch Unpublished Report, Nanaimo. 16 pp.

_____. 1981a. Swan survey of region 1 - February 1981. British Columbia Fish and Wildlife Branch Unpublished Report, Victoria. 8 pp. (Bibliography 2776).

_____. 1981b. Abundance and distribution of Mute Swans on Vancouver Island, British Columbia. British Columbia Fish and Wildlife Branch Unpublished Report, Victoria. 7 pp. (Bibliography 2777).

_____. 1981c. Status of swans wintering on Vancouver Island between 1971 and 1977. Pages 86-90 *in* Proceedings and Papers of the Sixth Trumpeter Swan Society Conference, Anchorage, Alaska, September 7-11, 1978. (Bibliography 2778).

Davis, T.A., M.F. Platter-Reiger, and R.A. Ackerman. 1984. Incubation water loss by Pied-billed Grebe eggs: adaptation to a hot, wet nest. Physiological Zoology 57:384-391.

Dawe, N.K. 1971. Nature interpretation report on Wasa, Moyie, and Jimsmith Provincial Parks, British Columbia. British Columbia Parks Branch Unpublished Report, Victoria. 97 pp. (Bibliography 1172).

_____. 1972. Franklin's Gull sighted in southeastern British Columbia. Vancouver Natural History Society Discovery 1:6.

_____. 1973. Sighting of a Bar-tailed Godwit at the George C. Reifel Waterfowl Refuge. Vancouver Natural History Society Discovery 1:110-111.

_____. 1976. Flora and fauna of the Marshall-Stevenson Wildlife area. Canadian Wildlife Service Report, Delta, British Columbia. 201 pp. (Bibliography 1862).

_____. 1980. Flora and fauna of the Marshall-Stevenson Unit, Qualicum National Wildlife Area (update to June 1979). Canadian Wildlife Service Report, Qualicum Beach, British Columbia. 149 pp. (Bibliography 2788).

Dawe, N.K. and B. Davies. 1975. A nesting study of Canada geese on the George C. Reifel Migratory Bird Sanctuary, British Columbia. Syesis 8:1-7.

Dawe, N.K. and L.E. Jones. 1986. Vegetation of the Koksilah Marsh, Cowichan estuary: a pre-restoration study, July 1985. Canadian Wildlife Service Technical Report Series No.9, Delta, British Columbia. 30 pp.

Dawe, N.K. and S.D. Lang. 1980. Flora and fauna of the Nanoose Unit, Qualicum National Wildlife Area. Canadian Wildlife Service Unpublished Report. Qualicum Beach, British Columbia. 117 pp. (Bibliography 2791).

Dawe, N.K. and J.D. McIntosh. 1987. Changes in vegetation following dyke removal on the Englishman River estuary (1979-1986). Research Note. Northwest Environmental Journal 3:150-151.

Dawe, N.K. and E.L. Nygren. 1989. Vancouver Island Brant: 1989 survey. B.C. Naturalist 27(3):18-19.

Dawe, N.K., W.S. Boyd, and D.E.C. Trethewey. 1987. Vegetation of man-made marshes on the Campbell River estuary: a five year study. Research Note. Northwest Environmental Journal 3:151-152.

Day, R.H., K.L. Oakley, and D.R. Barnard. 1983. Nest sites and eggs of Kittlitz's and Marbled murrelets. Condor 85:265-273.

Degner, M.A. 1988. Song, vegetation, and sound production in Blue Grouse. M.Sc. Thesis, University of Alberta, Edmonton. 140 pp.

de Goutiere, J. 1968. The pathless way. J.J. Douglas Ltd., Vancouver, British Columbia. 194 pp.

Delacour, J. 1954. The waterfowl of the world (Volume 1). Country Life Limited, London, England. 284 pp.

_____. 1956. The waterfowl of the world (Volume 2). Country Life Limited, London, England. 232 pp.

Demarchi, D.A. 1987. Defining British Columbia's regional ecosystem. Pages 57-68 *in* Bits and Pieces Symposium. Federation of British Columbia Naturalists, Vancouver, November 20-21, 1987.

_____. 1988a. A regional wildlife ecosystem classification for British Columbia. Pages 11-19 *in* H.A. Stelfox and G.R. Ironside (compilers). Land/Wildlife integration workshop No. 3, Mount Ste.-Marie, Quebec, 16-19 September 1985. Ecological Land Classification Series No. 22, Canadian Wildlife Service, Ottawa, Ontario. 215 pp.

_____. 1988b. Ecoregions of British Columbia. British Columbia Ministry of Environment and Parks, Wildlife Branch, Victoria. Map.

Demarchi, D.A. and E.C. Lea. 1987. Biophysical habitat classification in British Columbia: an interdisciplinary approach to ecosystem evaluation. Symposium on Land Classification based on Vegetation, Applications for Resource Management, Moscow, Idaho, 17-19 November 1987.

Demarchi, R.A. 1962. A study of the Chukar partridge in the Thompson valley of south-central British Columbia. B.Sc. Thesis, University of British Columbia, Vancouver. 61 pp. (Bibliography 2806).

Demarchi, R.A. and W.G. Smith. 1967. Spring and fall waterfowl surveys in the Columbia River marshes of the East Kootenay. British Columbia Fish and Wildlife Unpublished Report, Victoria. 44 pp. (Bibliography 2805).

Demaree, S.R. 1970. Nest-building, incubation period, and fledging in the Black-chinned Hummingbird. Wilson Bulletin 82:225.

Denson, E.P. 1964. Comparison of waterfowl hunting techniques at Humboldt Bay, California. Journal of Wildlife Management 28:103-119.

De Smet, K.D. 1982. Status of the Red-necked Grebe *(Podiceps grisegena)* in Canada. Committee on the Status of Endangered Wildlife in Canada Report, c/o Canadian Nature Federation, Ottawa, Ontario. 103 pp. (Bibliography 2809).

_____. 1983. Breeding ecology and productivity of Red-necked Grebes in Turtle Mountain Provincial Park, Manitoba. M.Sc. Thesis, University of North Dakota, Bismarck. 100 pp.

_____. 1986. A status report on the Golden Eagle *(Aquila chrysaetos)* in Canada. Committee on the Status of Endangered Wildlife in Canada, c/o Canadian Nature Federation, Ottawa, Ontario.

_____. 1987. First nesting record and status of the Clark's Grebe in Canada. Blue Jay 45:101-105.

Deusing, M. 1939. Nesting habits of the Pied-billed Grebe. Auk 56:367-373.

Devillers, P. 1970. Identification and distribution in California of the *Sphyrapicus varius* group of sapsuckers. California Birds 1:47-76.

_____. 1977. The skuas of the North American Pacific coast. Auk 94:417-429.

Dickinson, J.C. 1953. Report on the McCabe collection of British Columbia birds. Bulletin of the Museum of Comparative Zoology 100:123-209.

Dixon, K.R. and T.C. Juelson. 1987. The political economy of the Spotted Owl. Ecology 68:772-776.

Dobkin, D.S., J.A. Holmes, and B.A. Wilcox. 1986. Traditional nest-site use by White-throated Swifts. Condor 88:252-253.

Douglas, A. 1984. An evaluation of wintering raptors in the lower mainland of British Columbia. British Columbia Institute of Technology Unpublished Report, Burnaby. 60 pp.

Douglas, S.D. and T.E. Reimchen. 1988a. Habitat characteristics and population estimate of breeding Red-throated Loons, *Gavia stellata*, on the Queen Charlotte Islands, British Columbia. Canadian Field-Naturalist 102: 679-684.

_____. and _____. 1988b. Reproductive phenology and early survivorship in Red-throated Loons, *Gavia stellata*. Canadian Field-Naturalist 102: 701-704.

Dow, D.D. and W.H. Hesse. 1969. British Columbia record of Skua in terrestrial habitat. Canadian Field-Naturalist 83:402.

Dow, J.S. 1943. A study of nesting Canada geese in Honey Lake Valley, California. California Fish and Game 29:3-18.

Drent, R.H. 1961. On the supposed nesting of the Rhinoceros Auklet near Metlakahtla, Alaska. Auk 78:257-258.

_____. 1965. Breeding biology of the Pigeon Guillemot, *Cepphus columba*. Ardea 53:99-160.

Drent, R.H. and C.J. Guiguet. 1961. A catalogue of British Columbia sea-bird colonies. British Columbia Provincial Museum Occasional Paper No. 12, Victoria. 173 pp.

Drent, R. and J. Ward. 1970. Report on the sightings of wing-tagged Glaucous-winged Gulls, 1969/70. Vancouver Natural History Society Discovery 149:8-10.

Drent, R., G.R. van Tets, F. Tompa and K.Vermeer. 1964. The breeding birds of Mandarte Island, British Columbia. Canadian Field-Naturalist 78:208-263.

Drent, R.H., V. Gibbard, and W. Smith. 1971. British Columbia nest records scheme - 16th annual report, 1970. Federation of British Columbia Naturalists Newsletter 9(1):3-5.

_____, _____, and _____. 1972. British Columbia nest records scheme - 17th annual report, 1971. Federation of British Columbia Naturalists Newsletter 10(1):3-5.

Drewien, R.C. and E.C. Bizeau. 1974. Status and distribution of Greater Sandhill Cranes in the Rocky Mountains. Journal of Wildlife Management 38:720-742.

Drury, W.H. 1961. The breeding biology of shorebirds on Bylot Island, Northwest Territories, Canada. Auk 78:176-219.

Ducks Unlimited Canada. 1983. Annotated checklist of birds for the vicinity of eight Ducks Unlimited projects in the Cariboo-Chilcotin region of British Columbia. Ducks Unlimited (Canada) Unpublished Report, Kamloops, British Columbia. 29 pp. (Bibliography 2837).

Dunbar, D.L. 1984. The breeding ecology and management of White Pelicans at Stum Lake, British Columbia. British Columbia Fish and Wildlife Report R-6, Victoria. 85 pp.

Dunn, E.H. and C.D. MacInnes. 1987. Geographic variation in clutch size and body size of Canada Geese. Journal of Field Ornithology 58:355-371.

Dunn, J. 1978. The races of the Yellow-bellied Sapsucker. Birding 10:142-149.

Duvall, A.J. 1946. An early record of the Passenger Pigeon for British Columbia. Auk 63:598.

Dwight, J. 1925. The gulls (Laridae) of the world: their plumages, moults, variations, relationships and distribution. Bulletin of the American Museum of Natural History 52:63-401.

Dzubin, A. 1959. Growth and plumage development of wild-trapped juvenile Canvasback (*Aythya valisineria*). Journal of Wildlife Management 23:279-290.

_____. 1965. A study of migrating Ross' Geese in western Saskatchewan. Condor 67:511-534.

_____. 1979. Recent increase of blue geese in western North America. Pages 141-175 *in* R.L. Jarvis and J.C. Bartonek (editors). Management and Biology of Pacific Flyway Geese. United States Fish and Wildlife Service, Portland, Oregon.

Dzubin, A., H.W. Miller and G.V. Schildman. 1964. White-fronts. Pages 135-143 *in* J.P. Linduska (editor). Waterfowl Tomorrow. United States Government Printing Office, Washington, D.C.

Ealey, D.M. 1986. Tim Myres: recipient of the 11th Loran L. Goulden Memorial award. Alberta Naturalist 16:25-29.

Eamer, J. 1985. Winter habitat for dabbling ducks on southeastern Vancouver Island, British Columbia. M.Sc. Thesis, University of British Columbia, Vancouver. 103 pp.

Eastman, D.S. 1974. White-faced Ibis photographed in British Columbia. Canadian Field-Naturalist 88:354.

Ebel, G.R.A. 1973a. Band-tailed Pigeon in the northern interior of British Columbia. Murrelet 54:36-37.

_____. 1973b. Nechako River bird sanctuary - some thoughts and recommendations. Canadian Wildlife Service Unpublished Report, Delta, British Columbia. 76 pp. (Bibliography 2861).

Edgell, M.C.R. 1984. Trans-hemispheric movements of Holarctic Anatidae: the Eurasian Wigeon (*Anas penelope* L.) in North America. Journal of Biogeography 11:27-39.

Edson, J.M. 1935. Some records supplementary to the distributional checklist of the birds of the state of Washington. Murrelet 16:11-14.

Edwards, R.Y. 1949. A faunal investigation of E.C. Manning Park. British Columbia Parks Branch Unpublished Report, Victoria. 89 pp. (Bibliography 1396).

_____. 1953. Barrow's Goldeneye using crow nests in British Columbia. Wilson Bulletin 65:197-198.

_____. 1965. Birds seen in Active Pass, British Columbia. Pages EE19-EE22 in Provincial Museum of Natural History and Anthropology Report for the Year 1964, Victoria, British Columbia.

_____. 1968. Notes on gulls of southwestern British Columbia. Syesis 1:199-202.

Edwards, R.Y. and R.W. Ritcey. 1967. The birds of Wells Gray Park, British Columbia. British Columbia Parks Branch, Victoria. 37 pp. (Bibliography 1025).

Einarsen, A.S. 1965. Black Brant - sea goose of the Pacific coast. University of Washington Press, Seattle. 142 pp.

Elliott, J.E., R.W. Butler, R.J. Norstrom, and P.E.Whitehead. 1988. Levels of polychlorinated dibenzodioxins and polychlorinated dibenzofurans in eggs of Great Blue Herons (*Ardea herodias*) in British Columbia, 1983-87; possible impacts on reproductive success. Canadian Wildlife Service Progress Notes No. 176, Ottawa, Ontario. 7 pp.

Ellison, L.N. 1971. Territoriality in Alaskan Spruce Grouse. Auk 88:652-664.

Ellison, M. and W. Merilees. 1980. Winter Harlequins in the west Kootenay. Vancouver Natural History Society Discovery 9:17-18.

Emms, S.K. and K.H. Morgan. 1989. The breeding biology and distribution of the Pigeon Guillemot (*Cepphus columba*) in the Strait of Georgia. Pages 100-106 *in* Vermeer, K. and R.W. Butler (editors). The ecology and status of marine and shoreline birds in the Strait of Georgia, British Columbia. Canadian Wildlife Service Special Publication, Ottawa, Ontario.

Enderson, J.H. 1964. A study of the Prairie Falcon in the central Rocky Mountain region. Auk 81:332-352.

Ennis, T. 1969. Field characters of immature Little Gulls and Kittiwakes. British Birds 62:234-237.

Environment Canada. 1979. Canada's resource lands. Map Folio No.4, Environment Canada Lands Directorate, Ottawa. 232 pp.

Erasmus, G. and J. Erasmus. 1972. Mitlenatch Island Nature Park - summer 1972. British Columbia Parks Branch Unpublished Report, Victoria. 44 pp. (Bibliography 2883).

Erickson, R.C. 1948. Life history and ecology of the Canvas-back, *Nyroca valisinera* (Wilson), in south-eastern Oregon. Ph.D. Thesis, Iowa State College, Ames. 324 pp.

Erskine, A.J. 1959. A joint clutch of Barrow's Goldeneye and Bufflehead eggs. Canadian Field-Naturalist 73:131.

_____. 1960. Three sight records of unusual birds in the Vancouver, British Columbia area. Murrelet 41:9.

_____. 1962. Some new data on introgression in flickers from British Columbia. Canadian Field-Naturalist 76:82-87.

_____. 1964. Bird migration during April in southern British Columbia. Murrelet 45:15-22.

_____. 1968. Birds observed in north-central Alberta, summer 1964. Blue Jay 26:24-31.

_____. 1971. Growth and annual cycles in weights, plumages, and reproductive organs of Goosanders in eastern Canada. Ibis 113:42-58.

_____. 1971a. Nest record card program in Canada. Canadian Field-Naturalist 85:3-11.

_____. 1972. Buffleheads. Canadian Wildlife Service Monograph Series No.4, Ottawa, Ontario. 240 pp.

_____. 1978. Durability of tree holes used by Buffleheads. Canadian Field-Naturalist 92:94-95.

Erskine, A.J. and G.S. Davidson. 1976. Birds in the Fort Nelson lowlands of northeastern British Columbia. Syesis 9:1-11.

Erskine, A.J. and R.C. Stein. 1964. A re-evaluation of the avifauna of the Cariboo parklands. Pages 18-35 *in* Provincial Museum Natural History and Anthropology Report for the year 1963, Victoria, British Columbia.

Evans, D.L. 1982. Status reports on twelve raptors. United States Department of the Interior Fish and Wildlife Service Special Scientific Report - Wildlife No. 238, Washington, D.C. 68 pp.

Everett, W.T. 1988. Biology of the Black-vented Shearwater. Western Birds 19:89-104.

Fannin, J. 1891. Check-list British Columbia birds. British Columbia Provincial Museum, Victoria. 49 pp.

_____. 1895. The Emperor Goose in British Columbia. Auk 12:76.

_____. 1898. A preliminary catalogue of the collections of natural history and ethnology of the Provincial Museum, Victoria, British Columbia. British Columbia Provincial Museum, Victoria. 196 pp.

Farley, A.L. 1979. Atlas of British Columbia. University of British Columbia Press, Vancouver. 135 pp.

Farr, A. 1977. Observations of Sharp-tailed Grouse (*Pedioecetes phasianellus*) in the East Kootenay. British Columbia Fish and Wildlife Branch Unpublished Report, Cranbrook. 12 pp. (Bibliography 2903).

_____. 1987. Managing habitat for Bald Eagles in the Fraser valley of British Columbia: 1986-1987 observations. British Columbia Ministry of Environment and Parks Unpublished Report, Victoria. 40 pp.

Farr, A.C.M. and D.L. Dunbar. 1987. British Columbia's 1987 midwinter Bald Eagle survey. British Columbia Ministry of Environment and Parks Unpublished Report, Surrey. 23 pp.

_____. and _____. 1988. British Columbia's 1988 midwinter Bald Eagle survey. British Columbia Ministry of Environment, Surrey. 33 pp.

Farrand, John. 1977. What to look for: Eskimo and Little curlews compared. American Birds 31:137-138.

Feinstein, B. 1958. Xantus' Murrelet (*Endomychura hypoleuca scrippsi*) from the State of Washington. Auk 75:90-91.

Ferris, R.W. 1940. Eight years of banding of Western Gulls. Condor 42: 189-197

Findholt, S. and C.H. Trost. 1981. White Pelicans nesting in Idaho. Murrelet 62:19-20.

Finnegan, R.P. 1972. Pheasant counts on the Saanich Peninsula, 1966-1972. British Columbia Fish and Wildlife Branch Unpublished Report, Victoria. 75 pp. (Bibliography 2909)

Fisher, H.I. 1966. Airplane - albatross collisions on Midway Atoll. Conder 68:229-242.

Fisher, J. 1952. The Fulmar. Collins, St. James Place, London. 496 pp.

Fitch, H.S., F. Swenson, and D.F. Tillotson. 1946. Behavior and food habits of the Red-tailed Hawk. Condor 48:205-237.

Fitz-Gibbon, J. 1977. Wasa Lake Park - fauna records, 1977. British Columbia Parks Branch Unpublished Report, Victoria. 43 pp. (Bibliography 2914).

Fitzner, J.N. 1978. The ecology and behavior of the Long-billed Curlew (*Numenius americanus*) in southeastern Washington. PhD. Thesis, Washington State University, Pullman.

Fitzner, R.E. 1978. Behavioral ecology of the Swainson's Hawk (*Buteo swainsoni*) in southeastern Washington. Ph.D. Thesis, Washington State University, Pullman. 194 pp.

Fix, D. 1984. The spring migration-northern Pacific coast region. American Birds 38:948-952.

Flahaut, M.R. 1949. Spring migration - north Pacific coast region. Audubon Field Notes 3:220-222.

_____. 1950a. Fall migration - north Pacific coast region. Audubon Field Notes 4:30-32.

_____. 1950b. Winter season - north Pacific coast region. Audubon Field Notes 4:216-218.

_____. 1953a. The fall migration - north Pacific coast region. Audubon Field Notes 7:31-33.

_____. 1953b. The winter season - north Pacific coast region. Audubon Field Notes 7:230-231.

_____. 1953c. The spring migration - north Pacific coast region. Audubon Field Notes 7:287-288.

_____. 1953d. The spring migration - north Pacific coast region. Audubon Field Notes 7:322-324.

Flahaut, M.R. and Z.M.Schultz. 1954a. The fall migration - north Pacific coast region. Audubon Field Notes 8:36-38.

_____. and _____. 1954b. The spring migration - north Pacific coast region. Audubon Field Notes 8:324-326.

_____. and _____. 1955. The fall migration - north Pacific coast region. Audubon Field Notes 9:47-50.

_____. and _____. 1956. The fall migration - north Pacific coast region. Audubon Field Notes 10:47-50.

Fleming, J.H. 1907. The Fulvous Tree-Duck in British Columbia. Ottawa Naturalist 20:213.

Flint, V.E., R.L. Boehme, Y.V. Kostin, and A.A. Kuznepsov. 1984. A field guide to the birds of the USSR. Princeton University Press, New Jersey. 353 pp.

Flook, D.R. and L.S. Forbes. 1983. Ospreys and water management at Creston, British Columbia. Pages 281-286 *in* D.M. Bird (editor). Biology and Management of Bald Eagles and Ospreys. Proceedings of First International Symposium on Bald Eagles and Ospreys, Montreal, 28-29 October 1981. (Bibliography 2961).

Foottit, R. 1968. Summer report for 1968 - Mitlenatch Island Nature Park. British Columbia Parks Branch Unpublished Report, Victoria. 33 pp. (Bibliography 2962).

_____. 1969. Summer report for 1969 - Mitlenatch Island Nature Park. British Columbia Parks Branch Unpublished Report, Victoria. 25 pp. (Bibliography 2963).

_____. 1970. Summer report for 1970 - Mitlenatch Island Nature Park. British Columbia Parks Branch Unpublished Report, Victoria. 18 pp. (Bibliography 1910).

Forbes, L.S. 1984. The nesting ecology of the Western Grebe in British Columbia. Canadian Wildlife Service Report, Delta, British Columbia. 20 pp.

_____. 1985a. Nesting of Eared Grebes at Duck Lake, near Creston, British Columbia. Murrelet 66:20-21.

_____. 1985b. The feeding ecology of Western Grebes breeding at Duck Lake, British Columbia. M.Sc. Thesis, University of Manitoba, Winnipeg. 72 pp.

_____. 1988. Western Grebe nesting in British Columbia. Murrelet 69:28-33.

Forbes, L.S., K. Simpson, J.P. Kelsall, and D.R. Flook. 1985a. Great Blue Heron colonies in British Columbia. Canadian Wildlife Service Manuscript Report, Delta, British Columbia. 78 pp.

_____, _____, _____, and _____. 1985b. Reproductive success of Great Blue Herons in British Columbia. Canadian Journal of Zoology 63:1110-1113.

Force, M.P. and P.W. Mattocks. 1986. The winter season - northern Pacific coast region. American Birds 40:316-321.

Forsell, D.J. and P.J. Gould. 1980. Distribution and abundance of seabirds wintering in the Kodiak area of Alaska. United States Fish and Wildlife Service Unpublished Report, Anchorage, Alaska. 83 pp.

_____. and _____. 1981. Distribution and abundance of marine birds and mammals wintering in the Kodiak area of Alaska. United States Fish and Wildlife Service Report FWS/OBS-81-13, Washington, D.C. 72 pp.

Forsman, E.D. 1983. Methods and materials for locating and studying Spotted Owls. Pacific Northwest Forest and Range Experiment Station General Technical Report PNW-162, Portland, Oregon. 8 pp.

Forsman, E.D. and B. Booth. 1986. A survey of the Spotted Owl in the Skagit River region of British Columbia. British Columbia Wildlife Branch Unpublished Report, Surrey. 17 pp.

Forsman, E.D. and D. Dunbar. 1985. A survey of the Spotted Owl in British Columbia. British Columbia Wildlife Branch Unpublished Report, Surrey. 21 pp.

Forsman, E.D., E.C. Meslow, and M.J. Strub. 1977. Spotted Owl abundance in young versus old-growth forests, Oregon. Wildlife Society Bulletin 5:43-47.

Forsman, E.D., E.C. Meslow, and H.M. Wight. 1984. Distribution and biology of the Spotted Owl in Oregon. Wildlife Monographs 87:1-64.

Foster, B. 1974. A study of fall pheasant population dynamics on Westham Island, B.C. University of British Columbia Faculty of Forestry Unpublished Report, Vancouver. 16 pp. (Bibliography 2978).

Fox, G.A. 1971. Recent changes in reproductive success of the Pigeon Hawk. Journal of Wildlife Management 35:122-128.

Fraser, D.F. 1984. An annotated list of the birds of the Elk and Flathead drainages. Environmental Services Westar Mining Unpublished Report, Sparwood, British Columbia. 110 pp. (Bibliography 2989).

Fredrickson, L.H. 1967. Some aspects of reproductive behavior of American Coots (*Fulica americana*). Ph.D. Thesis, Iowa State University, Ames 113 pp.

Friedmann, H. 1943. A new race of Sharp-tailed Grouse. Journal of the Washington Academy of Science 33:189-191.

Frost, D.L. 1972. A recent nest record of a Pygmy Owl. Vancouver Natural History Society Discovery 1:35-36.

Fry, K. 1980. Aspects of the wintering ecology of the Dunlin (*Calidris alpina*) on the Fraser River delta. Canadian Wildlife Service Unpublished Report, Delta, British Columbia. 45 pp. (Bibliography 2997).

Fujimaki, Y. 1986. Seabird colonies on Hokkaido Island. Pages 152-165 *in* N. Litvinenko (editor). Seabirds of the Far East (Morskie ptitsy dalnego vostoka). Unedited translation number LSM-7-00912. Environment Canada, Ottawa.

Fuller, R.W. 1953. Studies in the life history and ecology of the American Pintail, *Anas acuta tzitzihoa* (Vieillot) in Utah. M.S. Thesis, Utah State Agricultural College, Logan.

Furness, R.W. 1987. The Skuas. T. and A.D. Poser Ltd. Calton, England. 363 pp.

Furrer, R.K. 1974. First spring sight record of the Yellow Rail for the Pacific Northwest. Murrelet 55:25-26.

Fyfe, R. and S.M. Teeple. 1968. 1968 field survey of colony fish-eating birds in the Kootenay River valley of British Columbia. Canadian Wildlife Service Manuscript Report No. 2051, Edmonton, Alberta. 16 pp.

Fyfe, R.W., R.W. Riseborough, and W. Walker. 1976. Pollutant effects on the reproduction of the Prairie Falcons and Merlins of the Canadian prairies. Canadian Field-Naturalist 90:346-355.

Gabrielson, I.N. and S.G. Jewett. 1940. Birds of Oregon. Oregon State College Monographs Studies in Zoology No.2, Corvallis, Oregon. 650 pp.

_____. and _____. 1970. Birds of the Pacific Northwest. Dover Publications, New York. 650 pp.

Gabrielson, I.N. and F.C. Lincoln. 1959. The birds of Alaska. The Stackpole Company, Harrisburg, Pennsylvania. 922 pp.

Gaines, D. 1974. Review of the status of the Yellow-billed Cuckoo in California: Sacramento Valley populations. Condor 76:204-209.

Garber, D.P. and J.R. Koplin. 1972. Prolonged and bisexual incubation by California Ospreys. Condor 74:201-202.

Gass, C.L. 1974. Feeding territoriality in postbreeding migratory Rufous Hummingbirds. Ph.D. Thesis, University of Oregon, Eugene. 138pp.

_____. 1978. Rufous Hummingbird feeding territoriality in a suboptimal habitat. Canadian Journal of Zoology 56:1535-1539.

_____. 1979. Territory regulation, tenure, and migration in Rufous Hummingbirds. Canadian Journal of Zoology 57:914-923.

Gass, C.L., G. Angehr, and J. Centa. 1976. Regulation of food supply by feeding territoriality in the Rufous Hummingbird. Canadian Journal of Zoology 54:2046-2054.

Gaston, A.J. and R. Decker. 1985. Interbreeding of Thayer's Gull, *Larus thayeri*, and Kumlien's Gull, *Larus glaucoides kumlieni*, on Southampton Island, Northwest Territories. Canadian Field-Naturalist 99:257-259.

Gaston, A.J. and D.N. Nettleship. 1981. The Thick-billed Murres of Prince Leopold Island. Canadian Wildlife Service Monograph Series No. 6, Ottawa,Ontario. 350 pp.

Gaston, A.J. and D.G. Noble. 1985. Studies on Ancient Murrelets at Reef Island, 1985. Canadian Wildlife Service Unpublished Report, Ottawa, Ontario. 46 pp.

Gaston, A.J. and D.W. Powell. 1989. Natural incubation, egg neglect, and hatchability in the Ancient Murrelet. Auk 106:433-438.

Gaston, A.J., I.L. Jones, D.G. Noble, and S.A. Smith. 1988. Orientation of Ancient Murrelet, *Synthliboramphus antiquus*, chicks during passage from the burrow to the sea. Animal Behaviour 36:300-303.

Gauthier, G. 1985. A functional analysis of territorial behaviour in breeding Bufflehead. Ph.D. Thesis, University of British Columbia, Vancouver. 165 pp.

Gehrman, K.H. 1951. An ecological study of the Lesser Scaup Duck (*Aythya affinis* Eyton) at West Medical Lake, Spokane County, Washington. M.S. Thesis, Washington State College, Pullman. 94 pp.

Geist, O.W. 1939. Sea birds found far inland in Alaska. Condor 41:68-70.

George, D.V. 1980. Hummingbird! B.C. Naturalist 18 (2 and 3):16.

Gerrard, J.M. 1983. A review of the current status of Bald Eagles in North America. Pages 5-21 *in* D.M. Bird (editor). Biology and Management of Bald Eagles and Ospreys. Proceedings of First International Symposium on Bald Eagles and Ospreys, Montreal, 28-29 October 1981. Harpell Press. Ste. Anne de Bellevue, Quebec.

Gerson, H. 1987. The status of the Black Tern (*Chlidonias niger*) in Canada. Committee on the Status of Endangered Wildlife in Canada, c/o Ontario Ministry of Natural Resources, Toronto, Ontario. 54 pp.

Gerstenberg, R.H. 1979. Habitat utilization by wintering and migrating shorebirds on Humboldt Bay, California. Studies in Avian Biology 2:33-40.

Gibson, D.D. 1981. Migrant birds at Shemya Island, Aleutian Islands, Alaska. Condor 83:65-77.

_____. 1986. The autumn migration - Alaska region. American Birds 40:155-156.

Gibson, D.D. and N.D. Hogg. 1982. Direct recovery in Alaska of California-banded Cattle Egret. American Birds 36:335.

Gibson, D.D. and B. Kessel. 1989. Geographic variation in the Marbled Godwit and description of an Alaskan subspecies. Condor 91:436-443.

Gibson, F. 1971. The breeding biology of the American Avocet (*Recurvirostra americana*) in central Oregon. Condor 73:444-454.

Gibson, G.G. 1965. The taxonomy and biology of Splendidofilariine nematodes of the Tetraonidae of British Columbia. Ph.D. Thesis, University of British Columbia, Vancouver. 241 pp.

Gilkey, A.K., W.D. Loomis, B.M. Breckenridge, and C.H. Richardson. 1944. The incubation period of the Great Horned Owl. Auk 60:272-273.

Gill, R. and P.D.Jorgenson. 1979. A preliminary assessment of timing and migration of shorebirds along the northcentral Alaska peninsula. Studies in Avian Biology 2:113-123.

Gill, R.E. 1977. Breeding avifauna of the south San Francisco Bay estuary. Western Birds. 8:1-12.

Gill, R.E. and L.R. Mewaldt. 1983. Pacific coast Caspian Terns: dynamics of an expanding population. Auk 100:369-381.

Gill, R.E., C.M. Handel, and L.A. Shelton. 1983. Memorial to a Black Turnstone: an exemplar of breeding and wintering site fidelity. North American Bird Bander 8:98-101.

Girard, G.L. 1939. Notes on the life history of the Shoveler. Transactions of the North American Wildlife Conference 4:364-371.

_____. 1941. The Mallard: its management in western Montana. Journal of Wildlife Management 5:223-259.

Gissing, A. 1959. Black-billed Cuckoo in British Columbia. Murrelet 40:12.

Glendenning, R. 1921. Notes on the fauna and flora of Mt. McLean, B.C. Proceedings of the Entomological Society of British Columbia 18:39-44.

Godfrey, W.E. 1947. A new Long-eared Owl. Canadian Field-Naturalist 61:196-197.

_____. 1952. Birds of the Lesser Slave Lake - Peace River areas, Alberta. National Museum of Canada Bulletin 126:142-175.

_____. 1954. Birds of Prince Edward Island. Pages 155-213 *in* National Museum of Canada Bulletin No. 132. Ottawa, Ontario.

_____. 1955. Additional notes on birds of the east Kootenay, British Columbia. National Museum of Canada Bulletin 136:89-94.

_____. 1958. Birds of Cape Breton Island, Nova Scotia. Canadian Field-Naturalist 73:7-27.

_____. 1966. The birds of Canada. National Museum of Canada Bulletin 203, Ottawa, Ontario. 428 pp.

_____. 1967. Some winter aspects of the Great Gray Owl. Canadian Field-Naturalist 81:99-101.

_____. 1970. Canada's endangered birds. Canadian Field-Naturalist 84:24-26.

_____. 1986. The birds of Canada, revised edition. National Museums of Canada, Ottawa, Ontario. 595 pp.

Goggans, R. 1986. Habitat use by Flammulated Owls in northeastern Oregon. M.Sc. Thesis, Oregon State University, Corvallis. 54 pp.

Goldman, L.J. 1936. Observations concerning waterfowl in Canada, with special reference to migratory species, May 19 to August 10, 1936. Canadian Wildlife Service Unpublished Report, Delta, British Columbia. 46 pp. (Bibliography 3033).

_____. 1940. Migratory waterfowl - British Columbia (May 25, 1940 to August 26, 1940). United States Fish and Wildlife Service Unpublished Report. California. 35 pp. (Bibliography 3034).

Gollop, J.B. and W.H. Marshall. 1954. A guide for aging duck broods in the field. Mississippi Flyway Council Technical Section Report, Jackson. 14 pp.

Golovkin, A.N. 1984. Seabirds nesting in the USSR: The status and protection of populations. Pages 473-486 *in* Croxall, J.P., P.G.H. Evans, and R.W. Schreiber (editors). Status and conservation of the world's seabirds. International Council for Bird Preservation Technical Publication No. 2. Cambridge, England.

Goodwill, M.E. and J.E.V. Goodwill. 1988. Terek Sandpiper in British Columbia, Canada. American Birds 42:177.

Goodwin, D. 1967. Pigeons and doves of the world. The British Museum (Natural History), London, England. 446 pp.

Goossen, J.P., R.W. Butler, B. Stushnoff, and D. Stirling. 1982. Distribution and breeding status of Forster's Tern, *Sterna forsteri*, in British Columbia. Canadian Field-Naturalist 96:345-346.

Gosselin, M. and N. David. 1975. Field identification of Thayer's Gull *Larus thayeri* in eastern North America. American Birds 29:1059-1066.

Gould, E. 1981. Ralph Edwards of Lonesome Lake. Hancock House Publishers Ltd. North Vancouver, British Columbia. 293 pp.

Gould, P.J., D.J. Forsell and C.J. Lensink. 1982. Pelagic distribution and abundance of seabirds in the Gulf of Alaska and the eastern Bering Seas. United States Fish and Wildlife Service Report FWS/OBS-82/48, Washington, D.C. 264 pp.

Goward, T. 1976. Addendum to the birds of Wells Gray Park - an annotated list. British Columbia Parks Branch Unpublished Report, Victoria. 8 pp. (Bibliography 3050).

Graf, R.P. 1978. The ecology of the Ring-necked Pheasant, *Phasianus colchicus*, on Westham Island, B.C. B.Sc. Thesis, University of British Columbia, Vancouver. 101 pp.

Grant, J. 1951. Christmas bird census, 1950 - Vernon, British Columbia. Canadian Field Naturalist 65:74-75.

_____. 1956. Christmas bird census for 1955, Vernon, British Columbia. Canadian Field-Naturalist 70:90-91.

_____. 1959. A summer record of the Great Gray Owl in southern British Columbia. Canadian Field-Naturalist 73:173.

_____. 1966a. A Black Swift nest in British Columbia. Canadian Field-Naturalist 80:60-61.

_____. 1966b. The Barred Owl in British Columbia. Murrelet 47:39-45.

_____. 1966c. The Red-headed Woodpecker near Vernon, British Columbia. Murrelet 47:45.

_____. 1975. Observations. North Okanagan Naturalists Club Newspacket 2:5-6 (Bibliography 3057).

Grant, K.A. and V. Grant. 1968. The hummingbirds and their flowers. Columbia University Press, New York. 115 pp.

Grant, P.J. 1979. Field identification of west Palearctic gulls. British Birds 72:142-182.

_____. 1981. Identification of Semipalmated Sandpiper. British Birds 74:505-509.

_____. 1982. Gulls - a guide to identification. Buteo Books, Vermillion, South Dakota. 280 pp.

Grant, P.J. and R.E. Scott. 1969. Field identification of juvenile Common, Arctic, and Roseate Terns. British Birds 62:297-299.

Grass, A. 1968. A Stilt Sandpiper sight record for British Columbia. Murrelet 49:28.

_____. 1971. Wells Gray Park naturalist's report. British Columbia Parks Branch Unpublished Report, Victoria. 45 pp. (Bibliography 1175).

Grass, A. and J. Grass. 1978. Squamish eagle count. Federation of British Columbia Naturalists Newsletter 16:9-10.

Greel, G.J. 1974. Sharp-tailed Sandpiper with flesh-coloured legs and feet. British Birds 67:211.

Green, C. deB. 1916. Note on the distribution and nesting-habits of *Falco peregrinus pealei* Ridgway. Ibis (Series 10) 4:473-476.

Green, D. and R.W. Campbell. 1984. The amphibians of British Columbia. British Columbia Provincial Museum Handbook No. 45, Victoria. 101 pp.

Greenwood, J.G. 1984. Migration of Dunlin *Calidris alpina*: a worldwide overview. Ringing and Migration 5:35-39.

_____. 1986. Geographical variation and taxonomy of the Dunlin *Calidris alpina* (L.). Bulletin of the British Ornithological Club 106:43-56.

Gregory, P.T. and R.W. Campbell. 1984. The reptiles of British Columbia. British Columbia Provincial Museum Handbook No. 44, Victoria, 103 pp.

Greyell, R. 1966. Report on wildlife survey, Creston flats, summer 1966. Canadian Wildlife Service Unpublished Report, Delta, British Columbia. 28 pp. (Bibliography 3080).

Grieb, J.R. 1970. The shortgrass prairie Canada Goose population. Wildlife Monographs 22:1-49.

Griffith, D.E. 1973. Notes on the birds of Summit Lake Pass, British Columbia. Vancouver Natural History Society Discovery. 2:45-51.

Grinnell, J. 1913. Two new races of the Pygmy Owl from the Pacific coast. Auk 30:222-224.

Gross, A.O. 1923. The Black-crowned Night Heron (*Nycticorax nycticorax naevius*) of Sandy Neck. Auk. 40:1-30.

_____. 1935. The life history cycle of the Leach's Petrel (*Oceanodroma leucorhoa*) on the outer sea islands of the Bay of Fundy. Auk 52:382-399.

_____. 1947. Cyclic invasions of the Snowy Owl and the migration of 1945-46. Auk 64:589-601.

Groves, S. 1982. Aspects of foraging in Black Oystercatchers (Aves: *Haematopodidae*). Ph.D. Thesis, University of British Columbia, Vancouver. 123 pp.

_____. 1984. Chick growth, sibling rivalry, and chick production in American Black Oystercatchers. Auk 101:525-531.

Grub, T.C. 1972. Smell and foraging in shearwaters and petrels. Nature 237:404-405.

Gruchy, C.G., A.A.R. Dykes and R.H. Bowen. 1972. The Short-tailed Albatross recorded at Ocean Station Papa, North Pacific Ocean, with notes on other birds. Canadian Field-Naturalist 86:285-287.

Grunberg, H. 1982. The spring migration - northwestern Canada region. American Birds 36:873-874.

_____. 1983a. The winter season - northwestern Canada region. American Birds 37:318-320.

_____. 1983b. The spring migration - northwestern Canada region. American Birds 37:890-891.

_____. 1983c. The autumn migration - northwestern Canada region. American Birds 37:201-202.

_____. 1984a. The autumn migration - northwestern Canada region. American Birds 38:223-224.

_____. 1984b. The winter season - northwestern Canada region. American Birds 38:336-337.

_____. 1984c. The spring migration - northwestern Canada region. American Birds 38:935-936.

_____. 1984d. The nesting season - northwestern Canada region. American Birds 38:1040-1041.

_____. 1985a. The autumn migration - northwestern Canada region. American Birds 38:77-78.

_____. 1985b. The winter season - northwestern Canada region. American Birds 39:187-189.

_____. 1985c. The spring season - northwestern Canada region. American Birds 39:326-327.

_____. 1985d. The nesting season - northwestern Canada region. American Birds 39:937-938.

_____. 1986. The autumn migration - northwestern Canada region. American Birds 40:141-142.

Guiguet, C.J. 1949. Kennicott's Screech Owl on British Columbia coastal islands. Canadian Field-Naturalist 63:206-207.

_____. 1950a. Notes on Common Murres nesting in British Columbia. Murrelet 31:12-13.

_____. 1950b. Saw-whet Owl at Victoria. Victoria Naturalist 7:55-56.

_____. 1952a. Report on the Francois-Ootsa Lake area visited in June, 1951. Pages B15-B18 *in* Provincial Museum of Natural History and Anthropology Report for the Year 1951, Victoria, British Columbia.

_____. 1952b. Christmas bird census, 1951 - Victoria, British Columbia. Canadian Field-Naturalist 66:56.

_____. 1953a. An ecological study of Goose Island, British Columbia, with special reference to mammals and birds. British Columbia Provincial Museum Occasional Paper No.10, Victoria. 78 pp.

_____. 1953b. Asiatic Chukar Partridge released on B.C. mainland. Victoria. Daily Colonist. Page 2.

_____. 1953c. Mountain Quail on Island shy and retiring species. Daily Colonist Newspaper, 22 November:2.

_____. 1954. The birds of British Columbia: (1) The woodpeckers, (2) The crows and their allies. British Columbia Provincial Museum Handbook No. 6, Victora. 51 pp.

_____. 1955a. The birds of British Columbia: (3) The shorebirds. British Columbia Provincial Museum Handbook No. 8, Victoria. 54 pp.

_____. 1955b. The birds of British Columbia: (4) Upland game birds. British Columbia Provincial Museum Handbook No. 10, Victoria. 47 pp.

_____. 1956. Enigma of the Pacific. Audubon Magazine 58:164-167, 174.

_____. 1957. The birds of British Columbia: (5) Gulls, terns, jaegers and skua. British Columbia Provincial Museum Handbook No. 13, Victoria. 42pp.

_____. 1958. The birds of British Columbia: (6) Waterfowl. British Columbia Provincial Museum Handbook No. 15, Victoria. 84 pp.

_____. 1959. Anna's Hummingbird (*Calypte anna*) at Victoria, British Columbia. Murrelet 40:13.

_____. 1960a. The Golden Plover (*Pluvialis dominica*) nesting in British Columbia. Page 40 *in* Provincial Museum of Natural History and Anthropology Report for the Year 1959, Victoria, British Columbia.

_____. 1960b. The birds of British Columbia: (7) Owls. British Columbia Provincial Museum Handbook No. 18, Victoria. 62 pp.

_____. 1964. The birds of British Columbia: (8) Chickadees, thrushes, kinglets, pipits, waxwings, and shrikes. British Columbia Provincial Museum Handbook No. 22, Victoria. 66 pp.

_____. 1971. A list of sea bird nesting sites in Barkley Sound, British Columbia. Syesis 4:253-259.

_____. 1972. The birds of British Columbia: (9) Diving birds and tube-nosed swimmers. British Columbia Provincial Museum Handbook No. 29, Victoria. 104 pp.

_____. 1978. The birds of British Columbia: (10) Goatsuckers, swifts, hummingbirds, and swallows. British Columbia Provincial Museum Handbook No. 37, Victoria. 58 pp.

_____. 1983. The birds of British Columbia: (11) Sparrows and finches. British Columbia Provincial Museum Handbook No. 42, Victoria. 122 pp.

Guillon, G.W. 1951. The frontal shield of the American Coot. Wilson Bulletin 63:157-166.

Gunn, W.W.H. 1972. Bald Eagles at Port Hardy airport: Interim Report No. 2, for the period November 1-21, 1972. LGL Limited Report, Toronto, Ontario. 3 pp. (Bibliography 3116).

Gutierrez, R.J. and A.B. Carey (editors). 1985. Ecology and management of the Spotted Owl in the Pacific Northwest. United States Department of Agriculture, Forest Service General Technical Report PNW-185 Portland, Oregon. 119 pp.

Guzman, J.R. 1981. The wintering of Sooty and Short-tailed shearwaters (Genus *Puffinus*) in the north Pacific. Ph.D. Thesis. University of Calgary, Calgary, Alberta. 510 pp.

Guzman, J.R. and M.T. Myres. 1983. The occurrence of shearwaters (*Puffinus* spp.) off the west coast of Canada. Canadian Journal of Zoology 61:2064-2077.

Hackman, C.D. and C.J. Henny. 1971. Hawk migration over White Marsh, Maryland. Chesapeake Science 12:137-141.

Hadow, H.H. 1973. Winter ecology of migrant and resident Lewis' Woodpeckers in southeastern Colorado. Condor 75:210-224.

_____. 1976. Growth and development of nesting Downy Woodpeckers. North American Bird Bander 1:155-164.

Hagar, D.C. 1957. Nesting populations of Red-tailed Hawks and Horned Owls in central New York. Wilson Bulletin 69:263-272.

Hagar, J.A. 1966. Nesting of the Hudsonian Godwit at Churchill, Manitoba. Living Bird 5:5-43.

Hagenstein, W. 1928. Miscellaneous observations from Washington and British Columbia. Murrelet 9:69.

Haig, B. 1980. In the footsteps of Thomas Blakiston: 1858. Historic Trails Society of Alberta, Lethbridge. 57 pp.

Haig, S. 1985. The status of the Piping Plover in Canada. Committee on the Status of Endangered Wildlife in Canada, c/o Canadian Nature Federation, Ottawa, Ontario 23 pp.

Hamel, P. 1983. The eighty-third Audubon Christmas bird count - Masset, B.C. American Birds 37:441-442.

Hamilton, R.C. 1975. Comparative behavior of the American Avocet and the Black-necked Stilt (Recurvirostridae). American Ornithologists' Union Ornithological Monographs No. 17, Lawrence, Kansas.

Hammond, M.C. and C.J. Henry. 1949. Success of Marsh Hawk nests in North Dakota. Auk 66:271-274.

Hancock, D.A. 1963. The abundance of wintering waterfowl in the Victoria, B.C. area. B.Sc. Thesis, Victoria College [University of Victoria], Victoria, British Columbia. 40 pp. (Bibliography 3143).

_____. 1964. Breeding record for Bufflehead west of the coast range in British Columbia. Canadian Field-Naturalist 78:64-65.

_____. 1970. New Rhinoceros Auklet colony for British Columbia. Condor 72:491.

Hannon, S.J. 1982. Female aggression, breeding density, and monogamy in Willow Ptarmigan. Ph.D. Thesis, University of British Columbia, Vancouver. 118 pp.

_____. 1983. Spacing and breeding density of Willow Ptarmigan in response to an experimental alteration of sex ratio. Journal of Animal Ecology 52:807-820.

Hannon, S.J. and J.N.M. Smith. 1984. Factors influencing age-related reproductive success in the Willow Ptarmigan. Auk 101:848-854.

Hannon, S.J., K. Martin, and J.O. Schieck. 1988. Timing of reproduction in two populations of Willow Ptarmigan in northern Canada. Auk 105:330-338.

Hansen, H.A. 1962. Canada geese of coastal Alaska. Transactions of the North American Wildlife Conference 27:301-319.

Hansen, H.A. and V.C. Nelson. 1957. Brant of the Bering Sea, migration, and mortality. Transactions of the North American Wildlife and Natural Resources Conference 22:237-254.

_____. and _____. 1964. Honkers large and small. Pages 109-124 *in* J.P. Linduska (editor). Waterfowl Tomorrow. United States Department of the Interior Fish and Wildlife Service, Washington, D.C.

Hansen, H.A., P.E.K. Shepherd, J.G. King, and W.T. Troyer. 1971. The Trumpeter Swan in Alaska. Wildlife Monographs No. 26:1-83.

Hanson, W.C. 1971. The 1966-67 Snowy Owl incursion in southeastern Washington and the Pacific northwest. Condor 73:114-116.

Hanson, W.C. and R.L. Browning. 1959. Hanford Reservation nesting geese. Journal of Wildlife Management 23:129-137.

Hardy, G.A. 1927. Report on a collecting trip to Garibaldi Park, B.C. Pages 15-26 *in* Report of the Provincial Museum of Natural History for the Year 1926, Victoria, British Columbia.

_____. 1957. Notes on the flora and fauna of Blenkinsop Lake area on southern Vancouver Island, British Columbia. Pages 25-66 *in* Provincial Museum of Natural History and Anthropology Report for the Year 1956, Victoria, British Columbia.

Hare, F.K. and M.K. Thomas. 1974. Climate Canada. Wiley Publishers of Canada Limited, Toronto, Ontario. 256 pp.

Harrington, B.A. 1983. The migration of the Red Knot. Oceanus 26:44-48.

Harrington, B.A. and R.I.G. Morrison. 1979. Semipalmated Sandpiper migration in North America. Studies in Avian Biology 2:83-100.

Harrington-Tweit, B. and P.W. Mattocks. 1984. The nesting season - northern Pacific coast region. American Birds 38:1054-1056.

_____. and _____. 1985. The nesting season - northern Pacific coast region. American Birds 39:953-956.

Harrington-Tweit, B., P.W. Mattocks, and E.S. Hunn. 1978. Nesting season - northern Pacific coast region. American Birds 32:1199-1203.

_____, _____, and _____. 1979. Nesting season - northern Pacific coast region. American Birds 33:890-893.

_____, _____, and _____. 1980. The nesting season - northern Pacific coast region. American Birds 34:922-925.

_____, _____, and _____. 1981. Nesting season - northern Pacific coast region. American Birds 35:970-973.

Harris, C. 1987. Black-chinned Hummingbird - first Vancouver record. Vancouver Natural History Society Discovery 16:126.

Harris, H. 1941. The annals of *Gymnogyps* to 1900. Condor 43:3-55.

Harris, M.P. 1964. Aspects of the breeding biology of the gulls *Larus argentatus, L. fuscus* and *L. marinus*. Ibis 106:432-456.

_____. 1969. The biology of storm petrels in the Galapagos Islands. Proceedings of the California Academy of Science 37:95-166.

Harris, R.D. 1971. Further evidence of tree nesting in the Marbled Murrelet. Canadian Field-Naturalist 85:67-68.

Harris, R.D. and E.J. O'Neil. 1967. Biological investigations, Duck Lake Creston, B.C. Canadian Wildlife Service Unpublished Report, Delta, British Columbia. 10 pp. (Bibliography 3166).

Harris, S.W. 1974. Status, chronology, and ecology of nesting storm petrels in northwestern California. Condor 76:249-261.

Harrison, C. 1978. A field guide to the nests, eggs, and nestlings of North American birds. Collins, Glasgow. 416 pp.

_____. 1979. Short-tailed Albatross. Oceans 12:24.

Harrison, C.S., M.B. Naughton, and S.I. Fefer, 1984. The status and conservation of seabirds in the Hawaiian Archipelago and Johnston Atoll. Pages 513-526 in Croxall, J.P., P.G.H. Evans, and R.W. Schreiber (editors). The status and conservation of the world's seabirds. International Council for Bird Preservation Technical Publication No. 2, Cambridge, England.

Harrison, G.H. 1979. Bird watching: the fastest growing family fun is an industry. Science Digest 86:74-80.

Harrison, P. 1983. Seabirds: an identification guide. Houghton Mifflin Company, Boston. 448 pp.

Hart, F.G. 1978. A January letter from Green Island lighthouse. Vancouver Natural History Society Discovery 7:30-32.

_____. 1978a. Green Island in summer. Vancouver Natural History Society Discovery 7:73-75.

Hart, J.L. 1973. Pacific fishes of Canada. Fisheries Research Board of Canada Bulletin No. 180, Ottawa, Ontario. 740 pp.

Hartwick, E.B. 1973. Foraging strategy of the Black Oystercatcher. Ph.D. Thesis, University of British Columbia, Vancouver. 138 pp.

_____. 1974. Breeding ecology of the Black Oystercatcher (*Haematopus bachmani* Audubon). Syesis 7:83-92.

Hartwick, E.B. and W. Blaylock. 1979. Winter ecology of a Black Oystercatcher population. Studies in Avian Biology 2:207-215.

Harwell, M. 1946. Vancouver Island bird list (June 2-6, 1946). Victoria Naturalist 3:54-57.

Hasbrouck, E.M. 1944. Apparent status of the European Widgeon in North America. Auk 61:93-104.

Hasegawa, H. 1978. The Laysan Albatross breeding in the Ogasawara Islands. Pacific Seabird Group Bulletin 5:16-17.

_____. 1982. The breeding status of the Short-tailed Albatross *Diomedea albatrus*, on Torishima, 1979/80-1980/81. Journal of the Yamashina Institute of Ornithology 14:16-24.

_____. 1984. Status and conservation of seabirds in Japan, with special attention to the Short-tailed Albatross. Pages 487-500 in Corxall, J.P., P.G.H. Evans, and R.W. Schreiber (editors). The status and conservation of the world's seabirds. International Council for Bird Preservation Technical Publication No. 2. Cambridge, England.

Hasegawa, H. and A.R. DeGange. 1982. The Short-tailed Albatross, *Diomedea albatrus*, its status, distribution, and natural history. American Birds 36:806-814.

Hatfield, J.P. 1979. Canada Goose production on Vaseux Lake. Canadian Wildlife Service Unpublished Report, Delta, British Columbia. 3 pp.

Hatler, D.F. 1973. An analysis of use, by waterfowl, of tideflats in southern Clayoquot Sound, British Columbia. Canadian Wildlife Service Unpublished Report, Edmonton, Alberta. 134 pp. (Bibliography 997).

_____. 1983. Concerns for ungulate collision mortality along new surface route - Rogers Pass project report. MacLaren Plansearch Corporation Unpublished Report, Vancouver, British Columbia. 109 pp. (Bibliography 3181).

Hatler, D.F., R.W. Campbell and A. Dorst. 1973. Birds of Pacific Rim National Park, British Columbia. Canadian Wildlife Service Unpublished Report, Edmonton, Alberta. 383 pp. (Bibliography 1147).

_____, _____, and _____ 1978. Birds of Pacific Rim National Park. British Columbia Provincial Museum Occasional Paper No.20, Victoria. 194 pp.

Hatter, I. and D. Bustard. 1975. A survey of an Ancient Murrelet colony on Lyell Island, Queen Charlotte Islands, British Columbia. British Columbia Fish and Wildlife Branch Unpublished Report, Smithers. 25 pp.

Hatter, I. and L. Stordeur. 1978. An inventory of Canada Geese and seabirds nesting in Juskatla, Masset, Skidegate, and Long inlets, Queen Charlotte Islands, British Columbia: British Columbia Fish and Wildlife Report, Victoria. 44 pp. (Bibliography 1896).

Hatter, J. 1955. Blue Grouse. British Columbia Fish and Wildlife Branch Unpublished Report, Victoria. 3 pp.

_____. 1960. Baikal Teal in British Columbia. Condor 62:480.

Hawkins, A.S. 1970. Honkers move to the city. Pages 120-130 in H.H. Hilland and F.B. Lee (editors). Home grown honkers. United States Department of the Interior, Fish and Wildlife Service, Washington, D.C. 154 pp.

Hay, R.B. 1976. An environmental study on the Kitimat region with special reference to the Kitimat River estuary. Canadian Wildlife Service Unpublished Report, Delta, British Columbia. 85 pp. (Bibliography 1204).

Hayman, P., J. Marchant, and T. Prater. 1986. Shorebirds: an identification guide to the waders of the world. Houghton Mifflin Company, Boston, Massachusetts. 412 pp.

Hays, H. 1973. Polyandry in the Spotted Sandpiper. Living Bird 11:43-57.

Hazelwood, W.G. 1973. Cape Scott Park - a preliminary look at its wildlife values, October 25-28. British Columbia Parks Branch Unpublished Report, Victoria. 11 pp. (Bibliography 3186).

_____. 1976a. Tweedsmuir Park initial wildlife and fisheries inventory (Area C and D). British Columbia Parks Branch Unpublished Report, Victoria. 116 pp. (Bibliography 1202).

_____. 1976b. Kwadacha Park 1976. British Columbia Parks Branch Unpublished Report, Victoria. 19 pp. (Bibliography 3191).

_____. 1976c. Atsutla Range report. British Columbia Parks Branch Unpublished Report, Victoria. 12 pp. (Bibliography 3194).

_____. 1979. Tatlatui Park summer trip report - August 2 and 3, 1979. British Columbia Parks Branch Unpublished Report. 6 pp. (Bibliography 3202).

Headley, P.C. 1967. Ecology of the Emperor Goose. Report of the Alaska Cooperative Wildlife Unit, University of Alaska College, Fairbanks. 106 pp.

Hearne, M. and J.M. Cooper. 1987. Aleutian Tern (*Sterna aleutica*), a new bird for Canada. Canadian Field-Naturalist 101:589-590.

Heath, H. 1915. Birds observed on Forrester Island, Alaska, during the summer of 1913. Condor 17:20-41.

Hegner, R.W. 1906. Life of the Redtail. Bird-Lore 8:151-157.

Hekstra, G.P. 1982. Description of twenty-four new subspecies of American *Otus*. Bulletin Zoologisch Museum Universiteit Van Amsterdam 9:49-63.

Henderson, B.A. 1972. The control and organization of parental feeding and its relationships to the food supply for the Glaucous-winged Gull *Larus glaucescens*. M.Sc. Thesis, University of British Columbia, Vancouver. 94 pp.

Hennan, E. 1977. Wildlife observations - Chilcotin Lake, 1977. Ducks Unlimited (Canada) Unpublished Report, Williams Lake, British Columbia. 37 pp. (Bibliography 1913).

_____. 1975. Columbia River marshes, British Columbia waterfowl habitat assessment. Ducks Unlimited (Canada) Special Report No. 7104, Kamloops, British Columbia. 48 pp. (Bibliography 3208).

_____. 1979. Upper Dean River project - waterfowl habitat assessment. Ducks Unlimited (Canada) Unpublished Report, Kamloops, British Columbia. 51 pp. (Bibliography 3209).

Henny, C.J. 1983. Distribution and abundance of nesting Ospreys in the United States. Pages 175-186 *in* D.M.Bird (editor). Biology and Management of Bald Eagles and Ospreys. Proceedings First International Symposium on Bald Eagles and Ospreys, Montreal, 28-29 October 1981. Harpell Press. Ste Anne de Bellevue, Quebec.

_____. 1986. Osprey (*Pandion haliaetus*): Section 4.3.1, United States Army Corps of Engineers Wildlife Resources Management Manual, Technical Report EL-86-5, prepared by the United States Fish and Wildlife Service, Corvallis, Oregon, for the United States Army Engineer Waterways Experiment Station, Vicksburg, Mississippi.

Henny, C.J. and N.E. Holgersen. 1974. Range expansion and population increase of the Gadwall in eastern North America. Wildfowl 25:95-101.

Henny, C.J. and H.M. Wight. 1969. An endangered osprey population: estimates of mortality and production. Auk 86:188-198.

_____. and _____. 1972. Population ecology and environmental pollution: Red-tailed and Cooper's hawks. Pages 229-250 *in* Population ecology of migratory birds. United States Fish and Wildlife Service Wildlife Resource Report No. 2, Washington, D.C. 278 pp.

Henshaw, H.W. 1881. On *Podiceps occidentalis* and *P. clarkii*. Bulletin Nuttall Ornithological Club 6:211-216.

Herrick, F.H. 1932. Daily life of the American eagle: early phase. Auk 49:307-323.

Herzog, P.W. 1977. Summer habitat use by White-tailed Ptarmigan in southwestern Alberta. Canadian Field-Naturalist 91:367-371.

_____. 1980. Winter habitat use by White-tailed Ptarmigan in southwestern Alberta. Canadian Field-Natralist 94:159-162.

Hesse, W. and H. Hesse. 1961. Sight record of the downy young Semipalmated Plover in the Chilcotin of British Columbia. Murrelet 42:3.

Hetherington, A.E., I.E. Teske, D.G. Milne, A. Von Sacken, and S. Myers. 1987. Spotted Owl and old-growth habitat survey, 1987. British Columbia Conservation Foundation Report, Langley. 91 pp.

Hilden, O. 1971. Occurrence, migration, and colour phases of the Arctic Skua (*Stercorarius parasiticus*) in Finland. Annales Zoologica Fennici 8:223-230.

Hilden, O. and S. Vuolanto. 1972. Breeding biology of the Red-necked Phalarope *Phalaropus lobatus* in Finland, Ornis Fennica 49:57-85.

Hills, G.A., D.A. Love, and D.S. Lacate. 1973. Developing a better environment: ecological land-use planning in Ontario. Ontario Economic Council, Toronto. 182 pp.

Hines, J.E. 1986. Social organization, movements, and home ranges of Blue Grouse in fall and winter. Wilson Bulletin 98:419-432.

Hirsch, K.V., D.A. Woodby, and L.B. Astheimer. 1981. Growth of a nestling Marbled Murrelet. Condor 83:264-265.

Hirst, S.M. and C.A. Easthope. 1981. Use of agricultural lands by waterfowl in southwestern British Columbia. Journal of Wildlife Management 45:454-462.

Hobson, K.A. and J.C. Driver. 1989. Archaeological evidence for the use of the Strait of Georgia by marine birds. Pages 168-173 *in* K. Vermeer and R.W. Butler (editors). The ecology and status of marine and shoreline birds in the Strait of Georgia, British Columbia. Canadian Wildlife Service Special Publication, Ottawa, Ontario.

Hobson, K.A. and S.G. Sealy. 1986. Use of diurnal roosting sites by Pelagic Cormorants in Barkley Sound, British Columbia. Murrelet 67:65-74.

Hobson, K.A. and D. Wilson. 1985. Colony establishment by Pelagic Cormorants on man-made structures in southwest coastal British Columbia. Murrelet 66:84-86.

Hobson, M. 1976. Naturalist's summer report - Miracle Beach Park, 1976. British Columbia Parks Branch Unpublished Report, Victoria. 23 pp. (Bibliography 3237).

Hochbaum, H.A. 1944. The Canvasback on a prairie marsh. North American Wildlife Institute, Washington, D.C. 201 pp.

Hodges, J.I., J.G. King and R. Davies. 1983. Bald Eagle breeding population survey of coastal British Columbia. Abstract only. Page 321 *in* D.M. Bird (editor). Biology and Management of Bald Eagles and Ospreys. Proceedings First International Symposium on Bald Eagles and Ospreys, Montreal, 28-29 October 1981. Harpell Press, Ste Anne de Bellevue, Quebec.

Hodges, J.I., E.L. Boeker, and A.J. Hansen. 1987. Movements of radio-tagged Bald Eagles, *Haliaeetus leucocephalus*, in and from southeastern Alaska. Canadian Field-Naturalist 101:136-140.

Hodson, K. 1980. Peregrine Falcons in British Columbia. Pages 85-87 *in* R. Stace-Smith, L. Johns, and P. Joslin (editors). Threatened and Endangered Species and Habitats in British Columbia and the Yukon. British Columbia Ministry of Environment, Victoria.

Hoffman, R. 1924. Breeding of the ancient murrelet in Washington. Condor 26:191.

Hoffman, R.W. and C.E. Braun. 1975. Migration of a wintering population of White-tailed Ptarmigan in Colorado. Journal of Wildlife Management 39:485-490.

Hoffman, W., W.P. Elliot, and J.M. Scott. 1975. The occurrence and status of the Horned Puffin in the western United States. Western Birds 6:87-94.

Hoffman, W., J.A. Wiens, and J.M. Scott. 1978. Hybridization between gulls (*Larus glaucescens and L. occidentalis*) in the Pacific Northwest. Auk 95:441-458.

Hohn, E.O. 1966. Ringing (banding) and recoveries of phalaropes, a summary of presently available information. Bird-Banding 37:197-200.

Holdom, M.W. 1943. Christmas bird census, 1942 - Crescent Beach, British Columbia. Canadian Field-Naturalist 57:57.

_____. 1945. Christmas bird census, 1944 - Crescent, British Columbia. Canadian Field-Naturalist 59:37-38.

_____. 1947. Christmas bird census, 1946 - Crescent, British Columbia. Canadian Field-Naturalist 61:66.

_____. 1948. Immature Snowy Egret (?) (*Leucophoyx thula*) at Crescent, B.C. Canadian Field-Naturalist 62:125.

_____. 1952. Glimpses of bird life in Surrey. The Surrey Leader, Cloverdale, British Columbia. 10 pp.

_____. 1954. Random bird notes. Surrey Leader, Cloverdale, British Columbia. 22 pp.

_____. 1962. Sixty-second Christmas bird count - Surrey Municipality, B.C. Audubon Field Notes 16:90.

Holland, S.S. 1964. Landforms of British Columbia: a physiograhic outline. British Columbia Department of Mines and Petroleum Resources Bulletin No. 48, Victoria. 138 pp.

Holmes, R.T. 1966. Breeding ecology and annual cycle adaptations of the Red backed Sandpiper (*Calidris alpina*) in northern Alaska. Condor 68:3-46.

Holmes, R.T. and F.A. Pitelka. 1964. Breeding behavior and taxonomic relationships of the Curlew Sandpiper. Auk 81:362-379.

Holroyd, G.L. and P.L. Jalkotzy. 1986. The breeding strategy of the Black Swift. Poster presented at the International Ornithological Congress, 22-28 June 1986, Ottawa, Ontario, Canada.

Honacki, J.H., K.E. Kinman, and J.W. Koeppl (editors). 1982. Mammal species of the world - a taxonomic and geographic reference. Association of Systematics Collections, Lawrence, Kansas.

Hooper, D.C. 1951. Waterfowl nesting at Minto Lakes, Alaska. Proceedings of the 2nd Alaskan Science Conference: 318-321.

Hooper, T.D. 1988. Habitat, reproductive parameters, and nest-site tenacity of urban-nesting Glaucous-winged Gulls at Victoria, British Columbia. Murrelet 69:10-14.

Hooper, T.D. and M. Nyhof. 1986. Food habits of the Long-eared Owl in south-central British Columbia. Murrelet 67:28-30.

Hooper, T.D. and K. Sars. 1986. An analysis of census methods and population trends for the Ring-necked Pheasant (*Phasianus colchicus*) on the Saanich Peninsula, Vancouver Island. British Columbia Ministry of Environment Wildlife Branch Unpublished Report, Victoria. 24 pp.

Horak, G.J. 1964. A comparative study of Virginia and Sora rails with emphasis on foods. M.S. Thesis, Iowa State University, Ames. 73 pp.

Horvath, O. 1963. Contributions to nesting ecology of forest birds. M.S.F. Thesis, University of British Columbia, Vancouver. 181 pp.

_____. 1964. Seasonal differences in Rufous Hummingbird nest height and their relation to nest climate. Ecology 45:235-241.

Hosford, H. 1975. Stray feathers - Daphne: early bird got carrots. Victoria Times Newspaper, 19 April.

Hoskins, H., M.W. Richards, and J.T.R. Sharrock. 1979. Best recent black-and-white bird photographs. British Birds 72:580-589.

Houston, C.S. 1963. R.F. Oldaker, the man who reads gull bands with a telescope. Blue Jay 21:53-57.

_____. 1977. Movements of Saskatchewan-banded California Gulls. Bird-Banding 48:158-161.

Houston, C.S. and P.W. Brown. 1983. Recoveries of Saskatchewan banded White-winged Scoters (*Melanitta fusca*). Canadian Field-Naturalist 97:454-455.

Hout, J.L. 1967. Contribution toward a bibliography on Brant. United States Department of the Interior Fish and Wildlife Service Special Scientific Report - Wildlife No. 103, Washington, D.C. 15 pp.

Howard, R.P. 1975. Breeding ecology of the Ferruginous Hawk in northern Utah and southern Idaho. M.S. Thesis, Utah State University, Logan. 60 pp.

Howe, M.A. 1975. Behavioural aspects of the pair bond in Wilson's Phalarope. Wilson Bulletin 87:248-270.

Howell, T.R. 1952. Natural history and differentiation in the Yellow-bellied Sapsucker. Condor 54:237-282.

_____. 1953. Racial and sexual differences in migration in *Sphyrapicus varius*. Auk 70:118-126.

Howie, R.R. 1975. The fall migration at Golden, B.C. and adjacent areas of the Rocky Mountain cordillera 1975. British Columbia Provincial Museum Unpublished Report, Victoria. 30 pp. (Bibliography 3272).

_____. 1980. The Burrowing Owl in British Columbia. Pages 88-95 *in* R. Stace-Smith, L. Johns and P. Joslin (editors). Threatened and Endangered Species and Habitats in British Columbia and the Yukon. British Columbia Ministry of Environment, Victoria.

_____. 1987. Status report on the Flammulated Owl (*Otus flammeolus*) in Canada - 1986. Committee on the Status of Endangered Wildlife in Canada Unpublished Report, c/o Canadian Nature Federation, Ottawa, Ontario. 58 pp.

Howie, R.R. and R. Ritcey. 1987. Distribution, habitat selection, and densities of Flammulated Owls in British Columbia. Pages 249-254 *in* R.W. Nero, R.J. Clark, R.J. Knapton, and R.H. Hamre (editors). Biology and Conservation of Northern Forest Owls: Symposium Proceedings. 1987 Feb. 3-7; Winnipeg, Manitoba. United States Department of Agriculture Forest Service General Technical Report RM-142, Fort Collins, Colorado.

Hoyt, J.S.Y. 1944. Preliminary notes on the development of nesting Pileated Woodpeckers. Auk 61:376-384.

Hoyt, S.F. 1957. The ecology of the Pileated Woodpecker. Ecology 38:246-256.

Hubbs, C.L. and G.A. Bartholomew. 1951. Persistence of a rare colour aberration in the Heermann Gull. Condor 53:221-227.

Hudson, G.E. and C.F. Yocom. 1954. A distributional list of the birds of southeastern Washington. Research Studies, State University of Washington 22:25.

Hughes, W.M. 1956. Observations of our less common birds. Vancouver Natural History Society News 105:4-6.

_____. 1961. Green Heron in southwestern British Columbia. Canadian Field-Naturalist 75:169-170.

_____. 1963. Sight record of the Tufted Duck at Vancouver, British Columbia. Canadian Field-Naturalist 77:62-63.

Huhtala, K., E. Korpimakl, and E. Pulliainen. 1987. Foraging activity and growth of nestlings in the Hawk Owl: adaptive strategies under northern conditions. Pages 152-156 *in* R.W. Nero, R.J. Clark, R.J. Knapton, and R.H. Hamre (editors). Biology and Conservation of Northern Forest Owls: Symposium Proceedings. 1987 Feb.3-7; Winnipeg, Manitoba. United States Department of Agriculture Forest Service General Technical Report RM-142, Fort Collins, Colorado.

Hume, S. 1988. Neighbors feud over peacocks. Times-Colonist 25 February, p. B1.

Hunn, E.S. and P.W. Mattocks. 1981a. Fall migration - northern Pacific coast region. American Birds 35:216-219.

_____. and _____. 1981b. The spring migration - northern Pacific coast region. American Birds 35:854-857.

_____. and _____. 1982. Fall migration - northern Pacific coast region. American Birds 36:208-211.

_____. and _____. 1983a. Fall migration - northern Pacific coast region. American Birds 37:214-218.

_____. and _____. 1983b. The spring migration - northern Pacific coast region. American Birds 37:903-906.

_____. and _____. 1984. The autumn migration - northern Pacific coast region. American Birds 38:236-240.

_____. and _____. 1985. The autumn migration - northern Pacific coast region. American Birds 39:92-96.

_____. and _____. 1986. The autumn migration - northern Pacific coast region. American Birds 40:321-324.

Inkster, C. 1971. Sibling competition in the Double-crested Cormorant (*Phalacrocorax auritus*). B.Sc. Thesis. Simon Fraser University, Burnaby, British Columbia. 60pp.

International Union for Conservation of Nature and Natural Resources. 1969. Red data book, Volume 2, *Aves*. American Peregrine Falcon. Sheet B/35/Falcon/Per/Ana.

Irving, E.B. 1953. Birds at Carmanah Point. Victoria Naturalist 10:19-22; 28-31.

Isleib, M.E. and B. Kessel. 1973. Birds of the North Gulf coast - Prince William Sound region, Alaska. Biological Papers of the University of Alaska No.14, Fairbanks. 149 pp.

Jackson, J.A. 1983. Nesting phenology, nest site selection, and reproductive success of Black and Turkey vultures. Pages 245-271 *in* S.R. Wilbur and J.A. Jackson (editors). Vulture biology and management. University of California Press, Berkeley.

Jacobson, T. 1974. Birds of Kamloops country. Published by the author, Kamloops, British Columbia. 34 pp. (Bibliography 1751).

James, R. 1980. Snowy Owl food in different habitats in the Toronto region. Ontario Field Biologist 34:11-16.

Jeffrey, R. and G. Kaiser. 1979. The Snow Goose flock of the Fraser and Skagit deltas. Pages 266-279 *in* R.L. Jarvis and J.C. Bartonek (editors). Management and Biology of Pacific Flyway Geese. A symposium sponsored by the Northwest Section, The Wildlife Society, 16 February 1979, Portland, Oregon. Oregon State University Book Store, Inc., Corvallis.

Jehl, J.R. 1968. Relationships in the Charadrii (shorebirds): a taxonomic study based on color patterns of the downy young. San Diego Society of Natural History Memoir No.3, San Diego, California.

_____. 1973a. Late autumn observations of pelagic birds off southern California. Western Birds 4:45-52.

_____. 1973b. Breeding biology and systematic relationships of the Stilt Sandpiper. Wilson Bulletin 85:115-147.

_____. 1979. The autumnal migration of Baird's Sandpiper. Studies in Avian Biology 2:55-68.

_____. 1982. The biology and taxonomy of Townsend's Shearwater. Le Gerfaut 72:121-135.

_____. 1985. Hybridization and evolution of oystercatchers on the Pacific coast of Baja California. Ornithological Monographs 6:484-504.

_____. 1987. Geographic variation and evolution in the California Gull (*Larus californicus*). Auk 104:421-428.

Jehl, J.R. and B.A. Smith. 1970. Birds of the Churchill region, Manitoba. Manitoba Museum of Man and Nature Special Publication No.1, Winnipeg. 87 pp.

Jehl, J.R., and P.K. Yochem. 1986. Movements of Eared Grebes indicated by banding recoveries. Journal of Field Ornithology 57:208-212.

Jenkins, J.A. 1969. A note on the local distribution of Buller's Shearwaters. Notornis 16:220.

_____. 1974. Local distribution and feeding habits of Buller's Shearwater (*Puffinus bulleri*). Notornis 21:109-120.

Jerema, R.S. 1973. Birds of Port Coquitlam. Published by City of Port Coquitlam, British Columbia. 59 pp. (Bibliography 811).

Jewett, S.A., W.A. Taylor, W.T. Shaw, and J.W. Aldrich. 1953. Birds of Washington state. University of Washington Press, Seattle. 767 pp.

Jewett, S.G. 1929. The Wedge-tailed Shearwater off the coast of Vancouver Island, British Columbia. Auk 46:224.

_____. 1942. Bird notes from southeastern Alaska. Murrelet 23:67-75.

Jobin, L. 1952a. Some uncommon birds collected in the Cariboo parkland area of British Columbia. Murrelet 33:9.

_____. 1952b. Records of *Somateria mollisima V-nigra* on the mainland of British Columbia. Murrelet 33:12.

_____. 1952c. Records of the Burrowing Owl and Long-eared Owl in the Cariboo, British Columbia, Canada. Murrelet 33:43.

_____. 1955. Notes on the Black Swift and Vaux Swift at their nesting sites in central British Columbia. Canadian Field-Naturalist 69:131-132.

Johns, J.E. 1969. Field studies of Wilson's Phalarope. Auk 86:660-670.

Johnsgard, P.A. 1965. Handbook of waterfowl behavior. Cornell University Press, Ithaca, New York. 378 pp.

_____. 1968. Waterfowl: their biology and natural history. University of Nebraska Press, Lincoln.

_____. 1973. Grouse and quails of North America. University of Nebraska Press, Lincoln. 553 pp.

_____. 1981. The plovers, sandpipers, and snipes of the world. University of Nebraska Press, Lincoln. 493 pp.

_____. 1983. The hummingbirds of North America. Smithsonian Institution Press, Washington, D.C. 303 pp.

_____. 1983a. The grouse of the world. University of Nebraska Press, Lincoln.

Johnson, D.H. and R.E. Stewart. 1983. Racial composition of migrant populations of Sandhill Cranes in the northern plains states. Wilson Bulletin 85:148-162.

Johnson, D.H., D.E. Timm, and P.F. Springer. 1979. Morphological characteristics of Canada geese in the Pacific flyway. Pages 56-76 *in* R.J. Jarvis and J.C. Bartonek (editors). Management and Biology of Pacific Flyway Geese. A symposium sponsored by the Northwest Section, The Wildlife Society, 16 February 1979, Portland, Oregon. Oregon State University Book Stores, Inc., Corvallis.

Johnson, N.K. and C.B. Johnson. 1985. Speciation in sapsuckers (*Sphyrapicus*): II. Sympatry, hybridization, and mate preference in S. *ruber daggetti* and S. *nuchalis*. Auk 102:1-15.

Johnson, R. and J.J. Dinsmore. 1986. Habitat use by breeding Virginia Rails and Soras. Journal of Wildlife Management 50:387-392.

Johnston, D.W. 1955. The Glaucous Gull in western North America south of its breeding range. Condor 57:202-207.

_____. 1961. Timing of annual molt in the Glaucous Gulls of northern Alaska. Condor 63:474-478.

Johnston, S. and H.R. Carter. 1985. Cavity-nesting Marbled Murrelets. Wilson Bulletin 97:1-3.

Johnston, W.G. and C. McEwen. 1986a. The winter season - northwestern Canada region. American Birds 40:303-304.

_____. and _____. 1986b. The nesting season - northwestern Canada region. American Birds 40:1228-1229.

Johnstone, S.T. 1970. Waterfowl eggs. Aviculture Magazine 76: 52-55.

Johnstone, W.B. 1949. An annotated list of the birds of the east Kootenay, British Columbia. British Columbia Provincial Museum Occasional Paper No.7, Victoria. 87pp.

_____. 1964. Two interior British Columbia records for the Ancient Murrelet. Canadian Field-Naturalist 78:199-200.

Jones, E.T. 1985. BC/Yukon bird observations - summer, 1984. Alberta Naturalist 15:72-73.

_____. 1987. Observations of the Northern Hawk Owl in Alberta. Pages 149-151 *in* R.W. Nero, R.J. Clark, R.J. Knapton, and R.H. Hamre (editors). Biology and conservation of Northern Forest Owls: Symposium Proceedings. 1987. Feb. 3-7; Winnipeg, Manitoba. United States Department of Agriculture Forest Service General Technical Report RM-142, Fort Collins, Colorado.

Jones, I.L. 1985. The structure and function of vocalizations and related behavior of the Ancient Murrelet *Synthliborhamphus antiquus*. M.Sc. Thesis. University of Toronto, Ontario. 178pp.

Jones, I.L. and J.B. Falls. 1987. Colony departure of family groups of Ancient Murrelets. Condor 89:940-943.

_____. and _____. 1989. The vocal repertoire of the Ancient Murrelet. Condor 91: 699-710.

Jones, I.L., J.B. Falls, and A.J. Gaston. 1987a. Vocal recognition between parents and young of Ancient Murrelets, *Synthliboramphus antiquus* (Aves:Alcidae). Animal Behaviour 35:1405-1415.

_____, _____, and _____. 1987b. Colony departure of family groups of Ancient Murrelets. Condor 89:940-943.

Jones, J.K., D.C. Carter, H.H. Genoways, R.S. Hoffman, D.W. Rice, and C. Jones. 1986. Revised checklist of North American mammals north of Mexico, 1986. Occasional Papers The Museum Texas Tech University No.107, Lubbock. 22 pp.

Jones, R.D. 1973. A method for appraisal of annual reproductive success in the Black Brant population. M.S. Thesis, University of Alaska, Fairbanks. 117 pp.

Jones, S. 1981. Habitat management series for unique or endangered species. Report No.17. The accipiters - Goshawk, Cooper's Hawk, Sharp-shinned hawk. United States Department of the Interior, Bureau of Land Management Technical Note 335, Denver, Colorado. 51 pp.

Kaiser, G. and M. Lemon. 1987. Protecting our seabird colonies. Vancouver Natural History Society Discovery 16:77-80.

Kaiser, G.W., R.W. McKelvey, and D.W. Smith. 1978. A preliminary report on the first set of aerial surveys to be conducted through a full annual cycle in the Columbia valley between the Libby Reservoir and Golden, British Columbia (1976-1977). Canadian Wildlife Service Unpublished Report, Delta, British Columbia. 54 pp. (Bibliography 3354).

Kaiser, G.W., D. Bertram, and D. Powell. 1984. A band recovery for the Rhinoceros Auklet. Murrelet 65:57.

Kautesk, B.M. 1985a. A possible sighting of the Little Curlew. Vancouver Natural History Society Discovery 14:12-13.

_____. 1985b. "Caribbean Coots" in British Columbia? Vancouver Natural History Society Discovery 14:49-51.

Kautesk, B.M., R.E. Scott, D.S. Aldcroft, and J. Ireland. 1983. Temminck's Stint at Vancouver, British Columbia. American Birds 37:347-349.

Keen, J.H. 1910. Bird migration in northern British Columbia. Ottawa Naturalist 24:116-117.

Keisker, D.G. 1986. Nest tree selection by primary cavity nesting birds in south-central British Columbia. M.Sc. Thesis, Simon Fraser University, Burnaby, British Columbia. 71 pp.

Keith, L.B. 1963. Wildlife's ten-year cycle. University of Wisconsin Press, Madison. 201 pp.

Kelleher, K.E. 1963. A study of the hole-nesting avifauna of southwestern British Columbia. M.Sc. Thesis, University of British Columbia, Vancouver. 169 pp.

Kellert, S.R. 1985. Birdwatching in American society. Leisure Sciences 7:343-360.

Kelso, J.E.H. 1924. The Osprey or fish hawk on Arrow Lake. Migrant 2:17 (Bibliography 1937).

_____. 1926. Birds of Arrow Lakes, Kootenay District, British Columbia. Ibis 2:689-723.

Kempton, R.M. 1927. Notes on the home life of the Turkey Vulture. Wilson Bulletin 39:142-145.

Kendrew, W.G. and D. Kerr. 1955. The climate of British Columbia and the Yukon Territory. Queens Printer, Ottawa, Ontario. 222 pp.

Kennedy, A.J., F.J. van Thienen, and R.M. McKelvey. 1982. Winter foods of Snowy Owls on the southern coast of British Columbia. Vancouver Natural History Society Discovery 11:119-121.

Kennedy, K. and B. Foottit. 1967. Summer report for 1967 - Mitlenatch Island Nature Park. British Columbia Parks Branch Unpublished Report, Victoria. 27 pp. (Bibliography 3372).

Kenyon, K.W. 1937. Two sea-bird records for southern California. Condor 39:257-258.

Kermode, F. 1904. Catalogue of British Columbia birds. British Columbia Provincial Museum, Victoria. 69 pp. (Bibliography 1003).

_____. 1923a. Notes on the occurrence of the Plumed Egret (*Mesophoyx intermedia*) in British Columbia. Canadian Field-Naturalist 37:64-65.

_____. 1923b. Notes on the Plumed Egret (*Mesophoyx intermedia*) in British Columbia. Murrelet 4:3-5.

_____. 1933. California Brown Pelican seen at Victoria, British Columbia. Murrelet 14:15.

Kermode, F. and E.M. Anderson. 1914. Report on birds collected and observed during September, 1913 on Atlin Lake, from Atlin to the south end of the lake. Pages G19-G21 *in* Annual Report of the British Columbia Provincial Museum of Natural History for the year 1913, Victoria.

Kessel, B. 1984. Migration of Sandhill Cranes, *Grus canadensis*, in east-central Alaska, with routes through Alaska and western Canada. Canadian Field-Naturalist 98:279-292.

_____. 1986. Yellow-bellied Sapsucker, *Sphyrapicus varius*, in Alaska. Journal of Field Ornithology 57:42-47.

Kessel, B. and D.D. Gibson. 1978. Status and distribution of Alaskan birds. Studies in Avian Biology No. 1:1-100.

Kevan, C.L. 1970. An ecological study of Red-necked Grebes on Astotin Lake, Alberta. M.Sc. Thesis, University of Alberta, Edmonton.

Kieser, J.A. and F.T.H. Smith. 1982. Field identification of the Pectoral Sandpiper *Calidris melanotos*. Australian Bird Watcher 9:137-146.

Kiff, L. 1981. Eggs of the Marbled Murrelet. Wilson Bulletin 93:400-403.

Kilham, L. 1962. Reproductive behavior of Downy Woodpeckers. Condor 64:126-133.

King, D.G. 1973. First records of nesting by Marsh Hawks on Vancouver Island. Canadian Field-Naturalist 87:470.

King, J.G. and B. Conant. 1981. The 1980 census of Trumpeter Swans on Alaska nesting habitats. American Birds 35: 789-793.

King, J.G. and G.A. Sanger. 1979. Oil vulnerability index for marine-oriented birds. Pages 227-239 *in* J.C. Bartonek and D.N. Nettleship (editors). Conservation of marine birds of northern North America. United States Fish and Wildlife Service Wildlife Research Report No. 11, Washington, D.C. 319 pp.

King, W.B. 1967. Sea-birds of the Tropical Pacific Ocean: preliminary Smithsonian identification manual. United States National Museum, Washington, D.C.

_____ (compiler). 1981. Endangered birds of the world - The ICB bird red data book. Smithsonian Institution Press, Washington, D.C.

_____. 1984. Incidental mortality of seabirds in gillnets in the North Pacific. Pages 709-716 *in* J.P. Croxall, P.G.H. Evans and R.W. Schreiber (editors). Status and conservation of the world's seabirds. International Council for Bird Preservation Technical Publication No. 2. Cambridge, England.

King, W.B., R.G.B. Brown and G.A. Sanger. 1979. Mortality to marine birds through commercial fishing. Pages 195-200 *in* J.C. Bartonek and D.N. Nettleship (editors). Conservation of marine birds of northern North America. United States Department of the Interior Fish and Wildlife Service Wildlife Research Report 11, Washington, D.C. 319 pp.

Kitchen, D.W. and G.S. Hunt. 1969. Brood habitat of the Hooded Merganser. Journal of Wildlife Management 33:605-609.

Knorr, O.N. 1961. The geographical and ecological distribution of the Black Swift in Colorado. Wilson Bulletin 73:155-170.

Kortright, F.H. 1942. The ducks, geese, and swans of North America. Stackpole Co., Harrisburg, Pennsylvania and Wildlife Management Institute, Washington, D.C. 476 pp.

Kozlik, F.M., A.W. Miller, and W.C. Rienecker. 1959. Color-marking white geese for determining migration routes. California Fish and Game 45:69-82.

Kragh, W.D. 1982. The Cattle Egret in the Fraser Delta area, British Columbia. Murrelet 63:86-89.

Kragh, W.D., B.M. Kautesk, J. Ireland, and E. Sian. 1986. Far Eastern Curlew in Canada. American Birds. 40:13-15.

Krajina, V.J. 1959. Bioclimatic zones in British Columbia. University of British Columbia Botanical Series No. 1, Vancouver. 47 pp.

———. 1965. Biogeoclimatic zones and biogeocoenoses of British Columbia. Ecology of Western North America 1:1-17.

———. 1969. Ecology of forest trees in British Columbia. Ecology of western North America. 2:1-146.

Kramer, G.W., L.R. Raven, and S.W. Harris. 1979. Populations, hunting mortality, and habitat use of Black Brant at San Quintin Bay, Baja California, Mexico. Pages 242-254 *in* R.L. Jarvis and J.C. Bartonek (editors). Management and Biology of Pacific flyway Geese. A symposium sponsored by the Northwest Section, The Wildlife Society, 16 February 1979, Portland, Oregon. Oregon State University Book Stores, Inc., Corvallis.

Krohn, W.B. and E.G. Bizeau. 1979. Molt migration of the Rocky Mountain population of the western Canada Goose. Pages 130-140 *in* R.L. Jarvis and J.C. Bartonek (editors). Management and Biology of Pacific Flyway Geese. A symposium sponsored by the Northwest Section, The Wildlife Society, 16 February 1979, Portland, Oregon. Oregon State University Book Stores, Inc., Corvallis.

Kurata, Y. 1978. Breeding record of the Laysan Albatross (*Diomedea immutabilis*) on the Ogasawara Islands (a preliminary report). Miscellaneous Report Yamashina Institute of Ornithology 10:185-187.

Kuroda, N. 1960. Analysis of seabird distribution in the northwest Pacific Ocean. Pacific Science 14:55-67.

———. 1962. On the melanic phase of the McCormick Great Skua. Miscellaneous Reports of the Yamashina Institute for Ornithology 3:212-217.

Kuroda, N. and a Special Committee of the Ornithological Society of Japan. 1958. A hand-list of the Japanese birds, fourth edition. Tokyo Ornithological Society of Japan.

Kuzyakin, A.P. 1963. On the biology of the Long-billed [Marbled] Murrelet. Ornitologiya 6:315-320 (translation in Van Tyne Memorial Library, University of Michigan, Ann Arbor).

Lack, D. 1967. Interrelationships in breeding adaptations as shown by marine birds. Proceedings of the 14th International Ornithological Congress:3-42.

Laing, H.M. 1932. White Pelican on Vancouver Island. Canadian Field-Naturalist 46:190.

———. 1934. Some Vancouver Island bird notes. Canadian-Field Naturalist 48:37-38.

———. 1935. Some Vancouver Island bird notes. Canadian Field-Naturalist 49:56-57.

———. 1937. Birds of River's Inlet region, B.C. - summer 1937. National Museum of Canada Unpublished Report, Ottawa, Ontario. 117 pp. (Bibliography 3397).

———. 1942. Birds of the coast of central British Columbia. Condor 44:175-181.

———. 1956. Nesting of Golden Eagle on Vancouver Island. Canadian Field-Naturalist 70:95-96.

———. 1979. Allan Brooks: Artist-Naturalist. British Columbia Provincial Museum, Victoria. 234 pp.

Lane, R.K. 1962. A Short-tailed Albatross off British Columbia. Canadian Field-Naturalist 76:178-179.

Larrison, E.J. and K.G. Sonnenberg. 1968. Washington birds - their location and identification. Seattle Audubon Society, Seattle, Washington. 258 pp.

Lauro, A.J. and B.J. Spencer. 1980. A method for separating juvenal and first-winter Ring-billed Gulls (*Larus delawarensis*) and Common Gulls (*Larus canus*). American Birds 34:111-117.

Laymon S.A. and M.D. Halterman. 1987. Can the western subspecies of the Yellow-billed Cuckoo be saved from extinction? Western Birds 18:19-25.

Leach, B.A. 1970. A "Slimbridge" in British Columbia. Wildfowl 21:112-114.

———. 1972. The waterfowl of the Fraser delta, British Columbia. Wildfowl 23:45-54.

———. 1982. Waterfowl on a Pacific estuary: a natural history of man and waterfowl on the lower Fraser River. British Columbia Provincial Museum Special Publication No. 5, Victoria. 211 pp.

Lee, P.L. 1985. History and current status of Spotted Owl (*Strix occidentalis*) habitat management in the Pacific Northweest region, USDA, Forest Service. Pages 5-9 *in* R.J. Gutierrez and A.B. Carey (editors). Ecology and management of the Spotted Owl in the Pacific Northwest. United States Department of Agriculture, Forest Service General Technical Report PNW-185, Portland Oregon.

Lees, J. 1946. All the year breeding of the Rock Dove. British Birds 39:136-141.

Le Franc, M.N., and W.S. Clark. 1983. Working bibliography of the Golden Eagle and the genus *Aquila*. National Wildlife Federation Scientific and Technical Series No. 7, Washington, D.C. 222 pp.

Lehman, P. 1980. The identification of the Thayer's Gull in the field. Birding 12:198-210.

Leinonen, A. 1978. Hawk Owl breeding biology and behaviour at nest. Lintumies 13:13-18.

Lemon, E.K. 1958. Bird watching at Drumadoon, 1957. Victoria Naturalist 14:93-94.

Lemon, M. and M. Rodway. 1983. Survey of breeding population of Ancient Murrelets of Lyell Island, in 1982. Canadian Wildlife Service Technical Report, Delta, British Columbia. 22 pp.

———. and ———. 1985a. Survey of breeding population of Ancient Murrelets and Cassin's Auklets on Hippa Island, 1983. Canadian Wildlife Service Technical Report, Delta, British Columbia. 45 pp.

———. and ———. 1985b. Census of Ancient Murrelets and Cassin's Auklets nesting on Ramsay Island, B.C. in 1984. Canadian Wildlife Service Technical Report, Delta, British Columbia. 49 pp.

Lemon, M., M. Rodway and A. Vallee. 1983. Census of Tufted Puffins breeding on Triangle Island, in 1982. Canadian Wildlife Service Technical Report, Delta, British Columbia. 22 pp.

Lensink, C.C. 1984. The status and conservation of seabirds in Alaska. Pages 13-28 *in* Croxall, J.P., P.G.H. Evans and R.W. Schreiber (editors). The satus and conservation of the world's seabirds. International Council for Bird Preservation Technical Publication No. 2. Cambridge, England.

Lensink, C.J. 1954. Waterfowl breeding ground survey, Ft. Yukon Flats, Alaska. Progress Report Federal Aid Project W-3-R-9, Alaska Game Commission, Juneau.

———. 1964. Distribution of recoveries from bandings of ducklings. United States Fish and Wildlife Service Special Scientific Report - Wildlife No. 89, Washington, D.C. 146 pp.

———. 1969. The distribution recoveries from White-fronted geese (*Anser albifrons frontalis*) banded in North America. United States Bureau of Sport Fisheries and Wildlife Unpublished Report, Bethel, Alaska. 63 pp.

Leopold, A.S. and R.H. Smith. 1953. Numbers and winter distribution of Pacific Black Brant in North America. California Fish and Game 39:95-101.Leschner, L.L. 1976. The breeding biology of the Rhinoceros Auklet on Destruction Island. M.Sc. Thesis. University of Washington, Seattle. 77 pp.

Leschner, L.L. 1976. The breeding biology of the Rhinoceros Auklet on Destruction Island. M.Sc. Thesis, University of Washington, Seattle. 77 pp.

Lewin, V. 1963. Reproduction and development of young in a population of California Quail. Condor 65:249-278.

_____. 1965. The introduction and present status of California Quail in the Okanagan valley of British Columbia. Condor 67:61-66.

Lewis, H.F. 1929. The natural history of the Double-crested Cormorant (*Phalacrocorax auritus auritus* (Lesson)). Ru-Mi-Lou Books, Ottawa, Ontario. 94 pp.

Lewis, R.A. 1984. Non-territorial adult males and breeding densities of Blue Grouse. Wilson Bulletin 96:723-725.

Lewis, R.A. and F.C. Zwickel. 1980. Removal and replacement of male Blue Grouse on persistent and transient territorial sites. Canadian Journal of Zoology 58:1417-1423.

LGL Limited. 1974. Use of the Morice, Nanika, and Entiako River drainage systems by migrating waterbirds; October 1974. Canadian Wildlife Service Unpublished Report, Delta, British Columbia. 38 pp. (Bibliography 3439).

L'Hyver, M-A. 1985. Intraspecific variability in nesting phenology, clutch size, and egg size in the Black Oystercatcher *Haematopus bachmani*. M.Sc. Thesis, University of Victoria, Victoria, British Columbia. 224 pp.

Lies, M.F. and W.H. Behle. 1966. Status of the White Pelican in the United States and Canada through 1964. Condor 68: 279-292.

Lincer, J.L., W.S. Clark, and M.N. LeFranc. 1979. Working bibliography of the Bald Eagle. National Wildlife Federation Scientific and Technical Series No .2, Washington, D.C. 219 pp.

Lincoln, R.C. 1986. Burrowing Owl recovery plan. B.C. Naturalist 24:20.

Lindvall, M.L. and J.B. Low. 1982. Nesting ecology and production of Western Grebes at Bear River Migratory Bird Refuge, Utah. Condor 84:66-70.

Littlefield, C.D. and S.P. Thompson. 1979. Distribution and status of the central valley population of greater Sandhill Cranes. Pages 113-120 in J.C. Lewis (editor). Proceedings 1978 Crane Workshop. Colorado State University Printing Service, Fort Collins, Colorado.

_____. and _____. 1981. History and status of the Franklin's Gull on Malheur National Wildlife Refuge, Oregon. Great Basin Naturalist 41:440-444.

_____. and _____. 1982. The Pacific coast population of lesser Sandhill Cranes in the contiguous United States. Pages 288-294 in J.C. Lewis (editor). Proceedings 1981 Crane Workshop. National Audubon Society, Tavernier, Florida.

Loomis, L.M. 1918. Expedition of the California Academy of Sciences to the Galapagos Islands, 1905-1906 - A review of the albatrosses, petrels, and diving petrels. Proceedings of the California Academy of Sciences 2:1-187.

Lord, J.K. 1866. The naturalist in Vancouver Island and British Columbia (Volume 2). London, Richard Bentley. 375 pp.

Lovvorn, J.R. and C.M. Kirkpatrick. 1981. Roosting behavior and habitat of migrant greater Sandhill Cranes. Journal of Wildlife Management 45:842-857.

Low, J.B. 1941. Nesting of the Ruddy Duck in Iowa. Auk 58: 506-517.

_____. 1945. Ecology and management of the Redhead, *Nyroca americana*, in Iowa. Ecological Monograph 15:35-69.

Lumsden, H.G. 1984. The pre-settlement breeding distribution of Trumpeter Swans (*Cygnus buccinator*) and Tundra Swans (*C. columbianus*) in eastern Canada. Canadian Field-Naturalist 98:415-424.Luttich, S.N., L.B. Keith, and J.D. Stephenson. 1971. Population dynamics of the Red-tailed Hawk (*Buteo jamaicensis*) at Rochester, Alberta. Auk 88:75-87.

Luttich, S.N., L.B. Keith, and J.D. Stephenson, 1971. Population dynamics of the Red-tailed Hawk (*Buteo jamaicensis*) at Rochester, Alberta. Auk 88:75-87.

Lynch, J.J. and J.F. Voelzer. 1974. 1973 productivity and mortality among geese, swans, and brant wintering in North America. United States Fish and Wildlife Service Unpublished Report, Albuquerque, New Mexico. 43 pp.

Lyons, J.R. 1982. Nonconsumptive wildlife-associated recreation in the U.S.: identifying the other constituency. Pages 667-685 in Transactions of the 47th North American and Natural Resources Conference, Portland, Oregon, March 28, 1982.

Macdonald, B.A. 1978a. Curlew Sandpiper at Iona Island. Vancouver Natural History Society Discovery 6:89-90.

_____. 1978b. Sighting of a Garganey at Iona Island. Vancouver Natural History Society Discovery 7:18-19.

MacDonald, S.D. 1968. The courtship and territorial behaviour of Franklin's race of Spruce Grouse. Living Bird 7:5-25.

Mace, P.M. 1983. Bird predation on juvenile salmonids in the Big Qualicum estuary, Vancouver Island. Canadian Technical Report of Fisheries and Aquatic Sciences No. 1176, Vancouver, British Columbia.

MacFarlane, R. and C. Mair. 1908. Notes on the mammals and birds of northern Canada. Pages 1-494 in A narrative of the Athabasca and Peace River Treaty Expedition of 1899. William Briggs, Toronto, Ontario.

Mackay, R.H. 1950. British Columbia Trumpeter Swan census, winter 1949-50. Canadian Wildlife Service Report CWSC 448, Ottawa, Ontario. 5 pp. (Bibliography 3459).

_____. 1957. Movements of Trumpeter Swans shown by band returns and observations. Condor 59:339.

Mackenzie-Grieve, R.C. and J.B. Tatum. 1974. Costa's Hummingbird, a new bird for Canada. Canadian Field-Naturalist 88:91-92.

Mackie, R. 1985. Hamilton Mack Laing: Hunter-Naturalist. Sono Nis Press, Victoria, British Columbia. 234 pp.

Mackie, R.J. and H.K. Buechner. 1963. The reproductive cycle of the Chukar. Journal of Wildlife Management 27:246-260.

MacLean, S.F. and R.T. Holmes. 1971. Bill lengths, wintering areas, and taxonomy of North American Dunlins, *Calidris alpina*. Auk 88:893-901.

Macoun, J. 1900. Catalogue of Canadian birds. Part 1. Waterbirds, gallinaceous birds, and pigeons. Geological Survey of Canada, 213 pp.

Macoun, J. and J.M. Macoun. 1909. Catalogue of Canadian birds. Canada Department of Mines Geological Survey Branch, Ottawa, Ontario. 761pp.

Macpherson, A.H. 1961. Observations on Canadian arctic *Larus* gulls, and on the taxonomy of *L. thayeri* Brooks. Arctic Institute of North America Technical Paper 7:1-40.

Maguire, W.S. 1950. Christmas bird census, 1949 - New Westminster, British Columbia. Canadian Field-Naturalist 64:81.

Maher, W.J. 1974. Ecology of Pomarine, Parasitic, and Long-tailed jaegers in northern Alaska. Pacific Coast Avifauna No. 37, Los Angeles, California. 148 pp.

Mailliard, J. 1932. Birds and mammals from the Kootenay valley, southeastern British Columbia. Proceedings of the California Academy of Science 20:269-290.

Manuwal, D.A. 1972. The population ecology of Cassin's Auklet on southeast Farallon Island, California. Ph.D. Thesis, University of California, Los Angeles. 298 pp.

_____. 1974a. The natural history of Cassin's Auklet (*Ptychoramphus aleuticus*). Condor 76:421-431.

_____. 1974b. Effects of territoriality on breeding in a population of Cassin's Auklet. Ecology 55:1399-1406.

_____. 1978. Criteria for aging Cassin's Auklet. Bird-Banding 49:157-161.

_____. 1979. Reproductive commitment and success of Cassin's Auklet. Condor 81:111-121.

Manuwal, D.A. and R.W. Campbell. 1979. Status and distribution of breeding seabirds of southeastern Alaska, British Columbia and Washington. Pages 73-91 *in* J.S. Bartonek and D. Nettleship (editors). Conservation of marine birds of northern North America. United States Fish and Wildlife Service, Wildlife Research Report No. 11, Washington, D.C.

Manuwal, D.A., P.W. Mattocks, and K.O. Richter. 1979. First Arctic Tern colony in the contiguous western United States. American Birds 33:144-145.

March, G.L. 1971. The biology of the Band-tailed Pigeon (*Columba fasciata*) in British Columbia. Ph.D. Thesis, Simon Fraser University, Burnaby, British Columbia. 97 pp.

March, G.L. and R.M.F.S. Sadleir. 1972. Studies on the Band-tailed Pigeon (*Columba fasciata*) in British Columbia. II. Food resource and mineral-gravelling activity. Syesis 5:279-284.

Mark, D.M. 1974. Preliminary results of some Great Blue Heron (*Ardea herodias*) studies in the Vancouver checklist area. Vancouver Natural History Society Discovery 3:38-45.

_____. 1976. An inventory of Great Blue Heron (*Ardea herodias*) nesting colonies in British Columbia. Northwest Science 50:32-41.

_____. 1981. Thayer's Gulls from western Christmas bird counts: a cautionary note. American Birds 35:898-900.

Marsh, R.D. 1988. Macroclimatic regions of British Columbia. Pages 22-32 *in* H.A. Stelfox and G.R. Ironside (*compilers*). Land/wildlife integration workshop No. 3, Mount Ste.-Marie, Quebec, 16-19 September 1985. Ecological Land Classification Series No. 22, Canadian Wildlife Service, Ottawa, Ontario. 215 pp.

Marshall, D.B. 1987. Status of the Marbled Murrelet with special emphasis on the Oregon population. Audubon Society of Portland Unpublished Report, Portland, Oregon. 46 pp.

Marshall, J.T. 1967. Parallel variation in north and middle American screech owls. Western Foundation Vertebrate Zoology Monograph No.1, Los Angeles, California. 72 pp.

_____. 1988. Status of the Marbled Murrelet in North America: with special emphasis on populations in California, Oregon, and Washington. United States Department of the Interior Fish and Wildlife Service Biological Report 88(30), Washington, D.C. 19 pp.

Marti, C.D., P.W. Wagner, and K.W. Denne. 1979. Nest boxes for the management of Barn Owls. Wildlife Society Bulletin 7:145-148.

Martin, P.W. 1942. Notes on some pelagic birds on the coast of British Columbia. Condor 44:27-29.

_____. 1955. Chukar partridge - summary of stocking, 1950-1955. British Columbia Fish and Wildlife Branch Unpublished Report, Kamloops. 7pp. (Bibliography 4339 - erroneously listed as authored by E.W. Taylor).

_____. 1978. A winter inventory of the shoreline and marine oriented birds and mammals of Chatham Sound. British Columbia Fish and Wildlife Branch Unpublished Report, Victoria. 47 pp. (Bibliography 3521).

Martin, P.W. and M.T. Myres. 1969. Observations on the distribution and migration of some seabirds off the outer coasts of British Columbia and Washington State, 1946-1949. Syesis 2:241-256.

Mathews, W.H. (compiler). 1986. Physiographic map of the Canadian Cordillera. Map 1701A, Geological Survey of Canada, Surveys and Mapping Branch, Ottawa, Ontario.

Mattocks, P.W. 1984. The winter season - northern Pacific coast region. American Birds 38:349-351.

_____. 1985a. The winter season - northern Pacific coast region. American Birds 39:201-204.

_____. 1985b. The spring season - northern Pacific coast region. American Birds 39:340-344.

_____. 1986a. The spring migration - northern Pacific coast region. American Birds 40:514-518.

_____. 1986b. The nesting season - northern Pacific coast region. American Birds 40(5):1244-1248.

Mattocks, P.W. and B. Harrington-Tweit. 1987. The autumn migration - northern Pacific coast region. American Birds 41:132-136.

_____. and _____. 1987a. The spring migration - northern Pacific Coast region. American Birds 41:478-482.

Mattocks, P.W. and E.S. Hunn. 1978. The spring season - northern Pacific coast region. American Birds 32:1045-1049.

_____. and _____. 1980. The autumn migration - northern Pacific coast region. American Birds 34:191-194.

_____. and _____. 1981. The winter season - northern Pacific coast region. American Birds 35:328-331.

_____. and _____. 1982. Spring migration - northern Pacific coast region. American Birds 36:886-888.

_____. and _____. 1983a. Spring migration - northern Pacific coast region. American Birds 37:903-906.

_____. and _____. 1983b. The nesting season - northern Pacific coast region. American Birds 37:1019-1022.

Mattocks, P.W., E.S. Hunn, and T.R. Wahl. 1976. A checklist of the birds of Washington state, with recent changes annotated. Western Birds 7:1-24.

Mattocks, P.W., B. Harrington-Tweit, and E.Hunn. 1983. The nesting season - northern Pacific coast region. American Birds 37:1019-1022.

Mayr, E. and L.L. Short. 1970. Species taxa of North American birds. Publications of the Nuttall Ornithological Club 9:1-127.

McAllister, N.M. 1958. Courtship, hostile behaviour, nest establishment, and egg laying in the Eared Grebe (*Podiceps caspicus*). Auk 75:290-311.

_____. 1963. Ontogeny of behaviour in five species of grebes. Ph.D. dissertation, University of British Columbia, Vancouver. 135 pp.

_____. N.M. 1980. Avian fauna from the Yuquot excavation. Pages 103-174 *in* W.J. Folan and J. Dewhirst (editors). The Yuquot project, volume 2. History and Archaeology 43. Parks Canada, Ottawa, Ontario.

McCabe, R.A. and A.S. Hawkins. 1946. The Hungarian Partridge in Wisconsin. American Midland Naturalist 36:1-75.

McCabe, T.R. 1976. First record of a Magnificent Frigatebird in inland Pacific Northwest. Murrelet 57:43-44.

McCabe, T.T. and I. McT. Cowan. 1945. *Peromyscus maniculatus macrorhinus* and the problem of insularity. Transactions of the Royal Canadian Institute 1945:117-215.

McCaskie, R.G. 1965. The Cattle Egret reaches the west coast of the United States. Condor 67:89.

_____. 1968. A Broad-winged Hawk in California. Condor 70:93.

_____. 1969. The fall migration - southern Pacific coast region. Audubon Field Notes 23:106-112.

_____. 1970. The occurrence of four species of Pelecaniformes in the southwestern United States. California Birds 1:117.

_____. 1973. A second look at the exotic waterfowl. Birding 5:45-47.

_____. 1979. The nesting season - southern Pacific coast region. American Birds 33:396-398.

_____. 1985. The winter season - southern Pacific coast region. American Birds 39:101-105.

McCourt, K.H. 1969. Dispersion and dispersal of female and juvenile Franklin's Grouse in lodgepole pine forest in southwestern Alberta. M.Sc. Thesis, University of Alberta, Edmonton. 137 pp.

McEwan, C. and W.G. Johnston. 1986. The spring migration - northwestern Canada region. American Birds 40:497-498.

_____. and _____. 1987. The autumn migration - northwestern Canada region. American Birds 41:116-118.

McEwan, E.H. and K. Fry. 1984. Food habits of wintering Dunlin (*Calidris alpina*). Canadian Wildlife Service Unpublished Report, Delta, British Columbia. 10 pp.

_____. and _____. 1986a. Activity budgets of Dunlin (*Calidris alpina*) overwintering in British Columbia. Canadian Wildlife Service Unpublished Report, Delta, British Columbia.

_____. and _____. 1986b. Foraging tactics of Dunlin (*Calidris alpina*). Canadian Wildlife Service Unpublished Report, Delta, British Columbia.

McEwan, E.H. and D.K. Gordon. 1985. Benthic invertebrates of Boundary Bay and Roberts Bank, British Columbia. Canadian Wildlife Service Unpublished Report, Delta, British Columbia. 18 pp.

McEwan, E.H. and P.M. Whitehead. 1984. Seasonal changes in body weight and composition of Dunlin (*Calidris alpina*). Canadian Journal of Zoology 62:154-156.

McFetridge, J. and J. Kirbyson. 1978. Mitlenatch interpretation report - 1978. British Columbia Parks Branch Unpublished Report, Victoria. 43 pp. (Bibliography 3546).

McGilvrey, F.B. 1966. Nesting of Hooded Mergansers on the Patuxent Wildlife Research Center, Laurel, Maryland. Auk 83:477-479.

McKay, W.A. 1957. This area could become fine game bird district past records show. Grand Forks Gazette, Grand Forks, British Columbia.

McKelvey, R.W. 1976. Fall aerial survey of marine birds and mammals off the British Columbia coast. Canadian Wildlife Service Unpublished Report, Delta, British Columbia. 8 pp. (Bibliography 3552).

_____. 1981a. Surveys of water birds in the Boudreau Lakes area, northeastern British Columbia. Canadian Wildlife Service Unpublished Report, Delta, British Columbia. 25 pp.

_____. 1981b. Some aspects of the winter feeding ecology of Trumpeter Swans at Port Alberni and Comox Harbour, British Columbia. M.Sc. Thesis, Simon Fraser University, Burnaby, British Columbia. 117 pp.

_____. 1986. The status of Trumpeter Swans in British Columbia and the Yukon, summer 1985. Canadian Wildlife Service Technical Report Series No. 8, Delta, British Columbia. 30 pp.

McKelvey, R.W. and C. Burton. 1983. A possible migration route for Trumpeter Swans (*Cygnus buccinator*) in British Columbia. Canadian Wildlife Service Progress Notes 138, Ottawa, Ontario. 4 pp.

McKelvey, R.W. and N.A.M. Verbeek. 1988. Habitat use, behaviour and management of Trumpeter Swans, *Cygnus buccinator*, wintering at Comox, British Columbia. Canadian Field-Naturalist 102:434-441.

McKelvey, R.W., I. Robertson, and P.E. Whitehead. 1978. The effect of non-petroleum oil spills on wintering birds near Vancouver, British Columbia. Canadian Wildlife Service Unpublished Report, Delta, British Columbia. 8 pp. (Bibliography 3560)

McKelvey, R.W., K.J. McCormick, and L.J. Shandruk. 1988. The status of Trumpeter Swans, *Cygnus buccinator*, in western Canada. Canadian Field-Naturalist 102:495-499.

McKinnon, D.T. and F.C. Zwickel. 1988. Length of incubation period of Blue Grouse. Murrelet 69:73-75.

McKnight, D.E. 1974. Dry-land nesting by Redheads and Ruddy Ducks. Journal of Wildlife Management 38:112-119.

McLandress, M.R. 1979. Status of Ross' Geese in California. Pages 255-265 *in* R.L. Jarvis and J.C. Bartonek (editors). Management and Biology of Pacific Flyway Geese. A symposium sponsored by the Northwest Section, The Wildlife Society, 16 February 1979, Portland, Oregon. Oregon State University Book Stores, Inc., Corvallis.

McLardy, R. 1983. The eighty-third Audubon Christmas Count - Pender Islands, B.C. American Birds 37:442-443.

McLaren, P.L. and M.A. McLaren. 1973. A sight record of the Ferruginous Hawk in British Columbia. Blue Jay 31:59.

McMannama, Z.V. 1951. Growth in the Glaucous-winged Gull, *Larus glaucescens*. M.Sc. Thesis, University of Washington, Seattle. 60 pp.

McMillan, W.J., A. Panteleyev, and T. Hoy. 1987. Mineral deposits in British Columbia: a review of their tectonic settings. Pages 1-18 *in* I.C. Elliott and B.W. Smee (editors). Proceedings of Exploration in the North American Cordillera. Association of Exploration Geochemists, May 12-14, 1986, Vancouver, British Columbia.

McNicholl, M.K. 1975. Sight record of White-throated Swift on Vancouver Island. Western Birds 6:10.

_____. 1988. Common Loon distribution and conservation problems in Canada. Pages 196-214 *in* P.I.V. Strong (editor). Papers from the 1987 Conference on Common Loon Research and Management. North American Loon Fund, Meredith, New Hampshire.

McNulty, F. 1966. The Whooping Crane: the bird that defies extinction. Clark, Irwin and Co., Ltd., Toronto. 190 pp.

Meehan, R.H. and R.J. Ritchie. 1982. Habitat requirements of Boreal and Hawk owls in interior Alaska. Pages 188-196 *in* W.N. Ladd and P.F. Schempf (editors). Proceedings of a Symposium and Workshop on Raptor Management and Biology in Alaska and Western Canada, February 17-20, 1981, Anchorage, Alaska. United States Department of the Interior, Fish and Wildlife Service Anchorage, Alaska.

Meidinger, D. (compiler). 1987. Recommended vernacular names for common plants of British Columbia. British Columbia Ministry of Forests and Lands, Research Branch, Victoria. 64 pp.

Mellen, T.K. 1987. Home range and habitat use of Pileated Woodpeckers, western Oregon. M.S. Thesis, Oregon State University, Corvallis. 96 pp.

Melville, D.S. 1984. Seabirds of China and the surrounding seas. Pages 501-511 *in* J.P. Croxell, P.G.H. Evans, and R.G. Schreiber (editors). Status and conservation of the world's seabirds. International Council for Bird Preservation Technical Publication No. 2, Cambridge, England.

Melvin, S.M. and S.A. Temple. 1982. Migration ecology of Sandhill Cranes: a review. Pages 73-87 *in* J.C. Lewis (editor). Proceedings 1981 Crane Workshop. National Audubon Society, Tavernier, Florida.

Mendall, H.L. 1958. The Ring-necked Duck in the northeast. University of Maine Bulletin No. 60, Orono. 317 pp.

Meng, H.K. 1951. The Cooper's Hawk. Ph.D. Thesis, Cornell University, Ithaca, New York. 216 pp.

Menzies, A. 1792. Menzies' Journal of Vancouver's voyage, April to October, 1792. *In* C.F. Newcombe (editor). Archives of British Columbia Memoir No. 5, Victoira, 1923. 171 pp.

Merilees, W.J. 1971. Observations of Turkeys in British Colum-bia. Blue Jay 29:25-27.

————. 1974a. Ring-billed and California gull nesting colony in south central British Columbia. Canadian Field-Naturalist 88:484-485.

————. 1974b. A Glaucous-winged Gull mated to a Herring Gull on Okanagan Lake, British Columbia. Canadian Field-Naturalist 88:485-486.

Merilees, W.J. and M. McNall. 1981. Cattle Egret update. Vancouver Natural History Society Discovery 10:18-20.

Merriam, C.H. 1890. Results of a biological survey of the San Francisco mountain region and desert of the Little Colorado in Arizona. North American Fauna No. 3:1-135.

Mershon, W.B. 1907. The Passenger Pigeon. Outing Publishing Company, New York.

Metras, L. 1986. Migratory birds killed in Canada during the 1985 season. Canadian Wildlife Service Progress Notes No. 166, Ottawa, Ontario. 42 pp.

Meugens, A.L. 1945. A trip to Bare Island. Victoria Naturalist 2:75-76.

Meugens, A.L. and J.K. Cooper. 1962. Notes on the bird fauna of the Richter Pass area. British Columbia Provincial Museum Unpublished Report, Victoria. 14 pp. (Bibliography 1999).

Middleton, H. 1949. Christmas bird census, 1948 - Vancouver, British Columbia. Canadian Field-Naturalist 63:65-66.

Miller, H.W., A. Dzubin, and J.T. Sweet. 1968. Distribution and mortality of Saskatchewan-banded White-fronted Geese. Transactions of the 33rd North American Wildlife and Natural Resources Conference: 101-118.

Mills, E.L. 1960a. Bird observations in the Queen Charlotte Islands, British Columbia. Canadian Field-Naturalist 74:156-158.

————. 1960b. Heermann's Gull in Barkley Sound, Vancouver Island. Canadian Field-Naturalist 74:162.

Millsap, B.A. 1986. Status of wintering Bald Eagles in the conterminous 48 states. Wildlife Society Bulletin 14:433-440.

Mindell, D.P. 1983. Harlan's hawk (*Buteo jamaicensis harlani*): a valid subspecies. Auk 100:161-169.

Mitchell, G.J. 1959. Bird observations at Tahsis Inlet, Vancouver Island, British Columbia. Canadian Field-Naturalist 73:6-13.

Mitchell, W.R. and R.E. Green. 1981. Identification and interpretation of ecosystems of the western Kamloops forest region. Volume 1. British Columbia Ministry of Forests Unpublished Report, Victoria.

Modafferi, R.D. 1975. Aspects of morphology in female Rock Ptarmigan (*Lagopus mutus*) during ovarian recrudescence. Ph.D. Thesis, University of Alaska, Fairbanks.

Moffit, J. 1939. Ninth annual Black Sea Brant census in California. California Fish and Game 25:335-342.

Moisan, G., R.I. Smith, and R.K. Martinson. 1967. The Green-winged Teal: its distribution, migration and population dynamics. United States Fish and Wildlife Service Special Scientific Report-Wildlife No. 100, Washington, D.C. 248 pp.

Monaghan, P. and N. Duncan. 1979. Plumage variation of known-age Herring Gulls. British Birds 72:100-103.

Monroe, B.L. 1973. Summary of all-time highest counts of individuals for Canada and the U.S. American Birds 27:541-547.

————. 1974. Summary of highest counts of individuals for Canada and the U.S. American Birds 28:568-576.

————. 1976. Summary of highest counts of individuals for Canada and the U.S. American Birds 30:637-641.

————. 1977. Summary of highest counts of individuals for Canada and the U.S. American Birds 31:910-915.

————. 1978. Summary of highest counts of individuals for Canada and the U.S. American Birds 32:924-930.

————. 1979. Summary of highest counts of individuals for Canada and the U.S. American Birds 33:703-707.

————. 1981. Summary of highest counts of individuals for Canada and the U.S. American Birds 35:758-762.

————. 1982. Summary of highest counts of individuals for Canada and the U.S. American Birds 36:779-783.

————. 1983. Summary of highest counts of individuals for Canada and the U.S. American Birds 37:793-796.

————. 1984. Summary of highest counts of individuals for Canada and the U.S. American Birds 38:837-839.

————. 1985a. Summary of highest counts of individuals for Canada and the U.S. American Birds 39:826-831.

————. 1985b. Summary of highest counts of individuals for Canada and the U.S. American Birds 39:832-834.

Morrison, K.P. 1969. Mourning Dove ecology in south-central British Columbia. M.Sc. Thesis, Colorado State University, Fort Collins. 116 pp.

Morse, D.H. 1970. Ecological aspects of some mixed species foraging flocks of birds. Ecological Monographs 40:119-168.

Morse, T.E., J.L. Jakabosky, and V.P. McCrow. 1969. Some aspects of the breeding biology of the Hooded Merganser. Journal of Wildlife Management 33:596-604.

Mousely, H. 1938. A study of the home life of the eastern Belted Kingfisher. Wilson Bulletin 50:3-12.

————. 1939. Home life of the American Bittern. Wilson Bulletin 51:83-85.

Moyle, J.B., F.B. Lee, R.L. Jessen, N.J. Ordal, R.I. Benson, J.P. Lindmeier, R.E. Farmes, and M.M. Nelson. 1964. Ducks and land use in Minnesota. Minnesota Department of Conservation Technical Bulletin No. 8, Minneapolis. 140 pp.

Mueller, H.C. and D.D. Berger. 1967. Some observations and comments on the periodic invasion of Goshawks. Auk 84:183-191.

Mueller, H.C., D.D. Berger, and G. Allez. 1976. Age and sex variation in the size of Goshawks. Bird-Banding 47:310-318.

————, ————, and ————. 1979a. Age and sex differences in size of Sharp-shinned Hawks. Bird-Banding 50:34-44.

————, ————, and ————. 1979b. The identification of North American accipiters. American Birds 33:236-240.

————, ————, and ————. 1981. Age, sex, and seasonal differences in size of Cooper's Hawks. Journal of Field Ornithology 52:112-126.

Mulholland, R. 1985. Habitat suitability index models: Lesser Scaup (wintering), United States Fish and Wildlife Service Biological Report 82 (10.91), Washington, D.C. 15 pp.

Munro, D. and K. Munro. 1987. Western Grebe a rare attraction. Salmon Arm Observer Newspaper, 6 May: 8.

Munro, D.A. 1947. A preliminary study of the waterfowl of Burnaby Lake, British Columbia. B.A. Thesis. University of British Columbia, Vancouver. 66 pp.

————. 1952. Ornithological investigations in British Columbia, 1950 and 1951. University of British Columbia Department of Zoology Unpublished Report, Vancouver. 122 pp. (Bibliography 3640).

————. 1953. Observations of Canada Geese in British Columbia and western Alberta in 1952. University of British Columbia Department of Zoology Unpublished Report, Vancouver. 33 pp. (Bibliography 3641).

————. 1954. Notes on the Western Grebe in British Columbia. Auk 71:333.

References Cited

Munro, J.A. 1917. Report on field work in Okanagan and Shuswap districts, 1916. Pages Q12-Q18 *in* Annual Report of the Provincial Museum of Natural History for 1916, Victoria, British Columbia.

_____. 1918. Notes on some British Columbia birds. Auk 35:234-235.

_____. 1919. Notes on some birds of the Okanagan valley, British Columbia. Auk 36:64-74.

_____. 1921. British Columbia bird notes, 1920-1. Murrelet 2:15-17.

_____. 1923. A preliminary report on the relation of various ducks and gulls to the propagation of sockeye salmon at Henderson Lake, Vancouver Island, British Columbia. Canadian Field-Naturalist 37:81-83; 107-116.

_____. 1925. The European Gray Partridge in the Okanagan valley, British Columbia. Canadian Field-Naturalist 29: 163-164.

_____. 1925a. Further notes from southern Vancouver Island, Canadian Field-Naturalist 39:156-158.

_____. 1925b. Some observations on Bare Island, B.C. Murrelet 6:55-57.

_____. 1927. Christmas bird census returns, 1926 - Okanagan Landing, British Columbia. Canadian Field-Naturalist 41:15.

_____. 1928. Horned owl migration in British Columbia. Auk 45:99.

_____. 1929a. A further note on the Horned Owl and Goshawk migration in British Columbia. Auk 46:387-388.

_____. 1929b. Status of sea birds on Bare Island, British Columbia, 1927. Canadian Field-Naturalist 43:167.

_____. 1935a. Recent records from British Columbia. Condor 37:178-179.

_____. 1935b. Bird life at Horse Lake, British Columbia. Condor 37:185-193.

_____. 1935c. Nesting colonies of the Herring Gull in British Columbia. Condor 37:214-215.

_____. 1935d. Glaucous Gull on the British Columbia coast. Condor 37:255-256.

_____. 1935e. Report of J.A. Munro, Okanagan Landing, B.C., summarizing activities for the month of March, 1935. Canadian Wildlife Service Unpublished Report, Delta, British Columbia. 33 pp. (Bibliography 3651).

_____. 1935f. Barrow's Goldeneye nesting in marmot's burrow. Condor 37:82-83.

_____. 1936a. A wader migration at Tlell, Queen Charlotte Islands, British Columbia. Condor 38:230-234.

_____. 1936b. Behaviour of White-fronted Goose at Tl-ell, Queen Charlotte Islands, B.C. Wilson Bulletin 48:137.

_____. 1936c. Water-fowl conditions in the Okanagan valley, April, May and June, 1936. Canadian Wildlife Service Unpublished Report, Delta, British Columbia. 6 pp. (Bibliography 3652).

_____. 1937. Nesting colonies of the Double-crested Cormorant in British Columbia. Pages K26-K30 *in* Annual report of the British Columbia Provincial Museum of Natural History for the year 1936, Victoria.

_____. 1938. Studies of waterfowl in the Cariboo region, British Columbia,1937-38. Canadian Wildlife Service Unpublished Report, Delta, British Columbia. 47 pp. (Bibliography 3657).

_____. 1939a. Studies of waterfowl in British Columbia - Barrow's Golden-eye, American Golden-eye. Transactions of the Royal Canadian Institute 22:259-318.

_____. 1939b. Nesting of the Western Grebe in British Columbia. Pages K16-K17 *in* Report of the Provincial Museum of Natural History for the year 1938, Victoria, British Columbia.

_____. 1939c. Waterfowl observations in the Okanagan district -October, 1939. Canadian Wildlife Service Unpublished Report, Delta, British Columbia. 4pp. (Bibliography 3661).

_____. 1939d. Waterfowl observations in the Okanagan district, British Columbia, November, 1939. Canadian Wildlife Service Unpublished Report, Delta, British Columbia. 3pp. (Bibliography 3662).

_____. 1939e. Food of ducks and coots at Swan Lake, British Columbia. Canadian Journal of Research D17: 178-186.

_____. 1939f. Studies of waterfowl in British Columbia 1938 (December) - 1939 covering parts of southern Vancouver Isand, Okanagan, Kamloops, Nicola and Cariboo. Canadian Wildlife Service Unpublished Report, Ottawa, Ontario.

_____. 1939g. Studies of waterfowl in British Columbia 1938 (December)-1939 covering parts of southern Vancouver Island, Okanagan, Kamloops, Nicola and Cariboo. Canadian Wildlife Service Unpublished Report, Ottawa, Ontario. 116 pp. (Bibliography 3658).

_____. 1941a. Studies of waterfowl in British Columbia - Greater Scaup Duck, Lesser Scaup Duck. Canadian Journal of Research D19:113-138.

_____. 1941b. The grebes: studies of waterfowl in British Columbia. British Columbia Provincial Museum Occasional Paper No.3, Victoria. 71 pp.

_____. 1942a. Studies of waterfowl in British Columbia - Bufflehead. Canadian Journal of Research D20:133-160.

_____. 1942b. Observations of waterfowl in British Columbia - September, October, November, 1942. Canadian Wildlife Service Unpublished Report, Delta, British Columbia. 15 pp. (Bibliography 3667).

_____. 1943. Studies of waterfowl in British Columbia - Mallard. Canadian Journal of Research D21:223-260.

_____. 1944. Studies of waterfowl in British Columbia. Canadian Wildlife Service Unpublished Report, Ottawa, Ontario. 8 pp. (Bibliography 3669).

_____. 1945a. Birds of the Cariboo parklands. Canadian Journal of Research D23:17-103.

_____. 1945b. Observations of waterfowl in southern British Columbia, 1944. Canadian Wildlife Service Unpublished Report, Ottawa, Ontario. 16pp. (Bibliography 3670).

_____. 1945c. Observations of the loon in the Cariboo Parklands, British Columbia. Auk 62:38-49.

_____. 1946. Birds and mammals of the Vanderhoof region, British Columbia, with comments on other resources. Canadian Wildlife Service Unpublished Report, Ottawa, Ontario. 161 pp.

_____. 1947a. Observations of birds and mammals in central British Columbia. British Columbia Provincial Museum Occasional Paper No. 6, Victoria. 165 pp.

_____. 1947b. A preliminary report on the Duck Lake area, British Columbia. Canadian Wildlife Service Unpublished Report, Delta, British Columbia. 19 pp. (Bibliography 3672).

_____. 1949. Studies of waterfowl in British Columbia - Green-winged Teal. Canadian Journal of Research D 27:149-178.

_____. 1949a. The birds and mammals of the Vanderhoof region, B.C. American Midland Naturalist 41:3-138.

_____. 1950. The birds and mammals of the Creston region, British Columbia. British Columbia Provincial Museum Occasional Paper No.8, Victoria. 90 pp.

_____. 1955a. Additional observations of birds and mammals in the Vanderhoof region, British Columbia. American Midland Naturalist 52:56-60.

_____. 1955b. A record of the Least Bittern in British Columbia. Murrelet 36:44.

_____. 1955c. The birds of the Cariboo parklands: a supplement. Pages 79-85 *in* Provincial Museum of Natural History and Anthropology Report for the year 1954, Victoria, British Columbia.

_____. 1958a. The birds and mammals of the Creston region, British Columbia: a supplement. Pages C65-C82 *in* British Columbia Provincial Museum of Natural History and Anthropology Report for the year 1957, Victoria, British Columbia.

_____. 1958b. The status of nesting waterfowl in the Cariboo parklands, British Columbia, in 1958. Canadian Wildlife Service Unpublished Report, Delta, British Columbia. 67 pp.

Munro, J.A. and W.A. Clemens. 1931. Waterfowl in relation to the spawning of herring in British Columbia. Bulletin of the Biological Board of Canada No. 17:1-46.

_____. and _____. 1937. The American Merganser in British Columbia and its relation to the fish population. Biological Board of Canada Bulletin No. 55, Ottawa, Ontario. 50 pp.

Munro, J.A. and I. Mc T. Cowan. 1947. A review of the bird fauna of British Columbia. British Columbia Provincial Museum Special Publication No. 2, Victoria. 285 pp.

Munro, W.T. 1967. Occurrence of the Fulvous Tree Duck in Canada. Canadian Field-Naturalist 81:151-152.

_____. 1979a. Preliminary Canada Goose management plan for British Columbia. British Columbia Fish and Wildlife Branch Report, Victoria. 15 pp. (Bibliography 3681).

_____. 1979b. Preliminary Brant management plan for British Columbia. British Columbia Ministry of Environment Fish and Wildlife Branch Report, Victoria. 18 pp. (Bibliography 3683).

Munro, W.T. and R.W. Campbell. 1979. Programs and authorities of the province of British Columbia related to marine bird conservation. Pages 247-250 *in* J.C. Bartonek and D.N. Nettleship (editors). Conservation of marine birds of northern North America. United States Department of the Interior Fish and Wildlife Service Wildlife Research Report No. 11, Washington, D.C.

Munro, W.T. and S.T. Goodchild. 1981. Preliminary duck management plan for British Columbia. British Columbia Ministry of Environment Unpublished Report, Victoria. 23 pp.

Munro, W.T. and R. McKelvey. 1983. Cooperative waterfowl management plan for British Columbia. British Columbia Ministry of Environment Unpublished Manuscript. Victoria. 29 pp.

Munro, W.T. and B. van Drimmelen. 1988. Status of peregrines in the Queen Charlotte Islands, British Columbia. Pages 69-72 *in* T.J. Cade, J.H. Enderson, C.G. Thelander, and C.M. White (editors). Peregrine Falcon populations - their management and recovery. The Peregrine Fund, Inc. Boise, Idaho.

Munyer, E.A. 1965. Inland wanderings of the Ancient Murrelet. Wilson Bulletin 77:235-242.

Murphy, D. 1984. Burrowing Owl project (1984). British Columbia Wildlife Branch Unpublished Report, Kamloops. 24 pp.

Myres, M.T. 1957. Clutch size and laying dates in Cliff Swallow colonies. Condor 59:311-316.

_____. 1986. Thomas W. Blakiston, Charles Waterton and John George Brown, and their interconnected associations with Waterton Lakes National Park, Alberta. Alberta Naturalist 16:29-31.

Myres, M.T., and S.R. Cannings. 1971. A Canada Goose migration through the southern interior of British Columbia. Pages 23-34 *in* Studies of Bird Hazards to Aircraft. Canadian Wildlife Service Report Series No.14, Ottawa, Ontario.

Myres, M.T. and J.R. Guzman. 1976-1977. Ecology and behaviour of southern hemisphere shearwater (genus *Puffinus*) and other seabirds, when over the Outer Continental Shelf of the Bering Sea and Gulf of Alaska during the northern summer. Environmental Assessment of the Alaskan Continental Shelf, Principal Investigator's Reports, for the year ending March 1977, Vol.3, Pages 179-191. United States Department of Commerce, National Oceanic and Atmospheric Administration, and United States Department of the Interior, Bureau of Land Management, Boulder, Colorado.

Myres, M.T., I.McT. Cowan and M.D.F. Udvardy. 1957. The British Columbia nest records scheme. Condor 59:308-310.

Nagy, A.C. 1977. Population trend indices based on 40 years of autumn counts at Hawk Mountain Sanctuary in north-eastern Pennsylvania. Pages 243-253 *in* R.D. Chancellor (editor). World Conference on Birds of Prey (1975). Report of Proceedings of the International Council for Bird Preservation. Cambridge, England.

National Audubon Society. 1983. The Audubon Society Master Guide to Birding. Volumes 1 and 2. Alfred A. Knopf, New York. 845 pp.

National Geographic Society. 1983. Field Guide to the birds of North America. National Geographic Society, Washington, D.C. 464 pp.

Neff, J.A. 1947. Habits, food, and economic status of the Band-tailed Pigeon. United States Fish and Wildlife Service North American Fauna No.58, Washington, D.C. 76 pp.

Nelson, B. 1979. Seabirds: their biology and ecology. A & W Publishers Inc., New York. 224 pp.

Nelson, R.W. 1970. Some aspects of the breeding behavior of peregrines on Langara Island, British Columbia. M.Sc. Thesis, University of Calgary, Alberta. 306 pp.

_____. 1977. Behavioral ecology of coastal peregrine (*Falco peregrinus pealei*). Ph.D. Thesis, University of Calgary, Alberta. 490 pp.

Nelson, R.W. and M.T. Myres. 1976. Declines in populations of Peregrine Falcons and their seabird prey at Langara Island, British Columbia. Condor 78:281-293.

Nelson, U.C. and H.A. Hansen. 1959. The cackling goose - its migration and management. Transactions of the North America Wildlife Conference 24:174-187.

Nero, R.W. 1969. The status of the Great Gray Owl in Manitoba, with special reference to the 1968-69 influx. Blue Jay 27:191-209.

_____. 1980. The Great Gray Owl - phantom of the northern forest. Smithsonian Institution Press, Washington, D.C. 167 pp.

Nettleship, D.N. 1973. Breeding ecology of turnstones *Arenaria interpres* at Hazen Camp, Ellesmere Island, N.W.T. Ibis 115:202-217.

_____. 1976. Census techniques for seabirds of arctic eastern Canada. Canadian Wildlife Service Occasional Paper No. 25, Ottawa, Ontario. 33 pp.

Newton, I. 1979. Population ecology of raptors. Buteo Books, Vermillion, South Dakota. 339 pp.

Nichols, J.T. 1927. Tubinares off the north-west coast. Auk 44:326-327.

Noble, M.D. 1972. Blue geese observation in British Columbia. Murrelet 53:13.

Norton, D.W. 1971. Two Soviet recoveries of Dunlins banded at Point Barrow, Alaska. Auk 88:927.

Nuechterlein, G.L. 1981. Courtship behavior and reproductive isolation between Western Grebe color morphs. Auk 98: 335-349.

O'Brien, D. 1974. Manning Park avifauna report - summer 1974. British Columbia Parks Branch Unpublished Report, Victoria. 12 pp. (Bibliography 3790).

O'Brien, D. and K.M. Bell. 1975. The avifauna of Bowron Lake Provincial Park - report for summer 1975. British Columbia Parks Branch Unpublished Report, Victoria. 22 pp. (Bibliography 3791).

Odlum, G.C. 1952. Banding at the Triple Island lightstation. News from the Bird-Banders 27:34.

O'Donald, P. 1983. The Arctic Skua: a study of the ecology and evolution of a seabird. Cambridge University Press, London, England 324 pp.

Oeming, A.F. 1955a. A preliminary study of the Great Gray Owl (*Scotiaptex nebulosa nebulosa* Forster) in Alberta with observations on some other species of owls. M.Sc. Thesis, University of Alberta, Edmonton.

_____. 1955b. In quest of the rare Great Gray Owl. Canadian Geographical Journal 73:236-243.

Ogden, V.T. 1973. Nesting density and reproductive success of the Prairie Falcon in southwesern Idaho. M.S. Thesis, University of Idaho, Moscow. 43 pp.

Ogi, H. 1984. Seabird mortality incidental to the Japanese salmon gill-net fishery. Pages 717-722 *in* J.P. Croxall, P.G.H. Evans and R.W. Schreiber (editors). Status and conservation of the world's seabirds. International Council for Bird Preservation Technical Report No. 2. Cambridge, England.

Ohanjanian, I.A. 1986a. Effects of a man-made dyke on the reproductive behavior and nesting success of Red-necked Grebes. M.Sc. thesis, Simon Fraser University, Burnaby. 83 pp.

_____. 1986b. The Long-billed Curlew in the east Kootenay - status report and enhancement schedule for Skookumchuck Prairie. British Columbia Wildlife Branch Unpublished Report, Cranbrook. 12 pp.

Oldaker, R.F. 1960. Band reading by telescope. News from the Bird-Banders 35:39-42.

_____. 1961. Survey of the California Gull. Western Bird Bander 36:26-30.

_____. 1963a. Unusual nest site of the Glaucous-winged Gull. Canadian Field-Naturalist 77:65-66.

_____. 1963b. Sight records of banded California Gulls. Western Bird Bander 38:7-10.

Oliphant, L.W. 1985, North American Merlin breeding survey. Raptor Research 19:37-41.

Oliphant, L.W. and E. Haug. 1985. Productivity, population density and rate of increase of an expanding Merlin population. Raptor Research 19:56-59.

Oliphant, L.W. and W.J.P. Thompson. 1978. Recent breeding success of Richardson's Merlin in Saskatchewan. Raptor Research 12: 35-39.

Olson, S.T. and W.H. Marshall. 1952. The Common Loon in Minnesota. Minnesota Museum of Natural History Occasional Papers No. 5, Minneapolis 77 pp.

Orcutt, L. 1967. Intermediate naturalists are busy birders. Vancouver Natural History Society News 134:5-8.

Orians, G. and F. Kuhlman. 1956. The Red-tailed Hawk and Great Horned Owl populations in Wisconsin. Condor 58:371-385.

Oring, L.W. 1966. Breeding biology and molts of the Gadwall, *Anas strepera* Linnaeus. Ph.D. Thesis, University of Oklahoma, Norman. 103 pp.

_____. 1968. Growth, molts, and plumages of the Gadwall. Auk 85:355-380.

_____. 1969. Summer biology of the Gadwall of Delta, Manitoba. Wilson Bulletin 81:44-54.

_____. 1973. Solitary Sandpiper early reproductive behavior. Auk 90:652-663.

Oring, L.W. and S.J. Maxon. 1978. Instances of simultaneous polyandry by a Spotted Sandpiper (*Actitis macularia*). Ibis 120:349-353.

Osgood, W.H. 1901. Natural History of the Queen Charlotte Islands, British Columbia - the Cook Inlet region Alaska. United States Department of Agriculture, Division of Biological Survey, North American Fauna 21:1-87.

Osmond-Jones, E.J., M. Sather, W.G. Hazelwood and B. Ford. 1977. Spatsizi and Tatlatui wilderness parks: an inventory of wildlife, fisheries, and recreational values in a northern wilderness park. British Columbia Parks Branch, Victoria. 292 pp.

Ouelet, H. 1987. Profile of a pioneer: P.A. Taverner. American Birds 41:20-25.

Owen, D.F. 1963a. Variation in North American screech owls and their sub-species concept. Systematic Zoology 12:8-14.

Pacific Flyway Study Committee. 1982. Pacific flyway management plan for the Pacific flyway population of lesser sandhill cranes. Pacific Flyway Council, c/o United States Fish and Wildlife Service, Portland, Oregon. 19 pp.

Pacific Flyway Study Committee. 1982a. Pacific flyway management plan for the Central Valley population of greater sandhill cranes. Pacific Flyway Council, c/o United States Fish and Wildlife Service, Portland, Oregon.

Page, G., B. Fearis and R.M. Jurek. 1972. Age and sex composition of Western Sandpipers on Bolinas Lagoon. California Birds 3:79-86.

Page, R. and A.T. Bergerud. 1979. The caribou calf mortality study-1979: a progress report. University of Victoria Department of Biology Unpublished Report, Victoria, British Columbia. 65 pp. (Bibliography 3808).

Palmer, D.A. 1986. Habitat selection, movements, and activity of Boreal and Saw-whet Owls. M.Sc. Thesis, Colorado State University, Fort Collins. 101 pp.

Palmer, R.S. (editor). 1962. Handbook of North American birds: Volume 1. Loons through Flamingos. Yale University Press, New Haven, Connecticut. 567 pp.

_____. 1967. Buff-breasted Sandpiper. Pages 212-214 *in* G.P. Stout (editor). The shorebirds of North America. Viking Press, New York.

_____. 1976a. Handbook of North American birds. Volume 2. Waterfowl (Part 1). Yale University Press, New Haven, Connecticut. 521 pp.

_____. 1976b. Handbook of North American birds. Volume 3. Waterfowl concluded. Yale University Press, New Haven, Connecticut. 560 pp.

_____. 1988a. Handbook of North American birds: Volume 4. Diurnal Raptors (Part 1). Yale University Press, New Haven, Connecticut. 433 pp.

_____. 1988b. Handbook of North American Birds: Volume 5. Diurnal Raptors (Part 2). Yale University Press, New Haven, Connecticut. 465 pp.

Parham, H.J. 1937. A nature lover in British Columbia. H.F. and G. Witherby Ltd., London. 292 pp.

Parkham, C.H. 1950. Two uncommon birds from Westport, Washington. Murrelet 31:46.

Parkin, D.T. and J.M. McMeeking. 1985. The increase of Canada Geese in Nottinghamshire from 1980. Bird Study 32:132-140.

Parmelee, D.F. and S.D. MacDonald. 1960. The birds of west-central Ellesmere Island and adjacent areas. National Museum of Canada Bulletin No. 169, Ottawa, Ontario. 103 pp.

Parmelee, D.F., D.W. Greiner, and W.D. Graul. 1968. Summer schedule and breeding biology of the White-rumped Sandpiper in the central Canadian Arctic. Wilson Bulletin 80:1-29.

Patch, C.A. 1922. A biological reconnaisance on Graham Island of the Queen Charlotte group. Canadian Field-Naturalist 36:101-105, 133-136.

Patten, S.M. 1974. Breeding ecology of the Glaucous-winged Gull (*Larus glaucescens*) in Glacier Bay, Alaska. M.Sc. Thesis, University of Washington, Seattle. 78 pp.

Patten, S. and A.R. Weisbrod. 1974. Sympatry and interbreeding of Herring and Glaucous-winged Gulls in southeastern Alaska. Condor 76:343-344.

Paul, W.A.B. 1959. The birds of Kleena Kleene, Chilcotin district, British Columbia, 1947-1958. Canadian Field-Naturalist 73:83-93.

_____. 1964. Birds of Kleena Kleene, Chilcotin district, British Columbia, 1959-1962. Canadian Field-Naturalist 78:13-16.

Paulson, D.R. 1986. Identification of juvenile tattlers, and a Gray-tailed Tattler record from Washington. Western Birds 17:33-36.

Payne, R.B. 1965. The molt of breeding Cassin Auklets. Condor 67:220-228.

Payne, R.B. and L.L. Master. 1983. Breeding of a mixed pair of white-shielded and red-shielded American Coots in Michigan. Wilson Bulletin 95:467-469.

Payne, R.B. and C.J. Risley. 1976. Systematics and evolutionary relationships among the herons. University of Michigan Museum of Zoology Miscellaneous Publication No. 150, Ann Arbor.

Peakall, D.B. 1965. The status of the Ruff in North America. Wilson Bulletin 77:294-296.

Pearse, T. 1923. Banding Glaucous-winged Gulls with other notes on a colony in southern British Columbia. Canadian Field-Naturalist 37:132-135.

_____. 1926. Notes on the birds seen on a trip off the east coast of Vancouver Island, June 1924. Migrant 3:37-39.

_____. 1931. The Burrowing Owl on Vancouver Island, British Columbia. Murrelet 12:81-82.

_____. 1935. Red Phalaropes on Vancouver Island. Murrelet 16:16-17.

_____. 1936. A record of the Passenger Pigeon in B.C. Auk 53:446-447.

_____. 1946. Nesting of the Western Gull off the coast of Vancouver Island, British Columbia, and possible hybridization with the Glaucous-winged Gull. Murrelet 27:39-40.

_____. 1947. Abnormal plumage of Glaucous-winged Gulls. Murrelet 28:39-40.

_____. 1948. The 1948 spring migration at Comox, B.C. Canadian Field-Naturalist 5:29-32.

_____. 1953. Franklin Gull on the Pacific coast of British Columbia. Condor 54:219.

_____. 1956. Changes in breeding populations of pelagic birds in the Gulf of Georgia, B.C. Murrelet 37:22-23.

_____. 1960. Christmas bird census, 1959-1960 - Comox, British Columbia. Canadian Field-Naturalist 74:44.

_____. 1963. Results from banding Glaucous-winged Gulls in the northern Gulf of Georgia, B.C., from 1922 to 1949. Bird-Banding 34:30-36.

_____. 1968. Birds of the early explorers in the northern Pacific. Published by the author, The Close, Comox, British Columbia. 275 pp.

Pearson, T.G. 1919. Turkey Vulture. Bird-Lore 21:319-322.

Peck, G.K. and R.D. James. 1983. Breeding birds of Ontario - nidiology and distribution - Volume 1: Nonpasserines. Royal Ontario Museum Life Sciences Miscellaneous Publication, Toronto, Ontario. 321 pp.

Pendergast, B.A. 1969. Nutrition of Spruce Grouse of the Swan Hills, Alberta. M.Sc. Thesis, University of Alberta, Edmonton. 73 pp.

Pendergast, B.A. and D.A. Boag. 1971. Maintenance and breeding of Spruce Grouse in captivity. Journal of Wildlife Management 35:177-179.

Penland, S.T. 1976. The natural history and current status of the Caspian Tern (*Hydroprogne caspia*) in Washington state. M.S. Thesis, University of Puget Sound, Tacoma, Washington.

_____. 1981. Natural history of the Caspian Tern in Gray's Harbor, Washington. Murrelet 62:66-72.

Pennant, T. 1785. Arctic Zoology, Volume 2, Class 2, Birds. London, England.

Penner, D.F. 1976. Peace River sites C and E environmental impact studies: wildlife resources. Renewable Resources Consulting Services Report, Edmonton, Alberta. 307 pp.

Peters, F.L. and successors. 1931-1979. Check-list of birds of the world. Volumes 1-10, 12-15. Museum of Comparative Zoology, Cambridge, Massachusetts.

Peters, J.L. 1931. Check-list of birds of the world. Volume 1. Harvard University Press, Cambridge, Massachusetts. 345 pp.

_____. 1934. Check-list of birds of the world. Volume 2. Harvard University Press, Cambridge, Massachusetts. 401 pp.

Peterson, B. and G. Gauthier. 1985. Nest site use by cavity-nesting birds of the Cariboo parkland, British Columbia. Wilson Bulletin 97:319-331.

Peterson, R.T. 1961. Bird's-eye view. Audubon 63:73.

Phillips, A.R. 1975. Semipalmated Sandpiper: identification, migrations, summer, and winter ranges. American Birds 29:799-806.

Phillips, J.C. 1928. Wild birds introduced or transplanted in North America. United States Department Agriculture Bulletin 61, Washington, D.C. 63 pp.

Phillips, J.H. 1963. The pelagic distribution of the Sooty Shearwater, *Procellaria grisea*. Ibis 105:340-353.

Pierce, D.J. and T.R. Simons. 1986. The influence of human disturbance on Tufted Puffin breeding success. Auk 103:214-216.

Pitelka, F.A. 1942. Territoriality and related problems in North American hummingbirds. Condor 44:189-204.

_____. 1950. Geographic variation and the species problem in the genus *Limnodromus*. University of California Publications in Zoology 50:1-108.

Pitman, R.L. and M.R. Graybill. 1985. Horned Puffin sightings in the eastern Pacific. Western Birds 16:99-102.

Pitman, R., M. Newcomer, J. Butler, J. Cotton, and G. Friedrichsen. 1983. A Crested Auklet from Baja California. Western Birds 14:47-48.

Pojar, J. 1980. Threatened forest ecosystems of British Columbia. Pages 28-39 in R. Stace-Smith, L. Johns, and P. Joslin (editors). Proceedings of the Symposium on Threatened and Endangered Species and Habitats in British Columbia and the Yukon. British Columbia Ministry of Environment, Victoria.

_____. 1983. Forest ecology. Pages 221-318 in S.B. Watts (editor). Forestry Handbook for British Columbia, 4th edition. University of British Columbia Faculty of Forestry, Vancouver.

Pojar, J., K. Klinka, and D.V. Meidinger. 1987. Biogeoclimatic classification in British Columbia. Forestry Ecology and Management 22:119-154.

Poll, D.M., M.M. Porter, G.L. Holroyd, R.M. Wershler, and L.W. Gyug. 1984. Ecological land classification of Kootenay National Park. Volume II. Wildlife resource. Canadian Wildlife Service, Edmonton. 260 pp.

Poole, F. 1966. Birds of the North Pacific. Sea Swallow 18:71-74.

Portenko, L. 1944. New subspecies of birds from Wrangel Island. C.R. (Doklady) Academy of Sciences U.R.S.S. 43:225-228.

Porter, J.M. 1980. The dynamics of seabird multispecies flocks in Barkley Sound, British Columbia. M.Sc. Thesis, University of Manitoba, Winnipeg. 135 pp.

Porter, J.M. and S.G. Sealy. 1981. Dynamics of seabird multispecies feeding flocks: chronology of flocking in Barkley Sound, British Columbia, in 1979. Colonial Waterbirds 4:104-113.

Porter, R.D., M.A. Jenkins, and A.L. Gaski. 1987. Working bibliography of the Peregrine Falcon. National Wildlife Federation Scientific and Technical Series No. 9, Washington, D.C. 185 pp.

Pospahala, R.S., D.R. Anderson, and C.J. Henny. 1974. Population ecology of the Mallard: II. Breeding habitat conditions, size of the breeding populations, and production indices. United States Department of the Interior Fish and Wildlife Service Resource Publication 115, Washington, D.C. 73 pp.Poston, H.J. 1974. Home range and breeding biology of the Shoveler. Canadian Wildlife Service Report Series No. 25, Ottawa, Ontario. 49 pp.

Potapov, R.L. 1985. Fauna of the USSR: birds. Volume III. Order Galliformes, Family Tetraonidae. Science Institute, Leningrad (In Russian).

Poynter, G.A. 1958. Bird notes. Victoria Naturalist 15:5-6.

_____. 1959. Discovery Island birds. Victoria Naturalist 16:37.

_____. 1960. A report on the birds of the lower Vancouver Island region for the year of 1959. Victoria Natural History Society Mimeo, Victoria. 27 pp. (Bibliography 308).

_____. 1972. British Columbia record of Snowy Plover. Vancouver Natural History Society Discovery 1:69-70.

_____. 1976. Glaucous-winged Gulls - unusual nesting sites. Vancouver Natural History Society Discovery 5:8-10.

Pratt, H.D. 1976. Field identification of White-faced and Glossy ibises. Birding 8:1-5.

Preble, E.A. 1922. Roderick Ross Macfarlane, 1833-1920. Auk 37:203-210.

Preece, W.H.A. 1925a. An Ivory Gull, *Pagophila alba* Gunn., observed at Victoria. British Columbia. Canadian Field-Naturalist 39:172-173.

_____. 1925b. January bird notes from Mount Tolmie, Victoria, British Columbia. Canadian Field-Naturalist 39:175-176.

Prose, B.L. 1985. Habitat suitability index models: Belted Kingfisher. United States Department of the Interior Fish and Wildlife Service Biological Report 82(10.87), Washington, D.C. 22 pp.

Pullianen, E. and K. Loisa. 1977. Breeding biology and food of the Great Gray Owl, *Strix nebulosa*, in northeastern Finnish Forest Lapland. Aquilo Serie. Zoologica 17:23-33.

Purdy, M.A. 1985. Parental behaviour and role differentiation in the Black Oystercatcher *Haematopus bachmani*. M.Sc. Thesis, University of Victoria, Victoria, British Columbia. 239 pp.

Purdy, R.M. 1978. The effect of radiant energy on the energy and activity budgets of the Rufous Hummingbird (*Selasphorus rufus*). B.Sc. Thesis, University of British Columbia, Vancouver. 104 pp.

Pyle, R. and J. Sarles. 1958. Glaucous-winged Gull banding sponsored by Pacific International Chapter, summer, 1958. News from the Bird-Banders 33:36-37.

Quinlan, S.E. 1979. Breeding biology of storm-petrels at Wooded Islands, Alaska. M.Sc. Thesis. University of Alaska, Fairbanks. 206 pp.

Racey, K. 1921. Notes on the Northwest coast Heron in Stanley Park, Vancouver, B.C. Canadian Field-Naturalist 35:118-119.

_____. 1926. Notes on the birds observed in the Alta Lake region, British Columbia. Auk 43:319-325.

_____. 1933. White Pelican (*Pelecanus erythrorhynchos*) in British Columbia. Auk 50:205.

_____. 1944. Extension of range of the Northern Spotted Owl (*Strix occidentalis caurina*). Canadian Field-Naturalist 58:104.

_____. 1945. Bird nesting notes from western British Columbia. Murrelet 26:38,46.

_____. 1946. Nesting of the Black Oystercatcher in B.C. Victoria Naturalist 2:138.

_____. 1947. Pallas' Murre in British Columbia. Canadian Field-Naturalist 61:116.

_____. 1948. Birds of the Alta Lake region, British Columbia. Auk 63:383-401.

_____. 1950. The Steller Eider in British Columbia. Canadian Field-Naturalist 64:51.

Rand, A.L. 1944. Birds of the Alaska Highway in British Columbia. Canadian Field-Naturalist 58:111-125.

Ransom, W.H. 1938. Yellow Rail (*Coturnicops noveboracensis*) recorded in the State of Washington. Murrelet 19:16.

Ratti, J.T. 1979. Reproductive separation and isolating mechanisms between sympatric dark- and light-phase Western Grebes. Auk 96:573-586.

_____. 1981. Identification and distribution of Clark's Grebe. Western Birds. 12:41-46.

Ratti, J.T. and D.E. Timm. 1979. Migratory behavior of Vancouver Canada geese: recovery rate bias. Pages 208 to 212 *in* R.L. Jarvis and J.C. Bartonek (editors). Management and Biology of Pacific Flyway Geese. A symposium sponsored by the Northwest Section, The Wildlife Society, 16 February 1979, Portland, Oregon. Oregon State University Book Stores, Inc., Corvallis.

Rawls, C.K. 1949. An investigation of the life history of the White-winged Scoter (*Melanitta fusca deglandi*). M.Sc. Thesis, University of Minnesota, Rochester. 128 pp.

Redfield, J.A. 1973. Variations in weight of Blue Grouse (*Dendragapus obscurus*). Condor 75:312-321.

Redmond, R.L. 1986. Egg size and laying date of Long-billed Curlews *Numenius americanus*: implications for female reproductive tactics. Oikos 46:330-338.

Redmond, R.L. and D.A. Jenni. 1982. Natal philopatry and breeding area fidelity of Long-billed Curlews (*Numenius americanus*): patterns and evolutionary consequences. Behavioural Ecology and Sociobiology 10:277-279.

_____. and _____. 1986. Population ecology of the Long-billed Curlew (*Numenius americanus*) in western Idaho. Auk 103:755-767.

Reese, J.G. 1975. Productivity and management of feral Mute Swans in Chesapeake Bay. Journal of Wildlife Management 39:280-286.

Reid, T.C. 1975. Liard River Hotsprings Park - natural history observations (autumn, 1974 and winter, spring, summer - 1975). British Columbia Parks Branch Unpublished Report, Victoria. 117 pp. (Bibliography 3893).

Reimchen, T.E. and S. Douglas. 1980. Observations of loons (*Gavia immer* and *G. stellata*) at a bog lake on the Queen Charlotte Islands. Canadian Field-Naturalist 94:398-404.

_____. and _____. 1984. Feeding schedule and daily food consumption in Red-throated Loons (*Gavia stellata*) over the prefledging period. Auk 101:593-599.

_____. and _____. 1985. Differential contribution of the sexes of prefledged young in Red-throated Loons. Auk 102:198-201.

Remsen, J.V. and L.C. Binford. 1975. Status of the Yellow-billed Loon (*Gavia adamsii*) in the western United States and Mexico. Western Birds 6:7-20.

Reynolds, R.T. 1983. Management of western coniferous forest habitat for nesting accipiter hawks. United States Department of Agriculture, Forest Service, General Technical Report RM-102, Fort Collins, Colorado. 7 pp.

Reynolds, R.T. and B.D. Linkhart. 1987a. Fidelity to territory and mate in Flammulated Owls. Pages 234-238 *in* R.W. Nero, R.J. Clark, R.J. Knapton, and R.H. Hamre (editors). Biology and Conservation of Northern Forest Owls: Symposium Proceedings. 1987 Feb. 3-7; Winnipeg, Manitoba. United States Department of Agriculture Forest Service General Technical Report RM-142, Fort Collins, Colorado.

_____. and _____. 1987b. The nesting biology of Flammulated Owls in Colorado. Pages 239-248 *in* R.W. Nero, R.J. Clark, R.J. Knapton, and R.H. Hamre (editors). Biology and Conservation of Northern Forest Owls: Symposium Proceedings. 1987 Feb. 3-7; Winnipeg, Manitoba. United States Department of Agriculture Forest Service General Technical Report RM-142, Fort Collins, Colorado.

Reynolds, R.T. and H.M. Wight. 1978. Distribution, density, and productivity of accipiter hawks breeding in Oregon. Wilson Bulletin 90:182-196.

Rhoads, S.N. 1891. The wild pigeon (*Ectopistes migratorius*) on the Pacific Coast. Auk 8:310-312.

_____. 1893a. The birds observed in British Columbia and Washington during spring and summer, 1892. Proceedings of the Academy of Natural Sciences of Philadelphia 45:21-65.

_____. 1893b. Notes on certain Washington and British Columbia birds. Auk 10:16-24.

Rice, D.W. 1959. Birds and aircraft on Midway Island - 1957-58 investigations. United States Department of the Interior, Fish and Wildlife Service Special Scientific Report - Wildlife No. 44, Washington, D.C. 49 pp.

Rice, D.W. and K.W. Kenyon. 1962. Breeding distribution, history, and populations of north Pacific albatrosses. Auk 79:365-386.

Richardson, F. 1961. Breeding biology of the Rhinoceros Auklet on Protection Islands, Washington. Condor 63:456-473.

_____. 1970. A North American record of the Bristle-thighed Curlew outside Alaska. Auk 87:815.

_____. 1971. Birds of Grant Bay and Browning Inlet, northwest Vancouver Island, British Columiba: a years phenology. Murrelet 52:29-40.

Richdale, L.E. 1963. Biology of the Sooty Shearwater, *Puffinus griseus*. Proceedings of the Zoological Society of London 141:1-117.

Ricker, W.E. 1937. Christmas bird census, 1936. Vedder Crossing, British Columbia, December 28, 1936. Canadian Field-Naturalist 51:27.

Rieck, C.A. 1962. A Common Egret in western Washington. Murrelet 43:52.

Riley, J.H. 1912. Birds collected or observed on the expedition of the Alpine Club of Canada to Jasper Park, Yellowhead Pass and Mount Robson region. Canadian Alpine Journal 1912:47-75.

Riske, M. 1976. Environmental and human impacts of grebes breeding in central Alberta. Ph.D. Thesis, University of Calgary, Calgary, Alberta.

Ritcey, R.W. 1953. Winter wildlife report - Wells Gray Park, 1952-1953. British Columbia Forest Service, Unpublished Report, Victoria. 56 pp. (Bibliography 3919).

_____. 1956. Report on Tweedsmuir reconnaisance - summer 1956. British Columbia Forest Service, Parks and Recreation Division Unpublished Report, Victoria. 55 pp. (Bibliography 3920).

_____. 1985. Progress Report - Thompson owls. British Columbia Wildlife Branch Unpublished Report, Kamloops. 6 pp.

Ritcey, R.W. and N.A.M. Verbeek. 1961. An annotated list of birds, Bowron Lake Park, 1961. British Columbia Provincial Park Unpublished Report, Victoria. 12 pp. (Bibliography 920).

Ritter, L.V. 1983. Growth, development, and behavior of nestling Turkey Vultures in central California. Pages 287-303 *in* S.R. Wilbur and J.A. Jackson (editors). Vulture biology and management. University of California Press, Berkeley.

Robbins, C.S. 1974. A history of North American hawkwatching. Pages 29-40 *in* Proceedings of the 1974 North American Hawk Migration Conference. Syracuse, New York, 18-21 April. 165 pp.

Roberson, D. 1980. Rare birds of the west coast of North America. Woodcock Publications, Pacific Grove, California. 496 pp.

Roberts, A. 1973. Birds of the Cariboo. Williams Lake Field Naturalists Club, Williams Lake. 11 pp. (Bibliography 1108).

Roberts, H.A. 1963. Aspects of the life history and food habits of Rock and Willow ptarmigan. M.Sc. Thesis, University of Alaska, Fairbanks. 108 pp.

Robertson, I. 1971. The influence of brood-size on reproductive success in two species of cormorant, *Phalacrocorax auritus* and *P. pelagicus*, and its relation to the problem of clutch-size. M.Sc. Thesis, University of British Columbia, Vancouver. 47 pp.

_____. 1974. An inventory of seabirds occurring along the west coast of Canada. Part II: the shoreline and inlet zone. Canadian Wildlife Service Unpublished Report, Delta, British Columbia. 64 pp. (Bibliography 3935).

_____. 1974a. The food of nesting Double-crested and Pelagic cormorants at Mandarte Island, British Columbia, with notes on feeding ecology. Condor 76:346-348.

Robinson, W.F. 1974. The greater Sandhill Cranes of the Pitt Polder. Issued by the author, Pitt Meadows, British Columbia. 24 pp. (Bibliography 1238)

Rodway, M.S. 1988. British Columbia Seabird Colony Inventory: Report No. 3-Census of Glaucous-winged Gulls, Pelagic Cormorants, Black Oystercatchers, and Pigeon Guillemots in the Queen Charlotte Islands, 1986. Canadian Wildlife Service Technical Report Series No. 43, Delta, British Columbia. 95 pp.

_____. 1989a. Distribution and abundance of waterbirds in Barkley Sound and the Long Beach/Tofino/Grice Bay area in spring 1989 following the Nestucca oil spill. Canadian Wildlife Service Technical Report Series No. 76, Delta, British Columbia.

_____. 1port on the Marbled Murrelet (*Brachyramphus marmoratus*) in Canada - 1990. Committee on the Status of Endange in Canada Report, Canadian Nature Federation, Ottawa, Ontario. 58 pp.

_____. In press. Status and conservation of breeding seabirds in British Columbia. Submitted to J.P. Croxall (editor). Status and conservation of the world's seabirds. International Council for Bird Preservation, Cambridge, England.

Rodway, M.S. and R.W. Campbell. 1977. Natural history theme study of marine bird and mammal habitats in the Gulf Islands, British Columbia. Parks Canada Unpublished Report, Ottawa, Ontario. 107 pp. (Bibliography 1900).

Rodway, M.S., N. Hillis, and L. Langley. 1983. Nesting population of Ancient Murrelets on Langara Island, British Columbia. Canadian Wildlfie Service Seabird Colony Report No. 1, Delta, British Columbia. 47 pp.

Rodway, M.S., M.J.F. Lemon, and G.W. Kaiser. 1988. British Columbia colony inventory: Report No. 1 - east coast Moresby Island. Canadian Wildlife Service, Technical Report Series No. 50 Delta, British Columbia. 276 pp.

_____, _____, and_____. 1989. British Columbia Seabirds Colony Inventory: Report No. 2 west coast Moresby Island. Canadian Wildlife Service Technical Report Series No. 65, Delta, British Columbia.

Rodway, M.S., R.W. Campbell, and M.J.F. Lemon. (In prep.) Breeding, seabirds of British Columbia: history, populations, and international significance. Environment Canada, Canadian Wildlife Service.

Rodway, M.S., M.J.F. Lemon, J.-P. Savard, and R. McKelvey. (In Press). Nestucca oil spill: Impact assessment on avian populations and habitat. Canadian Wildlife Service Technical Report No. 68, Delta, British Columbia. 48 pp.

Rogers, J.P. 1962. The ecological effects of drought on reproduction of the Lesser Scaup, *Aythya affinis* (Eyton). Ph.D. Thesis, University of Missouri, Columbia. 99 pp.

Rogers, T.H. 1963a. Fall migration - northern Rocky Mountain-Intermountain region. Audubon Field Notes 17:51-53.

_____. 1963b. The nesting season - northern Rocky Mountain-Intermountain region. Audubon Field Notes 17:472-474.

_____. 1964a. The fall migration - northern Rocky Mountain-Intermountain region. Audubon Field Notes 18:57-60.

_____. 1966a. The fall migration - northern Rocky Mountain-Intermountain region. Audubon Field Notes 20:72-76.

_____. 1966b. The winter season - northern Rocky Mountain-Intermountain region. Audubon Field Notes 20:442-445.

_____. 1968a. The spring migration - northern Rocky Mountain-Intermountain region. Audubon Field Notes 22:557-560.

_____. 1968b. The nesting season - northern Rocky Mountain-Intermountain region. Audubon Field Notes 22:628-632.

_____. 1969. The winter season - northern Rocky Mountain-Intermountain region. Audubon Field Notes 23:498-503.

_____. 1970a. The fall migration - northern Rocky Mountain-Intermountain region. Audubon Field Notes 24:70-74.

_____. 1970b. The winter season - northern Rocky Mountain-Intermountain region. Audubon Field Notes 24:521-524.

_____. 1970c. The spring migration - northern Rocky Mountain-Intermountain region. Audubon Field Notes 24:625-628.

_____. 1970d. The nesting season - northern Rocky Mountain-Intermountain region. Audubon Field Notes 24:699-702.

_____. 1971a. The fall migration - northern Rocky Mountain-Intermountain region. American Birds 25:80-84.

_____. 1971b. The winter season - northern Rocky Mountain-Intermountain region. American Birds 25:603-606.

_____. 1972. The fall migration - northern Rocky Mountain-Intermountain region. American Birds 26:88-92.

_____. 1973a. The fall migration - northern Rocky Mountain-Intermountain region. American Birds 27:85-91.

_____. 1973b. The winter season - northern Rocky Mountain-Intermountain region. American Birds 27:639-643.

_____. 1973c. The spring migration - northern Rocky Mountain-Intermountain region. American Birds 27:796-799.

_____. 1974a. The fall migration - northern Rocky Mountain-Intermountain region. American Birds 28:78-83.

_____. 1974b. The winter season - northern Rocky Mountain-Intermountain region. American Birds 28:665-668.

_____. 1974c. The spring migration - northern Rocky Mountain-Intermountain region. American Birds 28:828-832.

_____. 1981. The autumn migration - northern Rocky Mountain-Intermountain region. American Birds 35:205-208.

_____. 1983a. The autumn migration - northern Rocky Mountain-Intermountain region. American Birds 37:202-204.

_____. 1983b. The winter season - northern Rocky Mountain-Intermountain region. American Birds 37:320-322.

_____. 1983c. The spring migration - northern Rocky Mountain-Intermountain region. American Birds 37:892-894.

_____. 1983d. The nesting season - northern Rocky Mountain-Intermountain region. American Birds 37:1007-1009.

_____. 1984a. The autumn migration - northern Rocky Mountain-Intermountain region. American Birds 38:224-227.

_____. 1984b. The winter season - northern Rocky Mountain-Intermountain region. American Birds 38:337-340.

_____. 1984c. The spring migration - northern Rocky Mountain-Intermountain region. American Birds 38:936-939.

_____. 1984d. The nesting season - northern Rocky Mountain-Intermountain region. American Birds 38:1041-1044.

_____. 1985a. The autumn migration - northern Rocky Mountain-Intermountain region. American Birds 39:78-81.

_____. 1985b. The winter season - northern Rocky Mountain-Intermountain region. American Birds 39:189-191.

_____. 1985c. The spring season - northern Rocky Mountain-Intermountain region. American Birds 39:327-329.

_____. 1985d. The nesting season - northern Rocky Mountain-Intermountain region. American Birds 39:938-941.

_____. 1986a. The autumn migration - northern Rocky Mountain-Intermountain region. American Birds 40:142-145.

_____. 1986b. The winter season - northern Rocky Mountain-Intermountain region. American Birds 40:304-306.

_____. 1986c. The spring migration - northern Rocky Mountain-Intermountain region. American Birds 40:498-502.

_____. 1986d. The nesting season - northern Rocky Mountain-Intermountain region. American Birds 40:1229-1232.

_____. 1987. The autumn migration - northern Rocky Mountain-Intermountain region. American Birds 41:118-121.

Rohwer, S., D.F. Martin and G.G. Benson. 1979. Breeding of the Black-necked Stilt in Washington. Murrelet 60:67-61.

Rowan, W. 1925. On the wintering of *Perdix perdix* in Alberta, 1924-25. Canadian Field-Naturalist 39:114-115.

_____. 1927. Details of the release of the Hungarian Partridge (*Perdix perdix*) in central Alberta. Canadian Field-Naturalist 41:98-101.

_____. 1938. The Hungarian Partridge on the Canadian prairie. Outdoor America 3:6-7.

Rowe, J.S. 1984. Understanding forest landscapes: what you conceive is what you get. Leslie L. Schaffer Lectureship in Forest Science, University of British Columbia, Vancouver. 13 pp.

Runyan, B. 1971. Bowron Lake Park natural history report, 1971. British Columbia Parks Branch Unpublished Report, Victoria. 51 pp. (Bibliography 4043).

Runyan, C.S. 1978. Pitt wildlife management area wildlife inventory report. British Columbia Fish and Wildlife Branch Unpublished Report, Vancouver. 102 pp. (Bibliography 1192).

_____. 1987. Location and density of nests of the Red-tailed Hawk, *Buteo jamaicensis*, in Richmond, British Columbia. Canadian Field-Naturalist 101:415-418.

Ryder, G.R. 1972. Pelican park - naturalist report for 1971. British Columbia Parks Branch Unpublished Report, Victoria. 91 pp. (Bibliography 1295).

_____. 1973. Report on White Pelican Provincial Park, 1973. British Columbia Parks Branch Unpublished Report, Victoria. 122 pp. (Bibliography 1134).

_____. 1986. Rare sighting of Barred Owl recorded at park. Langley Advance, 19 July :20.

Rydzewski, W. 1956. The nomadic movements and migrations of the European Common Heron (*Ardea cinerea*). Ardea 44:71-253.

Rye, D. 1952. Factors affecting orchard pheasant populations in the Okanagan valley of British Columbia, with special reference to orchard insecticides. M.A. Thesis, University of British Columbia, Vancouver. 67 pp.

Salomonsen, F. 1950. The birds of Greenland. Parts 1-3. Ejnar Munksgaard, Copenhagen. 607 pp.

Salt, W.R. and J.R. Salt. 1976. The birds of Alberta. Hurtig Publishers, Edmonton, Alberta. 498 pp.

Salt, W.R. and A.L. Wilk. 1966. The birds of Alberta (Second Edition). Queen's Printer, Edmonton. 511 pp.

Salvin, O. 1883. A list of birds collected by Captain A.H. Markham on the west coast of America. Pages 419-432 *in* Proceedings of the Zoological Society of London.

Salwasser, H. 1987. Spotted Owls: turning a battleground into a blueprint. Ecology 68:776-779.

Sandilands, A.P. and C.A. Campbell. 1987. Status report on the Least Bittern *Ixobrychus exilis* in Canada. Committee on the Status of Endangered Wildlife in Canada Report, c/o Canadian Nature Federation, Toronto, Ontario. 29 pp.

Sanford, F.J. 1974. Gulls nesting on Water Street - 1972-73. Vancouver Natural History Society Discovery 2:119-120.

Sanger, G.A. 1964. A possible sight record of a Short-tailed Albatross. Murrelet 45:47.

_____. 1970. The seasonal distribution of some seabirds off Washington and Oregon, with notes on their ecology and behavior. Condor 72:339-357.

_____. 1972a. The recent pelagic status of the Short-tailed Albatross (*Diomedea albatrus*). Biological Conservation 4:189-193.

_____. 1972b. Checklist of bird observations from the Eastern North Pacific Ocean. Murrelet 53:16-21.

_____. 1973a. Pelagic records of Glaucous-winged and Herring gulls in the north Pacific Ocean. Auk 90:384-393.

_____. 1973b. New northern record for Xantus' Murrelet. Condor 75:253.

_____. 1974a. Pelagic studies of seabirds in the central and eastern North Pacific Ocean: III Black-footed Albatross (*Diomedea nigripes*). Smithsonian Contributions to Zoology 158:96-128.

_____. 1974b. Pelagic studies of seabirds in the central and eastern North Pacific Ocean: IV Laysan Albatross (*Diomedea immutabilis*). Smithsonian Contributions to Zoology 158:129-153.

Sarles, J. and R. Sarles. 1983. Golden Eagle on the 1955 Vancouver Christmas bird count. Vancouver Natural History Society Discovery 11(4):D.

Saunders, W.E. 1902. Canadian hummingbirds. Ottawa Naturalist 16:97-103.

Sauppe, B. 1980. Hawk migration observed from Cypress Provincial Park: fall 1979. Vancouver Natural History Society Discovery 8:75.

Sauppe, B., B.A. Macdonald, and D.M. Mark. 1978. First Canadian and third North American record of the Spoon-billed Sandpiper (*Eurynorhynchos pygmeus*). American Birds 32:1062-1064.

Savard, J.-P.L. 1978. Aerial surveys in Dixon Entrance, Hecate Strait and Chatham Sound (February 13, 15 and 16, 1978). Canadian Wildlife Service Unpublished Report, Delta, British Columbia. 27 pp. (Bibliography 4078).

_____. 1979. Marine birds of Dixon Entrance, Hecate Strait and Chatham Sound during fall 1977 and winter 1978 (number, species composition and distribution). Canadian Wildlife Service Technical Report, Delta, British Columbia. 106 pp.

_____. 1981. Molting ducks in the coastal waters of British Columbia - a progress report. Canadian Wildlife Service Unpublished Report, Delta, British Columbia. 21 pp. (Bibliography 4085).

_____. 1982. Intra- and inter-specific competition between Barrow's Goldeneye (*Bucephala islandica)* and Bufflehead (*Bucephala albeola*). Canadian Journal of Zoology 60:3439-3446.

_____. 1984. Territorial behaviour of Common Goldeneye, Barrow's Goldeneye and Bufflehead in areas of sympatry. Ornis Scandinavica 15:211-216.

_____. 1985a. Evidence of long-term pair bonds *in* Barrow's Goldeneye (*Bucephala islandica*). Auk 102:389-391.

_____. 1985b. Conservation of Barrow's Goldeneye (*Bucephala islandica*) - use of nest boxes. Pages 45-51 *in* B. Shautz and H. Shautz (editors). Proceedings of the eighth annual North American Bluebird Society Conference, Calgary, Alberta.

_____. 1986. Territorial behavior, nesting success, and brood survival in Barrow's Goldeneye and its congeners. Ph.D. Thesis, University of British Columbia, Vancouver. 219 pp.

_____. 1987. A summary of current knowledge on the distribution and abundance of moulting seaducks in the coastal waters of British Columbia. Canadian Wildlife Service Technial Report Series No. 45, Delta, British Columbia. 81 pp.

_____. 1987a. Status report on Barrow's Goldeneye. Canadian Wildlife Service Technical Report Series No. 23, Delta, British Columbia. 57 pp.

_____. In press. Causes and functions of brood amalgamation in Barrow's Goldeneye and Bufflehead. Canadian Journal of Zoology.

Savard, J.-P.L. and G.W. Kaiser. 1982. Reconnaissance of marine birds on the northwest coast of British Columbia during March and May. Canadian Wildlife Service Unpublished Report, Delta, British Columbia. 37 pp. (Bibliography 4087).

Savile, D.B.O. 1972. Evidence of tree nesting by the Marbled Murrelet in the Queen Charlotte Islands. Canadian Field-Naturalist 86:389-390.

Schaffner, F.C. 1986. Trends in Elegant Tern and northern anchovy populations in California. Condor 88:347-354.

Schlatter, R.P. 1984. The status and conservation of seabirds in Chile. Pages 261-269 *in* Croxall, J.P., P.G.H. Evans, and R.W. Schreiber (editors). The status and conservation of the world's seabirds. International Council for Bird Preservation Technical Publications No. 2, Cambridge, England.

Schmidt, V. 1964. Late nesting of a Gray Partridge. Blue Jay 22:149.

Schmutz, J.K. 1977. Relationships between three species of the genus *Buteo* (Aves) coexisting in the prairie-parkland ecotone of southeastern Alberta. M.S. Thesis, University of Alberta, Calgary. 126 pp.

Schnider, B., D. Beacham, and T. Stevens. 1971. Shuswap Lake nature house annual report (1971). British Columbia Parks Branch Unpublished Report, Victoria. 15 pp. (Bibliography 4089).

Schorger, A.W. 1955. The Passenger Pigeon, its natural history, and extinction. University of Wisconsin Press, Madison. 424 pp.

Schouten, M. 1979. The seventy-ninth Audubon Christmas Bird count - White Rock, B.C. American Birds 33:381.

Schreiber, R.W. and R.L. DeLong. 1969. Brown Pelican status in California. Audubon Field Notes 23:57-59.

Schreiber, R.W. and R.W. Risebrough. 1972. Studies of the Brown Pelican. I. Status of Brown Pelican populations in the United States. Wilson Bulletin 84:119-135.

Schultz, Z.M. 1958. The spring migration - northern Pacific coast region. Audubon Field Notes 12:377-379.

_____. 1970. The occurrence of the Yellow-billed Loon in Washington. Murrelet 51:23.

Scott, D.M., C.D. Ankney, and C.H. Jarosch. 1976. Sapsucker hybridization in British Columbia: changes in 25 years. Condor 78:253-257.

Scott, G. 1973. Avifauna of the Vermillion Pass burn. B.Sc. Thesis, University of Calgary, Alberta. 60 pp. (Bibliography 1155).

Scott, G.A. 1963. First nesting of the Little Gull (*Larus minutus*) in Ontario and the New World. Auk 80:548-549.

Scott, J.M. 1971. Interbreeding of the Glaucous-winged Gull and Western Gull in the Pacific Northwest. California Birds 2:129-133.

Scott, J.M., J. Butler, W.G. Pearcy, and G.A. Bertrand. 1971. Occurrence of the Xantus' Murrelet off the Oregon coast. Condor 73:254.

Scott, J.M., W. Hoffman, and C.F. Zeillemaker. 1974. Range expansion and activity patterns in Rhinoceros Auklets. Western Birds 5:13-20.

Scudder, G.G.E. 1980. The Osoyoos-arid biotic area. Pages 49-55 *in* R. Stace-Smith, L. Johns, and P. Joslin (editors). Proceedings of the Symposium on Threatened and Endangered Species and Habitats in British Columbia and the Yukon. British Columbia Ministry of Environment, Victoria.

Sealy, S.G. 1967. Notes on the breeding biology of the Marsh Hawk in Alberta and Saskatchewan. Blue Jay 25:63-69.

_____. 1972. Adaptive differences in breeding biology in the marine bird family Alcidae. Ph.D. Thesis, University of Michigan, Ann Arbor. 283 pp.

_____. 1973a. Interspecific feeding assemblages of marine birds off British Columbia. Auk 90:796-802.

_____. 1973b. Breeding biology of the Horned Puffin on St. Lawrence Island, Bering Sea, with zoo-geographical notes on the North Pacific puffins. Pacific Science 27:99-119.

_____. 1974. Breeding phenology and clutch size in the Marbled Murrelet. Auk 91:10-23.

_____. 1975a. Egg size in murrelets. Condor 77:500-501.

_____. 1975b. Aspects of the breeding biology of the Marbled Murrelet in British Columbia. Bird-Banding 46:141-154.

_____. 1975c. Feeding ecology of the Ancient and Marbled murrelets near Langara Island, British Columbia. Canadian Journal of Zoology 53:418-433.

_____. 1976. Biology of nesting Ancient Murrelets. Condor 78:294-306.

_____. 1984. Interruptions extend incubation by Ancient Murrelets, Crested Auklets, and Least Auklets. Murrelet 65:53-56.

Sealy, S.G. and R.W. Campbell. 1979. Post-hatching movements of young Ancient Murrelets. Western Birds 10:25-30.

Sealy, S.G. and H.R. Carter. 1984. At-sea distribution and nesting habitat of the Marbled Murrelet in British Columbia: problems in the conservation of a solitarily nesting seabird. Pages 737-756 *in* J.P. Croxall, P.G.H. Evans, and R.W. Schreiber (editors). Status and conservation of the world's seabirds. International Council for Bird Preservation Technical Publication No. 2. Cambridge, England.

Sealy, S.G. and N. Gessler. 1988. A specimen of the Long-eared Owl from the Queen Charlotte Islands. Murrelet 69:27-28.

Sealy, S.G. and R.W. Nelson. 1973. The occurrences and status of Horned Puffin in British Columbia. Syesis 6:51-55.

Sealy, S.G., H.R. Carter, and D. Allison. 1982. Occurrences of the Asiatic Marbled Murrelet [*Brachyramphus marmoratus perdix* (Pallas)] in North America. Auk 99: 778-781.

Seel, K.E. 1965. The birds of Kootenay National Park (First Report 1965) - field studies. Parks Canada Unpublished Report, Radium Hot Springs, British Columbia. 41 pp. (Bibliography 4123).

Senner, S.E. and E.F. Martinez. 1982. A review of Western Sandpiper migration in interior North America. Southwest Naturalist 27:149-159.

Senner, S.E., G.C. West, and D.W. Norton. 1981. The spring migration of Western Sandpipers and Dunlins in southcentral Alaska: numbers, timing, and sex ratio. Journal of Field Ornithology 52:271-284.

Serventy, D.L. 1957. The banding programme on *Puffinus tenuirostris* (Temminck): I. First Report. Commonwealth Scientific and Industrial Research Organization Wildlife Research 2:51-59.

_____. 1961. The banding programme on *Puffinus tenuirostris* (Temminck). I. Second Report. Commonwealth Scientific and Industrial Research Organization Wildlife Research 6:42-55.

_____. 1967. Aspects of the population ecology of the Short-tailed Shearwater *Puffinus tenuirostris*. Proceedings of the 14th International Ornithological Congress: 165-190.

Serventy, D.L., V. Serventy, and J. Warham. 1971. The handbook of Australian sea-birds. A.H. & A.W. Reed, Sydney, Australia. 254 pp.

Serveen, C.W. and W. English. 1979. Movements of rehabilitated Bald Eagles and proposed seasonal movement patterns of Bald Eagles in the Pacific Northwest. Raptor Research 13:79-88.

Shepard, M.G. 1974. British Columbia birds - winter season, 1973-1974. Vancouver Natural History Society Discovery 3:4-11.

_____. 1975a. British Columbia birds - spring and summer, 1974. Vancouver Natural History Society Discovery 3:32-38.

_____. 1975b. British Columbia birds - spring 1975. Vancouver Natural History Society Discovery 4:41-44.

_____. 1975c. British Columbia birds - July to September, 1975. Vancouver Natural History Society Discovery 4:67-69.

_____. 1975d. British Columbia birds - October to December, 1975. Vancouver Natural History Society Discovery 5:10-13.

_____. 1976a. Notes on the Laysan Albatross, New Zealand Shearwater, and Skua in the north Pacific Ocean. Murrelet 57:48-49.

_____. 1976b. British Columbia birds - October to December, 1975. Vancouver Natural History Society Discovery 5:10-13.

_____. 1976c. British Columbia birds - April to June, 1976. Vancouver Natural History Society Discovery 5:48-50.

_____. 1977a. British Columbia birds - July to September, 1976. Vancouver Natural History Society Discovery 5:65-67.

_____. 1977b. British Columbia birds - October to December, 1976. Vancouver Natural History Society Discovery 6:18-20.

_____. 1978. Pelagic birding trips - fall 1977. Vancouver Natural History Society Discovery 6:90-91.

Shepard, T. 1977. Naturalist's summer report, Lakelse Lake Park. British Columbia Parks Branch Unpublished Report, Victoria. 29 pp. (Bibliography 4144).

Sherman, A. 1910. At the sign of the Northern Flicker. Wilson Bulletin 22:135-171.

Sherman, A.R. 1911. Nest life of the Screech Owl. Auk 28:155-168.

_____. 1913. Nest life of the Sparrow Hawk. Auk 30:406-418.

Short, L.L. 1969. Taxonomic aspects of avian hybridization. Auk 86:84-105.

Shuntov, V.P. 1964. Transequatorial migrations of the Short-tailed Shearwater *Puffinus tenuirostris* (Temminck). Zoologichesky Zhurnal 43:36-48.

_____. 1974. Sea birds and the biological structure of the oceans. Translated from Russian by I. Allardt for United States Department of the Interior, Bureau of Sports Fisheries and Wildlife, Washington, D.C. 565 pp.

_____. 1986. Seabirds in the Sea of Okohotrk. *In* N.M. Litvinenko (editor), Seabirds of the Far East: Collection of scientific papers. USSR Academy of Sciences, Vladivostok (Translation for Environment Canada, Ottawa).

Siddle, C. 1981. Potential effects of the activities of the Scurry-Rainbow oil company on the avifauna of the south end of Charlie Lake. British Columbia Fish and Wildlife Branch Unpublished Report, Fort St. John. 12 pp. (Bibliography 4158).

_____. 1982. The status of birds in the Peace River area of British Columbia. British Columbia Provincial Museum Unpublished Report, Victoria. 319pp. (Bibliography 4159).

_____. 1984. Raptor mortality on northeastern British Columbia trapline. Blue Jay 42:184.

_____. 1986. The phenology of the Hudsonian Godwit in northeastern British Columbia, British Columbia Provincial Museum Unpublished Report, Victoria. 6 pp.

Siemens, A.H. 1968. The process of settlement in the lower Fraser valley - in its provincial context. Pages 27-50 *in* A.H.Siemens (editor). Lower Fraser valley: evolution of a cultural landscape. B.C. Geographical Series No.9, Tantalus Research Limited, Vancouver.

Silovsky, G.D. 1969. Distribution and mortality of Pacific coast Band-tailed Pigeons. M.S. Thesis, Oregon State University, Corvallis. 70 pp.

Simberloff, D. 1987. The Spotted Owl fracas: mixing academic, applied, and political ecology. Ecology 68:766-772.

Simons, T.R. 1979. Behavior and attendance patterns of the Fork-tailed Storm-Petrel. M.Sc. Thesis, University of Washington, Seattle. 35 pp.

_____. 1980. Discovery of a ground-nesting Marbled Murrelet. Condor 82:1-9.

_____. 1981. Behavior and attendance patterns of the Fork-tailed Storm-Petrel. Auk 98:145-158.

Simpson, G.B. 1925. Christmas bird censuses, 1924 - Lake Cowichan, V.I., British Columbia. Canadian Field-Naturalist 39:21.

_____. 1926. Christmas bird census from Lake Cowichan, B.C. Canadian Field-Naturalist 40:10.

_____. 1927. Christmas bird census at Lake Cowichan, B.C. Canadian Field-Naturalist 41:10.

Sirk, G. 1968. Summer and fall visitants to Vancouver. Vancouver Natural History Society News 137:6-7.

_____. 1972. Summer report for Monck Park, 1972. British Columbia Parks Branch Unpublished Report, Victoria. 11 pp. (Bibliography 4166).

Sirk, G. and L. Sirk. 1971. Mitlenatch Island Nature Park - annual report, 1971. British Columbia Parks Branch Unpublished Report, Victoria. 12 pp. (Bibliography 4168).

Sirk, G.P., R.J. Cannings, and M.G. Shepard. 1973. Shuswap Lake Park annual report, - 1973. British Columbia Parks Branch Unpublished Report, Victoria. 66 pp. (Bibliography 4169).

Skeel, M.A. 1983. Nesting success, density, philopatry, and nest site selection of the Whimbrel *(Numenius phaeopus)* in different habitats. Canadian Journal of Zoology 61:218-255.

Sladen, W.J.L. 1966. Additions to the avifauna of the Pribilof Islands, Alaska, including five species new to North America. Auk 83:130-135.

_____. 1973. A continental study of Whistling Swans using neck collars. Wildfowl 24:8-14.

Sladen, W.J. and A.A. Kistchinski. 1977. Some results from circumpolar marking programs on northern swans and snow geese. XIII International Congress of Game Biologists, Atlanta, Georgia. 631 pp.

Sloan, N.G. 1982. Status of breeding colonies of White Pelicans in the United States through 1979. American Birds 36:250-254.

Smith, C.C. 1963. First breeding record of the Spotted Owl in British Columbia. Condor 65:440.

Smith, D.A. 1970. Observations on nesting Hawk Owls at Mer Bleu, near Ottawa, Canada. Canadian Field-Naturalist 84:377-383.

Smith, D.G. and J.R.Murphy. 1973. Breeding ecology of raptors in the eastern Great Basin of Utah. Brigham Young University Science Bulletin Biological Series 18:1-76.

Smith, I.D. 1972. Status of the Nimpkish goose transplant program: Oct. 30, 1972. British Columbia Fish and Wildlife Branch Unpublished Report, Nanaimo. 4 pp. (Bibliography 4197).

_____. 1973. Report on the Nimpkish Valley goose transplant program: May 1, 1973. British Columbia Fish and Wildlife Branch, Victoria. 10 pp. (Bibliography 4198).

Smith, I.D. and D.A. Blood. 1972. Native swans wintering on Vancouver Island over the period 1969-71. Canadian Field-Naturalist 86:213-216.

Smith, I.D., D. Hatler, W. Munro, and K. Hodson. 1976. Queen Charlotte Islands, British Columbia in R.W. Fyfe, S.A.Temple, and T.J. Cade (editors). The 1976 North American Peregrine Falcon Survey. Canadian Field-Naturalist 90:228-273.

Smith, K.M., N.J. Anderson, and K.I. Beamish. 1973. Nature west coast: a study of plants, insects, birds, mammals and marine life as seen in Lighthouse Park. Discovery Press, Vancouver, British Columbia. 283 pp.

Smith, N.G. 1966. Evolution of some arctic gulls *(Larus)*: an experimental study of isolating mechanisms. Ornithological Monographs 4:1-99.

Smith, R.H. and G.H. Jensen. 1970. Black Brant on the mainland coast of Mexico. Transactions of the 35th North American Wildlife and Natural Resources Conference: 227-241.

Smith, S.M. 1965. Seasonal changes in the survival of the Black-capped Chickadee. M.Sc. Thesis, University of British Columbia, Vancouver. 31 pp.

Smith, W.G. 1952. The food habits of a population of Black Turnstones, Aleutian Sandpipers, and Surf-Birds wintering in southern British Columbia. B.A. Thesis, University of British Columbia, Vancouver. 51pp.

Snow, C. 1973. Habitat management series for unique or endangered species: the Golden Eagle. United States Department of the Interior, Bureau of Land Management Report No.7, Washington, D.C. 52 pp.

_____. 1974. Habitat management series for unique or endangered species Report No.9: Gyrfalcon *Falco rusticolus* L. United States Department of the Interior, Bureau of Land Management Technical Note 241, Denver, Colorado. 14 pp.

Snyder, L.L. 1935. A study of the Sharp-tailed Grouse. Contributions of the Royal Ontario Museum of Zoology No. 6, Toronto, Ontario. 66 pp.

Snyder, N.F.R., H.A. Snyder, J.C. Lincer, and R.T. Reynolds. 1973. Organochlorines, heavy metals, and the biology of North American accipiters. Bioscience 23:300-305.

Soikkeli, M. 1967. Breeding cycle and population dynamics of the Dunlin *(Calidris alpina schinzii)* in Finland. Annales Zoologica Fennici 4:158-198.

Somerville, A.J. 1985. Advantages to late breeding in Ruddy Ducks. M.Sc. Thesis. University of British Columbia, Vancouver. 107 pp.

Soper, J.D. 1949. Birds observed in the Grande Prairie - Peace River region of northwestern Alberta, Canada. Auk 66:233-257.

Sordahl, T.A. 1978. First record of the Curlew Sandpiper *(Calidris ferruginea)* in Utah, with comments on its occurrence in North America. American Birds 32:1065-1068.

Southern, H.N. 1943. The two phases of *Stercorarius parasiticus* (Linnaeus). Ibis 85:443-485.

Sowls, A.L., S.A. Hatch, and C.J. Lensink. 1978. Catalogue of Alaskan seabird colonies. United States Fish and Wildlife Service FWS/OBS-78/78, Washington, D.C. 249 pp.

Sowls, A.L., A.R. DeGange, R. Nelson, J.W. Lester, and G.S. Lester. 1980. Catalogue of California seabird colonies. United States Department of the Interior, Fish and Wildlife Service Biological Services Program FWS/OBS 37/80.

Spalding, D. 1966. Are pheasants a plague? Wildlife Review 3:4-6.

Spalding, D.J. and R.P .Stoneberg. 1981. A history of the pheasant in the Okanagan region of southern British Columbia. British Columbia Ministry of Environment and Parks Wildlife Report No. R-4, Victoria. 64 pp.

Sparling, D.B. and R. Sparling. 1974. The Bar-tailed Godwit. Victoria Naturalist 30:80.

Spear, L.B., M.J. Lewis, M.T. Myres, and R.L. Pyle. 1988. The recent occurrence of Garganey in North America and the Hawaiian Islands. American Birds 42:385-392.

Speich, S. and D.A. Manuwal. 1974. Gular pouch development and population structure of Cassin's Auklet. Auk 91:291-306.

Speich, S.M. and T.R. Wahl. 1989. Catalogue of Washington seabird colonies, United States Department of the Interior Fish and Wildlife Service Biological Report, Series 88(6), Washington, D.C.

Spencer, H.E. 1953. The Cinnamon Teal, *Anas cyanoptera* (Vieillot): its life history, ecology, and management. M.S. Thesis, Utah State University, Logan. 184 pp.

Spitzer, P.R., A.F. Poole, and M. Scheibel. 1983. Initial population recovery of breeding Ospreys in the region between New York city and Boston. Pages 231 - 241 *in* D.M. Bird (editor). Biology and Management of Bald Eagles and Ospreys. Proceeding First International Symposium on Bald Eagles and Ospreys, Montreal, 28-29 October 1981. Harpell Press, Ste. Anne de Bellevue, Quebec.

Spofford, W. 1969. Problems of the Golden Eagle in North America. Pages 345-347 *in* J. Hickey (editor). Peregrine Falcon populations; their biology and decline. University of Wisconsin Press, Madison.

Springer, P.R., G.V. Byrd, and D.W. Woolington. 1978. Reestablishing Aleutian Canada Geese. Pages 331-338 *in* S.A. Temple (editor). Endangered Birds. University of Wisconsin Press, Madison.

Sprot, G.D. 1936. A tree-nesting colony of White-crested Cormorants in Trincomali Channel, British Columbia. Condor 38:247-248.

Stallcup, R.W. 1976. Pelagic birds on Monterey Bay, California. Western Birds 7:113-136.

Stalmaster, M.V. and J.A. Gessaman. 1984. Ecological energetics and foraging behavior of overwintering Bald Eagles. Ecological Monographs 54:407-428.

Stalmaster, M.V. and J.R. Newman. 1978. Behavioral responses of wintering Bald Eagles to human activity. Journal of Wildlife Management 42:506-513.

Stanwell-Fletcher, J.F. and T.C. Stanwell-Fletcher. 1940. Naturalists in the wilds of British Columbia. Scientific Monthly 50:1-44.

_____. and _____. 1943. Some accounts of the flora and fauna of the Driftwood Valley region of northcentral British Columbia. British Columbia Provincial Museum Occasional Paper No. 4, Victoria. 97pp.

Steenhof, K. and J.M. Brown. 1978. Management of wintering Bald Eagles. United States Department of the Interior, Fish and Wildlife Service Biological Services Program FWS/OBS-78/79, Washington, D.C. 59 pp.

Sterling, J. and T.F. Campbell. 1985. The autumn migration - middle Pacific coast region. American Birds 39:96-101.

Stevens, T. 1969. Bird report for the Shuswap Lake region (prepared September 1969). British Columbia Parks Branch Unpublished Report, Victoria. 6 pp. (Bibliography 4261).

Stevens, T. and D. Belton. 1969. Annual report for the Shuswap Lake nature house - 1969. British Columbia Parks Branch Unpublished Report, Victoria. 19 pp. (Bibliography 4262).

Stevens, T., A. Grass, and G. Sirk. 1970. Shuswap Lake nature house annual report - 1970. British Columbia Parks Branch Unpublished Report, Victoria. 23 pp. (Bibliography 4260).

Stevenson, H.M. 1975. Identification of difficult birds. Part 3. Semi-palmated Sandpipers and Western Sandpipers. Florida Field Naturalist 3:39-44.

Stewart, P.A. 1985. Need for new direction in research on Black and Turkey Vultures in the USA. Vulture News 13:8-12.

Stewart, R.M. 1927. Marbled Murrelet taken at Harrison Lake, British Columbia. Murrelet 8:16.

Stiles, F.G. 1970. Food supply and the annual cycle of the Anna Hummingbird. Ph.D. Thesis, University of California, Los Angeles. 239 pp.

_____. 1971. On the field identification of California hummingbirds. California Birds 2:41-54.

Stirling, D. 1960a. Sight records of unusual birds in the Victoria area for 1959. Murrelet 41:10-11.

_____. 1960b. Bird life at Esquimalt Lagoon. Victoria Naturalist 16:61.

_____. 1961. Summer birds of Miracle Beach. British Columbia Parks Branch Unpublished Report, Victoria. 14 pp. (Bibliography 4278).

_____. 1962. Some bird notes from Vancouver Island - 1961. Victoria Natural History Society Mimeo, Victoria, British Columbia. 9 pp. (Bibliography 309).

_____. 1964. Western Grebe colony at Shuswap Lake re-visited. Murrelet 45:8-9.

_____. 1965a. Two new heron records for Vancouver Island. Murrelet 46:15.

_____. 1965b. A sight record of Emperor Goose at Victoria, British Columbia. Murrelet 46:36.

_____. 1966a. First nesting record of Brandt's Cormorant in Canadian waters. Victoria Naturalist 23:1-2.

_____. 1966b. Bird report (Victoria) number four - 1965. Victoria Natural History Society Mimeo, Victoria. 6 pp. (Bibliography 310).

_____. 1967. Ross' Gull *Rhodostethia rosea*, rarest of accidental stragglers. Victoria Naturalist 23:49-50.

_____. 1970. A sight record of the Barred Owl on Vancouver Island. Murrelet 51:19.

_____. 1971. Notes on birds of Mount Robson Provincial Park, 1970. Blue Jay 29:66-72.

_____. 1972a. More Franklin's Gulls in southeastern British Columbia. Vancouver Natural History Society Discovery 1:37.

_____. 1972b. Birds of Vancouver Island for birdwatchers. Published by the author, Victoria. 27 pp. (Bibliography 307).

_____. 1986. Mountain Quail returns? B.C. Naturalist 24:5.

Stirling, D. and R. Buffam. 1966. The first breeding record of Brandt's Cormorant in Canada. Canadian Field-Naturalist 80:117-118.

Stockman, B. 1972. The Pitt waterfowl study. Canadian Wildlife Service Unpublished Report, Delta, British Columbia. 84 pp. (Bibliography 4283).

Stoneberg, R.P. 1967. A preliminary study of the breeding biology of the Spruce Grouse in northwestern Montana. M.Sc. Thesis, University of Montana, Missoula.

Stonehouse, B. 1968. Penguins. Golden Press, New York. 96 pp.

Storer, R.W. 1952. A comparison of variation, behavior and evolution in the sea bird genera *Uria* and *Cepphus*. University of California Publications in Zoology 52:121-222.

Storer, R.W. and G.L. Nuechterlein. 1985. An analysis of plumage and morphological characters of the two color phases of the Western Grebe *(Aechmophorus)*. Auk 102:102-119.

Stotts, V.D. and C.J. Henny. 1975. The age at first flight for young American Ospreys. Wilson Bulletin 87:277-278.

Stresemann, E. and D. Amadon. 1979. Order Falconiformes. Pages 271-425 *in* E. Mayr and G.W. Cottrell (editors). Checklist of birds of the world. Museum of Comparative Zoology, Cambridge, Massachusetts.

Strong, P.I.V., J.A. Bissonette, and R. Souza. 1986. A case of brood mixing by Common Loons. Wilson Bulletin 98:478-479.

Stutz, S.S. 1965. Size of Common Merganser broods. Murrelet 46:47-48.

Sugden, L.G. 1963. Barrow's Goldeneye using crow nests. Condor 65:330.

Sullivan, T. 1985. A survey of Christie Islet Migratory Bird Sanctuary, B.C. Canadian Wildlife Service Unpublished Report, Delta, British Columbia. 8 pp.

Summers, K.R. 1974. Seabirds breeding along the east coast of Moresby Island, Queen Charlotte Islands, British Columbia. Syesis 7:1-12.

Summers, K.R. and R.H. Drent. 1979. Breeding biology and twinning experiments of Rhinoceros Auklet on Cleland Island, British Columbia. Murrelet 60:16-22.

Sutton, G.M. and D.F. Parmelee. 1955. Breeding of the Semipalmated Plover on Baffin Island. Bird-Banding 26:137-147.

Sutton, G.M. and J.B. Semple. 1941. An egg of the Marbled Murrelet. Auk 58:580-581.

Swarth, H.S. 1912. Report on a collection of birds and mammals from Vancouver Island. University of California Publications in Zoology 10:1-124.

_____. 1922. Birds and mammals of the Stikine River region of northern British Columbia and southeastern Alaska. University of California Publications in Zoology 24:125-314.

_____. 1924. Birds and mammals of the Skeena River region of northern British Columbia. University of California Publications in Zoology 24:315-394.

_____. 1926. Report on a collection of birds and mammals from the Atlin region, northern British Columbia. University of California Publications in Zoology 30:51-62.

_____. 1932. Status of the Baikal Teal in California. Condor 34:259.

_____. 1936. A list of the birds of the Atlin region, British Columbia. Proceedings of the California Academy of Sciences 23:35-58.

Swenson, J.E. 1983. Is the northern interior Bald Eagle population in North America increasing? Pages 23-34 *in* D.M. Bird (editor). Biology and Management of Bald Eagles and Ospreys. Proceedings of First International Symposium on Bald Eagles and Ospreys, Montreal, 28-29 October 1981. Harpell Press, Ste. Anne de Bellevue, Quebec.

Swift, P. 1975. Annotated list of birds of Goldstream Park, spring 1975. British Columbia Parks Branch Unpublished Report, Victoria. 5 pp. (Bibliography 4311).

Sykes, P.W. 1975. Caribbean Coot collected in southern Florida. Florida Field Naturalist 3:25-27.

Syroechkovskiy, Ye.V. and K.Ye. Litvin. 1986. Investigation of the migration of the Snow Geese of Wrangel Island by the method of individual marking. Pages 1-17 *in* V.Ye. Sokolov and I.N. Dobrinina (editors). The Ringing and Marking of Birds in the U.S.S.R. 1979-1982. Moscow: "Nauka":5-20. (Translation by M.A. Bousfield, Department of Zoology, University of Alberta, Edmonton).

Szuba, K.J. and J.F. Bendell. 1983. Population densities and habitats of Spruce Grouse in Ontario. Pages 199-213 *in* Proceedings of a conference held at Thunder Bay, Ontario, August, 1982. Association of Canadian Universities for Northern Studies, Ottawa.

Tacha, T.C., P.A. Vohs, and G.C. Iverson. 1984. Migration routes of Sandhill Cranes from mid-continental North America. Journal of Wildlife Management 48:1028-1033.

Tait, E.M. 1929. Christmas bird census, 1928 - Summerland, Okanagan Lake, British Columbia. Canadian Field-Naturalist 43:34.

_____. 1932. Black-crowned Night Heron in Okanagan Valley, British Columbia. Canadian Field-Naturalist 46:190.

_____. 1949. Nesting of the Pacific Harlequin Duck in vicinity of Penticton, B.C. Canadian Field-Naturalist 63:43.

Tamm, S. 1985. Breeding territory quality and agnostic behavior: effects of energy availability and intruder pressure in hummingbirds. Behavioral Ecology Sociobiology 16:203-207.

_____. 1986. Behavioural energetics: acquisition and use of energy by hummingbirds. Ph.D. Thesis, University of Stockholm, Sweden.

Tate, J. 1981. The blue list for 1981. American Birds 35:3-10.

_____. 1986. The blue list for 1986. American Birds 40:227-236.

Tate, J. and D.J. Tate. 1982. The blue list for 1982. American Birds 36:126-135.

Tatum J.B. (editor). 1970. Experimental annual bird report for southern Vancouver Island 1969. Victoria Natural History Society Mimeo, Victoria. 34 pp.

_____. (editor). 1971. Bird report for southern Vancouver Island (1970). Victoria Natural History Society, Victoria, British Columbia. 64 pp.

_____. (editor). 1972. Annual bird report - 1971 - for southern Vancouver Island. Victoria Natural History Society, Victoria, British Columbia. 66 pp.

_____. 1972a. A Canadian ornithological records committee. Canadian Field-Naturalist 86:181.

_____. (editor). 1973. Annual bird report - 1972 - for southern Vancouver Island. Victoria Natural History Society, Victoria, British Columbia. 80 pp.

_____. 1980. The effect of the Coriolis force on the flight of a bird. Auk 97:99-117.

Taverner, P.A. 1918. Summer birds of Alert Bay, British Columbia. Condor 20:183-186.

_____. 1919. The summer birds of Hazelton, British Columbia. Condor 21:80-86.

_____. 1919a. Birds of Eastern Canada. Canada Department of Mines Memoir 104, Number 3, Biological Series, Ottawa, Ontario. 297 pp.

_____. 1926. Birds of Western Canada. Canada Department of Mines Museum Bulletin Number 41, Ottawa, Ontarior. 380 pp.

_____. 1927. Some recent Canadian records. Auk 44:217-218.

_____. 1929. A study of the Canadian races of Rock Ptarmigan (*Lagopus rupestris*). Pages 28-38 *in* National Museum of Canada Annual Report for 1928, Ottawa, Ontario.

_____. 1936. Taxonomic comments on Red-tailed Hawk. Condor 38:66-71.

_____. 1940. Variation in the American Goshawk. Condor 42:157-160.

_____. 1942. The distribution and migration of the Hudsonian Curlew. Wilson Bulletin 54:3-11.

Taylor, A.L. and E.D. Forsman. 1976. Recent range extensions of the Barred Owl in western North America, including the first records for Oregon. Condor 78:560-561.

Taylor, E.W. 1950. A study of factors affecting reproduction and survival of the Ring-necked Pheasant in the lower Fraser River valley of British Columbia. M.A. Thesis, University of British Columbia, Vancouver. 116 pp.

_____. 1959. Reports of E.W. Taylor - 1954 to 1959. British Columbia Fish and Wildlife Branch Unpublished Report, Vancouver. 27 pp. (Bibliography 4344).

_____. 1962. A report on the Ringneck Pheasant population of the district municipality of Salmon Arm and the Salmon River valley. British Columbia Fish and Wildlife Branch Unpublished Report, Victoria. 23pp.

Taylor, R.L. and B. MacBryde. 1977. Vascular plants of British Columbia: a descriptive resource inventory. University of British Columbia Botanical Garden Technical Bulletin No. 4, Vancouver. 754 pp.

Telosky, H.A. 1977. Ruby-throated Hummingbird reported on north-eastern Vancouver Island. Vancouver Natural History Society Discovery 6:57-60.

Temple, S.A. 1972. Systematics and evolution of the North American Merlins. Auk 89:325-338.

Terres, J.K. 1980. The Audubon Society encyclopedia of North American birds. Alfred Knopf, New York. 1110 pp.

Thacker, B.M. and T.L. Thacker. 1923. Extracts from note-book for Little Mountain, Hope, B.C. - Year, 1922. Migrant 1:20-21 (Bibliography 1929).

Thacker, T.L. 1923. Bird notes made at Vaseux Lake, south Okanagan, British Columbia. Canadian Field-Naturalist 37:66-69.

_____. 1948. Sight record of Red-bellied Hawk at Hope, British Columbia. Murrelet 29:50.

Thompson, B.H. 1933. History and present status of the breeding colonies of the White Pelican (*Pelecanus erythrorhynchos*) in the United States. United States Department of Interior National Park Service Occasional Paper No. 1, Washington, D.C. 82 pp.

Thompson, D.Q. 1951. Notes on distribution of north Pacific albatrosses. Auk 68:227-235.

Thompson, M.C. 1974. Migratory patterns of Ruddy Turnstone in the central Pacific region. Living Bird 12:5-23.

Thompson, M.C. and R.L. DeLong. 1969. Birds new to North America and the Pribilof Islands, Alaska. Auk 86:744-749,

Thomson, A.L. (editor). 1964. A new dictionary of birds. McGraw-Hill Book Company, New York. 928 pp.

Thomson, D. 1974. Naturalist program at Black Tusk 1974. British Columbia Parks Branch Unpublished Report, Victoria. 17 pp. (Bibliography 4360).

Thomson, R.E. 1981. Oceanography of the British Columbia coast. Canadian Special Publication of Fisheries and Aquatic Sciences 56. Canada Department Fisheries and Oceans, Ottawa. 291 pp.

Thoresen, A.C. 1964. Breeding behavior of the Cassin Auklet. Condor 66:456-476.

Thoresen, A.C. and E.S. Booth. 1958. Breeding activities of the Pigeon Guillemot *Cepphus columba columba* (Pallas). Walla Walla College Publications in Biological Science No. 23, Walla Walla, Washington. 36 pp.

Tierney, R. 1974. Bowron Lake Provincial Park - bird report 1974. British Columbia Parks Branch Unpublished Report, Victoria. 14 pp. (Bibliography 4364).

Tilgham, N.G. 1980. The Black Tern survey, 1979. Passenger Pigeon 42:1-8.

Timm, D.E. and C.P. Dau. 1979. Productivity, mortality, distribution, and population status of Pacific White-fronted Geese. Pages 280-298 *in* R.L. Jarvis and J.C. Bartonek (editors). Management and Biology of Pacific Flyway Geese. A symposium sponsored by the Northwest Section, The Wildlife Society, 16 February 1979, Portland, Oregon. Oregon State University Book Stores, Inc., Corvallis.

Timm, D.E., M.L. Wege, and D.S. Gilmer. 1982. Current status and management challenges for Tule White-fronted Geese. Transactions of the North American Wildlife and Natural Resources Conference 47:453-463.

Tisdale, E.W. and A. McLean. 1957. The Douglas fir zone of southern British Columbia. Ecological Monographs 27:247-266.

Trapp, J.L., M.A. Robus, G.J. Tans, and M.A. Tans. 1981. First breeding record of the Sora and American Coot in Alaska - with comments on drought displacement. American Birds 35:901-902.

Trauger, D.L., A. Dzubin, and J.P. Ryder. 1971. White geese intermediate between Ross' Geese and Lesser Snow Geese. Auk 88:856-875.

Trethewey, R.B. and J.M. Cooper. 1975. Wood Duck project final report, 1972-1975. Pitt Waterfowl Management Association Unpublished Report, Pitt Meadows, British Columbia. 9 pp. (Bibliography 4381).

Trimble, S.A. 1975. Habitat management series for unique or endangered species Report No. 15: Merlin (*Falco columbarius*), United States Department of Interior, Bureau of Land Management Technical Note, Denver, Colorado.

Tuck, G. 1978. A field guide to the seabirds of Britain and the world. Collins, London, England.

Tuck, L.M. 1960. The murres: their distribution, populations and biology - a study of the genus *Uria*. Queens Printer, Ottawa, Ontario. 260 pp.

_____. 1972. The snipes. Canadian Wildlife Service Monograph Series No. 5, Ottawa, Ontario. 429 pp.

Tull, C.E. 1979. Raptor nest sites along segments 2-6, Shakwak highway British Columbia - Yukon, May to June, 1979. LGL Limited Unpublished Report, Edmonton, Alberta. 66 pp. (Bibliography 4389).

Turner, I.G. 1970. A daily record of Trumpeter Swans at Lonesome Lake, British Columbia (October to March, 1969-1970). Canadian Wildlife Service Unpublished Report, Delta. 47 pp. (Bibliography 4391).

Turner, J. 1971. Trumpeter Swans - Lonesome Lake, B.C. - winter 1970-71. Canadian Wildlife Service Unpublished Report, Delta, British Columbia. 68 pp.

Tyler, W.M. 1937. *Cathartes aura septentrionalis* Wied. Turkey Vulture. Pages 12-28 *in* A.C. Bent (editor). Life histories of North American birds of prey. United States National Museum Bulletin No. 167, Washington, D.C.

Udvardy, M.D.F. 1954. Summer movements of Black Swifts in relation to weather conditions. Condor 56:261-267.

Ulke, T. 1923. Birds observed in Yoho Park, B.C. in August 1922. Canadian Field-Naturalist 37:54-55.

United States Department of the Interior. 1982. 1980 national survey of fishing, hunting, and wildlife associated recreation. United States Department of the Interior Fish and Wildlife Service, Washington, D.C. 152 pp.

_____. 1988. Catalogue of Alaskan seabird colonies - computer data base. United States Department of Interior, Fish and Wildlife Service, Anchorage, Alaska.

United States Fish and Wildlife Service. 1973. Threatened wildlife of the United States. United States Fish and Wildlife Resource Publication 114, Washington, D.C. 289 pp.

Unitt, P. 1976. Occurrence and migration of the Long-tailed Jaeger in North America. Pacific Seabird Group Bulletin 3:31 (Abstract).

_____. 1977. The Little Blue Heron in California. Western Birds 8:151-154.

_____. 1984. The birds of San Diego county. San Diego Society of Natural History Memoir 13, San Diego, California. 276 pp.

Vallee, A. and R.J. Cannings. 1983. Nesting of the Thick-billed Murre, *Uria lomvia*, in British Columbia. Canadian Field-Naturalist 97:450-451.

Vance, H. 1970. Seventieth Christmas bird count - Terrace, B.C. Audubon Field Notes 24:125.

van Drimmelen, B. 1973. An analysis of the 1972 Pitt Polder Wood Duck nesting project. British Columbia Fish and Wildlife Branch Unpublished Report, Surrey. 19 pp. (Bibliography 4417).

_____. 1986. 1986 Queen Charlotte Islands Peale's Peregrine Falcon inventory. British Columbia Ministry of Environment Unpublished Report, Smithers.

van Drimmelen, B. and S.A. Sullivan. 1976. Report on the 1975 falcon survey in south-central B.C. (May 20 to July 23). British Columbia Fish and Wildlife Branch Unpublished Report, Victoria. 35 pp. (Bibliography 1897).

van Tets, G.F. 1959. A comparative study of the reproductive behaviour and natural history of three sympatric species of cormorants (*Phalacrocorax auritus*, *P. penicillatus*, and *P. pelagicus*) at Mandarte Island, B.C. M.A. Thesis, University of British Columbia, Vancouver. 86 pp.

_____. 1963. A report on the seabird colony at Mitlenatch Island. British Columbia Parks Branch Unpublished Report, Victoria. 133 pp. (Bibliography 1912).

_____. 1968. Seasonal fluctuations in the mortality rates of three northern-and three southern-hemisphere gulls. Commonwealth Scientific and Industrial Research Organization Wildlife Research 13:1-9.

van Tighem, K.J. 1977. The avifauna of Kootenay National Park. Parks Canada Unpublished Report, Radium Hotsprings, British Columbia. 151 pp. (Bibliography 4431).

van Tighem, K.J. and L.W. Gyug. 1983. Ecological land classification of Mount Revelstoke and Glacier National Parks, British Columbia. Volume II - Wildlife Resource. Canadian Wildlife Service and Parks Canada Report, Edmonton, Alberta. 254 pp.

Varoujean, D.H. and W.A. Williams. 1986. Nest locations and nesting habitat of the Marbled Murrelet (*Brachyramphus marmoratus*) in coastal Oregon. United States Department of the Interior, Fish and Wildlife Service Interim Report, Portland, Oregon. 33 pp.

Vaurie, C.A. 1959. The birds of the Palearctic fauna: Order Passeriformes. H.F. & G. Witherby, London, England. 762 pp.

_____. 1965. The birds of the Palearctic fauna: Non-passeriformes. H.F. & G. Witherby Limited, London, England 763 pp.

Veit, R. and L. Jonsson. 1984. Field identification of smaller sandpipers within the genus *Calidris*. American Birds 38:853-876.

Venables, E.P. 1909. The Burrowing Owl. Ottawa Naturalist 22:261.

Verbeek, N.A.M. 1966. Wanderings of the Ancient Murrelet: some additional comments. Condor 68:510-511.

_____. 1979. Timing of primary molt and egg-laying in Glaucous-winged Gulls. Wilson Bulletin 91:420-425.

_____. 1986. Aspects of the breeding biology of an expanded population of Glaucous-winged Gulls in British Columbia. Journal of Field Ornithology 57:22-33.

Vermeer, K. 1963. The breeding ecology of the Glaucous-winged Gull (*Larus glaucescens*) on Mandarte Island, B.C. British Columbia Provincial Museum Occasional Paper No. 13, Victoria. 104 pp.

_____. 1968. Ecological aspects of ducks nesting in high densities among larids. Wilson Bulletin 80:78-83.

_____. 1970. Breeding biology of California and Ring-billed Gulls. Canadian Wildlife Service Report Series No. 12, Ottawa, Ontario. 52 pp.

_____. 1971. The pelican - protection or extinction. Canadian Audubon 33:103-104.

_____. 1977. Comparison of White Pelican recoveries from colonies east and west of the Canadian Rocky Mountains. Murrelet 58:79-82.

_____. 1978. Extensive reproductive failure of Rhinoceros Auklets and Tufted Puffins. Ibis 120:112.

_____. 1979. Nesting requirements, food and breeding distribution of Rhinoceros Auklets, *Cerorhinca monocerata*, and Tufted Puffins, *Lunda cirrhata*. Ardea 67:101-110.

_____. 1980. The importance of timing and type of prey to reproductive success of Rhinoceros Auklets *Cerorhinca monocerata*. Ibis 122:343-350.

_____. 1981. The importance of plankton to Cassin's Auklets during breeding. Journal of Plankton Research 3:315-329.

_____. 1982. Foods and distribution of three *Bucephala* species in British Columbia waters. Wildfowl 33:22-30.

_____. 1983. Marine bird populations in the Strait of Georgia: comparison with the west coast of Vancouver Island. Canadian Technical Report of Hydrography and Ocean Sciences No. 19, Sydney, British Columbia. 18 pp.

Vermeer, K. and L. Cullen. 1979. Growth of Rhinoceros Auklets and Tufted Puffins, Triangle Island, British Columbia. Ardea 67:22-27.

_____. and _____. 1982. Growth comparison of a plankton-and a fish-feeding alcid. Murrelet 63:34-39.

Vermeer, K. and D. Devito. 1986. The nesting biology of Mew Gulls (*Larus canus*) on Kennedy Lake, British Columbia, Canada: comparison with Mew Gulls in northern Europe. Colonial Waterbirds 9:95-103.

_____. and _____. 1989. Population trends of nesting Glaucous-winged Gulls in the Strait of Georgia. Pages 89-93 *in* Vermeer, K. and R.W. Butler (editors). The ecology and status of marine and shoreline birds in the Strait of Georgia, British Columbia. Canadian Wildlife Service Special Publication, Ottawa, Ontario.

Vermeer, K. and M. Lemon. 1986. Nesting habits and habitats of Ancient Murrelets and Cassin's Auklets in the Queen Charlotte Islands, British Columbia. Murrelet 67:33-44.

Vermeer, K. and C.D. Levings. 1977. Populations, biomass and food habits of ducks on the Fraser Delta intertidal area, British Columbia. Wildfowl 28:49-60.

Vermeer, K. and L. Rankin. 1984. Population trends in nesting Double-crested Cormorants and Pelagic Cormorants in Canada. Murrelet 65:1-9.

Vermeer, K. and R. Vermeer. 1975. Oil threat to birds on the Canadian west coast. Canadian Field-Naturalist 89:278-298.

Vermeer, K., R.F. Oldaker, M.D.F. Udvardy, and K. Kelleher. 1963. Aberrant Glaucous-winged Gulls. Condor 65:332-333.

Vermeer, K., D.A. Manuwal and D.S. Bingham. 1976. Seabirds and pinnipeds of Sartine Island, Scott Island group, British Columbia. Murrelet 57:14-16.

Vermeer, K., K.R. Summers, and D.S. Bingham. 1976. Birds observed at Triangle Island, British Columbia, 1974 and 1975. Murrelet 57:35-42.

Vermeer, K., L. Cullen, and M. Porter. 1979a. A provisional explanation of the reproductive failure of Tufted Puffins (*Lunda cirrhata*) on Triangle Island, British Columbia. Ibis 121:348-354.

Vermeer, K., R. Vermeer, K.R. Summers, and R.R. Billings. 1979b. Numbers and habitat selection of Cassin's Auklets breeding on Triangle Island, British Columbia. Auk 96:143-151.

Vermeer, K., D. Power and G.E.J. Smith. 1988. Habitat selection and nesting biology of roof-nesting Glaucous-winged Gulls. Colonial Waterbirds II:109-201.

Vermeer, K., K. Morgan, and J. Smith. 1989. Population trends and nesting habitat of Double-crested and Pelagic cormorants in the Strait of Georgia. Pages 94-99 *in* Vermeer, K. and R.W. Butler (editors). The ecology and status of marine and shoreline birds in the Strait of Georgia, British Columbia. Canadian Wildlife Service Special Publication, Ottawa, Ontario.

Vesall, D.B. 1940. Notes on nesting habits of the American Bittern. Wilson Bulletin. 52:207-208.

Vickery, P.D., and R.P. Yunick. 1979. The 1978-1979 Great Gray Owl incursion across northeastern North America. American Birds 33:242-244.

Voous, K.H. 1973. List of recent holarctic bird species. Non-passerines. Ibis 115:612-638.

Vyatkin, P.S. 1986. Nesting cadastres of colonial birds in the Kamchatka regon. *In* N.M. Litvienko (editor). Seabirds of the Far East: collection of scientific papers. USSR Academy of Sciences, Vladivostok (Translation for Environment Canada).

Wade, C. 1977. The birds of Yoho National Park. Parks Canada Unpublished Report, Ottawa, Ontario. 799 pp. (Bibliography 1994).

Wahl, T.R. 1970. A Short-tailed Albatross record for Washington state. California Birds 1:113-114.

_____. 1972. Glaucous-winged Gull nesting at Lake Whatcom, Bellingham, Washington. Murrelet 53:51.

_____. 1975. Seabirds in Washington's offshore zone. Western Birds 6:117-134.

_____. 1985. The distribution of Buller's Shearwater, (*Puffinus bulleri*) in the North Pacific Ocean. Notornis 32:109-117.

Wahl, T.R., S.M. Speich, D.A. Manuwal, K.V. Hirsch, and C. Miller. 1981. Marine bird populations of the Strait of Juan de Fuca, Strait of Georgia, and adjacent waters in 1978 and 1979. Interagency Energy-Environment Research and Development Program Report, EPA-600/7-81-156. NOAA, Marine Ecosystems Analysis Program, Seattle, Washington. 391 pp.

Wakefield, K.S. 1987. Greylegs - a most uncommon bird. Vancouver Natural History Society. Discovery 16:47-48.

Walkinshaw, L.H. 1935. The incubation period of the Sora Rail. Wilson Bulletin 47:79-80.

_____. 1937. The Virginia Rail in Michigan. Auk 54:464-475.

_____. 1940. Summer life of the Sora Rail. Auk 57:153-168.

_____. 1949. The Sandhill Cranes. Cranbrook Institute of Science Bulletin No. 29, Bloomfield Hills, Michigan. 202 pp.

_____. 1981. The Sandhill Cranes. *in* Lewis, J.C. and H. Masatomi (editors). Crane Research Around the World. Proceedings of the International Crane Symposium at Sapporo, Japan in 1980 and papers from the World Working Group on Cranes, ICBP. International Crane Foundation, Baraboo, Wisconsin.

Wallace, D.I.M. 1974. Field identification of small species of the genus *Calidris*. British Birds 67:1-17.

_____. 1979. Review of British records of Semipalmated Sandpipers and claimed Red-necked Stints. British Birds 72:264-274.

Wallace, G.J. 1948. The Barn Owl in Michigan. Michigan State College Agriculture Experiment Station 208:1-61.

Wallace, W.M. 1961. Scaled Petrel in Oregon. Condor 63:417.

Walsh, T. 1988. Identifying Pacific loons - some old and new problems. Birding 20:12-28.

Ward, J.G. 1973. Reproductive success, food supply, and the evolution of clutch-size in the Glaucous-winged Gull. Ph.D. Thesis, University of British Columbia, Vancouver. 119 pp.

Ward, P.R.B. 1973. Further record of Snowy Plover in B.C. Vancouver Natural History Society Discovery 2:80-81.

Warren, C.L. and P.C. Rump. 1981. The urbanization of rural land in Canada: 1966-1971 and 1971-1976. Land Use in Canada Series No. 20, Environment Canada, Ottawa, Ontario. 283 pp.

Warren, W.H. 1970. Mute Swans in Victoria. Victoria Naturalist 27:11.

Watanuki, Y., M. Aotsuka and T. Terasawa. 1986. Status of seabirds breeding on Teuri Island. Tori 34:146-150.

Watson, A. 1956. The annual cycle of Rock Ptarmigan. Ph.D. Thesis, Aberdeen University, Aberdeen, Scotland. 333 pp.

Watson, D. 1977. The Hen Harrier. T. and A.D. Poyser Ltd., Berkharnsted, Hertfordshire, England. 307 pp.

Watson, G.E. 1962. Sympatry in Palearctic *Alectoris* partridges. Evolution 16:11-19.

Webb, R. 1952. Annotated bird list for Wells Gray Park, 1952. British Columbia Parks Branch Unpublished Report, Victoria. 41 pp. (Bibliography 4492).

Weber, J.W. and R.E. Fitzner. 1986. Nesting of the Glaucous-winged Gull east of the Washington Cascades. American Birds 40:567-569.

Weber, W.C. 1975. Occurrence and possible breeding of the White-throated Swift at Spence's Bridge, British Columbia. Murrelet 56:10-11.

_____. 1980. A proposed list of rare and endangered bird species for British Columbia. Pages 160-182 *in* R. Stace-Smith, L. Johns and, P. Joslin (editors). Proceedings of the Symposium on Threatened and Endangered Species and Habitats in British Columbia and the Yukon. British Columbia Ministry of Environment, Victoria.

_____. 1982. Vancouver bird records committee: first annual report. Vancouver Natural History Society Discovery 11:110-115.

_____. 1985. Vancouver bird records committee report for 1982. Vancouver Natural History Society Discovery 12:51-55.

Weber, W.C. and R.W. Campbell. 1978. Occurrence of the Smew in British Columbia, with comments on other North American Records. American Birds 32:1059-1061.

Weber, W.C. and S.R. Cannings. 1976. The White-headed Woodpecker (*Dendrocopos albolarvatus*) in British Columbia. Syesis 9:215-220.

Weber, W.C. and E.S. Hunn. 1978. First record of the Little Blue Heron for British Columbia and Washington. Western Birds 9:33-34.

Weber, W.C. and W.D. Kragh. 1986. The 86th Christmas bird count - British Columbia. American Birds 40:644-645.

_____. and _____. 1987. The 87th Christmas bird count - British Columbia. American Birds 41:647-665.

Weber, W.J. 1972. A new world for the Cattle Egret. Natural History 81:56-63.

Webster, J.D. 1969. Thirty-third breeding bird census - white spruce forest. Audubon Field Notes 23:717.

Wedgewood, I.A. 1978. The status of the Burrowing Owl in Canada. Committee on the Status of Endangered Wildlife in Canada Report. Canadian Wildlife Service, Ottawa, Ontario. 82 pp.

Weeden, R.B. 1959a. The ecology and distribution of ptarmigan wintering in North America. Ph.D. Thesis, University of British Columbia, Vancouver. 247 pp.

_____. 1959b. A new breeding record for the Wandering Tattler in Alaska. Auk 76:230-232.

_____. 1960. The birds of Chilkat Pass, British Columbia. Canadian Field-Naturalist 74:119-129.

_____. 1963. Management of ptarmigan in North America. Journal of Wildlife Management 27:673-683.

_____. 1965a. Further notes on Wandering Tattlers in central Alaska. Condor 67:87-89.

_____. 1965b. Breeding density, reproductive success, and mortality of Rock Ptarmigan at Eagle Creek, Alaska, from 1960-1964. Transactions of the North American Wildlife Conference 30:336-348.

Wehle, D.H.S. 1980. The breeding biology of the puffin: Tufted Puffin (*Lunda cirrhata*), Horned Puffin (*Fratercula corniculata*), Common Puffin (*F. arctica*), and Rhinoceros Auklet (*Cerorhinca monocerata*). Ph.D. Thesis, University of Alaska, Fairbanks.

_____. 1983. The food, feeding, and development of young Tufted and Horned Puffins in Alaska. Condor 85:427-442.

Weller, M.W. 1957. Growth, weight, and plumages of the Red-head, *Aythya americana*. Wilson Bulletin 69:5-38.

_____. 1959. Parasitic egg laying in the Redhead (*Aythya americana*) and other north American Anatidae. Ecological Monographs 29:333-365.

_____. 1964. Distribution and migration of the Redhead. Journal of Wildlife Management 28:64-103.

Wells, A.N. 1954. Green heron at Chilliwack, British Columbia. Murrelet 35:50.

Wenzel, B.M. 1980. Chemoreception in seabirds. Pages 41-67 *in* Burger, J., B.L. Olla and H.E. Winn (editors). Behavior of marine animals. Vol. 4. Plenum, New York.

Weseloh, D.V. 1981. Presidents of FAN - the first ten years: M.T. Myres - President 1970/71. Alberta Naturalist 1:71-74.

Westerborg, B.J. and D. Stirling. 1963. Twenty-seventh breeding bird census - disturbed second-growth coast forest. Audubon Field Notes 17:500-501.

Westerskov, K. 1956. Age determination and dating nesting events in the Willow Ptarmigan. Journal of Wildlife Management 20:274-279.

_____. 1965. Winter ecology of the partridge (*Perdix perdix*) in the Canadian prairie. Proceedings of the New Zealand Ecological Society 12:23-30.

_____. 1966. Winter food and feeding habits of the partridge (*Perdix perdix*) in the Canadian prairie. Canadian Journal of Zoology 44:303-322.

Weston, J.B. 1968. Nesting ecology of the Ferruginous Hawk (*Buteo regalis*). M.S. Thesis, Brigham Young University, Provo, Utah. 40 pp.

Wetmore, A. 1926. Food and economic relations of North American grebes. United States Department of Agriculture Bulletin 1196, Washington, D.C.

Wetmore, S.P., R.A. Keller, and G.E.J. Smith. 1985. Effects of logging on bird populations in British Columbia as determined by a modified point-count method. Canadian Field-Naturalist 99:224-233.

Whelton, B.D. 1989. Distribution of the Boreal Owl in eastern Washington and Oregon. Condor 91:712-716.

White, C.M. 1968. Diagnosis and relationships of the North American tundra-inhabiting Peregrine Falcons. Auk 85:179-191.

White, C.M. and D.A. Boyce. 1988. An overview of Peregrine Falcon subspecies. Pages 789-810 *in* T.J. Cade, J.H. Enderson, C.G. Thelander, and C.M. White (editors). Peregrine Falcon populations - their management and recovery. The Peregrine Fund, Inc., Boise, Idaho.

Whitelaw, V.R. 1977. The Anna's Hummingbird in British Columbia. Vancouver Natural History Society Discovery 6:53-56.

Whittaker, S. 1987. Wild Turkeys thriving in new Kootenay home. Kootenay Advertiser, 11 May 1987, p. 4.

Wik, D. and G. Streveler. 1968. Birds of Glacier Bay National Monument. Updated Edition. United States National Park Service. 80 pp.

Wiken, E. 1986. Terrestrial ecozones of Canada. Environment Canada Ecological Land Classification Series No. 19, Ottawa, Ontario. 26 pp.

Wilbur, S.R. 1978. Turkey Vulture eggshell thinning in California, Florida, and Texas. Wilson Bulletin 90:642-643.

_____. 1983. The status of vultures in the western hemisphere. Pages 113-123 *in* S.R. Wilbur and J.A. Jackson (editors). Vulture biology and management. University of California Press, Berkeley.

Wilbur, S.R. and J. A. Jackson (editors). 1983. Vulture biology and management. University of California Press, Berkeley. 550 pp.

Wilbur, S.R. and C.F. Yocom. 1972. Unusual geese in the Pacific coast states. Murrelet 52:16-19.

Wilds, C. and M. Newton. 1983. The identification of dowitchers. Birding 15:151-166.

Willett, G. 1915. Summer birds of Forrester Island, Alaska. Auk 32:295-305.

Willey, C.H. 1968. The ecology, distribution and abundance of the Mute Swan (*Cygnus olor*) in Rhode Island. M.S. Thesis, University of Rhode Island, Kingston. 93 pp.

Williams, J.H. 1978. Fort D'Epinette: a description of faunal remains from an early fur trade site in northern British Columbia. M.A. Thesis, Simon Fraser University, Burnaby, British Columbia.

Williams, M. 1964. Importation of game birds into British Columbia. British Columbia Fish and Wildlife Branch Unpublished Report, Victoria. 9 pp (Bibliography 4584).

Williams, M.Y. 1933a. Biological notes, covering parts of the Peace, Liard, Mackenzie and Great Bear River basins. Canadian Field-Naturalist 47:23-31.

_____. 1933b. Fauna of the former Dominion Peace River block, British Columbia. Pages 14-22 *in* Provincial Museum of Natural History and Anthropology for the year 1932, Victoria, British Columbia.

Williams, M.Y. and G.J. Spencer. 1942. The Flammulated Screech Owl at Kamloops. Canadian Field-Naturalist 56:138.

Williamson, F.S.L. and L.J. Peyton. 1963. Interbreeding of Glaucous-winged and Herring Gulls in the Cook Inlet region, Alaska. Condor 65:24-65.

Williamson, F.S.L. and M.A. Smith. 1964. The distribution and breeding status of the Hudsonian Godwit in Alaska. Condor 66:41-50.

Wilson, D. 1977. Wintering raptors in northern Pitt Meadows, B.C.: their distribution and significance. British Columbia Institute of Technology Unpublished Report, Burnaby. 46 pp. (Bibliography 4594).

Wilson, D.J. 1989. Avocets on the B.C. coast: first breeding record. Vancouver Natural History Society Discovery 18:95-97.

Wilson, M.C., E. Wilson, and L. Wilson. 1972. Ornithological notes from Columbia Lake, British Columbia. Syesis 5:63-65.

Wilson, U.W. 1977. A study of the biology of the Rhinoceros Auklet on Protection Island, Washington. M.Sc. Thesis, University of Washington, Seattle. 98 pp.

_____. 1986. Artificial Rhinoceros Auklet burrows: a useful tool for management and research. Journal of Field Ornithology 57:295-299.

Wilson, U.W. and D.A. Manuwal. 1986. Breeding biology of the Rhinoceros Auklet in Washington. Condor. 88:143-155.

Wilson-Jacobs, R. and E.C. Meslow. 1984. Distribution, abundance, and nesting characteristics of Snowy Plovers on the Oregon Coast. Northwest Science 58:40-48.

Winter, G.R. 1968. Agricultural development in the lower Fraser River valley. Pages 101-115 *in* A.H. Siemens (editor). Lower Fraser valley: evolution of a cultural landscape. B.C. Geographical Series No. 9, Tantalus Research Limited, Vancouver.

Winter, J. and D. Erickson. 1977. The fall migration - middle Pacific Coast region. American Birds 31:216-221.

Witherby, H.F., F.C.R. Jourdain, N.F. Ticehurst, and B.W. Tucker. 1943. The handbook of British birds. H.F. and G. Witherby Ltd., London, England.

Wohl, K.D. 1975. Sightings of New Zealand shearwaters in the northern Gulf of Alaska. Canadian Field-Naturalist 89:320-321.

Wood, C. 1976. First record of the Black-headed Gull for British Columbia. Syesis 9:361.

Wood, C.C. 1984. Foraging behaviour of Common Mergansers (*Mergus merganser*) and their dispersion in relation to the availability of juvenile Pacific salmon. Ph.D. Thesis, University of British Columbia, Vancouver.

_____. 1986. Dispersion of Common Merganser (*Mergus merganser*) breeding pairs in relation to the availability of juvenile Pacific salmon in Vancouver Island streams. Canadian Journal of Zoology 64:756-765.

Wood, K. 1964. Holidays at Invermere. Lake Windermere - Valley Echo, August 27, 1964.

Woodbury, A.M. and H. Knight. 1951. Results of the Pacific gull color-banding project. Condor 53:57-77.

Woods, J.G. 1979. Who gives a hoot. Revelstoke Review, November 28, 1979:. p. 9. (Bibliography 4612).

Woolington, D.W., P.F. Springer, and D.R. Yparraguirre. 1979. Migration and wintering distribution of Aleutian Canada Geese. Pages 299-309 *in* R.L. Jarvis and J.C. Bartonek (editors). Biology and Management of Pacific Flyway Geese. A symposium sponsored by the Northwest Section, The Wildlife Society, 16 February 1979, Portland, Oregon. Oregon State University Book Stores, Inc., Corvallis.

Wyatt, B. 1963. A Short-tailed Albatross sighted off the Oregon Coast. Condor 65:163.

Wylde, M.A. 1923. Ornithological Notes: Quail. Migrant 2:44.

Yesner, D.R. 1976. Aleutian Island albatrosses: a population history. Auk 93:263-280.

Yocom, C.F. 1943. The Hungarian partridge, *Perdix perdix* Linn., in the Palouse Region, Washington. Ecological Monographs 13:167-202.

_____. 1956. The Sage Hen in Washington State. Auk 73:540-550.

Young, C.J. 1930. A study of the Rhinoceros Auklet and other birds in British Columbia, 1929. Pages F16-F19 *in* British Columbia Provincial Museum of Natural History Annual Report for 1929, Victoria.

Zar, J.H. 1974. Biostatistical Analysis. Prentice-Hall Inc., Englewood Cliffe, New Jersey. 620 pp.

Zettergreen, B. 1988. Rare bird sighting. The Golden Times, 8 June 1988: p. 8.

Zimmerman, D.A. 1973. Range expansion of Anna's Hummingbird. American Birds 27:827-835.

Zwickel, F.C. 1967. Early behaviour in young Blue Grouse. Murrelet 48:2-7.

Zwickel, F.C. and J.F. Bendell. 1967. Early mortality and the regulation of numbers in Blue Grouse. Canadian Journal of Zoology 45:817-851.

_____. and _____. 1985. Blue Grouse - effects on, and influences of, a changing forest. Forestry Chronicle 1985:185-188.

Zwickel, F.C. and A.N. Lance. 1965. Renesting in Blue Grouse. Journal of Wildlife Management 29:202-204.

ADDENDA

Lesser Black-backed Gull
Larus fuscus Linnaeus

RANGE: Breeds from Iceland, the Faroe Islands, northern Scandinavia, and Russia, south to the British Isles and France. Winters from the British Isles, east to the Baltic, southward to central Africa and the Persian Gulf. In North America occurs regularly, and in increasing numbers, mainly from the Great Lakes region to Nova Scotia, south to the Gulf Coast and Florida. Casual elsewhere, including the Northwest Territories and Alaska.

STATUS: *Accidental.*

OCCURRENCE: An adult entering winter plumage was found on the Columbia River in Revelstoke on 26 October 1989 (W. Douglas Powell pers. comm.). It remained in the area, associating with Ring-billed, California, Herring, and Glaucous gulls until 10 November 1989. The bird was photographed at the local garbage dump on 4 November and again on 10 November (RBCM Photo 1248; Fig. 353).

Figure 353. *Adult Lesser Black-backed Gull at the Revelstoke landfill, 10 November 1989 (RBCM photo 1248; Orville Gordon). This is the first record for British Columbia.*

Great Black-backed Gull

Larus marinus Linnaeus

RANGE: Breeds in North America along the Atlantic coast from Labrador south to North Carolina and recently inland to the Great Lakes. Winters commonly from Newfoundland south to North Carolina, but regularly to Florida and inland on the Great Lakes. Also in the Old World.

STATUS: *Accidental.*

OCCURRENCE: An adult in winter plumage was found at the Kamloops landfill near the South Thompson River on 18 December 1988. The bird was photographed on 21 December with Herring and Glaucous-winged gulls (RBCM Photo 1243; Fig. 354). These photographs were subsequently examined by W. Earl Godfrey (National Museums of Canada) and Paul Lehman. The gull was last seen on 23 December 1988 (Campbell 1989c).

Figure 354. *Great Black-backed Gull in winter plumage at Kamloops landfill, South Thompson River, 21 December 1988 (Ralph W. Ritcey). Note the large bill and very dark mantle (left) and size comparison with Herring and immature Glaucous-winged gulls (right).*

Parakeet Auklet

PAAU

Cyclorrhynchus psittacula (Pallas)

RANGE: Breeds in North America in western Alaska south through the Bering Sea to the Aleutian Islands and east to islands in Prince William Sound. Winters off the Pacific coast from the Pribilof and Aleutian Islands south, mostly within the breeding range; also on the northern coast of Asia.

STATUS: *Casual.*

OCCURRENCE: As a result of the *Nestucca* barge oil spill off the Washington coast on 23 December 1988, an oil slick travelled north into British Columbia and from 3 January 1989 through the next month or so, it contaminated marine birds. Between 3 January and 8 February 1989, a total of 3,137 birds were found on beaches along the central west coast of Vancouver Island (Rodway et al. In press). Of those, 15 birds were identified as Parakeet Auklets, the first documented occurrence for the province. One carcass was found in Clayquot Sound, eight on Long Beach, four in the Barkley Sound to Pachena Bay area, and two were of unknown origin. Most carcasses will be preserved as skeleton specimens in the Royal British Columbia Museum collections.

Another record is noteworthy but is considered hypothetical because the bird was seen by a single observer. On 27 October 1988, a Parakeet Auklet was seen about 120 km west of Vancouver Island (48°19'N, 127°10'W).

See also the account in Hypothetical Species.

INDEX

R. Wayne Campbell was born in Edmonton, Alberta, in 1942. His fields of interest include zoogeography, feeding ecology of raptors, marine bird populations, and conservation of birds. He graduated from the University of Victoria in 1976 and received his M.Sc. degree from the University of Washington in 1983.

After high school, he worked as a seasonal naturalist with the British Columbia Parks Branch and in 1969 joined the staff at the University of British Columbia as Curator of the Cowan Vertebrate Museum in the Department of Zoology. Over the next 4 years he established the Photo-Records File, a system to document the occurrence of rare vertebrates in the province, and took over administrative responsibilities for the British Columbia Nest Records Scheme which he continues today. He also became very active in the executives of several conservation organizations including the British Columbia Waterfowl Society and the Vancouver Natural History Society.

In 1973 he moved to the then British Columbia Provincial Museum as Curator of Ornithology, a position he holds today. Over the next 15 years he conducted wildlife inventories of remote areas of the province including the first complete census of breeding seabird colonies. In addition, he amassed an enormous provincial vertebrate data base which includes details for 1-1/2 million specimen and sight records, 200,000 breeding records, and hard copies of nearly 10,000 published and unpublished articles on reptiles, amphibians, birds and mammals.

Wayne has written over 300 scientific and popular articles, government reports, and books on higher vertebrates. He has served as British Columbia coordinator for the North American Breeding Bird Survey since 1976, and as a select member of the national ornithology group for the Committee on the Status of Endangered Wildlife in Canada since 1980. He belongs to 22 professional and natural history organizations and is a Life Member and Elected Member of the American Ornithologists' Union, Life Member of the Cooper Ornithological Society, and Honourary Life Member of the Vancouver Natural History Society.

He has received numerous honours and awards for lecturing, writing, and conservation activities, and in 1989 received the "Award of Excellence in Biology" from the Association of Professional Biologists of British Columbia.

Neil K. Dawe was born in New Westminster, British Columbia, in 1943. After graduation from high school, his interest turned to the world of finance and banking became his vocation for the next 7 years. In 1970 he returned to the University of British Columbia where his interest in natural history was inspired by the enthusiasm and encouragement of Wayne Campbell. That interest grew into a career in habitat management and a commitment to the wildlife of the province.

In 1971 Neil worked as a seasonal naturalist for the British Columbia Parks Branch. Later that year he became Chief Naturalist at the George C. Reifel Migratory Bird Sanctuary where he developed interpretation and education programs for the British Columbia Waterfowl Society until 1975. Since 1975 he has worked for the Canadian Wildlife Service managing their wildlife areas, migratory bird sanctuaries, and working to protect migratory bird habitat on Vancouver Island.

Neil is a member of a number of conservation and scientific organizations including the Association of Professional Biologists of British Columbia, the Society of Wetland Scientists, and the Pacific Estuarine Research Society. He has served as first regional Vice-President of the Federation of British Columbia Naturalists and on the executive of the Vancouver Natural History Society, and has helped organize Christmas Bird Counts, raptor counts, and Brant surveys. He has also taught birding courses at regional colleges and school districts in British Columbia.

His research interests include garter snake ecology, the breeding biology of the Barn Swallow, and the enhancement and cre-ation of migratory bird habitats, with emphasis on wetlands. He has written over 30 popular and scientific papers and reports, and has recently co-authored a popular children's bird book.

Ian McTaggart-Cowan, born in Edinburgh, Scotland in 1910, is a career biologist with special concentration on the sytematics, biology, and conservation of birds and mammals. He graduated from the University of British Columbia in 1932 and earned a Ph.D. degree from the University of California in 1935. He has been awarded D.Sc. degrees by the University of British Columbia and the University of Victoria, LL.D. degrees by the University of Alberta and Simon Fraser University, and a Doctor of Environmental Studies by the University of Waterloo.

He was the biologist at the Provincial Museum in Victoria from 1935 until 1940 when he joined the Faculty of the University of British Columbia. During 35 years there he established and taught courses in vertebrate zoology, undertook research in ornithology and mammalogy and guided the research of some 100 graduate students. In the ensuing years his studies took him to 6 continents and resulted in more than 260 publications, 110 television programs, and 12 teaching films.

Public service related to vertebrate zoology and conservation includes 7 years on the National Research Council of Canada where he was the first Chairman of the Advisory Committee on Wildlife Research. He also served as Chairman of the Environmental Council of Canada, the Habitat Enhancement Committee of the Province of British Columbia, the Board of Governors of the Arctic Institute of North America, and Vice-President of the International Union for the Conservation of Nature and Natural Resources. In addition, he was a member of the Select Committee on National Parks for the United States Secretary of the Interior and the Nature Trust of British Columbia.

Honours received include: Officer of the Order of Canada, Fellow of the Royal Society of Canada, Leopold Medal of the Wildlife Society, Fry Medal of the Canadian Society of Zoologists, Einarsen Award in Conservation by the Northwest Section of the Wildlife Society, and the J. Dewey Soper Award by the Alberta Society of Professional Biologists.

John M. Cooper was born in New Westminster, British Columbia in 1956. His early interest in birds and the natural world was stimulated by his parents, Jack and Louise Cooper. Each spring, for nearly 2 decades, the Cooper family travelled throughout British Columbia and Alberta, often with close friends Lorne Frost and Glen Ryder, in search of birds and their nests. His passion for birds, wilderness, and environmental issues, was born from those experiences.

He graduated from the University of British Columbia, in zoology, in 1978 and worked as a biological consultant for several years. In 1981, he joined the British Columbia Provincial Museum and has since participated in several museum expeditions to inventory vertebrates in unknown and remote areas of the province. Presently he is enrolled at the University of Victoria and is studying the breeding biology of Least Sandpipers on the Queen Charlotte Islands.

John is a member of several scientific and conservation organizations and has directed fund-raising activities for Ducks Unlimited Canada to aid their wetland preservation program on Vancouver Island. He is also active in fund-raising activities for the Steelhead Society of British Columbia.

He has written 12 scientific and popular articles and reports on birds in British Columbia.

Gary W. Kaiser was born in Sussex, England in 1944. During his high school years, as a member of the Macoun field Club, he regularly visited the National Museum of Canada where he became a dedicated amateur coleopterist. He obtained a B.Sc.

from Carleton University in Ottawa, Ontario in 1966, and a M.Sc. 5 years later. During that same period he assisted with research on scarab beetles in Columbia and Ecuador in South America.

In 1968 ornithology first played a role in his career, with a temporary position studying bird hazards to aircraft. Later, the same year, he joined the Canadian Wildlife Service, and until early 1974 assisted with duck hunter surveys, breeding waterfowl surveys on the Prairies and throughout northern Ontario, and studies involving waterfowl banding. In later 1974 he moved to the British Columbia office of C.W.S. and began work in the province on waterfowl surveys of the Chilcotin-Cariboo region. During the next 15 years he participated in aerial surveys of Trumpeter Swans, waterfowl populations in the Rocky Mountain Trench, and organized shorebird banding programs on the Fraser River delta and breeding seabird surveys along the British Columbia coast.

In addition, he has maintained a keen interest in tropical ecology. Much of his free time is spent with wader banding projects, wildlife surveys, and teaching wildlife technique workshops in the Philippines, Borneo, Columbia and Peru.

His bibliography contains 20 scientific papers and internal government reports.

Michael C.E. McNall, born in Wingham, Ontario, spent much of his early life hunting, fishing, and studying nature. He obtained a diploma in Wildlife Management from Sir Sandford Fleming College, Ontario, in 1971. After graduation, he joined the Ornithology Department of the Royal Ontario Museum and spent the next 3 years on field expeditions in the West Indies, British Isles, Holland, Iceland, and throughout North America.

While at the Royal Ontario Museum, he was inspired by artist Terry Shortt to carry out his own research. In 1975 and 1976, with guidance and support from Henri Ouellet and Stewart MacDonald of the National Museum of Canada, he carried out a behavioral study of Parasitic and Long-tailed jaegers on Southampton Island and Bathurst Island in the Canadian arctic.

After his arctic experience, Michael moved to Victoria and in 1980 joined the staff of the British Columbia Provincial Museum. Since that time he has travelled throughout remote areas of the province collecting data for these books.

He is an accomplished photographer and decoy carver.

The authors, from left: John M. Cooper, Neil K. Dawe, Gary W. Kaiser, Michael C.E. McNall, R. Wayne Campbell, and Ian McTaggart-Cowan.